Interest Boxes

Organic Chemistry

SECOND CUSTOM EDITION FOR THE UNIVERSITY OF MISSISSIPPI

Paula Yurkanis Bruice

Taken From:
Organic Chemistry, Sixth Edition
by Paula Yurkanis Bruice

Learning Solutions

New York Boston San Francisco
London Toronto Sydney Tokyo Singapore Madrid
Mexico City Munich Paris Cape Town Hong Kong Montreal

Cover Art: Courtesy of PhotoDisc/Getty Images.

Taken from:

Organic Chemistry, Sixth Edition
by Paula Yurkanis Bruice
Copyright © 2011, 2007, 2004 by Pearson Education, Inc.
Published by Prentice Hall
Upper Saddle River, New Jersey 07458

This special edition published in cooperation with Pearson Learning Solutions.

Pearson Learning Solutions, 501 Boylston Street, Suite 900, Boston, MA 02116
A Pearson Education Company
www.pearsoned.com

Printed in the United States of America

2 3 4 5 6 7 8 9 10 V0ZG 15 14 13 12 11 10

0002000102705581056

AD

ISBN 10: 0-558-84358-1
ISBN 13: 978-0-558-84358-8

To Meghan, Kenton, and Alec

with love and immense respect

and to Tom, my best friend

BRIEF CONTENTS

CONTENTS

PART 2   ELECTROPHILIC ADDITION REACTIONS, STEREOCHEMISTRY, AND ELECTRON DELOCALIZATION   119

3   Alkenes: Structure, Nomenclature, and an Introduction to Reactivity • Thermodynamics and Kinetics   120

4   The Reactions of Alkenes   155

5 Stereochemistry: The Arrangement of Atoms in Space: The Stereochemistry of Addition Reactions 195

6 The Reactions of Alkynes · An Introduction to Multistep Synthesis 251

10 Reactions of Alcohols, Ethers, Epoxides, Amines, and Sulfur-Containing Compounds   410

11 Organometallic Compounds   450

12 Radicals • Reactions of Alkanes   468

PART 4   IDENTIFICATION OF ORGANIC COMPOUNDS 499

13 Mass Spectrometry, Infrared Spectroscopy, and Ultraviolet/Visible Spectroscopy 500

14 NMR Spectroscopy 553

PART 5   AROMATIC COMPOUNDS   623

15 Aromaticity · Reactions of Benzene   624

16 Reactions of Substituted Benzenes   660

PART 6   CARBONYL COMPOUNDS   705

17 Carbonyl Compounds I: Reactions of Carboxylic Acids and Carboxylic Acid Derivatives   706

18 Carbonyl Compounds II: Reactions of Aldehydes and Ketones • More Reactions of Carboxylic Acid Derivatives • Reactions of α,β-Unsaturated Carbonyl Compounds   771

19 Carbonyl Compounds III:
Reactions at the α-Carbon   831

PART 7   MORE ABOUT OXIDATION—REDUCTION
REACTIONS AND AMINES   885

20 More about Oxidation—Reduction Reactions   886

21   More about Amines · Heterocyclic Compounds   917

PART 8   BIOORGANIC COMPOUNDS   939

22   The Organic Chemistry of Carbohydrates   940

The Organic Chemistry of Amino Acids, Peptides, and Proteins   977

The Chemistry of the Nucleic Acids   1147

P R E F A C E

TO THE INSTRUCTOR

The guiding principle in writing this book has been to present organic chemistry as an exciting and vitally important science. Too many students look on organic chemistry as a necessary evil, a course they have to take for reasons that to them are unknown. Some suspect it has been designed as a kind of test of their ability to stick things out. Others equate learning organic chemistry with learning the language of a foreign country that they will never visit. They come to organic chemistry having taken other science courses, but they probably have not had the opportunity to study a science that is not a collection of individual topics, but one that unfolds and grows, allowing them to use what they learn at the beginning of the course to explain and predict what follows. To counter the impression that the study of organic chemistry consists primarily of memorizing a diverse collection of molecules and reactions, this book is organized around shared features and unifying concepts, and emphasizes principles that can be applied again and again. I want students to learn how to apply what they have learned to a new setting, reasoning their way to a solution rather than memorizing a multitude of facts. I also want them to see that organic chemistry is a fascinating discipline that is integral to biology as well as to their daily lives.

The comments I have received from colleagues and students who used previous editions suggest the book is working in the way I had hoped. As much as I enjoy having faculty tell me that their students are scoring higher than ever before on tests, nothing is more rewarding than hearing positive comments from the students themselves. Many students have generously credited their success in organic chemistry to this book, not giving themselves nearly enough credit for how hard they studied to achieve that success. They always seem surprised that they have come to love "orgo" (on the East Coast) or "o-chem" (on the West Coast). I also hear from many premedical students who say that the book gave them the permanent understanding of organic chemistry that made the organic chemistry section of the MCAT the easiest part for them.

In striving to make this edition of *Organic Chemistry* even more useful to students, I have relied on constructive comments from many of you. For these I am extremely grateful. I also kept a journal of questions students had when they came to my office. These questions let me know what sections in the book needed clarifying and what answers in the *Study Guide and Solutions Manual* needed more detailed explanations. Most importantly, they showed me where I should create new problems to reduce the likelihood that students using the new edition will ask the same questions. Because I teach large classes, I have a vested interest in foreseeing and preventing potential confusion before it arises. In this edition, many sections have been rewritten to optimize readability and comprehension. There are new in-chapter and end-of-chapter problems to enhance students' mastery through problem solving. There are also new interest boxes to show students the relevance of organic chemistry and additional margin notes to remind them of important concepts and principles.

I hope you find this edition even more appealing to your students than earlier versions have been. As always, I am eager to hear your comments, bearing in mind that positive comments are the most fun, but critical comments are the most useful.

CHANGES TO THIS EDITION

Responses from instructors and students have led to adjustments in the coverage and distribution of certain topics and encouraged expansion of the book's most successful pedagogical features.

Content and Organization

- Much of the book was rewritten to tighten up and streamline the narrative in order to facilitate understanding. Additional boxed material on biologically related topics has been added to the earlier chapters to let the students see sooner, and more frequently, how organic chemistry is related to biological systems and to their daily lives (Drugs Bind to Their Receptors, Cholesterol and Heart Disease, An S_N2 Reaction that Causes a Severe Clinical Disorder, Is Chocolate a Health Food?). Some reactions now rarely used have been omitted, and newer reactions have been added.

- The coverage of acid and base chemistry in Chapter 1 has been reorganized to aid understanding. Chapter 3 has a new discussion of catalysis. Chapter 6 now includes a discussion of green chemistry. There is a new chapter on organometallic chemistry (Chapter 11), giving students new ways to make carbon–carbon single bonds as well as carbon–carbon double and triple bonds. Chapter 10 is now focused primarily on the substitution and elimination reactions that occur with alcohols, ethers, epoxides, quaternary ammonium hydroxides, and sulfonium ions. A section on phase-transfer catalysis has been included in this chapter. All radical chemistry continues to be covered together in Chapter 12 and includes a new section on the formation (and mechanism) of explosive peroxides.

- Chapter 13 (the first of the two spectroscopy chapters) has a new section on the various ionizing techniques used in mass spectrometry; Chapter 14 has a new section on X-ray crystallography. The discussion of arene oxides has been moved to Chapter 15, the first chapter on benzene chemistry, and the reactions of substituents on benzene rings have been moved to Chapter 16. Chapters 20 and 21 have been rewritten so that they contain less duplication from earlier chapters, and Chapter 21 contains a new section on chemoselective reactions.

- The section on DNA sequencing in Chapter 28 has been updated, as has the section on biodegradable polymers in Chapter 29. Chapter 28 contains new material on how natural products modify DNA, and Chapter 29 contains a new section on recycling polymers.

- A significant percentage of the condensed structures in the book were changed to skeletal structures; students should now find themselves comfortable using either format, and they will be prepared for whatever format is used on standardized tests they may have to take.

- This edition also includes more voice boxes to aid student learning. In response to student comments, there are also more margin notes that succinctly repeat key points and facilitate review. Furthermore, there are more than 20 new interest boxes in this edition, including: How Tamiflu Works; Temolozolomide (the drug used to treat Senator Kennedy's brain tumor); Health Concerns: Bisphenol A and Phthalates; Melamine Poisoning.

- This edition has more than 200 new problems, both in-chapter and end-of-chapter. They include new solved problems, new problem-solving strategies, and new problems incorporating information from more than one chapter. I keep a list of questions my students have when they come to office hours. Many of the new problems were created as a result of these questions.

A Functional Group Approach with a Mechanistic Organization That Ties Together Synthesis and Reactivity

As mentioned earlier, this book is designed to discourage rote memorization. To this end, the presentation of functional groups is organized around mechanistic similarities: electrophilic addition reactions, nucleophilic substitution reactions, elimination reactions, radical addition and radical substitution reactions, electrophilic (and nucleophilic) aromatic substitution reactions, nucleophilic addition reactions, and nucleophilic addition–elimination reactions. This organization allows a great deal of material to be understood in light of unifying principles of reactivity.

Many organic chemistry textbooks discuss the synthesis of a functional group just after its reactivity is discussed; but these two groups of reactions generally have little to do with one another. Instead, when I discuss a functional group's reactivity, I cover the synthesis of compounds that are formed as a result of that reactivity, often by having students design synthetic schemes. In Chapter 4, for example, students learn about the reactions of alkenes but do *not* learn at this point about the synthesis of alkenes. Instead, they learn about the synthesis of alkyl halides, alcohols, ethers, epoxides, and alkanes—the compounds formed when alkenes react. Because alkenes are synthesized from the reactions of alkyl halides and alcohols, the synthesis of alkenes is covered when the reactions of alkyl halides and alcohols are discussed. The strategy of tying together the reactivity of a functional group and the synthesis of compounds resulting from its reactivity prevents the student from having to memorize lists of unrelated reactions. It also results in a certain economy of presentation, allowing more material to be covered in less time.

Although memorizing different ways a particular functional group can be prepared can be counterproductive to mastering organic chemistry, it is useful to have such a compilation of reactions when designing multistep syntheses. For this reason, lists of reactions that yield particular functional groups are compiled in Appendix IV. In the course of learning how to design syntheses, students come to appreciate the importance of reactions that change the carbon skeleton of a molecule; these reactions are compiled in Appendix V.

A Modular Format

Because different instructors teach organic chemistry in different ways, I have tried to make the book as modular as possible. For example, the spectroscopy chapters (Chapters 13 and 14) have been composed so that they may be covered at any time in the course. For those who prefer to teach spectroscopy at the beginning—or in a separate laboratory course—I have included a table of the functional groups at the beginning of Chapter 13. For those who prefer to cover carbonyl chemistry earlier in the course, Part 6 (Carbonyl Compounds) can be covered before Part 5 (Aromatic Compounds). I anticipate that most instructors will cover the first 23 chapters during a year-long course and will then choose among the remaining chapters depending on personal preference, the interests of the students enrolled in their class, and time permitted. Those whose students are primarily interested in the biological sciences might be more inclined to focus on Chapters 24–28, which discuss the organic chemistry of compounds found in biological systems. Those teaching courses designed for chemistry or engineering majors may focus instead on Chapter 29 (Synthetic Polymers) and Chapter 30 (Pericyclic Reactions). The book ends with a chapter on drug discovery and design, a topic that in my experience interests students sufficiently that they will choose to read it on their own, even if it is not assigned by their instructor.

A Bioorganic Emphasis

Today, many students taking organic chemistry are interested in the biological sciences. I have therefore introduced bioorganic material throughout the text to show these students that organic chemistry and biochemistry are not separate entities but are closely related on a continuum of knowledge. Once students learn how, for example, electron delocalization, leaving-group tendency, electrophilicity, and nucleophilicity affect the reactions of simple organic compounds, they can appreciate how these same factors influence the reactions of more complicated organic molecules such as enzymes, nucleic acids, and vitamins. I have found that the economy of presentation achieved in the first two-thirds of this text (explained above) makes it possible to devote time to bioorganic topics.

In the first two-thirds of the book, the bioorganic material is limited mostly to "interest boxes" and the last sections of the chapters. Thus, the material is available to the curious student without requiring the instructor to introduce bioorganic topics into the course. For example, after the stereochemistry of organic reactions is presented, the stereochemistry of enzyme catalyzed reactions is discussed; after alkyl halides are discussed, biological compounds used to methylate substrates are examined; after the methods chemists use to activate carboxylic acids are presented, the methods cells use to activate these acids are explained; after condensation reactions are discussed, examples of biological condensation reactions are shown.

In addition, seven chapters in the last part of the book (Chapters 22–28) focus on bioorganic chemistry. These chapters have the unique distinction of containing more chemistry than is typically found in the corresponding parts of a biochemistry text. Chapter 24 (Catalysis), for example, explains the various modes of catalysis employed in organic reactions and then shows that they are identical to the modes of catalysis found in reactions catalyzed by enzymes. All of this is presented in a way that allows students to understand the lightning-fast rates of enzymatic reactions. Chapter 25 (The Organic Chemistry of the Coenzymes, Compounds Derived from Vitamins) emphasizes the role of vitamin B_1 as an electron delocalizer, vitamin K as a strong base, vitamin B_{12} as a radical initiator, and biotin as a compound that transfers a carboxyl group by means of a nucleophilic addition–elimination reaction, and describes how the many different reactions of vitamin B_6 are controlled by the overlap of p orbitals. Chapter 26 (The Organic Chemistry of Metabolic Pathways) explains the chemical function of ATP. (Its role is not to provide a magic shot of energy that allows an endothermic reaction to take place—commonly called a coupled reaction. Rather, it provides a reaction pathway involving a good leaving group for a reaction that cannot occur because of a poor leaving group.) Chapter 27 (The Organic Chemistry of Lipids) presents the mechanisms for prostaglandin formation (allowing students to understand how aspirin works), fat breakdown, and terpene biosynthesis. In Chapter 28 (The Chemistry of the Nucleic Acids), students learn that DNA contains thymine instead of uracil because of imine hydrolysis, and they see how DNA strands are synthesized in the laboratory. Thus, these chapters do not replicate what will be covered in a biochemistry course; they bridge the two disciplines, allowing students to see that knowledge of organic chemistry is central to the understanding of biological processes.

With the conviction that learning should be fun, certain biologically oriented discussions presented in interest boxes serve as intriguing asides. Examples include: why Dalmatians are the only mammals that excrete uric acid; why life is based on carbon instead of silicon; how a microorganism has learned to use industrial waste as a source of carbon; the chemistry associated with SAMe (a product prominently displayed in health food stores); trans fats; melamine poisoning; and alkylating agents as cancer drugs.

An Early and Consistent Emphasis on Organic Synthesis

Students are introduced to synthetic chemistry and retrosynthetic analysis early in the book (Chapters 4 and 6, respectively), so they can use that technique throughout the course to design multistep syntheses. Nine special sections on synthesis design, each with a different focus, are introduced at appropriate intervals. One, for example, discusses the proper choice of reagents and reaction conditions for maximizing the yield of the target molecule (Chapter 9); one introduces disconnections, synthons, and synthetic equivalents (Chapter 18); one discusses making new carbon–carbon bonds (Chapter 19); and one focuses on controlling stereochemistry (Chapter 20). The use of combinatorial methods in organic synthesis is described in Chapter 31, which examines drug discovery and design.

PEDAGOGICAL FEATURES

The pedagogical features that appealed to students in earlier editions have been retained and enhanced.

Margin Notes and Boxed Material to Engage the Student

Margin notes and biographical sketches appear throughout the text. The margin notes encapsulate key points that students should remember, and the biographical sketches give students some appreciation of the history of chemistry and the people who contributed to that history. Interest boxes connect chemistry to real life (discussing, for example, Chiral Drugs, Measuring Toxicity, Chimney Sweeps and Cancer, Ultraviolet Light and Sunscreens, and Penicillin and Drug Resistance) or provide additional instruction (as in Calculating Kinetic Parameters, A Few Words about Curved Arrows, and Incipient Primary Carbocations).

Summaries and Voice Boxes to Help the Student

Each chapter concludes with a Summary to help students synthesize the key points, as well as a list of cross-referenced Key Terms. Chapters that cover reactions conclude with a Summary of Reactions. Annotations (voice boxes) help students focus on points being discussed.

Problems, Solved Problems, and Problem-Solving Strategies

The book contains more than 2000 problems, many with multiple parts. The answers (and explanations, when needed) to all the problems are in the accompanying *Study Guide and Solutions Manual*, which I authored to ensure consistency in language with the text. The problems within each chapter are primarily drill problems that allow students to test themselves on material just covered before moving on to the next section. Selected problems are accompanied by worked-out solutions to provide insight into problem-solving techniques. Short answers provided at the end of the book for problems marked with a diamond give students immediate feedback concerning their mastery of a skill or concept. There are 45 Problem-Solving Strategies throughout the book, a feature that teaches how to approach various kinds of problems. For example, a Problem-Solving Strategy in Chapter 4 teaches students how to plan the synthesis of an alkyl halide, and a Problem-Solving Strategy in Chapter 8 teaches students how to determine whether a reaction will be more apt to take place by an S_N1 or an S_N2 pathway. Each Problem-Solving Strategy is followed by an exercise giving the student an opportunity to use the problem-solving skill just learned.

The end-of-chapter problems vary in difficulty. They begin with drill problems that integrate material from the entire chapter, requiring the student to think in terms of all the material in the chapter rather than focusing on individual sections. The problems become more challenging as the student proceeds, often reinforcing concepts from prior chapters. The net result for the student is a progressive building of both problem-solving ability and confidence. (I have chosen not to label problems as particularly challenging so as not to intimidate the students before they try to solve the problem.)

ChemPlace Website   thechemistry place

Part of the revamped and bolstered ChemPlace Website (see the description on page xxviii) is a **Student Tutorials** quiz gallery. Each question contains a visual animation or an interactive tutorial, then asks a question about it, and provides feedback that includes links back to the relevant section of the book. Each student tutorial has a ChemPlace icon in the textbook (as shown here in the margin) to indicate where the tutorial relates to the content.

chem
place

Art Program: Rich in Three-Dimensional, Computer-Generated Structures

This edition continues to present energy-minimized, three-dimensional structures throughout the text that give students an appreciation of the three-dimensional shapes of organic molecules. Color in the illustration program is used not simply for show but to highlight and organize the information; in fact, the use of highlights to draw attention to points of interest has been increased in this edition. I have attempted to employ specific colors in consistent ways (for example, mechanism arrows are always red, brand names are green), but there is no need for a student to memorize a color palette.

A CLOSER LOOK AT COVERAGE AND ORGANIZATION

This book is divided into nine parts, each starting with a brief overview so that students can understand where they are "going." The first chapter in Part 1 provides a summary of material that students need to recall from general chemistry. The review of acids and bases emphasizes the relationship between acidity and the stability of the conjugate base, a theme recurrently raised throughout the text. (Acids and bases are covered even more extensively in the *Study Guide and Solutions Manual*.) In Chapter 2, students learn how to name five classes of organic compounds—those that will be the products of the reactions in the ten chapters that immediately follow. Chapter 2 also covers topics that must be mastered before the study of reactions can begin—structures, conformations, and physical properties of organic compounds.

The five chapters of Part 2 deal with electrophilic addition reactions, stereochemistry, and electron delocalization. Chapter 3 sets the stage for the study of organic reactions by giving the students the knowledge of thermodynamics and kinetics they will need as they progress through the course. Rate constants are derived in an appendix for those who wish to take a more mathematical approach to kinetics, and the *Study Guide and Solutions Manual* contains a section on calculating kinetic parameters. Chapter 3 also introduces students to the concept of "curved arrows." The *Study Guide and Solutions Manual* contains an extensive tutorial on "electron pushing." (I have found this tutorial to be very successful in making my students comfortable with a topic that should be easy, but somehow perplexes even the best of them unless they get sufficient practice.)

I lead off the study of reactions with the reactions of alkenes because of their simplicity. Thus, although Chapter 4 covers a wide variety of alkene reactions, they all have similar mechanisms—an electrophile adds to the least substituted sp^2 carbon and a nucleophile adds to the other sp^2 carbon—and differ only in the nature of the electrophile and the nucleophile. Because organic chemistry is all about the interactions of electrophiles and nucleophiles, it makes sense to begin the study of organic reactions by introducing students to a variety of electrophiles and nucleophiles. The reactions in Chapter 4 are discussed without regard to stereochemistry because I have found that students do well as long as only one new concept is introduced at a time. Understanding the mechanisms of the reactions is enough at this point.

Chapter 5 reviews the isomers introduced in Chapters 2 and 3 (constitutional isomers and cis–trans isomers) and then discusses isomers that result from an asymmetric center—one kind of stereogenic center. The *Study Guide and Solutions Manual* has an exercise that encourages students to open their box of molecular models and see how model building can help them learn. In addition, the ChemPlace Website gives students the opportunity to manipulate many molecules in three dimensions. Now that the students are comfortable with both isomers and electrophilic addition reactions, the two topics are considered together at the end of Chapter 5, where the stereochemistry of the electrophilic addition reactions covered in Chapter 4 is presented. My students have become much more comfortable with stereochemistry now that I introduce it in the context of reactions with which they are familiar. Chapter 6 covers the electrophilic addition reactions of alkynes and introduces students to multistep organic synthesis. This chapter builds the students' confidence because of the similarity of the material to that in Chapter 4.

Understanding electron delocalization is vitally important in organic chemistry, so this subject is covered in its own chapter (Chapter 7), which is a continuation of the introduction to this topic found in Chapter 1. Students see how electron delocalization affects stability and pK_a, and can affect the products of electrophilic addition reactions. The *Study Guide and Solutions Manual* contains an extensive tutorial on "Drawing Resonance Structures." It also contains a tutorial on "Molecular Orbital Theory" for instructors who want a more extensive treatment of this subject than the text provides.

The first three chapters of Part 3 discuss the reactions of compounds that have an electron-withdrawing group bonded to an sp^3 carbon. First, the substitution reactions of alkyl halides are discussed in Chapter 8. Chapter 9 presents elimination reactions of alkyl halides and then goes on to consider competition between substitution and elimination. Chapter 10 covers substitution and elimination reactions at an sp^3 carbon when a group other than a halogen is the leaving group—reactions of alcohols, ethers, epoxides, quaternary ammonium hydroxides, and sulfonium salts. Chapter 11 discusses organometallic compounds, including transition metal-catalyzed coupling reactions and alkene metathesis. Chapter 12 covers radical chemistry. Students learn that alkanes are largely unreactive due to the absence of a functional group, underscoring the importance of a functional group to chemical reactivity. A tutorial on "Drawing Curved Arrows in Radical Systems" is included in the *Study Guide and Solutions Manual*.

The two chapters in Part 4 discuss instrumental techniques. Mass spectrometry, IR spectroscopy, and UV/Vis spectroscopy are discussed in Chapter 13. Chapter 14 discusses NMR spectroscopy. Each spectral technique is written as a "stand-alone topic," so it can be covered independently at any time during the course. The first of these chapters opens with a table of functional groups for instructors who want to cover spectroscopy before students have been introduced to all the functional groups.

Part 5 is all about aromatic compounds. Chapter 15 covers aromaticity and the reactions of benzene. Chapter 16 discusses the reactions of substituted benzenes. Because not all organic courses cover the same amount of material in a semester, Chapters 11–16 have been strategically placed to come near the end of the first semester. Ending a semester before Chapter 11, 12, 13, 14, or after Chapter 11, 12, 13, 14, or 16 will not leave students suspended halfway through a topic.

Part 6 is devoted to the chemistry of carbonyl compounds. Instructors who had never covered carboxylic acid derivatives before aldehydes and ketones were initially skeptical about this order. However, when the opinions of those who had used previous editions of the book were sought, almost all preferred this order. Chapter 17 starts the treatment of carbonyl chemistry by discussing the reactions of carboxylic acids and their derivatives with oxygen and nitrogen nucleophiles. In this way, students are introduced to carbonyl chemistry by learning how tetrahedral intermediates partition. The first part of Chapter 18 discusses the reactions of carboxylic acid derivatives, aldehydes, and ketones with carbon and hydrogen nucleophiles. By studying all these carbonyl compounds together, students see how the reactions of aldehydes and ketones differ from those of carboxylic acid derivatives. Then, when they move on to study the formation and hydrolysis of imines, enamines, and acetals in the second part of Chapter 18, they can easily understand these mechanisms because they are well versed in how tetrahedral intermediates partition. Over the years I have experimented with my classes, and I believe this to be the most effective and easiest way to teach carbonyl chemistry. That being said, Chapters 17 and 18 can easily be switched as long as Sections 18.4, 18.5, and 18.6 are skipped and then covered with Chapter 17. Chapter 19 discusses reactions at the α-carbon of carbonyl compounds.

Chapter 20, the first chapter in Part 7, revisits oxidation and reduction reactions and discusses new ones. Students have already seen most of these reactions but can better appreciate them when they are presented as a unit. Chapter 21 reviews some of the material on amines that was covered in previous chapters and then explores those topics in greater detail. The chapter concludes with a discussion of heterocyclic compounds.

Part 8 covers bioorganic topics. Part 9 covers synthetic polymers, pericyclic reactions, and drug discovery and design.

SUPPLEMENTS

For the Instructor

Instructor Resource Center on CD/DVD (0-321-67683-1). This CD/ DVD includes all the art and tables in .JPG, .PDF and PowerPoint^{TM} formats for use in classroom projection or for creating study materials and tests. In addition, the instructor can access three pre-built PowerPoint^{TM} presentations. The first contains a complete lecture outline; the second presentation contains the in-chapter **PROBLEM** boxes from the text; and the third contains questions you can use in class along with your Classroom Response System (CRS). This CD/DVD set also contains TestGen test-generation software and a TestGen version of the Test Item File that enables professors to create and tailor exams to their needs, or to create online quizzes for delivery in WebCT, Blackboard, or CourseCompass. Word^{TM} files of the Test Item File are also included.

Transparency Acetates (0-321-67240-2) by Paula Yurkanis Bruice, University of California, Santa Barbara. This set features 250 full-color images from the text.

Printed Test Bank (0-321-67239-9) by Gary Hollis, Roanoke College. Includes a selection of over 2500 multiple-choice, short answer, and essay test questions.

Course and Homework Management Tools Blackboard and **WebCT** offer the best teaching and learning resources for your course. Conveniently organized by textbook chapters for *Organic Chemistry, 6th Edition*, these resources help you save time and help your students reinforce and apply what they have learned in class.

ACE—Achieving Chemistry Excellence Prentice Hall, in conjunction with Robert B. Grossman, Raphael A. Finkel, and a team of programmers at the University of Kentucky, has developed a homework system for organic chemistry that can finally support the types of problems assigned in organic chemistry. *Achieving Chemistry Excellence: Organic Chemistry*, or ACE, is a Web-based program that has been developed specifically for instructors and students of introductory organic chemistry. In the typical organic chemistry course, students work questions out of a textbook for which a solutions manual is available. Students struggle with a question for a few minutes, look up the answer, and then feel as if they understand how to answer the question. It isn't until exam time that they realize that learning an answer to a question and knowing how to answer a question are two entirely different things.

Computer programs that can tell students that their responses are incorrect without giving away the correct answer are an ideal solution to this problem. Many Web-based chemistry homework programs exist, but most require text-based, numeric, or multiple-choice responses. By contrast, ACE permits students to draw structural responses to posed questions with a graphical structure-drawing interface. They submit their structure to a server, and, if their response is incorrect, they are given feedback and asked to try again. Moreover, ACE is the only program that provides specific feedback for incorrect structural responses, effectively teaching students how to solve the problem without giving away correct answers. Please contact your local Prentice Hall representative for more information.

For the Student

Study Guide and Solutions Manual (0-321-67682-3) by Paula Yurkanis Bruice. This *Study Guide and Solutions Manual* contains complete and detailed explanations of the solutions to the problems in the text and definitions of all the key terms used in each chapter. In addition, you will find a section on advanced acid–base chemistry with an additional set of problems, two tutorials on "pushing electrons," (one for two electrons systems, one for radials), a section on molecular orbital theory, a tutorial on drawing resonance contributors, an exercise on building molecular models, and an exercise on calculating kinetic parameters, as well as 28 practice tests.

Virtual ChemLab Workbook and CD (0-13-238827-8) Prepared by Brian F. Woodfield of Brigham Young University. This virtual laboratory is a realistic, simulated laboratory environment where students can get a feel for what to expect in a real wet lab, or conduct experiments that are not included in the department's lab program. Students may experiment on their own in the full virtual lab environment, or choose prearranged labs that are referenced in the workbook and at the end of the chapter in the textbook. Virtual ChemLab CD can be run directly from the CD or installed on the student's computer.

Molecular Modeling Workbook & CD (0-13-222044-X) Features SpartanView™ and SpartanBuild™ software. This workbook includes a software tutorial and numerous challenging exercises students can tackle to solve problems involving structure building and analysis using the tools included in the two pieces of Spartan software. Contact your Prentice Hall representative for details.

ChemPlace Website with GradeTracker (*http://www.chemplace.com*) Available with GradeTracker to provide flexible gradebook functionality for instructors who wish to use it. The text-specific ChemPlace Website for *Organic Chemistry, Sixth Edition* has been thoroughly updated and enhanced from the previous edition, and provides students with a collection of learning and assessment tools for each chapter. The ChemPlace Website for the Sixth Edition includes:

- The revised **Student Tutorials quiz** gallery. Each question contains a visual animation or interactive tutorial, then asks a question about it, and provides feedback that includes links back to the relevant section of the book. By providing assessment tightly wrapped around the tutorial elements, including feedback on incorrect responses, and references to the book, the concept is reinforced. See the associated icons within the text, at point of use.

- A **Molecule Gallery**, with a vast selection of 3-D (jmol) renderings of most of the important molecules in the text. Students can rotate the molecule in three dimensions, change its representation, and explore its structure in detail.

- **Exercise Sets** and **Quizzes** with hints and instant feedback, including links to relevant sections from the book.

- The **MCAT Study Guide** consists of 200 questions and can be a vital career resource.

- For students who are using ChemOffice Ltd., a workbook featuring **ChemOffice Exercises** is also available on the Website.

Collaborators for this edition's Website are Bette Kreuz, Matt Dintzner, and Ronald Wikholm.

Pearson eText A full electronic version of *Organic Chemistry, Sixth Edition* is available as an eText. Pearson eText pages look exactly like the printed text, offering powerful new functionality for students and instructors. Users can create notes, highlight text in different colors, create book marks, zoom, view in single-page or two-page view, etc.

ChemOffice Student CD This software includes ChemDraw LTD and Chem3D LTD. A free workbook is available on the ChemPlace Website and includes a software tutorial and numerous exercises for each chapter of the text. The software is sold at the instructor's discretion and is available at a substantial discount if purchased with the textbook.

Prentice Hall Molecular Model Kit (0-205-508136-3) This best-selling model kit allows students to build space-filling and ball-and-stick models of common organic molecules. It allows accurate depiction of double and triple bonds, including heteroatomic molecules (which some model kits cannot handle well).

Organic Molecular Model Kit (0-13-233471-2) by Steve Darling. Darling Models™ contain various pieces used to build atoms, bonds, and molecules. This model kit allows you to build molecules and see the three-dimensional aspects of organic chemistry that can only be imagined on a two-dimensional drawing.

Prentice Hall Framework Molecular Model Kit (0-13-330076-5) This model kit allows students to build scale models that show the mutual relations of atoms in organic molecules, including precise interatomic distances and bond angles. This is the most accurate model kit available.

TO THE STUDENT

Welcome to organic chemistry. You are about to embark on an exciting journey. This book has been written with students like you in mind—those who are encountering the subject for the first time. The journey into organic chemistry can be an exciting one. The book's central goal is to make this journey both stimulating and enjoyable by helping you understand the central principles of the subject and asking you to apply them as you progress through the pages. You will be reminded about these principles at frequent intervals in references back to sections you have already mastered.

You should start by familiarizing yourself with the book. The inside front and back covers display information you may want to refer to often during the course. Chapter Summaries, Key Terms, and Reaction Summaries at each chapter's end provide helpful checklists of the terms and concepts you should understand after studying the chapter. The Glossary at the end of the book can also be a useful study aid, as can the Appendices, which were written to consolidate useful categories of information. The molecular models and electrostatic potential maps that you will find throughout the book are provided to give you an appreciation of what molecules look like in three dimensions and to show how charge is distributed within a molecule. Think of the margin notes as the author's opportunity to inject personal reminders of ideas and facts that are important to remember. Be sure to read them.

Work all the problems within each chapter. These are drill problems that allow you to check whether you have mastered the skills and concepts the particular section is teaching before you go on to the next section. Some of these problems are solved for you in the text. Short answers to some of the others—those marked with a diamond—are provided at the end of the book. Do not overlook the "Problem-Solving Strategies" that are also sprinkled throughout the text; they provide practical suggestions on the best way to approach important types of problems.

In addition to the within-chapter problems, work as many end-of-chapter problems as you can. The more problems you work, the more comfortable you will be with the subject matter and the better prepared you will be for the material in subsequent chapters. Do not let any problem frustrate you. If you cannot figure out the answer in a reasonable amount of time, turn to the *Study Guide and Solutions Manual* to learn how you should have approached the problem. Later on, go back and try to work the problem on your own again. Be sure to visit the ChemPlace Website (*www.chemplace.com*) to try out some of the study tools like the Student Tutorials, Molecule Gallery, and Exercise Sets and Quizzes.

The most important advice to remember (and follow) in studying organic chemistry is DO NOT FALL BEHIND! The individual steps to learning organic chemistry are quite simple; each by itself is relatively easy to master. But they are numerous, and the subject can quickly become overwhelming if you do not keep up.

Before many of the theories and mechanisms were figured out, organic chemistry was a discipline that could be mastered only through memorization. Fortunately, that is no longer true. You will find many unifying ideas that allow you to use what you have learned in one situation to predict what will happen in other situations. So, as you read the book and study your notes, always try to understand *why* each chemical event or behavior happens. For example, when the reasons behind reactivity are understood, most reactions can be predicted. Approaching the course with the misconception that to succeed you must memorize hundreds of unrelated reactions could be your downfall. There is simply too much material to memorize. Understanding and reasoning, not memorization, provides the necessary foundation on which to lay subsequent learning. Nevertheless, from time to time some memorization will be required: some fundamental rules will have to be memorized, and you will need to memorize the common names of a number of organic compounds. But that should not be a problem; after all, your friends have common names that you have been able to learn.

Students who study organic chemistry to gain entrance into medical school sometimes wonder why medical schools pay so much attention to this topic. The importance of organic chemistry is not in the subject matter alone, however. Mastering organic chemistry requires a thorough understanding of certain fundamental principles and the ability to use those fundamentals to analyze, classify, and predict. The study of medicine makes similar demands: a physician uses an understanding of certain fundamental principles to analyze, classify, and diagnose.

Good luck in your study. I hope you will enjoy studying organic chemistry and learn to appreciate the logic of this fascinating discipline. If you have any comments about the book or any suggestions for improving it, I would love to hear from you. Remember, positive comments are the most fun, but negative comments are the most useful.

Paula Yurkanis Bruice
pybruice@chem.ucsb.edu

ACKNOWLEDGMENTS

It gives me great pleasure to acknowledge the dedicated efforts of many good friends who made this book a reality. The many contributions of Ed Skibo of Arizona State University, Ron Magid of the University of Tennessee, Ron Starkey of the University of Wisconsin–Green Bay continue in this edition. Particular thanks go to Jordan Fantini, who checked every inch of the book for accuracy; David Yerzley, M.D., for his assistance with the section on MRI; Warren Hehre of Wavefunction, Inc., and Alan Shusterman of Reed College for their advice on the electrostatic potential maps that appear in the book; and Jeremy Davis who created the art that appears on page 127. I am also very grateful to my students, who pointed out sections that needed clarification, worked the problems and suggested new ones, and searched for errors.

The following reviewers have played an enormously important role in the development of this book.

Sixth Edition Reviewers

Igor Alabugin, *Florida State University*
Angela Allen, *University of Michigan—Dearborn*
Taghg Begley, *Cornell University*
Maggie Bobbit Bump, *Virginia Tech*
Barbara Colonna, *University of Miami*
Lee Friedman, *University of Maryland—College Park*
Nathaniel Grove, *Clemson University*
Doug Heller, *University of Miami*
Jason Locklin, *University of Georgia*
Jeffrey Moore, *University of Illinois—Urbana*
Venugopal Mukku, *University of Minnesota Crookston*
Edward Skibo, *Arizona State University*
Stacey Stoffregen, *University of Wisconsin—River Falls*
Timothy Trygstad, *The College of St. Scholastica*
Coran Watanabe, *Texas A&M University*

Sixth Edition Accuracy Reviewers

Paul Cassidy, *Texas State University*
Jordan Fantini, *Denison University*
Paul Floreancig, *University of Pittsburgh*
Christopher Roy, *Duke University*

Fifth Edition Manuscript Reviewers

Jon C. Antilla, *University of Mississippi*
Arthur J. Ashe, *III, University of Michigan*
William F. Bailey, *University of Connecticut*
Chad Booth, *Texas State University*
Gary Breton, *Berry College*
Lale Aka Burk, *Smith College*
Dorian Canelas, *North Carolina State University*
Robert Coleman, *Ohio State University*

S. Todd Deal, *Georgia Southern University*
Malcolm D.E. Forbes, *University of North Carolina*
Annaliese Franz, *Harvard University*
Alison J. Frontier, *University of Rochester*
Albert Fry, *Wesleyan University*
Jose J. Gutierrez, *The University of Texas Pan American*
Christopher M. Hadad, *Ohio State University*
C. Frederick Jury, *Collin County Community College*
Bob Kane, *Baylor University*
Angela King, *Wake Forest University*
Irene Lee, *Case Western Reserve University*
Philip Lukeman, *New York University*
Neil Miranda, *University of Illinois at Chicago*
Robert P. O'Fee, *The College of New Jersey*
JaimeLee Iolani Rizzo, *Pace University*
Alexander J. Seed, *Kent State University*
William N. Setzer, *University of Alabama-Huntsville*
Thomas E. Sorensen, *University of Wisconsin-Milwaukee*
Jennifer A. Tripp, *University of Scranton*
Linda Waldman, *Cerritos College*
Ronald Wikholm, *University of Connecticut*
Emel L. Yakali, *Raymond Walters College*

Accuracy Reviewers

S. Todd Deal, *Georgia Southern University*
Malcolm Forbes, *University of North Carolina*
Steven Graham, *St. John's University*
Christopher Roy, *Duke University*
Susan Schelble, *University of Colorado at Denver*

I am deeply grateful to my editor, Dawn Giovanniello, whose talents guided this book and caused it to be as good as it could be and to my assistant editor, Jessica Neumann, whose gentle prodding and attention to detail made the book actually happen. I also want to thank the other talented and dedicated people at Prentice Hall whose contributions made this book a reality. I am enormously grateful to Daniel Schiller, the developmental editor, both for his creativity and uncanny ability to find just the right word. And thank you to Kristin Mayo and Angela Bernhardt, the creative brains behind the technology, and the student and instructor resources to accompany the book.

I particularly want to thank the many wonderful and talented students I have had over the years, who taught me how to be a teacher. And I want to thank my children, from whom I may have learned the most. Three special people—Dante Talbot Bruice, Jensen Lewis Bruice, and Valen Talbot Bruice—were born while I wrote this edition. I look forward to the day when they can recognize their names in print.

To make this textbook as user friendly as possible, I would appreciate any comments that will help me achieve this goal in future editions. If you find sections that could be clarified or expanded, or examples that could be added, please let me know. Finally, this edition has been painstakingly combed for typographical errors. Any that remain are my responsibility; if you find any, please send me a quick e-mail so they can be corrected in future printings of this edition.

Paula Yurkanis Bruice
University of California, Santa Barbara
pybruice@chem.ucsb.edu

This innovative text organizes functional groups around mechanistic similarities, emphasizing how functional groups react and the compounds synthesized as a result of that reactivity.

Focus on Mechanistic Similarities

The unique organization of the text—functional groups assembled by mechanistic similarities—allows you to understand a great deal of material in light of unifying principles of reactivity.

Tying Together Synthesis and Reactivity

The strategy of tying together the reactivity of a functional group and the synthesis of compounds resulting from its reactivity prevents you from having to memorize lists of unrelated actions.

MECHANISM FOR THE S_N1 REACTION OF AN ALCOHOL

reaction of the carbocation with a nucleophile

protonation of the most basic atom

formation of a carbocation

substitution product

HBr

an alkene product undergoes an addition reaction

elimination product

An acid protonates the most basic atom in a molecule.

- An acid always reacts with an organic molecule in the same way: it protonates the most basic atom in the reactant.
- Weakly basic water is the leaving group that is expelled, forming a carbocation.
- The carbocation has two possible fates: it can combine with a nucleophile and form a substitution product, or it can lose a proton and form an elimination product.

Stepped-out Mechanisms

Stepped-out mechanisms clearly illustrate the mechanisms of the reactions.

biological systems and to your daily life

9.10 DESIGNING A SYNTHESIS II: APPROACHING THE PROBLEM

When you are asked to design a synthesis, one way to approach the task is to think about the starting material you have been given and ask yourself if there is an obvious series of reactions beginning with the starting material that can get you on the road to the **target molecule** (the desired product). Sometimes this is the best way to approach a *simple* synthesis. The following examples will give you practice employing this strategy.

Example 1. Using the given starting material, how could you prepare the target molecule?

Adding HBr to the alkene would form a compound with a leaving group that can be replaced by a nucleophile. Because ¯C≡N is a relatively weak base (the pK_a of HC≡N is 9.1), the desired substitution reaction will be favored over the competing elimination reaction.

synthesis

Example 2. Starting with 1-bromo-1-methylcyclohexane, how could you prepare *trans*-2-methylcyclohexanol?

The elimination reaction should be carried out under E2 conditions because under these conditions tertiary alkyl halides undergo only elimination, so there will be no competing substitution product. Because hydroboration–oxidation overall results in the syn addition of water, the target molecule (as well as its enantiomer) is obtained.

synthesis

As you saw in Section 6.12, working backward can be a useful way to design a synthesis, particularly when the starting material does not clearly indicate how to proceed. Look at the target molecule and ask yourself how it could be prepared. Once you have an answer, look at the precursor you have identified for the target molecule and ask yourself how that precursor could be prepared. Keep working backward one step at a time, until you get to a readily available starting material. We learned that this technique is called *retrosynthetic analysis*. (Section 6.12).

Example 3. How could you prepare ethyl methyl ketone from 1-bromobutane?

$$CH_3CH_2CH_2CH_2Br \xrightarrow{\text{?}} CH_3CH_2\overset{\text{O}}{\overset{\|}{C}}CH_3$$

At this point in your study of organic chemistry, you know only two ways to synthesize a ketone: (1) the addition of water to an alkyne (Section 6.7) and (2) hydroboration–oxidation

Designing a Synthesis

Designing a Synthesis sections appear throughout the text and help you learn to design multi-step syntheses. Many synthesis problems include the synthesis of compounds that you will recognize such as Novocaine, Valium, and ketoprofen.

You will learn how to design a synthesis and how to approach different types of problems.

Problem-Solving Strategies

Problem solving strategies are followed by an exercise that gives you an opportunity to use the problem-solving skill just learned. You will learn how to approach a variety of problems, organize your thoughts, and improve your problem-solving abilities.

PROBLEM-SOLVING STRATEGY

Determining Relative Acid Strength from Structure

a. Which is a stronger acid?

CH₃CHCH₂OH   or   CH₃CHCH₂OH
        | |
        F   Br

When you are asked to compare two items, pay attention to how they differ; ignore where they are the same. These two compounds differ only in the halogen atom attached to the middle carbon of the molecule. Because fluorine is more electronegative than bromine, there is greater electron withdrawal from the oxygen atom in the fluorinated compound. The fluorinated compound, therefore, will have the more stable conjugate base, so it will be the stronger acid.

b. Which is a stronger acid?

         Cl   Cl
         | |
CH₃CCH₂OH   or   CH₃CHCH₂OH
         | |
         Cl   Cl

These two compounds differ in the location of one of the chlorine atoms. Because the second chlorine in the compound on the left is closer to the O—H bond than is the second chlorine in the compound on the right, the former is more effective at withdrawing electrons from the oxygen atom. Thus, the compound on the left will have the more stable conjugate base, so it will be the stronger acid.

Now continue on to Problem 55.

PROBLEM 6   SOLVED

Explain why the ether obtained by treating an optically active alcohol with PBr₃ followed by sodium methoxide has the same configuration as the alcohol, whereas the ether obtained by treating the alcohol with tosyl chloride followed by sodium methoxide has a configuration opposite that of the alcohol.

same configuration as the alcohol

configuration opposite to that of the alcohol

Solution   Conversion of the alcohol to the ether by way of the alkyl halide requires two successive S$_N$2 reactions: (1) attack of Br¯ on the bromophosphite and (2) attack of CH₃O¯ on the alkyl halide. Each S$_N$2 reaction takes place with inversion of configuration, so the final product has the same configuration as the starting material. In contrast, conversion of the alcohol to the ether by way

Problem Solving

Solved problems appear throughout the chapter and help to walk you through the steps involved in solving a particular type of problem.

Make connections between core ideas

Features throughout the book help you to synthesize key points, connect chemistry to real life, and give you some appreciation of the history of chemistry.

BIOGRAPHY

Dr. Frances O. Kelsey receives the President's medal for Distinguished Federal Civilian Service from President John F. Kennedy, in 1962, for preventing the sale of thalidomide.

Frances Oldmam Kelsey was born in British Columbia in 1914. She received a B.Sc. in 1934 and a M.Sc. in pharmacology in 1936 from McGill University. In 1938, she received a Ph.D. and an M.D. from the University of Chicago, where she became a member of the faculty. She married Fremont Kelsey, a fellow faculty member, and they had two daughters. She joined the FDA in 1960 and worked there until 2005, when she retired at the age of 90. Also see Section 31.4.

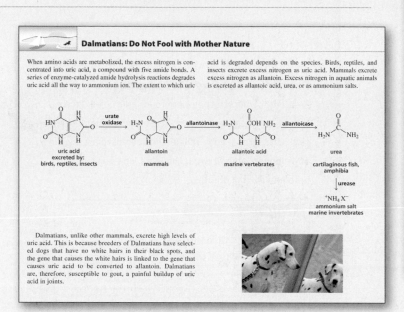

Dalmatians: Do Not Fool with Mother Nature

When amino acids are metabolized, the excess nitrogen is concentrated into uric acid, a compound with five amide bonds. A series of enzyme-catalyzed amide hydrolysis reactions degrades uric acid all the way to ammonium ion. The extent to which uric acid is degraded depends on the species. Birds, reptiles, and insects excrete excess nitrogen as uric acid. Mammals excrete excess nitrogen as allantoin. Excess nitrogen in aquatic animals is excreted as allantoic acid, urea, or as ammonium salts.

Dalmatians, unlike other mammals, excrete high levels of uric acid. This is because breeders of Dalmatians have selected dogs that have no white hairs in their black spots, and the gene that causes the white hairs is linked to the gene that causes uric acid to be converted to allantoin. Dalmatians are, therefore, susceptible to gout, a painful buildup of uric acid in joints.

Bioorganic Emphasis

Coverage of bioorganic chemistry connects organic chemistry to biochemistry to present content as a continuum of knowledge. This material is incorporated throughout the text in several ways: special interest boxes, specific chapter sections, and chapters that focus on bioorganic topics.

Biographical Sketches

Biographical sketches give you an appreciation of the history of chemistry and the people who contributed to it.

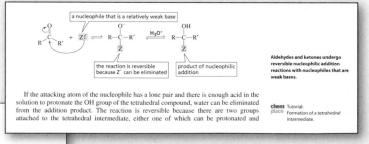

If the attacking atom of the nucleophile has a lone pair and there is enough acid in the solution to protonate the OH group of the tetrahedral compound, water can be eliminated from the addition product. The reaction is reversible because there are two groups attached to the tetrahedral intermediate, either one of which can be protonated and

Aldehydes and ketones undergo reversible nucleophilic addition reactions with nucleophiles that are weak bases.

chemplace Tutorial: Formation of a tetrahedral intermediate.

SUMMARY OF REACTIONS

1. S_N2 reaction: a one-step mechanism

   $$\overline{Nu} + \overset{|}{\underset{|}{C}} - X \longrightarrow \overset{|}{\underset{|}{C}} - Nu + X^-$$

   Relative reactivities of alkyl halides: $CH_3X > 1° > 2° > 3°$.
   Only the inverted product is formed.

2. S_N1 reaction: a two-step mechanism with a carbocation intermediate

   $$\overset{|}{\underset{|}{C}} - X \longrightarrow \overset{|}{\underset{|}{C^+}} \quad \overline{Nu} \longrightarrow \overset{|}{\underset{|}{C}} - Nu$$
   $$+ \ X^-$$

   Relative reactivities of alkyl halides: $3° > 2° > 1° > CH_3X$
   Both the inverted and noninverted products are formed.

Margin Notes

These notes emphasize core ideas and remind you of important principles to help you grasp concepts in the text.

Summary of Reactions

Reaction summaries are included in each chapter that covers reactions. This ensures that you can understand and explain how each reaction occurs.

Bring organic chemistry to life with outstanding learning tools

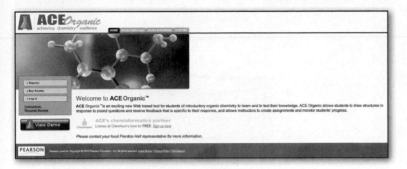

ACE Organic—Online Tutorial and Assessment for Organic Chemistry

www.aceorganic.com

You answer organic chemistry problems by drawing structures. When you draw organic structures, ACE Organic evaluates your responses and provides feedback to help guide you to the correct answer without giving it away. The system grades your responses automatically and stores your activity in a gradebook, providing a better way to track your learning while saving time.

---

www.chemplace.com

TheChemistryPlace® Website gives you everything you need to delve deeper into learning chemistry:

- **Review Activities** provide you with a variety of assessment opportunities that help you check your understanding of key concepts with the choice to view helpful hints and receive instant feedback on selected answers.

- **Media Enhancements** include selected review questions that are enhanced with media—short movies, animations, and 3-D molecules—to help you visualize key concepts.

- **ChemOffice** offers activities using ChemOffice Lite, appropriate for material in the chapter.

- **Pearson eText** features all chapters of the text available for you in TheChemistryPlace.

Building on Fundamentals

Now found on the Chemistry Place for *Organic Chemistry*, the Building on Fundamentals lists show how key topics in the chapter are connected to material already learned. They reveal organic chemistry as a unified, unfolding story, rather than a series of disparate topics.

Modeling Kits

Organic Molecular Model Kit
Steve Darling
ISBN-13: 978-0-13-233471-6
ISBN-10: 0-13-233471-2

Molecular Model Kit for Organic Chemistry
Prentice Hall
ISBN-13: 978-0-205-08136-3
ISBN-10: 0-205-08136-3

SpartanModel: An Electronic Model Kit (CD, Guide, and 3-D glasses)
Warren J. Hehre
ISBN-13: 978-0-13-222044-6
ISBN-10: 0-13-222044-X

Framework Molecular Model Student Kit
George Brumlik
ISBN-13: 978-0-13-330076-5
ISBn-10: 0-13-330076-5

Organic and Inorganic Molecular Model Kit
Steve Darling
ISBN-13: 978-0-13-33470-9
ISBN-10: 0-13-233470-4

Molecular Model Set for General and Organic Chemistry
Prentice Hall
ISBN-13: 978-0-13-955444-5
ISBN-10: 0-13-955444-0

Paula Bruice with Zeus and Abigail

Paula Yurkanis Bruice was raised primarily in Massachusetts. After graduating from the Girls' Latin School in Boston, she earned an A.B. from Mount Holyoke College and a Ph.D. in chemistry from the University of Virginia. She then received an NIH postdoctoral fellowship for study in the Department of Biochemistry at the University of Virginia Medical School and held a postdoctoral appointment in the Department of Pharmacology at Yale Medical School.

Paula has been a member of the faculty at the University of California, Santa Barbara since 1972, where she has received the Associated Students Teacher of the Year Award, the Academic Senate Distinguished Teaching Award, two Mortar Board Professor of the Year Awards, and the UCSB Alumni Association Teaching Award. Her research interests center on the mechanism and catalysis of organic reactions, particularly those of biological significance. Paula has a daughter and a son who are physicians and a son who is a lawyer. Her main hobbies are reading mystery and suspense novels and enjoying her pets (two dogs, two cats, and a parrot).

An Introduction to the Study of Organic Chemistry

The first two chapters of the text cover a variety of topics that you need to be familiar with in order to start your study of organic chemistry.

CHAPTER 1
Electronic Structure and Bonding • Acids and Bases

Chapter 1 reviews the topics from general chemistry that will be important to your study of organic chemistry. The chapter starts with a description of the structure of atoms and then proceeds to a description of the structure of molecules. Molecular orbital theory is introduced. Acid–base chemistry, which is central to understanding many organic reactions, is reviewed. You will see how the structure of a molecule affects its acidity and how the acidity of a solution affects molecular structure.

CHAPTER 2
An Introduction to Organic Compounds: Nomenclature, Physical Properties, and Representation of Structure

To discuss organic compounds, you must be able to name them and to visualize their structures when you read or hear their names. In **Chapter 2**, you will learn how to name five different classes of organic compounds. This will give you a good understanding of the basic rules for naming compounds. Because the compounds examined in the chapter are reactants or products of many of the reactions presented in the first third of the book, you will have numerous opportunities to review the nomenclature of these compounds as you proceed through those chapters. Chapter 2 also compares and contrasts the structures and physical properties of these compounds, which makes learning about them a little easier than if the structure and physical properties of each class of compound were presented separately. Because organic chemistry is a study of compounds that contain carbon, the last part of Chapter 2 discusses the spatial arrangement of the atoms in both chains and rings of carbon atoms.

1

Electronic Structure and Bonding · Acids and Bases

HF

HCl

HBr

HI

TO STAY ALIVE, EARLY HUMANS MUST HAVE BEEN ABLE TO TELL THE DIFFERENCE between the kinds of materials in their world. "You can live on roots and berries," they might have said, "but you can't eat dirt. You can stay warm by burning tree branches, but you can't burn rocks."

By the early eighteenth century, scientists thought they had grasped the nature of that difference, and in 1807 Jöns Jakob Berzelius gave names to the two kinds of materials. Compounds derived from living organisms were believed to contain an unmeasurable vital force—the essence of life. These he called "organic." Compounds derived from minerals—those lacking that vital force—were "inorganic."

Because chemists could not create life in the laboratory, they assumed they could not create compounds that had a vital force. Since this was their mind-set, you can imagine how surprised chemists were in 1828 when Friedrich Wöhler produced urea—a compound known to be excreted by mammals—by heating ammonium cyanate, an inorganic mineral.

$$\overset{+}{N}H_4 \ \overset{-}{O}CN \xrightarrow{\text{heat}} \underset{\text{urea}}{H_2N \overset{\overset{\displaystyle O}{\|}}{C} NH_2}$$

ammonium cyanate

For the first time, an "organic" compound had been obtained from something other than a living organism and certainly without the aid of any kind of vital force. Clearly, chemists needed a new definition for "organic compounds." **Organic compounds** are now defined as *compounds that contain carbon.*

Why is an entire branch of chemistry devoted to the study of carbon-containing compounds? We study organic chemistry because just about all of the molecules that make life possible—proteins, enzymes, vitamins, lipids, carbohydrates, and nucleic acids—contain carbon. Thus the chemical reactions that take place in living systems, including our own bodies, are reactions of organic compounds. Most of the compounds found in nature—those we rely on for food, medicine, clothing (cotton, wool, silk), and energy (natural gas, petroleum)—are organic as well.

Organic compounds are not, however, limited to those found in nature. Chemists have learned to synthesize millions of organic compounds never found in nature, including synthetic fabrics, plastics, synthetic rubber, medicines, and even things like photographic film and Super Glue. Many of these synthetic compounds prevent shortages of naturally occurring products. For example, it has been estimated that if synthetic materials were not available for clothing, all of the arable land in the United States would have to be used for the production of cotton and wool just to provide enough material to clothe us. Currently, there are about 16 million known organic compounds, and many more are possible.

What makes carbon so special? Why are there so many carbon-containing compounds? The answer lies in carbon's position in the periodic table. Carbon is in the center of the second row of elements. We will see that the atoms to the left of carbon have a tendency to give up electrons, whereas the atoms to the right have a tendency to accept electrons (Section 1.3).

the second row of the periodic table

Because carbon is in the middle, it neither readily gives up nor readily accepts electrons. Instead, it shares electrons. Carbon can share electrons with several different kinds of atoms, and it can also share electrons with other carbon atoms. Consequently, carbon is able to form millions of stable compounds with a wide range of chemical properties simply by sharing electrons.

When we study organic chemistry, we study how organic compounds react. When an organic compound reacts, some bonds break and some new bonds form. Bonds form when two atoms share electrons, and bonds break when two atoms no longer share electrons. How readily a bond forms and how easily it breaks depend on the particular electrons that are shared, which, in turn, depend on the atoms to which the electrons belong. So if we are going to start our study of organic chemistry at the beginning, we must start with an understanding of the structure of an atom—what electrons an atom has and where they are located.

Natural Versus Synthetic

It is a popular belief that natural substances—those made in nature—are superior to synthetic ones—those made in the laboratory. Yet when a chemist synthesizes a compound, such as penicillin or estradiol, it is exactly the same in all respects as the compound synthesized in nature. Sometimes chemists can improve on nature. For example, chemists have synthesized analogs of morphine—compounds with structures similar to but not identical to that of morphine—that have pain-killing effects like morphine but, unlike morphine, are not habit forming (Section 31.3). Chemists have synthesized analogs of penicillin that do not produce the allergic responses that a significant fraction of the population experiences from naturally produced penicillin, or that do not have the bacterial resistance of the naturally produced antibiotic (Section 17.17).

A field of poppies growing in Afghanistan. Commercial morphine is obtained from opium, the juice obtained from this species of poppy. Morphine is the starting material for the synthesis of heroin (Section 30.3). Nearly three-quarters of the world's supply of heroin comes from the poppy fields of Afghanistan.

nucleus (protons + neutrons)

electron cloud

1.1 THE STRUCTURE OF AN ATOM

An atom consists of a tiny dense nucleus surrounded by electrons that are spread throughout a relatively large volume of space around the nucleus. The nucleus contains *positively charged protons* and *neutral neutrons*, so it is positively charged. The *electrons are negatively charged*. They are moving continuously. Like anything that moves, electrons have kinetic energy, and this energy is what counters the attractive force of the positively charged protons that would otherwise pull the negatively charged electrons into the nucleus.

Because the amount of positive charge on a proton equals the amount of negative charge on an electron, a neutral atom has an equal number of protons and electrons. Atoms can gain electrons and thereby become negatively charged, or they can lose electrons and become positively charged, but the number of protons in an atom does not change.

Protons and neutrons have approximately the same mass and are about 1800 times more massive than an electron. This means that most of the mass of an atom is in its nucleus. However, most of the *volume* of an atom is occupied by its electrons, and that is where our focus will be because it is the electrons that form chemical bonds.

The **atomic number** of an atom equals the *number of protons* in its nucleus. The atomic number is also the number of electrons that surround the nucleus of a neutral atom. For example, the atomic number of carbon is 6, which means that a neutral carbon atom has six protons and six electrons.

The **mass number** of an atom is the *sum of its protons and neutrons*. All carbon atoms have the same atomic number because they all have the same number of protons. They do not all have the same mass number because they do not all have the same number of neutrons. For example, 98.89% of naturally occurring carbon atoms have six neutrons—giving them a mass number of 12—and 1.11% have seven neutrons—giving them a mass number of 13. These two different kinds of carbon atoms (^{12}C and ^{13}C) are called isotopes. **Isotopes** have the same atomic number (that is, the same number of protons), but different mass numbers because they have different numbers of neutrons.

Naturally occurring carbon also contains a trace amount of ^{14}C, which has six protons and eight neutrons. This isotope of carbon is radioactive, decaying with a half-life of 5730 years. (The *half-life* is the time it takes for one-half of the nuclei to decay.) As long as a plant or animal is alive, it takes in as much ^{14}C as it excretes or exhales. When it dies, it no longer takes in ^{14}C, so the ^{14}C in the organism slowly decreases. Therefore, the age of a substance derived from a living organism can be determined by its ^{14}C content.

The **atomic weight** of a naturally occurring element is the *average mass of its atoms*. Because an *atomic mass unit (amu)* is defined as exactly 1/12 of the mass of ^{12}C, the atomic mass of ^{12}C is 12.0000 amu; the atomic mass of ^{13}C is 13.0034 amu. Therefore, the atomic weight of carbon is 12.011 amu because $(0.9889 \times 12.0000) + (0.0111 \times 13.0034) = 12.011$. The **molecular weight** of a compound is the *sum of the atomic weights* of all the atoms in the molecule.

Chlorine

PROBLEM 1 ♦

Oxygen has three isotopes with mass numbers of 16, 17, and 18. The atomic number of oxygen is eight. How many protons and neutrons does each of the isotopes have?

1.2 HOW THE ELECTRONS IN AN ATOM ARE DISTRIBUTED

For a long time, electrons were perceived to be particles—infinitesimal "planets" orbiting the nucleus of an atom. In 1924, however, a French physicist named Louis de Broglie showed that electrons also have wavelike properties. He did this by combining a formula developed by Albert Einstein that relates mass and energy with a formula developed by Max Planck that relates frequency and energy. The realization that electrons have wavelike properties spurred physicists to propose a mathematical concept known as quantum mechanics.

Quantum mechanics uses the same mathematical equations that describe the wave motion of a guitar string to characterize the motion of an electron around a nucleus. The

The bronze sculpture of Albert Einstein, on the grounds of the National Academy of Sciences in Washington, D.C., measures 21 feet from the top of the head to the tip of the feet and weighs 7000 pounds. In his left hand, Einstein holds the mathematical equations that represent his three most important contributions to science: the photoelectric effect, the equivalency of energy and matter, and the theory of relativity. At his feet is a map of the sky.

version of quantum mechanics most useful to chemists was proposed by Erwin Schrödinger in 1926. According to Schrödinger, the behavior of each electron in an atom can be described by a **wave equation**. The solutions to the Schrödinger equation are called **wave functions** or **orbitals**. They tell us the *energy* of the electron and the *volume of space* around the nucleus where an electron is most likely to be found.

According to quantum mechanics, the electrons in an atom can be thought of as occupying a set of concentric shells that surround the nucleus. The first shell is the one closest to the nucleus. The second shell lies farther from the nucleus, and even farther out lie the third and higher numbered shells. Each shell contains subshells known as **atomic orbitals**. Each atomic orbital has a characteristic shape and energy and occupies a characteristic volume of space, which is predicted by the Schrödinger equation. An important point to remember is that *the closer the atomic orbital is to the nucleus, the lower is its energy.*

The first shell consists of only an *s* atomic orbital; the second shell consists of *s* and *p* atomic orbitals; the third shell consists of *s*, *p*, and *d* atomic orbitals; and the fourth and higher shells consist of *s, p, d,* and *f* atomic orbitals (Table 1.1).

B I O G R A P H Y

Louis Victor Pierre Raymond duc de Broglie (1892–1987) *was born in France and studied history at the Sorbonne. During World War I, he was stationed in the Eiffel Tower as a radio engineer. Intrigued by this exposure to radio communications, he returned to school after the war, earned a Ph.D. in physics, and became a professor of theoretical physics at the Faculté des Sciences at the Sorbonne. He received the Nobel Prize in Physics in 1929, five years after obtaining his degree, for his work that showed electrons to have properties of both particles and waves. In 1945, he became an adviser to the French Atomic Energy Commissariat.*

Table 1.1	Distribution of Electrons in the First Four Shells That Surround the Nucleus			
	First shell	**Second shell**	**Third shell**	**Fourth shell**
Atomic orbitals	*s*	*s, p*	*s, p, d*	*s, p, d, f*
Number of atomic orbitals	1	1, 3	1, 3, 5	1, 3, 5, 7
Maximum number of electrons	2	8	18	32

The closer the orbital is to the nucleus, the lower is its energy.

Each shell contains one *s* orbital. The second and higher shells—in addition to their *s* orbital—each contain three *degenerate p* orbitals. **Degenerate orbitals** are orbitals that have the same energy. The third and higher shells—in addition to their *s* and *p* orbitals—contain five degenerate *d* orbitals, and the fourth and higher shells also contain seven degenerate *f* orbitals. Because a maximum of two electrons can coexist in an atomic orbital (see the Pauli exclusion principle, below), the first shell, with only one atomic orbital, can contain no more than two electrons. The second shell, with four atomic orbitals—one *s* and three *p*—can have a total of eight electrons. Eighteen electrons can occupy the nine atomic orbitals—one *s*, three *p*, and five *d*—of the third shell, and 32 electrons can occupy the 16 atomic orbitals of the fourth shell. In studying organic chemistry, we will be concerned primarily with atoms that have electrons only in the first and second shells.

Degenerate orbitals are orbitals that have the same energy.

The **ground-state electronic configuration** of an atom describes the orbitals occupied by the atom's electrons when they are all in the available orbitals with the lowest energy. If energy is applied to an atom in the ground state, one or more electrons can jump into a higher energy orbital. The atom then would be in an **excited-state electronic configuration**. The ground-state electronic configurations of the 11 smallest atoms are shown in Table 1.2. (Each arrow—whether pointing up or down—represents one electron.) The following three rules specify which orbitals an atom's electrons occupy:

1. The **aufbau principle** (*aufbau* is German for "building up") tells us the first thing we need to know to be able to assign electrons to the various atomic orbitals. According to this principle, *an electron always goes into the available orbital with the lowest energy.*

An important point to remember is that *the closer the atomic orbital is to the nucleus, the lower is its energy.* Because a 1*s* orbital is closer to the nucleus, it is lower in energy than a 2*s* orbital, which is lower in energy—and closer to the nucleus—than a 3*s* orbital. Comparing atomic orbitals in the same shell, we see that an *s* orbital is lower in energy than a *p* orbital, and a *p* orbital is lower in energy than a *d* orbital.

Relative energies of atomic orbitals:

$$1s < 2s < 2p < 3s < 3p < 4s < 3d < 4p < 5s < 4d < 5p < 6s < 4f < 5d < 6p < 7s < 5f$$

2. The **Pauli exclusion principle** states that (a) *no more than two electrons can occupy each atomic orbital*, and (b) *the two electrons must be of opposite spin*.

B I O G R A P H Y

Erwin Schrödinger (1887–1961) *was teaching physics at the University of Berlin when Hitler rose to power. Although not Jewish, Schrödinger left Germany to return to his native Austria, only to see it taken over later by the Nazis. He moved to the School for Advanced Studies in Dublin and then to Oxford University. In 1933, he shared the Nobel Prize in Physics with Paul Dirac, a professor of physics at Cambridge University, for mathematical work on quantum mechanics.*

Albert Einstein

Albert Einstein (1879–1955) was born in Germany. When he was in high school, his father's business failed and his family moved to Milan, Italy. Although Einstein wanted to join his family in Italy, he had to stay behind because German law required military service after high school. To help him, his high school mathematics teacher wrote a letter saying that Einstein could have a nervous breakdown without his family and also that there was nothing left to teach him. Eventually, Einstein was asked to leave the school because of his disruptive behavior. Popular folklore says he left because of poor grades in Latin and Greek, but his grades in those subjects were fine. Einstein and his first wife, Mileva Maric, who was also a scientist, had a daughter and two sons. After their divorce, he married his cousin Elsa.

Einstein was visiting the United States when Hitler came to power, so he accepted a position at the Institute for Advanced Study in Princeton, New Jersey, becoming a U.S. citizen in 1940. Although a lifelong pacifist, he wrote a letter to President Roosevelt warning of ominous advances in German nuclear research. This led to the creation of the Manhattan Project, which developed the atomic bomb and tested it in New Mexico in 1945.

 Max Karl Ernst Ludwig Planck

Max Planck (1858–1947) was born in Germany, the son of a professor of civil law. He himself was a professor at the Universities of Kiel (1885–1889) and Berlin (1889–1926). Two of his daughters died in childbirth, and one of his sons was killed in action in World War I. In 1918, Planck received the Nobel Prize in Physics for his development of quantum theory. He became president of the Kaiser Wilhelm Society of Berlin—later renamed the Max Planck Society—in 1930. Planck felt that it was his duty to remain in Germany during the Nazi era, but he never supported the Nazi regime. He unsuccessfully interceded with Hitler on behalf of his Jewish colleagues and, as a consequence, was forced to resign from the presidency of the Kaiser Wilhelm Society in 1937. A second son was accused of taking part in the plot to kill Hitler and was executed. Planck lost his home to Allied bombings. He was rescued by Allied forces during the final days of the war.

It is called an exclusion principle because it limits the number of electrons that can occupy any particular shell. (Notice in Table 1.2 that spin in one direction is designated by ↑, and spin in the opposite direction by ↓.)

From these first two rules, we can assign electrons to atomic orbitals for atoms that contain one, two, three, four, or five electrons. The single electron of a hydrogen atom occupies a $1s$ orbital, the second electron of a helium atom fills the $1s$ orbital, the third electron of a lithium atom occupies a $2s$ orbital, the fourth electron of a beryllium atom fills the $2s$ orbital, and the fifth electron of a boron atom occupies one of the $2p$ orbitals. (The subscripts x, y, and z distinguish the three $2p$ orbitals.) Because the three p orbitals are degenerate, the electron can be put into any one of them. Before we can discuss atoms containing six or more electrons, we need Hund's rule:

3. **Hund's rule** states that when there are degenerate orbitals—two or more orbitals with the same energy—an electron will occupy an empty orbital before it will pair up with another electron. In this way, electron repulsion is minimized.

Atom	Name of element	Atomic number	1s	2s	2p$_x$	2p$_y$	2p$_z$	3s
H	Hydrogen	1	↑					
He	Helium	2	↑↓					
Li	Lithium	3	↑↓					
Be	Beryllium	4	↑↓	↑↓				
B	Boron	5	↑↓	↑↓	↑			
C	Carbon	6	↑↓	↑↓	↑	↑		
N	Nitrogen	7	↑↓	↑↓	↑	↑	↑	
O	Oxygen	8	↑↓	↑↓	↑↓	↑	↑	
F	Fluorine	9	↑↓	↑↓	↑↓	↑↓	↑	
Ne	Neon	10	↑↓	↑↓	↑↓	↑↓	↑↓	
Na	Sodium	11	↑↓	↑↓	↑↓	↑↓	↑↓	↑

Table 1.2   The Electronic Configurations of the Smallest Atoms

As a teenager, Austrian **Wolfgang Pauli (1900–1958)** *wrote articles on relativity that caught the attention of Albert Einstein. Pauli went on to teach physics at the University of Hamburg and at the Zurich Institute of Technology. When World War II broke out, he immigrated to the United States, where he joined the Institute for Advanced Study at Princeton.*

The sixth electron of a carbon atom, therefore, goes into an empty 2*p* orbital, rather than pairing up with the electron already occupying a 2*p* orbital (see Table 1.2). There is one more empty 2*p* orbital, so that is where nitrogen's seventh electron goes. The eighth electron of an oxygen atom pairs up with an electron occupying a 2*p* orbital rather than going into the higher-energy 3*s* orbital.

The locations of the electrons in the remaining elements can be assigned using these three rules.

Electrons in inner shells (those below the outermost shell) are called **core electrons**. Core electrons do not participate in chemical bonding. Electrons in the outermost shell are called **valence electrons**. Carbon, for example, has two core electrons and four valence electrons (Table 1.2). Lithium and sodium each have one valence electron. If you examine the periodic table inside the back cover of this book, you will see that lithium and sodium are in the same column. Elements in the same column of the periodic table have the same number of valence electrons. Because the number of valence electrons is the major factor determining an element's chemical properties, elements in the same column of the periodic table have similar chemical properties. Thus, the chemical behavior of an element depends on its electronic configuration.

chem Tutorial:
place   Electrons in orbitals

PROBLEM 2♦

How many valence electrons do the following atoms have?
a. boron   **b.** nitrogen   **c.** oxygen   **d.** fluorine

PROBLEM 3♦

a. Write electronic configurations for chlorine (atomic number 17), bromine (atomic number 35), and iodine (atomic number 53).
b. How many valence electrons do chlorine, bromine, and iodine have?

PROBLEM 4

Look at the relative positions of each pair of atoms in the periodic table. How many core electrons does each have? How many valence electrons does each have?

a. carbon and silicon   **c.** nitrogen and phosphorus
b. oxygen and sulfur   **d.** magnesium and calcium

Friedrich Hermann Hund (1896–1997) *was born in Germany. He was a professor of physics at several German universities, the last being the University of Göttingen. He spent a year as a visiting professor at Harvard University. In February 1996, the University of Göttingen held a symposium to honor Hund on his 100th birthday.*

1.3 IONIC AND COVALENT BONDS

In trying to explain why atoms form bonds, G. N. Lewis proposed that *an atom is most stable if its outer shell is either filled or contains eight electrons, and it has no electrons of higher energy.* According to Lewis's theory, an atom will give up, accept, or share electrons in order to achieve a filled outer shell or an outer shell that contains eight electrons. This theory has come to be called the **octet rule** (even though hydrogen has only two electrons in its filled outer shell).

Lithium (Li) has a single electron in its $2s$ orbital. If it loses this electron, the lithium atom ends up with a filled outer shell—a stable configuration. Lithium, therefore, loses an electron relatively easily. Sodium (Na) has a single electron in its $3s$ orbital, so it too loses an electron easily. Elements (such as lithium and sodium) that readily lose an electron and thereby become positively charged are said to be **electropositive**. The elements in the first column of the periodic table are all electropositive—each readily loses an electron because each has a single electron in its outermost shell.

When we draw the electrons around an atom, as in the following equations, core electrons are not shown; only valence electrons are shown because only valence electrons are used in bonding. Each valence electron is shown as a dot. Notice that when the single valence electron of lithium or sodium is removed, the species that is formed is called an ion because it carries a charge.

Fluorine has seven valence electrons (Table 1.2). Consequently, it readily acquires an electron in order to have an outer shell of eight electrons. Elements in the same column as fluorine (for example, chlorine, bromine, and iodine) also need only one electron to have an outer shell of eight, so they, too, readily acquire an electron. Elements that readily acquire an electron are said to be **electronegative**—they acquire an electron easily and thereby become negatively charged.

PROBLEM 5♦

  a. Find potassium (K) in the periodic table and predict how many valence electrons it has.
  b. What orbital does the unpaired electron occupy?

Ionic Bonds Are Formed by the Attraction Between Ions of Opposite Charge

We have just seen that sodium gives up an electron easily and chlorine readily acquires an electron. Therefore, when sodium metal and chlorine gas are mixed, each sodium atom transfers an electron to a chlorine atom, and crystalline sodium chloride (table salt) is formed as a result. The positively charged sodium ions and negatively charged chloride ions are independent species held together by the attraction of opposite charges (Figure 1.1).

A **bond** is an attractive force between two ions or between two atoms. Attractive forces between opposite charges are called **electrostatic attractions**. A **bond** that results from *the electrostatic attraction between ions of opposite charge* is called an **ionic bond**.

an ionic bond is the attraction between ions of opposite charges

$:\ddot{\underset{..}{Cl}}:^-$ Na^+ $:\ddot{\underset{..}{Cl}}:^-$

Na^+ $:\ddot{\underset{..}{Cl}}:^-$ Na^+

$:\ddot{\underset{..}{Cl}}:^-$ Na^+ $:\ddot{\underset{..}{Cl}}:^-$

sodium chloride

a.

b.

◄ **Figure 1.1**
(a) Crystalline sodium chloride. (b) The electron-rich chloride ions are red, and the electron-poor sodium ions are blue. Each chloride ion is surrounded by six sodium ions, and each sodium ion is surrounded by six chloride ions. Ignore the sticks holding the balls together; they are there only to keep the model from falling apart.

Sodium chloride is an example of an ionic compound. **Ionic compounds** are formed when an element on the left side of the periodic table (an electropositive element) transfers one or more electrons to an element on the right side of the periodic table (an electronegative element).

Covalent Bonds Are Formed by Sharing Electrons

Instead of giving up or acquiring electrons, an atom can achieve a filled outer shell by sharing electrons. For example, two fluorine atoms can each attain a filled second shell by sharing their unpaired valence electrons. A bond formed as a result of *sharing electrons* is called a **covalent bond**.

a covalent bond is formed by sharing electrons

$:\ddot{\underset{..}{F}}\cdot \;+\; \cdot\ddot{\underset{..}{F}}: \;\longrightarrow\; :\ddot{\underset{..}{F}}\!:\!\ddot{\underset{..}{F}}:$

Two hydrogen atoms can form a covalent bond by sharing electrons. As a result of covalent bonding, each hydrogen acquires a stable, filled first shell.

$$H\cdot \;+\; \cdot H \;\longrightarrow\; H\!:\!H$$

Similarly, hydrogen and chlorine can form a covalent bond by sharing electrons. In doing so, hydrogen fills its only shell, and chlorine achieves an outer shell of eight electrons.

$$H\cdot \;+\; \cdot\ddot{\underset{..}{Cl}}: \;\longrightarrow\; H\!:\!\ddot{\underset{..}{Cl}}:$$

A hydrogen atom can achieve a completely empty shell by losing an electron. Loss of its sole electron results in a positively charged **hydrogen ion**. A positively charged hydrogen ion is called a **proton** because when a hydrogen atom loses its valence electron, only the hydrogen nucleus—which consists of a single proton—remains. A hydrogen atom can achieve a filled outer shell by gaining an electron, thereby forming a negatively charged hydrogen ion, called a **hydride ion**.

$$H\cdot \;\longrightarrow\; H^+ \;+\; e^-$$
a hydrogen atom **a proton**

$$H\cdot \;+\; e^- \;\longrightarrow\; H\!:^-$$
a hydrogen atom **a hydride ion**

Because oxygen has six valence electrons, it needs to form two covalent bonds to achieve an outer shell of eight electrons. Nitrogen, with five valence electrons, must form three covalent bonds, and carbon, with four valence electrons, must form four covalent bonds to achieve a filled outer shell. Notice that all the atoms in water, ammonia, and methane have filled outer shells.

$$2\ \text{H·} + \text{·}\ddot{\text{O}}\text{:} \longrightarrow \text{H:}\ddot{\text{O}}\text{:} \quad \boxed{\text{oxygen has formed 2 covalent bonds}}$$
$$\overset{..}{\underset{\text{H}}{}}$$

water

$$3\ \text{H·} + \text{·}\dot{\ddot{\text{N}}}\text{·} \longrightarrow \text{H:}\ddot{\text{N}}\text{:H} \quad \boxed{\text{nitrogen has formed 3 covalent bonds}}$$
$$\underset{\text{H}}{}$$

ammonia

$$4\ \text{H·} + \text{·}\dot{\text{C}}\text{·} \longrightarrow \overset{\text{H}}{\text{H:}\overset{..}{\text{C}}\text{:H}} \quad \boxed{\text{carbon has formed 4 covalent bonds}}$$
$$\underset{\text{H}}{}$$

methane

Polar Covalent Bonds

The atoms that share the bonding electrons in the F—F and H—H covalent bonds are identical. Therefore, they share the electrons equally; that is, each electron spends as much time in the vicinity of one atom as in the other. Such a bond is called a **nonpolar covalent bond**.

In contrast, the bonding electrons in hydrogen chloride, water, and ammonia are more attracted to one atom than to another because the atoms that share the electrons in these molecules are different and have different electronegativities. **Electronegativity** is a measure of the ability of an atom to pull the bonding electrons toward itself. The bonding electrons in hydrogen chloride, water, and ammonia are more attracted to the atom with the greater electronegativity. The bonds in these compounds are called polar covalent bonds. A **polar covalent bond** is a covalent bond between atoms of different electronegativities. The electronegativities of some of the elements are shown in Table 1.3. Notice that electronegativity increases from left to right across a row of the periodic table or going up any of the columns.

chem Tutorial:
place Periodic trends in electronegativity

Table 1.3   The Electronegativities of Selected Elements[a]

IA	IIA	IB	IIB	IIIA	IVA	VA	VIA	VIIA
H 2.1								
Li 1.0	Be 1.5			B 2.0	C 2.5	N 3.0	O 3.5	F 4.0
Na 0.9	Mg 1.2			Al 1.5	Si 1.8	P 2.1	S 2.5	Cl 3.0
K 0.8	Ca 1.0							Br 2.8
								I 2.5

increasing electronegativity →

increasing electronegativity ↑

[a]Electronegativity values are relative, not absolute. As a result, there are several scales of electronegativities. The electronegativities listed here are from the scale devised by Linus Pauling.

A polar covalent bond has a slight positive charge on one end and a slight negative charge on the other. Polarity in a covalent bond is indicated by the symbols δ^+ and δ^-, which denote partial positive and partial negative charges, respectively. The negative end of the bond is the end that has the more electronegative atom. The greater the difference in electronegativity between the bonded atoms, the more polar the bond will be. (Notice that a pair of shared electrons can be shown as a line between two atoms.)

The direction of bond polarity can be indicated with an arrow. By convention, chemists draw the arrow so that it points in the direction in which the electrons are pulled. Thus, the head of the arrow is at the negative end of the bond; a short perpendicular line near the tail of the arrow marks the positive end of the bond. (Physicists draw the arrow in the opposite direction.)

You can think of ionic bonds and nonpolar covalent bonds as being at the opposite ends of a continuum of bond types. All bonds fall somewhere on this line. At one end is an ionic bond, a bond in which there is no sharing of electrons. At the other end is a nonpolar covalent bond, a bond in which the electrons are shared equally. Polar covalent bonds fall somewhere in between. The greater the difference in electronegativity between the atoms forming the bond, the closer the bond is to the ionic end of the continuum.

C—H bonds are relatively nonpolar, because carbon and hydrogen have similar electronegativities (electronegativity difference = 0.4; see Table 1.3); N—H bonds are more polar (electronegativity difference = 0.9), but not as polar as O—H bonds (electronegativity difference = 1.4). Even closer to the ionic end of the continuum is the bond between sodium and chloride ions (electronegativity difference = 2.1), but sodium chloride is not as ionic as potassium fluoride (electronegativity difference = 3.2).

PROBLEM 6◆

Which bond is more polar?

a. H—CH$_3$ or Cl—CH$_3$ **c.** H—Cl or H—F

b. H—OH or H—H   **d.** Cl—Cl or Cl—CH$_3$

PROBLEM 7◆

Which of the following has

a. the most polar bond?   **b.** the least polar bond?

    NaI   LiBr   Cl$_2$ KCl

chem place Tutorial: Electronegativity differences and bond types

A polar bond has a **dipole**—it has a negative end and a positive end. The size of the dipole is indicated by the dipole moment, symbolized by the Greek letter μ. The **dipole moment** of a bond is equal to the magnitude of the charge (e) on the atom (either the partial positive charge or the partial negative charge, because they have the same magnitude) times the distance between the two charges (d):

$$\text{dipole moment} = \mu = e \times d$$

Peter Debye (1884–1966) *was born in the Netherlands. He taught at the Universities of Zürich (succeeding Einstein), Leipzig, and Berlin, but returned to his homeland in 1939 when the Nazis ordered him to become a German citizen. Upon visiting Cornell to give a lecture, he decided to stay in the United States, and he became a U.S. citizen in 1946. He received the Nobel Prize in chemistry in 1936 for his work on dipole moments and on the diffraction of X-rays and electrons in gases.*

A dipole moment is reported in a unit called a **debye (D)** (pronounced de-bye). Because the charge on an electron is 4.80×10^{-10} electrostatic units (esu) and the distance between charges in a polar bond will have units of 10^{-8} cm, the product of charge and distance will have units of 10^{-18} esu cm. Thus, $1.0\,D = 1.0 \times 10^{-18}$ esu cm, so a dipole moment of 1.5×10^{-18} esu cm can be more simply stated as 1.5 D. The dipole moments of some bonds commonly found in organic compounds are listed in Table 1.4.

Table 1.4	The Dipole Moments of Some Commonly Encountered Bonds		
Bond	**Dipole moment (D)**	**Bond**	**Dipole moment (D)**
H—C	0.4	C—C	0
H—N	1.3	C—N	0.2
H—O	1.5	C—O	0.7
H—F	1.7	C—F	1.6
H—Cl	1.1	C—Cl	1.5
H—Br	0.8	C—Br	1.4
H—I	0.4	C—I	1.2

When a molecule has only one covalent bond and the bond is polar, the molecule has a dipole moment that is identical to the dipole moment of the bond. For example, the dipole moment of hydrogen chloride (HCl) is 1.1 D because the dipole moment of the H—Cl bond is 1.1 D. The dipole moment of a molecule with more than one covalent bond depends on the dipole moments of all the bonds in the molecule and the geometry of the molecule. We will examine the dipole moments of molecules with more than one covalent bond in Section 1.15 after you learn about the geometry of molecules.

PROBLEM 8   **SOLVED**

Determine the partial negative charge on the fluorine atom in a C—F bond. The bond length is 1.39 Å* and the bond dipole moment is 1.60 D.

Solution   If there were a full negative charge on the fluorine atom, the dipole moment would be

$$(4.80 \times 10^{-10}\ \text{esu})\,(1.39 \times 10^{-8}\ \text{cm}) = 6.97\ \text{esu cm} = 6.97\ \text{D}$$

Knowing that the dipole moment is 1.60 D, we calculate that the partial negative charge on the fluorine atom is about 0.23 of a full charge:

$$\frac{1.60}{6.97} = 0.23$$

PROBLEM 9

Explain why HCl has a smaller dipole moment than HF, even though the H—Cl bond is longer than the H—F bond.

PROBLEM 10♦

Use the symbols δ^+ and δ^- to show the direction of polarity of the indicated bond in each of the following compounds, for example,

$$\overset{\delta^+\quad\ \delta^-}{H_3C—OH}$$

a. HO—H   **c.** $H_3C—NH_2$ **e.** HO—Br   **g.** I—Cl
b. F—Br   **d.** $H_3C—Cl$ **f.** $H_3C—MgBr$ **h.** $H_2N—OH$

---

*The angstrom (Å) is not a Système International unit. Those who opt to adhere strictly to SI units can convert it into picometers: 1 picometer (pm) $= 10^{-12}$ m; 1 Å $= 10^{-10}$ m $= 100$ pm. Because the angstrom continues to be used by many organic chemists, we will use angstroms in this book.

Understanding bond polarity is critical to understanding how organic reactions occur, because a central rule governing the reactivity of organic compounds is that *electron-rich atoms or molecules are attracted to electron-deficient atoms or molecules* (Section 3.6). **Electrostatic potential maps** (often called simply potential maps) are models that show how charge is distributed in the molecule under the map. They, therefore, show the kind of electrostatic attraction an atom or molecule has for another atom or molecule. The potential maps for LiH, H_2, and HF are shown below.

LiH H_2 HF

The colors on a potential map indicate the degree to which a molecule or an atom in a molecule attracts charged particles. Red, signifying the most negative electrostatic potential, is used for regions that attract positively charged molecules most strongly. Blue is used for areas with the most positive electrostatic potential, regions that attract negatively charged molecules most strongly. Other colors indicate intermediate levels of attraction.

The colors on a potential map can also be used to estimate charge distribution. For example, the potential map for LiH indicates that the hydrogen atom is more electron-rich than the lithium atom. By comparing the three maps, we can tell that the hydrogen in LiH is more electron-rich than a hydrogen in H_2, and the hydrogen in HF is less electron-rich than a hydrogen in H_2.

A molecule's size and shape are determined by the number of electrons in the molecule and by the way these electrons move. Because a potential map roughly marks the "edge" of the molecule's electron cloud, the map tells us something about the relative size and shape of the molecule. Notice that a given kind of atom can have different sizes in different molecules. The negatively charged hydrogen in LiH is bigger than a neutral hydrogen in H_2, which, in turn, is bigger than the positively charged hydrogen in HF.

PROBLEM 11 ◆

After examining the potential maps for LiH, HF, and H_2, answer the following questions:

a. Which compounds are polar?

b. Why does LiH have the largest hydrogen?

c. Which compound has the hydrogen that would be most apt to attract a negatively charged molecule?

1.4 HOW THE STRUCTURE OF A COMPOUND IS REPRESENTED

First we will see how compounds are drawn using Lewis structures. Then we will look at the kinds of structures that are used more commonly for organic compounds.

Lewis Structures

The chemical symbols we have been using, in which the valence electrons are represented as dots, are called **Lewis structures**. Lewis structures are useful because they show us which atoms are bonded together and tell us whether any atoms possess *lone-pair electrons* or have a *formal charge*, two concepts we describe below. The Lewis structures for H_2O, H_3O^+, HO^-, and H_2O_2 are:

Notice that the atoms in Lewis structures are always lined up linearly or at right angles. Therefore, they do not tell us anything about the bond angles in the actual molecule.

When you draw a Lewis structure, make sure that hydrogen atoms are surrounded by no more than two electrons and that C, O, N, and halogen (F, Cl, Br, I) atoms are surrounded by no more than eight electrons, in accordance with the octet rule. Valence electrons not used in bonding are called **nonbonding electrons** or **lone-pair electrons**.

Once you have the atoms and the electrons in place, you must examine each atom to see whether a formal charge should be assigned to it. A **formal charge** is the *difference* between the number of valence electrons an atom has when it is not bonded to any other atoms and the number it "owns" when it is bonded. An atom "owns" all of its lone-pair electrons and half of its bonding (shared) electrons.

formal charge = number of valence electrons

      − (number of lone-pair electrons + 1/2 number of bonding electrons)

For example, an oxygen atom has six valence electrons (Table 1.2). In water (H_2O), oxygen "owns" six electrons (four lone-pair electrons and half of the four bonding electrons). Because the number of electrons it "owns" is equal to the number of its valence electrons ($6 - 6 = 0$), the oxygen atom in water has no formal charge. The oxygen atom in the hydronium ion (H_3O^+) "owns" five electrons: two lone-pair electrons plus three (half of six) bonding electrons. Because the number of electrons it "owns" is one less than the number of its valence electrons ($6 - 5 = 1$), its formal charge is +1. The oxygen atom in the hydroxide ion (HO^-) "owns" seven electrons: six lone-pair electrons plus one (half of two) bonding electron. Because it "owns" one more electron than the number of its valence electrons ($6 - 7 = -1$), its formal charge is −1.

H_2O H_3O^+ HO^-

PROBLEM 12 ◆

A formal charge does not necessarily indicate that the atom with the formal change has greater or less electron density than atoms in the molecule without formal charges. We can see this by examining the potential maps for H_2O, H_3O^+, and HO^-.

a. Which atom bears the formal negative charge in the hydroxide ion?
b. Which atom has the greater electron density in the hydroxide ion?
c. Which atom bears the formal positive charge in the hydronium ion?
d. Which atom has the least electron density in the hydronium ion?

Nitrogen has five valence electrons (Table 1.2). Prove to yourself that the appropriate formal charges have been assigned to the nitrogen atoms in the following Lewis structures:

Carbon has four valence electrons. Take a moment to make sure you understand why the carbon atoms in the following Lewis structures have the indicated formal charges:

$$H:\overset{\displaystyle H}{\underset{\displaystyle H}{\overset{\cdot\cdot}{C}}}:H \qquad H:\overset{\displaystyle H}{\underset{\displaystyle H}{C^{+}}} \qquad H:\overset{\displaystyle H}{\underset{\displaystyle H}{\overset{\cdot\cdot}{C}}}:^{-} \qquad H:\overset{\displaystyle H}{\underset{\displaystyle H}{\overset{\cdot}{C}}}\cdot \qquad H:\overset{\displaystyle H\ H}{\underset{\displaystyle H\ H}{C:C}}:H$$

| methane | methyl cation a carbocation | methyl anion a carbanion | methyl radical | ethane |

A species containing a positively charged carbon atom is called a **carbocation**, and a species containing a negatively charged carbon atom is called a **carbanion**. (Recall that a *cation* is a positively charged ion and an *anion* is a negatively charged ion.) A species containing an atom with a single unpaired electron is called a **radical** (often called a **free radical**).

Hydrogen has one valence electron, and each halogen (F, Cl, Br, I) has seven valence electrons, so the following species have the indicated formal charges:

$$H^{+} \qquad H:^{-} \qquad H\cdot \qquad :\overset{\cdot\cdot}{\underset{\cdot\cdot}{Br}}:^{-} \qquad :\overset{\cdot\cdot}{\underset{\cdot\cdot}{Br}}\cdot \qquad :\overset{\cdot\cdot}{\underset{\cdot\cdot}{Br}}:\overset{\cdot\cdot}{\underset{\cdot\cdot}{Br}}: \qquad :\overset{\cdot\cdot}{\underset{\cdot\cdot}{Cl}}:\overset{\cdot\cdot}{\underset{\cdot\cdot}{Cl}}:$$

| hydrogen ion | hydride ion | hydrogen radical | bromide ion | bromine radical | bromine | chlorine |

PROBLEM 13

Give each atom the appropriate formal charge:

a. $CH_3-\overset{\cdot\cdot}{\underset{\displaystyle H}{O}}-CH_3$

b. $H-\overset{\cdot\cdot}{\underset{\displaystyle H}{C}}-H$

c. $CH_3-\overset{\displaystyle CH_3}{\underset{\displaystyle CH_3}{N}}-CH_3$

d. $H-\overset{\displaystyle H\ \ H}{\underset{\displaystyle H\ \ H}{N-B}}-H$

chem place Tutorial: Formal charges

In studying the molecules in this section, notice that when the atoms do not bear a formal charge or an unpaired electron, hydrogen and the halogens always have *one* covalent bond, oxygen always has *two* covalent bonds, nitrogen always has *three* covalent bonds, and carbon has *four* covalent bonds. Atoms that have more bonds or fewer bonds than the number required for a neutral atom will have either a formal charge or an unpaired electron. These numbers are very important to remember when you are first drawing structures of organic compounds because they provide a quick way to recognize when you have made a mistake.

$$H- \qquad \overset{\displaystyle :\overset{\cdot\cdot}{\underset{\cdot\cdot}{F}}-\ :\overset{\cdot\cdot}{\underset{\cdot\cdot}{Cl}}-}{:\overset{\cdot\cdot}{\underset{\cdot\cdot}{I}}-\ :\overset{\cdot\cdot}{\underset{\cdot\cdot}{Br}}-} \qquad :\overset{\cdot\cdot}{\underset{\displaystyle |}{O}}- \qquad -\overset{\cdot\cdot}{\underset{\displaystyle |}{N}}- \qquad -\overset{\displaystyle |}{\underset{\displaystyle |}{C}}-$$

| one bond | one bond | two bonds | three bonds | four bonds |

In the following Lewis structures notice that each atom has a filled outer shell. Also notice that since none of the molecules has a formal charge or an unpaired electron, H and Br each form one bond, O forms two bonds (these can be two single bonds or one double bond), N forms three bonds (these can be three single bonds, one double bond and one single bond, or one triple bond), and C forms a total of four bonds. (In drawing the Lewis structure for a compound that has two or more oxygen atoms, avoid oxygen–oxygen single bonds. These are weak bonds, and few compounds have them.)

When it is neutral:
C forms 4 bonds
N forms 3 bonds
O forms 2 bonds
H forms 1 bond
Halogen forms 1 bond

two covalent bonds holding two atoms together is called a double bond

three covalent bonds holding two atoms together is called a triple bond

We have seen that a pair of shared electrons can also be shown as a line between two atoms (Section 1.3). Compare the preceding structures with the following ones:

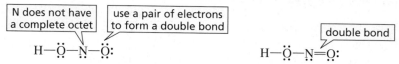

PROBLEM-SOLVING STRATEGY

Drawing Lewis Structures

Draw the Lewis structure for HNO_2.

1. Determine the total number of valence electrons (1 for H, 5 for N, and 6 for each O adds up to $1 + 5 + 12 = 18$.
2. Use the total number of valence electrons to form bonds and fill octets with lone-pair electrons.
3. If after all the electrons have been assigned, an atom (other than hydrogen) does not have a complete octet, use a lone pair to form a double bond to that atom.
4. Assign a formal charge to any atom whose number of valence electrons is not equal to the number of its lone-pair electrons plus one-half its bonding electrons. (None of the atoms in HNO_2 has a formal charge.)

N does not have a complete octet	use a pair of electrons to form a double bond

$$H—\overset{..}{\underset{..}{O}}—N—\overset{..}{\underset{..}{O}}:$$

18 electrons have been assigned

double bond

$$H—\overset{..}{\underset{..}{O}}—N=\overset{..}{\underset{}{O}}:$$

using one of oxygen's lone pairs to form a double bond gives N a complete octet

Now continue on to Problem 14.

PROBLEM 14   SOLVED

Draw the Lewis structure for each of the following:

a. NO_3^- c. $^-C_2H_5$ e. $CH_3\overset{+}{N}H_3$ g. HCO_3^-
b. NO_2^+ d. $^+C_2H_5$ f. NaOH   h. H_2CO

Solution to 14a   The only way we can arrange one N and three O's and avoid O—O single bonds is to place the three O's around the N. The total number of valence electrons is 23 (5 for N, and 6 for each of the three O's). Because the species has one negative charge, we must add 1 to the number of valence electrons, for a total of 24. We then use the 24 electrons to form bonds and fill octets with lone-pair electrons.

$$:\overset{..}{\underset{}{O}}:$$
$$:\overset{..}{\underset{..}{O}}—N—\overset{..}{\underset{..}{O}}:$$

incomplete octet

When all 24 electrons have been assigned, we see that N does not have a complete octet. We complete N's octet by using one of oxygen's lone pairs to form a double bond. (It does not make a difference which oxygen atom we choose.) When we check each atom to see whether it has a formal charge, we find that two of the O's are negatively charged and the N is positively charged, for an overall charge of -1.

$$:\overset{..}{\underset{}{O}}:$$
$$:\overset{..}{\underset{..}{O}}—\overset{+}{N}—\overset{..}{\underset{..}{O}}:$$

Solution to 14b   The total number of valence electrons is 17 (5 for N and 6 for each of the two O's). Because the species has one positive charge, we must subtract 1 from the number of valence electrons, for a total of 16. The 16 electrons are used to form bonds and then fill octets with lone-pair electrons.

$$\boxed{\text{incomplete octet}}$$
$$:\ddot{O}\!-\!N\!-\!\ddot{O}:$$

Two double bonds are necessary to complete N's octet. The N has a formal charge of $+1$.

$$:\ddot{O}\!=\!\overset{+}{N}\!=\!\ddot{O}:$$

chem Tutorial:
place Lewis structure

PROBLEM 15◆

a. Draw two Lewis structures for C_2H_6O.
b. Draw three Lewis structures for C_3H_8O.

(*Hint:* The two Lewis structures in part **a** are **constitutional isomers**, molecules that have the same atoms, but differ in the way the atoms are connected; see page 195. The three Lewis structures in part **b** are also constitutional isomers.)

Kekulé Structures

In **Kekulé structures**, the bonding electrons are drawn as lines and the lone-pair electrons are usually left out entirely, unless they are needed to draw attention to some chemical property of the molecule. (Although lone-pair electrons are not shown, you should remember that neutral nitrogen, oxygen, and halogen atoms always have them: one pair in the case of nitrogen, two pairs in the case of oxygen, and three pairs in the case of a halogen.)

Condensed Structures

Frequently, structures are simplified by omitting some (or all) of the covalent bonds and listing atoms bonded to a particular carbon (or nitrogen or oxygen) next to it with subscripts as necessary. These structures are called **condensed structures**. Compare the following examples with the Kekulé structures shown above:

$$CH_3Br \qquad CH_3OCH_3 \qquad HCO_2H \qquad CH_3NH_2 \qquad N_2$$

You can find more examples of condensed structures and the conventions commonly used to create them in Table 1.5. Notice that since none of the molecules in Table 1.5 has a formal charge or an unpaired electron, each C has four bonds, each N has three bonds, each O has two bonds, and each H or halogen has one bond.

PROBLEM 16◆

Draw the lone-pair electrons that are not shown in the following structures:

a. $CH_3CH_2NH_2$ c. CH_3CH_2OH e. CH_3CH_2Cl
b. CH_3NHCH_3 d. CH_3OCH_3 f. $HONH_2$

Table 1.5   Kekulé and Condensed Structures

Kekulé structure	Condensed structures

Atoms bonded to a carbon are shown to the right of the carbon. Atoms other than H can be shown hanging from the carbon.

$CH_3CHBrCH_2CH_2CHClCH_3$ or $CH_3CHCH_2CH_2CHCH_3$ with Br and Cl hanging below.

Repeating CH_2 groups can be shown in parentheses.

$CH_3CH_2CH_2CH_2CH_2CH_3$ or $CH_3(CH_2)_4CH_3$

Groups bonded to a carbon can be shown (in parentheses) to the right of the carbon, or hanging from the carbon.

$CH_3CH_2CH(CH_3)CH_2CH(OH)CH_3$ or $CH_3CH_2CHCH_2CHCH_3$ with CH_3 and OH hanging below.

Groups bonded to the far-right carbon are not put in parentheses.

$CH_3CH_2C(CH_3)_2CH_2CH_2OH$ or $CH_3CH_2CCH_2CH_2OH$ with CH_3 above and CH_3 below.

Two or more identical groups considered bonded to the "first" atom on the left can be shown (in parentheses) to the left of that atom, or hanging from the atom.

$(CH_3)_2NCH_2CH_2CH_3$ or $CH_3NCH_2CH_2CH_3$ with CH_3 hanging below.

$(CH_3)_2CHCH_2CH_2CH_3$ or $CH_3CHCH_2CH_2CH_3$ with CH_3 hanging below.

An oxygen doubly bonded to a carbon can be shown hanging off the carbon or to the right of the carbon.

$$CH_3CH_2\overset{\overset{\displaystyle O}{\|}}{C}CH_3 \quad \text{or} \quad CH_3CH_2COCH_3 \quad \text{or} \quad CH_3CH_2C(=\!\!=\!O)CH_3$$

$$CH_3CH_2CH_2\overset{\overset{\displaystyle O}{\|}}{C}H \quad \text{or} \quad CH_3CH_2CH_2CHO \quad \text{or} \quad CH_3CH_2CH_2CH=\!\!=O$$

$$CH_3CH_2\overset{\overset{\displaystyle O}{\|}}{C}OH \quad \text{or} \quad CH_3CH_2CO_2H \quad \text{or} \quad CH_3CH_2COOH$$

$$CH_3CH_2\overset{\overset{\displaystyle O}{\|}}{C}OCH_3 \quad \text{or} \quad CH_3CH_2CO_2CH_3 \quad \text{or} \quad CH_3CH_2COOCH_3$$

PROBLEM 17 ◆

Draw condensed structures for the compounds represented by the following models (black = C, white = H, red = O, blue = N, green = Cl):

a.

b.

c.

d.

PROBLEM 18 ◆

Which of the atoms in the molecular models in Problem 17 have:

a. three lone pairs   b. two lone pairs   c. one lone pair   d. no lone pairs

PROBLEM 19

Expand the following condensed structures to show the covalent bonds and lone-pair electrons:

a. $CH_3NH(CH_2)_2CH_3$ c. $(CH_3)_3CBr$
b. $(CH_3)_2CHCl$ d. $(CH_3)_3C(CH_2)_3CH(CH_3)_2$

1.5 ATOMIC ORBITALS

We have seen that electrons are distributed into different atomic orbitals (Table 1.2), three-dimensional regions around the nucleus where electrons are most likely to be found. The **Heisenberg uncertainty principle**, however, states that both the precise location and the momentum of an atomic particle cannot be simultaneously determined. This means that we can never say precisely where an electron is—we can only describe its probable location. Mathematical calculations indicate that an *s* atomic orbital is a sphere with the nucleus at its center, and experimental evidence supports this theory. Thus, when we say that an electron occupies a 1*s* orbital, we mean that there is a greater than 90% probability that the electron is in the space defined by the sphere.

An orbital tells us the volume of space around the nucleus where an electron is most likely to be found.

Because the second shell lies farther from the nucleus than the first shell (Section 1.2), the average distance from the nucleus is greater for an electron in a 2*s* orbital than it is for an electron in a 1*s* orbital. A 2*s* orbital, therefore, is represented by a larger sphere. Because of the greater size of a 2*s* orbital, the average electron density there is less than the average electron density in a 1*s* orbital.

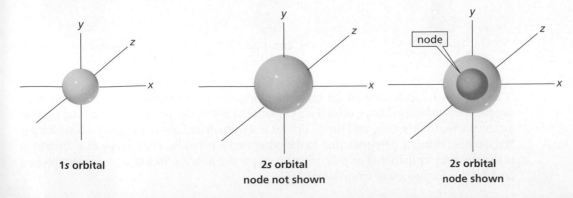

1s orbital

2s orbital
node not shown

2s orbital
node shown

An electron in a 1*s* orbital can be anywhere within the 1*s* sphere, but a 2*s* orbital has a region where the probability of finding an electron falls to zero. This is called a **node**, or, more precisely a **radial node** since this absence of electron density lies at one set distance from the nucleus. So a 2*s* electron can be found anywhere within the 2*s* sphere—including the region of space defined by the 1*s* sphere—except at the node.

To understand why nodes occur, you need to remember that electrons have both particlelike and wavelike properties. A node is a consequence of the wavelike properties of an electron. There are two types of waves: traveling waves and standing waves. Traveling waves move through space; light is an example of a traveling wave. A standing wave, in contrast, is confined to a limited space. A vibrating string of a guitar is an example of a standing wave—the string moves up and down, but does not travel through space. If you were to write a wave equation for the guitar string, the wave function would be (+) in the region above where the guitar string is at rest and (−) in the region below where the guitar string is at rest—the regions are of opposite phase. The regions where the guitar string has no transverse displacement are called *nodes*. A node is at the region where a standing wave has an amplitude of zero.

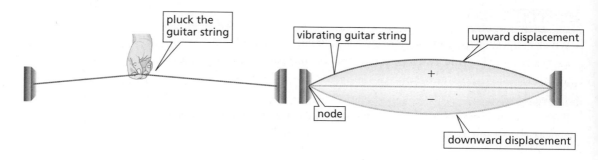

An electron behaves like a standing wave, but, unlike the wave created by a vibrating guitar string, it is three dimensional. This means that the node of a 2*s* orbital is actually a spherical surface within the 2*s* orbital. Because the electron wave has zero amplitude at the node, there is zero probability of finding an electron at the node.

Unlike *s* orbitals, which resemble spheres, *p* orbitals have two lobes. Generally, the lobes are depicted as teardrop shaped, but computer-generated representations reveal that they are shaped more like doorknobs (as shown on the right below). Like the vibrating guitar string, the lobes are of opposite phase, which can be designated by plus (+) and minus (−) or by two different colors. (In this context, + and − indicate the phase of the orbital; they do not indicate charge.) The node of the *p* orbital is a plane—called a **nodal plane**—that passes through the center of the nucleus, between its two lobes. There is zero probability of finding an electron in the nodal plane of the *p* orbital.

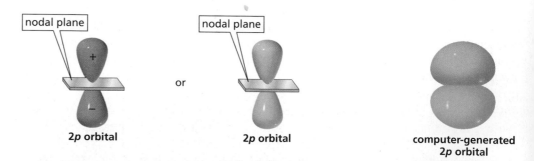

In Section 1.2, we saw that the second and higher numbered shells each contain three degenerate *p* orbitals. The p_x orbital is symmetrical about the *x*-axis, the p_y orbital is symmetrical about the *y*-axis, and the p_z orbital is symmetrical about the *z*-axis. This means that each *p* orbital is perpendicular to the other two *p* orbitals. The energy of a 2*p* orbital is slightly greater than that of a 2*s* orbital because the average location of an electron in a 2*p* orbital is farther away from the nucleus.

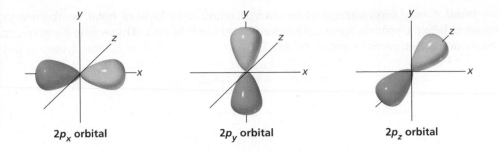

$2p_x$ orbital   **$2p_y$ orbital**   **$2p_z$ orbital**

1.6 AN INTRODUCTION TO MOLECULAR ORBITAL THEORY

How do atoms form covalent bonds in order to form molecules? The Lewis model, which shows atoms attaining a complete octet by sharing electrons, tells only part of the story. A drawback of the model is that it treats electrons like particles and does not take into account their wavelike properties.

Molecular orbital (MO) theory combines the tendency of atoms to fill their octets by sharing electrons (the Lewis model) with their wavelike properties, assigning electrons to a volume of space called an orbital. According to MO theory, covalent bonds result when atomic orbitals combine to form *molecular orbitals*. A **molecular orbital** belongs to the whole molecule rather than to a single atom. Like an atomic orbital, which describes the volume of space around an atom's nucleus where an electron is likely to be found, a molecular orbital describes the volume of space around a molecule where an electron is likely to be found. Molecular orbitals, too, have specific sizes, shapes, and energies.

Let's look first at the bonding in a hydrogen molecule (H_2). Imagine a meeting of two separate H atoms. As one atom with its $1s$ atomic orbital approaches the other with its $1s$ atomic orbital, the orbitals begin to overlap. The atoms continue to move closer, and the amount of overlap increases until the orbitals combine to form a molecular orbital. The covalent bond that is formed when the two *s* orbitals overlap is called a **sigma (σ) bond**. A σ bond is cylindrically symmetrical—the electrons in the bond are symmetrically distributed about an imaginary line connecting the centers of the two atoms joined by the bond.

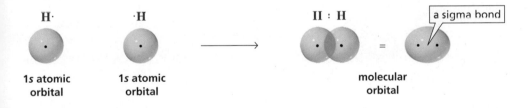

H·   **·H**   **H : H**   [a sigma bond]

1s atomic   **1s atomic**   **molecular**
orbital   **orbital**   **orbital**

An atomic orbital surrounds an atom.

A molecular orbital surrounds a molecule.

As the two orbitals start to overlap, energy is released (stability is increased) because the electron in each atom is attracted both to its own nucleus and to the positively charged nucleus of the other atom (Figure 1.2). The attraction of the negatively charged electrons for the two positively charged nuclei is what holds the atoms together. The more the orbitals overlap, the more the energy decreases until the atoms are so close that their positively charged nuclei start to repel each other. This repulsion causes a large increase in energy. Figure 1.2 shows that minimum energy (maximum stability) is achieved when the nuclei are a certain distance apart. This distance is the **bond length** of the new covalent bond. The bond length of the H—H bond is 0.74 Å.

As Figure 1.2 shows, energy is released when a covalent bond forms. When the H—H bond forms, 105 kcal/mol (or 439 kJ/mol)[*] of energy is released. Breaking the bond requires precisely the same amount of energy. Thus, the **bond strength**, also called

Minimum energy corresponds to maximum stability.

[*]Joules are the Système International (SI) units for energy, although many chemists use calories (1 kcal = 4.184 kJ). We will use both in this book.

the **bond dissociation energy**, is the energy required to break a bond, or the energy released when a bond is formed. Every covalent bond has a characteristic bond length and bond strength.

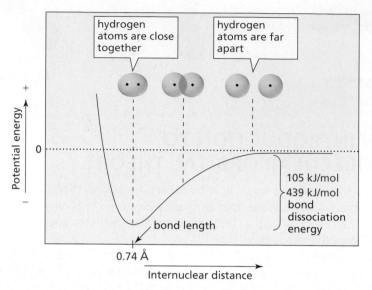

▶ **Figure 1.2**
The change in energy that occurs as two 1s atomic orbitals approach each other. The internuclear distance at minimum energy is the length of the H—H covalent bond.

Orbitals are conserved. In other words, the number of molecular orbitals formed must equal the number of atomic orbitals combined. In describing the formation of an H—H bond, we combined two atomic orbitals but discussed only one molecular orbital. Where is the other molecular orbital? We will see that it is there, but it does not contain any electrons.

Atomic orbitals can combine in two different ways: constructively and destructively. They can combine in a constructive, additive manner, just as two light waves or sound waves may reinforce each other (Figure 1.3). The constructive combination of two s orbitals is called a **σ (sigma) bonding molecular orbital**. Atomic orbitals can also combine in a destructive way, canceling each other. The cancellation is similar to the darkness that results when two light waves cancel each other or to the resulting silence when two sound waves cancel each other (Figure 1.3). The destructive combination of two s orbitals is called a **σ* antibonding molecular orbital**. An antibonding orbital is indicated by an asterisk (*).

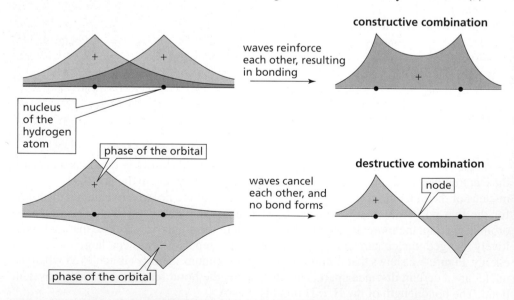

▶ **Figure 1.3**
The wave functions of two hydrogen atoms can interact to reinforce each other (*top*) or can interact to cancel each other (*bottom*). Note that waves that interact constructively are in-phase (have the same phase), whereas waves that interact destructively are out-of-phase (have different phases).

The σ bonding molecular orbital and σ* antibonding molecular orbital are shown in the molecular orbital (MO) diagram in Figure 1.4. In an MO diagram, the energies of the orbitals are represented as horizontal lines; the bottom line is the lowest energy level, the top line the highest energy level. We see that any electrons in the bonding molecular orbital will most likely be found between the nuclei, attracting both nuclei simultaneously. This increased electron density between the nuclei is what binds the atoms together.

Because there is a node between the nuclei in the antibonding molecular orbital, any electrons in that orbital are more likely to be found anywhere except between the nuclei, so the nuclei are more exposed to one another and will be forced apart by electrostatic repulsion. Thus, electrons that occupy this orbital detract from, rather than aid, the formation of a bond between the atoms.

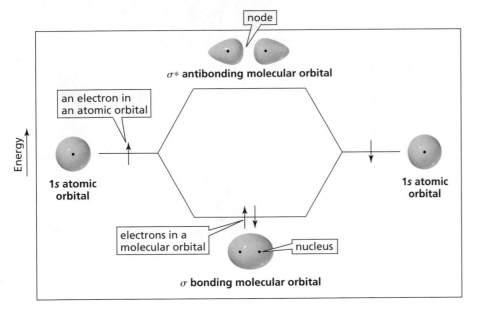

◀ **Figure 1.4**
Atomic orbitals of H· and molecular orbitals of H_2. Before covalent bond formation, each electron is in an atomic orbital. After covalent bond formation, both electrons are in the bonding molecular orbital. The antibonding molecular orbital is empty.

The MO diagram shows that the bonding molecular orbital is lower in energy, and therefore more stable, than the individual atomic orbitals. This is because the more nuclei an electron "feels," the more stable it is. The antibonding molecular orbital, with less electron density between the nuclei, is less stable—is of higher energy—than the atomic orbitals.

Electrons are assigned to the molecular orbitals using the same rules used to assign electrons to atomic orbitals: electrons always occupy available orbitals with the lowest energy (the aufbau principle), and no more than two electrons can occupy a molecular orbital (the Pauli exclusion principle). Thus, the two electrons of the H—H bond occupy the lower energy bonding molecular orbital (Figure 1.4), where they are attracted to both positively charged nuclei. It is this electrostatic attraction that gives a covalent bond its strength. Therefore, the greater the overlap of the atomic orbitals, the stronger is the covalent bond. *The strongest covalent bonds are formed by electrons that occupy the molecular orbitals with the lowest energy.*

The MO diagram in Figure 1.4 allows us to predict that H_2^+ would not be as stable as H_2 because H_2^+ has only one electron in the bonding orbital. Using the same diagram, we can also predict that He_2 does not exist: because each He atom would bring two electrons, He_2 would have four electrons—two filling the lower energy bonding molecular orbital and the remaining two filling the higher energy antibonding molecular orbital. The two electrons in the antibonding molecular orbital would cancel the advantage to bonding gained by the two electrons in the bonding molecular orbital.

When two atomic orbitals overlap, two molecular orbitals are formed—one lower in energy and one higher in energy than the atomic orbitals.

In-phase overlap forms a bonding MO; out-of-phase overlap forms an antibonding MO.

chem Tutorial:
place H_2 bond formation

PROBLEM 20 ◆

Predict whether or not He_2^+ exists.

When *p* orbitals overlap, the side of one *p* orbital overlaps the side of the other *p* orbital. The bond that is formed is called a **pi (π) bond**. Side-to-side overlap of two in-phase *p* atomic orbitals (blue lobes overlap blue lobes and green lobes overlap green lobes) forms a π bonding molecular orbital, whereas side-to-side overlap of two out-of-phase *p* orbitals (blue lobes overlap green lobes) forms a $\pi*$ antibonding

Side-to-side overlap of two *p* atomic orbitals forms a π bond. All other covalent bonds in organic molecules are σ bonds.

molecular orbital (Figure 1.5). The π bonding molecular orbital has one node—a nodal plane that passes through both nuclei. The antibonding molecular orbital has two nodal planes.

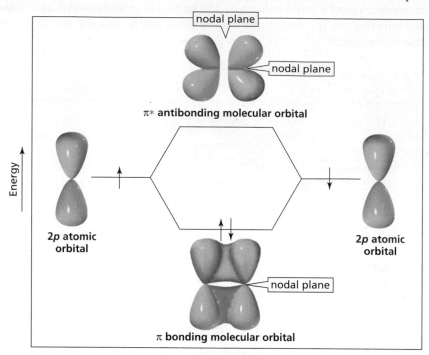

▶ **Figure 1.5**
Side-to-side overlap of two parallel *p* orbitals to form a π bonding molecular orbital and a π* antibonding molecular orbital.

Now let's look at the MO diagram for side-to-side overlap of a *p* orbital of carbon with a *p* orbital of oxygen—the orbitals are the same type, but they belong to different kinds of atoms. When the two *p* atomic orbitals combine to form molecular orbitals, the atomic orbital of the more electronegative atom contributes more to the bonding molecular orbital, and the atomic orbital of the less electronegative atom contributes more to the antibonding molecular orbital (Figure 1.6). This means that if we were to put electrons in the bonding MO, they would be more apt to be around the oxygen atom than around the carbon atom. Thus, both Lewis theory and molecular orbital theory tell us that the electrons shared by carbon and oxygen are not shared equally—the oxygen atom of a carbon–oxygen bond has a partial negative charge and the carbon atom has a partial positive charge.

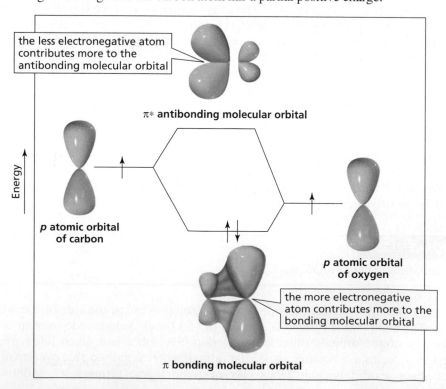

▶ **Figure 1.6**
Side-to-side overlap of a *p* orbital of carbon with a *p* orbital of oxygen to form a π bonding molecular orbital and a π* antibonding molecular orbital.

Organic chemists find that the information obtained from MO theory, where valence electrons occupy bonding and antibonding molecular orbitals, does not always yield the needed information about the bonds in a molecule. The **valence-shell electron-pair repulsion (VSEPR) model** combines the Lewis concept of shared electron pairs and lone-pair electrons with the concept of atomic orbitals and adds a third principle: *the minimization of electron repulsion*. In this model, atoms share electrons by overlapping their atomic orbitals, and because electron pairs repel each other, the bonding electrons and lone-pair electrons around an atom are positioned as far apart as possible. Thus, a Lewis structure gives us a first approximation of the structure of a simple molecule, and VSEPR gives us a first glance at the shape of the molecule.

Because organic chemists generally think of chemical reactions in terms of the changes that occur in the bonds of the reacting molecules, the VSEPR model often provides the easiest way to visualize chemical change. However, the model is inadequate for some molecules because it does not allow for antibonding orbitals. We will use both the MO and the VSEPR models in this book. Our choice will depend on which model provides the best description of the molecule under discussion. We will use the VSEPR model in Sections 1.7–1.13.

You can find a more extensive discussion of molecular orbital theory in Special Topic VI in the *Study Guide and Solutions Manual.*

PROBLEM 21 ◆

Indicate the kind of molecular orbital (σ, σ^*, π, or π^*) that results when atomic orbitals are combined as indicated:

a.

c.

b.

d.

1.7 HOW SINGLE BONDS ARE FORMED IN ORGANIC COMPOUNDS

We will begin the discussion of bonding in organic compounds by looking at the bonding in methane, a compound with only one carbon atom. Then we will examine the bonding in ethane, a compound with two carbons attached by a carbon–carbon single bond.

The Bonds in Methane

Methane (CH_4) has four covalent C—H bonds. Because all four bonds have the same length (1.10 Å) and all the bond angles are the same (109.5°), we can conclude that the four C—H bonds in methane are identical. Four different ways to represent a methane molecule are shown here.

perspective formula
of methane

ball-and-stick model
of methane

space-filling model
of methane

electrostatic potential
map for methane

In a **perspective formula**, bonds in the plane of the paper are drawn as solid lines, bonds protruding out of the plane of the paper toward the viewer are drawn as solid wedges, and those projecting back from the plane of the paper away from the viewer are drawn as hatched wedges.

The potential map of methane shows that neither carbon nor hydrogen carries much of a charge: there are neither red areas, representing partially negatively charged atoms, nor blue areas, representing partially positively charged atoms. (Compare this map with the potential map for water on p. 35.) The absence of partially charged atoms can be explained by the similar electronegativities of carbon and hydrogen, which cause them to share their bonding electrons relatively equally. Methane is therefore a **nonpolar molecule**.

You may be surprised to learn that carbon forms four covalent bonds since you know that carbon has only two unpaired electrons in its ground-state electronic configuration (Table 1.2). But if carbon formed only two covalent bonds, it would not complete its octet. We therefore need to come up with an explanation that accounts for carbon's forming four covalent bonds.

If one of the electrons in carbon's 2s orbital were promoted into the empty 2p orbital, the new electronic configuration would have four unpaired electrons; thus, four covalent bonds could be formed.

But we have seen that the four C—H bonds in methane are identical. How can they be identical if carbon uses an s orbital and three p orbitals to form these four bonds? Wouldn't the bond formed with the s orbital be different from the three bonds formed with p orbitals? The four C—H bonds are identical because carbon uses *hybrid orbitals.*

Hybrid orbitals are mixed orbitals that result from combining atomic orbitals. The concept of combining orbitals, called **hybridization**, was first proposed by Linus Pauling in 1931. If the one s and three p orbitals of the second shell are all combined and then apportioned into four equal orbitals, each of the four resulting orbitals will be one part s and three parts p. This type of mixed orbital is called an sp^3 (pronounced "s-p-three," not "s-p-cubed") orbital. (The superscript 3 means that three p orbitals were mixed with one s orbital—the superscript 1 on the s is implied—form the hybrid orbitals.) Each sp^3 orbital has 25% s character and 75% p character. The four sp^3 orbitals are degenerate—they all have the same energy.

Linus Carl Pauling (1901–1994) *was born in Portland, Oregon. A friend's home chemistry laboratory sparked Pauling's early interest in science. He received a Ph.D. from the California Institute of Technology and remained there for most of his academic career. He received the Nobel Prize in Chemistry in 1954 for his work on molecular structure. Like Einstein, Pauling was a pacifist, winning the 1962 Nobel Peace Prize for his work on behalf of nuclear disarmament.*

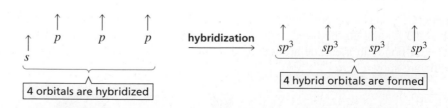

Like a p orbital, an sp^3 orbital has two lobes. The lobes differ in size, however, because the s orbital adds to one lobe of the p orbital and subtracts from the other lobe of the p orbital (Figure 1.7). The stability of an sp^3 orbital reflects its composition; it is more stable than a p orbital, but not as stable as an s orbital (Figure 1.8). The larger lobe of the sp^3 orbital is used in covalent bond formation.

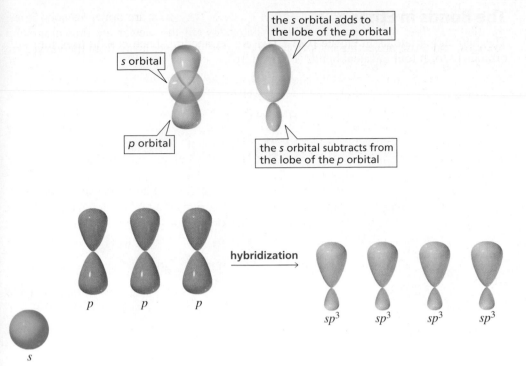

▸ **Figure 1.7**
The *s* orbital adds to one lobe of the *p* orbital and subtracts from the other lobe of the *p* orbital.

▸ **Figure 1.8**
An *s* orbital and three *p* orbitals hybridize to form four sp^3 orbitals. An sp^3 orbital is more stable than a *p* orbital, but not as stable as an *s* orbital.

The four sp^3 orbitals adopt a spatial arrangement that keeps them as far away from each other as possible. They do this because electrons repel each other, and moving as far from each other as possible minimizes the repulsion (Section 1.6). When four orbitals move as far from each other as possible, they point toward the corners of a regular tetrahedron—a pyramid with four faces, each an equilateral triangle (Figure 1.9a). Each of the four C—H bonds in methane is formed from overlap of an sp^3 orbital of carbon with the *s* orbital of a hydrogen (Figure 1.9b). This explains why the four C—H bonds are identical.

Electron pairs stay as far from each other as possible.

▸ **Figure 1.9**
(a) The four sp^3 orbitals are directed toward the corners of a tetrahedron, causing each bond angle to be 109.5°.
(b) An orbital of methane, showing the overlap of each sp^3 orbital of carbon with the *s* orbital of a hydrogen. (For clarity, the smaller lobes of the sp^3 orbitals are not shown.)

The angle between any two lines that point from the center to the corners of a tetrahedron is 109.5°. The bond angles in methane therefore are 109.5°. This is called a **tetrahedral bond angle**. A carbon, such as the one in methane, that forms covalent bonds using four equivalent sp^3 orbitals is called a **tetrahedral carbon**.

Hybrid orbital theory may appear to have been contrived just to make things fit—and that is exactly the case. Nevertheless, it gives us a very good picture of the bonding in organic compounds.

NOTE TO THE STUDENT
It is important to understand what molecules look like in three dimensions. Therefore be sure to visit the textbook's website (http://www.chemplace.com) and look at the three-dimensional representations of molecules that can be found in the molecule gallery prepared for each chapter.

The Bonds in Ethane

The two carbon atoms in ethane (CH_3CH_3) are tetrahedral. Each carbon uses four sp^3 orbitals to form four covalent bonds (Figure 1.10):

ethane

▲ **Figure 1.10**
An orbital picture of ethane. The C—C bond is formed by sp^3–sp^3 overlap, and each C—H bond is formed by sp^3–s overlap. (The smaller lobes of the sp^3 orbitals are not shown.)

One sp^3 orbital of one carbon overlaps an sp^3 orbital of the other carbon to form the C—C bond. Each of the remaining three sp^3 orbitals of each carbon overlaps the s orbital of a hydrogen to form a C—H bond. Thus, the C—C bond is formed by sp^3–sp^3 overlap, and each C—H bond is formed by sp^3–s overlap. Each of the bond angles in ethane is nearly the tetrahedral bond angle of 109.5°, and the length of the C—C bond is 1.54 Å. Ethane, like methane, is a nonpolar molecule.

perspective formula of ethane   ball-and-stick model of ethane   space-filling model of ethane   electrostatic potential map for ethane

All single bonds found in organic compounds are sigma bonds.

Sigma bonds are cylindrically symmetrical.

All the bonds in methane and ethane are sigma (σ) bonds because they are all formed by the end-on overlap of atomic orbitals. One bond connecting two atoms is called a **single bond**. *All single bonds found in organic compounds are sigma bonds.*

The MO diagram illustrating the overlap of an sp^3 orbital of one carbon with an sp^3 orbital of another carbon shows that the two sp^3 orbitals overlap end-on (Figure 1.11). End-on overlap forms a cylindrically symmetrical bond that is, therefore, a σ bond (Section 1.6). The electron density of the σ bonding MO is concentrated between the nuclei, which causes the back lobes (the nonoverlapping green lobes) to be quite small.

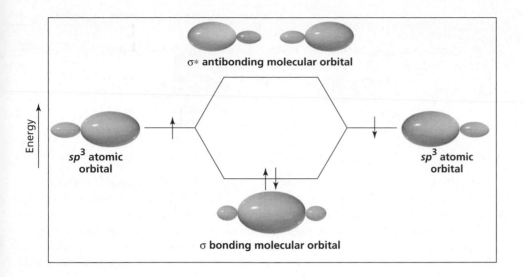

σ* antibonding molecular orbital

Energy

*sp*³ atomic orbital

*sp*³ atomic orbital

σ bonding molecular orbital

◀ **Figure 1.11**
End-on overlap of two *sp*³ orbitals to form a σ bonding molecular orbital and a σ* antibonding molecular orbital.

PROBLEM 22◆

What orbitals are used to form the 10 covalent bonds in propane ($CH_3CH_2CH_3$)?

1.8 HOW A DOUBLE BOND IS FORMED: THE BONDS IN ETHENE

Each of the carbon atoms in ethene (also called ethylene) forms four bonds, but each is bonded to only three atoms:

$$\begin{array}{c} H \qquad\quad H \\ \diagdown\qquad\diagup \\ C=C \\ \diagup\qquad\diagdown \\ H \qquad\quad H \end{array}$$

ethene
ethylene

To bond to three atoms, each carbon hybridizes three atomic orbitals: an *s* orbital and two of the *p* orbitals. Because three orbitals are hybridized, three hybrid orbitals are obtained. These are called *sp*² orbitals. After hybridization, each carbon atom has three degenerate *sp*² orbitals and one unhybridized *p* orbital:

To minimize electron repulsion, the three *sp*² orbitals need to get as far from each other as possible. Therefore, the axes of the three orbitals lie in a plane, directed toward the corners of an equilateral triangle with the carbon nucleus at the center. This means that the bond angles are all close to 120°. Because an *sp*² hybridized carbon is bonded to three atoms that define a plane, it is called a **trigonal planar carbon**. The unhybridized *p* orbital is perpendicular to the plane defined by the axes of the *sp*² orbitals (Figure 1.12).

▶ **Figure 1.12**
(a) The three degenerate sp^2 orbitals lie in a plane.
(b) The unhybridized p orbital is perpendicular to the plane. (The smaller lobes of the sp^2 orbitals are not shown.)

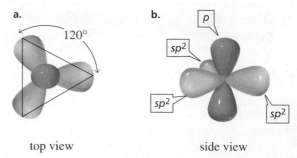

top view   side view

The carbons in ethene form two bonds with each other. Two bonds connecting two atoms is called a **double bond**. The two carbon–carbon bonds in the double bond are not identical. One of them results from the overlap of an sp^2 orbital of one carbon with an sp^2 orbital of the other carbon; this is a sigma (σ) bond because it is cylindrically symmetrical (Figure 1.13a). Each carbon uses its other two sp^2 orbitals to overlap the s orbital of a hydrogen to form the C—H bonds. The second carbon–carbon bond results from side-to-side overlap of the two unhybridized p orbitals. Side-to-side overlap of p orbitals forms a pi (π) bond (Figure 1.13b). Thus, one of the bonds in a double bond is a σ bond, and the other is a π bond (Figure 1.13c). All the C—H bonds are σ bonds.

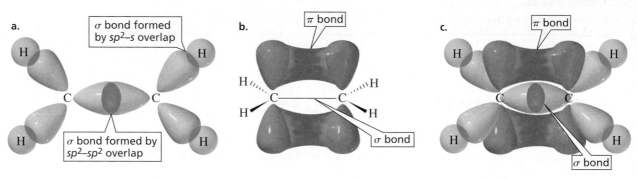

▲ **Figure 1.13**
(a) One C—C bond in ethene is a σ bond formed by sp^2–sp^2 overlap, and the C—H bonds are σ bonds formed by sp^2–s overlap. (b) The second C—C bond is a π bond formed by side-to-side overlap of a p orbital of one carbon with a p orbital of the other carbon. (c) There is an accumulation of electron density above and below the plane containing the two carbons and four hydrogens.

The two p orbitals that overlap to form the π bond must be parallel to each other for maximum overlap to occur. This forces the triangle formed by one carbon and two hydrogens to lie in the same plane as the triangle formed by the other carbon and two hydrogens. As a result, all six atoms of ethene lie in the same plane, and the electrons in the p orbitals occupy a volume of space above and below the plane (Figure 1.13c). The potential map for ethene shows that it is a nonpolar molecule with a slight accumulation of negative charge (the pale orange area) above the two carbons. (If you could turn the potential map over to show the hidden side, a similar accumulation of negative charge would be found there.)

a double bond consists of   ball-and-stick model   space-filling model   electrostatic potential map
one σ bond and one π bond   of ethene   of ethene   for ethene

Four electrons hold the carbons together in a carbon–carbon double bond; only two electrons hold the carbons together in a carbon–carbon single bond. With more electrons holding the carbons together, a carbon–carbon double bond is stronger (174 kcal/mol or 728 kJ/mol) and shorter (1.33 Å) than a carbon–carbon single bond (90 kcal/mol or 377 kJ/mol, and 1.54 Å).

Diamond, Graphite, and Fullerenes: Substances Containing Only Carbon Atoms

The difference that hybridization can make is illustrated by diamond and graphite. Diamond is the hardest of all substances. Graphite, in contrast, is a slippery, soft solid most familiar to us as the "lead" in pencils. Both materials, in spite of their very different physical properties, contain only carbon atoms. The two substances differ solely in the nature of the bonds holding the carbon atoms together.

Diamond consists of a rigid three-dimensional network of carbon atoms, with each bonded to four others via sp^3 orbitals. The carbon atoms in graphite, on the other hand, are sp^2 hybridized, so each bonds to only three other carbons. This trigonal planar arrangement causes the atoms in graphite to lie in flat, layered sheets. Since there are no covalent bonds between the sheets, they can shear off from neighboring sheets.

Diamond and graphite have been known since ancient times—but a third substance found in nature that contains only carbon atoms was discovered just 25 years ago. Like graphite, fullerenes consist solely of sp^2 carbons, but instead of forming planar sheets, the carbons join to form spherical structures. (Fullerenes are discussed in Section 15.3.)

diamond

graphite

1.9 HOW A TRIPLE BOND IS FORMED: THE BONDS IN ETHYNE

The carbon atoms in ethyne (also called acetylene) are each bonded to only two atoms—a hydrogen and another carbon:

$$H-C\equiv C-H$$
ethyne
acetylene

Because each carbon forms covalent bonds with two atoms, only two of each carbon's orbitals are hybridized: an s and a p. Two degenerate sp orbitals result. Each carbon atom in ethyne, therefore, has two sp orbitals and two unhybridized p orbitals. To minimize electron repulsion, the two sp orbitals point in opposite directions (Figure 1.14).

▲ **Figure 1.14**
The two sp orbitals are oriented 180° away from each other, perpendicular to the two unhybridized p orbitals. (The smaller lobes of the sp orbitals are not shown.)

The carbon atoms in ethyne are held together by three bonds. Three bonds connecting two atoms is called a **triple bond**. One of the sp orbitals of one carbon in ethyne overlaps an sp orbital of the other carbon to form a carbon–carbon σ bond. The other sp orbital of each carbon overlaps the s orbital of a hydrogen to form a C—H σ bond (Figure 1.15a). Because the two sp orbitals point in opposite directions, the bond angles are 180°. The two unhybridized p orbitals are perpendicular to each other, and both are perpendicular to the sp orbitals. Each of the unhybridized p orbitals engages in side-to-side overlap with a parallel p orbital on the other carbon, with the result that two π bonds are formed (Figure 1.15b).

▶ **Figure 1.15**
(a) The C—C σ bond in ethyne is formed by *sp–sp* overlap, and the C—H bonds are formed by *sp–s* overlap. The carbon atoms and the atoms bonded to them are in a straight line.
(b) The two carbon–carbon π bonds are formed by side-to-side overlap of the *p* orbitals of one carbon with the *p* orbitals of the other carbon.
(c) The triple bond has an electron-dense region above and below and in front of and in back of the internuclear axis of the molecule.

A triple bond therefore consists of one σ bond and two π bonds. Because the two unhybridized *p* orbitals on each carbon are perpendicular to each other, they create regions of high electron density above and below *and* in front of and back of the internuclear axis of the molecule (Figure 1.15c). The potential map for ethyne shows that negative charge accumulates in a cylinder that wraps around the egg-shaped molecule.

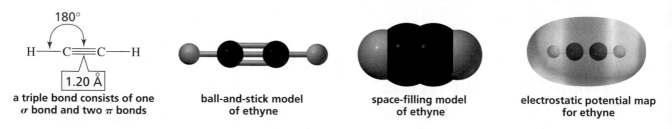

a triple bond consists of one σ bond and two π bonds | ball-and-stick model of ethyne | space-filling model of ethyne | electrostatic potential map for ethyne

Because the two carbon atoms in a triple bond are held together by six electrons, a triple bond is stronger (231 kcal/mol or 967 kJ/mol) and shorter (1.20 Å) than a double bond (174 kcal/mol or 728 kJ/mol, and 1.33 Å).

PROBLEM 23   **SOLVED**

For each of the given species:
a. Draw its Lewis structure.
b. Describe the orbitals used by each carbon atom in bonding and indicate the approximate bond angles.

    1. HCOH   **2.** CCl$_4$ **3.** CH$_3$COH   **4.** HCN

Solution to 23a1. Our first attempt at a Lewis structure (drawing the atoms in the order given by the condensed structure) shows that carbon is the only atom that does not form the needed number of bonds.

$$H{-}C{-}O{-}H$$

If we place a double bond between carbon and oxygen and move an H, all the atoms end up with the correct number of bonds. Lone-pair electrons are used to give each atom a filled outer shell. When we check to see if any atom needs to be assigned a formal charge, we find that none of them does.

$$\overset{\displaystyle :\!\ddot{O}\!:}{\underset{\displaystyle H{-}C{-}H}{\|}}$$

Solution to 23b1.   Because the carbon atom forms a double bond, we know that carbon uses sp^2 orbitals (as it does in ethene) to bond to the two hydrogens and the oxygen. It uses its "left-over" p orbital to form the second bond to oxygen. Because carbon is sp^2 hybridized, the bond angles are approximately 120°.

$$120° \quad \overset{\cdot\overset{\cdot\cdot}{O}\cdot}{\underset{\underset{120°}{H \qquad H}}{\overset{\|}{C}}} \quad 120°$$

1.10 THE BONDS IN THE METHYL CATION, THE METHYL RADICAL, AND THE METHYL ANION

Not all carbon atoms form four bonds. A carbon with a positive charge, a negative charge, or an unpaired electron forms only three bonds. Now we will see what orbitals carbon uses when it forms three bonds.

The Methyl Cation ($^+CH_3$)

The positively charged carbon in the methyl cation is bonded to three atoms, so it hybridizes three orbitals—an s orbital and two p orbitals. Therefore, it forms its three covalent bonds using sp^2 orbitals. Its unhybridized p orbital remains empty. The positively charged carbon and the three atoms bonded to it lie in a plane. The p orbital stands perpendicular to the plane.

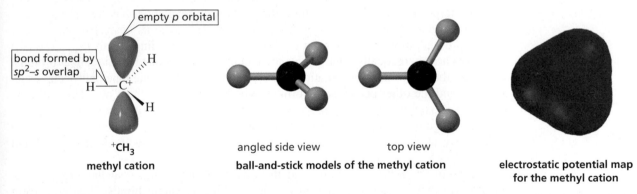

empty p orbital

bond formed by sp^2–s overlap

$^+CH_3$
methyl cation

angled side view   top view

ball-and-stick models of the methyl cation

electrostatic potential map for the methyl cation

The Methyl Radical ($\cdot CH_3$)

The carbon atom in the methyl radical is also sp^2 hybridized. The methyl radical differs by one unpaired electron from the methyl cation. That electron is in the p orbital, with half of the electron density in each lobe. Notice the similarity in the ball-and-stick models of the methyl cation and the methyl radical. The potential maps, however, are quite different because of the additional electron in the methyl radical.

p orbital contains the unpaired electron

bond formed by sp^2–s overlap

$\cdot CH_3$
methyl radical

angled side view   top view

ball-and-stick models of the methyl radical

electrostatic potential map for the methyl radical

The Methyl Anion ($\overset{..}{-}CH_3$)

The negatively charged carbon in the methyl anion has three pairs of bonding electrons and one lone pair. The four pairs of electrons are farthest apart when the four orbitals containing the bonding and lone-pair electrons point toward the corners of a tetrahedron. In other words, a negatively charged carbon is sp^3 hybridized. In the methyl anion, three of carbon's sp^3 orbitals each overlap the s orbital of a hydrogen, and the fourth sp^3 orbital holds the lone pair.

methyl anion   ball-and-stick model of the methyl anion   electrostatic potential map
for the methyl anion

Take a moment to compare the potential maps for the methyl cation, the methyl radical, and the methyl anion.

1.11   THE BONDS IN WATER

The oxygen atom in water (H_2O) forms two covalent bonds. Because the electronic configuration of oxygen shows that it has two unpaired electrons (Table 1.2), oxygen does not need to promote an electron to form the number of covalent bonds (two) required to achieve an outer shell of eight electrons—that is, to complete its octet. But this simple picture presents a problem. Oxygen has two pairs of nonbonding electrons. These two lone pairs are energetically identical, which means that they must be in identical orbitals. However, the electronic configuration of oxygen indicates that one lone pair occupies an s orbital and the other occupies a p orbital, which would make them nonidentical. Furthermore, if oxygen uses p orbitals to form the two O—H bonds, as predicted by its electronic configuration, we would expect a bond angle of about 90° because the two p orbitals are at right angles to each other. However, the experimentally observed bond angle is 104.5°.

The identity of the lone pairs and the observed bond angle can be explained if we assume that oxygen uses hybrid orbitals to form covalent bonds—just as carbon does. The s orbital and the three p orbitals must hybridize to produce four identical sp^3 orbitals.

The bond angles in a molecule indicate which orbitals are used in bond formation.

Each of the two O—H bonds is formed by the overlap of an sp^3 orbital of oxygen with the s orbital of a hydrogen. A lone pair occupies each of the two remaining sp^3 orbitals.

The bond angle in water (104.5°) is a little smaller than the bond angle in methane (109.5°) presumably because each of the lone pairs is held by only one nucleus, which makes a lone pair more diffuse than a bonding pair that is shared by two nuclei and is therefore relatively confined between them. Consequently, lone pairs exert more electron repulsion, causing the O—H bonds to squeeze closer together, thereby decreasing the bond angle.

water   ball-and-stick model of water   electrostatic potential map for water

Compare the potential map for water with that for methane. Water is a polar molecule; methane is nonpolar.

PROBLEM 24 ♦

The bond angles in H_3O^+ are greater than _____ and less than _____.

Water—A Unique Compound

Water is the most abundant compound found in living organisms. Its unique properties have allowed life to originate and evolve. Its high heat of fusion (the heat required to convert a solid to a liquid) protects organisms from freezing at low temperatures because a lot of heat must be removed from water to freeze it. Its high heat capacity (the heat required to raise the temperature of a substance by a given amount) minimizes temperature changes in organisms, and its high heat of vaporization (the heat required to convert a liquid to a gas) allows animals to cool themselves with a minimal loss of body fluid. Because liquid water is denser than ice, ice formed on the surface of water floats and insulates the water below. That is why oceans and lakes don't freeze from the bottom up, and why plants and aquatic animals can survive when the ocean or lake they live in freezes.

1.12 THE BONDS IN AMMONIA AND IN THE AMMONIUM ION

The experimentally observed bond angles in NH_3 are 107.3°. The bond angles indicate that nitrogen also uses hybrid orbitals when it forms covalent bonds. Like carbon and oxygen, the one s and three p orbitals of the second shell of nitrogen hybridize to form four degenerate sp^3 orbitals:

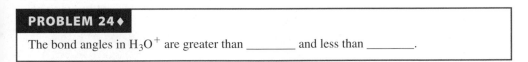

Each of the N—H bonds in NH_3 is formed from the overlap of an sp^3 orbital of nitrogen with the s orbital of a hydrogen. The single lone pair occupies an sp^3 orbital. The bond angle (107.3°) is smaller than the tetrahedral bond angle (109.5°) because of the relatively diffuse lone pair. Notice that the bond angles in NH_3 (107.3°) are larger than the bond angles in H$_2$O (104.5°) because nitrogen has only one lone pair, whereas oxygen has two lone pairs.

NH$_3$
ammonia

ball-and-stick model of ammonia

electrostatic potential map
for ammonia

Because the ammonium ion ($^+$NH$_4$) has four identical N—H bonds and no lone pairs, all the bond angles are 109.5°, just like the bond angles in methane.

$^+$NH$_4$
ammonium ion

ball-and-stick model of the ammonium ion

electrostatic potential map
for the ammonium ion

PROBLEM 25 ◆

Predict the approximate bond angles in the methyl carbanion.

PROBLEM 26 ◆

According to the potential map for the ammonium ion, which atom has the greatest electron density?

PROBLEM 27 ◆

Compare the potential maps for methane, ammonia, and water. Which is the most polar molecule? Which is the least polar?

electrostatic potential
map for methane

electrostatic potential map
for ammonia

electrostatic potential map
for water

1.13 THE BOND IN A HYDROGEN HALIDE

Fluorine, chlorine, bromine, and iodine are known as the halogens, so HF, HCl, HBr, and HI are called hydrogen halides. Bond angles will not help us determine the orbitals that form a hydrogen halide bond, as they did with other molecules, because hydrogen halides have only one bond and therefore no bond angles. We do know, however, that a halogen's three lone pairs are energetically identical and that lone-pair electrons position themselves to minimize electron repulsion. Both of these observations suggest that the halogen's three lone pairs are in hybrid orbitals. Therefore, we will assume that the hydrogen–halogen bond is formed by the overlap of an sp^3 orbital of the halogen with the s orbital of hydrogen.

H—F̈:
hydrogen fluoride

ball-and-stick model of hydrogen fluoride

electrostatic potential map for hydrogen fluoride

In the case of fluorine, the sp^3 orbital used in bond formation belongs to the second shell of electrons. In chlorine, the sp^3 orbital belongs to the third shell. Because the average distance from the nucleus is greater for an electron in the third shell than it is for an electron in the second shell, the average electron density is less in a $3sp^3$ orbital than it is in a $2sp^3$ orbital. This means that the electron density in the region where the s orbital of hydrogen overlaps the sp^3 orbital of the halogen decreases as the size of the halogen increases (Figure 1.16). Therefore, the hydrogen–halogen bond becomes longer and weaker as the size (atomic weight) of the halogen increases (Table 1.6).

◄ Figure 1.16
There is greater electron density in the region of overlap of an s orbital with a $2sp^3$ orbital than in the region of overlap of an s orbital with a $3sp^3$ orbital.

| overlap of an s orbital with a $2sp^3$ orbital | overlap of an s orbital with a $3sp^3$ orbital |

Table 1.6   Hydrogen–Halogen Bond Lengths and Bond Strengths

Hydrogen halide		Bond length (Å)	Bond strength (kcal/mol)	(kJ/mol)
H—F	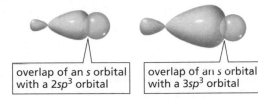	0.917	136	571
H—Cl		1.2746	103	432
H—Br		1.4145	87	366
H—I		1.6090	71	298

hydrogen fluoride

hydrogen chloride

hydrogen bromide

hydrogen iodide

PROBLEM 28 ◆

a. Predict the relative lengths and strengths of the bonds in Cl_2 and Br_2.
b. Predict the relative lengths and strengths of the carbon–halogen bonds in CH_3F, CH_3Cl, and CH_3Br.

PROBLEM 29 ◆

a. Which bond would be longer?
b. Which bond would be stronger?
   1. C—Cl or C—I   **2.** C—C or C—Cl   **3.** H—Cl or H—F

1.14 SUMMARY: HYBRIDIZATION, BOND LENGTHS, BOND STRENGTHS, AND BOND ANGLES

We have seen that all *single bonds* are σ bonds. All *double bonds* are composed of one σ bond and one π bond. All *triple bonds* are composed of one σ bond and two π bonds. The easiest way to determine the hybridization of a carbon, oxygen, or nitrogen atom is to look at the number of π bonds it forms: if it forms no π bonds, it is sp^3 hybridized; if it forms one π bond, it is sp^2 hybridized; if it forms two π bonds, it is sp hybridized. The exceptions are carbocations and carbon radicals, which are sp^2 hybridized—not because they form a π bond, but because they have an empty or a half-filled p orbital (Section 1.10).

The hybridization of a C, O, or N is $sp^{(3\text{ minus the number of }\pi\text{ bonds})}$.

Ethane

Ethene

Ethyne

In comparing the lengths and strengths of carbon–carbon single, double, and triple bonds, we see that the more bonds holding two carbon atoms together, the shorter and stronger is the carbon–carbon bond (Table 1.7): triple bonds are shorter and stronger than double bonds, which are shorter and stronger than single bonds.

The data in Table 1.7 indicate that a C—H σ bond is shorter and stronger than a C—C σ bond. This is because the s orbital of hydrogen is closer to the nucleus than is the sp^3 orbital of carbon. Consequently, the nuclei are closer together in a bond formed by sp^3–s overlap than they are in a bond formed by sp^3–sp^3 overlap. In addition to being shorter, a C—H σ bond is stronger than a C—C σ bond because there is greater electron density in the region of overlap of an sp^3 orbital with an s orbital than in the region of overlap of an sp^3 orbital with an sp^3 orbital.

The length and strength of a C—H bond depend on the hybridization of the carbon atom to which the hydrogen is attached. The more s character in the orbital used by carbon to form the bond, the shorter and stronger is the bond—again, because an s orbital is closer to the nucleus than is a p orbital. So a C—H bond formed by an sp carbon (50% s) is shorter and stronger than a C—H bond formed by an sp^2 carbon (33.3% s), which in turn is shorter and stronger than a C—H bond formed by an sp^3 carbon (25% s).

A double bond (a σ bond plus a π bond) is stronger (174 kcal/mol) than a single bond (a σ bond), but it is not twice as strong, so we can conclude that the π bond of a

Table 1.7	Comparison of the Bond Angles and the Lengths and Strengths of the Carbon–Carbon and Carbon–Hydrogen Bonds in Ethane, Ethene, and Ethyne							
Molecule	Hybridization of carbon	Bond angles	Length of C—C bond (Å)	Strength of C—C bond (kcal/mol)	(kJ/mol)	Length of C—H bond (Å)	Strength of C—H bond (kcal/mol)	(kJ/mol)
H—C—C—H (ethane)	sp^3	109.5°	1.54	90	377	1.10	101	423
C=C (ethene)	sp^2	120°	1.33	174	728	1.08	111	466
H—C≡C—H (ethyne)	sp	180°	1.20	231	967	1.06	131	548

double bond is weaker than the σ bond. Table 1.7 indicates that the strength of a $C-C$ σ bond formed by sp^3-sp^3 overlap is 90 kJ/mol. However, a $C-C$ σ bond formed by sp^2-sp^2 overlap is expected to be stronger because of the greater s character in the overlapping orbitals; it has been estimated to be ~112 kcal/mol. We can conclude then, that the strength of the π bond of ethene is about 62 kcal/mol, because $174 - 112 = 62$. We expected the π bond to be weaker than the σ bond because side-to-side overlap that forms a π bond is less effective than the end-on overlap that forms a σ bond (Section 1.6).

The bond angle, too, depends on the orbital used by carbon to form the bond. The greater the amount of s character in the orbital, the larger is the bond angle. For example, sp carbons have bond angles of 180°, sp^2 carbons have bond angles of 120°, and sp^3 carbons have bond angles of 109.5°.

You may wonder how an electron "knows" what orbital it should go into. In fact, electrons know nothing about orbitals. They simply occupy the space around atoms in the most stable arrangement possible. It is chemists who use the concept of orbitals to explain this arrangement.

> The shorter the bond, the stronger it is.
>
> A π bond is weaker than a σ bond.
>
> The greater the electron density in the region of orbital overlap, the stronger the bond.
>
> The more s character in an orbital, the shorter and stronger the bond it forms.
>
> The more s character in the orbitals, the larger the bond angle they form.

PROBLEM 30♦

Which of the bonds in a carbon–oxygen double bond has more effective orbital–orbital overlap, the σ bond or the π bond?

PROBLEM 31♦

Would you expect a $C-C$ σ bond formed by sp^2-sp^2 overlap to be stronger or weaker than a $C-C$ σ bond formed by sp^3-sp^3 overlap?

PROBLEM 32

a. What is the hybridization of each of the carbon atoms in the following compound?

$$CH_3CHCH{=}CHCH_2C{\equiv}CCH_3$$
$$\quad\quad |$$
$$\quad\quad CH_3$$

b. What is the hybridization of each of the carbon and oxygen atoms in the following compounds?

vitamin C   demerol

chem Tutorial:
place Hybridization 1

Tutorial:
Hybridization 2

PROBLEM-SOLVING STRATEGY

Predicting Bond Angles

Predict the approximate bond angle of the $C-N-H$ bond in $(CH_3)_2NH$.

First we need to determine the hybridization of the central atom (the N). Because the nitrogen atom forms only single bonds, we know it is sp^3 hybridized. Next we look to see if there are lone pairs that will affect the bond angle. A neutral nitrogen has one lone pair. Based on these observations, we can predict that the $C-N-H$ bond angle will be about 107.3°, the same as the $H-N-H$ bond angle in NH_3, another compound with a neutral sp^3 nitrogen.

Now continue on to Problem 33.

PROBLEM 33◆

Predict the approximate bond angles:
a. the C—N—C bond angle in $(CH_3)_2\overset{+}{N}H_2$
b. the C—N—H bond angle in $CH_3CH_2NH_2$
c. the H—C—N bond angle in $(CH_3)_2NH$
d. the H—C—O bond angle in CH_3OCH_3

PROBLEM 34

Describe the orbitals used in bonding and the bond angles in the following compounds. (*Hint:* See Table 1.7.)
a. BeH_2
b. BH_3
c. CCl_4
d. CO_2
e. $HCOOH$
f. N_2

1.15 THE DIPOLE MOMENTS OF MOLECULES

In Section 1.3, we saw that in molecules with one covalent bond, the dipole moment of the molecule is identical to the dipole moment of the bond. When molecules have more than one covalent bond, the geometry of the molecule must be taken into account because both the *magnitude* and the *direction* of the individual bond dipole moments (the vector sum) determine the overall dipole moment of the molecule. Totally symmetrical molecules, therefore, have no dipole moment. For example, let's look at the dipole moment of carbon dioxide (CO_2). Because the carbon is bonded to two atoms, it uses *sp* orbitals to form the C—O σ bonds. The remaining two *p* orbitals on carbon form the two C—O π bonds. The *sp* orbitals form a bond angle of 180°, so the individual carbon–oxygen bond dipole moments cancel each other. Therefore, carbon dioxide has a dipole moment of 0 D. Another symmetrical molecule is carbon tetrachloride (CCl_4). The four atoms bonded to the sp^3 carbon atom are identical and project symmetrically out from the carbon atom. Thus, as with CO_2, the symmetry of the molecule causes the bond dipole moments to cancel. Methane also has no dipole moment.

carbon dioxide
μ = **0 D**

carbon tetrachloride
μ = **0 D**

The dipole moment of chloromethane (CH_3Cl) is greater (1.87 D) than the dipole moment of the C—Cl bond (1.5 D) because the C—H dipoles are oriented so that they reinforce the dipole of the C—Cl bond: all the electrons are pulled in the same relative direction. The dipole moment of water (1.85 D) is greater than the dipole moment of a single O—H bond (1.5 D) because the dipoles of the two O—H bonds reinforce each other. The lone-pair electrons also contribute to the dipole moment. Similarly, the dipole moment of ammonia (1.47 D) is greater than the dipole moment of a single N—H bond (1.3 D).

chloromethane
μ = **1.87 D**

water
μ = **1.85 D**

ammonia
μ = **1.47 D**

PROBLEM 35 ◆

If the dipole moment of CH_3F is 1.847 D and the dipole moment of CD_3F is 1.858 D, which is more electronegative, hydrogen or deuterium?

PROBLEM 36

Account for the difference in the shape and color of the potential maps for ammonia and the ammonium ion in Section 1.12.

PROBLEM 37 ◆

Which of the following molecules would you expect to have a dipole moment of zero? To answer parts g and h, you may need to consult your answers to Problem 34a and b.

a. CH_3CH_3
b. $H_2C{=}O$
c. CH_2Cl_2
d. NH_3
e. $H_2C{=}CH_2$
f. $H_2C{=}CHBr$
g. $BeCl_2$
h. BF_3

1.16 AN INTRODUCTION TO ACIDS AND BASES

Early chemists called any compound that tasted sour an acid (from *acidus*, Latin for "sour"). Some familiar acids are citric acid (found in lemons and other citrus fruits), acetic acid (found in vinegar), and hydrochloric acid (found in stomach acid—the sour taste associated with vomiting). Compounds that neutralize acids, eliminating their acidic properties, were called bases, or alkaline compounds ("ash" in Arabic is *al kalai*). Glass cleaners and solutions designed to unclog drains are familiar alkaline solutions.

There are two definitions for the terms *acid* and *base,* the Brønsted–Lowry definitions and the Lewis definitions (Section 1.27). According to Brønsted and Lowry, an **acid** is a species that donates a proton, and a **base** is a species that accepts a proton. (Remember that positively charged hydrogen ions are called protons.) In the reaction shown below, hydrogen chloride (HCl) is an acid because it donates a proton to water, and water is a base because it accepts a proton from HCl. Water can accept a proton because it has two lone pairs, either of which can form a covalent bond with a proton. In the reverse reaction, H_3O^+ is an acid because it donates a proton to Cl^-, and Cl^- is a base because it accepts a proton from H_3O^+. The reaction of an acid with a base is called an **acid–base reaction** or a **proton-transfer reaction**. Both an acid and a base must be present in an acid–base reaction, because an acid cannot donate a proton unless a base is present to accept it.

$$H\ddot{C}l: \ +\ H_2\ddot{O}: \ \rightleftharpoons\ :\ddot{C}l:^- \ +\ H_3\ddot{O}^+$$
$$\text{an acid} \qquad \text{a base} \qquad\qquad \text{a base} \qquad \text{an acid}$$

Notice that according to the Brønsted–Lowry definitions, *any species that has a hydrogen can potentially act as an acid, and any compound possessing a lone pair can potentially act as a base.*

When a compound loses a proton, the resulting species is called its **conjugate base**. Thus, Cl^- is the conjugate base of HCl, and H_2O is the conjugate base of H_3O^+. When a compound accepts a proton, the resulting species is called its **conjugate acid**. Thus, HCl is the conjugate acid of Cl^-, and H_3O^+ is the conjugate acid of H_2O.

In a reaction between ammonia and water, ammonia (NH_3) is a base because it accepts a proton, and water is an acid because it donates a proton. Thus, HO^- is the conjugate base of H_2O, and $^+NH_4$ is the conjugate acid of NH_3. In the reverse reaction, ammonium ion ($^+NH_4$) is an acid because it donates a proton, and hydroxide ion (HO^-) is a base because it accepts a proton.

Notice that water can behave as either an acid or a base. It can behave as an acid because it has a proton that it can donate, but it can also behave as a base because it has a lone pair that can accept a proton. In Section 1.19, we will see how we can predict that water acts as a base in the first reaction and acts as an acid in the second reaction.

A strong base has a high affinity for a proton.

Acidity is a measure of the tendency of a compound to give up a proton. **Basicity** is a measure of a compound's affinity for a proton. A strong acid is one that has a strong tendency to give up its proton. This means that its conjugate base must be weak because it has little affinity for the proton. A weak acid has little tendency to give up its proton, indicating that its conjugate base is strong because it has a high affinity for the proton. Thus, the following important relationship exists between an acid and its conjugate base: *the stronger the acid, the weaker is its conjugate base.* For example, since HBr is a stronger acid than HCl, we know that Br^- is a weaker base than Cl^-.

The stronger the acid, the weaker is its conjugate base.

PROBLEM 38 ◆

a. What is the conjugate acid of each of the following?
   1. NH_3 **2.** Cl^- **3.** HO^- **4.** H_2O
b. What is the conjugate base of each of the following?
   1. NH_3 **2.** HBr   **3.** HNO_3 **4.** H_2O

1.17 pK_a AND pH

When a strong acid such as hydrogen chloride is dissolved in water, almost all the molecules dissociate (break into ions), which means that the *products* are favored at equilibrium—the equilibrium lies to the right. When a much weaker acid, such as acetic acid, is dissolved in water, very few molecules dissociate, so the *reactants* are favored at equilibrium—the equilibrium lies to the left. Two half-headed arrows are used to designate equilibrium reactions. A longer arrow is drawn toward the species favored at equilibrium.

The degree to which an acid (HA) dissociates in aqueous solution is indicated by the **equilibrium constant** of the reaction, K_{eq}. Brackets are used to indicate the concentration in moles/liter, that is, the molarity (M).

$$HA + H_2O \rightleftharpoons H_3O^+ + A^-$$

$$K_{eq} = \frac{[H_3O^+][A^-]}{[H_2O][HA]}$$

The degree to which an acid (HA) dissociates is normally determined in a dilute solution, so the concentration of water remains nearly constant. The equilibrium expression, therefore, can be rewritten using a new constant called the **acid dissociation constant**, (K_a).

$$K_a = \frac{\left[H_3O^+\right]\left[A^-\right]}{\left[HA\right]} = K_{eq}\left[H_2O\right]$$

The acid dissociation constant is the equilibrium constant multiplied by the molar concentration of water (55.5 M).

The larger the acid dissociation constant, the stronger is the acid—that is, the greater is its tendency to give up a proton. Hydrogen chloride, with an acid dissociation constant of 10^7, is a stronger acid than acetic acid, with an acid dissociation constant of 1.74×10^{-5}. For convenience, the strength of an acid is generally indicated by its **pK_a** value rather than its K_a value, where

$$pK_a = -\log K_a$$

The pK_a of hydrogen chloride is -7 and the pK_a of acetic acid, a much weaker acid, is 4.76. Notice that *the smaller the pK_a, the stronger the acid.*

The stronger the acid, the smaller is its pK_a value.

very strong acids	$pK_a < 1$
moderately strong acids	$pK_a = 1-3$
weak acids	$pK_a = 3-5$
very weak acids	$pK_a = 5-15$
extremely weak acids	$pK_a > 15$

Unless otherwise stated, the pK_a values given in this text indicate the strength of the acid *in water*. Later (in Section 8.9), you will see how the pK_a value of an acid is affected when the solvent is changed.

The concentration of positively charged hydrogen ions in a solution is indicated by **pH**. This concentration can be described as either [H^+] or, because a hydrogen ion in water is solvated, as [H_3O^+].

$$pH = -\log\left[H^+\right]$$

The lower the pH, the more acidic is the solution. Acidic solutions have pH values less than 7; basic solutions have pH values greater than 7. The pH values of some commonly encountered solutions are shown in the margin. The pH of a solution can be changed simply by adding acid or base to the solution. Do not confuse pH and pK_a: the pH scale is used to describe the acidity of a *solution*; the pK_a is characteristic of a particular *compound*, much like a melting point or a boiling point—it indicates the tendency of the compound to give up its proton. The importance of organic acids and bases will become clear when we discuss how and why organic compounds react.

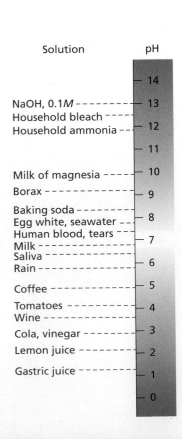

Solution	pH
	14
NaOH, 0.1M	13
Household bleach	
Household ammonia	12
	11
Milk of magnesia	10
Borax	9
Baking soda	
Egg white, seawater	8
Human blood, tears	7
Milk	
Saliva	6
Rain	
Coffee	5
Tomatoes	4
Wine	
Cola, vinegar	3
Lemon juice	2
Gastric juice	1
	0

Acid Rain

Rain is mildly acidic (pH = 5.5) because when water reacts with the CO_2 in the air, a weak acid—carbonic acid (pK_a = 6.4)—is formed.

$$CO_2 + H_2O \rightleftharpoons H_2CO_3$$
carbonic acid

In some parts of the world, rain has been found to be much more acidic—with pH values as low as 4.3. Acid rain is formed where sulfur dioxide and nitrogen oxides are produced, because when water reacts with these gases, strong acids—sulfuric acid (pK_a = −5.0) and nitric acid (pK_a = −1.3)—are formed. Burning fossil fuels for the generation of electric power is the factor most responsible for forming these acid-producing gases.

Acid rain has many deleterious effects. It can destroy aquatic life in lakes and streams; it can make soil so acidic that crops cannot grow; and it can cause the deterioration of paint and building materials, including monuments and statues that are part of our cultural heritage. Marble—a form of calcium carbonate—decays because acid reacts with CO_3^{2-} to

form carbonic acid, which decomposes to CO_2 and H_2O, the reverse of the reaction shown to the left.

$$CO_3^{2-} \overset{H^+}{\rightleftharpoons} HCO_3^- \overset{H^+}{\rightleftharpoons} H_2CO_3 \rightleftharpoons CO_2 + H_2O$$

photo taken in 1935   photo taken in 1994

Statue of George Washington in Washington Square Park, in Greenwich Village, New York.

PROBLEM 39 ♦

a. Which is a stronger acid, one with a pK_a of 5.2 or one with a pK_a of 5.8?

b. Which is a stronger acid, one with an acid dissociation constant of 3.4×10^{-3} or one with an acid dissociation constant of 2.1×10^{-4}?

PROBLEM 40 ♦

An acid has a K_a of 4.53×10^{-6} in water. What is its K_{eq}? ([H_2O] = 55.5 M)

PROBLEM-SOLVING STRATEGY

Determining K_a from pK_a

Vitamin C has a pK_a value of 4.17. What is its K_a value?

You will need a calculator to answer this question. Remember that $pK_a = -\log K_a$.

1. Enter the pK_a value on your calculator.
2. Multiply it by −1.
3. Determine the inverse log by pressing the key labeled 10^x.

You should find that vitamin C has a K_a value of 6.76×10^{-5}.

Now continue on to Problem 41.

---

chem Tutorial:
place Introduction to Acids

PROBLEM 41 ♦

Butyric acid, the compound responsible for the unpleasant odor and taste of sour milk, has a pK_a value of 4.82. What is its K_a value? Is it a stronger or a weaker acid than vitamin C?

PROBLEM 42

Antacids are compounds that neutralize stomach acid. Write the equations that show how Milk of Magnesia, Alka-Seltzer, and Tums remove excess acid.

a. Milk of Magnesia: $Mg(OH)_2$
b. Alka-Seltzer: $KHCO_3$ and $NaHCO_3$
c. Tums: $CaCO_3$

1.18 ORGANIC ACIDS AND BASES

The most common organic acids are carboxylic acids—compounds that have a COOH group. Acetic acid and formic acid are examples of carboxylic acids. Carboxylic acids have pK_a values ranging from about 3 to 5. (They are weak acids.) The pK_a values of a wide variety of organic compounds are given in Appendix II.

acetic acid
pK_a = 4.76

formic acid
pK_a = 3.75

Alcohols—compounds that have an OH group—are much weaker acids than carboxylic acids, with pK_a values close to 16. Methyl alcohol and ethyl alcohol are examples of alcohols.

CH_3OH
methyl alcohol
pK_a = 15.5

CH_3CH_2OH
ethyl alcohol
pK_a = 15.9

A compound with an NH_2 group is an amine. Amines and ammonia have such high pK_a values that they rarely behave as acids—they are much more likely to act as bases. In fact, they are the most common organic bases.

CH_3NH_2
methylamine
pK_a = 40

NH_3
ammonia
pK_a = 36

We can assess the strength of a base by considering the strength of its conjugate acid, as indicated by its pK_a value—remembering that the stronger the acid, the weaker is its conjugate base. For example, from their pK_a values we see that protonated methylamine is a stronger acid than protonated ethylamine, which means that methylamine is a weaker base than ethylamine. (A protonated compound is a compound that has gained an additional proton.) Notice that the pK_a values of protonated amines are in the range of 10 to 11.

$CH_3\overset{+}{N}H_3$
protonated methylamine
pK_a = 10.7

$CH_3CH_2\overset{+}{N}H_3$
protonated ethylamine
pK_a = 11.0

Protonated alcohols and protonated carboxylic acids are very strong acids. For example, protonated methyl alcohol has a pK_a of −2.5, protonated ethyl alcohol has a pK_a of −2.4, and protonated acetic acid has a pK_a of −6.1.

protonated methanol
pK_a = −2.5

protonated ethanol
pK_a = −2.4

protonated acetic acid
pK_a = −6.1

Notice that it is the sp^2 oxygen of the carboxylic acid that is protonated (acquires the proton). We will see why this is so in Section 17.11.

We have seen that water can behave both as an acid and as a base. An alcohol behaves similarly: it can behave as an acid and donate a proton, or as a base and accept a proton.

a curved arrow indicates where the electrons start from and where they end up

new bond

a curved arrow indicates where the electrons start from and where they end up

$$CH_3\overset{\cdot\cdot}{\underset{\cdot\cdot}{O}}-H \ + \ H-\overset{\cdot\cdot}{\underset{\cdot\cdot}{O}}{:}^{-} \ \rightleftharpoons \ CH_3\overset{\cdot\cdot}{\underset{\cdot\cdot}{O}}{:}^{-} \ + \ H-\overset{\cdot\cdot}{\underset{\cdot\cdot}{O}}-H$$

an acid

$$CH_3\overset{\cdot\cdot}{\underset{\cdot\cdot}{O}}-H \ + \ H-\overset{+}{\underset{H}{\overset{\cdot\cdot}{O}}}-H \ \rightleftharpoons \ CH_3\overset{+}{\underset{H}{\overset{\cdot\cdot}{O}}}-H \ + \ H-\overset{\cdot\cdot}{\underset{\cdot\cdot}{O}}-H$$

a base

new bond

Chemists frequently use curved arrows to indicate the bonds that are broken and formed as reactants are converted into products. The arrows show where the electrons start from and where they end up. In an acid–base reaction, one arrow is drawn *from* a lone pair on the base (the tail of the arrow) *to* the proton of the acid (the point of the arrow). A second arrow is drawn *from* the electrons that the proton shared *to* the atom on which they are left behind. These are called "curved" arrows to distinguish them from the "straight" arrows used to link reactants with products in the equation for a chemical reaction. Notice that the curved arrows let you follow the electrons to see how bonds are being formed and broken.

A carboxylic acid also can behave as an acid and donate a proton, or as a base and accept a proton.

an acid

a base

Similalry, an amine can behave as an acid and donate a proton, or as a base and accept a proton.

$$CH_3\overset{\cdot\cdot}{\underset{H}{N}}H \ + \ H-\overset{\cdot\cdot}{\underset{\cdot\cdot}{O}}{}^{-} \ \rightleftharpoons \ CH_3\overset{-}{\underset{}{N}}H \ + \ H-\overset{\cdot\cdot}{\underset{\cdot\cdot}{O}}-H$$

an acid

$$CH_3\overset{\cdot\cdot}{\underset{H}{N}}H \ + \ H-\overset{+}{\underset{H}{\overset{\cdot\cdot}{O}}}-H \ \rightleftharpoons \ CH_3\overset{+}{\underset{H}{N}}H \ + \ H-\overset{\cdot\cdot}{\underset{\cdot\cdot}{O}}-H$$

a base

It is important to know the approximate pK_a values of the various classes of compounds we have discussed. An easy way to remember them is in units of five, as shown in Table 1.8. (R is used when the particular carboxylic acid, alcohol, or amine is not specified.) Protonated alcohols, protonated carboxylic acids, and protonated water have pK_a values less than 0, carboxylic acids have pK_a values of about 5, protonated amines have pK_a values of about 10, and alcohols and water have pK_a values of about 15. These values are also listed inside the back cover of this book for easy reference.

Be sure to learn the approximate pK_a values given in Table 1.8.

Table 1.8   Approximate pK_a Values

pK_a < 0	pK_a ~ 5	pK_a ~ 10	pK_a ~ 15

$R\overset{+}{O}H_2$
a protonated
alcohol

$R\overset{O}{\underset{\overset{\|}{}}{C}}OH$
a carboxylic
acid

$R\overset{+}{N}H_3$
a protonated
amine

ROH
an alcohol

$\overset{+}{O}H$ ... $R\overset{\|}{C}OH$
a protonated
carboxylic acid

H_2O
water

H_3O^+
protonated
water

PROBLEM 44 ◆

Draw the conjugate acid of each of the following:

a. CH_3CH_2OH **b.** $CH_3CH_2O^-$ **c.** $CH_3CH_2NH_2$ **d.** $CH_3CH_2\overset{O}{\underset{\overset{\|}{}}{C}}OH$

PROBLEM 45 ◆

a. Which is a stronger base, CH_3COO^- or $HCOO^-$? (The pK_a of CH_3COOH is 4.8; the pK_a of $HCOOH$ is 3.8.)
b. Which is a stronger base, HO^- or $^-NH_2$? (The pK_a of H_2O is 15.7; the pK_a of NH_3 is 36.)
c. Which is a stronger base, H_2O or CH_3OH? (The pK_a of H_3O^+ is −1.7; the pK_a of $CH_3\overset{+}{O}H_2$ is −2.5.)

PROBLEM 46 ◆

Using the pK_a values in Section 1.18, rank the following species in order of decreasing base strength (that is, list the strongest base first):

CH_3NH_2 CH_3NH^- CH_3OH CH_3O^- $CH_3\overset{O}{\underset{\overset{\|}{}}{C}}O^-$

chem Tutorial:
place   Important pK_a values

1.19   HOW TO PREDICT THE OUTCOME OF AN ACID—BASE REACTION

Now let's see how we can predict that water will act as a base in the first reaction in Section 1.16 and as an acid in the second reaction. To determine which of two reactants will be the acid, we need to compare their pK_a values: in the first reaction, the pK_a of hydrogen chloride is −7 and the pK_a of water is 15.7. Because hydrogen chloride is the stronger acid, it will donate a proton to water. Water, therefore, is a base in this reaction. When we compare the pK_a values of the two reactants of the second reaction, we see that the pK_a of ammonia is 36 and the pK_a of water is 15.7. In this case, water is the stronger acid, so it donates a proton to ammonia. Water, therefore, is an acid in this reaction.

this is the acid   this is the acid

HCl + H_2O NH_3 + H_2O
pK_a = −7   pK_a = 15.7   pK_a = 36   pK_a = 15.7

1.20 HOW TO DETERMINE THE POSITION OF EQUILIBRIUM

To determine the position of equilibrium for an acid–base reaction (that is, whether reactants or products are favored at equilibrium), we need to compare the pK_a value of the acid on the left of the arrow with the pK_a value of the acid on the right of the arrow. The equilibrium favors *reaction* of the stronger acid (the one with the lower pK_a) and *formation* of the weaker acid (the one with the higher pK_a). In other words, *strong reacts to form weak.* Thus, the equilibrium lies away from the stronger acid and toward the weaker acid. Notice that the stronger acid has the weaker conjugate base.

Strong reacts to form weak.

$$
\text{CH}_3\text{CH}_2\text{OH} \ + \ \text{CH}_3\text{NH}_2 \ \rightleftharpoons \ \text{CH}_3\text{CH}_2\text{O}^- \ + \ \text{CH}_3\overset{+}{\text{N}}\text{H}_3
$$

weaker acid   weaker base   stronger base   stronger acid
$pK_a = 15.9$ $pK_a = 10.7$

PROBLEM 47

a. Write an equation showing CH_3OH reacting as an acid with NH_3 and an equation showing it reacting as a base with HCl.

b. Write an equation showing NH_3 reacting as an acid with CH_3O^- and an equation showing it reacting as a base with HBr.

PROBLEM 48

a. For each of the acid–base reactions in Section 1.18, compare the pK_a values of the acids on either side of the equilibrium arrows to prove that the equilibrium lies in the direction indicated. (The pK_a values you need can be found in Section 1.18 or in Problem 45.)

b. Do the same for the equilibria in Section 1.16. (The pK_a of $^+\text{NH}_4$ is 9.4.)

PROBLEM 49

Ethyne has a pK_a value of 25, water has a pK_a value of 15.7, and ammonia (NH_3) has a pK_a value of 36. Draw the equation, showing equilibrium arrows that indicate whether reactants or products are favored, for the acid–base reaction of ethyne with:

a. HO^- b. $^-\text{NH}_2$

c. Which would be a better base to use if you wanted to remove a proton from ethyne, HO^- or $^-\text{NH}_2$?

The precise value of the equilibrium constant can be calculated by dividing the K_a of the reactant acid by the K_a of the product acid.

$$
K_{eq} = \frac{K_a \text{ reactant acid}}{K_a \text{ product acid}}
$$

Thus, the equilibrium constant for the reaction of acetic acid with ammonia is 4.0×10^4, and the equilibrium constant for the reaction of ethyl alcohol with methylamine is 6.3×10^{-6}. The calculations are:

for the reaction of acetic acid with ammonia:

$$
K_{eq} = \frac{10^{-4.8}}{10^{-9.4}} = 10^{4.6} = 4.0 \times 10^4
$$

for the reaction of ethyl alcohol with methylamine:

$$
K_{eq} = \frac{10^{-15.9}}{10^{-10.7}} = 10^{-5.2} = 6.3 \times 10^{-6}
$$

Calculate the equilibrium constant for the acid–base reaction between the reactants in each of the following pairs:

a. $HCl + H_2O$

b. $CH_3COOH + H_2O$

c. $CH_3NH_2 + H_2O$

d. $CH_3\overset{+}{N}H_3 + H_2O$

chem Tutorial:
place Acid-Base Reaction

1.21 HOW THE STRUCTURE OF AN ACID AFFECTS ITS pK_a VALUE

The strength of an acid is determined by the stability of the conjugate base formed when the acid gives up its proton: the more stable the base, the stronger is its conjugate acid. (The reason for this will be explained in Section 3.7.) A stable base is a base that readily bears the electrons it formerly shared with a proton. In other words, stable bases are weak bases—they do not share their electrons well—allowing us to say, *the weaker the base, the stronger is its conjugate acid*, or *the more stable the base, the stronger is its conjugate acid*.

The weaker the base, the stronger is its conjugate acid.

Stable bases are weak bases.

The more stable the base, the stronger is its conjugate acid.

Electronegativity

Two factors that affect the stability of a base are its *electronegativity* and its size. The atoms in the second row of the periodic table are all similar in size, but they have very different electronegativities, which increase across the row from left to right. Of the atoms shown, carbon is the least electronegative and fluorine is the most electronegative.

relative electronegativities: C < N < O < F
most electronegative

If we look at the acids formed by attaching hydrogens to these elements, we see that the most acidic compound is the one that has its hydrogen attached to the most electronegative atom. Thus, HF is the strongest acid and methane is the weakest acid.

relative acidities: CH_4 < NH_3 < H_2O < HF
strongest acid

If we look at the stabilities of the conjugate bases of these acids, we find that they too increase from left to right because the more electronegative the atom, the better it can bear its negative charge. Thus, we see that the strongest acid has the most stable (most electronegative) conjugate base.

relative stabilities: $^-CH_3$ < $^-NH_2$ < HO^- < F^-
most stable

We therefore can conclude that *when the atoms are similar in size, the strongest acid will have its hydrogen attached to the most electronegative atom.*

The effect that the electronegativity of the atom bonded to a hydrogen has on the acidity of that hydrogen can be appreciated when the pK_a values of alcohols and amines are compared. Because oxygen is more electronegative than nitrogen, an alcohol is more acidic than an amine.

When atoms are similar in size, the strongest acid will have its hydrogen attached to the most electronegative atom.

CH_3OH CH_3NH_2
methyl alcohol   methylamine
pK_a = 15.5   pK_a = 40

Similarly, a protonated alcohol is more acidic than a protonated amine.

$$CH_3\overset{+}{O}H_2$$
protonated methyl alcohol
pK_a = −2.5

$$CH_3\overset{+}{N}H_3$$
protonated methylamine
pK_a = 10.7

Hybridization

An *sp* carbon is more electronegative than an sp^2 carbon, which is more electronegative than an sp^3 carbon.

The hybridization of an atom affects the acidity of a hydrogen bonded to the atom because its hybridization affects its electronegativity: an *sp* hybridized atom is more electronegative than the same atom that is sp^2 hybridized, which is more electronegative than the same atom that is sp^3 hybridized.

relative electronegativities of carbon atoms

most electronegative $> sp > sp^2 > sp^3 <$ least electronegative

Because the electronegativity of carbon atoms follows the order $sp > sp^2 > sp^3$, ethyne is a stronger acid than ethene, and ethene is a stronger acid than ethane—the most acidic compound is the one with the hydrogen attached to the most electronegative atom.

most acidic $>$ $HC{\equiv}CH$ $H_2C{=}CH_2$ CH_3CH_3 $<$ least acidic
ethyne   **ethene**   **ethane**
pK_a = 25   **pK_a = 44**   **pK_a > 60**

Why does the hybridization of the atom affect its electronegativity? Electronegativity is a measure of the ability of an atom to pull the bonding electrons toward itself. Thus, the most electronegative atom will be the one with its bonding electrons closest to the nucleus. The average distance of a 2*s* electron from the nucleus is less than the average distance of a 2*p* electron from the nucleus. Therefore, an *sp* hybridized atom with 50% *s* character is the most electronegative, an sp^2 hybridized atom with 33.3% *s* character is next, and an sp^3 hybridized atom with 25% *s* character is the least electronegative.

Pulling the electrons closer to the nucleus stabilizes the carbanion. Once again we see that the stronger the acid, the more stable (weaker) is its conjugate base. Notice that the weakest base is the least electron-rich (less red).

most stable   least stable
$HC{\equiv}C^-$ $H_2C{=}\overset{-}{C}H$ $CH_3\overset{-}{C}H_2$

Size

In comparing atoms that are very different in size, the *size* of the atom is more important than its *electronegativity* in determining how well it bears its negative charge. For example, as we proceed down a column in the periodic table, the atoms get larger and their electronegativity *decreases*. But the stability of the bases increases down the column, so the strength of the conjugate acids *increases*. Thus, HI is the strongest acid of the hydrogen halides, even though iodine is the least electronegative of the halogens.

Therefore, *when atoms are very different in size, the strongest acid will have its hydrogen attached to the largest atom.*

Size overrides electronegativity.

relative electronegativities: F > Cl > Br > I

most electronegative

largest

relative stabilities: F⁻ < Cl⁻ < Br⁻ < I⁻

most stable

relative acidities: HF < HCl < HBr < HI

strongest acid

Why does the size of an atom have such a significant effect on the stability of the base that it more than overcomes any difference in electronegativity? The valence electrons of F⁻ are in a $2sp^3$ orbital, the valence electrons of Cl⁻ are in a $3sp^3$ orbital, those of Br⁻ are in a $4sp^3$ orbital, and those of I⁻ are in a $5sp^3$ orbital. The volume of space occupied by a $3sp^3$ orbital is significantly greater than the volume of space occupied by a $2sp^3$ orbital because a $3sp^3$ orbital extends out farther from the nucleus. Because its negative charge is spread over a larger volume of space, Cl⁻ is more stable than F⁻.

Thus, as the halide ion increases in size, its stability increases because its negative charge is spread over a larger volume of space (its electron density decreases). The *more stable the halide ion is as a base, the stronger is its conjugate acid*. Therefore, HI is the strongest acid of the hydrogen halides because I⁻ is the most stable halide ion, even though iodine is the least electronegative of the halogens (Table 1.9). The potential maps illustrate the large difference in size of the hydrogen halides:

When atoms are very different in size, the strongest acid will have its hydrogen attached to the largest atom.

Table 1.9 The pK_a Values of Some Simple Acids			
CH$_4$	NH$_3$	H$_2$O	HF
pK_a = 60	pK_a = 36	pK_a = 15.7	pK_a = 3.2
		H$_2$S	HCl
		pK_a = 7.0	pK_a = 7
			HBr
			pK_a = −9
			HI
			pK_a = −10

HF   HCl   HBr   HI

In summary, as we move across a row of the periodic table, the atoms' orbitals have approximately the same volume, so it is electronegativity that determines the stability of the base and, therefore, the acidity of a proton bonded to that base. As we move down a column of the periodic table, the volume of the orbitals increases. The increase in volume causes the electron density of the orbital to decrease. The electron density of the orbitals is more important than electronegativity in determining the stability of a base and, therefore, the acidity of its conjugate acid.

CH₃O⁻

CH₃S⁻

PROBLEM 51♦

a. Which is more electronegative, oxygen or sulfur?
b. Which is a stronger acid, H_2O or H_2S?
c. Which is a stronger acid, CH_3OH or CH_3SH?

PROBLEM 52♦

For each of the following pairs, indicate which is the stronger acid:
a. HCl or HBr

b. $CH_3CH_2CH_2\overset{+}{N}H_3$ or $CH_3CH_2CH_2\overset{+}{O}H_2$

c. or

black = C, white = H, blue = N, red = O

d. or

PROBLEM 53♦

a. Which of the halide ions (F^-, Cl^-, Br^-, I^-) is the strongest base?
b. Which is the weakest base?

PROBLEM 54♦

For each of the following pairs, indicate which is the stronger base:

a. H_2O or HO^- **b.** H_2O or NH_3 **c.** CH_3CO^- or CH_3O^- **d.** CH_3O^- or CH_3S^-

1.22 HOW SUBSTITUENTS AFFECT THE STRENGTH OF AN ACID

Although the acidic proton of each of the following four carboxylic acids is attached to the same atom (an oxygen atom), the four compounds have different acidities as reflected in their pK_a values:

least acidic ⟶ pK_a = 4.76   pK_a = 2.86   pK_a = 2.81   pK_a = 2.66 ⟵ most acidic

This difference indicates that in addition to the nature of the atom to which the hydrogen is bonded, there must be another factor that affects acidity.

From the pK_a values of the four carboxylic acids, we see that replacing one of the hydrogen atoms of the CH_3 group with a halogen atom affects the acidity of the compound. (The term for replacing an atom in a compound is *substitution*, and the new atom is called a *substituent*.) The acidity increases because a halogen is more electronegative than hydrogen. An electronegative halogen atom pulls the bonding electrons toward itself. Pulling electrons through sigma (σ) bonds is called **inductive electron withdrawal**. If we look at the conjugate base of a carboxylic acid, we see that inductive electron withdrawal stabilizes the base by *decreasing the electron density* about the oxygen atom. Stabilizing a base increases the acidity of its conjugate acid.

inductive electron withdrawal toward the bromine atom

As the pK_a values of the four carboxylic acids on page 52 show, inductive electron withdrawal increases the acidity of a compound. The greater the electron-withdrawing ability (electronegativity) of the halogen substituent, the more the acidity is increased because the more its conjugate base is stabilized. Thus, the fluoro-substituted compound is the strongest acid.

The effect of a substituent on the acidity of a compound decreases as the distance between the substituent and the acidic proton increases.

most acidic $pK_a = 2.97$ $pK_a = 4.01$ $pK_a = 4.59$ $pK_a = 4.71$ least acidic

PROBLEM-SOLVING STRATEGY

Determining Relative Acid Strength from Structure

a. Which is a stronger acid?

$$CH_3CHCH_2OH \quad or \quad CH_3CHCH_2OH$$
$$\quad\quad | \quad\quad\quad\quad\quad\quad\quad\quad | $$
$$\quad\quad F \quad\quad\quad\quad\quad\quad\quad\quad Br$$

When you are asked to compare two items, pay attention to how they differ; ignore where they are the same. These two compounds differ only in the halogen atom attached to the middle carbon of the molecule. Because fluorine is more electronegative than bromine, there is greater electron withdrawal from the oxygen atom in the fluorinated compound. The fluorinated compound, therefore, will have the more stable conjugate base, so it will be the stronger acid.

b. Which is a stronger acid?

$$\quad\quad Cl \quad\quad\quad\quad\quad Cl$$
$$\quad\quad | \quad\quad\quad\quad\quad\quad |$$
$$CH_3CCH_2OH \quad or \quad CH_2CHCH_2OH$$
$$\quad\quad | \quad\quad\quad\quad\quad\quad |$$
$$\quad\quad Cl \quad\quad\quad\quad\quad\quad Cl$$

These two compounds differ in the location of one of the chlorine atoms. Because the second chlorine in the compound on the left is closer to the O—H bond than is the second chlorine in the compound on the right, the former is more effective at withdrawing electrons from the oxygen atom. Thus, the compound on the left will have the more stable conjugate base, so it will be the stronger acid.

Now continue on to Problem 55.

PROBLEM 55 ◆

For each of the following pairs, indicate which is the stronger acid:

a. $CH_3OCH_2CH_2OH$ or $CH_3CH_2CH_2CH_2OH$

b. $CH_3CH_2CH_2\overset{+}{N}H_3$ or $CH_3CH_2CH_2\overset{+}{O}H_2$

c. $CH_3OCH_2CH_2CH_2OH$ or $CH_3CH_2OCH_2CH_2OH$

d. $CH_3\overset{O}{\overset{||}{C}}CH_2OH$ or $CH_3CH_2\overset{O}{\overset{||}{C}}OH$

PROBLEM 56 ◆

List the following compounds in order of decreasing acidity:

$$\underset{\underset{F}{|}}{CH_3CHCH_2OH} \qquad CH_3CH_2CH_2OH \qquad \underset{\underset{Cl}{|}}{CH_2CH_2CH_2OH} \qquad \underset{\underset{Cl}{|}}{CH_3CHCH_2OH}$$

PROBLEM 57 ◆

For each of the following pairs, indicate which is the stronger base:

a.
$$\underset{\underset{Br}{|}}{CH_3CHC\overset{O}{\overset{\|}{C}}O^-} \quad or \quad \underset{\underset{F}{|}}{CH_3CHC\overset{O}{\overset{\|}{C}}O^-}$$

c.
$$BrCH_2CH_2\overset{O}{\overset{\|}{C}}O^- \quad or \quad CH_3CH_2\overset{O}{\overset{\|}{C}}O^-$$

b.
$$\underset{\underset{Cl}{|}}{CH_3CHCH_2\overset{O}{\overset{\|}{C}}O^-} \quad or \quad \underset{\underset{Cl}{|}}{CH_3CH_2CHC\overset{O}{\overset{\|}{C}}O^-}$$

d.
$$CH_3\overset{O}{\overset{\|}{C}}CH_2CH_2O^- \quad or \quad CH_3CH_2\overset{O}{\overset{\|}{C}}CH_2O^-$$

PROBLEM 58 **SOLVED**

If HCl is a weaker acid than HBr, why is $ClCH_2COOH$ a stronger acid than $BrCH_2COOH$?

Solution To compare the acidities of HCl and HBr, we need to compare the stabilities of their conjugate bases, Cl^- and Br^-. Because we know that size is more important than electronegativity in determining stability, we know that Br^- is more stable than Cl^-. Therefore, HBr is a stronger acid than HCl. In comparing the acidities of the two carboxylic acids, we need to compare the stabilities of their conjugate bases, $RCOO^-$ and $R'COO^-$. (Notice that an O—H bond is broken in both compounds.) The only way the conjugate bases differ is in the electronegativity of the atom that is pulling electrons away from the negatively charged oxygen. Because Cl is more electronegative than Br, Cl exerts greater inductive electron withdrawal. Thus, it has a greater stabilizing effect on the base that is formed when the proton leaves, so the chloro-substituted compound is the stronger acid.

1.23 AN INTRODUCTION TO DELOCALIZED ELECTRONS

We have seen that a carboxylic acid has a pK_a value of about 5, whereas the pK_a value of an alcohol is about 15. Because a carboxylic acid is a much stronger acid than an alcohol, we know that a carboxylic acid has a considerably more stable conjugate base.

$$\underset{pK_a = 4.76}{CH_3\overset{O}{\overset{\|}{\underset{}{C}}}O-H} \qquad \underset{pK_a = 15.9}{CH_3CH_2O-H}$$

Two factors cause the conjugate base of a carboxylic acid to be more stable than the conjugate base of an alcohol. First, the conjugate base of a carboxylic acid has a doubly bonded oxygen in place of two hydrogens in the conjugate base of an alcohol. Inductive electron withdrawal by this electronegative oxygen decreases the electron density of the negatively charged oxygen. Second, oxygen's electron density is further decreased by *electron delocalization*.

When an alcohol loses a proton, the negative charge resides on its single oxygen atom: electrons that belong to only one atom are called *localized* electrons. In contrast, when a carboxylic acid loses a proton, the negative charge is shared by both oxygen atoms because the electrons are *delocalized*.

The two structures shown for the conjugate base of the carboxylic acid are called **resonance contributors**. Neither resonance contributor alone represents the actual structure of the conjugate base. Instead, the actual structure—called a **resonance hybrid**—is a composite of the two resonance contributors. The double-headed arrow between the two resonance contributors is used to indicate that the actual structure is a hybrid. Notice that the two resonance contributors differ only in the location of their π electrons and lone-pair electrons—all the atoms stay in the same place. In the resonance hybrid, an electron pair is spread over *two oxygens and a carbon*. The negative charge is shared equally by the two oxygens, and both carbon–oxygen bonds are the same length—they are not as long as a single bond, but they are longer than a double bond. A resonance hybrid can be drawn by using dotted lines to show the delocalized electrons.

The following potential maps show that the negative charge is on one oxygen in the conjugate base of the alcohol (red region) and is shared by both oxygens in the conjugate base of the carboxylic acid (orange-red region):

Delocalized electrons are shared by more than two atoms.

$CH_3CH_2O^-$

CH_3-C with $O^{\delta-}$ (double bond) and $O^{\delta-}$

Thus, the combination of inductive electron withdrawal and the ability of two atoms to share the negative charge makes the conjugate base of the carboxylic acid more stable than the conjugate base of the alcohol.

We will discuss delocalized electrons in greater detail in Chapter 7. By that time, you will be thoroughly comfortable with compounds that have only localized electrons, and we can then further explore how delocalized electrons affect the stability and reactivity of organic compounds.

PROBLEM 59 ♦

Which compound would you expect to be a stronger acid? Why?

$$CH_3\overset{O}{\overset{\|}{C}}-O-H \quad \text{or} \quad CH_3\overset{O}{\underset{\underset{O}{\|}}{\overset{\|}{S}}}-O-H$$

PROBLEM 60 ◆

Draw resonance contributors for the following compounds:

a.   b.

1.24 A SUMMARY OF THE FACTORS THAT DETERMINE ACID STRENGTH

We have seen that the strength of an acid depends on five factors: the *size* of the atom to which the hydrogen is attached, the *electronegativity* of the atom to which the hydrogen is attached, the *hybridization* of the atom to which the hydrogen is attached, *inductive effects*, and *electron delocalization*. All five factors affect acidity by stabilizing the conjugate base.

1. **Size:** As the atom attached to the hydrogen increases in size (going down a column of the periodic table), the strength of the acid increases.

2. **Electronegativity:** As the atom attached to the hydrogen increases in electronegativity (going across a row of the periodic table), the strength of the acid increases.

3. **Hybridization:** The relative electronegativities of an atom are: $sp > sp^2 > sp^3$. Because hybridization affects the electronegativity of an atom, a hydrogen attached to an sp carbon is the most acidic and a hydrogen attached to an sp^3 carbon is the least acidic.

most acidic > HC≡CH > H₂C=CH₂ > CH₃CH₃ < least acidic

    sp sp^2 sp^3

4. **Inductive effect:** An electron-withdrawing group increases acid strength: the more electronegative the electron-withdrawing group and the closer it is to the acidic hydrogen, the stronger is the acid.

most acidic > CH₃CHCH₂OH > CH₃CHCH₂OH > CH₃CHCH₂OH > CH₃CH₂CH₂OH < least acidic
              F   Cl   Br

most acidic > CH₃CHCH₂OH > CH₂CH₂CH₂OH > CH₃CH₂CH₂OH < least acidic
              F   F

5. Electron delocalization: An acid whose conjugate base has delocalized electrons is more acidic than a similar acid whose conjugate base has only localized electrons.

PROBLEM 61♦

Using the table of pK_a values given in Appendix II, answer the following:

a. Which is the most acidic organic compound in the table?

b. Which is the least acidic organic compound in the table?

c. Which is the most acidic carboxylic acid in the table?

d. Which is more electronegative, an sp^3 oxygen or an sp^2 oxygen? (*Hint:* Pick a compound in Appendix II with a hydrogen attached to an sp^2 oxygen and one with a hydrogen attached to an sp^3 oxygen, and compare their pK_a values.)

e. What compounds illustrate that the relative electronegativities of a hybridized nitrogen atom are $sp > sp^2 > sp^3$?

f. Which is more acidic, HNO_3 or HNO_2? Why?

1.25 HOW pH AFFECTS THE STRUCTURE OF AN ORGANIC COMPOUND

Whether a given acid will lose a proton in an aqueous solution depends both on the pK_a of the acid and the pH of the solution. The relationship between the two is given by the **Henderson–Hasselbalch equation**. This is an extremely useful equation because it tells us whether a compound will exist in its acidic form (with its proton retained) or in its basic form (with its proton removed) at a particular pH.

the Henderson–Hasselbalch equation

$$pK_a = pH + \log \frac{[HA]}{[A^-]}$$

The Henderson–Hasselbalch equation tells us that when the pH of a solution equals the pK_a of the compound that undergoes dissociation, the concentration of the compound in its acidic form [HA] will equal the concentration of the compound in its basic form [A^-] (because $\log 1 = 0$). If the pH of the solution is less than the pK_a of the compound, the compound will exist primarily in its acidic form. If the pH of the solution is greater than the pK_a of the compound, the compound will exist primarily in its basic form. In other words, *compounds exist primarily in their acidic forms in solutions that are more acidic than their pK_a values and primarily in their basic forms in solutions that are more basic than their pK_a values.*

> A compound will exist primarily in its acidic form if the pH of the solution is less than the compound's pK_a.

> A compound will exist primarily in its basic form if the pH of the solution is greater than the compound's pK_a.

If we know the pH of the solution and the pK_a of the compound, the Henderson–Hasselbalch equation allows us to calculate precisely how much of the compound will be in its acidic form, and how much will be in its basic form. For example, when a compound with a pK_a of 5.2 is in a solution of pH 5.2, half the compound will be in the acidic form and the other half will be in the basic form (Figure 1.17). If the pH is one unit less than the pK_a of the compound (pH = 4.2), there will be 10 times more compound present in the acidic form than in the basic form (because $\log 10 = 1$). If the pH is two units less than the pK_a of the compound (pH = 3.2), there will be 100 times more compound present in the acidic form than in the basic form (because $\log 100 = 2$). If the pH is 6.2, there will be 10 times more compound in the basic form than in the acidic form, and at pH = 7.2 there will be 100 times more compound present in the basic form than in the acidic form.

▶ Figure 1.17
The relative amounts of a compound with a pK_a of 5.2 in the acidic and basic forms at different pH values.

Derivation of the Henderson—Hasselbalch Equation

The Henderson–Hasselbalch equation can be derived from the expression that defines the acid dissociation constant:

$$K_a = \frac{[H_3O^+][A^-]}{[HA]}$$

Taking the logarithms of both sides of the equation remembering that when things are multiplied their logs are added, we obtain

$$\log K_a = \log[H_3O^+] + \log \frac{[A^-]}{[HA]}$$

Multiplying both sides of the equation by −1 give us

$$-\log K_a = -\log[H_3O^+] - \log \frac{[A^-]}{[HA]}$$

Substituting and remembering that when a fraction is inverted, the sign of its log changes, we get

$$pK_a = pH + \log \frac{[HA]}{[A^-]}$$

PROBLEM-SOLVING STRATEGY

Determining the Structure at a Particular pH

Write the form in which the following compounds will predominate in a solution of pH 5.5:

a. CH_3CH_2OH (pK_a = 15.9)

b. $CH_3CH_2\overset{+}{O}H_2$ (pK_a = −2.5)

c. $CH_3\overset{+}{N}H_3$ (pK_a = 11.0)

To answer this kind of question, we need to compare the pH of the solution with the pK_a value of the compound's dissociable proton.

a. The pH of the solution is more acidic (5.5) than the pK_a value of the OH group (15.9). Therefore, the compound will exist primarily as CH_3CH_2OH (with its proton).

b. The pH of the solution is more basic (5.5) than the pK_a value of the $^+OH_2$ group (−2.5). Therefore, the compound will exist primarily as CH_3CH_2OH (without its proton).

c. The pH of the solution is more acidic (5.5) than the pK_a value of the $^+NH_3$ group (11.0). Therefore, the compound will exist primarily as $CH_3\overset{+}{N}H_3$ (with its proton).

Now continue on to Problem 62.

PROBLEM 62◆

For each of the following compounds, shown in their acidic forms, write the form that will predominate in a solution of pH = 5.5:

a. CH_3COOH (pK_a = 4.76)

b. $CH_3CH_2\overset{+}{N}H_3$ (pK_a = 11.0)

c. H_3O^+ (pK_a = −1.7)

d. HBr (pK_a = −9)

e. $^+NH_4$ (pK_a = 9.4)

f. $HC\equiv N$ (pK_a = 9.1)

g. HNO_2 (pK_a = 3.4)

h. HNO_3 (pK_a = −1.3)

PROBLEM 63 ♦ SOLVED

a. Indicate whether a carboxylic acid (RCOOH) with a pK_a value of 4.5 will have more charged molecules or more neutral molecules in a solution with the following pH:

1. pH = 1   3. pH = 5   5. pH = 10
2. pH = 3   4. pH = 7   6. pH = 13

b. Answer the same question for a protonated amine (RNH_3^+) with a pK_a value of 9.
c. Answer the same question for an alcohol (ROH) with a pK_a value of 15.

Solution to 63a   First determine whether the compound is charged or neutral in its acidic form and charged or neutral in its basic form: a carboxylic acid is neutral in its acidic form (RCOOH) and charged in its basic form ($RCOO^-$). Then compare the pH and pK_a values remembering that if the pH of the solution is less than the pK_a value of the compound, more molecules will be in the acidic form, but if the pH is greater than the pK_a value of the compound, more molecules will be in the basic form. Therefore, at pH = 1 and 3, there will be more neutral molecules, and at pH = 5, 7, 10, and 13, there will be more charged molecules.

You are what you're in: a compound will be mostly in the acidic form in an acidic solution (pH < pK_a) and mostly in the basic form in a basic solution (pH > pK_a).

PROBLEM 64 ♦

A naturally occurring amino acid such as alanine has both a carboxylic acid group and an amine group. The pK_a values of the two groups are shown.

$pK_a = 2.34$

$pK_a = 9.69$

alanine
an amino acid

a. Draw the structure of alanine in a solution at physiological pH (pH 7.3).
b. Is there a pH at which alanine will be neutral (neither group will have a charge)?
c. At what pH will alanine have no net charge (the amount of negative charge will be the same as the amount of positive charge)?

The Henderson–Hasselbalch equation can be very useful in the laboratory for separating the compounds in a mixture. Water and diethyl ether are liquids of very limited mutual solubility and, therefore, will form two layers when combined; the ether layer will lie above the more dense water layer. Charged compounds are more soluble in water, whereas neutral compounds are more soluble in diethyl ether (Section 2.9). Two compounds, such as a carboxylic acid (RCOOH) with a pK_a of 5.0 and a protonated amine (RNH_3^+) with a pK_a of 10.0, dissolved in a mixture of water and diethyl ether, can be separated by adjusting the pH of the water layer. For example, if the pH of the water layer is 2, the carboxylic acid and the protonated amine will both be in their acidic forms because the pH of the water is less than the pK_a values of both compounds. The acidic form of a carboxylic acid is neutral, whereas the acidic form of an amine is charged. Therefore, the carboxylic acid will be more soluble in the ether layer, and the protonated amine will be more soluble in the water layer.

—ether

—water

acidic form   basic form

$RCOOH \rightleftharpoons RCOO^- + H^+$

$RNH_3^+ \rightleftharpoons RNH_2 + H^+$

For the most effective separation, the pH of the water layer should be at least two units away from the pK_a values of the compounds being separated. Then the relative amounts of the compounds in their acidic and basic forms will be at least 100:1 (Figure 1.17).

PROBLEM 65♦ **SOLVED**

a. At what pH will the concentration of a compound with a pK_a of 8.4 be 100 times greater in its basic form than in its acidic form?
b. At what pH will the concentration of a compound with a pK_a of 3.7 be 10 times greater in its acidic form than in its basic form?
c. At what pH will the concentration of a compound with a pK_a of 8.4 be 100 times greater in its acidic form than in its basic form?
d. At what pH will 50% of a compound with a pK_a of 7.3 be in its basic form?
e. At what pH will the concentration of a compound with a pK_a of 4.6 be 10 times greater in its basic form than in its acidic form?

Solution to 65a   If the concentration in the basic form is 100 times greater than the concentration in the acidic form, the Henderson–Hasselbalch equation becomes

$$pK_a = pH + \log 1/100$$
$$8.4 = pH + \log .01$$
$$8.4 = pH - 2.0$$
$$pH = 10.4$$

There is a faster way to get the answer: if 100 times more compound is present in the basic form than in the acidic form, the pH will be two units more basic than the pK_a. Thus, pH = 8.4 + 2.0 = 10.4.

Solution to 65b   If 10 times more compound is present in the acidic form than in the basic form, the pH will be one unit more acidic than the pK_a. Thus, pH = 3.7 − 1.0 = 2.7.

PROBLEM 66♦

For each of the following compounds, indicate the pH at which
a. 50% of the compound will be in a form that possesses a charge.
b. more than 99% of the compound will be in a form that possesses a charge.
  1. CH_3CH_2COOH (pK_a = 4.9)
  2. $CH_3\overset{+}{N}H_3$ (pK_a = 10.7)

PROBLEM 67♦

As long as the pH is greater than _____, more than 50% of a protonated amine with a pK_a of 10.4 will be in its neutral, nonprotonated form.

1.26 BUFFER SOLUTIONS

A solution of a weak acid (HA) and its conjugate base (A⁻) is called a **buffer solution**. A buffer solution will maintain nearly constant pH when small amounts of acid or base are added to it, because the weak acid can donate a proton to any HO⁻ added to the solution, and its conjugate base can accept any H⁺ that is added to the solution.

can donate an H⁺ to HO⁻

$$HA + HO^- \longrightarrow A^- + H_2O$$
$$A^- + H_3O^+ \longrightarrow HA + H_2O$$

can accept an H⁺ from H₃O⁺

NOTE TO THE STUDENT
Buffer solutions are discussed in detail in Special Topic I in the *Study Guide and Solutions Manual*. By working the problems you will find there, you will see the usefulness of the Henderson–Hasselbalch equation for dealing with buffer solutions.

PROBLEM 68 ◆

Write the equation that shows how a buffer made by dissolving CH_3COOH and $CH_3COO^- Na^+$ in water prevents the pH of a solution from changing appreciably when:

a. a small amount of H^+ is added to the solution.

b. a small amount of HO^- is added to the solution.

Blood: A Buffered Solution

Blood is the fluid that transports oxygen to all the cells of the human body. The normal pH of human blood is 7.3 to 7.4. Death will result if this pH decreases to a value less than ~6.8 or increases to a value greater than ~8.0 for even a few seconds.

Oxygen is carried to cells by a protein in the blood called hemoglobin (HbH^+). When hemoglobin binds O_2, hemoglobin loses a proton, which would make the blood more acidic if it did not contain a buffer to maintain its pH.

$$HbH^+ + O_2 \rightleftharpoons HbO_2 + H^+$$

A carbonic acid/bicarbonate (H_2CO_3 / HCO_3^-) buffer controls the pH of blood. An important feature of this buffer is that carbonic acid decomposes to CO_2 and H_2O:

$$\underset{\textbf{carbonic acid}}{CO_2 + H_2O \rightleftharpoons H_2CO_3} \rightleftharpoons \underset{\textbf{bicarbonate}}{HCO_3^-} + H^+$$

During exercise our metabolism speeds up, producing large amounts of CO_2. The increased concentration of CO_2 shifts the equilibrium between carbonic acid and bicarbonate to the right, which increases the concentration of H^+. Significant amounts of lactic acid are also produced during exercise, and this further increases the concentration of H^+. Receptors in the brain respond to the increased concentration of H^+ by triggering a reflex that increases the rate of breathing. Hemoglobin then releases more oxygen to the cells and more CO_2 is eliminated by exhalation. Both processes decrease the concentration of H^+ in the blood by shifting both equilibria to the left.

Thus, any disorder that decreases the rate and depth of ventilation, such as emphysema, will decrease the pH of the blood—a condition called acidosis. In contrast, any excessive increase in the rate and depth of ventilation, as with hyperventilation due to anxiety, will increase the pH of blood—a condition called alkalosis.

1.27 LEWIS ACIDS AND BASES

In 1923, G. N. Lewis (page 8) offered new definitions for the terms *acid* and *base*. He defined an acid as *a species that accepts a share in an electron pair* and a base as *a species that donates a share in an electron pair*. All proton donating acids fit the Lewis definition because all proton-donating acids lose a proton and the proton accepts a share in an electron pair.

the curved arrow indicates where the electrons start from and where they end up

$$\underset{\textbf{acid}}{H^+} + \underset{\textbf{base}}{:NH_3} \rightleftharpoons H-\overset{+}{N}H_3$$

accepts a share in an electron pair

donates a share in an electron pair

new bond

Lewis acids, however, are not limited to compounds that donate protons. Compounds such as aluminum chloride ($AlCl_3$), boron trifluoride (BF_3), and borane (BH_3) are acids according to the Lewis definition because they have unfilled valence orbitals and thus can accept a share in an electron pair. These compounds react with a compound that has a lone pair, just as a proton reacts with ammonia. Thus, the Lewis definition of an acid includes all proton-donating compounds and some additional compounds that do not have protons. Throughout this text, the term *acid* is used to mean a Brønsted-Lowery proton-donating acid, and the term **Lewis acid** is used to refer to non-proton-donating acids such as $AlCl_3$ or BF_3.

Lewis base: Have pair, will share.

Lewis acid: Need two from you.

All bases are **Lewis bases** because they all have a pair of electrons that they can share, either with a proton or with an atom such as aluminum or boron.

the curved arrow indicates where the electrons start from and where they end up

new bond

Cl—Al + CH₃ÖCH₃ ⇌ Cl—Al—Ö—CH₃

aluminum trichloride   dimethyl ether
a Lewis acid   a Lewis base

H—B + :N—H ⇌ H—B—N—H

borane   ammonia
a Lewis acid   a Lewis base

PROBLEM 69

Give the products of the following reactions using arrows to show where the pair of electrons starts and where it ends up.

a. $ZnCl_2$ + $CH_3\ddot{O}H$ ⇌

b. $FeBr_3$ + $:\ddot{Br}:^-$ ⇌

c. $AlCl_3$ + $:\ddot{Cl}:^-$ ⇌

PROBLEM 70

Show how each of the following compounds reacts with HO^-:

a. CH_3OH **c.** $CH_3\overset{+}{N}H_3$ **e.** $^+CH_3$ **g.** $AlCl_3$

b. $^+NH_4$ **d.** BF_3 **f.** $FeBr_3$ **h.** CH_3COOH

SUMMARY

Organic compounds are compounds that contain carbon. The **atomic number** of an atom is the number of protons in its nucleus. The **mass number** of an atom is the sum of its protons and neutrons. **Isotopes** have the same atomic number, but different mass numbers.

An **atomic orbital** indicates where there is a high probability of finding an electron. The closer the atomic orbital is to the nucleus, the lower is its energy. **Degenerate orbitals** have the same energy. Electrons are assigned to orbitals following the **aufbau principle**, the **Pauli exclusion principle**, and **Hund's rule**.

The **octet rule** states that an atom will give up, accept, or share electrons in order to fill its outer shell or attain an outer shell with eight electrons. **Electropositive** elements readily lose electrons; **electronegative** elements readily acquire electrons. The **electronic configuration** of an atom describes the orbitals occupied by the atom's electrons. Electrons in inner shells are called **core electrons**; electrons in the outermost shell are called **valence electrons**. **Lone-pair electrons** are valence electrons that are not used in bonding. Attractive forces between opposite charges are called **electrostatic**

attractions. An **ionic bond** is formed by a transfer of electrons; a **covalent bond** is formed by sharing electrons. A **polar covalent bond** is a covalent bond between atoms with different **electronegativites**. Therefore, a polar covalent bond has a **dipole**, measured by a **dipole moment**. The **dipole moment** of a molecule depends on the magnitudes and directions of the bond dipole moments.

Lewis structures indicate which atoms are bonded together and show **lone pairs** and **formal charges**. A **carbocation** has a positively charged carbon, a **carbanion** has a negatively charged carbon, and a **radical** has an unpaired electron.

According to **molecular orbital (MO) theory**, covalent bonds result when atomic orbitals combine to form **molecular orbitals**. Atomic orbitals combine to give a **bonding MO** and a higher energy **antibonding MO**. Cylindrically symmetrical bonds are called **sigma** (σ) bonds; **pi** (π) bonds form when p orbitals overlap side to side. Bond strength is measured by the **bond dissociation energy**. A σ bond is stronger than a π bond. All **single bonds** in organic compounds are σ bonds, a **double bond** consists of one σ bond and one π bond, and a **triple bond** consists of one σ bond and two π bonds.

Triple bonds are shorter and stronger than double bonds, which are shorter and stronger than single bonds.

To form four bonds, carbon promotes an electron from a $2s$ to a $2p$ orbital. C, N, and O form bonds using **hybrid orbitals**. The **hybridization** of C, N, or O depends on the number of π bonds the atom forms: no π bonds means that the atom is sp^3 **hybridized**, one π bond indicates that it is sp^2 **hybridized**, and two π bonds signifies that it is sp **hybridized**. Exceptions are carbocations and carbon radicals, which are sp^2 hybridized. The more s character in the orbital used to form a bond, the shorter and stronger the bond and the larger the bond angle. Bonding and lone-pair electrons around an atom are positioned as far apart as possible.

An **acid** is a species that donates a proton, and a **base** is a species that accepts a proton. A **Lewis acid** is a species that accepts a share in an electron pair; a **Lewis base** is a species that donates a share in an electron pair.

Acidity is a measure of the tendency of a compound to give up a proton. **Basicity** is a measure of a compound's affinity for a proton. The stronger the acid, the weaker is its conjugate base. The strength of an acid is given by the **acid dissociation constant** (K_a). Approximate pK_a values are as follows: protonated alcohols, protonated carboxylic acids, protonated water < 0; carboxylic acids ~ 5; protonated amines ~ 10; alcohols and water ~ 15. The **pH** of a solution indicates the concentration of positively charged hydrogen ions in the solution. In **acid–base reactions**, the equilibrium favors reaction of the strong acid and formation of the weak acid. Curved arrows indicate the bonds that are broken and formed as reactants are converted into products.

The strength of an acid is determined by the stability of its conjugate base: the more stable the base, the stronger is its conjugate acid. When atoms are similar in size, the more acidic compound will have its hydrogen attached to the more electronegative atom. When atoms are very different in size, the more acidic compound will have its hydrogen attached to the larger atom. Hybridization affects acidity because an sp hybridized atom is more electronegative than an sp^2 hybridized atom, which is more electronegative than an sp^3 hybridized atom. **Inductive electron withdrawal** increases acidity: the more electronegative the electron-withdrawing group and the closer it is to the acidic hydrogen, the stronger is the acid.

Delocalized electrons, which are electrons shared by more than two atoms, stabilize a compound. A **resonance hybrid** is a composite of the **resonance contributors**, structures that differ only in the location of their lone-pair and π electrons.

The **Henderson–Hasselbalch equation** gives the relationship between pK_a and pH: a compound exists primarily in its acidic form in solutions more acidic than its pK_a value and primarily in its basic form in solutions more basic than its pK_a value. A **buffer solution** contains both a weak acid and its conjugate base.

KEY TERMS

acid (p. 41)
acid–base reaction (p. 41)
acid dissociation constant (K_a) (p. 43)
acidity (p. 42)
antibonding molecular orbital (p. 22)
atomic number (p. 4)
atomic orbital (p. 5)
atomic weight (p. 4)
aufbau principle (p. 5)
base (p. 41)
basicity (p. 42)
bond (p. 9)
bond dissociation energy (p. 22)
bond length (p. 21)
bond strength (p. 21)
bonding molecular orbital (p. 22)
buffer solution (p. 60)
carbanion (p. 15)
carbocation (p. 15)
condensed structure (p. 17)
conjugate acid (p. 41)
conjugate base (p. 41)
constitutional isomer (p. 17)
core electrons (p. 6)
covalent bond (p. 9)
degenerate orbitals (p. 5)
delocalized electrons (p. 54)
debye (D) (p. 12)
dipole (p. 11)
dipole moment (μ) (p. 11)
double bond (p. 30)
electronegative (p. 8)

electronegativity (p. 10)
electropositive (p. 8)
electrostatic attraction (p. 9)
electrostatic potential map (p. 13)
equilibrium constant (p. 43)
excited-state electronic configuration (p. 5)
formal charge (p. 14)
free radical (p. 15)
ground-state electronic configuration
    (p. 5)
Heisenberg uncertainty principle (p. 19)
Henderson–Hasselbalch equation (p. 57)
Hund's rule (p. 6)
hybrid orbital (p. 26)
hybridization (p. 26)
hydride ion (p. 9)
hydrogen ion (p. 9)
inductive electron withdrawal (p. 52)
ionic bond (p. 9)
ionic compound (p. 9)
isotopes (p. 4)
Kekulé structure (p. 17)
Lewis acid (p. 61)
Lewis base (p. 62)
Lewis structure (p. 13)
lone-pair electrons (p. 14)
mass number (p. 4)
molecular orbital (p. 2)
molecular orbital (MO) theory (p. 21)
molecular weight (p. 4)
nodal plane (p. 20)
node (p. 20)

nonbonding electrons (p. 14)
nonpolar covalent bond (p. 10)
nonpolar molecule (p. 26)
octet rule (p. 7)
orbital (p. 5)
organic compound (p. 2)
Pauli exclusion principle (p. 5)
pH (p. 43)
perspective formula (p. 26)
pi (π) bond (p. 23)
pK_a (p. 43)
polar covalent bond (p. 10)
proton (p. 9)
proton-transfer reaction (p. 41)
quantum mechanics (p. 4)
radial node (p. 20)
radical (p. 15)
resonance contributors (p. 55)
resonance hybrid (p. 55)
sigma (σ) bond (p. 21)
sigma bonding molecular orbital
    (p. 22)
single bond (p. 28)
tetrahedral bond angle (p. 27)
tetrahedral carbon (p. 27)
trigonal planar carbon (p. 29)
triple bond (p. 31)
valence electrons (p. 6)
valence-shell electron-pair repulsion
    (VSEPR) model (p. 25)
wave equation (p. 5)
wave function (p. 5)

PROBLEMS

71. Draw a Lewis structure for each of the following species:
  a. H_2CO_3 c. CH_2O e. CH_3NH_2 g. CO_2
  b. CO_3^{2-} d. N_2H_4 f. $CH_3N_2^{+}$ h. NH_2O^{-}

72. What is the hybridization of the central atom of each of the following species? Are the bonds around it linear, trigonal planar, or tetrahedral?
  a. NH_3 c. $^{-}CH_3$ e. $^{+}NH_4$ g. HCN   i. H_3O^{+}
  b. BH_3 d. $\cdot CH_3$ f. $^{+}CH_3$ h. $C(CH_3)_4$ j. $H_2C{=}O$

73. Draw the condensed structure of a compound that contains only carbon and hydrogen atoms and that has
  a. three sp^3 hybridized carbons.
  b. one sp^3 hybridized carbon and two sp^2 hybridized carbons.
  c. two sp^3 hybridized carbons and two sp hybridized carbons.

74. a. List the following alcohols in order of decreasing acidity (that is, list the most acidic alcohol first):

$$CCl_3CH_2OH \qquad\qquad CH_2ClCH_2OH \qquad\qquad CHCl_2CH_2OH$$
$$K_a = 5.75 \times 10^{-13} \qquad K_a = 1.29 \times 10^{-13} \qquad K_a = 4.90 \times 10^{-13}$$

  b. Explain the relative acidities.

75. Predict the approximate bond angles:
  a. the $C{-}N{-}H$ bond angle in $(CH_3)_2NH$
  b. the $C{-}N{-}C$ bond angle in $(CH_3)_2NH$
  c. the $C{-}N{-}C$ bond angle in $(CH_3)_2NH_2^{+}$
  d. the $C{-}O{-}C$ bond angle in CH_3OCH_3
  e. the $C{-}O{-}H$ bond angle in CH_3OH
  f. the $H{-}C{-}H$ bond angle in $H_2C{=}O$
  g. the $F{-}B{-}F$ bond angle in $^{-}BF_4$
  h. the $C{-}C{-}N$ bond angle in $CH_3C{\equiv}N$
  i. the $C{-}C{-}N$ bond angle in $CH_3CH_2NH_2$

76. Draw the ground-state electronic configuration for:
  a. Ca   b. Ca^{2+} c. Ar   d. Mg^{2+}

77. List the bonds in order of decreasing polarity (that is, list the most polar bond first).
  a. $C{-}O, C{-}F, C{-}N$ b. $C{-}Cl, C{-}I, C{-}Br$ c. $H{-}O, H{-}N, H{-}C$ d. $C{-}H, C{-}C, C{-}N$

78. Which is the stronger base?
  a. HS^{-} or HO^{-} b. CH_3O^{-} or $CH_3\overset{-}{N}H$ c. CH_3OH or CH_3O^{-} d. Cl^{-} or Br^{-}

79. Write the Kekulé structure for each of the following compounds:
  a. CH_3CHO c. CH_3COOH e. $CH_3CH(OH)CH_2CN$
  b. CH_3OCH_3 d. $(CH_3)_3COH$ f. $(CH_3)_2CHCH(CH_3)CH_2C(CH_3)_3$

80. Draw curved arrows to show the electron flow in the following reactions:

  a. $\ddot{N}H_3 \; + \; H{-}\ddot{\underset{..}{C}}l{:} \;\;\rightleftharpoons\;\; {^{+}}NH_4 \; + \; {:}\ddot{\underset{..}{C}}l{:}^{-}$

  b. $BF_3 \; + \; CH_3\ddot{N}H_2 \;\;\rightleftharpoons\;\; CH_3\overset{\displaystyle H}{\underset{\displaystyle H}{\overset{|}{\underset{|}{N^{+}}}}}{-}\bar{B}F_3$

  c.
$$\underset{H}{\overset{\overset{\textstyle \ddot{O}{:}}{\|}}{C}}{\overset{}{\diagdown}}OH \; + \; H{-}\ddot{\underset{..}{C}}l{:} \;\;\rightleftharpoons\;\; \underset{H}{\overset{\overset{\textstyle {^{+}}\ddot{O}H}{\|}}{C}}{\overset{}{\diagdown}}OH \; + \; {:}\ddot{\underset{..}{C}}l{:}^{-}$$

81. Show the direction of the dipole moment in each of the following bonds (use the electronegativities given in Table 1.3):
  a. $H_3C{-}Br$ b. $H_3C{-}Li$ c. $HO{-}NH_2$ d. $I{-}Br$ e. $H_3C{-}OH$ f. $(CH_3)_2N{-}H$

82. What is the hybridization of the indicated atom in each of the following molecules?
  a. $CH_3\overset{\downarrow}{CH}{=}CH_2$ c. $CH_3CH_2\overset{\downarrow}{O}H$ e. $CH_3CH{=}\overset{\downarrow}{N}CH_3$
  b. $CH_3\overset{\overset{\textstyle O\leftarrow}{\|}}{C}CH_3$ d. $CH_3\overset{\downarrow}{C}{\equiv}N$ f. $CH_3\overset{\downarrow}{O}CH_2CH_3$

83. Draw the missing lone-pair electrons and assign the missing formal charges.

a. H—C(—H)(—H)—O—H   b. H—C(—H)(—H)—O—H(—H)   c. H—C(—H)(—H)—O   d. H—C(—H)(—H)—N—H(—H)

84. a. List the following carboxylic acids in order of decreasing acidity:

$CH_3CH_2CH_2COOH$
$K_a = 1.52 \times 10^{-5}$

$CH_3CH_2CHCOOH$
Cl
$K_a = 1.39 \times 10^{-3}$

$ClCH_2CH_2CH_2COOH$
$K_a = 2.96 \times 10^{-5}$

CH_3CHCH_2COOH
Cl
$K_a = 8.9 \times 10^{-5}$

b. How does the presence of an electronegative substituent such as Cl affect the acidity of a carboxylic acid?
c. How does the location of the substituent affect the acidity of the carboxylic acid?

85. Draw the products of the following reactions:

a. $CH_3\ddot{O}CH_3$ + BF_3 $\longrightarrow$

b. $CH_3\ddot{O}CH_3$ + H—Cl $\longrightarrow$

c. $CH_3\ddot{N}H_2$ + $AlCl_3$ $\longrightarrow$

86. a. Which of the indicated bonds in each molecule is shorter?
b. Indicate the hybridization of the C, O, and N atoms in each of the molecules.

1. $CH_3CH{=}CHC{\equiv}CH$

2. $CH_3CCH_2{-}OH$ (with O double bond)

3. $CH_3NH{-}CH_2CH_2N{=}CHCH_3$

4. $\underset{H}{\overset{H}{C}}{=}CHC{\equiv}C{-}H$

5. $\underset{H}{\overset{H}{C}}{=}CHC{\equiv}C{-}\underset{CH_3}{\overset{CH_3}{C}}{-}H$

87. List the following compounds in order of decreasing acidity.

CH_3CH_2OH $CH_3CH_2NH_2$ CH_3CH_2SH $CH_3CH_2CH_3$

88. For each of the following compounds, draw the form in which it will predominate at pH = 3, pH = 6, pH = 10, and pH = 14:

a. CH_3COOH
$pK_a = 4.8$

b. $CH_3CH_2\overset{+}{N}H_3$
$pK_a = 11.0$

c. CF_3CH_2OH
$pK_a = 12.4$

89. Do the sp^2 carbons and the indicated sp^3 carbons lie in the same plane?

$\underset{H}{\overset{H_3C}{}}C{=}C\underset{CH_3}{\overset{H}{}}$ $\underset{H}{\overset{H_3C}{}}C{=}C\underset{CH_2CH_3}{\overset{H}{}}$ (ring with CH_3)   (ring with CH_3)

90. Give the products of the following acid–base reactions, and indicate whether reactants or products are favored at equilibrium (use the pK_a values that are given in Section 1.18):

a. CH_3COH (with O double bond) + CH_3O^- $\rightleftharpoons$

b. CH_3COH (with O double bond) + CH_3NH_2 $\rightleftharpoons$

c. CH_3CH_2OH + $^-NH_2$ $\rightleftharpoons$

d. CH_3CH_2OH + HCl $\rightleftharpoons$

91. a. List the following alcohols in order of decreasing acidity:
   b. Explain the relative acidities.

$$CH_2=CHCH_2OH \qquad CH_3CH_2CH_2OH \qquad HC≡CCH_2OH$$

92. Which of the following species have a bond angle of 109.5°?

$$H_2O \quad H_3O^+ \quad {}^+CH_3 \quad BF_3 \quad NH_3 \quad {}^+NH_4 \quad {}^-CH_3$$

93. For each of the following molecules, indicate the hybridization of each carbon atom and give the approximate values of all the bond angles:
   a. $CH_3C≡CH$ **b.** $CH_3CH=CH_2$ **c.** $CH_3CH_2CH_3$ **d.** $CH_2=CH—CH=CH_2$

94. a. Estimate the pK_a value of each of the following acids without using a calculator (that is, between 3 and 4, between 9 and 10, etc.):
   1. nitrous acid (HNO_2), $K_a = 4.0 \times 10^{-4}$
   2. nitric acid (HNO_3), $K_a = 22$
   3. bicarbonate (HCO_3^-), $K_a = 6.3 \times 10^{-11}$
   4. hydrogen cyanide (HCN), $K_a = 7.9 \times 10^{-10}$
   5. formic acid (HCOOH), $K_a = 2.0 \times 10^{-4}$
   b. Determine the pK_a values, using a calculator.
   c. Which is the strongest acid?

95. Histamine is the compound that causes the symptoms associated with the common cold and with allergic responses. Which of the two nitrogen atoms in the ring is the most basic? Explain its greater basicity.

histamine

96. a. List the following carboxylic acids in order of decreasing acidity:

$$
\begin{array}{cccc}
CH_3CH_2CHCOOH & CH_3CH_2CH_2COOH & CH_3CH_2CHCOOH & CH_3CH_2CHCOOH \\
\quad\;\; | & & \qquad | & \qquad | \\
\quad\;\; Br & & \qquad OH & \qquad Cl \\
K_a = 1.02 \times 10^{-3} & K_a = 1.51 \times 10^{-5} & K_a = 6.03 \times 10^{-5} & K_a = 1.45 \times 10^{-3}
\end{array}
$$

   b. Which is a more electronegative substituent, Cl or OH?

97. Draw a Lewis structure for each of the following species:

   a. $CH_3N_2^+$ **b.** CH_2N_2 **c.** N_3^- **d.** N_2O (arranged NNO)

98. a. For each of the following pairs of reactions, indicate which one has the more favorable equilibrium constant (that is, which one most favors products):
   1. $CH_3CH_2OH + NH_3 \rightleftharpoons CH_3CH_2O^- + {}^+NH_4$
   or
   $CH_3OH + NH_3 \rightleftharpoons CH_3O^- + {}^+NH_4$
   2. $CH_3CH_2OH + NH_3 \rightleftharpoons CH_3CH_2O^- + {}^+NH_4$
   or
   $CH_3CH_2OH + CH_3NH_2 \rightleftharpoons CH_3CH_2O^- + CH_3{}^+NH_3$
   b. Which of the four reactions has the most favorable equilibrium constant?

99. Citrus fruits are rich in citric acid, a compound with three COOH groups. Explain why:
   a. The first pK_a (for the COOH group in the center of the molecule) is lower than the pK_a of acetic acid.

b. The third pK_a is greater than the pK_a of acetic acid.

$$pK_a = 4.5 \quad HOCCH_2CCH_3COH \quad pK_a = 5.8$$

with structure showing O (pKa groups):

$$\begin{array}{c} O \quad OH \quad O \\ \parallel \quad | \quad \parallel \\ HOCCH_2CCH_3COH \\ | \\ COH \\ \parallel \\ O \quad pK_a = 3.1 \end{array}$$

100. The following compound has two isomers:

$$ClCH=CHCl$$

One isomer has a dipole moment of 0 D, and the other has a dipole moment of 2.95 D. Propose structures for the two isomers that are consistent with these data.

101. Explain why the following compound is not stable:

102. Given that $pH + pOH = 14$ and that the concentration of water in a solution of water is 55.5 M, show that the pK_a of water is 15.7. (*Hint:* $pOH = -\log [HO^-]$.)

103. Water and diethyl ether are immiscible liquids. Charged compounds dissolve in water, and uncharged compounds dissolve in ether. Given that $C_6H_{11}COOH$ has a pK_a of 4.8 and $C_6H_{11}\overset{+}{N}H_3$ has a pK_a of 10.7.
a. What pH would you make the water layer in order to cause both compounds to dissolve in it?
b. What pH would you make the water layer in order to cause the acid to dissolve in the water layer and the amine to dissolve in the ether layer?
c. What pH would you make the water layer in order to cause the acid to dissolve in the ether layer and the amine to dissolve in the water layer?

104. How could you separate a mixture of the following compounds? The reagents available to you are water, ether, 1.0 M HCl, and 1.0 M NaOH. (*Hint:* See Problem 103.)

COOH	$\overset{+}{N}H_3Cl^-$	OH	Cl	$\overset{+}{N}H_3Cl^-$
$pK_a = 4.17$	$pK_a = 4.60$	$pK_a = 9.95$		$pK_a = 10.66$

105. Show that $K_{eq} = \dfrac{K_a \text{ reactant acid}}{K_a \text{ product acid}} = \dfrac{[\text{products}]}{[\text{reactants}]}$

For help in answering Problems 106–108, see Special Topic I in the *Study Guide and Solutions Manual*.

106. Carbonic acid has a pK_a of 6.1 at physiological temperature. Is the carbonic acid/bicarbonate buffer system that maintains the pH of the blood at 7.3 better at neutralizing excess acid or excess base?

107. a. If an acid with a pK_a of 5.3 is in an aqueous solution of pH 5.7, what percentage of the acid is present in the acidic form?
b. At what pH will 80% of the acid exist in the acidic form?

108. Calculate the pH values of the following solutions:
a. a 1.0 M solution of acetic acid ($pK_a = 4.76$)
b. a 0.1 M solution of protonated methylamine ($pK_a = 10.7$)
c. a solution containing 0.3 M HCOOH and 0.1 M HCOO$^-$ (pK_a of HCOOH $= 3.76$)

2

An Introduction to Organic Compounds

Nomenclature, Physical Properties, and Representation of Structure

CH₃CH₂Cl

CH₃CH₂OH

CH₃OCH₃

CH₃CH₂NH₂

CH₃CH₂Br

IN THIS BOOK, THE PRESENTATION OF ORGANIC CHEMISTRY IS ORGANIZED ACCORDING TO HOW organic compounds react. When a compound undergoes a reaction, a new compound is synthesized. In other words, while you are learning how organic compounds react, you are simultaneously learning how to synthesize organic compounds.

Y is reacting   Z is being synthesized

The main classes of compounds that are synthesized by the reactions we will look at in Chapters 3–10 are alkanes, alkyl halides, ethers, alcohols, and amines. As we learn about the reactions and synthesis of organic compounds, we will need to be able to refer to them by name. Therefore, we will begin the study of organic chemistry by learning how to name these five classes of compounds.

First we will see how *alkanes* are named because their names form the basis for the names of all the other organic compounds. **Alkanes** are composed of only carbon atoms and hydrogen atoms and contain only *single bonds*. Compounds that contain only carbon and hydrogen are called **hydrocarbons**. Thus, an alkane is a hydrocarbon that has only single bonds.

Alkanes in which the carbons form a continuous chain with no branches are called **straight-chain alkanes**. The names of several straight-chain alkanes are listed in Table 2.1. It is important that you learn the names of at least the first 10.

The family of alkanes shown in the table is an example of a homologous series. A **homologous series** (*homos* is Greek for "the same as") is a family of compounds in which each member differs from the one before it in the series by one **methylene (CH₂) group**. The members of a homologous series are called **homologs**. Propane (CH₃CH₂CH₃) and butane (CH₃CH₂CH₂CH₃) are homologs.

If you look at the relative numbers of carbon and hydrogen atoms in the alkanes listed in Table 2.1, you will see that the general molecular formula for an alkane is C_nH_{2n+2}, where n is any integer. So, if an alkane has one carbon, it must have four hydrogens; if it has two carbons, it must have six hydrogens.

Table 2.1   Nomenclature and Physical Properties of Straight-Chain Alkanes

Number of carbons	Molecular formula	Name	Condensed structure	Boiling point (°C)	Melting point (°C)	Density[a] (g/mL)
1	CH_4	methane	CH_4	−167.7	−182.5	
2	C_2H_6	ethane	CH_3CH_3	−88.6	−183.3	
3	C_3H_8	propane	$CH_3CH_2CH_3$	−42.1	−187.7	
4	C_4H_{10}	butane	$CH_3CH_2CH_2CH_3$	−0.5	−138.3	
5	C_5H_{12}	pentane	$CH_3(CH_2)_3CH_3$	36.1	−129.8	0.5572
6	C_6H_{14}	hexane	$CH_3(CH_2)_4CH_3$	68.7	−95.3	0.6603
7	C_7H_{16}	heptane	$CH_3(CH_2)_5CH_3$	98.4	−90.6	0.6837
8	C_8H_{18}	octane	$CH_3(CH_2)_6CH_3$	125.7	−56.8	0.7026
9	C_9H_{20}	nonane	$CH_3(CH_2)_7CH_3$	150.8	−53.5	0.7177
10	$C_{10}H_{22}$	decane	$CH_3(CH_2)_8CH_3$	174.0	−29.7	0.7299
11	$C_{11}H_{24}$	undecane	$CH_3(CH_2)_9CH_3$	195.8	−25.6	0.7402
12	$C_{12}H_{26}$	dodecane	$CH_3(CH_2)_{10}CH_3$	216.3	−9.6	0.7487
13	$C_{13}H_{28}$	tridecane	$CH_3(CH_2)_{11}CH_3$	235.4	−5.5	0.7546
⋮	⋮	⋮	⋮	⋮	⋮	⋮
20	$C_{20}H_{42}$	eicosane	$CH_3(CH_2)_{18}CH_3$	343.0	36.8	0.7886
21	$C_{21}H_{44}$	heneicosane	$CH_3(CH_2)_{19}CH_3$	356.5	40.5	0.7917
⋮	⋮	⋮	⋮	⋮	⋮	⋮
30	$C_{30}H_{62}$	triacontane	$CH_3(CH_2)_{28}CH_3$	449.7	65.8	0.8097

[a]Density is temperature dependent. The densities given are those determined at 20 °C $(d^{20°})$.

We have seen that carbon forms four covalent bonds and hydrogen forms only one covalent bond (Section 1.4). This means that there is only one possible structure for an alkane with molecular formula CH_4 (methane) and only one structure for an alkane with molecular formula C_2H_6 (ethane). We examined the structures of these compounds in Section 1.7. There is also only one possible structure for an alkane with molecular formula C_3H_8 (propane).

name	Kekulé structure	condensed structure	ball-and-stick model

However, there are two possible structures for an alkane with molecular formula C_4H_{10}. In addition to butane—a straight-chain alkane—there is a branched butane called isobutane. Both of these structures fulfill the requirement that each carbon forms four bonds and each hydrogen forms one bond.

$$CH_3CH_2CH_2CH_3$$
butane

$$CH_3CHCH_3$$
$$|$$
$$CH_3$$
isobutane

$$CH_3CH—$$
$$|$$
$$CH_3$$
an "iso"
structural unit

Compounds such as butane and isobutane that have the same molecular formula but differ in the order in which the atoms are connected are called **constitutional isomers**—their molecules have different constitutions. In fact, isobutane got its name because it is an "iso"mer of butane. The structural unit consisting of a carbon bonded to a hydrogen and two CH_3 groups—that occurs in isobutane—has come to be called "iso." Thus, the name isobutane tells you that the compound is a four-carbon alkane with an iso structural unit.

There are three alkanes with molecular formula C_5H_{12}. You have already learned how to name two of them. Pentane is the straight-chain alkane. Isopentane, as its name indicates, has an iso structural unit and five carbons. We cannot name the other branched-chain alkane without defining a name for a new structural unit. (For now, ignore the names written in blue.)

$$CH_3\overset{2}{C}H_2\overset{3}{C}H_2\overset{4}{C}H_2\overset{5}{C}H_3$$
pentane

$$CH_3CHCH_2CH_3$$
$$|$$
$$CH_3$$
isopentane

$$CH_3\overset{CH_3}{\underset{CH_3}{|{\atop|}}}CCH_3$$
2,2-dimethylpropane

There are five constitutional isomers with molecular formula C_6H_{14}. Again, we are able to name only two of them, unless we define new structural units.

common name:
systematic name:

$$CH_3\overset{2}{C}H_2\overset{3}{C}H_2\overset{4}{C}H_2\overset{5}{C}H_2\overset{6}{C}H_3$$
hexane
hexane

$$CH_3CHCH_2CH_2CH_3$$
$$|$$
$$CH_3$$
isohexane
2-methylpentane

$$CH_3\overset{CH_3}{\underset{CH_3}{|{\atop|}}}CCH_2CH_3$$
2,2-dimethylbutane

$$CH_3CH_2CHCH_2CH_3$$
$$|$$
$$CH_3$$
3-methylpentane

$$CH_3CH—CHCH_3$$
$$|\quad\quad|$$
$$CH_3\;\;CH_3$$
2,3-dimethylbutane

There are nine alkanes with molecular formula C_7H_{16}. We can name only two of them (heptane and isoheptane).

common name:
systematic name:

$$CH_3CH_2CH_2CH_2CH_2CH_2CH_3$$
heptane
heptane

$$CH_3CHCH_2CH_2CH_2CH_3$$
$$|$$
$$CH_3$$
isoheptane
2-methylhexane

$$CH_3CH_2CHCH_2CH_2CH_3$$
$$|$$
$$CH_3$$
3-methylhexane

$$CH_3CH—CHCH_2CH_3$$
$$|\quad\quad|$$
$$CH_3\;\;CH_3$$
2,3-dimethylpentane

$$CH_3CHCH_2CHCH_3$$
$$|\quad\quad\quad|$$
$$CH_3\quad\;CH_3$$
2,4-dimethylpentane

$$CH_3CH_2CHCH_2CH_3$$
$$|$$
$$CH_2CH_3$$
3-ethylpentane

$$CH_3\overset{CH_3}{\underset{CH_3}{|{\atop|}}}CCH_2CH_2CH_3$$
2,2-dimethylpentane

$$CH_3CH_2\overset{CH_3}{\underset{CH_3}{|{\atop|}}}CCH_2CH_3$$
3,3-dimethylpentane

$$CH_3\overset{CH_3}{\underset{CH_3}{|{\atop|}}}C—\overset{CH_3}{\underset{}{|}}CHCH_3$$
2,2,3-trimethylbutane

The number of constitutional isomers increases rapidly as the number of carbons in an alkane increases. For example, there are 75 alkanes with molecular formula $C_{10}H_{22}$ and 4347 alkanes with molecular formula $C_{15}H_{32}$. To avoid having to memorize the names of thousands of structural units, chemists have devised rules for creating systematic names that describe the compound's structure. That way, only the rules have to be learned. Because the name describes the structure, these rules make it possible to deduce the structure of a compound from its name.

This method of nomenclature is called **systematic nomenclature**. It is also called **IUPAC nomenclature** because it was designed by a commission of the International Union of Pure and Applied Chemistry (abbreviated IUPAC and pronounced "eye-you-pack") at a meeting in Geneva, Switzerland, in 1892. The IUPAC rules have been continually revised by the commission since then. A name such as isobutane—a nonsystematic name—is called a **common name**. When both names are shown in this book, common names will be shown in red and systematic (IUPAC) names in blue. Before we can understand how a systematic name for an alkane is constructed, we must learn how to name alkyl substituents.

2.1 HOW ALKYL SUBSTITUENTS ARE NAMED

Removing a hydrogen from an alkane results in an **alkyl substituent** (or an alkyl group). Alkyl substituents are named by replacing the "ane" ending of the alkane with "yl." The letter "R" is used to indicate any alkyl group.

CH_3- CH_3CH_2- $CH_3CH_2CH_2-$ $CH_3CH_2CH_2CH_2-$

a methyl group   **an ethyl group**   **a propyl group**   **a butyl group**

$CH_3CH_2CH_2CH_2CH_2-$ $R-$

a pentyl group   **any alkyl group**

If a hydrogen in an alkane is replaced by an OH, the compound becomes an **alcohol**; if it is replaced by an NH_2, the compound becomes an **amine**; if it is replaced by a halogen, the compound becomes an **alkyl halide**, and if it is replaced by an OR, the compound becomes an **ether**.

$R-OH$ $R-NH_2$ $R-X$ [X = F, Cl, Br, or I] $R-O-R$

an alcohol   **an amine**   **an alkyl halide**   **an ether**

The alkyl group name followed by the name of the class of the compound (alcohol, amine, etc.) yields the common name of the compound. The two alkyl groups in ethers are listed in alphabetical order. The following examples show how alkyl group names are used to build common names:

CH_3OH $CH_3CH_2NH_2$ $CH_3CH_2CH_2Br$ $CH_3CH_2CH_2CH_2Cl$

methyl alcohol   **ethylamine**   **propyl bromide**   **butyl chloride**

CH_3I CH_3CH_2OH $CH_3CH_2CH_2NH_2$ $CH_3CH_2OCH_3$

methyl iodide   **ethyl alcohol**   **propylamine**   **ethyl methyl ether**

Notice that for most compounds there is a space between the name of the alkyl group and the name of the class of compound. For amines, however, the entire name is written as one word.

methyl alcohol

methyl chloride

methylamine

PROBLEM 1 ◆

Name each of the following:

a.   b.   c.

Two alkyl groups—the propyl group and the isopropyl group—have three carbons. A propyl group is obtained when a hydrogen is removed from a *primary carbon* of propane. A **primary carbon** is a carbon bonded to only one other carbon. An isopropyl group is obtained when a hydrogen is removed from the *secondary carbon* of propane. A **secondary carbon** is a carbon bonded to two other carbons. Notice that an isopropyl group, as its name indicates, has its three carbon atoms arranged as an iso structural unit.

a primary carbon	a secondary carbon
$CH_3CH_2CH_2-$	CH_3CHCH_3
a propyl group	**an isopropyl group**

$CH_3CH_2CH_2Cl$	CH_3CHCH_3 $\vert$ Cl
propyl chloride	**isopropyl chloride**

Molecular structures can be drawn in different ways. Isopropyl chloride, for example, is drawn below in two different ways. Both representations depict the same compound, although, at first glance, the two-dimensional representations appear to be different: the methyl groups are placed at opposite ends in one structure and at right angles in the other. The structures are identical, however, because carbon is tetrahedral. The four groups bonded to the central carbon—a hydrogen, a chlorine, and two methyl groups—point to the corners of a tetrahedron. If you rotate the three-dimensional model on the right 90° in a clockwise direction, you should be able to see that the two models are the same. (If you visit the Molecule Gallery for Chapter 2 on the website (*http://www.chemplace.com*), you will be able to actually rotate isopropyl chloride to prove that the two molecules are identical.)

Build models of the two representations of isopropyl chloride to see that they represent the same compound.

two different ways to draw isopropyl chloride

CH_3CHCH_3 $\vert$ Cl	CH_3CHCl $\vert$ CH_3
isopropyl chloride	isopropyl chloride

There are four alkyl groups that have four carbons. Two of them, the butyl and isobutyl groups, have a hydrogen removed from a primary carbon. A *sec*-butyl group has a hydrogen removed from a secondary carbon (*sec*-, often abbreviated *s*-, stands for secondary), and a *tert*-butyl group has a hydrogen removed from a tertiary carbon (*tert*-, sometimes abbreviated *t*-, stands for tertiary). A **tertiary carbon** is a carbon that is bonded to three other carbons. Notice that the isobutyl group is the only group with an iso structural unit.

a primary carbon	a primary carbon	a secondary carbon	a tertiary carbon
$CH_3CH_2CH_2CH_2-$	CH_3CHCH_2- $\vert$ CH_3	CH_3CH_2CH- $\vert$ CH_3	CH_3 $\vert$ CH_3C- $\vert$ CH_3
a butyl group	**an isobutyl group**	**a *sec*-butyl group**	**a *tert*-butyl group**

A primary carbon is bonded to one carbon, a secondary carbon is bonded to two carbons, and a tertiary carbon is bonded to three carbons.

The names of straight-chain alkyl groups often have the prefix "*n*" (for "normal") to emphasize that the carbons are in an unbranched chain. If a name does not have a prefix such as "*n*" or "iso," we assume that the carbons are in an unbranched chain.

$$CH_3CH_2CH_2CH_2Br \qquad CH_3CH_2CH_2CH_2CH_2F$$

butyl bromide   **pentyl fluoride**

or   or

n-butyl bromide   **n-pentyl fluoride**

Like the carbons, the hydrogens in a molecule are also referred to as primary, secondary, and tertiary. **Primary hydrogens** are attached to primary carbons, **secondary hydrogens** to secondary carbons, and **tertiary hydrogens** to tertiary carbons.

primary hydrogens
$CH_3CH_2CH_2CH_2OH$

secondary hydrogens
CH_3CH_2CHOH
      CH_3

tertiary hydrogen
CH_3CHCH_2OH
      CH_3

A chemical name must specify one compound only. The prefix "*sec,*" therefore, can only be used with *sec*-butyl compounds. The name "*sec*-pentyl" cannot be used because pentane has two different secondary carbons, which means that removing a hydrogen from a secondary carbon of pentane produces one of two different alkyl groups, depending on which hydrogen is removed. As a result, *sec*-pentyl chloride would specify two different alkyl chorides, and, therefore, it is not a correct name.

Both alkyl halides have five carbon atoms with a chlorine attached to a secondary carbon, but two compounds cannot be named *sec*-pentyl chloride.

$CH_3CHCH_2CH_2CH_3$ $CH_3CH_2CHCH_2CH_3$
   Cl   Cl

The prefix "*tert*" can be used for both *tert*-butyl and *tert*-pentyl compounds because each of these substituent names describes only one alkyl group. The name "*tert*-hexyl" cannot be used because it describes two different alkyl groups.

CH_3
CH_3C-Br
CH_3
tert-butyl bromide

CH_3
CH_3C-Br
CH_2CH_3
tert-pentyl bromide

CH_2CH_3
CH_3CH_2C-Br
CH_3

CH_3
$CH_3CH_2CH_2C-Br$
CH_3

Both alkyl bromides have six carbon atoms with a bromine attached to a tertiary carbon, but two compounds cannot be named *tert*-hexyl bromide.

If you examine the following structures, you will see that whenever the prefix "iso" is used, the iso structural unit will be at one end of the molecule and any group replacing a hydrogen will be at the other end:

$CH_3CHCH_2CH_2OH$
   CH_3
isopentyl alcohol

$CH_3CHCH_2CH_2CH_2Cl$
   CH_3
isohexyl chloride

$CH_3CHCH_2NH_2$
   CH_3
isobutylamine

CH_3CHCH_2Br
   CH_3
isobutyl bromide

$CH_3CHCH_2CH_2OH$
   CH_3
isopentyl alcohol

CH_3CHBr
   CH_3
isopropyl bromide

Notice that an iso group has a methyl group on the next-to-the-last carbon in the chain. Notice also that all isoalkyl compounds have the substituent (OH, Cl, NH_2, etc.) on a primary carbon, except for isopropyl, which has the substituent on a secondary carbon. Thus, the isopropyl group could have been called a *sec*-propyl group. Either name would have been appropriate because the group has an iso structural unit and a hydrogen has been removed from a secondary carbon. Chemists decided to call it isopropyl, however, which means that "*sec*" is used only for *sec*-butyl.

Alkyl group names are used so frequently that you need to learn them. Some of the most common alkyl group names are compiled in Table 2.2.

Table 2.2	Names of Some Common Alkyl Groups				
methyl	CH_3	isobutyl	CH_3CHCH_2	pentyl	$CH_3CH_2CH_2CH_2CH_2$
ethyl	CH_3CH_2		$\quad\quad\,\,CH_3$	isopentyl	$CH_3CHCH_2CH_2$
propyl	$CH_3CH_2CH_2$	sec-butyl	CH_3CH_2CH		$\quad\quad CH_3$
isopropyl	CH_3CH		$\quad\quad\quad\quad CH_3$	hexyl	$CH_3CH_2CH_2CH_2CH_2CH_2$
	$\quad CH_3$		$\quad\quad\quad\quad CH_3$	isohexyl	$CH_3CHCH_2CH_2CH_2$
butyl	$CH_3CH_2CH_2CH_2$	tert-butyl	CH_3C		$\quad\quad CH_3$
			$\quad\,\,\,CH_3$		

PROBLEM 2 ♦

Draw the structure and give the systematic name of a compound with molecular formula C_5H_{12} that has

a. one tertiary carbon.

b. no secondary carbons.

PROBLEM 3 ♦

Draw the structures and name the four constitutional isomers with molecular formula C_4H_9Br.

PROBLEM 4 ♦

Which of the following statements can be used to prove that carbon is tetrahedral?

a. Methyl bromide does not have constitutional isomers.
b. Tetrachloromethane does not have a dipole moment.
c. Dibromomethane does not have constitutional isomers.

PROBLEM 5 ♦

Write a structure for each of the following:

a. isopropyl alcohol   c. sec-butyl iodide   e. tert-butylamine
b. isopentyl fluoride   d. tert-pentyl alcohol   f. n-octyl bromide

PROBLEM 6 ♦

Name the following:

a. $CH_3OCH_2CH_3$ c. $CH_3CH_2CHNH_2$ e. CH_3CHCH_2Br
                                            $\quad\quad\quad\quad\,\,|$ $\quad\quad\quad|$
                                            $\quad\quad\quad\quad CH_3$ $\quad\quad CH_3$

b. $CH_3OCH_2CH_2CH_3$ d. $CH_3CH_2CH_2CH_2OH$ f. CH_3CH_2CHCl
                                                                                                     $\quad\quad\quad\quad|$
                                                                                                     $\quad\quad\quad CH_3$

chem place Tutorial:
Degree of alkyl substitution

2.2 THE NOMENCLATURE OF ALKANES

The systematic name of an alkane is obtained using the following rules:

1. Determine the number of carbons in the longest continuous carbon chain. This chain is called the **parent hydrocarbon**. The name that indicates the number of carbons in the parent hydrocarbon becomes the alkane's "last name." For example, a parent hydrocarbon with eight carbons would be called *octane*. The longest continuous chain is not always a straight chain; sometimes you have to "turn a corner" to obtain the longest continuous chain.

$$\overset{8}{CH_3}\overset{7}{CH_2}\overset{6}{CH_2}\overset{5}{CH_2}\overset{4}{CH}\overset{3}{CH_2}\overset{2}{CH_2}\overset{1}{CH_3}$$
$$| $$
$$CH_3$$

4-methyloctane

three different alkanes with an eight-carbon parent hydrocarbon

$$\overset{8}{CH_3}\overset{7}{CH_2}\overset{6}{CH_2}\overset{5}{CH_2}\overset{4}{CH}CH_2CH_3$$
$$| $$
$$\underset{3}{CH_2}\underset{2}{CH_2}\underset{1}{CH_3}$$

4-ethyloctane

First, determine the number of carbons in the longest continuous chain.

$$\overset{4}{CH_3}CH_2\overset{3}{CH_2}\overset{2}{CH}\overset{1}{CH_2}CH_2CH_3$$
$$| $$
$$\underset{5}{CH_2}\underset{6}{CH_2}\underset{7}{CH_2}\underset{8}{CH_3}$$

4-propyloctane

2. The name of any alkyl substituent that hangs off the parent hydrocarbon is placed in front of the name of the parent hydrocarbon, together with a number to designate the carbon to which the alkyl substituent is attached. The carbons in the parent chain are numbered in the direction that gives the substituent as low a number as possible. The substituent's name and the name of the parent hydrocarbon are joined into one word, preceded by a hyphen that connects the number and the substituent's name.

$$\overset{1}{CH_3}\overset{2}{CH}\overset{3}{CH_2}\overset{4}{CH_2}\overset{5}{CH_3}$$
$$| $$
$$CH_3$$

2-methylpentane

$$\overset{6}{CH_3}\overset{5}{CH_2}\overset{4}{CH_2}\overset{3}{CH}\overset{2}{CH_2}\overset{1}{CH_3}$$
$$| $$
$$CH_2CH_3$$

3-ethylhexane

$$\overset{1}{CH_3}\overset{2}{CH_2}\overset{3}{CH_2}\overset{4}{CH}\overset{5}{CH_2}\overset{6}{CH_2}\overset{7}{CH_2}\overset{8}{CH_3}$$
$$| $$
$$CHCH_3$$
$$| $$
$$CH_3$$

4-isopropyloctane

Number the chain in the direction that gives the substituent the lower number.

Notice that only systematic names have numbers; common names never contain numbers.

$$CH_3$$
$$| $$
$$CH_3CHCH_2CH_2CH_3$$

common name: isohexane
systematic name: 2-methylpentane

Numbers are used only for systematic names, never for common names.

3. If more than one substituent is attached to the parent hydrocarbon, the chain is numbered in the direction that will produce a name containing the lowest of the possible numbers. The substituents are listed in alphabetical (not numerical) order, with each substituent preceded by the appropriate number. In the following example, the correct name (5-ethyl-3-methyloctane) contains a 3 as its lowest number, whereas the incorrect name (4-ethyl-6-methyloctane) contains a 4 as its lowest number:

$$CH_3CH_2CHCH_2CHCH_2CH_2CH_3$$
$$| \qquad\quad | $$
$$CH_3 \quad CH_2CH_3$$

5-ethyl-3-methyloctane
not
4-ethyl-6-methyloctane
because 3 < 4

Substituents are listed in alphabetical order.

If two or more substituents are the same, the prefixes "di," "tri," and "tetra" are used to indicate how many identical substituents the compound has. The numbers indicating the locations of the identical substituents are listed together, separated by commas. Notice that there must be as many numbers in a name as there are substituents. The prefixes "di," "tri," "tetra," *sec*, and *tert* are ignored in alphabetizing substituent groups, but the prefixes "iso" and "cyclo" ("cyclo" is introduced in Section 2.3) are not ignored.

$$CH_3CH_2CHCH_2CHCH_3$$
$$| \qquad\quad | $$
$$CH_3 \quad CH_3$$

2,4-dimethylhexane

$$CH_2CH_3$$
$$| $$
$$CH_3CH_2CCH_2CH_2CHCH_3$$
$$| \qquad\qquad\quad | $$
$$CH_3 \qquad\quad CH_3$$

5-ethyl-2,5-dimethylheptane

A number and a word are separated by a hyphen; numbers are separated by a comma.

di, tri, tetra, *sec*, and *tert* are ignored in alphabetizing.

iso and cyclo are not ignored in alphabetizing.

$$CH_3CH_2\overset{\overset{\displaystyle CH_2CH_3}{|}}{C}CH_2CH_2\overset{\overset{\displaystyle CH_3}{|}}{CH}CHCH_2CH_2CH_3$$
$$\underset{\underset{\displaystyle CH_2CH_3 \quad CH_2CH_3}{|}}{}$$
3,3,6-triethyl-7-methyldecane

$$CH_3CH_2CH_2\overset{}{CH}CH_2CH_2\overset{\overset{\displaystyle CH_3}{|}}{CH}CH_3$$
$$\underset{\underset{\displaystyle CH_3CHCH_3}{|}}{}$$
5-isopropyl-2-methyloctane

4. When numbering in either direction leads to the same lowest number for one of the substituents, the chain is numbered in the direction that gives the lowest possible number to one of the remaining substituents.

$$CH_3\overset{\overset{\displaystyle CH_3}{|}}{C}CH_2\overset{}{CH}CH_3$$
$$\underset{\underset{\displaystyle CH_3 \quad CH_3}{|}}{}$$

2,2,4-trimethylpentane
not
2,4,4-trimethylpentane
because 2 < 4

$$CH_3CH_2\overset{}{CH}\overset{\overset{\displaystyle CH_2CH_3}{|}}{CH}CH_2\overset{}{CH}CH_2CH_3$$
$$\underset{\underset{\displaystyle CH_3}{|}}{}$$

6-ethyl-3,4-dimethyloctane
not
3-ethyl-5,6-dimethyloctane
because 4 < 5

5. If the same substituent numbers are obtained in both directions, the first group listed receives the lower number.

Only if the same set of numbers is obtained in both directions does the first group listed get the lower number.

$$CH_3\overset{\overset{\displaystyle Cl}{|}}{CH}CHCH_3$$
$$\underset{\underset{\displaystyle Br}{|}}{}$$

2-bromo-3-chlorobutane
not
3-bromo-2-chlorobutane

$$CH_3CH_2\overset{\overset{\displaystyle CH_2CH_3}{|}}{CH}CH_2\overset{}{CH}CH_2CH_3$$
$$\underset{\underset{\displaystyle CH_3}{|}}{}$$

3-ethyl-5-methylheptane
not
5-ethyl-3-methylheptane

6. If a compound has two or more chains of the same length, the parent hydrocarbon is the chain with the greatest number of substituents.

In the case of two hydrocarbon chains with the same number of carbons, choose the one with the most substituents.

$$\overset{3 \quad 4 \quad 5 \quad 6}{CH_3CH_2CHCH_2CH_2CH_3}$$
$$\underset{\underset{\displaystyle {}_1CH_3}{|}}{{}_2CHCH_3}$$

3-ethyl-2-methylhexane (two substituents)

$$\overset{1 \quad 2 \quad 3 \quad 4 \quad 5 \quad 6}{CH_3CH_2CHCH_2CH_2CH_3}$$
$$\underset{\underset{\displaystyle CH_3}{|}}{CHCH_3}$$

not
3-isopropylhexane (one substituent)

7. Names such as "isopropyl," "*sec*-butyl," and "*tert*-butyl" are acceptable substituent names in the IUPAC system of nomenclature, but systematic substituent names are preferred. Systematic substituent names are obtained by numbering the alkyl substituent starting at the carbon attached to the parent hydrocarbon. This means that the carbon attached to the parent hydrocarbon is always the number-1 carbon of the substituent. In a compound such as 4-(1-methylethyl)octane, the substituent name is in parentheses; the number inside the parentheses indicates a position on the substituent, whereas the number outside the parentheses indicates a position on the parent hydrocarbon. (Note that if a prefix such as "di" is part of a branch name, it *is* included in the alphabetization.)

$$CH_3CH_2CH_2\overset{}{CH}CH_2CH_2CH_3$$
$$\underset{\underset{\displaystyle CH_3}{|}}{{}_1CHCH_3}$$

4-isopropylheptane
or
4-(1-methylethyl)heptane

$$CH_3CH_2CH_2CH_2\overset{}{CH}CH_2CH_2CH_2CH_3$$
$$\underset{\underset{\displaystyle CH_3}{|}}{\overset{2 \quad 3}{CH_2CHCH_3}}$$
$$_1$$

5-isobutyldecane
or
5-(2-methylpropyl)decane

$$CH_3CH_2\overset{\overset{\displaystyle CH_3CH_2}{|}}{CH}CH_2\overset{}{CH}CH_2CH_2CH_3$$
$$\underset{\underset{\displaystyle CH_3}{|}}{CH_3CCH_3}$$

5-*tert*-butyl-3-ethyloctane
or
5-(1,1-dimethylethyl)-3-ethyloctane

Some substituents have only a systematic name.

CH₂CH₂CH₃

CH₃CH₂CH₂CH₂CHCH₂CHCH₂CH₂CH₃
                        2   3
            CH₃CHCHCH₃
                1
                CH₃

6-(1,2-dimethylpropyl)-4-propyldecane

CH₃   CH₃

CH₃CHCHCH₂CHCH₂CHCH₂CH₃
         | 2   3   4
        CH₃   CH₂CH₂CH₂CH₂CH₃

2,3-dimethyl-5-(2-methylbutyl)decane

These rules will allow you to name thousands of alkanes, and eventually you will learn the additional rules necessary to name many other kinds of compounds. The rules are important for looking up a compound in the scientific literature, because it usually will be listed by its systematic name. Nevertheless, you must still learn common names because they are so entrenched in chemists' vocabularies that they are widely used in scientific conversation and are often found in the literature.

Look at the systematic names (the ones written in blue) for the isomeric hexanes and isomeric heptanes shown on page 70 to make sure you understand how they are constructed.

Octane Number

Gasoline engines like those used in most cars operate by creating a series of carefully-timed, controlled explosions. In the engine cylinders, fuel is mixed with air, compressed, and then ignited by a spark. When the fuel used is too easily ignited, however, the heat of compression can initiate combustion before the spark plug fires. A pinging or knocking may then be heard in the running engine.

As the quality of the fuel improves, the engine is less likely to knock. The quality of a fuel is indicated by its octane number. Straight-chain hydrocarbons have low octane numbers and make poor fuels. Heptane, for example, with an arbitrarily assigned octane number of 0, causes engines to knock badly. Branched-chain alkanes have more hydrogens bonded to primary carbons. These are the bonds that require the most energy to break and, therefore, make combustion more difficult to initiate, thereby reducing knocking. 2,2,4-Trimethylpentane, for example, does not cause knocking and has arbitrarily been assigned an octane number of 100.

The octane number of a gasoline is determined by comparing its knocking with the knocking of mixtures of heptane and

CH₃CH₂CH₂CH₂CH₂CH₂CH₃
heptane
octane number = 0

CH₃ CH₃

CH₃CCH₂CHCH₃
     |
     CH₃
2,2,4-trimethylpentane
octane number = 100

2,2,4-trimethylpentane. The octane number given to the gasoline corresponds to the percent of 2,2,4-trimethylpentane in the matching mixture. Thus, a gasoline with an octane rating of 91 has the same "knocking" property as a mixture of 91% 2,2,4-trimethylpentane and 9% heptane. The term *octane number* originated from the fact that 2,2,4-trimethylpentane contains eight carbons. Because slightly different methods are used to determine the octane number, gasoline in Canada and the United States will have an octane number that is 4 to 5 points less than the same gasoline in Europe and Australia.

PROBLEM 7 ♦

Draw the structure for each of the following:

a. 2,3-dimethylhexane
b. 4-isopropyl-2,4,5-trimethylheptane
c. 4,4-diethyldecane
d. 2,2-dimethyl-4-propyloctane
e. 4-isobutyl-2,5-dimethyloctane
f. 4-(1,1-dimethylethyl)octane

PROBLEM 8   SOLVED

a. Draw the 18 isomeric octanes.
b. Give each isomer its systematic name.
c. How many isomers have common names?
d. Which isomers contain an isopropyl group?
e. Which isomers contain a *sec*-butyl group?
f. Which isomers contain a *tert*-butyl group?

Solution to 8a   Start with the isomer with an eight-carbon continuous chain. Then draw isomers with a seven-carbon continuous chain plus one methyl group. Next, draw isomers with a six-carbon continuous chain plus two methyl groups or one ethyl group. Then draw isomers with a five-carbon continuous chain plus three methyl groups or one methyl group and one ethyl group. Finally, draw a four-carbon continuous chain with four methyl groups. (You will be able to tell whether you have drawn duplicate structures by your answers to Problem 8b, because if two structures have the same systematic name, they represent the same compound.)

PROBLEM 9◆

Give the systematic name for each of the following:

a. $CH_3CH_2CHCH_2\overset{\overset{\displaystyle CH_3}{|}}{\underset{\underset{\displaystyle CH_3}{|}}{C}}CH_3$

b. $CH_3CH_2C(CH_3)_3$

c. $CH_3CH_2CH_2CHCH_2CH_2CH_3$
      $CH_3CHCH_2CH_3$

d. $CH_3\overset{\overset{\displaystyle CH_3}{|}}{CH}CH_2CH_2\overset{\overset{\displaystyle CH_3}{|}}{\underset{\underset{\displaystyle CH_3}{|}}{C}}CH_3$

e. $CH_3CH_2C(CH_2CH_3)_2CH(CH_3)CH(CH_2CH_2CH_3)_2$

f. $CH_3\overset{\overset{\displaystyle CH_3}{|}}{\underset{\underset{\displaystyle CH_2CH_2CH_3}{|}}{C}}\overset{\overset{\displaystyle CH_2CH_2CH_3}{}}{CHCH_2CH_3}$

g. $CH_3CH_2C(CH_2CH_3)_2CH_2CH_2CH_3$

h. $CH_3CH_2CH_2CH_2\overset{}{CHCH_2CH_2CH_3}$
                      $\underset{\underset{\displaystyle CH(CH_3)_2}{|}}{}$

i. $CH_3\overset{}{CHCH_2CH_2}\overset{\overset{\displaystyle CH_3}{|}}{CHCH_3}$
      $\underset{\underset{\displaystyle CH_2CH_3}{|}}{}$

PROBLEM 10◆

Draw the structure and give the systematic name of a compound with molecular formula C_5H_{12} that has

a. only primary and secondary hydrogens.

b. only primary hydrogens.

c. one tertiary hydrogen.

d. two secondary hydrogens.

chem place Tutorial:
Basic nomenclature of alkanes

2.3 THE NOMENCLATURE OF CYCLOALKANES • SKELETAL STRUCTURES

Cycloalkanes are alkanes with their carbon atoms arranged in a ring. Because of the ring, a cycloalkane has two fewer hydrogens than an acyclic (noncyclic) alkane with the same number of carbons. This means that the general molecular formula for a cycloalkane is C_nH_{2n}. Cycloalkanes are named by adding the prefix "cyclo" to the alkane name that signifies the number of carbons in the ring.

cyclopropane   cyclobutane   cyclopentane   cyclohexane

Cycloalkanes are almost always written as **skeletal structures**. Skeletal structures show the carbon–carbon bonds as lines, but do not show the carbons or the hydrogens bonded to carbons. Atoms other than carbon are shown, and hydrogens bonded to atoms other than carbon are shown. Each vertex in a skeletal structure represents a carbon, and each carbon is understood to be bonded to the appropriate number of hydrogens to give the carbon four bonds.

cyclopropane   cyclobutane   cyclopentane   cyclohexane

Acyclic molecules can also be represented by skeletal structures. In skeletal structures of acyclic molecules, the carbon chains are represented by zigzag lines. Again, each vertex represents a carbon, and carbons are assumed to be present where a line begins or ends.

butane   2-methylhexane   3-methyl-4-propylheptane   6-ethyl-2,3-dimethylnonane

The rules for naming cycloalkanes resemble the rules for naming acyclic alkanes:

1. In a cycloalkane with an attached alkyl substituent, the ring is the parent hydrocarbon unless the substituent has more carbons than the ring. In that case, the substituent is the parent hydrocarbon and the ring is named as a substituent. There is no need to number the position of a single substituent on a ring.

methylcyclopentane   ethylcyclohexane   1-cyclobutylpentane

If there is only one substituent on a ring, do not give that substituent a number.

2. If the ring has two different substituents, they are listed in *alphabetical order* and the number-1 position is given to the substituent listed first.

1-methyl-2-propylcyclopentane   1-ethyl-3-methylcyclopentane   1,3-dimethylcyclohexane

3. If there are more than two substituents on the ring, they are listed in alphabetical order, and the substituent given the number-1 position is the one that results in a second substituent getting as low a number as possible. If two substituents have the same low numbers, the ring is numbered—either clockwise or counterclockwise—in the direction that gives the third substituent the lowest possible number. For example, the correct name of the compound below on the left is 4-ethyl-2-methyl-1-propylcyclohexane, not 5-ethyl-1-methyl-2-propylcyclohexane:

4-ethyl-2-methyl-1-propylcyclohexane	1,1,2-trimethylcyclopentane
not	not
1-ethyl-3-methyl-4-propylcyclohexane	1,2,2-trimethylcyclopentane
because 2 < 3	because 1 < 2
not	not
5-ethyl-1-methyl-2-propylcyclohexane	1,1,5-trimethylcyclopentane
because 4 < 5	because 2 < 5

PROBLEM-SOLVING STRATEGY

Interpreting a Skeletal Structure

Write the number of hydrogens attached to each of the indicated carbons in the following compound:

cholesterol

All the carbons in the compound are neutral, so each needs to be bonded to four atoms. Thus if the carbon has only one bond showing, it must be attached to three hydrogens that are not shown; if the carbon has two bonds showing, it must be attached to two hydrogens that are not shown, and so on.

Now continue on to Problem 11.

PROBLEM 11

Write the number of hydrogens attached to each of the indicated carbons in the following compound:

morphine

PROBLEM 12 ◆

Convert the following condensed structures into skeletal structures (remember that condensed structures show atoms but few, if any, bonds, whereas skeletal structures show bonds but few, if any, atoms):

a. $CH_3CH_2CH_2CH_2CH_2CH_2OH$

b. $CH_3CH_2CH_2CH_2CH_2CH_3$

c. $CH_3CH_2\overset{\displaystyle CH_3}{CH}CH_2\overset{\displaystyle CH_3}{CH}CH_2CH_3$

d. $CH_3CH_2CH_2CH_2OCH_3$

e. $CH_3CH_2NHCH_2CH_2CH_3$

f. $CH_3\overset{\displaystyle CH_3}{CH}CH_2CH_2\underset{\displaystyle Br}{CH}CH_3$

PROBLEM 13

Convert the structures in Problem 9 into skeletal structures.

PROBLEM 14

Draw the condensed and skeletal structures for:

a. 4-ethyl-3-isopropylheptane

b. 2,2,5-trimethylhexane

PROBLEM 15◆

Give the systematic name for each of the following:

a.

b.

c.

d.

e.

f.

g.

h.

chem Tutorial:
place Alkyl group nomenclature

Tutorial:
Advanced alkane nomenclature

2.4 THE NOMENCLATURE OF ALKYL HALIDES

An **alkyl halide** is a compound in which a hydrogen of an alkane has been replaced by a halogen. Alkyl halides are classified as primary, secondary, or tertiary, depending on the carbon to which the halogen is attached. **Primary alkyl halides** have a halogen bonded to a primary carbon, **secondary alkyl halides** have a halogen bonded to a secondary carbon, and **tertiary alkyl halides** have a halogen bonded to a tertiary carbon (Section 2.1). The lone-pair electrons on the halogens are generally not shown unless they are needed to draw your attention to some chemical property of the atom.

The number of alkyl groups attached to the carbon to which the halogen is bonded determines whether an alkyl halide is primary, secondary, or tertiary.

a primary carbon	a secondary carbon	a tertiary carbon
R—CH₂—Br	R—CH—R Br	R—C—R (R above) Br
a primary alkyl halide	a secondary alkyl halide	a tertiary alkyl halide

CH₃F
methyl fluoride

The common names of alkyl halides consist of the name of the alkyl group, followed by the name of the halogen—with the "ine" ending of the halogen name replaced by "ide" (that is, fluoride, chloride, bromide, iodide).

	CH₃Cl	CH₃CH₂F	CH₃CHI CH₃	CH₃CH₂CHBr CH₃
common name:	methyl chloride	ethyl fluoride	isopropyl iodide	*sec*-butyl bromide
systematic name:	chloromethane	fluoroethane	2-iodopropane	2-bromobutane

CH₃Cl
methyl chloride

CH₃Br
methyl bromide

In the IUPAC system, alkyl halides are named as substituted alkanes. The prefixes for the halogens end with "o" (that is, "fluoro," "chloro," "bromo," "iodo"). Therefore, alkyl halides are often called haloalkanes. Notice that although a name must specify only one compound, a compound can have more than one name.

CH₃I
methyl iodide

$$CH_3CH_2CHCH_2CH_2CHCH_3$$

with CH₃ above and Br below

2-bromo-5-methylheptane

1-chloro-6,6-dimethylheptane

1-ethyl-2-iodocyclopentane

4-bromo-2-chloro-1-methylcyclohexane

A compound can have more than one name, but a name must specify only one compound.

PROBLEM 16 ◆

Give two names for each of the following, and tell whether each alkyl halide is primary, secondary, or tertiary:

a. $CH_3CH_2CHCH_3$ with Cl below

c. $CH_3CHCH_2CH_2CH_2Cl$ with CH_3 below

b. cyclohexane with Br

d. structure with F below

PROBLEM 17

Draw the structures and provide systematic names for parts **a**, **b**, and **c** by substituting a chlorine for a hydrogen of methylcyclohexane:

a. a primary alkyl halide

b. a tertiary alkyl halide

c. three secondary alkyl halides

2.5 THE NOMENCLATURE OF ETHERS

Chemists sometimes neglect the prefix "di" when they name symmetrical ethers. Try not to make this oversight a habit.

An **ether** is a compound in which an oxygen is bonded to two alkyl substituents. If the alkyl substituents are identical, the ether is a **symmetrical ether**. If the substituents are different, the ether is an **unsymmetrical ether**.

$$R—O—R \qquad R—O—R'$$

a symmetrical ether   an unsymmetrical ether

The common name of an ether consists of the names of the two alkyl substituents (in alphabetical order), followed by the word "ether." The smallest ethers are almost always named by their common names.

dimethyl ether

$CH_3OCH_2CH_3$
ethyl methyl ether

$CH_3CH_2OCH_2CH_3$
diethyl ether
often called ethyl ether

$CH_3CHCH_2OCCH_3$ with CH_3 above and CH_3, CH_3 below
***tert*-butyl isobutyl ether**

$CH_3CHOCHCH_2CH_3$ with CH_3 above and CH_3 below
***sec*-butyl isopropyl ether**

$CH_3CHCH_2CH_2O—$ cyclohexyl with CH_3 below
cyclohexyl isopentyl ether

diethyl ether

The IUPAC system names an ether as an alkane with an RO substituent. The substituents are named by replacing the "yl" ending in the name of the alkyl substituent with "oxy."

$$CH_3O—$$
methoxy

$$CH_3CH_2O—$$
ethoxy

$$CH_3CHO—$$
$$\quad\ \ |$$
$$\quad\ \ CH_3$$
isopropoxy

$$CH_3CH_2CHO—$$
$$\qquad\ \ |$$
$$\qquad\ \ CH_3$$
sec-butoxy

$$\qquad\ CH_3$$
$$\qquad\ \ |$$
$$CH_3CO—$$
$$\qquad\ \ |$$
$$\qquad\ \ CH_3$$
tert-butoxy

chem Tutorial:
place   Nomenclature of ethers

Tutorial:
Ether nomenclature

$$CH_3CHCH_2CH_3$$
$$\quad\ \ |$$
$$\quad\ \ OCH_3$$
2-methoxybutane

$$CH_3CH_2CHCH_2CH_2OCH_2CH_3$$
$$\qquad\quad |$$
$$\qquad\quad CH_3$$
1-ethoxy-3-methylpentane

1-butoxy-2,3-dimethylpentane

$$CH_3CHOCH_2CH_2CH_2CH_2OCHCH_3$$
$$\quad\ |\qquad\qquad\qquad\qquad\ |$$
$$\quad\ CH_3\qquad\qquad\qquad\quad\ \ CH_3$$
1,4-diisopropoxybutane

PROBLEM 18 ◆

a. Give the systematic (IUPAC) name for each of the following ethers:

   1. $CH_3OCH_2CH_3$

   2. $CH_3CH_2OCH_2CH_3$

   3. $CH_3CH_2CH_2CH_2CHCH_2CH_2CH_3$
                         |
                         OCH_3

   4. $CH_3CHOCH_2CH_2CHCH_3$
            | |
           CH_3 CH_3

   5. [structure]

   6. [structure]

b. Do all of these ethers have common names?
c. What are their common names?

2.6 THE NOMENCLATURE OF ALCOHOLS

An **alcohol** is a compound in which a hydrogen of an alkane has been replaced by an OH group. Alcohols are classified as **primary alcohols**, **secondary alcohols**, or **tertiary alcohols**, depending on whether the OH group is bonded to a primary, secondary, or tertiary carbon—just like the way alkyl halides are classified.

> The number of alkyl groups attached to the carbon to which the OH group is attached determines whether an alcohol is primary, secondary, or tertiary.

$$R—CH_2—OH$$

a primary alcohol

$$\qquad R$$
$$\qquad |$$
$$R—CH—OH$$

a secondary alcohol

$$\qquad R$$
$$\qquad |$$
$$R—C—OH$$
$$\qquad |$$
$$\qquad R$$

a tertiary alcohol

methyl alcohol

The common name of an alcohol consists of the name of the alkyl group to which the OH group is attached, followed by the word "alcohol."

$$CH_3CH_2OH$$
ethyl alcohol

$$CH_3CH_2CH_2OH$$
propyl alcohol

$$CH_3CHOH$$
$$\quad\ \ |$$
$$\quad\ \ CH_3$$
isopropyl alcohol

$$CH_3CHCH_2OH$$
$$\quad\ \ |$$
$$\quad\ \ CH_3$$
isobutyl alcohol

The **functional group** is the center of reactivity in an organic molecule. In an alcohol, the OH is the functional group. The IUPAC system uses *suffixes* to denote certain functional groups. The systematic name of an alcohol, for example, is obtained by replacing the "e" at the end of the name of the parent hydrocarbon with the suffix "ol."

$$CH_3OH$$
methanol

$$CH_3CH_2OH$$
ethanol

ethyl alcohol

When necessary, the position of the functional group is indicated by a number immediately preceding the name of the alcohol or immediately preceding the suffix. The most recently approved IUPAC names are those with the number immediately preceding the suffix. However, names with the number preceding the name of the alcohol have been in

propyl alcohol

use for a long time, so those are the ones most likely to appear in the literature, on reagent bottles, and on standardized tests. They will also be the ones that appear most often in this book.

$$CH_3CH_2CHCH_2CH_3$$
$$|$$
$$OH$$

3-pentanol
or
pentan-3-ol

3-methyl-1-hexanol
or
3-methylhexan-1-ol

The following rules are used to name a compound that has a functional group suffix:

1. The parent hydrocarbon is the longest continuous chain *containing the functional group.*

2. The parent hydrocarbon is numbered in the direction that gives the *functional group suffix the lowest possible number.*

$$\overset{1}{C}H_3\overset{2}{C}HCH_2\overset{3}{C}H_3 \qquad \overset{4}{C}H_3$$

$$CH_3\overset{1}{C}HCH_2\overset{4}{C}H_3$$
$$|$$
$$OH$$

2-butanol
or
butan-2-ol

$$\overset{5}{C}H_3\overset{4}{C}H_2\overset{3}{C}H_2\overset{2}{C}H\overset{1}{C}H_2OH$$
$$|$$
$$CH_2CH_3$$

2-ethyl-1-pentanol
or
2-ethylpentan-1-ol

$$CH_3CH_2CH_2CH_2O\overset{3}{C}H_2\overset{2}{C}H_2\overset{1}{C}H_2OH$$

3-butoxy-1-propanol
or
3-butoxypropan-1-ol

$$CH_3CHCH_2CHCH_2CH_3$$
$$|\qquad\quad|$$
$$OH\quad OH$$

2,4-hexanediol
or
hexane -1,4-diol

| The longest continuous chain has six carbons, but the longest continuous chain containing the OH functional group has five carbons so the compound is named as a pentanol. |

| The longest continuous chain has four carbons, but the longest continuous chain containing the OH functional group has three carbons, so the compound is named as a propanol. |

3. If there are two OH groups, the suffix "diol" is added to the name of the parent hydrocarbon.

$$CH_3CHCH_2CHCH_2CH_3$$
$$|\qquad\quad|$$
$$OH\quad OH$$

2,4-hexanediol
or
hexane-1,4-diol

When there is only a substituent, the substituent gets the lowest possible number.

When there is only a functional group suffix, the functional group suffix gets the lowest possible number.

When there is both a functional group suffix and a substituent, the functional group suffix gets the lowest possible number.

4. If there is a functional group suffix and a substituent, the functional group suffix gets the lowest possible number.

$$HO\overset{1}{C}H_2\overset{2}{C}H_2\overset{3}{C}H_2Br$$

$$\overset{4}{C}lCH_2\overset{3}{C}H_2\overset{2}{C}HCH_3$$
$$|$$
$$OH$$

$$CH_3$$
$$\overset{5}{C}H_3\overset{4}{C}|CH_2\overset{2}{C}HCH_3$$
$$|\qquad\quad|$$
$$CH_3\quad OH$$

3-bromo-1-propanol   **4-chloro-2-butanol**   **4,4-dimethyl-2-pentanol**

5. If counting in either direction gives the same number for the functional group suffix, the chain is numbered in the direction that gives a substituent the lowest possible number. Notice that a number is not needed to designate the position of a functional group suffix in a cyclic compound, because it is assumed to be at the 1-position.

$$CH_3CHCHCH_2CH_3$$
$$|\quad\ |$$
$$Cl\ OH$$

$$CH_3CH_2CH_2CHCH_2CHCH_3$$
$$|\qquad\quad|$$
$$OH\qquad CH_3$$

2-chloro-3-pentanol
not
4-chloro-3-pentanol

2-methyl-4-heptanol
not
6-methyl-4-heptanol

3-methylcyclohexanol
not
5-methylcyclohexanol

6. If there is more than one substituent, the substituents are listed in alphabetical order.

7-bromo-4-ethyl-2-octanol   3,4-dimethylcyclopentanol   2-ethyl-5-methylcyclohexanol

Remember that the name of a substituent is stated *before* the name of the parent hydrocarbon, and the functional group suffix is stated *after* the name of the parent hydrocarbon.

[substituent] [parent hydrocarbon] [functional group suffix]

PROBLEM 19

Draw the structures of a homologous series of alcohols that have from one to six carbons, and then give each of them a common name and a systematic name.

PROBLEM 20 ♦

Give each of the following a systematic name, and indicate whether each is a primary, secondary, or tertiary alcohol:

a. $CH_3CH_2CH_2CH_2CH_2OH$

b. $CH_3\overset{\overset{\displaystyle OH}{|}}{C}CH_2CH_2CH_2Cl$

c. $CH_3\overset{\overset{\displaystyle CH_3}{|}}{C}HCH_2\overset{\overset{\displaystyle OH}{|}}{C}HCH_2CH_3$

d. $CH_3\overset{\overset{\displaystyle CH_3}{|}}{C}HCH_2\overset{\overset{\displaystyle OH}{|}}{C}HCH_2\overset{\overset{\displaystyle OH}{|}}{C}HCH_2CH_3$

chem Tutorial:
place Nomenclature of alcohols

PROBLEM 21 ♦

Write the structures of all the tertiary alcohols with molecular formula $C_6H_{14}O$, and give each a systematic name.

PROBLEM 22 ♦

Give each of the following a systematic name, and indicate whether each is a primary, secondary, or tertiary alcohol:

a.

b.

c.

d.

2.7 THE NOMENCLATURE OF AMINES

An **amine** is a compound in which one or more hydrogens of ammonia have been replaced by alkyl groups. There are **primary amines**, **secondary amines**, and **tertiary amines**. The classification depends on how many alkyl groups are bonded to the nitrogen. Primary amines have one alkyl group bonded to the nitrogen, secondary amines have two, and tertiary amines have three.

NH_3 $R-NH_2$ $R-\overset{\overset{\displaystyle R}{|}}{N}H$ $R-\overset{\overset{\displaystyle R}{|}}{N}-R$

ammonia   a primary amine   a secondary amine   a tertiary amine

The number of alkyl groups attached to the nitrogen determines whether an amine is primary, secondary, or tertiary.

Notice that the number of alkyl groups *attached to the nitrogen* determines whether an amine is primary, secondary, or tertiary. For an alkyl halide or an alcohol, on the other hand, the number of alkyl groups *attached to the carbon* to which the halogen or the OH is bonded determines the classification (Sections 2.4 and 2.6).

nitrogen is attached to one alkyl group	carbon is attached to three alkyl groups	

$$R-\underset{\underset{R}{|}}{\overset{\overset{R}{|}}{C}}-NH_2$$

a primary amine

$$R-\underset{\underset{R}{|}}{\overset{\overset{R}{|}}{C}}-Cl$$

a tertiary alkyl chloride

$$R-\underset{\underset{R}{|}}{\overset{\overset{R}{|}}{C}}-OH$$

a tertiary alcohol

The common name of an amine consists of the names of the alkyl groups bonded to the nitrogen, in alphabetical order, followed by "amine." The entire name is written as one word (unlike the common names of alcohols, ethers, and alkyl halides, in which "alcohol," "ether," and "halide" are separate words).

CH_3NH_2
methylamine

$CH_3NHCH_2CH_2CH_3$
methylpropylamine

$CH_3CH_2NHCH_2CH_3$
diethylamine

$$CH_3\overset{\overset{CH_3}{|}}{N}CH_3$$
trimethylamine

$$CH_3\overset{\overset{CH_3}{|}}{N}CH_2CH_2CH_2CH_3$$
butyldimethylamine

$$CH_3CH_2\overset{\overset{CH_3}{|}}{N}CH_2CH_2CH_3$$
ethylmethylpropylamine

The IUPAC system uses the suffix "amine" to denote the amine functional group. The "e" at the end of the name of the parent hydrocarbon is replaced by "amine"—similar to the way in which alcohols are named. Also similar to the way alcohols are named, a number identifies the carbon to which the nitrogen is attached, and the number can appear before the name of the parent hydrocarbon or before "amine." The name of any alkyl group bonded to nitrogen is preceded by an "*N*" (in italics) to indicate that the group is bonded to a nitrogen rather than to a carbon.

$\overset{4}{C}H_3\overset{3}{C}H_2\overset{2}{C}H_2\overset{1}{C}H_2NH_2$
1-butanamine
or
butan-1-amine

$\overset{1}{C}H_3\overset{2}{C}H_2\overset{3}{C}H\overset{4}{C}H_2\overset{5}{C}H_2\overset{6}{C}H_3$
$|$
$NHCH_2CH_3$
***N*-ethyl-3-hexanamine**
or
***N*-ethylhexan-3-amine**

$\overset{3}{C}H_3\overset{2}{C}H_2\overset{1}{C}H_2NCH_2CH_3$
$|$
CH_3
***N*-ethyl-*N*-methyl-1-propanamine**
or
***N*-ethyl-*N*-methylpropan-1-amine**

The substituents—regardless of whether they are attached to the nitrogen or to the parent hydrocarbon—are listed in alphabetical order, and then an "*N*" or a number is assigned to each one. The chain is numbered in the direction that gives the functional group suffix the lowest number.

$\overset{4}{C}H_3\overset{3}{C}H\overset{2}{C}H_2\overset{1}{C}H_2NHCH_3$
$|$
Cl
3-chloro-*N*-methyl-1-butanamine

$\overset{1}{C}H_3\overset{2}{C}H_2\overset{3}{C}H\overset{4}{C}H_2\overset{5}{C}H\overset{6}{C}H_3$
$\qquad\qquad\quad|\qquad\quad\overset{|}{C}H_3$
$\qquad\qquad\quad NHCH_2CH_3$
***N*-ethyl-5-methyl-3-hexanamine**

4-bromo-*N*,*N*-dimethyl-2-pentanamine

2-ethyl-*N*-propylcyclohexanamine

Nitrogen compounds with four alkyl groups bonded to the nitrogen—thereby giving the nitrogen a positive formal charge—are called **quaternary ammonium salts**. Their names consist of the names of the alkyl groups in alphabetical order, followed by "ammonium" (all in one word), and then the name of the accompanying anion as a separate word.

$$CH_3-\overset{\overset{\displaystyle CH_3}{|}}{\underset{\underset{\displaystyle CH_3}{|}}{N}}\!{}^{\pm}\!-CH_3 \quad HO^-$$

tetramethylammonium hydroxide

$$CH_3CH_2CH_2-\overset{\overset{\displaystyle CH_3}{|}}{\underset{\underset{\displaystyle CH_2CH_3}{|}}{N}}\!{}^{\pm}\!-CH_3 \quad Cl^-$$

ethyldimethylpropylammonium chloride

Bad-Smelling Compounds

Amines are associated with some of nature's unpleasant odors. Amines with relatively small alkyl groups, for example, have a fishy smell. Thus, fermented shark, a traditional dish in Iceland, smells exactly like triethylamine. The amines putrescine and cadaverine are poisonous compounds formed when amino acids are degraded. Because the body excretes them in the quickest ways possible, their odors may be detected in the urine and breath. They are also responsible for the odor of decaying flesh.

$$H_2N\diagup\diagdown\diagup NH_2$$

1,4-butanediamine
putrescine

$$H_2N\diagup\diagdown\diagup\diagdown NH_2$$

1,5-pentanediamine
cadaverine

Table 2.3 summarizes the ways in which alkyl halides, ethers, alcohols, and amines are named.

Table 2.3   Summary of Nomenclature

	Systematic name	Common name
Alkyl halide	substituted alkane $\quad CH_3Br$ bromomethane $\quad CH_3CH_2Cl$ chloroethane	alkyl group to which halogen is attached, plus *halide* $\quad CH_3Br$ methyl bromide $\quad CH_3CH_2Cl$ ethyl chloride
Ether	substituted alkane $\quad CH_3OCH_3$ methoxymethane $\quad CH_3CH_2OCH_3$ methoxyethane	alkyl groups attached to oxygen, plus *ether* $\quad CH_3OCH_3$ dimethyl ether $\quad CH_3CH_2OCH_3$ ethyl methyl ether
Alcohol	functional group suffix is *ol* $\quad CH_3OH$ methanol $\quad CH_3CH_2OH$ ethanol	alkyl group to which OH is attached, plus *alcohol* $\quad CH_3OH$ methyl alcohol $\quad CH_3CH_2OH$ ethyl alcohol
Amine	functional group suffix is *amine* $\quad CH_3CH_2NH_2$ ethanamine $\quad CH_3CH_2CH_2NHCH_3$ *N*-methyl-1-propanamine	alkyl groups attached to N, plus *amine* $\quad CH_3CH_2NH_2$ ethylamine $\quad CH_3CH_2CH_2NHCH_3$ methylpropylamine

PROBLEM 23 ◆

Tell whether the following are primary, secondary, or tertiary:

a. $CH_3-\overset{\overset{\displaystyle CH_3}{|}}{\underset{\underset{\displaystyle CH_3}{|}}{C}}-Br$

b. $CH_3-\overset{\overset{\displaystyle CH_3}{|}}{\underset{\underset{\displaystyle CH_3}{|}}{C}}-OH$

c. $CH_3-\overset{\overset{\displaystyle CH_3}{|}}{\underset{\underset{\displaystyle CH_3}{|}}{C}}-NH_2$

PROBLEM 24 ♦

Give a common name (if it has one) and a systematic name for each of the following amines and tell whether each is a primary, secondary, or tertiary amine:

a. $CH_3CH_2CH_2CH_2CH_2CH_2NH_2$

b. $CH_3CHCH_2NHCHCH_2CH_3$
         | |
        CH_3 CH_3

c. $(CH_3CH_2)_2NCH_3$

d. $CH_3CH_2CH_2NHCH_2CH_2CH_2CH_3$

e. $CH_3CH_2CH_2NCH_2CH_3$
                |
                CH_2CH_3

f. H_3C ⬠ $NHCH_2CH_3$

PROBLEM 25 ♦

Draw the structure for each of the following:

a. 2-methyl-*N*-propyl-1-propanamine
b. *N*-ethylethanamine
c. 5-methyl-1-hexanamine

d. methyldipropylamine
e. *N,N*-dimethyl-3-pentanamine
f. cyclohexylethylmethylamine

PROBLEM 26 ♦

For each of the following, give the systematic name and the common name (if it has one), and indicate whether it is a primary, secondary, or tertiary amine:

a.

b.

c.

d.

chem place   Tutorial:
Summary of systematic nomenclature

2.8 THE STRUCTURES OF ALKYL HALIDES, ALCOHOLS, ETHERS, AND AMINES

The classes of compounds we have been looking at in this chapter have structural resemblances to the simpler compounds introduced in Chapter 1. Let's begin by looking at alkyl halides and their resemblance to alkanes. Both classes of compounds have the same geometry; the only difference is that a C—X bond of an alkyl halide (where X denotes a halogen) has replaced a C—H bond of the alkane (Section 1.7). The C—X bond of an alkyl halide is formed from the overlap of an sp^3 orbital of the halogen with an sp^3 orbital of carbon. Fluorine uses a $2sp^3$ orbital to overlap with a $2sp^3$ orbital of carbon, chlorine uses a $3sp^3$ orbital, bromine a $4sp^3$ orbital, and iodine a $5sp^3$ orbital. As you can see in Table 2.4, because the electron density of the orbital decreases with increasing volume, the C—X bond becomes longer and weaker as the size of the halogen increases. Notice that this is the same trend shown by the H—X bond of hydrogen halides in Table 1.6 on page 37.

Now consider the geometry of the oxygen in an alcohol, which is the same as the geometry of the oxygen in water (Section 1.11). In fact, an alcohol molecule can be thought of structurally as a water molecule with an alkyl group in place of one of the hydrogens. The oxygen atom in an alcohol is sp^3 hybridized, as it is in water. One of the sp^3 orbitals of oxygen overlaps an sp^3 orbital of a carbon, one sp^3 orbital overlaps the *s* orbital of a hydrogen, and the other two sp^3 orbitals each contain a lone pair.

Table 2.4   Carbon–Halogen bond lengths and bond strengths

	Orbital interactions	Bond lengths	Bond strength (kcal/mol)	(kJ/mol)
H$_3$C—F		H—C 1.39 Å	108	451
H$_3$C—Cl		H—C 1.78 Å	84	350
H$_3$C—Br		H—C 1.93 Å	70	294
H$_3$C—I		H—C 2.14 Å	57	239

sp^3 hybridized

an alcohol

electrostatic potential map for methyl alcohol

The oxygen in an ether also has the same geometry as the oxygen in water. An ether molecule can be thought of structurally as a water molecule with alkyl groups in place of both hydrogens.

sp^3 hybridized

an ether

electrostatic potential map for dimethyl ether

The nitrogen in an amine has the same geometry as the nitrogen in ammonia (Section 1.12). It is *sp*^{3} hybridized as in ammonia, with one, two, or three of the hydrogens replaced by alkyl groups. Remember that the number of hydrogens replaced by alkyl groups determines whether the amine is primary, secondary, or tertiary (Section 2.7).

sp^3 hybridized

methylamine
a primary amine

dimethylamine
a secondary amine

trimethylamine
a tertiary amine

electrostatic potential maps for

methylamine   dimethylamine   trimethylamine

PROBLEM 27 ◆

Predict the approximate size of the following bond angles. (*Hint*: See Sections 1.11 and 1.12.)
a. the C—O—C bond angle in an ether
b. the C—N—C bond angle in a secondary amine
c. the C—O—H bond angle in an alcohol
d. the C—N—C bond angle in a quaternary ammonium salt

2.9 THE PHYSICAL PROPERTIES OF ALKANES, ALKYL HALIDES, ALCOHOLS, ETHERS, AND AMINES

Now we will look at the physical properties of the classes of compounds whose names and structures we have just examined.

Boiling Points

The **boiling point (bp)** of a compound is the temperature at which the liquid form becomes a gas (vaporizes). In order for a compound to vaporize, the forces that hold the individual molecules close to each other in the liquid must be overcome. This means that the boiling point of a compound depends on the strength of the attractive forces between the individual molecules. If the molecules are held together by strong forces, a lot of energy will be needed to pull the molecules away from each other and the compound will have a high boiling point. In contrast, if the molecules are held together by weak forces, only a small amount of energy will be needed to pull the molecules away from each other and the compound will have a low boiling point.

The attractive forces between alkane molecules are relatively weak. Alkanes contain only carbon and hydrogen atoms, and the electronegativities of carbon and hydrogen are similar. As a result, the bonds in alkanes are nonpolar—there are no significant partial charges on any of the atoms. Therefore, alkanes are neutral (nonpolar) molecules. The nonpolar nature of alkanes gives them their oily feel.

However, it is only the average charge distribution over the alkane molecule that is neutral. The electrons are moving continuously, and at any instant the electron density on one side of the molecule can be slightly greater than that on the other side, causing the molecule to have a temporary dipole. Recall that a molecule with a dipole has a negative end and a positive end (Section 1.3).

Johannes Diderik van der Waals (1837–1923) *was a Dutch physicist. He was born in Leiden, the son of a carpenter, and was largely self-taught when he entered the University of Leiden, where he earned a Ph.D. Van der Waals was a professor of physics at the University of Amsterdam from 1877 to 1907. He won the 1910 Nobel Prize in Physics for his research on the gaseous and liquid states of matter.*

A temporary dipole in one molecule can induce a temporary dipole in a nearby molecule. As a result, the (temporarily) negative side of one molecule ends up adjacent to the (temporarily) positive side of another, as shown in Figure 2.1. Because the dipoles in the molecules are induced, the interactions between the molecules are called **induced-dipole–induced-dipole interactions**. The molecules of an alkane are held together by these induced-dipole–induced-dipole interactions, which are known as **van der Waals forces**. Van der Waals forces are the weakest of all the intermolecular attractions.

The magnitude of the van der Waals forces that hold alkane molecules together depends on the area of contact between the molecules. The greater the area of contact, the stronger the van der Waals forces and the greater the amount of energy needed to overcome them. If you look at the boiling points of the alkanes listed in Table 2.1, you will see that they increase as their size increases. This relationship holds because each additional methylene (CH_2) group increases the area of contact between the molecules. The four smallest alkanes have boiling points below room temperature (which is about 25 °C), so they exist as gases at room temperature.

Because the strength of the van der Waals forces depends on the area of contact between the molecules, branching in a compound lowers the compound's boiling point by reducing the area of contact. If you think of pentane, an unbranched alkane, as a cigar and think of branched 2,2-dimethylpropane as a tennis ball, you can see that branching decreases the area of contact between molecules: two cigars make contact over a greater area than do two tennis balls. Thus, if two alkanes have the same molecular weight, the more highly branched alkane will have a lower boiling point.

▲ **Figure 2.1**
Van der Waals forces are induced-dipole–induced-dipole interactions.

CH₃CH₂CH₂CH₂CH₃
pentane
bp = 36.1 °C

CH₃CHCH₂CH₃ | CH₃
2-methylbutane
bp = 27.9 °C

CH₃CCH₃ | CH₃ | CH₃
2,2-dimethylpropane
bp = 9.5 °C

PROBLEM 28 ♦

What is the smallest alkane that is a liquid at room temperature?

The boiling points of a series of ethers, alkyl halides, alcohols, or amines also increase with increasing molecular weight because of the increase in van der Waals forces. (See Appendix I.) The boiling points of these compounds, however, are also affected by the polar C—Z bond (where Z denotes N, O, F, Cl, or Br). Recall that the C—Z bond is polar because nitrogen, oxygen, and the halogens are more electronegative than the carbon to which they are attached (Section 1.3).

R—C—Z   Z = N, O, F, Cl, or Br

Molecules with polar bonds are attracted to one another because they can align themselves in such a way that the positive end of one dipole is adjacent to the negative end of another dipole. These electrostatic attractive forces, called **dipole–dipole interactions**, are stronger than van der Waals forces, but not as strong as ionic or covalent bonds.

dipole–dipole interaction

As you can see in Table 2.5, ethers generally have higher boiling points than alkanes of comparable molecular weight. This is because both van der Waals forces and dipole–dipole interactions must be overcome for an ether to boil.

cyclopentane
bp = 49.3 °C

tetrahydrofuran
bp = 65 °C

The boiling point of a compound depends on the strength of the attraction between the individual molecules.

Table 2.5	Comparative Boiling Points (°C)		
Alkanes	**Ethers**	**Alcohols**	**Amines**
$CH_3CH_2CH_3$	CH_3OCH_3	CH_3CH_2OH	$CH_3CH_2NH_2$
−42.1	−23.7	78	16.6
$CH_3CH_2CH_2CH_3$	$CH_3OCH_2CH_3$	$CH_3CH_2CH_2OH$	$CH_3CH_2CH_2NH_2$
−0.5	10.8	97.4	47.8

Alcohols have much higher boiling points than ethers with similar molecular weights (as Table 2.5 also shows) because, in addition to van der Waals forces and the dipole–dipole interactions of the polar C—O bond, alcohols can form **hydrogen bonds**. A hydrogen bond is a special kind of dipole–dipole interaction that occurs between a hydrogen that is bonded to an oxygen, nitrogen, or fluorine and the lone-pair electrons of an oxygen, nitrogen, or fluorine in another molecule.

The length of the covalent bond between oxygen and hydrogen is 0.96 Å. The hydrogen bond between an oxygen of one molecule and a hydrogen of another molecule is almost twice as long (1.69−1.79 Å), which means that a hydrogen bond is not as strong as an O—H covalent bond. A hydrogen bond is, however, stronger than other dipole–dipole interactions. The strongest hydrogen bonds are linear, meaning the two electronegative atoms and the hydrogen between them lie on a straight line.

Hydrogen bonds are stronger than other dipole–dipole interactions, which are stronger than van der Waals forces.

hydrogen bond

hydrogen bonding in water

Although each individual hydrogen bond is weak, requiring about 5 kcal/mol (or 21 kJ/mol) to break, there are many such bonds holding alcohol molecules together. The extra energy required to break these hydrogen bonds is the reason alcohols have much higher boiling points than ethers with similar molecular weights.

The boiling point of water illustrates the dramatic effect that hydrogen bonding has on boiling points. Water has a molecular weight of 18 and a boiling point of 100 °C. The alkane nearest in size is methane, with a molecular weight of 16. Methane boils at −167.7 °C.

Primary and secondary amines also form hydrogen bonds, so these amines have higher boiling points than ethers with similar molecular weights. Nitrogen is not as electronegative as oxygen, however, which means that the hydrogen bonds between amine molecules are weaker than the hydrogen bonds between alcohol molecules. An amine, therefore, has a lower boiling point than an alcohol with a similar molecular weight (Table 2.5).

Because primary amines have two N—H bonds, hydrogen bonding is more significant in primary amines than in secondary amines. Tertiary amines cannot form hydrogen bonds between their own molecules because they do not have a hydrogen attached to the nitrogen. Consequently, when we compare amines with the same molecular weight and similar structures, we find that a primary amine has a higher boiling point than a secondary amine and a secondary amine has a higher boiling point than a tertiary amine.

a primary amine
bp = 97 °C

a secondary amine
bp = 84 °C

a tertiary amine
bp = 65 °C

Hydrogen bonds play an important role in biology. We will see that proteins are shaped by hydrogen bonding (Section 23.14), and DNA relies on hydrogen bonding to copy all its hereditary information (Section 28.3).

PROBLEM-SOLVING STRATEGY

Predicting Hydrogen Bonding

a. Which of the following compounds will form hydrogen bonds between its molecules?

   1. $CH_3CH_2CH_2OH$ **2.** $CH_3CH_2CH_2F$ **3.** $CH_3OCH_2CH_3$

b. Which of these compounds will form hydrogen bonds with a solvent such as ethanol?

   To solve this type of question, start by defining the kind of compound that will do what is being asked.

a. A hydrogen bond forms when a hydrogen attached to an O, N, or F of one molecule interacts with a lone pair on an O, N, or F of another molecule. Therefore, a compound that will form hydrogen bonds with itself must have a hydrogen bonded to an O, N, or F. Only compound 1 will be able to form hydrogen bonds with itself.

b. Ethanol has an H bonded to an O, so it will be able to form hydrogen bonds with a compound that has a lone pair on an O, N, or F. All three compounds will be able to form hydrogen bonds with ethanol.

   Now continue on to Problem 29.

PROBLEM 29 ◆

a. Which of the following will form hydrogen bonds between its molecules?

   1. $CH_3CH_2CH_2COOH$ **4.** $CH_3CH_2CH_2NHCH_3$

   2. $CH_3CH_2N(CH_3)_2$ **5.** $CH_3CH_2OCH_2CH_2OH$

   3. $CH_3CH_2CH_2CH_2Br$ **6.** $CH_3CH_2CH_2CH_2F$

b. Which of the preceding compounds will form hydrogen bonds with a solvent such as ethanol?

Both van der Waals forces and dipole–dipole interactions must be overcome for an alkyl halide to boil. Moreover, as the halogen atom increases in size, these interactions become stronger. A larger electron cloud means that the van der Waals contact area is greater and the electron cloud's polarizability is also greater. **Polarizability** indicates how readily an electron cloud can be distorted. The larger the atom, the more loosely it holds the electrons in its outermost shell, and the more they can be distorted to create a strong induced dipole. Therefore, an alkyl fluoride has a lower boiling point than an alkyl chloride with the same alkyl group. Similarly, alkyl chlorides have lower boiling points than alkyl bromides, which have lower boiling points than alkyl iodides (Table 2.6).

A more extensive tables of physical properties can be found in Appendix I.

Table 2.6 Comparative Boiling Points of Alkanes and Alkyl Halides (°C)

—Y	H	F	Cl	Br	I
CH_3—Y	−161.7	−78.4	−24.2	3.6	42.4
CH_3CH_2—Y	−88.6	−37.7	12.3	38.4	72.3
$CH_3CH_2CH_2$—Y	−42.1	−2.5	46.6	71.0	102.5
$CH_3CH_2CH_2CH_2$—Y	−0.5	32.5	78.4	101.6	130.5
$CH_3CH_2CH_2CH_2CH_2$—Y	36.1	62.8	107.8	129.6	157.0

Drugs Bind to Their Receptors

Many drugs exert their physiological effects by binding to specific binding sites called *receptors* (Sections 5.21 and 31.6). A drug binds to a receptor using the same kinds of bonding interactions—van der Waals interactions, dipole–dipole interactions, hydrogen bonding—that molecules use to bind to each other. The most important factor in the interaction between a drug and its receptor is a snug fit. Therefore, drugs with similar shapes often have similar physiological effects. For example, each of the compounds shown here has a nonpolar, planar six-membered ring and substituents with similar polarities, and they all have anti-inflammatory activity. Salicylic acid has been used for the relief of fever and arthritic pain since 500 B.C. In 1897, acetylsalicylic acid (aspirin) was found to be a more potent anti-inflammatory agent and less irritating to the stomach; it became commercially available in 1899.

salicylic acid

acetylsalicylic acid

acetaminophen
Tylenol®

Changing the relative positions of the substituents on the ring produced acetaminophen (Tylenol), which was introduced in 1955. It became a widely used drug because it causes no gastric irritation. However, its effective dose is not far from its toxic dose. Subsequently, ibufenac emerged; adding a methyl group to ibufenac produced ibuprofen (Advil), a much safer drug. Naproxen (Aleve), which has twice the potency of ibuprofen, was introduced in 1976.

ibufenac

ibuprofen
Advil®

naproxen
Aleve®

PROBLEM 30

Explain why
a. H_2O has a higher boiling point than CH_3OH (65 °C).
b. H_2O has a higher boiling point than NH_3 (−33 °C).
c. H_2O has a higher boiling point than HF (20 °C).

PROBLEM 31 ◆

List the following compounds in order of decreasing boiling point:

PROBLEM 32

List the compounds in each set in order of decreasing boiling point:

a.

b.

c.

Melting Points

The **melting point (mp)** of a compound is the temperature at which its solid form is converted into a liquid. If you examine the melting points of the alkanes listed in Table 2.1, you will see that they increase (with a few exceptions) as the molecular weight increases. The increase in melting point is less regular than the increase in boiling point because, in addition to the intermolecular attractions we considered above, the melting point is influenced by the type of **packing** (that is, the arrangement, including the closeness and compactness, of the molecules) in the crystal lattice. The tighter the fit, the more energy is required to break the lattice and melt the compound.

Figure 2.2 shows that the melting points of alkanes with an even number of carbons fall on a smooth curve (the red line). The melting points of alkanes with an odd number of carbons also fall on a smooth curve (the green line). The two curves do not overlap, however, because alkanes with an odd number of carbons pack less tightly than alkanes with an even number of carbons.

Alkanes with an odd number of carbons pack less tightly because the molecules, each a zigzag chain with its ends tilted the same way, can lie next to each other with a methyl group on the end of one facing and repelling the methyl group on the end of the other, thus increasing the average distance between the chains. Consequently, they have weaker intermolecular attractions and correspondingly lower melting points.

◀ Figure 2.2
Melting points of straight-chain alkanes. Alkanes with an even number of carbons fall on a melting-point curve that is higher than the melting-point curve for alkanes with an odd number of carbons.

odd number of carbons   even number of carbons

Solubility

The general rule that governs **solubility** is "like dissolves like." In other words, *polar compounds dissolve in polar solvents, and nonpolar compounds dissolve in nonpolar solvents.* The reason "polar dissolves polar" is that a polar solvent, such as water, has partial charges that can interact with the partial charges on a polar compound. The negative poles of the solvent molecules surround the positive pole of the polar compound, and the positive poles of the solvent molecules surround the negative pole of the polar compound. Clustering of the solvent molecules around the polar molecules separates them from each other, which is what makes them dissolve. The interaction between solvent molecules and solute molecules (molecules dissolved in a solvent) is called **solvation**.

"Like dissolves like."

solvation of a polar compound by water

Because nonpolar compounds have no net charge, polar solvents are not attracted to them. In order for a nonpolar molecule to dissolve in a polar solvent such as water, the nonpolar molecule would have to push the water molecules apart, disrupting their hydrogen bonding. Hydrogen bonding is strong enough to exclude the nonpolar compound. In contrast, nonpolar solutes dissolve in nonpolar solvents because the van der Waals interactions between solvent molecules and solute molecules are about the same as between solvent–solvent molecules and solute–solute molecules.

Alkanes are nonpolar, which causes them to be soluble in nonpolar solvents and insoluble in polar solvents such as water. The densities of alkanes (Table 2.1) increase with increasing molecular weight, but even a 30-carbon alkane (density at 20 °C, or $d^{20°} = 0.8097$ g/mL) is less dense than water ($d^{20°} = 1.00$ g/mL). This means that a mixture of an alkane and water will separate into two distinct layers, with the less dense alkane floating on top. The Alaskan oil spill of 1989, the Persian Gulf spill of 1991, and the spill off the northwest coast of Spain in 2002 are large-scale examples of this phenomenon. (Crude oil is primarily a mixture of alkanes.)

An alcohol has both a nonpolar alkyl group and a polar OH group. So is an alcohol molecule nonpolar or polar? Is it soluble in a nonpolar solvent, or is it soluble in water? The answer depends on the size of the alkyl group. As the alkyl group increases in size, becoming a more significant fraction of the alcohol molecule, the compound becomes less and less soluble in water. In other words, the molecule becomes more and more like an alkane. Groups with four carbons tend to straddle the dividing line at room temperature: alcohols with fewer than four carbons are soluble in water, but alcohols with more than four carbons are insoluble in water. In other words, an OH group can drag about three or four carbons into solution in water.

The four-carbon dividing line is only an approximate guide because the solubility of an alcohol also depends on the structure of the alkyl group. Alcohols with branched alkyl groups are more soluble in water than alcohols with nonbranched alkyl groups having the same number of carbons, because branching minimizes the contact surface of the nonpolar portion of the molecule. So *tert*-butyl alcohol is more soluble than *n*-butyl alcohol in water.

Similarly, the oxygen atom of an ether can drag only about three carbons into solution in water (Table 2.7). As the photo on page 59 shows, diethyl ether—an ether with four carbons—is not soluble in water.

Oil from a 70,000-ton oil spill in 1996 off the coast of Wales.

Table 2.7	Solubilities of Ethers in Water	
2 C's	CH_3OCH_3	soluble
3 C's	$CH_3OCH_2CH_3$	soluble
4 C's	$CH_3CH_2OCH_2CH_3$	slightly soluble (10 g/100 g H_2O)
5 C's	$CH_3CH_2OCH_2CH_2CH_3$	minimally soluble (1.0 g/100 g H_2O)
6 C's	$CH_3CH_2CH_2OCH_2CH_2CH_3$	insoluble (0.25 g/100 g H_2O)

Low-molecular-weight amines are soluble in water because amines can form hydrogen bonds with water. Comparing amines with the same number of carbons, we find that primary amines are more soluble than secondary amines because primary amines have two hydrogens that can engage in hydrogen bonding. Tertiary amines, like primary and secondary amines, have lone-pair electrons that can accept hydrogen bonds, but unlike primary and secondary amines, tertiary amines do not have hydrogens to donate for hydrogen bonds. Tertiary amines, therefore, are less soluble in water than are secondary amines with the same number of carbons.

Alkyl halides have some polar character, but only alkyl fluorides have an atom that can form a hydrogen bond with water. This means that alkyl fluorides are the most water soluble of the alkyl halides. The other alkyl halides are less soluble in water than ethers or alcohols with the same number of carbons (Table 2.8).

Table 2.8   Solubilities of Alkyl Halides in Water

CH_3F	CH_3Cl	CH_3Br	CH_3I
very soluble	soluble	slightly soluble	slightly soluble
CH_3CH_2F	CH_3CH_2Cl	CH_3CH_2Br	CH_3CH_2I
soluble	slightly soluble	slightly soluble	slightly soluble
$CH_3CH_2CH_2F$	$CH_3CH_2CH_2Cl$	$CH_3CH_2CH_2Br$	$CH_3CH_2CH_2I$
slightly soluble	slightly soluble	slightly soluble	slightly soluble
$CH_3CH_2CH_2CH_2F$	$CH_3CH_2CH_2CH_2Cl$	$CH_3CH_2CH_2CH_2Br$	$CH_3CH_2CH_2CH_2I$
insoluble	insoluble	insoluble	insoluble

PROBLEM 33◆

Rank the following groups of compounds in order of decreasing solubility in water:

a.

b. $CH_3CH_2CH_2OH$ $CH_3CH_2CH_2CH_2Cl$ $CH_3CH_2CH_2CH_2OH$ $HOCH_2CH_2CH_2OH$

PROBLEM 34◆

In which solvent would cyclohexane have the lowest solubility, 1-pentanol, diethyl ether, ethanol, or hexane?

2.10 ROTATION OCCURS ABOUT CARBON—CARBON SINGLE BONDS

We have seen that a carbon–carbon single bond (a σ bond) is formed when an sp^3 orbital of one carbon overlaps an sp^3 orbital of another carbon (Section 1.7). Figure 2.3 shows that rotation about a carbon–carbon single bond can occur without any change in the amount of orbital overlap. The different spatial arrangements of the atoms that result from rotation about a single bond are called **conformations**. Molecules with different conformations are called **conformational isomers** or **conformers**.

The conformers produced by rotation about the carbon–carbon bond of ethane represent a continuum between the two extremes shown below: a *staggered conformer* and an *eclipsed conformer*. An infinite number of conformers between these two extremes are also possible.

Our drawings of molecules are two-dimensional attempts to communicate three-dimensional structures. Chemists commonly use *Newman projections* to represent the three-dimensional spatial arrangements resulting from rotation about a σ bond. A **Newman projection** assumes that the viewer is looking along the longitudinal axis of a particular C—C bond. The carbon in front is represented by a point (where three lines are seen to intersect), and the carbon at the back is represented by a circle. The three lines emanating from each of the carbons represent its other three bonds.

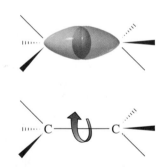

▲ Figure 2.3
A carbon–carbon bond is formed by the overlap of cylindrically symmetrical sp^3 orbitals. Therefore, rotation about the bond can occur without changing the amount of orbital overlap.

H_3C—CH_3
ethane

Newman projections

staggered conformer from rotation about the C—C bond in ethane	eclipsed conformer from rotation about the C—C bond in ethane

A **staggered conformer** is more stable, and therefore lower in energy, than an **eclipsed conformer**. Because of this energy difference, rotation about a carbon–carbon single bond is not completely free since an energy barrier must be overcome when rotation about the C—C bond occurs (Figure 2.4). However, the energy barrier in ethane is small enough (2.9 kcal/mol or 12 kJ/mol) to allow continuous rotation. A molecule's conformation changes from staggered to eclipsed millions of times per second at room temperature. Because of this continuous interconversion, the conformers cannot be separated from each other. Nevertheless, at any one time approximately 99% of the ethane molecules will be in a staggered conformation because of its greater stability, and only 1% will be in the less stable eclipsed conformation. The investigation of the various conformations of a compound and their relative stabilities is called **conformational analysis**.

Figure 2.4 shows the potential energies of all the conformers of ethane obtained in one complete 360° rotation about the C—C bond. Notice that staggered conformers are at energy minima, whereas eclipsed conformers are at energy maxima.

Why is a staggered conformer more stable than an eclipsed conformer? The major contribution to the energy difference between them is a stabilizing interaction between the C—H σ bonding orbital on one carbon and the C—H σ* antibonding orbital on the other carbon: the electrons in the filled bonding orbital move partially into the unoccupied antibonding orbital. This interaction is greatest in a staggered conformation because only in this conformation are the two orbitals parallel. Such a delocalization of electrons by the overlap of an σ orbital with an empty orbital is called **hyperconjugation**.

A staggered conformer is more stable than an eclipsed conformer.

▶ **Figure 2.4** Potential energy of ethane as a function of the angle of rotation about the carbon–carbon bond.

Butane has three carbon–carbon single bonds, and rotation can occur about each of them. The Newman projections below show the staggered and eclipsed conformers that result from rotation about the C-1—C-2 bond:

the C-2—C-3 bond

$$\overset{1}{CH_3}-\overset{2}{CH_2}-\overset{3}{CH_2}-\overset{4}{CH_3}$$

butane

the C-1—C-2 bond   the C-3—C-4 bond

ball-and-stick model of butane

staggered conformer that results from rotation about the C-1—C-2 bond in butane

eclipsed conformer that results from rotation about the C-1—C-2 bond in butane

Notice that the carbon with the lower number is placed in the foreground in a Newman projection.

Although the staggered conformers resulting from rotation about the C-1—C-2 bond in butane all have the same energy, the staggered conformers resulting from rotation about the C-2—C-3 bond do not. The staggered and eclipsed conformers from rotation about the C-2—C-3 bond in butane are:

A   B   C   D   E   F   A

Of the staggered conformers, D, in which the two methyl groups are as far apart as possible, is more stable than the other two staggered conformers (B and F). The most stable staggered conformer (in this case, D) is called the **anti conformer**, and the other two staggered conformers (in this case, B and F) are called **gauche** ("goesh") **conformers**. (*Anti* is Greek for "opposite of"; *gauche* is French for "left.") In the anti conformer, the largest substituents are opposite each other; in a gauche conformer, they are adjacent. The two gauche conformers have the same energy, which is higher than the energy of the anti conformer.

The anti and gauche conformers do not have the same energy because of steric strain. **Steric strain** is the strain experienced by a molecule (that is, the additional energy it possesses) when atoms or groups are close enough to one another for their electron clouds to repel each other. There is more steric strain in a gauche conformer than in the anti conformer because the two substituents (in this case, the two methyl groups of butane) are closer together in a gauche conformer. This type of steric strain is called a **gauche interaction**. In general, steric strain in molecules increases as the size of the interacting atoms or groups increases.

The eclipsed conformers resulting from rotation about the C-2—C-3 bond in butane also have different energies. The eclipsed conformer in which the two methyl groups are closest to each other (A) is less stable than the eclipsed conformer in which they are farther apart (C and E).

The energies of the conformers obtained from rotation about the C-2—C-3 bond of butane are shown in Figure 2.5. The letters in Figure 2.5 correspond to the letters that identify the above structures. The degree of rotation of each conformer is identified by the dihedral angle—the angle formed in a Newman projection by a bond on the nearer carbon and a bond on the far carbon. For example, the conformer in which one methyl

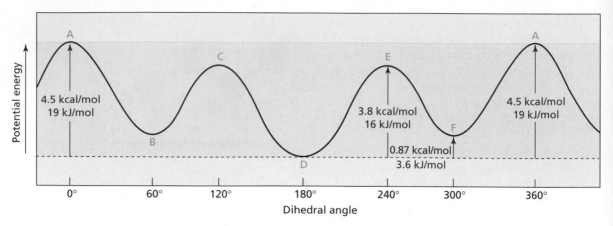

▶ **Figure 2.5**
Potential energy of butane as a function of the degree of rotation about the C-2—C-3 bond. Green letters refer to the conformers (A–F) shown on page 99.

group stands directly in front of the other—the least stable conformer—has a dihedral angle of 0°.

Because there is continuous rotation about all the C—C single bonds in a molecule, organic molecules with C—C single bonds are not static balls and sticks—they have many interconvertible conformers. The relative number of molecules in a particular conformation at any one time depends on its stability: the more stable it is, the greater the fraction of molecules that will be in that conformation. Most molecules, therefore, are in staggered conformations at any given instant, and more molecules are in the anti conformation than in a gauche conformation. The preference for the staggered conformation gives carbon chains a tendency to adopt zigzag arrangements, as seen in the ball-and-stick model of decane.

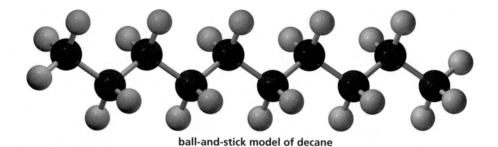

ball-and-stick model of decane

PROBLEM 35

a. Draw all the staggered and eclipsed conformers that result from rotation about the C-2—C-3 bond of pentane.

b. Draw a potential-energy diagram for rotation about the C-2—C-3 bond of pentane through 360°, starting with the least stable conformer.

PROBLEM 36 ♦

Using Newman projections, draw the most stable conformer for each of the following:

a. 3-methylpentane, viewed along the C-2—C-3 bond

b. 3-methylhexane, viewed along the C-3—C-4 bond

c. 3,3-dimethylhexane, viewed along the C-3—C-4 bond

2.11 SOME CYCLOALKANES HAVE ANGLE STRAIN

Early chemists observed that cyclic compounds found in nature generally have five- or six-membered rings. Compounds with three- and four-membered rings are much less common. This observation suggests that compounds with five- and six-membered rings are more stable than compounds with three- or four-membered rings.

eclipsed hydrogens

cyclopropane

In 1885, the German chemist Adolf von Baeyer proposed that the instability of three- and four-membered rings is due to angle strain. We know that, ideally, an sp^3 carbon has bond angles of 109.5° (Section 1.7). Baeyer suggested that the stability of a cycloalkane could be predicted by assessing the difference between this ideal bond angle and the bond angle in the planar cycloalkane. The bond angles in an equilateral triangle, for example, are 60°, representing a 49.5° deviation from the tetrahedral 109.5°. According to Baeyer, this deviation causes **angle strain**, and thus instability, in cyclopropane.

The angle strain in a three-membered ring can be understood by looking at the overlap of the orbitals that form the σ bonds in cyclopropane (Figure 2.6). Normal σ bonds are formed by the overlap of two sp^3 orbitals that point directly at each other. In cyclopropane, the overlapping orbitals cannot point directly at each other, so the amount of overlap between them is less than in a normal C—C bond. The smaller degree of overlap causes the C—C bonds in cyclopropane to be weaker than normal C—C bonds. This weakness is what we have described as angle strain.

a.

good overlap
strong bond

b.

poor overlap
weak bond

orbitals forming the C—C bonds of cyclopropane

◀ **Figure 2.6**
(a) Overlap of sp^3 orbitals in a normal σ bond.
(b) Overlap sp^3 of orbitals in cyclopropane.

Because the C—C bonding orbitals in cyclopropane cannot point directly at each other, the bonds they form have shapes that resemble bananas and, consequently, are sometimes called **banana bonds**. In addition to the angle strain of the C—C bonds, all the adjacent C—H bonds in cyclopropane are eclipsed rather than staggered, making it even more unstable.

banana bonds

The bond angles in a hypothetical planar cyclobutane molecule would have to be compressed from 109.5° to 90°, the bond angle associated with a planar four-membered ring. Planar cyclobutane would therefore have less angle strain than cyclopropane because the bond angles in cyclobutane are only 19.5° away from the ideal bond angle. It would, however, have eight pairs of eclipsed hydrogens, compared with six pairs in cyclopropane. Because of the eclipsed hydrogens, a cyclobutane molecule is not planar. (Its structure is explained and shown on page 102.)

Highly Strained Hydrocarbons

Organic chemists have been able to synthesize some highly strained cyclic hydrocarbons, such as bicyclo[1.1.0]butane, cubane, and prismane. Bicyclo[1.1.0] butane was synthesized by David Lemal, Fredric Menger, and George Clark at the University of Wisconsin. Cubane was synthesized by Philip Eaton and Thomas Cole Jr. at the University of Chicago. Prismane was synthesized by Thomas Katz and Nancy Acton at Columbia University.

bicyclo[1.1.0]butane

cubane

prismane

Philip Eaton, the first to synthesize cubane, also synthesized octanitrocubane, which is cubane with an NO_2 group bonded to each of the eight corners. It turned out to be less powerful an explosive than expected.

PROBLEM 37 ◆

The bond angles in a regular polygon with n sides are equal to

$$180° - \frac{360°}{n}$$

a. What are the bond angles in a regular octagon?
b. What are the bond angles in a regular nonagon?

Baeyer predicted that cyclopentane would be the most stable of the cycloalkanes because its bond angles (108°) are closest to the ideal tetrahedral bond angle. He predicted that cyclohexane, with bond angles of 120°, would be less stable and that as the number of sides in the cycloalkanes increases beyond six, their stability would decrease.

Contrary to what Baeyer predicted, however, cyclohexane is more stable than cyclopentane. Furthermore, cyclic compounds do not thereafter become less and less stable as the number of sides increases. The mistake Baeyer made was to assume that all cyclic molecules are planar. Because three points define a plane, the carbons of cyclopropane must lie in a plane. The other cycloalkanes, however, are not planar but twist and bend in order to attain a structure that maximizes their stability by minimizing ring strain and the number of eclipsed hydrogens. Therefore, instead of being planar as in the hypothetical example described on page 101, the cyclobutane molecule is bent, with one of its methylene groups extending at an angle of about 25° from the plane defined by the other three carbons.

If the cyclopentane ring were planar, as Baeyer had predicted, it would have essentially no angle strain, but it would have 10 pairs of eclipsed hydrogens. So cyclopentane puckers, allowing some of the hydrogens to become nearly staggered but, in the process, the molecule acquires some angle strain. The puckered form of cyclopentane is called the *envelope conformation*, because the shape of the ring resembles a squarish envelope with the flap up.

cyclobutane

Von Baeyer and Barbituric Acid

Johann Friedrich Wilhelm Adolf von Baeyer (1835–1917), a German chemist, was a professor of chemistry at the University of Strasbourg and later at the University of Munich. In 1864, he discovered barbituric acid—the first of a group of sedatives known as barbiturates—and named it after a woman named Barbara. Who Barbara was is not certain. Some say she was his girlfriend, but because Baeyer discovered barbituric acid in the same year that Prussia defeated Denmark, some believe he named it after Saint Barbara, the patron saint of artillerymen. Baeyer is also known as the first to synthesize indigo, the dye used in the manufacture of blue jeans. He received the Nobel Prize in Chemistry in 1905 for his work in synthetic organic chemistry.

PROBLEM 38♦

The effectiveness of a barbiturate as a sedative is related to its ability to penetrate the nonpolar membrane of a cell. Which of the following barbiturates would you expect to be the more effective sedative?

hexethal   barbital

cyclopentane

2.12 CONFORMERS OF CYCLOHEXANE

The cyclic compounds most commonly found in nature contain six-membered rings because carbon rings of that size can exist in a conformation—called a *chair conformer*—that is almost completely free of strain. All the bond angles in a **chair conformer** are 111°, which is very close to the ideal tetrahedral bond angle of 109.5°, and all the adjacent bonds are staggered (Figure 2.7).

chair conformer of
cyclohexane

Newman projection of
the chair conformer

ball-and-stick model of
the chair conformer

◀ **Figure 2.7**
The chair conformer of cyclohexane,
a Newman projection of the chair
conformer showing that all the
bonds are staggered, and a ball-and-
stick model.

The chair conformer is such an important conformer that you should learn how to draw it:

1. Draw two parallel lines of the same length, slanted upward and beginning at the same height.

2. Connect the tops of the lines with a V whose left side is slightly longer than its right side. Connect the bottoms of the lines with an inverted V. (The bottom-left and top-right lines should be parallel; and the top-left and bottom-right lines should be parallel.) This completes the framework of the six-membered ring.

3. Each carbon has an axial bond and an equatorial bond. The **axial bonds** (red lines) are vertical and alternate above and below the ring. The axial bond on one of the uppermost carbons is up, the next is down, the next is up, and so on.

4. The **equatorial bonds** (red lines with blue balls) point outward from the ring. Because the bond angles are greater than 90°, the equatorial bonds are on a slant. If the axial bond points up, the equatorial bond on the same carbon is on a downward slant. If the axial bond points down, the equatorial bond on the same carbon is on an upward slant.

Notice that each equatorial bond is parallel to two ring bonds (two carbons over).

Remember that in this depiction cyclohexane is viewed edge-on. The lower bonds of the ring are in front and the upper bonds of the ring are in back.

▲ = axial bond
● = equatorial bond

PROBLEM 39

Draw 1,2,3,4,5,6-hexachlorocyclohexane with

a. all the chloro groups in axial positions.
b. all the hexachloro groups in equatorial positions.

PROBLEM-SOLVING STRATEGY

Calculating the Strain Energy of a Cycloalkane

If we assume that cyclohexane is completely free of strain, we can use the **heat of formation**—the heat given off when a compound is formed from its elements under standard conditions—to calculate the total strain energy of the other cycloalkanes. Taking the heat of formation of cyclohexane (Table 2.9) and dividing by 6 for its six CH_2 groups gives us a value of -4.92 kcal/mol for a "strainless" CH_2 group ($-29.5/6 = -4.92$). With this value, we can calculate the heat of formation of any other "strainless" cycloalkane: we simply multiply the number of CH_2 groups in its ring by -4.92 kcal/mol. The total strain in the compound is the difference between its "strainless" heat of formation and its actual heat of formation (Table 2.9). For example, cyclopentane has a "strainless" heat of formation of $(5)(-4.92) = -24.6$ kcal/mol and an actual heat of formation of -18.4 kcal/mol. Therefore, cyclopentane has a total strain energy of 6.2 kcal/mol, because $[-18.4 - (-24.6) = 6.2]$. Dividing the total strain energy by the number of CH_2 groups in the cyclic compound gives the strain energy per CH_2 group.

Now continue on to Problem 40.

PROBLEM 40♦

Calculate the total strain energy of cycloheptane.

Table 2.9 Heats Formation and Strain Energies of Cyloalkanes

	Heat of formation (kcal/mol)	"Strainless" heat of formation (kcal/mol)	Total Strain energy (kcal/mol)	Strain energy per CH_2 group (kcal/mol)
cyclopropane	+12.7	-14.6	27.3	9.1
cyclobutane	+6.8	-19.7	26.5	6.6
cyclopentane	-18.4	-24.6	6.2	1.2
cyclohexane	-29.5	-29.5	0	0
cycloheptane	-28.2	-34.4	6.2	0.9
cyclooctane	-29.7	-39.4	9.7	1.2
cyclononane	-31.7	-44.3	12.6	1.4
cyclodecane	-36.9	-49.2	12.3	1.2
cycloundecane	-42.9	-54.1	11.2	1.0

Bonds that are equatorial in one chair conformer are axial in the other chair conformer.

Cyclohexane rapidly interconverts between two stable chair conformers because of the ease of rotation about its C—C bonds. This interconversion is called **ring flip** (Figure 2.8). When the two chair conformers interconvert, bonds that are equatorial in one chair conformer become axial in the other chair conformer and vice versa.

▶ **Figure 2.8**
The bonds that are axial in one chair conformer are equatorial in the other chair conformer. The bonds that are equatorial in one chair conformer are axial in the other chair conformer.

pull this carbon down

push this carbon up

ring flip

Cyclohexane can also exist as a **boat conformer**, shown in Figure 2.9. Like the chair conformer, the boat conformer is free of angle strain. However, the boat conformer is not as stable because some of the bonds are eclipsed. The boat conformer is further destabilized by the close proximity of the **flagpole hydrogens**—the hydrogens at the "bow" and "stern" of the boat—which causes steric strain.

boat conformer of cyclohexane	**Newman projection of the boat conformer**	**ball-and-stick model of the boat conformer**

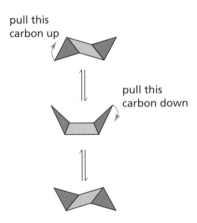

◀ **Figure 2.9**
The boat conformer of cyclohexane, a Newman projection of the boat conformer showing that some of the bonds are eclipsed, and a ball-and-stick model.

The conformers that cyclohexane assumes when interconverting from one chair conformer to the other are shown in Figure 2.10. To convert from the boat conformer to a chair conformer, one of the two topmost carbons of the boat conformer must be pulled down so that it becomes the bottommost carbon of the chair conformer. When the carbon is pulled down just a little, the **twist-boat** (or **skew-boat**) **conformer** is obtained. The twist-boat conformer is more stable than the boat conformer because the flagpole hydrogens have moved away from each other, thus relieving some steric strain. When the carbon is pulled down to the point where it is in the same plane as the sides of the boat, the very unstable **half-chair conformer** is obtained. Pulling the carbon down farther produces the *chair conformer*. The graph in Figure 2.10 shows the energy of a cyclohexane molecule as it interconverts from one chair conformer to the other; the energy barrier for interconversion is 12.1 kcal/mol (50.6 kJ/mol). From this value, it can be calculated that cyclohexane undergoes 10^5 ring flips per second at room temperature. In other words, the two chair conformers are in rapid equilibrium.

pull this carbon up

pull this carbon down

Build a model of cyclohexane. Convert it from one chair conformer to the other by pulling the topmost carbon down and pushing the bottommost carbon up.

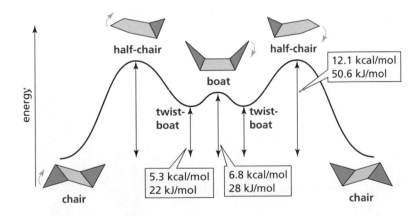

half-chair	boat	half-chair
	12.1 kcal/mol 50.6 kJ/mol	
	twist- boat	twist- boat
	5.3 kcal/mol 22 kJ/mol	6.8 kcal/mol 28 kJ/mol
chair		chair

energy

◀ **Figure 2.10**
The conformers of cyclohexane— and their relative energies—as one chair conformer interconverts to the other chair conformer.

The chair conformers are the most stable of cyclohexane's conformers, so at any instant more molecules of cyclohexane are in a chair conformation than in any other conformation. For every 10,000 molecules of cyclohexane in a chair conformation, there is no more than one molecule in the next most stable conformation, the twist-boat.

Go to the website to see three-dimensional representations of the conformers of cyclohexane.

2.13 CONFORMERS OF MONOSUBSTITUTED CYCLOHEXANES

Unlike cyclohexane, which has two equivalent chair conformers, the two chair conformers of a monosubstituted cyclohexane, such as methylcyclohexane, are not equivalent. The methyl substituent is in an equatorial position in one conformer and in an axial position in the other (Figure 2.11), because as we have just seen, substituents that are equatorial in one chair conformer are axial in the other (Figure 2.8).

▶ Figure 2.11
A substituent is in an equatorial position in one chair conformer and in an axial position in the other. The conformer with the substituent in the equatorial position is more stable.

The chair conformer with the methyl substituent in an equatorial position is the more stable of the two conformers because a substituent has more room and, therefore, fewer steric interactions when it is in an equatorial position. This can be best understood from a drawing like that in Figure 2.12a, which shows that when the methyl group is in an equatorial position, it extends into space, away from the rest of the molecule.

▶ Figure 2.12
  a. An equatorial substituent
  b. An axial substituent

In contrast, because the three axial bonds on the same side of the ring are parallel to each other, any axial substituent will be relatively close to the axial substituents on the other two carbons (Figure 2.12b).

Because the interacting hydrogens or substituents are in 1,3-positions relative to each other, these unfavorable steric interactions are called **1,3-diaxial interactions**. If you take a few minutes to build models, you will see that a substituent has more room if it is in an equatorial position than if it is in an axial position.

A gauche conformer of butane and the axially substituted conformer of methylcyclohexane are compared in Figure 2.13. Notice that the gauche interaction in butane is the same as a 1,3-diaxial interaction in methylcyclohexane. Butane has one gauche interaction and methylcyclohexane has two 1,3-diaxial interactions.

▶ Figure 2.13
The steric strain of gauche butane is the same as the steric strain between an axial methyl group of methylcyclohexane and one of its axial hydrogens. Butane has one gauche interaction between a methyl group and a hydrogen; methylcyclohexane has two.

gauche butane

**axial
methylcyclohexane**

In Section 2.10, we saw that the gauche interaction between the methyl groups of butane caused a gauche conformer to be 0.87 kcal/mol (3.6 kJ/mol) less stable than the anti conformer. Because there are two such gauche interactions in the chair conformer of methylcyclohexane when the methyl group is in an axial position, this conformer is 1.74 kcal/mol (7.2 kJ/mol) less stable than the chair conformer with the methyl group in the equatorial position.

Because of the difference in stability of the two chair conformers, a sample of methyl-cyclohexane or any other substituted cycloalkane will at any point in time contain more chair conformers with the substituent in the equatorial position than with the substituent in the axial position. The relative amounts of the two chair conformers depend on the substituent (Table 2.10).

Table 2.10 Equilibrium Constants for Several Monosubstituted Cyclohexanes at 25 °C

Substituent	Axial $\overset{K_{eq}}{\rightleftharpoons}$ Equatorial	Substituent	Axial $\overset{K_{eq}}{\rightleftharpoons}$ Equatorial
H	1	CN	1.4
CH_3	18	F	1.5
CH_3CH_2	21	Cl	2.4
$\underset{CH_3CH}{\overset{CH_3}{\mid}}$	35	Br	2.2
		I	2.2
$\underset{\overset{\mid}{CH_3}}{\overset{CH_3}{\mid}} CH_3C$	4800	HO	5.4

The substituent with the greater bulk in the vicinity of the 1,3-diaxial hydrogens will have a greater preference for the equatorial position because it will have stronger 1,3-diaxial interactions. For example, the experimental equilibrium constant (K_{eq}) for the conformers of methylcyclohexane (Table 2.10) indicates that 95% of methylcyclohexane molecules have the methyl group in the equatorial position at 25 °C:

$$K_{eq} = \frac{\left[\text{equatorial conformer} \right]}{\left[\text{axial conformer} \right]} = \frac{18}{1}$$

$$\% \text{ of equatorial conformer} = \frac{\left[\text{equatorial conformer} \right]}{\left[\text{equatorial conformer} \right] + \left[\text{axial conformer} \right]} \times 100$$

$$\% \text{ of equatorial conformer} = \frac{18}{18 + 1} \times 100 = 95\%$$

In *tert*-butylcyclohexane, where the 1,3-diaxial interactions are even more destabilizing because a *tert*-butyl group is larger than a methyl group, more than 99.9% of the molecules have the *tert*-butyl group in the equatorial position.

> The larger the substituent on a cyclohexane ring, the more the equatorial-substituted conformer will be favored.

PROBLEM 41♦

The chair conformer of fluorocyclohexane is 0.25 kcal/mol more stable when the fluoro substituent is in the equatorial position than when it is in the axial position. How much more stable is 1-fluoropropane when it is in the anti conformation than when it is in a gauche conformation?

PROBLEM 42 ◆

From the data in Table 2.10, calculate the percentage of molecules of cyclohexanol that have the OH group in the equatorial position at 25 °C.

2.14 CONFORMERS OF DISUBSTITUTED CYCLOHEXANES

If a cyclohexane ring has two substituents, we must take both substituents into account when predicting which of the two chair conformers is more stable. Let's use 1,4-dimethylcyclohexane as an example. First of all, note that there are two different dimethylcyclohexanes. One has both methyl substituents on the *same side* of the cyclohexane ring (both point downward); it is called the **cis isomer** (*cis* is Latin for "on this side"). The other has the two methyl substituents on *opposite sides* of the ring (one points upward and one points downward); it is called the **trans isomer** (*trans* is Latin for "across").

The cis isomer of a disubstituted cyclic compound has its substituents on the same side of the ring.

The trans isomer of a disubstituted cyclic compound has its substituents on opposite sides of the ring.

the two methyl groups are on the *same* side of the ring

cis-1,4-dimethylcyclohexane

the two methyl groups are on *opposite* sides of the ring

trans-1,4-dimethylcyclohexane

cis-1,4-Dimethylcyclohexane and *trans*-1,4-dimethylcyclohexane are examples of **cis–trans isomers** or **geometric isomers**; **cis–trans isomers** are compounds containing the same atoms, and the atoms are linked in the same order, but the atoms exhibit two different spatial arrangements. The cis and trans isomers are different compounds with different melting and boiling points. They can, therefore, be separated from one another.

PROBLEM-SOLVING STRATEGY

Differentiating Cis–Trans Isomers

Is the conformer of 1,2-dimethylcyclohexane with one methyl group in an equatorial position and the other in an axial position the cis isomer or the trans isomer?

Is this the cis isomer or the trans isomer?

To solve this kind of problem we need to determine whether the two substituents are on the same side of the ring (cis) or on opposite sides of the ring (trans). If the bonds bearing the substituents are both pointing upward or both pointing downward, the compound is the cis isomer; if one bond is pointing upward and the other downward, the compound is the trans isomer. Because the conformer in question has both methyl groups attached to downward-pointing bonds, it is the cis isomer.

the cis isomer   the trans isomer

The isomer that is the most misleading when drawn in two dimensions is a *trans*-1,2-disubstituted isomer. At first glance, the methyl groups of *trans*-1,2-dimethylcyclohexane (on the right, above) appear to be oriented in the same direction, so you might think the compound is the cis isomer. Closer inspection shows, however, that one bond points upward and the other downward, so we know that it is the trans isomer. Alternatively, if you look at the two axial hydrogens, they are clearly trans (one points straight up and the other straight down), so the methyl groups must also be trans.

Now continue on to Problem 43.

PROBLEM 43 ◆

Determine whether each of the following is a cis isomer or a trans isomer:

a.

b.

c.

d.

e.

f.

Every compound with a cyclohexane ring has two chair conformers; thus, both the cis and the trans isomers of disubstituted cyclohexanes have two chair conformers. Let's compare the structures of the two chair conformers of *cis*-1,4-dimethylcyclohexane to see if we can predict any difference in their stabilities.

cis-1,4-dimethylcyclohexane

The conformer shown on the left has one methyl group in an equatorial position and one methyl group in an axial position. The conformer shown on the right also has one methyl group in an equatorial position and one methyl group in an axial position. Therefore, both chair conformers are equally stable.

In contrast, the two chair conformers of *trans*-1,4-dimethylcyclohexane have different stabilities because one has both methyl substituents in equatorial positions and the other has both methyl groups in axial positions. The conformer with both substituents in equatorial positions is more stable.

trans-1,4-dimethylcyclohexane

The chair conformer with both substituents in axial positions has four 1,3-diaxial interactions, causing it to be about 4×0.87 kcal/mol $= 3.5$ kcal/mol (or 14.6 kJ/mol) less stable than the chair conformer with both methyl groups in equatorial positions. We can, therefore, predict that *trans*-1,4-dimethylcyclohexane will exist almost entirely in the chair conformer with both substituents in equatorial positions.

this chair conformer has four 1,3-diaxial interactions

Now let's look at the geometric isomers of 1-*tert*-butyl-3-methylcyclohexane. Both substituents of the cis isomer are in equatorial positions in one conformer and in axial positions in the other conformer. The conformer with both substituents in equatorial positions is more stable.

cis-1-*tert*-butyl-3-methylcyclohexane

Both conformers of the trans isomer have one substituent in an equatorial position and the other in an axial position. Because the *tert*-butyl group is larger than the methyl group, the 1,3-diaxial interactions will be stronger when the *tert*-butyl group is in the axial position. Therefore, the conformer with the *tert*-butyl group in the equatorial position is more stable.

more stable   **less stable**

trans-1-*tert*-butyl-3-methylcyclohexane

PROBLEM 44 ◆

Which will have a higher percentage of the diequatorial-substituted conformer compared with the diaxial-substituted conformer: *trans*-1,4-dimethylcyclohexane or *cis*-1-*tert*-butyl-3-methylcyclohexane?

PROBLEM 45   SOLVED

a. Draw the more stable chair conformer of *cis*-1-ethyl-2-methylcyclohexane.
b. Draw the more stable conformer of *trans*-1-ethyl-2-methylcyclohexane.
c. Which is more stable, *cis*-1-ethyl-2-methylcyclohexane or *trans*-1-ethyl-2-methylcyclohexane?

Solution to 45a   If the two substituents of a 1,2-disubstituted cyclohexane are to be on the same side of the ring, one must be in an equatorial position and the other must be in an axial position. The more stable chair conformer is the one in which the larger of the two substituents (the ethyl group) is in the equatorial position.

PROBLEM 46 ◆

For each of the following disubstituted cyclohexanes, indicate whether the substituents in the two chair conformers would be both equatorial in one chair conformer and both axial in the other *or* one equatorial and one axial in each of the chair conformers:
a. *cis*-1,2-   d. *trans*-1,3-
b. *trans*-1,2-   e. *cis*-1,4-
c. *cis*-1,3-   f. *trans*-1,4-

PROBLEM 47 ◆

a. Calculate the energy difference between the two chair conformers of *trans*-1,4-dimethylcyclohexane.
b. What is the energy difference between the two chair conformers of *cis*-1,4-dimethylcyclohexane?

2.15 FUSED CYCLOHEXANE RINGS

When two cyclohexane rings are fused together, the second ring can be considered to be a pair of substituents bonded to the first ring. As with any disubstituted cyclohexane, the two substituents can be either cis or trans. The trans isomer (in which one substituent bond points upward and the other downward) has both substituents in the equatorial position. The cis isomer has one substituent in the equatorial position and one in the axial position. **Trans-fused** rings, therefore, are more stable than **cis-fused** rings.

trans-fused rings
more stable

cis-fused rings
less stable

Michael S. Brown *and* **Joseph Leonard Goldstein** *shared the 1985 Nobel Prize in Physiology or Medicine for their work on the regulation of cholesterol metabolism and the treatment of disease caused by elevated cholesterol levels in the blood. Brown was born in New York in 1941, Goldstein in South Carolina in 1940. They are both professors of medicine at the University of Texas Southwestern Medical Center.*

Hormones are chemical messengers—organic compounds synthesized in glands and delivered by the bloodstream to target tissues in order to stimulate or inhibit some process. Many hormones are **steroids**. The four rings in steroids are designated A, B, C, and D. The B, C, and D rings are all trans fused, and in most naturally occurring steroids, the A and B rings are also trans fused.

the steroid ring system

all the rings are trans fused

The most abundant member of the steroid family in animals is **cholesterol**, the precursor of all other steroids. Cholesterol is an important component of cell membranes. Its ring structure makes it more rigid than other membrane components (Section 27.4). Cholesterol and other steroid hormones are discussed in Section 27.8.

cholesterol

Cholesterol and Heart Disease

Cholesterol is probably the best-known steroid because of the widely publicized correlation between cholesterol levels in the blood and heart disease. This compound is synthesized in the liver and is present in almost all body tissues. Cholesterol is also found in many foods, but we do not require it in our diet because the body can synthesize all we need. A diet high in cholesterol can lead to high levels of cholesterol in the bloodstream, and the excess can accumulate on the walls of arteries, restricting the flow of blood. This disease of the circulatory system is known as *atherosclerosis* and is a primary cause of heart disease. Cholesterol travels through the bloodstream packaged in particles that are classified according to their density. Low-density lipoprotein (LDL) particles transport cholesterol from the liver to other tissues. Receptors on the surfaces of cells bind LDL particles, allowing them to be brought into the cell so that it can use the cholesterol. High-density lipoprotein (HDL) is a cholesterol scavenger, removing cholesterol from the surfaces of membranes and delivering it back to the liver, where it is converted into bile acids. LDL is the so-called "bad" cholesterol, whereas HDL is the "good" cholesterol. The more cholesterol we eat, the less the body synthesizes. But this does not mean that dietary cholesterol has no effect on the total amount of cholesterol in the bloodstream, because dietary cholesterol also inhibits the synthesis of the LDL receptors. So the more cholesterol we eat, the less the body synthesizes, but also the less the body can get rid of by bringing it into target cells.

Clinical Treatment of High Cholesterol

Statins are the newest class of cholesterol-reducing drugs. Statins reduce serum cholesterol levels by inhibiting the enzyme that catalyzes the formation of a compound needed for the synthesis of cholesterol (Section 27.9). As a consequence of diminished cholesterol synthesis in the liver, the liver forms more LDL receptors—the receptors that help clear LDL (the so-called "bad" cholesterol) from the bloodstream. Studies show that for every 10% that cholesterol is reduced, deaths from coronary heart disease are reduced by 15% and total death risk is reduced by 11%.

Lovastatin and simvastatin are natural statins used clinically under the trade names Mevacor and Zocor. Atorvastatin (Lipitor), a synthetic statin, is now the most popular statin. It has greater potency and lasts longer in the body than natural statins because the products of its breakdown are as active as the parent drug in reducing cholesterol levels. Therefore, smaller doses of the drug may be administered. In addition, Lipitor is less polar than lovastatin and simvastatin, so it persists longer in liver cells, where it is needed. Lipitor has been the most widely prescribed drug in the United States for the past two years (Section 31.0).

lovastatin
Mevacor®

simvastatin
Zocor®

atorvastatin
Lipitor®

SUMMARY

Alkanes are **hydrocarbons** that contain only single bonds. Their general molecular formula is C_nH_{2n+2}. **Constitutional isomers** have the same molecular formula, but their atoms are linked differently. Alkanes are named by determining the number of carbons in their **parent hydrocarbon**—the longest continuous chain. Substituents are listed in alphabetical order, with a number to designate their position on the chain. When there is only a substituent, the substituent gets the lower of the possible numbers; when there is only a functional group suffix, the functional group suffix gets the lower of the possible numbers; when there is both a functional group suffix and a substituent, the functional group suffix gets the lower of the possible numbers. A **functional group** is a center of reactivity in a molecule.

Alkyl halides and **ethers** are named as substituted alkanes. **Alcohols** and **amines** are named using a functional group suffix. **Systematic names** can contain numbers; **common names** never do. A compound can have more than one name, but a name must specify only one compound. Whether alkyl halides or alcohols are **primary**, **secondary**, or **tertiary** depends on whether the X (halogen) or OH group is bonded to a primary, secondary, or tertiary carbon. A **primary carbon** is bonded to one carbon, a **secondary carbon** is bonded to two carbons, and a **tertiary carbon** is bonded to three carbons. Whether amines are **primary**, **secondary**, or **tertiary** depends on the number of alkyl groups bonded to the nitrogen. Compounds with four alkyl groups bonded to nitrogen are called **quaternary ammonium salts**.

The oxygen of an alcohol or an ether has the same geometry as the oxygen in water; the nitrogen of an amine has the same geometry as the nitrogen in ammonia. The greater the attractive forces between molecules—**van der Waals forces**, **dipole–dipole interactions, hydrogen bonds**—the higher is the **boiling point** of the compound. A **hydrogen bond** is an interaction between a hydrogen bonded to an O, N, or F and a lone pair of an O, N, or F in another molecule. In a series of homologs, the boiling point increases with increasing molecular weight. Branching lowers the boiling point. **Polarizability** indicates the ease with which an electron cloud can be distorted: larger atoms are more polarizable.

Polar compounds dissolve in polar solvents, and nonpolar compounds dissolve in nonpolar solvents. The interaction between a solvent and a molecule or an ion dissolved in that solvent is called **solvation**. The oxygen of an alcohol or an ether can usually drag three or four carbons into solution in water.

Rotation about a C—C bond results in two extreme **conformations**, staggered and eclipsed, that rapidly interconvert. A **staggered conformer** is more stable than an **eclipsed conformer** because of **hyperconjugation**. There can be two different staggered conformers: the **anti conformer** is more stable than a **gauche conformer** because of **steric strain**—repulsion between the electron clouds of atoms or groups. The steric strain in a gauche conformer is called a **gauche interaction**.

Five- and six-membered rings are more stable than three- and four-membered rings because of the **angle strain** that results when bond angles deviate from the ideal bond angle of 109.5°. In a process called **ring flip**, cyclohexane rapidly interconverts between two stable chair conformers. **Bonds that are axial** in one chair conformer are **equatorial** in the other and vice versa. The chair conformer with a substituent in the equatorial position is more stable, because there is more room, and hence less steric strain, in an equatorial position. A substituent in an axial position experiences unfavorable

1,3-diaxial interactions. In the case of disubstituted cyclohexanes, the more stable conformer will have its larger substituent in the equatorial position. Cis and trans isomers are called **geometric isomers** or **cis–trans isomers**. A **cis isomer** has its two substituents on the same side of the ring; a **trans isomer** has its substituents on opposite sides of the ring. Cis and trans isomers are different compounds. **Conformers** are different conformations of the same compound.

KEY TERMS

alcohol (p. 83)
alkane (p. 68)
alkyl halide (p. 81)
alkyl substituent (p. 71)
amine (p. 85)
angle strain (p. 101)
anti conformer (p. 99)
axial bond (p. 103)
banana bond (p. 101)
boat conformer (p. 105)
boiling point (bp) (p. 90)
chair conformer (p. 102)
cis fused (p. 111)
cis isomer (p. 108)
cis–trans isomers (p. 108)
common name (p. 71)
conformation (p. 97)
conformational analysis (p. 98)
conformational isomers (p. 97)
conformer (p. 97)
constitutional isomers (p. 70)
cycloalkane (p. 78)
1,3-diaxial interaction (p. 106)
dipole–dipole interaction (p. 91)
eclipsed conformer (p. 98)
equatorial bond (p. 103)
ether (p. 82)

flagpole hydrogen (p. 105)
functional group (p. 83)
gauche conformer (p. 99)
gauche interaction (p. 99)
geometric isomers (p. 108)
half-chair conformer (p. 105)
heat of formation (p. 104)
homolog (p. 68)
homologous series (p. 68)
hormones (p. 112)
hydrocarbon (p. 68)
hydrogen bond (p. 92)
hyperconjugation (p. 98)
induced-dipole–induced-dipole
    interaction (p. 91)
IUPAC nomenclature (p. 71)
melting point (mp) (p. 95)
methylene (CH_2) group (p. 68)
Newman projection (p. 97)
packing (p. 95)
parent hydrocarbon (p. 74)
polarizability (p. 93)
primary alcohol (p. 83)
primary alkyl halide (p. 81)
primary amine (p. 85)
primary carbon (p. 72)
primary hydrogen (p. 73)

quaternary ammonium salt (p. 87)
ring flip (p. 104)
secondary alcohol (p. 83)
secondary alkyl halide (p. 81)
secondary amine (p. 85)
secondary carbon (p. 72)
secondary hydrogen (p. 73)
skeletal structure (p. 78)
skew-boat conformer (p. 105)
solubility (p. 95)
solvation (p. 95)
staggered conformer (p. 98)
steric strain (p. 99)
steroids (p. 112)
straight-chain alkane (p. 68)
symmetrical ether (p. 82)
systematic nomenclature (p. 71)
tertiary alcohol (p. 83)
tertiary alkyl halide (p. 81)
tertiary amine (p. 85)
tertiary carbon (p. 72)
tertiary hydrogen (p. 73)
trans fused (p. 111)
trans isomer (p. 108)
twist-boat conformer (p. 105)
unsymmetrical ether (p. 82)
van der Waals forces (p. 91)

PROBLEMS

48. Draw a condensed structure for each of the following:
   a. *sec*-butyl *tert*-butyl ether
   b. isoheptyl alcohol
   c. *sec*-butylamine
   d. isopentyl bromide
   e. 4,5-diisopropylnonane
   f. triethylamine
   g. 4-*tert*-butylheptane
   h. 5,5-dibromo-2-methyloctane
   i. 3-ethoxy-2-methylhexane
   j. 5-(1,2-dimethylpropyl)nonane
   k. 3,4-dimethyloctane
   l. 4-(1-methylethyl)nonane

49. List the following compounds in order of decreasing boiling point. (Label the highest boiling compound #1.)

50. a. Give the systematic name for each of the following:

   1. $(CH_3)_3CCH_2CH_2CH_2CH(CH_3)_2$
   2.
   3. $CH_3CHCH_2CHCH_2CH_3$

4. $(CH_3CH_2)_4C$

5. $BrCH_2CH_2CH_2CH_2CH_2NHCH_2CH_3$

6.

7. $CH_3CH_2CHOCH_2CH_3$
     $\qquad\quad |$
     $\qquad\ CH_2CH_2CH_2CH_3$

8. $CH_3OCH_2CH_2CH_2OCH_3$

9.
CH_3
NCH_3

10.
CH_2CH_3
ethyl
2 ethyl cyclohexane
OH

C2H

11.
CH_3
Br

1 bromo 4 methylcyclohexane

2

b. Draw skeletal structures for these compounds.

51. Which of the following structures represents a cis isomer?

A   B   C   D

52. a. How many primary carbons does each of the following compounds have?

1.
CH_2CH_3
CH_2CHCH_3
CH_3

2.

b. How many secondary carbons does each one have?
c. How many tertiary carbons does each one have?

53. Which of the following conformers of isobutyl chloride is the most stable?

54. Draw the structural formula for an alkane that has
a. six carbons, all secondary
b. eight carbons and only primary hydrogens
c. seven carbons with two isopropyl groups

55. Give two names for each of the following:

a. $CH_3CH_2CHCH_3$
     $\qquad\quad |$
     $\qquad\ NH_2$

e. $CH_3CHCH_2CH_2CH_3$
     $\qquad |$
     $\qquad CH_3$

h. $CH_3CHCH_2CH_2CH_2OH$
     $\qquad |$
     $\qquad CH_3$

b. $CH_3CH_2CHCH_3$
     $\qquad\quad |$
     $\qquad\ Cl$

f. CH_3CHNH_2
     $\qquad |$
     $\qquad CH_3$

i.
Br

c. $CH_3CH_2CHNHCH_2CH_3$
     $\qquad\quad\ |$
     $\qquad\ CH_3$

g. CH_3CBr
     $\qquad\ \ CH_3$
     $\qquad\ \ |$
     $\qquad\ \ CH_2CH_3$

j.
OH

dimethyl cyclohexane

d. $CH_3CH_2CH_2OCH_2CH_3$

56. Which compound has
   a. the higher boiling point: 1-bromopentane or 1-bromohexane?
   b. the higher boiling point: pentyl chloride or isopentyl chloride?
   c. the greater solubility in water: 1-butanol or 1-pentanol?
   d. the higher boiling point: 1-hexanol or 1-methoxypentane?
   e. the higher melting point: hexane or isohexane?
   f. the higher boiling point: 1-chloropentane or 1-pentanol?
   g. the higher boiling point: 1-bromopentane or 1-chloropentane?
   h. the higher boiling point: diethyl ether or butyl alcohol?
   i. the greater density: heptane or octane?
   j. the higher boiling point: isopentyl alcohol or isopentylamine?
   k. the higher boiling point: hexylamine or dipropylamine?

57. a. Draw Newman projections of the two conformers of *cis*-1,3-dimethylcyclohexane.
   b. Which of the conformers would predominatae at equilibrium?
   c. Draw Newman projections of the two conformers of the trans isomer.
   d. Which of the conformers would predominate at equilibrium?

58. Ansaid and Motrin belong to the group of drugs known as nonsteroidal anti-inflammatory drugs (NSAIDs). Both are only slightly soluble in water, but one is a little more soluble than the other. Which of the drugs has the greater solubility in water?

Ansaid®

Motrin®

59. Draw a picture of the hydrogen bonding in methanol.

60. A student was given the structural formulas of several compounds and was asked to give them systematic names. How many did the student name correctly? Correct those that are misnamed.
   a. 4-bromo-3-pentanol
   b. 2,2-dimethyl-4-ethylheptane
   c. 5-methylcyclohexanol
   d. 1,1-dimethyl-2-cyclohexanol
   e. 5-(2,2-dimethylethyl)nonane
   f. isopentyl bromide
   g. 3,3-dichlorooctane
   h. 5-ethyl-2-methylhexane
   i. 1-bromo-4-pentanol
   j. 3-isopropyloctane
   k. 2-methyl-2-isopropylheptane
   l. 2-methyl-*N,N*-dimethyl-4-hexanamine

61. Which of the following conformers has the highest energy?

CH$_3$ CH$_3$ CH$_3$

Cl   Cl   CH$_3$ Cl

A   B   C

62. Give systematic names for all the alkanes with molecular formula C$_7$H$_{16}$ that do not have any secondary hydrogens.

63. Draw skeletal structures for the following:
   a. 5-ethyl-2-methyloctane
   b. 1,3-dimethylcyclohexane
   c. 2,3,3,4-tetramethylheptane
   d. propylcyclopentane
   e. 2-methyl-4-(1-methylethyl)octane
   f. 2,6-dimethyl-4-(2-methylpropyl)decane

64. For rotation about the C-3 — C-4 bond of 2-methylhexane:
   a. Draw the Newman projection of the most stable conformer.
   b. Draw the Newman projection of the least stable conformer.
   c. About which other carbon–carbon bonds may rotation occur?
   d. How many of the carbon–carbon bonds in the compound have staggered conformers that are all equally stable?

65. Draw all the isomers that have molecular formula C$_5$H$_{11}$Br. (*Hint:* There are eight such isomers.)
   a. Give the systematic name for each of the isomers.
   b. Give a common name for each isomer that has a common name.

c. How many isomers do not have common names?
d. How many of the isomers are primary alkyl halides?
e. How many of the isomers are secondary alkyl halides?
f. How many of the isomers are tertiary alkyl halides?

66. Give the systematic name for each of the following:

a.

f.

b.

g.

c.

h.

d.

i.

e.

j.

67. Draw the two chair conformers for each of the following, and indicate which conformer is more stable:
  a. *cis*-1-ethyl-3-methylcyclohexane
  b. *trans*-1-ethyl-2-isopropylcyclohexane
  c. *trans*-1-ethyl-2-methylcyclohexane
  d. *cis*-1,2-diethylcyclohexane
  e. *cis*-1-ethyl-3-isopropylcyclohexane
  f. *cis*-1-ethyl-4-isopropylcyclohexane

68. Why are lower molecular weight alcohols more soluble in water than higher molecular weight alcohols?

69. a. Draw a potential energy diagram for rotation about the C—C bond of 1,2-dichloroethane through 360°, starting with the least stable conformer. The anti conformer is 1.2 kcal/mol more stable than a gauche conformer. A gauche conformer has two energy barriers, 5.2 kcal/mol and 9.3 kcal/mole.
  b. Draw the conformer that would be present in greatest concentration.
  c. How much more stable is the most stable staggered conformer than the most stable eclipsed conformer?
  d. How much more stable is the most stable staggered conformer than the least stable eclipsed conformer?

70. How many ethers have molecular formula $C_5H_{12}O$? Draw their structures and give each a systematic name. What are their common names?

71. Draw the most stable conformer of the following molecule:

72. Give the systematic name for each of the following:

a. CH₃CH₂CHCH₂CH₂CHCH₃
      | |
    NHCH₃   CH₃
            CH₃

b. CH₃CH₂CHCH₂CHCH₂CH₃
         |
    CH₃CHCH₃
    CH₂CH₃

c. CH₃CHCHCH₂Cl
      |
     Cl

d. CH₃CH₂CHCH₃
    CH₃CHCH₃

e.

f.

73. Calculate the energy difference between the two chair conformers of *trans*-1,2-dimethylcyclohexane.

74. The most stable form of glucose (blood sugar) is a six-membered ring in a chair conformation with its five substituents all in equatorial positions. Draw the most stable conformer of glucose by putting the OH groups on the appropriate bonds in the structure on the right.

CH₂OH

HO

HO   OH

OH

glucose

CH₂OH

75. Give the systematic name for each of the following:

a. CH₃CHCH₂CHCH₂CH₃
    CH₃   OH

b.

Br

c. CH₃CHCHCH₂CH₃
    CH₃
    OH

d. CH₃CHCH₂CH₂CHCH₂CH₂CH₃
    CH₃   Br

e. OH ... OH

f. OH ... Br

g. HO

h. Br

76. Explain the following facts:
a. 1-Hexanol has a higher boiling point than 3-hexanol.
b. Diethyl ether has very limited solubility in water, but tetrahydrofuran is completely soluble.

tetrahydrofuran

77. One of the chair conformers of *cis*-1,3-dimethylcyclohexane has been found to be 5.4 kcal/mol (or 23 kJ/mol) less stable than the other. How much steric strain does a 1,3-diaxial interaction between two methyl groups introduce into the conformer?

78. Bromine is a larger atom than chlorine, but the equilibrium constants in Table 2.10 indicate that a chloro substituent has a greater preference for the equatorial position than a bromo substituent does. Suggest an explanation for this fact.

79. Name the following:

a.

b.

c.

80. Calculate the amount of steric strain in each of the chair conformers of 1,1,3-trimethylcyclohexane. Which conformer would predominate at equilibrium?

81. Using the data obtained in Problem 73, calculate the percentage of molecules of *trans*-1,2-dimethylcyclohexane that will have both methyl groups in equatorial positions.

Electrophilic Addition Reactions, Stereochemistry, and Electron Delocalization

The reactions of organic compounds can be divided into three main types: **addition reactions, substitution reactions**, and **elimination reactions**. The particular type of reaction a compound undergoes depends on the functional group in the compound. **Part 2** discusses the reactions of compounds that have carbon–carbon double bonds and carbon–carbon triple bonds. We will see that these compounds undergo addition reactions, or, more precisely, **electrophilic addition reactions**. **Part 2** also examines two topics that can be important when determining the outcome of a reaction. The first of these is stereochemistry, and the second is electron delocalization.

CHAPTER 3
Alkenes: Structure, Nomenclature, and an Introduction to Reactivity • Thermodynamics and Kinetics

Chapter 3 begins with a look at the structure, nomenclature, and stability of alkenes—*compounds that contain carbon–carbon double bonds*—and then introduces some fundamental principles that govern the reactions of organic compounds. You will learn how to draw curved arrows to show how electrons move during the course of a reaction as new covalent bonds are formed and existing covalent bonds are broken. This chapter also discusses the principles of thermodynamics and kinetics, which are central to an understanding of how and why organic reactions take place.

CHAPTER 4
The Reactions of Alkenes

Organic compounds can be divided into families, and fortunately, all members of a family react in the same way. In **Chapter 4**, you will learn how the family of compounds known as alkenes reacts and what kinds of products are formed from the reactions. Although many different reactions are covered, you will see that they all take place by a similar pathway.

CHAPTER 5
Stereochemistry: The Arrangement of Atoms in Space; The Stereochemistry of Addition Reactions

Chapter 5 is all about stereochemistry. After learning about the different kinds of isomers that are possible for organic compounds, you will revisit the reactions that you learned in

Chapter 4 to see whether the products of these reactions can exist as isomers and, if so, which isomers are formed.

CHAPTER 6
The Reactions of Alkynes • An Introduction to Multistep Synthesis

Chapter 6 covers the reactions of alkynes—*compounds that contain carbon–carbon triple bonds*. Because alkenes and alkynes both have reactive carbon–carbon π bonds, you will discover that their reactions have many similarities. This chapter will also introduce you to some of the techniques chemists use to design syntheses of organic compounds, and you will then have your first opportunity to design a multistep synthesis.

CHAPTER 7
Delocalized Electrons and Their Effect on Stability, Reactivity, and pK_a • More about Molecular Orbital Theory

In **Chapter 7**, you will learn more about delocalized electrons, which were introduced in Chapter 1. You will see how they influence some of the chemical properties with which you are already familiar—acidity, the stability of carbocations, and the reactions of alkenes. At this point we will turn to the reactions of dienes, compounds *that have two carbon–carbon double bonds*. You will see that if the two double bonds in a diene are sufficiently separated, the reactions of a diene are identical to the reactions of an alkene (Chapter 4). However, if the double bonds are separated by only one single bond, electron delocalization affects the nature of the products obtained from the reactions of a diene.

3

Alkenes

Structure, Nomenclature, and an Introduction to Reactivity
• Thermodynamics and Kinetics

E isomer
of 2-butene

Z isomer
of 2-butene

Tomatoes are shipped green so they will arrive unspoiled. Ripening can be started by exposure to ethene.

IN CHAPTER 2, WE SAW THAT ALKANES ARE HYDROCARBONS THAT CONTAIN ONLY CARBON–carbon *single* bonds. Hydrocarbons that contain a carbon–carbon *double* bond are called **alkenes**. Early chemists noted that an oily substance was formed when ethene ($H_2C = CH_2$), the smallest alkene, reacted with chlorine. On the basis of this observation, alkenes were originally called *olefins* ("oil forming").

Alkenes play many important roles in biology. Ethene, for example, is a plant hormone—a compound that controls growth and other changes in the plant's tissues. Among other things, ethene affects seed germination, flower maturation, and fruit ripening. Many of the flavors and fragrances produced by plants also belong to the alkene family.

citronellol
in rose and
geranium oils

limonene
in lemon and
orange oils

β-phellandrene
oil of eucalyptus

We will begin our study of alkenes by looking at their structures and how they are named. Then we will examine a reaction of an alkene, paying close attention to the steps by which it occurs and the energy changes that accompany them. You will see that some of the discussion in the chapter revolves around concepts with which you are already familiar, while some of the information is new and will broaden the foundation of knowledge that you will be building on in subsequent chapters.

Pheromones

Insects communicate by releasing pheromones—chemical substances that other insects of the same species detect with their antennae. Many of the sex, alarm, and trail pheromones are alkenes. Interfering with an insect's ability to send or receive chemical signals is an environmentally safe way to control insect populations. For example, traps containing synthetic sex attractants have been used to capture such crop-destroying insects as the gypsy moth and the boll weevil.

muscalure
sex attractant of the housefly

sex attractant of
the gypsy moth

3.1 MOLECULAR FORMULAS AND THE DEGREE OF UNSATURATION

We have seen that the general molecular formula for a noncyclic alkane is C_nH_{2n+2} (Section 2.0). We have also seen that the general molecular formula for a cyclic alkane is C_nH_{2n} because the cyclic structure reduces the number of hydrogens by two (Section 2.2). Noncyclic compounds are also called **acyclic** compounds (the prefix "*a*" is Greek for "non" or "not").

The general molecular formula for an *acyclic alkene* is also C_nH_{2n} because, as a result of the double bond, an alkene has two fewer hydrogens than an alkane with the same number of carbons. Thus, the general molecular formula for a *cyclic alkene* must be C_nH_{2n-2}.

$CH_3CH_2CH_2CH_2CH_3$
an alkane
C_5H_{12}
C_nH_{2n+2}

$CH_3CH_2CH_2CH{=}CH_2$
an alkene
C_5H_{10}
C_nH_{2n}

a cyclic alkane
C_5H_{10}
C_nH_{2n}

a cyclic alkene
C_5H_8
C_nH_{2n-2}

We can therefore make the following statement: *the general molecular formula for a hydrocarbon is C_nH_{2n+2} minus two hydrogens for every π bond or ring in the molecule.* The total number of π bonds and rings in an alkene is called the alkene's **degree of unsaturation**. Thus, C_8H_{14}, which is missing four hydrogens from C_nH_{2n+2}, has two degrees of unsaturation. In other words, the sum of its π bonds and rings is two.

several compounds with molecular formula C_8H_{14}

$CH_3CH{=}CH(CH_2)_3CH{=}CH_2$

CH_2CH_3

$CH_3(CH_2)_5C{\equiv}CH$

A

B

C

D

> The general molecular formula for a hydrocarbon is C_nH_{2n+2} minus two hydrogens for every π bond or ring present in the molecule.

Because alkanes contain the maximum number of C—H bonds possible—that is, they are saturated with hydrogen—they are called **saturated hydrocarbons**. In contrast, alkenes are called **unsaturated hydrocarbons** because they have fewer than the maximum number of hydrogens.

$CH_3CH_2CH_2CH_3$
a saturated hydrocarbon

$CH_3CH{=}CHCH_3$
an unsaturated hydrocarbon

PROBLEM 1♦ SOLVED

Determine the molecular formula for each of the following:

a. a 5-carbon hydrocarbon with one π bond and one ring.
b. a 4-carbon hydrocarbon with two π bonds and no rings.
c. a 10-carbon hydrocarbon with one π bond and two rings.

Solution to 1a For a 5-carbon hydrocarbon with no π bonds and no rings, $C_nH_{2n+2} = C_5H_{12}$. A 5-carbon hydrocarbon with one π bond and one ring has four fewer hydrogens, because two hydrogens are subtracted for every π bond or ring in the molecule. The molecular formula is therefore C_5H_8.

PROBLEM 2♦ SOLVED

Determine the degree of unsaturation for hydrocarbons with the following molecular formulas:

a. $C_{10}H_{16}$ **b.** $C_{20}H_{34}$ **c.** C_8H_{16} **d.** $C_{12}H_{20}$ **e.** $C_{40}H_{56}$

Solution to 2a For a 10-carbon hydrocarbon with no π bonds and no rings, $C_nH_{2n+2} = C_{10}H_{22}$. A 10-carbon compound with molecular formula $C_{10}H_{16}$ has six fewer hydrogens. The degree of unsaturation is therefore $6/2 = 3$.

PROBLEM 3

Determine the degree of unsaturation, and then draw possible structures, for compounds with the following molecular formulas:

a. C_3H_6 **b.** C_3H_4 **c.** C_4H_6

3.2 THE NOMENCLATURE OF ALKENES

We have seen that the IUPAC system uses a suffix to denote certain functional groups (Sections 2.6 and 2.7). The double bond is the functional group of an alkene, and its presence is denoted by the suffix "ene." Therefore, the systematic (IUPAC) name of an alkene is obtained by replacing the "ane" ending of the corresponding alkane with "ene." For example, a two-carbon alkene is called ethene, and a three-carbon alkene is called propene. Ethene also is frequently called by its common name: ethylene.

	$H_2C{=}CH_2$	$CH_3CH{=}CH_2$	cyclopentene	cyclohexene
systematic name:	ethene	propene		
common name:	ethylene	propylene		

Most alkene names need a number to indicate the position of the double bond. (The four names above do not because there is no ambiguity.) The IUPAC rules you learned in Chapter 2 apply to alkenes as well:

Number the longest continuous chain containing the functional group in the direction that gives the functional group suffix the lowest possible number.

1. The longest continuous chain containing the functional group (in this case, the carbon–carbon double bond) is numbered in a direction that gives the functional group suffix the lowest possible number. For example, 1-butene signifies that the double bond is between the first and second carbons of butene; 2-hexene signifies that the double bond is between the second and third carbons of hexene.

$$\overset{4}{C}H_3\overset{3}{C}H_2\overset{2}{C}H{=}\overset{1}{C}H_2$$
1-butene

$$\overset{1}{C}H_3\overset{2}{C}H{=}\overset{3}{C}H\overset{4}{C}H_3$$
2-butene

$$\overset{1}{C}H_3\overset{2}{C}H{=}\overset{3}{C}H\overset{4}{C}H_2\overset{5}{C}H_2\overset{6}{C}H_3$$
2-hexene

$$\overset{6}{C}H_3\overset{5}{C}H_2\overset{4}{C}H_2\overset{3}{C}H_2\overset{2}{C}CH_2CH_2CH_3$$
$$\underset{1\ CH_2}{\|}$$
2-propyl-1-hexene

the longest continuous chain has eight carbons but the longest continuous chain containing the functional group has six carbons, so the parent name of the compound is hexene

Notice that 1-butene does not have a common name. You might be tempted to call it "butylene," which is analogous to "propylene" for propene, but butylene is not an appropriate name. A name must be unambiguous, and "butylene" could signify either 1-butene or 2-butene.

2. For a compound with two double bonds, the suffix is "diene."

$$\overset{1}{C}H_3\overset{2}{C}H=\overset{3}{C}H-\overset{4}{C}H=\overset{5}{C}H\overset{6}{C}H_2\overset{7}{C}H_3$$
2,4-heptadiene

$$\overset{5}{C}H_3\overset{4}{C}H=\overset{3}{C}H-\overset{2}{C}H=\overset{1}{C}H_2$$
1,3-pentadiene

1,4-pentadiene

3. The name of a substituent is stated before the name of the longest continuous chain that contains the functional group, together with a number to designate the carbon to which the substituent is attached. Notice that *if a compound's name contains both a functional group suffix and a substituent, the functional group suffix gets the lowest possible number.*

> When there are both a functional group suffix and a substituent, the functional group suffix gets the lowest possible number.

$$\overset{1}{C}H_3\overset{2}{C}H=\overset{3}{C}H\overset{4}{\underset{|}{C}}H\overset{5}{C}H_3$$
$$\underset{CH_3}{}$$
4-methyl-2-pentene

$$\overset{2}{C}H_2\overset{1}{C}H_3$$
$$\overset{3}{C}H_3\overset{|}{C}=\overset{4}{C}H\overset{5}{C}H_2\overset{6}{C}H_2\overset{7}{C}H_3$$
3-methyl-3-heptene

4-pentoxy-1-butene

4-methyl-1,3-pentadiene

4. If a chain has more than one substituent, the substituents are stated in alphabetical order, using the same rules for alphabetizing discussed in Section 2.2. Then the appropriate number is assigned to each substituent.

> Substituents are stated in alphabetical order.

$$\underset{1}{C}H_3\underset{2}{C}H_2\underset{3}{\overset{CH_3}{\underset{|}{C}}}=\underset{4}{C}H\underset{5}{C}H_2\underset{6}{\overset{CH_3}{\underset{|}{C}}}H\underset{7}{C}H_2\underset{8}{C}H_3$$
3,6-dimethyl-3-octene

5-bromo-4-chloro-1-heptene

5. If counting in either direction results in the same number for the alkene functional group suffix, the correct name is the one containing the lowest substituent number. For example, 2,5-dimethyl-4-octene is a 4-octene whether the longest continuous chain is numbered from left to right or from right to left. If you number from left to right, the substituents are at positions 4 and 7, but if you number from right to left, they are at positions 2 and 5. Of those four substituent numbers, 2 is the lowest, so the compound is named 2,5-dimethyl-4-octene, *not* 4,7-dimethyl-4-octene.

> A substituent receives the lowest possible number only if there is no functional group suffix or if the same number for the functional group suffix is obtained in both directions.

$$CH_3CH_2CH_2C=CHCH_2CHCH_3$$
$$\underset{CH_3}{|}\qquad\underset{CH_3}{|}$$
2,5-dimethyl-4-octene
not
4,7-dimethyl-4-octene
because 2 < 4

$$CH_3CHCH=CCH_2CH_3$$
$$\underset{Br}{|}\qquad\underset{CH_3}{|}$$
2-bromo-4-methyl-3-hexene
not
5-bromo-3-methyl-3-hexene
because 2 < 3

6. A number is not needed to denote the position of the double bond in a cyclic alkene because the ring is always numbered so that the double bond is between carbons 1 and 2. To assign numbers to any substituents, count around the ring in the direction (clockwise or counterclockwise) that puts the lowest number into the name.

3-ethylcyclopentene

4,5-dimethylcyclohexene

4-ethyl-3-methylcyclohexene

For example, 1,6-dichlorocyclohexene is *not* called 2,3-dichlorocyclohexene because 1,6-dichlorocyclohexene has the lowest substituent number (1), even though it does not have the lowest sum of substituent numbers (1 + 6 = 7 versus 2 + 3 = 5).

1,6-dichlorocyclohexene
not
2,3-dichlorocyclohexene
because 1 < 2

5-ethyl-1-methylcyclohexene
not
4-ethyl-2-methylcyclohexene
because 1 < 2

7. If counting in either direction leads to the same number for the alkene functional group suffix and the same lowest number or numbers for one or more of the substituents, then ignore those substituents and choose the direction that gives the lowest number to one of the remaining substituents.

$$CH_3CHCH_2CH = CCH_2CHCH_3$$
$$\quad | \qquad\qquad\qquad | $$
$$\quad CH_3 \qquad\qquad CH_2CH_3$$

2-bromo-4-ethyl-7-methyl-4-octene
not
7-bromo-5-ethyl-2-methyl-4-octene
because 4 < 5

6-bromo-3-chloro-4-methylcyclohexene
not
3-bromo-6-chloro-5-methylcyclohexene
because 4 < 5

The sp^2 carbons of an alkene are called **vinylic carbons**. An sp^3 carbon that is adjacent to a vinylic carbon is called an **allylic carbon**.

vinylic carbons

$$RCH_2-CH=CH-CH_2R$$

allylic carbons

Two groups containing a carbon–carbon double bond are used in common names—the **vinyl group** and the **allyl group**. The vinyl group is the smallest possible group containing a vinylic carbon; the allyl group is the smallest possible group containing an allylic carbon. When "vinyl" or "allyl" is used in a name, the substituent must be attached to the vinylic or allylic carbon, respectively. A hydrogen bonded to a vinylic carbon is called a **vinylic hydrogen**; a hydrogen bonded to an allylic carbon is called an **allylic hydrogen**.

$$CH_2=CH-$$
the vinyl group

$$CH_2=CHCH_2-$$
the allyl group

$$CH_2=CHCl$$
$$CH_2=CHCH_2Br$$

systematic name: chloroethene   3-bromopropene
common name: vinyl chloride   allyl bromide

Notice how the groups shown below can be used as substituent names in systematic nomenclature.

| a vinyl group | an allyl group | a methylene group | a chloromethyl group |

vinylcyclohexane   **allylcyclohexane**   **methylenecyclohexane**   **chloromethylcyclohexane**

PROBLEM 4◆

Draw the structure for each of the following:
a. 3,3-dimethylcyclopentene
b. 6-bromo-2,3-dimethyl-2-hexene
c. ethyl vinyl ether
d. allyl alcohol

PROBLEM 5 ◆

Give the systematic name for each of the following:

a. $CH_3CHCH{=}CHCH_3$
    $\overset{\displaystyle |}{CH_3}$

b. $CH_3CH_2C{=}\overset{\displaystyle }{C}CHCH_3$
    $\overset{\displaystyle |}{CH_3}\ \overset{\displaystyle |}{Cl}$
    (with CH_3 above the C)

c. $\overset{Br}{\ }$ (bromo-cyclopentene structure)

d. $BrCH_2CH_2CH{=}\overset{\displaystyle }{C}CH_3$
    $\overset{\displaystyle |}{CH_2CH_3}$

e. (cyclohexene ring with CH_3 groups)
    $CH_3 \qquad CH_3$

f. $CH_3CH{=}CHOCH_2CH_2CH_2CH_3$

g. (branched alkene structure)

chem Tutorial:
place Alkene nomenclature

Tutorial:
Common names of alkyl groups

3.3 THE STRUCTURE OF ALKENES

The structure of the smallest alkene (ethene) was described in Section 1.8. Other alkenes have similar structures. Each double-bonded carbon of an alkene has three sp^2 orbitals that lie in a plane with angles of 120°. Each of these sp^2 orbitals overlaps an orbital of another atom to form a σ bond. Thus, one of the carbon–carbon bonds in a double bond is a σ bond, formed by the overlap of an sp^2 orbital of one carbon with an sp^2 orbital of the other carbon. The second carbon–carbon bond in the double bond (the π bond) is formed from side-to-side overlap of the remaining p orbital of one of the sp^2 carbons with the remaining p orbital of the other sp^2 carbon. Because three points determine a plane, each sp^2 carbon and the two atoms singly bonded to it lie in a plane. In order to achieve maximum orbital–orbital overlap, the two p orbitals must be parallel to each other. Therefore, all six atoms of the double-bond system are in the same plane.

$$H_3C \qquad CH_3$$
$$\underset{H_3C}{\overset{}{\diagdown}}C{=}C\underset{CH_3}{\overset{}{\diagup}}$$

**the six carbon atoms
are in the same plane**

It is important to remember that the π bond consists of the cloud of electrons distributed above and below the plane defined by the two sp^2 carbons and the four atoms bonded to them.

p orbitals overlap to form
a π bond

PROBLEM 6 ◆   **SOLVED**

For each of the following compounds, tell how many carbons are in its planar double-bond system:

a. (cyclohexene with CH_3)   **b.** (methylcyclohexene, CH_3 top)   **c.** (dimethylcyclohexene, CH_3)   **d.** (dimethylcyclohexene, two CH_3)

> **Solution to 6a**   Five carbons are in its planar double-bond system: the two sp^2 carbons (blue dots) and the three carbons bonded to the sp^2 carbons (red dots).
>
>

3.4 ALKENES CAN HAVE CIS AND TRANS ISOMERS

We have just seen that the two *p* orbitals forming the π bond must be parallel to achieve maximum overlap. Therefore, rotation about a double bond does not readily occur. If rotation were to occur, the two *p* orbitals would cease to overlap, and the π bond would break (Figure 3.1). The energy barrier to rotation about a double bond is about 62 kcal/mol or 259 kJ/mol (Section 1.14). Compare this to the energy barrier 2.9 kcal/mol or 12 kJ/mol to rotation about a carbon–carbon single bond (Section 2.10).

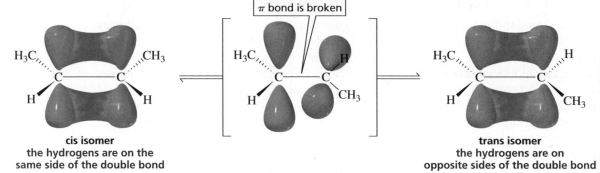

▶ **Figure 3.1**
Rotation about the carbon–carbon double bond would break the π bond.

Because of the high energy barrier to rotation about a carbon–carbon double bond, an alkene such as 2-butene can exist in two distinct forms: the hydrogens bonded to the sp^2 carbons can be on the same side of the double bond or on opposite sides of the double bond.

The compound with the hydrogens on the same side of the double bond is called the **cis isomer**, and the compound with the hydrogens on opposite sides of the double bond is called the **trans isomer**. A pair of isomers such as *cis*-2-butene and *trans*-2-butene are called **cis–trans isomers** or **geometric isomers**. This should remind you of the cis–trans isomers of disubstituted cyclohexanes you encountered in Section 2.14—the cis isomer had its substituents on the same side of the ring, and the trans isomer had its substituents on opposite sides of the ring. Notice that the cis and trans isomers have the same molecular formula and the same bonds but have different configurations—they differ in the way the atoms are oriented in space.

Do not confuse the terms *conformation* and *configuration*.

- Conformations are different spatial arrangements of the same compound (for example, anti and gauche conformers; Section 2.10). They cannot be separated. Some conformations are more stable than others.

Different Conformations

Stable   Unstable

- Compounds with different configurations are different compounds. They can be separated from each other. Bonds have to be broken to interconvert compounds with different configurations.

Different Configurations

If one of the sp^2 carbons of the double bond is attached to two identical substituents, there is only one possible structure for the alkene. In other words, cis and trans isomers are not possible for an alkene that has identical substituents attached to one of the sp^2 carbons.

cis and trans isomers are not possible for these compounds because two substituents on an sp^2 carbon are the same

---

PROBLEM 7 ♦

a. Which of the following compounds can exist as cis–trans isomers?
b. For those compounds, draw and label the cis and trans isomers.

   1. $CH_3CH{=}CHCH_2CH_2CH_3$ **3.** $CH_3CH{=}CHCH_3$

   2. $CH_3CH_2C{=}CHCH_3$ **4.** $CH_3CH_2CH{=}CH_2$
   　　　　　$|$
   　　　CH_2CH_3

Because of the energy barrier to rotation about a double bond, cis and trans isomers of alkenes cannot interconvert (except under conditions extreme enough to overcome the energy barrier and break the π bond). This means that they can be separated from each other. In other words, the two isomers are different compounds with different physical properties, such as different boiling points and different dipole moments. Notice that *trans*-2-butene and *trans*-1,2-dichloroethene, unlike their respective cis isomers, have dipole moments (μ) of zero because the bond dipole moments cancel (Section 1.15).

cis-2-butene
bp = 3.7 °C
μ = 0.33 D

trans-2-butene
bp = 0.9 °C
μ = 0 D

cis-1,2-dichloroethene
bp = 60.3 °C
μ = 2.95 D

trans-1,2-dichloroethene
bp = 47.5 °C
μ = 0 D

Because cis and trans isomers can be interconverted (in the absence of any added reagents) only when the molecule absorbs sufficient heat or light energy to cause the π bond to break, cis–trans interconversion is not a practical laboratory process.

cis-2-pentene   > 180 °C or *hv*   **trans-2-pentene**

Cis—Trans Interconversion in Vision

The ability to see depends in part on a cis–trans interconversion that takes place in our eyes. A protein called opsin binds to *cis*-retinal (formed from vitamin A) in photoreceptor cells (called rod cells) in the retina of the eye to form rhodopsin. When rhodopsin absorbs light, a double bond interconverts between the cis and trans configurations, triggering a nerve impulse that plays an important role in vision. *trans*-Retinal is then released from opsin, isomerizing back to *cis*-retinal, and another cycle begins. To trigger the nerve impulse, a group of about 500 rod cells must register five to seven rhodopsin isomerizations within a few tenths of a second.

cis double bond — *cis*-retinal   + H_2N—opsin   cis double bond — rhodopsin   light

trans double bond — *trans*-retinal   + H_2N—opsin   trans double bond — N—opsin

PROBLEM 10◆

Which of the following compounds have a dipole moment of zero?

$$\begin{array}{cccc}
\underset{\overset{|}{H}}{\overset{H}{|}}C=\underset{\overset{|}{Cl}}{\overset{Cl}{|}}C & \underset{\overset{|}{Cl}}{\overset{H}{|}}C=\underset{\overset{|}{H}}{\overset{H}{|}}C & \underset{\overset{|}{Cl}}{\overset{H}{|}}C=\underset{\overset{|}{H}}{\overset{Cl}{|}}C & \underset{\overset{|}{Cl}}{\overset{H}{|}}C=\underset{\overset{|}{Cl}}{\overset{H}{|}}C \\
\text{A} & \text{B} & \text{C} & \text{D}
\end{array}$$

3.5 NAMING ALKENES USING THE *E,Z* SYSTEM

As long as each of the sp^2 carbons of an alkene is bonded to only one substituent, we can use the terms *cis* and *trans* to designate the structure of the alkene: *if the hydrogens are on the same side of the double bond, it is the cis isomer; if they are on opposite sides of the double bond, it is the trans isomer.* But how do we designate the isomers of a compound such as 1-bromo-2-chloropropene?

$$\begin{array}{cc}
\underset{\overset{|}{H}}{\overset{Br}{|}}C=\underset{\overset{|}{CH_3}}{\overset{Cl}{|}}C & \underset{\overset{|}{H}}{\overset{Br}{|}}C=\underset{\overset{|}{Cl}}{\overset{CH_3}{|}}C
\end{array}$$

Which isomer is cis and which is trans?

The *E,Z* system of nomenclature was devised for alkenes with two substituents on one or both of the sp^2 carbons.*

To name an isomer by the *E,Z* system, we first determine the relative priorities of the two groups bonded to one of the sp^2 carbons and then the relative priorities of the two groups bonded to the other sp^2 carbon. (The rules for assigning relative priorities are explained below.)

low priority   low priority
$$C=C$$
high priority   high priority

the *Z* isomer has the high priority groups on the same side of the double bond

low priority   high priority
$$C=C$$
high priority   low priority

the *E* isomer has the high priority groups on opposite sides of the double bond

If the two high-priority groups (one from each carbon) are on the same side of the double bond, it is the Z isomer (Z is for *zusammen*, German for "together"). If the high-priority groups are on opposite sides of the double bond, it is the E isomer (E is for *entgegen*, German for "opposite").

The relative priorities of the two groups bonded to an sp^2 carbon are determined using the following rules:

> **The *Z* isomer has the high-priority groups on the same side.**

1. The relative priorities of the two groups depend on the atomic numbers of the atoms bonded directly to the sp^2 carbon. The greater the atomic number, the higher the priority.

---

*The IUPAC prefers the *E* and *Z* designations because they can be used for all alkene isomers. Many chemists, however, continue to use the "cis" and "trans" designations for simple molecules.

The greater the atomic number of the atom bonded to the sp^2 carbon, the higher the priority of the substituent.

For example, in the following pair of isomers, one of the sp^2 carbons is bonded to a Br and to an H:

Bromine has a greater atomic number than hydrogen, so **Br** has a higher priority than **H**. The other sp^2 carbon is bonded to a Cl and to a C. Chlorine has the greater atomic number, so **Cl** has a higher priority than **C**. (Notice that you use the atomic number of C, not the mass of the CH_3 group, because the priorities are based on the atomic numbers of atoms, *not* on the masses of groups.) The isomer on the left has the high-priority groups (Br and Cl) on the same side of the double bond, so it is the **Z isomer**. (Zee groups are on Zee Zame Zide.) The isomer on the right has the high-priority groups on opposite sides of the double bond, so it is the **E isomer**.

2. If the two groups bonded to an sp^2 carbon start with the same atom (there is a tie), you then move outward from the point of attachment and consider the atomic numbers of the atoms that are attached to the "tied" atoms.

If the atoms attached to the sp^2 carbon are the same, the atoms attached to the tied atoms are compared; the one with the greater atomic number belongs to the group with the higher priority.

For example, in the following pair of isomers, both atoms bonded to the sp^2 carbon on the left are C's (in a CH_2Cl group and a CH_2CH_2Cl group), so there is a tie.

The C of the CH_2Cl group is bonded to **Cl, H, H**, and the C of the CH_2CH_2Cl group is bonded to **C, H, H**. Cl has a greater atomic number than C, so the CH_2Cl group has the higher priority. Both atoms bonded to the other sp^2 carbon are C's (in a CH_2OH group and a $CH(CH_3)_2$ group), so there is a tie on that side as well. The C of the CH_2OH group is bonded to **O, H**, and **H**, and the C of the $CH(CH_3)_2$ group is bonded to **C, C**, and **H**. Of these six atoms, O has the greatest atomic number, so **CH_2OH** has a higher priority than **$CH(CH_3)_2$**. (Note that you do not add the atomic numbers; you consider the single atom with the greatest atomic number.) The E and Z isomers are as shown above.

3. If an atom is doubly bonded to another atom, the priority system treats it as if it were singly bonded to two of those atoms. If an atom is triply bonded to another atom, the priority system treats it as if it were singly bonded to three of those atoms.

If an atom is doubly bonded to another atom, treat it as if it were singly bonded to two of those atoms.

If an atom is triply bonded to another atom, treat it as if it were singly bonded to three of those atoms.

For example, one of the sp^2 carbons in the following pair of isomers is bonded to a CH_2CH_2OH group and to a $CH_2C≡CH$ group:

Because the carbons immediately bonded to the sp^2 carbon on the left are both bonded to **C, H**, and **H**, we ignore them and turn our attention to the groups attached to them. One of these groups is CH_2OH, and the other is C≡CH. One C is bonded react in similar ways. What makes learning organic chemistry even easier is that only a few rules govern the reactivity of each family.

The family that an organic compound belongs to is determined by its functional group. The **functional group** is the center of reactivity of a molecule (Section 2.6). You will find a table of common functional groups inside the back cover of this book. You are already familiar with the functional group of an alkene: the carbon–carbon double bond. All compounds with a carbon–carbon double bond react in similar ways, whether the compound is a small molecule like ethene or a large molecule like cholesterol.

First, we need to understand *why* a functional group reacts the way it does. It is not sufficient to know that a compound with a carbon–carbon double bond reacts with HBr to form a product in which the H and Br atoms have taken the place of the π bond; we also need to understand *why* the compound reacts with HBr. In each chapter that discusses the reactivity of a particular functional group, we will see how the nature of the functional group allows us to predict the kind of reactions it will undergo. Then, when you are confronted with a reaction you have never seen before, knowledge of how the structure of the molecule affects its reactivity will help you predict the products of the reaction.

In essence, organic chemistry is all about the interaction between electron-rich atoms or molecules and electron-deficient atoms or molecules. These are the forces that make chemical reactions happen. From this observation follows a very important rule for predicting the reactivity of organic compounds: *electron-rich atoms or molecules are attracted to electron-deficient atoms or molecules.* Each time you study a new functional group, remember that the reactions it undergoes can be explained by this very simple rule.

Therefore, to understand how a functional group reacts, you must first learn to recognize electron-deficient and electron-rich atoms and molecules. An electron-deficient atom or molecule is called an **electrophile**. Literally, "electrophile" means "electron loving" (*phile* is the Greek suffix for "loving"). An electrophile looks for a pair of electrons. An electrophile has either a positive charge or an incomplete octet that can accept electrons.

> Electron-rich atoms or molecules are attracted to electron-deficient atoms or molecules.

$$H^+ \quad CH_3\overset{+}{C}H_2 \quad BH_3$$

these are electrophiles because they can accept a pair of electrons

An electron-rich atom or molecule is called a **nucleophile**. A nucleophile has a pair of electrons it can share. Because a nucleophile has electrons to share and an electrophile is seeking electrons, it should not be surprising that they attract each other. Thus, the preceding rule can be restated as *a nucleophile reacts with an electrophile.*

> A nucleophile reacts with an electrophile.

$$H\ddot{O}:^- \quad :\ddot{C}l:^- \quad CH_3\ddot{N}H_2 \quad H_2\ddot{O}:$$

these are nucleophiles because they have a pair of electrons to share

PROBLEM 17

Identify the nucleophile and the electrophile in the following acid–base reactions.

a. $AlCl_3$ + NH_3 $\rightleftharpoons$ $Cl_3\bar{Al}-\overset{+}{N}H_3$

b. $H-Br$ + HO^- $\rightleftharpoons$ Br^- + H_2O

Let's now see how the rule "a nucleophile reacts with an electrophile" allows us to predict the characteristic reaction of an alkene. We have seen that the π bond of an alkene consists of a cloud of electrons above and below the σ bond. As a result of this cloud of electrons, an alkene is an electron-rich molecule—it is a nucleophile. (Notice the relatively electron-rich pale orange area in the electrostatic potential maps for *cis*- and *trans*-2-butene in Section 3.4.) We have also seen that a π bond is weaker than a σ bond (Section 1.14). The π bond, therefore, is the bond that is most easily broken when an alkene undergoes a reaction. For these reasons, we can predict that an alkene will react with an electrophile, and, in the process, the π bond will break. So if a reagent such as hydrogen bromide is added to an alkene, the alkene (a nucleophile) will react with the partially positively charged hydrogen (an electrophile) of hydrogen bromide; the product of the reaction will be a carbocation. In the second step of the reaction, the positively charged carbocation (an electrophile) will react with the negatively charged bromide ion (a nucleophile) to form an alkyl halide.

The step-by-step description of the process by which reactants (for example, alkene + HBr) are changed into products (an alkyl halide) is called the **mechanism of the reaction**. To help us understand a mechanism, curved arrows are drawn to show how the electrons move as new covalent bonds are formed and existing covalent bonds are broken. Each arrow represents the simultaneous movement of two electrons (an electron pair) from an electron-rich center (at the tail of the arrow) toward an electron-deficient center (at the point of the arrow). In this way, the arrows show which bonds are formed and which are broken.

> Curved arrows show the flow of electrons; they are drawn from an electron-rich center to an electron-deficient center.
>
> An arrowhead with two barbs signifies the movement of two electrons.

For the reaction of 2-butene with HBr, an arrow is drawn to show that the two electrons of the π bond of the alkene are attracted to the partially positively charged hydrogen of HBr. The hydrogen is not immediately free to accept this pair of electrons because it is already bonded to a bromine, and hydrogen can be bonded to only one atom at a time (Section 1.4). However, as the π electrons of the alkene move toward the hydrogen, the H—Br bond breaks, with bromine keeping the bonding electrons. Notice that the π electrons are pulled away from one carbon, but remain attached to the other. Thus, the two electrons that originally formed the π bond now form a new σ bond between carbon and the hydrogen from HBr. The product is positively charged, because the sp^2 carbon that did not form the new bond with hydrogen has lost a share in an electron pair (the electrons of the π bond).

In the second step of the reaction, a lone pair on the negatively charged bromide ion forms a bond with the positively charged carbon of the carbocation. Notice that in both steps of the reaction *a nucleophile reacts with an electrophile.*

$$CH_3\overset{+}{C}H-CHCH_3 \;+\; :\ddot{B}\ddot{r}:^- \longrightarrow CH_3CH-CHCH_3$$

H	:Ḃr: H

new σ bond

A curved arrow indicates where the electrons start from and where they end up.

Solely from the knowledge that a nucleophile reacts with an electrophile and a π bond is the weakest bond in an alkene, we have been able to predict that the product of the reaction of 2-butene and HBr is 2-bromobutane. The overall reaction involves the addition of 1 mole of HBr to 1 mole of the alkene. The reaction, therefore, is called an **addition reaction**. Because the first step of the reaction is the addition of an electrophile (H^+) to the alkene, the reaction is more precisely called an **electrophilic addition reaction**. *Electrophilic addition reactions are the characteristic reactions of alkenes.*

At this point, you may think it would be easier just to memorize the fact that 2-bromobutane is the product of the reaction, without trying to understand the mechanism that explains why 2-bromobutane is the product. Keep in mind, however, that you will soon be encountering a great many reactions, and you will not be able to memorize them all. *It will be a lot easier to learn a dozen mechanisms that are based on similar rules than to try to memorize thousands of reactions.* And if you understand the mechanism of each reaction, the unifying principles of organic chemistry will soon be clear to you, making mastery of the material much easier and a lot more fun.

PROBLEM 18 ♦

Which of the following are electrophiles, and which are nucleophiles?

$$H^- \qquad CH_3O^- \qquad CH_3C\equiv CH \qquad CH_3\overset{+}{C}HCH_3 \qquad NH_3$$

PROBLEM 19

Draw the consequence of following the incorrect arrows in item 1 of the box on page 136, "A Few Words about Curved Arrows." What is wrong with the structures that you obtain?

PROBLEM 20

Use curved arrows to show the movement of electrons in each of the following reaction steps. (*Hint*: Look at the starting material and look at the products, then draw the arrows.)

a.
$$CH_3\overset{O}{\overset{\|}{C}}\diagdown O-H \;+\; H\ddot{O}:^- \longrightarrow CH_3\overset{O}{\overset{\|}{C}}\diagdown O^- \;+\; H_2\ddot{O}:$$

b.
$$\bigcirc\!\!= \;+\; \ddot{B}\ddot{r}:^+ \longrightarrow$$ cyclohexane ring with :Ḃr: and + charge

c.
$$CH_3\overset{\ddot{O}:}{\overset{\|}{C}}\diagdown OH \;+\; H-\overset{+}{\underset{H}{\ddot{O}}}-H \longrightarrow CH_3\overset{^+\ddot{O}H}{\overset{\|}{C}}\diagdown OH \;+\; H_2O$$

d.
$$CH_3\overset{CH_3}{\underset{CH_3}{\overset{|}{C^+}}} \;+\; :\ddot{C}\ddot{l}:^- \longrightarrow CH_3\overset{CH_3}{\underset{CH_3}{\overset{|}{C}}}-\ddot{C}\ddot{l}:$$

PROBLEM 21

For each of the reactions in Problem 20, indicate which reactant is the nucleophile and which is the electrophile.

A Few Words about Curved Arrows

1. Draw the arrows so that they point in the direction of the electron flow and never against the flow. This means that *an arrow will point away from a negative charge and toward a positive charge.* An arrow is used to show both the bond that forms and the bond that breaks.

2. Curved arrows are meant to indicate the movement of electrons. *Never use a curved arrow to indicate the movement of an atom.* For example, do not use an arrow as a lasso to remove a proton, as shown in the equation on the right:

3. *The head of a curved arrow always points at an atom or at a bond.* Never draw the head of the arrow pointing out into space.

4. *A curved arrow starts at an electron source; it does not start at an atom.* In the following example, the arrow starts at the electron-rich π bond, not at a carbon atom:

NOTE TO THE STUDENT

It is critically important that you learn how to draw curved arrows. Be sure to do the exercise in Special Topic II in the *Study Guide and Solutions Manual.* It should take no more than 15 minutes, yet it can make an enormous difference to your success in this course.

3.7 THERMODYNAMICS AND KINETICS

To understand the energy changes that take place in a reaction such as the addition of HBr to an alkene, you need to understand some of the basic concepts of *thermodynamics*, which describes a reaction at equilibrium, and *kinetics*, which explains the rates of chemical reactions.

Consider a reaction in which Y is converted to Z: the *thermodynamics* of the reaction tells us the relative amounts of reactants (Y) and products (Z) present when the reaction has reached equilibrium, whereas the *kinetics* of the reaction tells us how fast reactants are converted into products.

A Reaction Coordinate Diagram Describes the Reaction Pathway

The mechanism of a reaction, as we have shown, describes the steps known to occur as reactants are converted into products. A **reaction coordinate diagram** shows the energy changes that take place in each of these steps. In a reaction coordinate diagram, the total energy of all species is plotted against the progress of the reaction. A reaction progresses from left to right as written in a chemical equation, so the energy of the reactants is plotted on the left-hand side of the *x*-axis and the energy of the products is plotted on the right-hand side. A typical reaction coordinate diagram is shown in Figure 3.2. It describes the reaction of A—B with C to form A and B—C. Remember that *the more stable the species, the lower is its energy.*

The more stable the species, the lower is its energy.

$$A-B + C \rightleftharpoons A + B-C$$

reactants ⎯⎯⎯⎯⎯⎯⎯⎯⎯ products

As the reactants are converted into products, the reaction passes through a *maximum* energy state called a **transition state**. The height of the transition state (the difference between the energy of the reactants and the energy of the transition state) tells us how likely it is that the reaction will occur; if the height is too great, the reactants will not be able to be converted into products, so no reaction will take place. The structure of the transition state is intermediate between the structure of the reactants and the structure of the products. Bonds that break and bonds that form, as reactants are converted to products, are partially broken and partially formed in the transition state. Dashed lines are used to show partially broken or partially formed bonds.

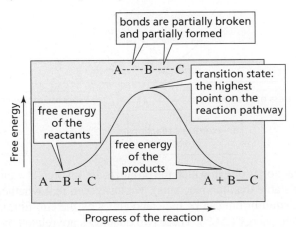

◀ **Figure 3.2**
A reaction coordinate diagram. The dashed lines in the transition state indicate bonds that are partially formed or partially broken.

Thermodynamics: How Much Product Is Formed?

Thermodynamics is the field of chemistry that describes the properties of a system at equilibrium. The relative concentrations of reactants and products at equilibrium can be expressed numerically by an equilibrium constant, K_{eq} (Section 1.17). For example, in a reaction in which *m* moles of A react with *n* moles of B to form *s* moles of C and *t* moles of D, K_{eq} is equal to the relative concentrations of products and reactants at equilibrium.

$$m\,A \; + \; n\,B \; \rightleftharpoons \; s\,C \; + \; t\,D$$

$$K_{eq} = \frac{[\text{products}]}{[\text{reactants}]} = \frac{[C]^s\,[D]^t}{[A]^m\,[B]^n}$$

The relative concentrations of products and reactants at equilibrium depend on their relative stabilities: *the more stable the compound, the greater is its concentration at equilibrium.* Thus, if the products are more stable (have a lower free energy) than the reactants (Figure 3.3a), there will be a higher concentration of products than reactants at equilibrium, and K_{eq} will be greater than 1. On the other hand, if the reactants are more stable than the products (Figure 3.3b), there will be a higher concentration of reactants than products at equilibrium, and K_{eq} will be less than 1. Now you can understand why the strength of an acid is determined by the stability of its conjugate base (Section 1.21). In other words, as the base becomes more stable, the equilibrium constant (K_a) for its formation becomes larger.

The difference between the free energy of the products and the free energy of the reactants under standard conditions is called the **Gibbs free-energy change**, $\Delta G°$. The symbol ° indicates standard conditions, which means that all species are at a concentration of 1 M, a temperature of 25°C, and a pressure of 1 atm.

$$\Delta G° = \text{(free energy of the products)} - \text{(free energy of the reactants)}$$

From this equation, we can see that $\Delta G°$ will be negative if the products have a lower free energy (are more stable) than the reactants. In other words, the reaction will release more energy than it will consume; such a reaction is called an **exergonic reaction** (Figure 3.3a). If the products have a higher free energy (are less stable) than the reactants, $\Delta G°$ will be positive, and the reaction will consume more energy than it will release; such a reaction is called an **endergonic reaction** (Figure 3.3b). (Notice that the terms *exergonic* and *endergonic* refer to whether the reaction has a negative $\Delta G°$ or a positive $\Delta G°$, respectively. Do not confuse these terms with *exothermic* and *endothermic*, which we will define later.)

▶ **Figure 3.3**
Reaction coordinate diagrams for
(a) a reaction in which the products are more stable than the reactants (an exergonic reaction) and
(b) a reaction in which the products are less stable than the reactants (an endergonic reaction).

The more stable the compound, the greater is its concentration at equilibrium.

When products are favored at equilibrium, $\Delta G°$ is negative and K_{eq} is greater than 1.

When reactants are favored at equilibrium, $\Delta G°$ is positive and K_{eq} is less than 1.

A successful reaction is one in which the products are favored at equilibrium (that is, the products are more stable than the reactants). We have seen that whether reactants or products are favored at equilibrium can be indicated either by the equilibrium constant (K_{eq}) or by the change in free energy ($\Delta G°$). These two quantities are related by the equation

$$\Delta G° = -RT \ln K_{eq}$$

where *R* is the gas constant ($1.986 \times 10^{-3}\,\text{kcal mol}^{-1}\,\text{K}^{-1}$, or $8.314 \times 10^{-3}\,\text{kJ mol}^{-1}\,\text{K}^{-1}$, recall 1 kcal = 4.184 kJ) and *T* is the temperature in kelvins. (The Kelvin scale avoids negative temperatures by assigning 0 K to −273 °C, the lowest temperature known. Thus, K = °C + 273; therefore, 25 °C = 298 K).

A small difference in $\Delta G°$ corresponds to a large difference in K_{eq} and, therefore, a large difference in the relative concentrations of reactants and products. For example, for a reaction carried out at 25 °C, the ratio of product to reactant changes by a factor of 10 when $\Delta G°$ becomes 1.36 kcal/mol (or 5.7 kJ/mol) more negative (Table 3.1). When you solve Problem 23, you will see that a small difference in $\Delta G°$ makes a big difference in the amount of product obtained at equilibrium.

Table 3.1   The Relationship between $\Delta G°$ and K_{eq} at 25 °C

$\Delta G°$ (kcal/mol)	K_{eq}	B $\rightleftharpoons$ C % C at equilibrium
−0.1	1.2	54.5
−1	5.4	84.4
−2.36	5.4 × 10	98.1
−5	4.6 × 10³	99.98
−5.36	4.6 × 10⁴	99.9998

B I O G R A P H Y

The gas constant R is thought to be named after **Henri Victor Regnault (1810–1878)**, *who was commissioned by the French Minister of Public Works in 1842 to recalculate all the physical constants required for the design and operation of the steam engine. Regnault was known for his work on the thermal properties of gases. Later, while studying the thermodynamics of dilute solutions, van't Hoff (p. 207) found that R could be used for all chemical equilibria.*

PROBLEM 22 ◆

a. Which of the monosubstituted cyclohexanes in Table 2.10 has a negative $\Delta G°$ for the conversion of an axial-substituted chair conformer to an equatorial-substituted chair conformer?

b. Which monosubstituted cyclohexane has the most negative $\Delta G°$ value?

c. Which monosubstituted cyclohexane has the greatest preference for the equatorial position?

d. Calculate $\Delta G°$ for conversion of "axial" methylcyclohexane to "equatorial" methylcyclohexane at 25 °C.

PROBLEM 23   **SOLVED**

a. The $\Delta G°$ for the conversion of "axial" fluorocyclohexane to "equatorial" fluorocyclohexane at 25 °C is −0.25 kcal/mol. Calculate the percentage of fluorocyclohexane molecules that have the fluoro substituent in the equatorial position at equilibrium.

b. Do the same calculation for isopropylcyclohexane (its $\Delta G°$ at 25 °C is −2.1 kcal/mol).

c. Why is the percentage of molecules with the substituent in the equatorial position greater for isopropylcyclohexane?

Solution to 23a

$$\text{fluorocyclohexane} \rightleftharpoons \text{fluorocyclohexane}$$
$$\textbf{axial} \qquad\qquad\qquad \textbf{equatorial}$$

$$\Delta G° = -0.25 \text{ kcal/mol at 25 °C}$$

$$\Delta G° = -RT \ln K_{eq}$$

$$-0.25 \frac{\text{kcal}}{\text{mol}} = -1.986 \times 10^{-3} \frac{\text{kcal}}{\text{mol K}} \times 298 \text{ K} \times \ln K_{eq}$$

$$\ln K_{eq} = 0.422$$

$$K_{eq} = 1.53 = \frac{[\text{fluorocyclohexane}]\ \textbf{equatorial}}{[\text{fluorocyclohexane}]\ \textbf{axial}} = \frac{1.53}{1}$$

Now we must determine the percentage of the total that is equatorial:

$$\frac{[\text{fluorocyclohexane}]\ \textbf{equatorial}}{[\text{fluorocyclohexane}]\ \textbf{equatorial} + [\text{fluorocyclohexane}]\ \textbf{axial}} = \frac{1.53}{1.53 + 1} = \frac{1.53}{2.53} = 0.60 \text{ or } 60\ \%$$

If an equilibrium is disturbed, the system will adjust to offset the disturbance.

BIOGRAPHY

Henri Louis Le Châtelier (1850–1936), *born in France, was the son of France's inspector-general of mines. He studied mining engineering and, understandably considering his father's position, was particularly interested in mine safety and learning how to prevent explosions. Le Châtelier's research into explosions led him to study heat and its measurement, which stimulated his interest in thermodynamics.*

Fortunately, there are ways to increase the amount of product formed in a reaction. **Le Châtelier's principle** states that *if an equilibrium is disturbed, the system will adjust to offset the disturbance.* In other words, if the concentration of C or D is decreased, A and B will react to form more C and D to maintain the value of the equilibrium constant. Thus, if a product crystallizes out of solution as it is formed, or if it can be distilled off as a liquid or driven off as a gas, the reactants will continue to react to replace the departing product, in order to maintain the relative concentrations of products and reactants at the value of the equilibrium constant. More products can also be formed if the equilibrium is disturbed by increasing the concentration of one of the reactants.

$$A + B \rightleftharpoons C + D$$

$$K_{eq} = \frac{[C][D]}{[A][B]}$$

The Gibbs standard free-energy change ($G°$) has an enthalpy ($H°$) component and an entropy ($\Delta S°$) component (T is the temperature in kelvins):

$$\Delta G° = \Delta H° - T\Delta S°$$

The **enthalpy** term ($\Delta H°$) is the heat given off or the heat consumed during the course of a reaction. Heat is given off when bonds are formed, and heat is consumed when bonds are broken. Thus, $\Delta H°$ is a measure of the energy of the bond-making and bond-breaking processes that occur as reactants are converted into products.

$\Delta H°$ = (energy of the bonds being broken) − (energy of the bonds being formed)

If the bonds that are formed in a reaction are stronger than the bonds that are broken, more energy will be released in the bond-forming process than will be consumed in the bond-breaking process, and $\Delta H°$ will be negative. A reaction with a negative $\Delta H°$ is called an **exothermic reaction**. If the bonds that are formed are weaker than those that are broken, $\Delta H°$ will be positive. A reaction with a positive $\Delta H°$ is called an **endothermic reaction**.

Entropy ($\Delta S°$) is a measure of the freedom of movement in a system. Restricting the freedom of movement of a molecule decreases its entropy. For example, in a reaction in which two molecules come together to form a single molecule, the entropy in the product will be less than the entropy in the reactants because two separate molecules can move in ways that are not possible when they are bound together in a single molecule. In such a reaction, $\Delta S°$ will be negative. In a reaction in which a single molecule is cleaved into two separate molecules, the products will have greater freedom of motion than the reactant, and $\Delta S°$ will be positive.

$\Delta S°$ = (freedom of motion of the products) − (freedom of motion of the reactants)

Entropy is a measure of the freedom of motion of a system.

PROBLEM 24 ♦

a. For which reaction in each set below will $\Delta S°$ be more significant?
b. For which reaction will $\Delta S°$ be positive?
   1. A $\rightleftharpoons$ B or A + B $\rightleftharpoons$ C
   2. A + B $\rightleftharpoons$ C or A + B $\rightleftharpoons$ C + D

The formation of products with stronger bonds and greater freedom of motion causes $\Delta G°$ to be negative.

A reaction with a negative $\Delta G°$ has a favorable equilibrium constant ($K_{eq} > 1$); that is, the reaction is favored as written from left to right because the products are more stable than the reactants. If you examine the expression for the Gibbs standard free-energy change, you will find that negative values of $\Delta H°$ and positive values of $\Delta S°$ contribute to make $\Delta G°$ negative. In other words, *the formation of products with stronger bonds and greater freedom of motion causes $\Delta G°$ to be negative.* Notice that the entropy term is temperature dependent and becomes more important as the temperature increases. Therefore, a reaction with a positive $\Delta S°$ may be endergonic at low temperatures, but exergonic at high temperatures.

PROBLEM 25♦

a. For a reaction with $\Delta H° = -12$ kcal/mol and $\Delta S° = 0.01$ kcal mol^{-1}K^{-1}, calculate the $\Delta G°$ and the equilibrium constant at (**1.**) 30 °C and (**2.**) 150 °C.

b. How does $\Delta G°$ change as T increases?

c. How does K_{eq} change as T increases?

Values of $\Delta H°$ are relatively easy to calculate, so organic chemists frequently evaluate reactions in terms of that quantity alone, since $\Delta S°$ values cannot be calculated but must be experimentally determined. However, you can ignore the entropy term only if the reaction involves just a small change in entropy, because then the $T\Delta S°$ term will be small and the value of $\Delta H°$ will be very close to the value of $\Delta G°$. Remember, though, that many organic reactions occur with a significant change in entropy or occur at high temperatures and so have significant $T\Delta S°$ terms; ignoring the entropy term in such cases can lead to wrong conclusions. It is permissible to use $\Delta H°$ values to *approximate* whether a reaction has a favorable equilibrium constant, but if a precise answer is needed, $\Delta G°$ values must be used. When $\Delta G°$ values are used to construct reaction coordinate diagrams, the *y*-axis represents free energy; when $\Delta H°$ values are used, the *y*-axis represents potential energy.

Values of $\Delta H°$ can be calculated from bond dissociation energies (Table 3.2), as shown in the following example. The bond dissociation energy is indicated by the special

BIOGRAPHY

William Thomson (1824–1907) *was born in Belfast, Northern Ireland. He was a professor of natural philosophy at the University of Glasgow, Scotland. For developing the Kelvin scale of absolute temperature and other important work in mathematical physics, he was given the title Baron Kelvin, which allowed him to be called **Lord Kelvin**. The name comes from the river Kelvin that flows by the University of Glasgow. His statue is in the botanic gardens that are adjacent to The Queen's University of Belfast.*

Table 3.2   Bond Dissociation Energies for Y—Z → Y· + ·Z

Bond	DH (kcal/mol)	DH (kJ/mol)	Bond	DH (kcal/mol)	DH (kJ/mol)
CH_3-H	105	439	$H-H$	104	435
CH_3CH_2-H	101	423	$F-F$	38	159
$CH_3CH_2CH_2-H$	101	423	$Cl-Cl$	58	242
$(CH_3)_2CH-H$	99	414	$Br-Br$	46	192
$(CH_3)_3C-H$	97	406	$I-I$	36	150
			$H-F$	136	571
CH_3-CH_3	90.1	377	$H-Cl$	103	432
$CH_3CH_2-CH_3$	89.0	372	$H-Br$	87	366
$(CH_3)_2CH-CH_3$	88.6	371	$H-I$	71	298
$(CH_3)_3C-CH_3$	87.5	366			
			CH_3-F	115	481
$H_2C=CH_2$	174	728	CH_3-Cl	84	350
$HC≡CH$	231	966	CH_3CH_2-Cl	85	356
			$(CH_3)_2CH-Cl$	85	356
			$(CH_3)_3C-Cl$	85	356
$HO-H$	119	497	CH_3-Br	72	301
CH_3O-H	105	439	CH_3CH_2-Br	72	301
CH_3-OH	92	387	$(CH_3)_2CH-Br$	74	310
			$(CH_3)_3C-Br$	73	305
			CH_3-I	58	243
			CH_3CH_2-I	57	238

S. J. Blanksby and G. B. Ellison, *Acc. Chem. Res.*, **2003**, *36*, 255.

term *DH*. Recall from Section 3.4 that the barrier to rotation about the π bond of ethene has been estimated to be 62 kcal/mol. In other words, the π bond has a bond dissociation energy of 62 kcal/mol. (Notice that this value cannot be obtained by subtracting the bond dissociation energy of the C—C σ bond of ethane from ethene's total bond energy, because a σ bond formed from sp^2—sp^2 overlap is stronger than σ bond formed from sp^3—sp^3 overlap, since the more σ character, the stronger is the bond; Section 1.14.)

$$
\begin{array}{ccc}
\text{C=C} + \text{H—Br} & \longrightarrow & \text{H—C—C—H}
\end{array}
$$

<u>bonds being broken</u>

<u>bonds being formed</u>

π bond of ethene	DH	=	62 kcal/mol	C—H	DH	=	101 kcal/mol
H—Br	DH	=	87 kcal/mol	C—Br	DH	=	72 kcal/mol
	DH_{total}	=	149 kcal/mol		DH_{total}	=	173 kcal/mol

$$\Delta H° \text{ for the reaction } = DH \text{ for bonds being broken} - DH \text{ for bonds being formed}$$

$$= 149 \text{ kcal/mol} - 173 \text{ kcal/mol}$$

$$= -24 \text{ kcal/mol}$$

The value of -24 kcal/mol—calculated for $\Delta H°$ by subtracting the sum of the $\Delta H°$ values for the bonds being formed from the sum of the $\Delta H°$ values for the bonds being broken—indicates that the addition of HBr to ethene is an exothermic reaction. But does this mean that $\Delta G°$ for the reaction is also negative? In other words, is the reaction exergonic as well as exothermic? Because $\Delta H°$ has a significant negative value (-24 kcal/mol), we can assume that $\Delta G°$ is also negative. If the value of $\Delta H°$ were close to zero, however, we could no longer assume that $\Delta H°$ has the same sign as $\Delta G°$.

Keep in mind that two conditions must be met to justify using $\Delta H°$ values to predict values of $\Delta G°$. First, the entropy change must be small, and second, the reaction must take place in the gas phase.

When reactions occur in solution, which is the case for the vast majority of organic reactions, the solvent molecules can solvate the reagents and products (Section 2.9). Solvation can have a large effect on both $\Delta H°$ and $\Delta S°$. For example, in a reaction of a solvated polar reagent, the $\Delta H°$ for breaking the dipole–dipole interactions between the solvent and the reagent has to be taken into account, and in a reaction having a polar product that becomes solvated, the $\Delta H°$ for forming the dipole–dipole interactions between the solvent and the product has to be taken into account. In addition, solvation of a polar reagent or a polar product by a polar solvent can greatly reduce the freedom of movement of the solvent molecules, thus affecting $\Delta S°$.

PROBLEM 26♦

a. Using the bond dissociation energies in Table 3.2, calculate the $\Delta H°$ for the addition of HCl to ethene.
b. Calculate the $\Delta H°$ for the addition of H_2 to ethene.
c. Are the reactions exothermic or endothermic?
d. Do you expect the reactions to be exergonic or endergonic?

Kinetics: How Fast Is the Product Formed?

Knowing whether a given reaction is exergonic or endergonic will not tell us how fast the reaction occurs, because $\Delta G°$ describes only the difference between the stability of the reactants and the stability of the products. It does not indicate anything about the energy barrier of the reaction, which is the energy "hill" that must be climbed for the reactants to be converted into products. The higher the energy barrier, the slower is the reaction. **Kinetics** is the field of chemistry that studies the rates of chemical reactions and the factors that affect those rates.

The energy barrier of a reaction, indicated in Figure 3.4 by $\Delta G^{\ddagger}$, is called the **free energy of activation**. It is the difference between the free energy of the transition state and the free energy of the reactants:

$$\Delta G^{\ddagger} = \text{(free energy of the transition state)} - \text{(free energy of the reactants)}$$

The smaller the $\Delta G^{\ddagger}$, the faster is the reaction. Thus, *anything that destabilizes the reactant or stabilizes the transition state will make the reaction go faster.*

The higher the energy barrier, the slower is the reaction.

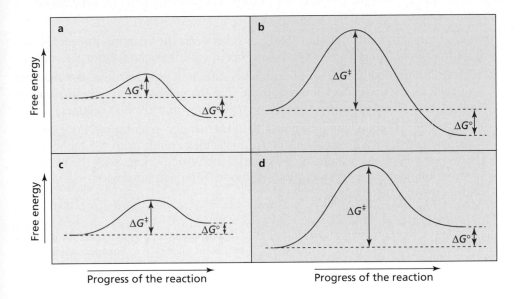

◀ **Figure 3.4**
Reaction coordinate diagrams for (a) a fast exergonic reaction, (b) a slow exergonic reaction, (c) a fast endergonic reaction, and (d) a slow endergonic reaction. (The four reaction coordinates are drawn on the same scale.)

Like ΔG°, $\Delta G^{\ddagger}$ has both an enthalpy component and an entropy component. Notice that any quantity that refers to the transition state is represented by a double-dagger superscript ($\ddagger$).

$$\Delta G^{\ddagger} = \Delta H^{\ddagger} - T\Delta S^{\ddagger}$$

$$\Delta H^{\ddagger} = \text{(enthalpy of the transition state)} - \text{(enthalpy of the reactants)}$$

$$\Delta S^{\ddagger} = \text{(entropy of the transition state)} - \text{(entropy of the reactants)}$$

Some exergonic reactions have small free energies of activation and therefore can take place at room temperature (Figure 3.4a). In contrast, some exergonic reactions have free energies of activation that are so large that the reaction cannot take place unless energy is supplied in addition to that provided by the existing thermal conditions (Figure 3.4b). Endergonic reactions can also have either small free energies of activation, as in Figure 3.4c, or large free energies of activation, as in Figure 3.4d.

Notice that ΔG° is related to the *equilibrium constant* of the reaction, whereas $\Delta G^{\ddagger}$ is related to the *rate* of the reaction. **Thermodynamic stability** is indicated by ΔG°. If ΔG° is negative, for example, the product is *thermodynamically stable* compared with the reactant, and if ΔG° is positive, the product is *thermodynamically unstable* compared with the reactant. **Kinetic stability** is indicated by $\Delta G^{\ddagger}$. If $\Delta G^{\ddagger}$ for a reaction is large, the reactant is *kinetically stable* because it does not undergo the reaction rapidly. If $\Delta G^{\ddagger}$ is small, the reactant is *kinetically unstable*—it undergoes the reaction rapidly. Generally, when chemists use the term *stability*, they are referring to thermodynamic stability.

PROBLEM 27 ◆

a. Which of the reactions in Figure 3.4 has a product that is thermodynamically stable compared with the reactant?

b. Which of the reactions in Figure 3.4 has the most kinetically stable product?

c. Which of the reactions in Figure 3.4 has the least kinetically stable product?

**Ludwig Eduard Boltzmann
(1844–1906)** *was born in Vienna,
Austria. He received a Ph.D. from
the University of Vienna in 1866;
his dissertation was on the kinetic
theory of gases. Boltzmann started
his career as a professor of mathematical physics at the University
of Graz. In 1872 he met Henriette
van Aigentier, an aspiring teacher
of mathematics and physics, who
had not been allowed to audit
lectures at the university because
they were not open to women.
Boltmann encouraged her to ap-
peal, which she did with success.
In 1873 Boltzmann returned to
the University of Vienna as a professor of mathematics. He and
Henriette were married in 1876 and
had five children. He went back to
the University of Graz in 1887 to
become its president. Boltzmann
was subject to alternating moods
of high elation and severe depression, which he attributed to having been born during the night
between Mardi Gras and Ash
Wednesday. The Boltzmann distribution (the number of molecules
as a function of energy) and
Maxwell-Boltzmann statistics
provided the foundation for
classical statistical mechanics.*

PROBLEM 28

Draw a reaction coordinate diagram for a reaction in which
a. the product is thermodynamically unstable and kinetically unstable.
b. the product is thermodynamically unstable and kinetically stable.

The rate of a chemical reaction is the speed at which the reacting substances are used up or the speed at which the products are formed. The rate of a reaction depends on the following factors:

1. **The number of collisions that take place between the reacting molecules in a given period of time.** The greater the number of collisions, the faster is the reaction.

2. **The fraction of collisions that occur with sufficient energy to get the reacting molecules over the energy barrier.** If the free energy of activation is small, more collisions will lead to reaction than if the free energy of activation is large.

3. **The fraction of collisions that occur with the proper orientation.** For example, 2-butene and HBr will react only if the molecules collide with the hydrogen of HBr approaching the π bond of 2-butene. If a collision occurs with the hydrogen approaching a methyl group of 2-butene, no reaction will take place, regardless of the energy of the collision.

$$\text{rate of a reaction} = \left(\begin{array}{c} \textbf{number of collisions} \\ \textbf{per unit of time} \end{array} \right) \times \left(\begin{array}{c} \textbf{fraction with} \\ \textbf{sufficient energy} \end{array} \right) \times \left(\begin{array}{c} \textbf{fraction with} \\ \textbf{proper orientation} \end{array} \right)$$

Increasing the concentration of the reactants increases the rate of a reaction because it increases the number of collisions that occur in a given period of time. Increasing the temperature at which the reaction is carried out also increases the rate of a reaction because it increases the kinetic energy of the molecules, which increases both the frequency of collisions (molecules that are moving faster collide more frequently) and the number of collisions that have sufficient energy to get the reacting molecules over the energy barrier (Figure 3.5).

The rate of a reaction can also be increased by adding a catalyst to the reaction mixture.

A catalyst gives the reactants a new pathway to follow—one with a smaller $\Delta G^{\ddagger}$. Thus, a **catalyst** increases the rate of a reaction by decreasing the energy barrier that has to be overcome in the process of converting the reactants into products (Figure 3.6).

A catalyst must participate in the reaction if it is going to make it go faster, but it is not consumed or changed during the reaction. Because the catalyst is not used up, only a small amount of it is needed to catalyze the reaction (typically, 1 to 10% of the number of moles of reactant). Notice in Figure 3.6 that the stability of the reactants and products is the same in both the catalyzed and uncatalyzed reactions. In other words, the catalyst

---

▶ **Figure 3.5**
Boltzmann distribution curves at two different temperatures. The curve shows the distribution of molecules with a particular kinetic energy. The energy of most molecules cluster about an average, but there are some with much lower and some with much higher energy. At a higher temperature, there will be more molecules with sufficient energy to get over the energy barrier.

◀ **Figure 3.6**
A catalyst provides a pathway with a lower energy barrier but it does not change the energy of the starting point (the reactants) or the end point (the products).

does not change the relative concentrations of products and reactants when the system reaches equilibrium. Thus, the catalyst does not change the *amount* of product formed; it changes only the *rate* at which it is formed. Catalysis and the kinds of species that can be used to catalyze a reaction are discussed in detail in Chapter 24.

A catalyst gives the reagents a new pathway with a lower "energy hill."

3.8 THE RATE OF A REACTION AND THE RATE CONSTANT FOR A REACTION

For a reaction in which a single reactant molecule A is converted into a product molecule B, *the rate of the reaction* is proportional to the concentration of A. If the concentration of A is doubled, the rate of the reaction will double; if the concentration of A is tripled, the rate of the reaction will triple; and so on. When you know the relationship between the rate of a reaction and the concentration of the reactants, you can write a **rate law** for the reaction.

$$\text{rate} \propto [A]$$

Because the rate of this reaction is proportional to the concentration of only *one* reactant, it is called a **first-order reaction**.

$$\text{a first-order reaction:} \quad A \longrightarrow B$$

We can replace the proportionality symbol ($\propto$) with an equal sign if we use a proportionality constant k, which is called a **rate constant**. The rate constant of a first-order reaction is called a **first-order rate constant**.

The smaller the rate constant, the slower is the reaction.

first-order rate constant

$$\text{rate} = k[A]$$

A reaction whose rate depends on the concentrations of *two* reactants, A and B, is called a **second-order reaction**. If the concentration of either A or B is doubled, the rate of the reaction will double; if the concentrations of both A and B are doubled, the rate of the reaction will quadruple; and so on. In this case, the rate constant k is a **second-order rate constant**.

$$\text{a second-order reaction:} \quad A + B \longrightarrow C + D$$

$$\text{rate} = k[A][B]$$

rate law   second-order rate constant

Notice that the order of a reaction is the sum of the exponents of the concentration terms in the rate law. Therefore, a reaction in which two molecules of A combine to form a molecule of B is also a second-order reaction: if the concentration of A is doubled, the rate of the reaction will quadruple.

$$\text{a second-order reaction:} \quad A + A \longrightarrow B$$

$$\text{rate} = k[A]^2$$

Do not confuse the *rate constant* of a reaction (*k*) with the *rate* of a reaction. The *rate constant* tells us how easy it is to reach the transition state (how easy it is to get over the energy barrier). Low-energy barriers are associated with large rate constants (Figure 3.4a and c), whereas high-energy barriers have small rate constants (Figure 3.4b and d). The reaction *rate* is a measure of the amount of product that is formed per unit of time. The preceding equations show that the *rate* is the product of the *rate constant and the reactant concentration or concentrations. Thus, reaction rates depend on concentration, whereas rate constants are independent of concentration.* Therefore, when we compare two reactions to see which one occurs more readily, we must compare their rate constants and not their concentration-dependent rates of reaction. (How rate constants are determined is explained in Appendix III.)

Although rate constants are independent of concentration, they are dependent on temperature. The **Arrhenius equation** relates the rate constant of a reaction to the experimental energy of activation and to the temperature at which the reaction is carried out:

The Arrhenius equation

$$k = Ae^{-E_a/RT}$$

In this expression, k is the rate constant, R is the gas constant, T is the temperature in kelvins, and A is the frequency factor, which represents the fraction of collisions that occurs with the proper orientation for reaction. E_a is the experimental energy of activation, an approximate activation energy (see the box, "The Difference between $\Delta G^{\ddagger}$ and E_a," on page 147). The term $e^{-E_a/RT}$ is the fraction of collisions with the minimum energy (E_a) needed to react. A good rule of thumb is that an increase of 10 °C in temperature will double the rate constant for a reaction and, therefore, double the rate of the reaction. Taking the logarithm of both sides of the Arrhenius equation, we obtain

$$\ln k = \ln A - \frac{E_a}{RT}$$

Problem 60 on page 154 shows how this form of the equation is used to calculate values of E_a, $\Delta G^{\ddagger}$, $\Delta H^{\ddagger}$, and $\Delta S^{\ddagger}$ for a reaction.

PROBLEM 29 **SOLVED**

At 30 °C, the second-order rate constant for the reaction of methyl chloride and HO^- is $1.0 \times 10^{-5}\,M^{-1}s^{-1}$.

a. What is the rate of the reaction when [CH₃Cl] = 0.10 M and [HO⁻] = 0.10 M?
b. If the concentration of methyl chloride is decreased to 0.01 M, what will be the effect on the *rate* of the reaction?
c. If the concentration of methyl chloride is decreased to 0.01 M, what will be the effect on the *rate constant* of the reaction?

Solution to 29a The rate of the reaction is given by

$$\text{rate} = k[\text{methyl chloride}]\,[HO^-]$$

Substituting the given rate constant and reactant concentrations yields

$$\text{rate} = 1.0 \times 10^{-5}\,M^{-1}s^{-1}[0.10\ M][0.10\ M]$$
$$= 1.0 \times 10^{-7}\,M\ s^{-1}$$

PROBLEM 30 ♦

The rate constant for a reaction can be increased by _____ the stability of the reactant or by _____ the stability of the transition state.

The Difference between $\Delta G^{\ddagger}$ and E_a

Do not confuse the *free energy of activation*, $\Delta G^{\ddagger}$, with the **experimental energy of activation**, E_a, in the Arrhenius equation. The free energy of activation ($\Delta G^{\ddagger} = \Delta H^{\ddagger} - T\Delta S^{\ddagger}$) has both an enthalpy component and an entropy component, whereas the experimental energy of activation ($E_a = \Delta H^{\ddagger} + RT$) has only an enthalpy component since the entropy component is implicit in the A term in the Arrhenius equation. Therefore, the experimental energy of activation is an approximate energy barrier to a reaction. The true energy barrier is given by $\Delta G^{\ddagger}$ because, although some reactions are driven by a change in enthalpy and some by a change in entropy, most reactions depend on changes in both of these properties.

PROBLEM 31 ◆

From the Arrhenius equation, predict how
a. increasing the experimental activation energy will affect the rate constant of a reaction.
b. increasing the temperature will affect the rate constant of a reaction.

The next question to consider is, how are the rate constants for a reaction related to the equilibrium constant? At equilibrium, the rate of the forward reaction must be equal to the rate of the reverse reaction because the amounts of reactants and products are not changing:

$$A \underset{k_{-1}}{\overset{k_1}{\rightleftharpoons}} B$$

forward rate = reverse rate

$$k_1[A] = k_{-1}[B]$$

Therefore,

$$K_{eq} = \frac{k_1}{k_{-1}} = \frac{[B]}{[A]}$$

From this equation, we can see that the equilibrium constant for a reaction can be determined from the relative concentrations of the products and reactants at equilibrium or from the relative rate constants for the forward and reverse reactions. The reaction shown in Figure 3.3a has a large equilibrium constant because the products are much more stable than the reactants. We could also say that it has a large equilibrium constant because the rate constant of the forward reaction is much greater than the rate constant of the reverse reaction.

PROBLEM 32 ◆

a. Which reaction has the greater equilibrium constant, one with a rate constant of $1 \times 10^{-3}\,\text{sec}^{-1}$ for the forward reaction and a rate constant of $1 \times 10^{-5}\,\text{sec}^{-1}$ for the reverse reaction or one with a rate constant of $1 \times 10^{-2}\,\text{sec}^{-1}$ for the forward reaction and a rate constant of $1 \times 10^{-3}\,\text{sec}^{-1}$ for the reverse reaction?

b. If both reactions start with a reactant concentration of 1.0 M, which reaction will form the most product?

NOTE TO THE STUDENT
Additional problems on kinetics and the solutions to the problems can be found in Special Topic III in the *Study Guide and Solutions Manual*. See also Appendix III.

3.9 A REACTION COORDINATE DIAGRAM DESCRIBES THE ENERGY CHANGES THAT TAKE PLACE DURING A REACTION

We have seen that the addition of HBr to 2-butene is a two-step process (Section 3.6). In each step, the reactants pass through a transition state as they are converted into products. The structure of the transition state for each of the steps is shown below in brackets. Notice that the bonds that break and the bonds that form during the course of the reaction are partially broken and partially formed in the transition state, as indicated by dashed lines. Similarly, atoms that either become charged or lose their charge during the course of the reaction are partially charged in the transition state. Transition states are always shown in brackets with a double-dagger superscript.

‡ symbolizes the transition state

$$CH_3CH{=}CHCH_3 \; + \; HBr \quad \left[\begin{array}{c} \overset{\delta+}{CH_3CH{=\!=}CHCH_3} \\ | \\ H \\ \vdots \\ \overset{\delta-}{Br} \end{array} \right]^{‡} \longrightarrow \; CH_3\overset{+}{C}HCH_2CH_3 \; + \; Br^-$$

partially formed bond

partially broken bond

transition state

$$CH_3\overset{+}{C}HCH_2CH_3 \; + \; Br^- \quad \left[\begin{array}{c} \overset{\delta+}{CH_3CHCH_2CH_3} \\ \vdots \\ \overset{\delta-}{Br} \end{array} \right]^{‡} \longrightarrow \; \begin{array}{c} CH_3CHCH_2CH_3 \\ | \\ Br \end{array}$$

transition state

A reaction coordinate diagram can be drawn for each of the steps in the reaction (Figure 3.7). In the first step, the alkene is converted into a carbocation that is higher in energy (less stable) than the reactants. The first step, therefore, is endergonic ($\Delta G°$ is positive). In the second step, the carbocation reacts with a nucleophile to form a product that is lower in energy (more stable) than the carbocation reactant. This step, therefore, is exergonic ($\Delta G°$ is negative).

▶ **Figure 3.7**
Reaction coordinate diagrams for the two steps in the addition of HBr to 2-butene: (a) the first step; (b) the second step.

Because the products of the first step are the reactants for the second step, we can hook the two reaction coordinate diagrams together to obtain the reaction coordinate diagram that describes the reaction pathway for the overall reaction (Figure 3.8). The $\Delta G°$ for the overall reaction is the difference between the free energy of the final products and the free energy of the initial reactants. Figure 3.8 shows that $\Delta G°$ for the overall reaction is negative. The overall reaction, therefore, is exergonic.

A chemical species that is a product of one step of a reaction and a reactant for the next step is called an **intermediate**. The carbocation intermediate of this reaction is too unstable to be isolated, but some reactions have more stable intermediates that can be isolated. **Transition states**, in contrast, represent the highest-energy structures that are involved in

◀ **Figure 3.8**
Reaction coordinate diagram for the addition of HBr to 2-butene.

the reaction. They exist only fleetingly and can never be isolated (Figure 3.2). Do not confuse transition states with intermediates: *transition states have partially formed bonds, whereas intermediates have fully formed bonds.*

Transition states have partially formed bonds. Intermediates have fully formed bonds.

Figure 3.8 shows that the free energy of activation for the first step of the reaction is greater than the free energy of activation for the second step. In other words, the rate constant for the first step is smaller than the rate constant for the second step. This is what we would expect, considering that the molecules in the first step of this reaction must collide with sufficient energy to break covalent bonds, whereas no bonds are broken in the second step.

If a reaction has two or more steps, the step that has its transition state *at the highest point on the reaction coordinate* is called the **rate-determining step** or **rate-limiting step**. The rate-determining step controls the overall rate of the reaction because the overall rate of a reaction such as that shown in Figure 3.8 cannot exceed the rate of the rate-determining step. Thus, the rate-determining step for the reaction of 2-butene with HBr is the first step—the addition of the electrophile (the proton) to the alkene.

Reaction coordinate diagrams can also be used to explain why a given reaction forms a certain product and not others. We will see the first example of this use in Section 4.3.

PROBLEM 33

Draw a reaction coordinate diagram for a two-step reaction in which the first step is endergonic, the second step is exergonic, and the overall reaction is endergonic. Label the reactants, products, intermediates, and transition states.

PROBLEM 34 ◆

a. Which step in the reaction diagrammed below has the greatest free energy of activation?

b. Is the first-formed intermediate more apt to revert to reactants or go on to form products?

c. Which step in the reaction sequence is rate determining?

PROBLEM 35 ♦

Draw a reaction coordinate diagram for the following reaction in which C is the most stable and B the least stable of the three species and the transition state going from A to B is more stable than the transition state going from B to C:

$$A \; \underset{k_{-1}}{\overset{k_1}{\rightleftarrows}} \; B \; \underset{k_{-2}}{\overset{k_2}{\rightleftarrows}} \; C$$

a. How many intermediates are there?
b. How many transition states are there?
c. Which step has the greater rate constant in the forward direction?
d. Which step has the greater rate constant in the reverse direction?
e. Of the four steps, which has the greatest rate constant?
f. Which is the rate-determining step in the forward direction?
g. Which is the rate-determining step in the reverse direction?

SUMMARY

An **alkene** is a hydrocarbon that contains a double bond. The double bond is the **functional group**, or center of reactivity of the alkene. The **functional group suffix** of an alkene is "ene." The general molecular formula for a hydrocarbon is C_nH_{2n+2}, minus two hydrogens for every π bond or ring in the molecule. The number of π bonds and rings is called the **degree of unsaturation**. Because alkenes contain fewer than the maximum number of hydrogens, they are called **unsaturated hydrocarbons**.

Rotation about the double bond is restricted, so an alkene can exist as **cis–trans isomers**. The **cis isomer** has its hydrogens on the same side of the double bond; the **trans isomer** has its hydrogens on opposite sides of the double bond. The **Z isomer** has the high-priority groups on the same side of the double bond; the **E isomer** has the high-priority groups on opposite sides of the double bond. The relative priorities depend on the atomic numbers of the atoms bonded directly to the sp^2 carbon.

All compounds with a particular **functional group** react similarly. Due to the cloud of electrons above and below its π bond, an alkene is an electron-rich species, or a **nucleophile**. Nucleophiles are attracted to electron-deficient species, called **electrophiles**. Alkenes undergo **electrophilic addition reactions**.

The description of the step-by-step process by which reactants are changed into products is called the **mechanism of the reaction**. **Curved arrows** show which bonds are formed and which are broken and the direction of the electron flow that accompanies these changes.

Thermodynamics describes a reaction at equilibrium; **kinetics** describes how fast the reaction occurs. A **reaction coordinate diagram** shows the energy changes that take place in a reaction. The more stable a species, the lower is its energy. As reactants are converted into products, a reaction passes through a maximum-energy **transition state**. An **intermediate** is a product of one step of a reaction and a reactant of the next step. Transition states have partially formed bonds; intermediates have fully formed bonds. The **rate-determining step** has its transition state at the highest point on the reaction coordinate.

The relative concentrations of reactants and products at equilibrium are given by the equilibrium constant K_{eq}. The more stable the product relative to the reactant, the greater is its concentration at equilibrium. **Le Châtelier's principle** states that if an equilibrium is disturbed, the system will adjust to offset the disturbance. If products are more stable than reactants: K_{eq} is >1, $\Delta G°$ is negative, and the reaction is **exergonic**; if reactants are more stable than products: K_{eq} is <1, $\Delta G°$ is positive, and the reaction is **endergonic**. $\Delta G°$ is the **Gibbs free-energy change**, with $\Delta G° = \Delta H° - T\Delta S°$. $\Delta H°$ is the change in **enthalpy**, the heat given off or consumed as a result of bond making and bond breaking. An **exothermic reaction** has a negative $\Delta H°$; an **endothermic reaction** has a positive $\Delta H°$. $\Delta S°$ is the change in **entropy**, the change in the freedom of motion of the system. A reaction with a negative $\Delta G°$ has a **favorable equilibrium constant**: the formation of products with stronger bonds and greater freedom of motion causes $\Delta G°$ to be negative. $\Delta G°$ and K_{eq} are related by the formula $\Delta G° = -RT \ln K_{eq}$.

The free energy of activation, $\Delta G^{\ddagger}$, is the energy barrier of a reaction. It is the difference between the free energy of the reactants and the free energy of the transition state. The smaller the $\Delta G^{\ddagger}$, the faster is the reaction. Anything that destabilizes the reactant or stabilizes the transition state makes the reaction go faster. **Kinetic stability** is given by $\Delta G^{\ddagger}$, **thermodynamic stability** by $\Delta G°$. The **rate** of a reaction depends on the concentration of the reactants, the temperature, and the rate constant. The **rate constant**, which is independent of concentration, indicates how easy or difficult it is for reactants to reach the transition state. A **first-order reaction** depends on the concentration of one reactant, and a **second-order reaction** on the concentration of two reactants.

KEY TERMS

acyclic (p. 121)
addition reaction (p. 135)
alkene (p. 120)
allyl group (p. 124)
allylic carbon (p. 124)
allylic hydrogen (p. 124)
Arrhenius equation (p. 146)
catalyst (p. 144)
cis isomer (p. 126)
cis–trans isomers (p. 126)
degree of unsaturation (p. 121)
E isomer (p. 130)
electrophile (p. 133)
electrophilic addition reaction (p. 135)
endergonic reaction (p. 138)
endothermic reaction (p. 140)
enthalpy (p. 140)

entropy (p. 140)
exergonic reaction (p. 138)
exothermic reaction (p. 140)
experimental energy of activation (p. 147)
first-order rate constant (p. 145)
first-order reaction (p. 145)
free energy of activation (p. 143)
functional group (p. 133)
geometric isomers (p. 126)
Gibbs free-energy change (p. 138)
intermediate (p. 148)
kinetics (p. 142)
kinetic stability (p. 143)
Le Châtelier's principle (p. 140)
mechanism of the reaction (p. 134)
nucleophile (p. 133)
rate constant (p. 145)

rate-determining step (p. 149)
rate law (p. 145)
rate-limiting step (p. 149)
reaction coordinate diagram (p. 137)
saturated hydrocarbon (p. 121)
second-order rate constant (p. 145)
second-order reaction (p. 145)
thermodynamics (p. 137)
thermodynamic stability (p. 143)
trans isomer (p. 126)
transition state (p. 137)
unsaturated hydrocarbon (p. 121)
vinyl group (p. 124)
vinylic carbon (p. 124)
vinylic hydrogen (p. 124)
Z isomer (p. 130)

PROBLEMS

36. Give the systematic name for each of the following:

a. $CH_3CH_2CHCH=CHCH_2CH_2CHCH_3$ with Br substituents

c. structure with CH_3 groups

e. cyclohexene with CH_3

b. structure: H_3C, CH_2CH_3, $C=C$, CH_3CH_2, $CH_2CH_2CHCH_3$, CH_3

d. structure: H_3C, CH_2CH_3, $C=C$, H_3C, $CH_2CH_2CH_2CH_3$

f. cyclohexene with CH_2CH_3 and CH_3

37. Give the structure of a hydrocarbon that has six carbon atoms and
   a. three vinylic hydrogens and two allylic hydrogens.
   b. three vinylic hydrogens and one allylic hydrogen.
   c. three vinylic hydrogens and no allylic hydrogens.

38. Draw the condensed structure for each of the following:
   a. (Z)-1,3,5-tribromo-2-pentene
   b. (Z)-3-methyl-2-heptene
   c. (E)-1,2-dibromo-3-isopropyl-2-hexene
   d. vinyl bromide
   e. 1,2-dimethylcyclopentene
   f. diallylamine

39. Draw the skeletal structures for the compounds in Problem 38.

40. a. Draw the condensed structures and give the systematic names for all alkenes with molecular formula C_6H_{12}, ignoring cis–trans isomers. (*Hint:* There are 13.)
   b. Which of the compounds have E and Z isomers?

41. Name the following:

a. skeletal structure

c. skeletal structure with Br

e. skeletal structure

b. skeletal structure

d. skeletal structure

f. skeletal structure

42. Draw curved arrows to show the flow of electrons responsible for the conversion of the reactants into the products:

$$H-\ddot{O}:^- + H-\underset{H}{\overset{H}{C}}-\underset{Br}{\overset{H}{C}}-H \longrightarrow H_2O + \underset{H}{\overset{H}{C}}=\underset{H}{\overset{H}{C}} + Br^-$$

43. Tamoxifen slows the growth of some breast tumors by binding to estrogen receptors. Is tamoxifen an *E* or a *Z* isomer?

tamoxifen

44. Draw the skeletal structure of 6-*sec*-butyl-7-isopropyl-3,3-dimethyldecane.

45. In a reaction in which reactant A is in equilibrium with product B at 25 °C, what are the relative amounts of A and B present at equilibrium if $\Delta G°$ at 25 °C is
  a. 2.72 kcal/mol?   **c.** −2.72 kcal/mol?
  b. 0.65 kcal/mol?   **d.** −0.65 kcal/mol?

46. Several studies have shown that β-carotene, a precursor of vitamin A, may play a role in preventing cancer. β-Carotene has a molecular formula of $C_{40}H_{56}$ and contains two rings and no triple bonds. How many double bonds does it have?

47. For each pair of bonds, which has the greater strength? Briefly explain why.
  a. $CH_3{-}Cl$ or $CH_3{-}Br$ **b.** $I{-}Br$ or $Br{-}Br$

48. Tell whether each of the following compounds has the *E* or the *Z* configuration:

49. Squalene, a hydrocarbon with molecular formula $C_{30}H_{50}$, is obtained from shark liver. (*Squalus* is Latin for "shark.") If squalene is an acyclic compound, how many π bonds does it have?

50. Assign relative priorities to each set of substituents:
  a. $-CH_2CH_2CH_3$, $-CH(CH_3)_2$, $-CH{=}CH_2$, $-CH_3$
  b. $-CH_2NH_2$, $-NH_2$, $-OH$, $-CH_2OH$
  c. $-C({=}O)CH_3$, $-CH{=}CH_2$, $-Cl$, $-C{\equiv}N$

51. Draw the geometric isomers for the following compounds, and name each one:
  a. 2-methyl-2,4-hexadiene   **b.** 1,5-heptadiene   **c.** 1,4-pentadiene

52. By following the curved red arrows, draw the product(s) of each of the reactions.

53. How many of the following names are correct? Correct the incorrect names.
  a. 3-pentene   **d.** 1-ethyl-1-pentene   **g.** 2-ethyl-2-butene
  b. 2-octene   **e.** 5-ethylcyclohexene   **h.** (*E*)-2-methyl-1-hexene
  c. 2-vinylpentane   **f.** 5-chloro-3-hexene   **i.** 2-methylcyclopentene

54. Draw structures for the following compounds:
  a. (2*E*,4*E*)-1-chloro-3-methyl-2,4-hexadiene   **c.** (3*Z*,5*Z*)-4,5-dimethyl-3,5-nonadiene
  b. (3*Z*,5*E*)-4-methyl-3,5-nonadiene   **d.** (3*E*,5*E*)-2,5-dibromo-3,5-octadiene

55. Given the reaction coordinate diagram for the reaction of A to form G, answer the following questions:

a. How many intermediates are formed in the reaction?
b. Which letters represent transition states?
c. What is the fastest step in the reaction?
d. Which is more stable, A or G?
e. Does A or E form faster from C?
f. What is the reactant of the rate-determining step?
g. Is the first step of the reaction exergonic or endergonic?
h. Is the overall reaction exergonic or endergonic?
i. Which is the more stable intermediate?
j. Which step in the forward direction has the smallest rate constant?
k. Which step in the reverse direction has the smallest rate constant?

56. a. What is the equilibrium constant of a reaction that is carried out at 25 °C (298 K) with $\Delta H° = 20$ kcal/mol and $\Delta S° = 25$ cal mol^{-1}K^{-1}?
b. What is the equilibrium constant of the same reaction carried out at 125 °C?

57. Using curved arrows, show the mechanism for the following reaction.

$$
\begin{array}{c}
\overset{\displaystyle\ddot{\text{O}}:}{\underset{R}{\overset{\parallel}{\text{C}}}}\ \text{H}-\overset{+}{\ddot{\text{O}}}-\text{H} \\
R \qquad R \qquad \text{H}
\end{array}
\rightleftharpoons
\begin{array}{c}
\overset{+\ddot{\text{O}}\text{H}}{\underset{R}{\overset{\parallel}{\text{C}}}}\ \text{H}_2\ddot{\text{O}}: \\
R \qquad R
\end{array}
\rightleftharpoons
\begin{array}{c}
:\ddot{\text{O}}\text{H} \\
R-\underset{+:\text{OH}}{\overset{|}{\text{C}}}-R \\
\text{H}\ \ \text{H}_2\ddot{\text{O}}:
\end{array}
\rightleftharpoons
\begin{array}{c}
:\ddot{\text{O}}\text{H} \\
R-\underset{:\underset{\cdot\cdot}{\text{O}}\text{H}}{\overset{|}{\text{C}}}-R \\
\text{H}_3\overset{+}{\text{O}}:
\end{array}
$$

58. a. For a reaction that is carried out at 25 °C, how much must $\Delta G°$ change in order to increase the equilibrium constant by a factor of 10?
b. How much must $\Delta H°$ change if $\Delta S° = 0$ kcal mol^{-1}K^{-1}?
c. How much must $\Delta S°$ change if $\Delta H° = 0$ kcal mol^{-1}?

59. Given that the twist-boat conformer of cyclohexane is 5.3 kcal/mole higher in free energy than the chair conformer, calculate the percentage of twist-boat conformers present in a sample of cyclohexane at 25 °C. Does your answer agree with the statement made in Section 2.12 about the relative number of molecules in these two conformations?

 Calculating Kinetic Parameters

After obtaining rate constants at several temperatures, you can calculate E_a, $\Delta H^{\ddagger}$, $\Delta G^{\ddagger}$, and $\Delta S^{\ddagger}$ for a reaction as follows:

- The Arrhenius equation allows E_a to be obtained from the slope of a plot of $\ln k$ versus $1/T$, because

$$\ln k_2 - \ln k_1 = -E_a/R\left(\frac{1}{T_2} - \frac{1}{T_1}\right)$$

- You can determine $\Delta H^{\ddagger}$ at a given temperature from E_a because $\Delta H^{\ddagger} = E_a - RT$.

- You can determine $\Delta G^{\ddagger}$, in kJ/mol, from the following equation, which relates $\Delta G^{\ddagger}$ to the rate constant at a given temperature:

$$-\Delta G^{\ddagger} = RT \ln \frac{kh}{Tk_B}$$

In this equation, h is Planck's constant (6.62608×10^{-34} Js) and k_B is the Boltzmann constant (1.38066×10^{-23} JK^{-1})
- You can determine the entropy of activation from the other two kinetic parameters via the formula $\Delta S^{\ddagger} = (\Delta H^{\ddagger} - \Delta G^{\ddagger})/T$.

Use this information to answer Problem 60.

60. From the following rate constants, determined at five temperatures, calculate the experimental energy of activation and $\Delta G^{\ddagger}$, $\Delta H^{\ddagger}$, and $\Delta S^{\ddagger}$ for the reaction at 30 °C:

Temperature	Observed rate constant
31.0 °C	$2.11 \times 10^{-5}\,\text{s}^{-1}$
40.0 °C	$4.44 \times 10^{-5}\,\text{s}^{-1}$
51.5 °C	$1.16 \times 10^{-4}\,\text{s}^{-1}$
59.8 °C	$2.10 \times 10^{-4}\,\text{s}^{-1}$
69.2 °C	$4.34 \times 10^{-4}\,\text{s}^{-1}$

CHAPTER

4

The Reactions of Alkenes

a cyclic bromonium ion

WE HAVE SEEN THAT AN **ALKENE** SUCH AS 2-BUTENE UNDERGOES AN **ELECTROPHILIC addition reaction** with HBr (Section 3.6). The first step of the reaction is a relatively slow addition of the electrophilic proton to the nucleophilic alkene to form a **carbocation intermediate**. In the second step, the positively charged carbocation intermediate (an electrophile) reacts rapidly with the negatively charged bromide ion (a nucleophile).

the electrophile adds to an sp^2 carbon of the alkene

a carbocation intermediate

the nucleophile adds to the carbocation

A curved arrow with a two-barbed arrowhead signifies the movement of two electrons.

In this chapter, we will look at a wide variety of reactions that alkenes undergo. You will see that some of the reactions form carbocation intermediates like the one formed when HBr reacts with an alkene, some form other kinds of intermediates, and some form no intermediates at all. At first glance, the reactions covered in this chapter may appear to be quite different, but you will see that they all occur by similar mechanisms. As you study each reaction, look for the feature that all alkene reactions have in common: *the relatively loosely held π electrons of the carbon–carbon double bond are attracted to an electrophile. Thus, each reaction starts with the addition of an electrophile to one of the sp^2 carbons of the alkene and concludes with the addition of a nucleophile to the other sp^2 carbon.* The end result is that the π bond breaks and the electrophile and nucleophile form new σ

bonds with the sp^2 carbons. Notice that the sp^2 carbons in the reactant have become sp^3 carbons in the product.

the double bond is composed of a σ bond and π bond

electrophile   nucleophile

the π bond has broken and new σ bonds have formed

This reactivity makes alkenes an important class of organic compounds, because they can be used to synthesize a wide variety of other compounds. For example, we will see that alkyl halides, alcohols, ethers, epoxides, and alkanes all can be synthesized from alkenes by electrophilic addition reactions. The particular product obtained depends only on the *electrophile* and the *nucleophile* used in the addition reaction.

4.1 THE ADDITION OF A HYDROGEN HALIDE TO AN ALKENE

If the electrophilic reagent that adds to an alkene is a hydrogen halide (HF, HCl, HBr, or HI), then the product of the reaction will be an alkyl halide:

2,3-dimethyl-2-butene   + HBr $\longrightarrow$ 2-bromo-2,3-dimethylbutane

cyclohexene   + HI $\longrightarrow$ iodocyclohexane

Because the alkenes in the preceding reactions have the same substituents on both sp^2 carbons, it is easy to predict the product of the reaction: the electrophile (H^+) adds to one of the sp^2 carbons, and the nucleophile (X^-) adds to the other sp^2 carbon. It does not matter which sp^2 carbon the electrophile attaches to, because the same product will be obtained in either case.

But what happens if the alkene does not have the same substituents on both sp^2 carbons? Which sp^2 carbon gets the hydrogen? For example, does the addition of HCl to 2-methylpropene produce *tert*-butyl chloride or isobutyl chloride?

2-methylpropene   +   HCl $\longrightarrow$ *tert*-butyl chloride   or   isobutyl chloride

To answer this question, we need to carry out the reaction, isolate the products, and identify them. When we do, we find that the only product of the reaction is *tert*-butyl chloride. Now we need to find out why this is the only product so that we can use this knowledge to predict the products of other alkene reactions. To do this, we need to look again at the **mechanism of the reaction** (Section 3.6).

Recall that the first step of the reaction—the addition of H^+ to an sp^2 carbon to form either the *tert*-butyl cation or the isobutyl cation—is the rate-determining step (Section 3.7). If there is any difference in the rate of formation of these two carbocations, then the one that is formed faster will be the predominant product of the first step.

Moreover, because carbocation formation is rate determining, the particular carbocation that is formed in the first step determines the final product of the reaction. That is, if the *tert*-butyl cation is formed, it will react rapidly with Cl⁻ to form *tert*-butyl chloride. On the other hand, if the isobutyl cation is formed, it will react rapidly with Cl⁻ to form isobutyl chloride. Since the only product of the reaction is *tert*-butyl chloride, we know that the *tert*-butyl cation is formed much faster than the isobutyl cation.

$$
CH_3\overset{CH_3}{\underset{+}{C}}CH_3 + :\ddot{C}l:^- \longrightarrow CH_3\overset{CH_3}{\underset{Cl}{C}}CH_3
$$

tert-butyl cation

tert-butyl chloride
only product formed

$$
CH_3\overset{CH_3}{\underset{}{C}}{=}CH_2 + H{-}Cl
$$

$$
CH_3\overset{CH_3}{\underset{+}{C}H}CH_2 + :\ddot{C}l:^- \longrightarrow CH_3\overset{CH_3}{\underset{}{C}H}CH_2Cl
$$

isobutyl cation

isobutyl chloride
not formed

The *sp²* carbon that does *not* become attached to the proton is the carbon that is positively charged in the carbocation.

The question now is, why is the *tert*-butyl cation formed faster than the isobutyl cation? To answer this, we need to look at the factors that affect the stability of carbocations and thus the ease with which they are formed.

4.2 CARBOCATION STABILITY DEPENDS ON THE NUMBER OF ALKYL GROUPS ATTACHED TO THE POSITIVELY CHARGED CARBON

Carbocations are classified according to the carbon atom that carries the positive charge: a **primary carbocation** has a positive charge on a primary carbon, a **secondary carbocation** has a positive charge on a secondary carbon, and a **tertiary carbocation** has a positive charge on a tertiary carbon. Thus, the stability of a carbocation increases as the number of alkyl substituents bonded to the positively charged carbon increases. In other words, tertiary carbocations are more stable than secondary carbocations, and secondary carbocations are more stable than primary carbocations. Keep in mind, however, that these stabilities are relative stabilities. Carbocations are rarely stable enough to isolate.

relative stabilities of carbocations

$$
\boxed{\text{most stable}} \; R{-}\overset{R}{\underset{R}{C}}{+} \; > \; R{-}\overset{R}{\underset{H}{C}}{+} \; > \; R{-}\overset{H}{\underset{H}{C}}{+} \; > \; H{-}\overset{H}{\underset{H}{C}}{+} \; \boxed{\text{least stable}}
$$

a tertiary
carbocation

a secondary
carbocation

a primary
carbocation

methyl cation

Alkyl groups stabilize carbocations: the greater the number of alkyl groups bonded to the positively charged carbon, the more stable the carbocation.

The reason for this pattern of decreasing stability is that alkyl groups bonded to the positively charged carbon decrease the concentration of positive charge on the carbon, and decreasing the concentration of positive charge makes the carbocation more stable. Notice that the blue (representing positive charge) in these electrostatic potential maps is most intense for the least stable methyl cation and is least intense for the most stable *tert*-butyl cation.

Carbocation stability: 3° > 2° > 1°

electrostatic
potential map
for the *tert*-butyl cation

electrostatic
potential map
for the isopropyl cation

electrostatic
potential map
for the ethyl cation

electrostatic
potential map
for the methyl cation

How do alkyl groups decrease the concentration of positive charge on the carbon? Recall that the positive charge on a carbon signifies an empty *p* orbital (Section 1.10). Figure 4.1 shows that in the ethyl cation, the orbital of an adjacent C—H σ bond can overlap the empty *p* orbital. No such overlap is possible in the methyl cation. Movement of electrons from the σ bond orbital toward the vacant *p* orbital of the ethyl cation decreases the charge on the sp^2 carbon and causes a partial positive charge to develop on the atoms bonded by the σ bond. Therefore, the positive charge is no longer concentrated solely on one atom, but is delocalized—that is, spread out over a larger volume of space. This dispersion of positive charge stabilizes the carbocation because a charged species is more stable if its charge is spread out (delocalized) over more than one atom (Section 1.23). Delocalization of electrons by the overlap of a σ bond orbital with an empty orbital on an adjacent carbon is called **hyperconjugation** (Section 2.10). The simple molecular orbital diagram in Figure 4.2 is another way of depicting the stabilization achieved by the overlap of a filled C—H σ bond orbital with an empty *p* orbital.

▶ **Figure 4.1**
Stabilization of a carbocation by hyperconjugation. The electrons of an adjacent C—H σ bond orbital of the ethyl cation spread into the empty *p* orbital. Note that hyperconjugation cannot occur in a methyl cation.

▶ **Figure 4.2**
A molecular orbital diagram showing the stabilization achieved by overlapping the electrons of a C—H bond with an empty *p* orbital.

Hyperconjugation occurs only if the σ bond orbital and the empty *p* orbital have the proper orientations. The proper orientations are easily achieved because there is free rotation about the carbon–carbon σ bond (Section 2.10). Notice that the σ bonds capable of overlapping the empty *p* orbital are those *attached to an atom that is attached to the positively charged carbon.* In the *tert*-butyl cation, nine σ bond orbitals can potentially overlap the empty *p* orbital of the positively charged carbon. (The nine σ bonds are indicated below by red dots.) The isopropyl cation has six such orbitals, and the ethyl and propyl cations each have three. Therefore, there is greater stabilization through hyperconjugation in the tertiary *tert*-butyl cation than in the secondary isopropyl cation, and greater stabilization in the secondary isopropyl cation than in the primary ethyl or primary propyl cation. Notice that the ethyl and propyl cations each have about the same stability, because both C—H and C—C σ bond orbitals can overlap the empty *p* orbital.

tert-butyl cation   isopropyl cation   ethyl cation   propyl cation

---

PROBLEM 1◆

a. How many σ bond orbitals are available for overlap with the vacant p orbital in the methyl cation?

b. Which is more stable, a methyl cation or an ethyl cation?

PROBLEM 2◆

a. How many σ bond orbitals are available for overlap with the vacant p orbital in

    1. the isobutyl cation   **2.** the n-butyl cation   **3.** the sec-butyl cation

b. Which of the carbocations in part **a** is most stable?

PROBLEM 3◆

List the following carbocations in order of decreasing stability:

$$\underset{\quad+}{\text{a.}}\ \ CH_3CH_2\overset{\displaystyle CH_3}{\underset{\displaystyle |}{C}}CH_3 \qquad CH_3CH_2\overset{+}{C}HCH_3 \qquad CH_3CH_2CH_2\overset{+}{C}H_2$$

$$\text{b.}\ \ CH_3CHCH_2\overset{+}{C}H_2 \qquad CH_3CHCH_2\overset{+}{C}H_2 \qquad CH_3CHCH_2\overset{+}{C}H_2$$
$$\underset{\displaystyle Cl}{|} \qquad\qquad\qquad \underset{\displaystyle CH_3}{|} \qquad\qquad\qquad \underset{\displaystyle F}{|}$$

4.3 WHAT DOES THE STRUCTURE OF THE TRANSITION STATE LOOK LIKE?

Knowing something about the structure of the transition state can help you predict the products of a reaction. In Section 3.7, you saw that the structure of the transition state resembles both the structure of the reactants and the structure of the products. But which does it resemble more closely? Is its structure more similar to that of the reactants (I in the reaction scheme below), or to that of the products (III), or is its structure about equally similar to that of the reactants and that of the products (II)?

$$A{-}B\ +\ C \longrightarrow \left[\begin{array}{l}\text{(I)}\ \ \ A\text{----}B\text{----------}C \\ \text{(II)}\ \ A\text{-------}B\text{-------}C \\ \text{(III)}\ A\text{----------}B\text{----}C\end{array}\right]^{\ddagger} \longrightarrow A\ +\ B{-}C$$

reactants   transition state   products

‡ symbolizes the transition state

This question is answered by the **Hammond postulate**, which says that *the transition state is more similar in structure to the species to which it is more similar in energy.* In an exergonic reaction, the energy of the transition state is more similar to the energy to the reactants than to the energy of the products (Figure 4.3, curve I), so its structure will more closely resemble that of the reactants. In an endergonic reaction (curve III), the energy of the transition state is more similar to the energy of the products, so its structure will more closely resemble that of the products. Only when the reactants and products have identical energies (curve II) would we expect the structure of the transition state to be exactly halfway between that of the reactants and that of the products.

BIOGRAPHY

George Simms Hammond (1921–2005) *was born in Maine and received a B.S. from Bates College in 1943 and a Ph.D. from Harvard University in 1947. He was a professor of chemistry at Iowa State University and at the California Institute of Technology and was a scientist at Allied Chemical Co.*

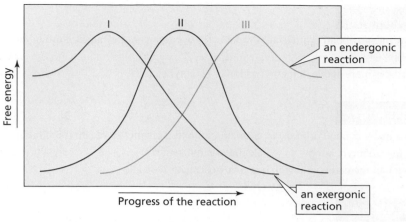

▶ **Figure 4.3**
Reaction coordinate diagrams for reactions with an early transition state (I), a midway transition state (II), and a late transition state (III).

The transition state is more similar in structure to the species to which it is more similar in energy.

In an exergonic reaction, the transition state is more similar in energy to the reactants, so its structure resembles that of the reactants.

In an endergonic reaction, the transition state is more similar in energy to the products, so its structure resembles that of the products.

Now we can understand why the *tert*-butyl cation is formed faster than the isobutyl cation when 2-methylpropene reacts with HCl. Because the formation of a carbocation is an endergonic reaction (Figure 4.4), the structure of the transition state resembles the structure of the carbocation product. This means that the transition state has a significant amount of positive charge on a carbon. The same factors that stabilize the positively charged carbocation stabilize the partially positively charged transition state. We know that the *tert*-butyl cation (a tertiary carbocation) is more stable than the isobutyl cation (a primary carbocation). Therefore, the transition state leading to the *tert*-butyl cation is more stable (lower in energy) than the transition state leading to the isobutyl cation. Note, however, that because the amount of positive charge in the transition state is not as great as the amount of positive charge in the carbocation product, the difference in the stabilities of the two transition states is not as great as the difference in the stabilities of the two carbocation products (Figure 4.4).

▶ **Figure 4.4**
Reaction coordinate diagram for the addition of H⁺ to 2-methylpropene to form the primary isobutyl cation and the tertiary *tert*-butyl cation.

We have seen that the rate of a reaction is determined by the free energy of activation, which is the difference between the free energy of the transition state and the free energy of the reactant (Section 3.7). Thus, the *tert*-butyl cation, with a smaller energy of activation, is formed faster than the isobutyl cation. *In an electrophilic addition reaction, the more stable carbocation is the one that is formed more rapidly.*

Formation of the carbocation is the rate-limiting step of the reaction. Therefore, the relative rates of formation of the two carbocations determine the relative amounts of the products that are formed. If the difference in the rates is small, both products will be formed, but the major product will be the one formed from reaction of the nucleophile with the more stable (faster formed) carbocation. If the difference in the rates is sufficiently large, the product formed from reaction of the nucleophile with the more stable carbocation will be the only product of the reaction. For example, when HCl adds to 2-methylpropene, the rates of formation of the two possible carbocation intermediates—one primary and the other tertiary—are sufficiently different to cause *tert*-butyl chloride to be the only product of the reaction.

PROBLEM 4 ♦

For each of the following reaction coordinate diagrams, tell whether the structure of the transition state will be more similar to the structure of the reactants or to the structure of the products:

a.   b.   c.   d.

4.4 ELECTROPHILIC ADDITION REACTIONS ARE REGIOSELECTIVE

When an alkene that has different substituents on its sp^2 carbons undergoes an electrophilic addition reaction, the electrophile can add to two different sp^2 carbons. We have just seen that the major product of the reaction is the one obtained by adding the electrophile to the sp^2 carbon that results in formation of the more stable carbocation (Section 4.3). For example, when propene reacts with HCl, the proton can add to the number-1 carbon (C-1) to form a secondary carbocation, or it can add to the number-2 carbon (C-2) to form a primary carbocation. Because the secondary carbocation is more stable, it is formed more rapidly. (Primary carbocations are so unstable that they form only with great difficulty.) The product of the reaction, therefore, is 2-chloropropane.

$$\underset{\substack{2\quad\ 1\\ CH_3CH=CH_2}}{} \quad \xrightarrow{\textbf{HCl}} \quad \overset{+}{CH_3}\overset{}{C}HCH_3 \quad \xrightarrow{\textbf{Cl}^-} \quad \underset{\textbf{2-chloropropane}}{CH_3\overset{\overset{\displaystyle Cl}{|}}{C}HCH_3}$$

a secondary carbocation

$$\xrightarrow{\textbf{HCl}} \quad \times\!\!\rightarrow \quad CH_3CH_2\overset{+}{C}H_2$$

a primary carbocation

The major product obtained from the addition of HI to 2-methyl-2-butene is 2-iodo-2-methylbutane; only a small amount of 2-iodo-3-methylbutane is obtained. The major product obtained from the addition of HBr to 1-methylcyclohexene is 1-bromo-1-methylcyclohexane. In both cases, the major product is the one that results from forming the more stable tertiary carbocation because it is formed more rapidly.

$$\underset{\textbf{2-methyl-2-butene}}{CH_3CH=\overset{\overset{\displaystyle CH_3}{|}}{C}CH_3} + HI \longrightarrow \underset{\substack{\textbf{2-iodo-2-methylbutane}\\ \textbf{major product}}}{CH_3CH_2\overset{\overset{\displaystyle CH_3}{|}}{\underset{\underset{\displaystyle I}{|}}{C}}CH_3} + \underset{\substack{\textbf{2-iodo-3-methylbutane}\\ \textbf{minor product}}}{CH_3\overset{\overset{\displaystyle CH_3}{|}}{C}H\overset{\overset{}{}}{\underset{\underset{\displaystyle I}{|}}{C}}HCH_3}$$

1-methylcyclohexene + HBr ⟶ 1-bromo-1-methyl-cyclohexane **major product** + 1-bromo-2-methyl-cyclohexane **minor product**

The two products of each of these reactions are *constitutional isomers*. We saw in Chapter 2 that **constitutional isomers** have the same molecular formula, but differ in how their atoms are connected. A reaction (such as either of those just shown) in which two or more constitutional isomers could be obtained as products, but one of them predominates, is called a **regioselective reaction**.

There are degrees of **regioselectivity**: a reaction can be *moderately regioselective, highly regioselective,* or *completely regioselective.* In a completely regioselective reaction, one of the possible products is not formed at all. The addition of a hydrogen halide to 2-methylpropene (where the two possible carbocations are tertiary and primary) is more highly regioselective than the addition of a hydrogen halide to 2-methyl-2-butene (where the two possible carbocations are tertiary and secondary) because the two carbocations formed from 2-methyl-2-butene are closer in stability.

The addition of HBr to 2-pentene is not regioselective. Because the addition of H^+ to either of the sp^2 carbons produces a secondary carbocation, both carbocation intermediates have the same stability, so both are formed with equal ease. Thus, approximately equal amounts of the two alkyl halides are formed.

> **Regioselectivity is the preferential formation of one constitutional isomer over another.**

$$CH_3CH=CHCH_2CH_3 \ + \ HBr \ \longrightarrow \ CH_3\overset{\underset{\mid}{Br}}{C}HCH_2CH_2CH_3 \ + \ CH_3CH_2\overset{\underset{\mid}{Br}}{C}HCH_2CH_3$$

2-pentene   2-bromopentane   3-bromopentane

50%   50%

Vladimir Markovnikov was the first to recognize that the major product obtained when a hydrogen halide is added to an alkene results from addition of the H^+ to the sp^2 carbon that is bonded to the greater number of hydrogens. As a result, this is often referred to as **Markovnikov's rule**. However, Markovnikov's rule is valid only for alkene addition reactions in which the electrophile is H^+. A better rule, and the one we will use in this book, is one that applies to all alkene addition reactions: *the electrophile adds to the* sp^2 *carbon that is bonded to the greater number of hydrogens.*

> **The electrophile adds to the sp^2 carbon that is bonded to the greater number of hydrogens.**

The rule is simply a quick way to determine the major product of an electrophilic addition reaction. The answer you get by using the rule will be the same as the answer you get by determining relative carbocation stabilities. In the following reaction, for example,

$$CH_3CH_2\overset{2}{C}H=\overset{1}{C}H_2 \ + \ HCl \ \longrightarrow \ CH_3CH_2\overset{\underset{\mid}{Cl}}{C}HCH_3$$

we can say that the electrophile (in this case, H^+) adds preferentially to C-1 because C-1 is bonded to two hydrogens, whereas C-2 is bonded to only one hydrogen. Or we can say that H^+ adds to C-1 because that results in the formation of a secondary carbocation, which is more stable than the primary carbocation that would have to be formed if H^+ added to C-2.

B I O G R A P H Y

Vladimir Vasilevich Markovnikov (1837–1904) *was born in Russia, the son of an army officer, and was a professor of chemistry at Kazan, Odessa, and Moscow universities. By synthesizing rings containing four carbons and seven carbons, he disproved the notion that carbon could form only five- and six-membered rings.*

PROBLEM 5◆

What would be the major product obtained from the addition of HBr to each of the following compounds?

a. $CH_3CH_2CH=CH_2$

c. (cyclopentene with CH_3)

e. (cyclohexane with $=CH_2$)

b. $CH_3CH=\overset{\underset{\mid}{CH_3}}{C}CH_3$

d. $CH_2=\overset{\underset{\mid}{CH_3}}{C}CH_2CH_2CH_3$

f. $CH_3CH=CHCH_3$

PROBLEM-SOLVING STRATEGY

Planning the Synthesis of an Alkyl Halide

a. What alkene should be used to synthesize 3-bromohexane?

$$? \; + \; HBr \; \longrightarrow \; CH_3CH_2CHCH_2CH_2CH_3$$
$$\qquad\qquad\qquad\qquad\qquad\quad |$$
$$\qquad\qquad\qquad\qquad\qquad\; Br$$

3-bromohexane

The best way to answer this kind of question is to begin by listing all the alkenes that could be used. Because you want to synthesize an alkyl halide that has a bromo substituent at the 3-position, the alkene should have an sp^2 carbon at that position. Two alkenes fit the description: 2-hexene and 3-hexene.

$$CH_3CH{=}CHCH_2CH_2CH_3 \qquad\qquad CH_3CH_2CH{=}CHCH_2CH_3$$

2-hexene **3-hexene**

Because there are two possibilities, we next need to decide whether there is any advantage to using one over the other. The addition of H^+ to 2-hexene can form two different carbocations, but they are both secondary carbocations. Because they have the same stability, approximately equal amounts of each will be formed. Therefore, half of the product will be 3-bromohexane and half will be 2-bromohexane.

The addition of H^+ to either of the sp^2 carbons of 3-hexene, on the other hand, forms the same carbocation because the alkene is symmetrical. Therefore, all of the product will be the desired 3-bromohexane.

Because all the alkyl halide formed from 3-hexene is the desired product (3-bromohexane), but only half the alkyl halide formed from 2-hexene is 3-bromohexane, 3-hexene is the best alkene to use to prepare 3-bromohexane.

b. What alkene should be used to synthesize 2-bromopentane?

$$? \; + \; HBr \; \longrightarrow \; CH_3CHCH_2CH_2CH_3$$
$$\qquad\qquad\qquad\qquad\qquad\; |$$
$$\qquad\qquad\qquad\qquad\quad Br$$

2-bromopentane

Either 1-pentene or 2-pentene could be used because both have an sp^2 carbon at the 2-position.

$$CH_2{=}CHCH_2CH_2CH_3 \qquad\qquad CH_3CH{=}CHCH_2CH_3$$

1-pentene **2-pentene**

When H^+ adds to 1-pentene, one of the carbocations that could be formed is secondary and the other is primary. A secondary carbocation is more stable than a primary carbocation, which is so unstable that little, if any, will be formed. Thus, 2-bromopentane will be the only product of the reaction.

$$CH_2=CHCH_2CH_2CH_3 \quad \xrightarrow[HBr]{} \quad \underset{+}{CH_3CHCH_2CH_2CH_3} \quad \xrightarrow{Br^-} \quad \underset{|}{CH_3CHCH_2CH_2CH_3}$$

1-pentene

Br

2-bromopentane

$$\xrightarrow[HBr]{\times} \quad \underset{+}{CH_2CH_2CH_2CH_2CH_3}$$

When H^+ adds to 2-pentene, on the other hand, the two carbocations that can be formed are both secondary. Because they have the same stability, they will be formed in approximately equal amounts. Thus, only about half of the product of the reaction will be 2-bromopentane. The other half will be 3-bromopentane.

$$CH_3CH=CHCH_2CH_3$$

2-pentene

$$\xrightarrow[HBr]{} \quad \underset{+}{CH_3CHCH_2CH_2CH_3} \quad \xrightarrow{Br^-} \quad \underset{|}{CH_3CHCH_2CH_2CH_3}$$

Br

2-bromopentane

$$\xrightarrow[HBr]{} \quad \underset{+}{CH_3CH_2CHCH_2CH_3} \quad \xrightarrow{Br^-} \quad \underset{|}{CH_3CH_2CHCH_2CH_3}$$

Br

3-bromopentane

Because all the alkyl halide formed from 1-pentene is the desired product (2-bromopentane), but only half the alkyl halide formed from 2-pentene is 2-bromopentane, 1-pentene is the best alkene to use to prepare 2-bromopentane.

Now continue on to Problem 6.

---

chem place Tutorial:
First step in addition of hydrogen halides to alkenes

Tutorial:
Second step in addition of hydrogen halides to alkenes

Mechanistic Tutorial:
Addition of HBr to an alkene

PROBLEM 6 ◆

What alkene should be used to synthesize each of the following alkyl bromides?

a.
$$\underset{Br}{\overset{CH_3}{\underset{|}{\overset{|}{CH_3CCH_3}}}}$$

c.
[cyclohexane with] $\underset{Br}{\overset{CH_3}{\underset{|}{\overset{|}{CCH_3}}}}$

b.
[cyclohexane]—$\underset{Br}{\overset{}{\underset{|}{CH_2CHCH_3}}}$

d.
[cyclohexane with] $\overset{CH_2CH_3}{\underset{Br}{}}$

PROBLEM 7 ◆

To which compound in each of the following pairs is the addition of HBr more highly regioselective?

a. $\underset{CH_3CH_2\overset{CH_3}{\underset{|}{C}}=CH_2}{}$ or $\underset{CH_3\overset{CH_3}{\underset{|}{C}}=CHCH_3}{}$

b. [cyclohexane with =CH_2] or [cyclohexene with CH_3]

4.5 THE ADDITION OF WATER TO AN ALKENE

An alkene does not react with water, because there is no electrophile present to start a reaction by adding to the nucleophilic alkene. The O—H bonds of water are too strong—water is too weakly acidic—to allow the hydrogen to act as an electrophile for this reaction.

$$CH_3CH=CH_2 \quad + \quad H_2O \quad \longrightarrow \quad \text{no reaction}$$

If an acid (the acid used most often is H_2SO_4) is added to the solution, then the outcome is much different: a reaction will occur because the acid provides an electrophile

(H^+). The product of the reaction is an *alcohol*. The addition of water to a molecule is called **hydration**, so we can say that an alkene will be *hydrated* in the presence of water and acid.*

$$\boxed{\pi \text{ bond breaks}}$$

$$CH_3CH\!\!=\!\!CH_2 \ + \ \boxed{H_2O} \ \xrightleftharpoons{H_2SO_4} \ CH_3CH\!-\!CH_2$$

$$\boxed{\text{new } \sigma \text{ bond}} \qquad \boxed{\text{new } \sigma \text{ bond}}$$
$$\underset{\text{OH \quad H}}{}$$
2-propanol
an alcohol

H_2SO_4 ($pK_a = -5$) is a strong acid, so it dissociates almost completely in an aqueous solution (Section 1.17). The acid that participates in the reaction, therefore, is most apt to be a hydrated proton—called a hydronium ion, which we will write as H_3O^+.

$$H_2SO_4 \ + \ H_2O \ \rightleftharpoons \ H_3O^+ \ + \ HSO_4^-$$
hydronium ion

Notice that the first two steps of the *mechanism for the acid-catalyzed addition of water to an alkene* are essentially the same as the two steps of the *mechanism for the addition of a hydrogen halide to an alkene* (Section 4.1):

MECHANISM FOR THE ACID-CATALYZED ADDITION OF WATER

- The electrophile (H^+) adds to the sp^2 carbon that is bonded to the greater number of hydrogens.
- The nucleophile (H_2O) adds to the carbocation, forming a protonated alcohol.
- The protonated alcohol loses a proton because the pH of the solution is greater than the pK_a of the protonated alcohol (Section 1.25). (We have seen that protonated alcohols are very strong acids; Section 1.18).

As we saw in Section 3.7, the addition of the electrophile to the alkene is relatively slow, whereas the subsequent addition of the nucleophile to the carbocation occurs rapidly. The reaction of the carbocation with a nucleophile is so fast, in fact, that the carbocation combines with whatever nucleophile it collides with. Notice that there are two nucleophiles in solution, water and the conjugate base (HSO_4^-) of the acid that was used to start the reaction. (HO^- is not a nucleophile in this reaction because there is no

chem
place

Mechanistic Tutorial:
First step in the mechanism of hydration

Mechanistic Tutorial:
Second step in the mechanism of hydration

Mechanistic Tutorial:
Third step in the mechanism of hydration

*Because an alkene is not soluble in water, water is not the solvent used in this reaction. A solvent, such as DMSO (Section 8.2), is required that will not react with the reactants, the products, or any intermediates formed in the reaction but in which both the alkene and water can dissolve.

Do not memorize the products of alkene addition reactions. Instead, for each reaction, ask yourself, "What is the electrophile?" and "What nucleophile is present in the greatest concentration?"

appreciable concentration of HO^- in an acidic solution.)* Because the concentration of water is much greater than the concentration of HSO_4^-, the carbocation is much more likely to collide with water. The final product of the addition reaction, therefore, is an alcohol.

A proton adds to the alkene in the first step, but a proton is returned to the reaction mixture in the final step. Overall, then, a proton is not consumed. A species that increases the rate of a reaction but is not consumed during the course of the reaction is called a **catalyst**. Catalysts increase the reaction rate by decreasing the free energy of activation (Section 3.7). They do *not* affect the equilibrium constant of the reaction. In other words, a catalyst increases the *rate* at which a product is formed, but does not affect the *amount* of product formed when the reaction has reached equilibrium. The catalyst employed in the hydration of an alkene is an acid, so the hydration reaction is called an **acid-catalyzed reaction**.

chem place
Mechanistic Tutorial:
First step in the mechanism of hydration showing orientation

Mechanistic Tutorial:
Second step in the mechanism of hydration showing orientation

Mechanistic Tutorial:
Addition of water to an alkene

Tutorial:
Addition of water to an alkene

PROBLEM 8 ◆

The pK_a of a protonated alcohol is about -2.5, and the pK_a of an alcohol is about 15. Therefore, as long as the pH of the solution is greater than _____ and less than _____, more than 50% of 2-propanol (the product of the reaction on page 166) will be in its neutral, nonprotonated form.

PROBLEM 9 ◆

Answer the following questions about the mechanism for the acid-catalyzed hydration of an alkene:
a. How many transition states are there?
b. How many intermediates are there?
c. Which step in the forward direction has the smallest rate constant?

PROBLEM 10 ◆

Give the major product obtained from the acid-catalyzed hydration of each of the following alkenes:

a. $CH_3CH_2CH_2CH{=}CH_2$ c. $CH_3CH_2CH_2CH{=}CHCH_3$

b. ⬡   d. ⬡$={=}CH_2$

4.6 THE ADDITION OF AN ALCOHOL TO AN ALKENE

Alcohols react with alkenes in the same way that water does, so this reaction, too, requires an acid catalyst. The product of the reaction is an *ether*.

$$CH_3CH{=}CH_2 \ + \ CH_3OH \ \xrightarrow{H_2SO_4} \ CH_3CH{-}CH_2$$

π bond breaks
new σ bond OCH_3 H   new σ bond
2-methoxypropane
an ether

The *mechanism for the acid-catalyzed addition of an alcohol* is essentially the same as the *mechanism for the acid-catalyzed addition of water*. The only difference is the nucleophile is ROH instead of HOH.

---

*At pH = 4, for example, the concentration of HO^- is 1×10^{-10} M, whereas the concentration of water in a dilute aqueous solution is 55.5 M.

MECHANISM FOR THE ACID-CATALYZED ADDITION OF AN ALCOHOL

$$CH_3CH=CH_2 \ + \ H-\overset{+}{\overset{\cdot\cdot}{O}}CH_3 \ \overset{slow}{\rightleftharpoons} \ CH_3\overset{+}{CH}CH_3 \ + \ CH_3\overset{\cdot\cdot}{\overset{\cdot\cdot}{O}}H \ \overset{fast}{\rightleftharpoons} \ CH_3CHCH_3$$

$$\overset{+}{:}OCH_3$$

- The electrophile (H^+) adds to the sp^2 carbon that is bonded to the greater number of hydrogens.
- The nucleophile (CH_3OH) adds to the carbocation, forming a protonated ether.
- The protonated ether loses a proton, because the pH of the solution is greater than the pK_a of the protonated ether ($pK_a \sim -3.6$).

chem place Synthetic Tutorial: Addition of an alcohol to an alkene

---

PROBLEM 11

a. Give the major product of each of the following reactions:

$$\text{CH}_3$$
1. $CH_3C=CH_2 \ + \ HCl \longrightarrow$

$$\text{CH}_3$$
2. $CH_3C=CH_2 \ + \ HBr \longrightarrow$

$$\text{CH}_3$$
3. $CH_3C=CH_2 \ + \ H_2O \ \xrightarrow{H_2SO_4}$

$$\text{CH}_3$$
4. $CH_3C=CH_2 \ + \ CH_3OH \ \xrightarrow{H_2SO_4}$

b. What do all the reactions have in common?
c. How do all the reactions differ?

PROBLEM 12   SOLVED

How could the following compound be prepared, using an alkene as one of the starting materials?

$$\text{CH}_3$$
$$CH_3CHOCHCH_2CH_3$$
$$\text{CH}_3$$

Solution

The desired compound—called a target molecule—can be prepared by the acid-catalyzed addition of an alcohol to an alkene. For the synthesis of this ether, there are two different combinations of an alkene and an alcohol that could be used.

$$CH_3CH=CH_2 \ + \ CH_3CHCH_2CH_3 \ \xrightarrow{H_2SO_4} \ CH_3CHOCHCH_2CH_3$$
$$\qquad\qquad\qquad\qquad OH \qquad\qquad\qquad\qquad CH_3$$

or

$$CH_3CH=CHCH_3 \ + \ CH_3CHCH_3 \ \xrightarrow{H_2SO_4} \ CH_3CHOCHCH_2CH_3$$
$$\qquad\qquad\qquad\qquad OH \qquad\qquad\qquad\qquad CH_3$$

PROBLEM 13

How could the following compounds be prepared, using an alkene as one of the starting materials?

a. ⬡—OCH_3

b. CH_3OCCH_3 with CH_3 above and CH_3 below

c. ⬠—OH

d. $CH_3CHCH_2CH_3$ with OH below

PROBLEM 14

Propose a mechanism for the following reaction (remember to use curved arrows when showing a mechanism):

$$CH_3CHCH_2CH_2OH \quad + \quad CH_3C{=}CH_2 \quad \xrightarrow{H_2SO_4} \quad CH_3CHCH_2CH_2OCCH_3$$
with CH_3 groups below the first carbon and below the alkene carbon, and CH_3 above and below the product carbon.

4.7 A CARBOCATION WILL REARRANGE IF IT CAN FORM A MORE STABLE CARBOCATION

BIOGRAPHY

Frank (Rocky) Clifford Whitmore (1887–1947) *was born in Massachusetts, received a Ph.D. from Harvard University, and was a professor of chemistry at Minnesota, Northwestern, and Pennsylvania State universities. Whitmore never slept a full night; he put in 20-hour workdays, and when he got tired, he took a one-hour nap. He generally had 30 graduate students working in his lab at a time. He wrote an advanced textbook that was considered a milestone in the field of organic chemistry.*

Some electrophilic addition reactions give products that clearly are not what you would get from adding an electrophile to the sp^2 carbon bonded to the greater number of hydrogens and a nucleophile to the other sp^2 carbon. For example, the addition of HBr to 3-methyl-1-butene forms two products. 2-Bromo-3-methylbutane (the minor product) is the one you would predict from adding H^+ to the sp^2 carbon bonded to the greater number of hydrogens and Br^- to the other sp^2 carbon. 2-Bromo-2-methylbutane, however, is an "unexpected" product, and yet it is the major product of the reaction.

In another example, the addition of HCl to 3,3-dimethyl-1-butene forms both 3-chloro-2,2-dimethylbutane (the expected product) and 2-chloro-2,3-dimethylbutane (the unexpected product). Again, the unexpected product is the major product of the reaction.

F. C. Whitmore was the first to suggest that the unexpected product results from a *rearrangement* of the carbocation intermediate. Not all carbocations rearrange. In fact, none of the carbocation intermediates that we have seen up to this point rearranges. Carbocations rearrange only if they become more stable as a result of the rearrangement. For example, when an electrophile adds to 3-methyl-1-butene, a *secondary* carbocation is formed initially. However, the secondary carbocation has a hydrogen that can shift with its pair of electrons to the adjacent positively charged carbon, creating a more stable *tertiary* carbocation.

Rearrangement results in a change in the way the atoms are connected.

As a result of the **carbocation rearrangement**, two alkyl halides are formed, one from the addition of the nucleophile to the unrearranged carbocation and one from the addition of the nucleophile to the rearranged carbocation. The major product is the one that results from adding the nucleophile to the rearranged carbocation. Because it entails the shifting of a hydrogen with its pair of electrons, the rearrangement is called a hydride shift. (Recall that H:$^-$ is a hydride ion.) More specifically, it is called a **1,2-hydride shift** because the hydride ion moves from one carbon to an *adjacent* carbon. (Notice that this does not mean it moves from C-1 to C-2.)

In the following reaction, after 3,3-dimethyl-1-butene acquires an electrophile to form a *secondary* carbocation, one of the methyl groups, with its pair of electrons, shifts to the adjacent positively charged carbon to form a more stable *tertiary* carbocation. This kind of shift is called a **1,2-methyl shift**. Again, the major product is the one formed by adding the nucleophile to the rearranged carbocation.

A shift is the movement of a species from one carbon to an adjacent carbon; 1,3-shifts normally do not occur. Furthermore, if a rearrangement does not lead to a more stable carbocation, then the rearrangement typically does not occur. For example, when a proton adds to 4-methyl-1-pentene, a secondary carbocation is formed. A 1,2-hydride shift would form a different secondary carbocation, but because both carbocations are equally stable, there is no energetic advantage to the shift. Consequently, the rearrangement does not occur, and only one alkyl halide is formed.

Carbocation rearrangements also can occur by *ring expansion*, another type of 1,2-shift.

In this example, ring expansion produces a carbocation that is more stable because it is tertiary rather than secondary and because a five-membered ring has less angle strain than a four-membered ring (Section 2.11).

In subsequent chapters, you will study other reactions that form carbocation intermediates. Keep in mind that *whenever a reaction leads to the formation of a carbocation, you must check its structure for the possibility of rearrangement.*

Whenever a reaction forms a carbocation intermediate, check to see if the carbocation will rearrange.

PROBLEM 15   SOLVED

Which of the following carbocations would be expected to rearrange?

a.
$\overset{+}{C}H_2$ (on cyclohexane ring)

d. $CH_3\overset{CH_3}{\underset{+}{C}}CH_2CH_3$

b. $CH_3\overset{CH_3}{CH}\overset{}{\underset{+}{C}}HCH_3$

e.
CH_3 (on cyclohexane ring with +)

c.
CH_3 (on cyclohexane ring with +)

f. $CH_3CH_2\overset{}{\underset{+}{C}}HCH_3$

Solution

a. This primary carbocation will rearrange because a 1,2-hydride shift converts it into a tertiary carbocation.

$$H\overset{+}{\curvearrowright}CH_2 \quad \longrightarrow \quad CH_3 \;\; +$$

b. This secondary carbocation will rearrange because a 1,2-hydride shift converts it into a tertiary carbocation.

$$CH_3\overset{CH_3}{\underset{H}{C}}\overset{+}{\text{—}}CHCH_3 \quad \longrightarrow \quad CH_3\overset{CH_3}{\underset{+}{C}}CH_2CH_3$$

c. This carbocation will not rearrange because it is tertiary and its stability cannot be improved by a carbocation rearrangement.

d. This carbocation will not rearrange because it is tertiary and its stability cannot be improved by a carbocation rearrangement.

e. This secondary carbocation will rearrange because a 1,2-hydride shift converts it into a tertiary carbocation.

$$CH_3 \overset{H}{\curvearrowright} \quad \longrightarrow \quad CH_3 \;\; +$$

f. This carbocation will not rearrange because it is secondary and a carbocation rearrangement would only yield another secondary carbocation.

PROBLEM 16 ♦

Give the major product obtained from the reaction of HBr with each of the following:

a. $CH_3\overset{}{\underset{CH_3}{CH}}CH{=}CH_2$

d. $CH_3\overset{}{\underset{CH_3}{CH}}CH_2CH{=}CH_2$

b.
CH_2 (on cyclohexane ring)

e. $CH_2{=}CH\overset{CH_3}{\underset{CH_3}{C}}CH_3$

c.
CH_3 (on cyclohexene ring)

f.
CH_3 (on cyclohexene ring)

4.8 THE ADDITION OF A HALOGEN TO AN ALKENE

The halogens Br_2 and Cl_2 add to alkenes. This may surprise you because it is not immediately apparent that an electrophile—which is necessary to start an electrophilic addition reaction—is present.

$$CH_3CH{=}CH_2 + Br_2 \longrightarrow CH_3CH{-}CH_2$$
$$\hspace{5cm} | \hspace{0.5cm} |$$
$$\hspace{5cm} Br \hspace{0.3cm} Br$$

$$CH_3CH{=}CH_2 + Cl_2 \longrightarrow CH_3CH{-}CH_2$$
$$\hspace{5cm} | \hspace{0.5cm} |$$
$$\hspace{5cm} Cl \hspace{0.3cm} Cl$$

The reaction is made possible by the fact that the bond joining the two halogen atoms is relatively weak (see the bond dissociation energies listed in Table 3.2) and, therefore, is easily broken. The mechanism for the addition of bromine to an alkene is shown below. (The mechanism for the addition of chlorine is the same.)

MECHANISM FOR THE ADDITION OF BROMINE TO AN ALKENE

cyclic bromonium ion
formed from the reaction
of Br_2 with *cis*-2-butene

- As the π electrons of the alkene approach a molecule of Br_2, one of the bromine atoms accepts those electrons and releases the electrons of the $Br{-}Br$ bond to the other bromine atom. Notice that a lone pair on bromine is the nucleophile that attaches to the other sp^2 carbon. Thus, the same atom is both the electrophile and the nucleophile, and it adds to the double bond in a single step.

- The intermediate, a cyclic bromonium ion, is unstable because there is still considerable positive charge on what was the sp^2 carbon. (See the electrostatic potential maps on the right and on page 155.) Therefore, the cyclic bromonium ion reacts with a nucleophile, the bromide ion. The product is a *vicinal dibromide*. **Vicinal** indicates that the two bromines are on adjacent carbons (*vicinus* is the Latin word for "near").

The product of the first step is a cyclic bromonium ion rather than a carbocation, because bromine's electron cloud is close enough to the other sp^2 carbon to form a bond. The cyclic bromonium ion is not stable but is more stable than the carbocation would have been, since all the atoms (except hydrogen) in the bromonium ion have complete octets, whereas the positively charged carbon of the carbocation does not have a complete octet. (To review the octet rule, see Section 1.3.)

chem Tutorial:
place Formation of a bromonium ion

The electrostatic potential maps for the cyclic bromonium ions show that the electron-deficient region (the blue area) encompasses the carbons, even though the formal positive charge is on the bromine.

When Cl_2 adds to an alkene, a cyclic chloronium ion is formed. The final product of the reaction is a vicinal dichloride. Reactions of alkenes with Br_2 or Cl_2 are generally carried out by mixing the alkene and the halogen in an inert solvent, such as dichloromethane (CH_2Cl_2), that readily dissolves both reactants, but does not participate in the reaction.

$$CH_3C{=}CH_2 \ + \ Cl_2 \ \xrightarrow{CH_2Cl_2} \ CH_3\overset{\underset{\displaystyle Cl}{|}}{\underset{}{\overset{\displaystyle CH_3}{|}}}CCH_2Cl$$

2-methylpropene

1,2-dichloro-2-methylpropane
a vicinal dichloride

Because a carbocation is not formed when Br_2 or Cl_2 adds to an alkene, carbocation rearrangements do not occur in these reactions.

$$CH_3\overset{\overset{\displaystyle CH_3}{|}}{CH}CH{=}CH_2 \ + \ Br_2 \ \xrightarrow{CH_2Cl_2} \ CH_3\overset{\overset{\displaystyle CH_3}{|}}{CH}\overset{\underset{\displaystyle Br}{|}}{CH}CH_2Br$$

| the carbon skeleton does not rearrange |

3-methyl-1-butene

1,2-dibromo-3-methylbutane
a vicinal dibromide

PROBLEM 17 ♦

What would have been the product of the preceding reaction if HBr had been used as a reagent instead of Br_2?

PROBLEM 18

a. How does the first step in the reaction of propene with Br_2 differ from the first step in the reaction of propene with HBr?

b. To understand why Br^- attacks a carbon atom of the bromonium ion rather than the positively charged bromine atom, draw the product that would be obtained if Br^- *did* attack the bromine atom.

---

chem place Mechanistic Tutorial:
Addition of halogen to an alkene

Synthetic Tutorial:
Addition of halogen to an alkene

The foregoing examples illustrate the way organic reactions are typically written. The reactants are placed to the left of the reaction arrow, and the products are placed to the right of the arrow. Any conditions that need to be stipulated, such as the solvent, the temperature, or a catalyst, are written above or below the arrow. Sometimes only the organic (carbon-containing) reagent is placed to the left of the arrow, and any other reagents are written above or below the arrow.

$$CH_3CH{=}CHCH_3 \ \xrightarrow[CH_2Cl_2]{Cl_2} \ CH_3\overset{\underset{\displaystyle Cl}{|}}{CH}\overset{\underset{\displaystyle Cl}{|}}{CH}CH_3$$

Although F_2 and I_2 are halogens, they are not used as reagents in electrophilic addition reactions. Fluorine reacts explosively with alkenes, so the electrophilic addition of F_2 is not useful for synthesizing new compounds. The addition of I_2 to an alkene is thermodynamically unfavorable. The vicinal diiodides are unstable at room temperature, decomposing back to the alkene and I_2.

$$CH_3CH{=}CHCH_3 \ + \ I_2 \ \underset{CH_2Cl_2}{\rightleftharpoons} \ CH_3\overset{\underset{\displaystyle I}{|}}{CH}\overset{\underset{\displaystyle I}{|}}{CH}CH_3$$

unstable

If H_2O rather than CH_2Cl_2 is used as a solvent, the major product of the reaction will be a vicinal halohydrin (or, more specifically, a bromohydrin or a chlorohydrin). A **halohydrin** is an organic molecule that contains both a halogen and an OH group. In a vicinal halohydrin, the halogen and the OH group are bonded to adjacent carbons.

$$CH_3CH{=}CH_2 \ + \ Br_2 \ \xrightarrow{\ H_2O\ } \ CH_3\underset{OH}{CH}CH_2Br \ + \ CH_3\underset{Br}{CH}CH_2Br \ + \ HBr$$

propene   a bromohydrin major product   minor product

$$CH_3CH{=}\overset{CH_3}{\underset{}{C}}CH_3 \ + \ Cl_2 \ \xrightarrow{\ H_2O\ } \ CH_3\underset{Cl}{CH}\overset{CH_3}{\underset{OH}{C}}CH_3 \ + \ CH_3\underset{Cl}{CH}\overset{CH_3}{\underset{Cl}{C}}CH_3 \ + \ HCl$$

2-methyl-2-butene   a chlorohydrin major product   minor product

The mechanism for halohydrin formation has three steps.

MECHANISM FOR HALOHYDRIN FORMATION

- A cyclic bromonium ion (or chloronium ion) is formed in the first step because Br^+ (or Cl^+) is the only electrophile in the reaction mixture.
- The relatively unstable cyclic bromonium ion rapidly reacts with any nucleophile it bumps into. Two nucleophiles—H_2O and Br^-—are present in the solution, but because H_2O is the solvent, its concentration far exceeds that of Br^-. Consequently, the bromonium ion is more likely to collide with water than with Br^-.
- The protonated halohydrin is a strong acid (Section 1.18), so it loses a proton.

chem
place Synthetic Tutorial: Halohydrin reaction

How can we explain the regioselectivity of the preceding addition reaction? In other words, why does the electrophile (Br^+) end up on the sp^2 carbon bonded to the greater number of hydrogens? In the two possible transition states for the second step of the reaction, the C—Br bond has broken to a greater extent than the C—O bond has formed. As a result, there is a partial positive charge on the carbon that is attacked by the nucleophile.

more stable transition state   less stable transition state

Therefore, the more stable transition state is the one achieved by adding the nucleophile to the more substituted sp^2 carbon—the carbon bonded to the fewer hydrogens—because in that case the partial positive charge is on a secondary carbon rather than on a primary carbon. Thus, this reaction, too, follows the general rule for electrophilic addition reactions: the electrophile (here, Br^+) adds to the sp^2 carbon that is bonded to the greater number of hydrogens.

When nucleophiles other than H_2O are added to the reaction mixture, they, too, change the product of the reaction, just as water changed the product of Br_2 addition from a vicinal dibromide to a vicinal bromohydrin. Because the concentration of the added nucleophile will be greater than the concentration of the halide ion generated from Br_2 or Cl_2, the added nucleophile will be the one most likely to participate in the second step of the reaction.

$$\underset{\text{CH}_3}{\overset{\text{CH}_3}{\text{CH}_3\text{CH}=\text{CCH}_3}} + \text{Cl}_2 + \text{CH}_3\text{OH} \longrightarrow \underset{\underset{\text{Cl}}{|}\ \underset{\text{OCH}_3}{|}}{\text{CH}_3\text{CHCCH}_3} + \text{HCl}$$

$$\text{CH}_3\text{CH}=\text{CH}_2 + \text{Br}_2 + \text{NaCl} \longrightarrow \underset{\underset{\text{Cl}}{|}}{\text{CH}_3\text{CHCH}_2\text{Br}} + \text{NaBr}$$

Remember that ions such as Na^+ and K^+ cannot form covalent bonds, so they do not react with organic compounds. They serve only as counterions to negatively charged species, so their presence generally is ignored in writing chemical reactions.

$$\underset{\overset{|}{\text{CH}_3}}{\text{CH}_3\text{C}=\text{CH}_2} + \text{Br}_2 + \text{Cl}^- \longrightarrow \underset{\underset{\text{Cl}}{|}}{\overset{\overset{\text{CH}_3}{|}}{\text{CH}_3\text{C}-\text{CH}_2\text{Br}}} + \text{Br}^- \cdot$$

PROBLEM 19

There are two nucleophiles in each of the following reactions:

a. $\underset{\overset{|}{\text{CH}_3}}{\text{CH}_2=\text{CCH}_3} + \text{Cl}_2 \xrightarrow{\text{CH}_3\text{OH}}$

b. $\text{CH}_2=\text{CHCH}_3 + 2\,\text{NaI} + \text{HBr} \longrightarrow$

c. $\text{CH}_3\text{CH}=\text{CHCH}_3 + \text{HCl} \xrightarrow{\text{H}_2\text{O}}$

d. $\text{CH}_3\text{CH}=\text{CHCH}_3 + \text{HBr} \xrightarrow{\text{CH}_3\text{OH}}$

For each reaction, explain why there is a greater concentration of one nucleophile than the other. What will be the major product of each reaction?

PROBLEM 20

Why are Na^+ and K^+ unable to form covalent bonds?

PROBLEM 21 ♦

What is the product of the addition of I—Cl to 1-butene? [*Hint:* Chlorine is more electronegative than iodine (Table 1.3).]

PROBLEM 22 ♦

What would be the major product obtained from the reaction of Br_2 with 1-butene if the reaction were carried out in

a. dichloromethane? **c.** ethyl alcohol?
b. water? **d.** methyl alcohol?

PROBLEM-SOLVING STRATEGY

Proposing a Mechanism

Propose a reasonable mechanism for the following reaction:

The electrophile will add to sp^2 carbon of the alkene that is bonded to the greater number of hydrogens.

There are two nucleophiles that could add to the carbocation, OH and Cl⁻. The nucleophile that is present in the highest concentration is the OH group. Only a small amount of HCl is added to the reaction mixture, since it is a catalyst and catalysts are regenerated (Section 4.5).

Now continue on to Problem 23.

PROBLEM 23

Propose a mechanism for the following reaction:

4.9 OXYMERCURATION—REDUCTION AND ALKOXYMERCURATION—REDUCTION ARE OTHER WAYS TO ADD WATER OR AN ALCOHOL TO AN ALKENE

In Section 4.5, you saw that water adds to an alkene if an acid catalyst is present. This is the process used in industry for converting alkenes into alcohols. In most laboratories, however, water is added to an alkene by a procedure known as **oxymercuration–reduction**. The addition of water by oxymercuration–reduction has two advantages over acid-catalyzed addition: it does not require acidic conditions, which are harmful to many organic molecules; and because carbocation intermediates are not formed, carbocation rearrangements do not occur.

In oxymercuration, the alkene is treated with mercuric acetate in aqueous tetrahydrofuran (THF). After that reaction is finished, sodium borohydride is added to the reaction mixture.

The numbers in front of the reagents above and below the reaction arrow indicate that two reactions are run in sequence; the second reagent is not added until reaction with the first reagent is completed.

MECHANISM FOR OXYMERCURATION

The steps of the oxymercuration mechanism are as follows:

- The electrophilic mercury of mercuric acetate adds to the double bond. (Two of mercury's $5d$ electrons are shown.) Because chemists have found that carbocation rearrangements do not occur, we can conclude that the product of the addition reaction is a cyclic mercurinium ion rather than a carbocation. As in the formation of a cyclic bromonium ion (Section 4.7), the electrophile has a lone pair that serves as the nucleophile.

- Water attacks the more substituted carbon of the unstable cyclic mercurinium ion—the carbon bonded to the fewer hydrogens—for the same reason that water attacks the more substituted carbon of the cyclic bromonium ion in halohydrin formation (Section 4.7). That is, attacking at the more substituted carbon leads to the more stable transition state because the partial positive charge is on a secondary carbon rather than on a primary carbocation.

chem place Mechanism: Oxymercuration-reduction

- The protonated alcohol loses a proton because the pH of the solution is greater than the pK_a of the protonated alcohol group (Section 1.25).

In the second of the two reactions, sodium borohydride ($NaBH_4$) converts the C—Hg bond into a C—H bond. A reaction that increases the number of C—H bonds in a compound is called a **reduction reaction**. Consequently, the reaction with sodium borohydride is a reduction reaction. The mechanism of this reaction is not fully understood.

A reduction reaction increases the number of C—H bonds.

$$CH_3CHCH_2-Hg-O_2CCH_3 \xrightarrow{\textbf{NaBH}_4} CH_3CHCH_3 + Hg + CH_3CO_2^-$$
$$\overset{|}{OH} \qquad\qquad\qquad\qquad\qquad \overset{|}{OH}$$

Notice in the reactions shown above that the oxymercuration–reduction of propene forms the same product that would be obtained from the acid-catalyzed addition of water: the hydrogen adds to the sp^2 carbon bonded to the greater number of hydrogens, and OH adds to the other sp^2 carbon.

The products obtained from oxymercuration–reduction and acid-catalyzed addition of water will be different *only* if the carbocation formed in the latter reaction rearranges.

Acid-catalyzed addition will give the rearranged product because the reaction forms a carbocation intermediate, whereas oxymercuration–reduction will give the unrearranged product because a carbocation intermediate is not formed in this reaction.

acid-catalyzed addition of water

oxymercuration-reduction

We have seen that alkenes react with alcohols in the presence of an acid catalyst to form ethers (Section 4.5). Adding the alcohol in the presence of mercuric acetate rather than in the presence of a strong acid has the same advantages as adding water in the presence of mercuric acetate rather than in the presence of a strong acid. Mercuric trifluoroacetate, $Hg(O_2CCF_3)_2$, works even better. This reaction is called **alkoxymercuration–reduction**.

1-methylcyclohexene

1-methoxy-1-methylcyclohexane
an ether

The mechanisms for oxymercuration and alkoxymercuration are essentially identical; the only difference is that water is the nucleophile in oxymercuration and an alcohol is the nucleophile in alkoxymercuration. Therefore, the product of oxymercuration–reduction is an alcohol, whereas the product of alkoxymercuration–reduction is an ether.

PROBLEM 24

How could the following compounds be synthesized from an alkene?

a.

c. $CH_3CHCH_2CH_3$
   $\quad\;\; OCH_2CH_3$

b.

d. $CH_3\overset{\displaystyle CH_3}{\underset{\displaystyle OCH_3}{C}}CH_2CH_3$

PROBLEM 25

How could the following compounds be synthesized from 3-methyl-1-butene?

a. $CH_3\overset{\displaystyle CH_3}{\underset{\displaystyle OH}{C}}CH_2CH_3$

b. $CH_3\overset{\displaystyle CH_3}{\underset{\displaystyle OH}{C}}HCHCH_3$

4.10 THE ADDITION OF A PEROXYACID TO AN ALKENE

An alkene can be converted to an *epoxide* by a peroxyacid. An **epoxide** is an ether in which the oxygen atom is incorporated into a three-membered ring; a **peroxyacid** is a carboxylic acid with an extra oxygen atom. The overall reaction amounts to the transfer of an oxygen from the peroxyacid to the alkene; it is an oxidation reaction. An **oxidation reaction** increases the number of C—O, C—N, or C—X bonds in a compound or decreases the number of C—H bonds. Other oxidation reactions of alkenes are discussed in Chapter 20.

An oxidation reaction increases the number of C—O, C—N, or C—X bonds.

Recall that an O—O bond is weak and, therefore, easily broken (Section 1.4).

a peroxyacid

MECHANISM FOR EPOXIDATION OF AN ALKENE

- The oxygen atom of the OH group of the peroxyacid is electron deficient and is therefore an electrophile. It accepts a pair of electrons from the π bond of the alkene, which causes the weak O—O bond to break. The electrons from the O—O bond are delocalized (Section 1.23). The electrons left behind as the O—H bond breaks add to the other sp^2 carbon of the alkene.

The mechanism for formation of the epoxide shows that it is a *concerted* reaction. A **concerted reaction** is a reaction in which all the bond-making and bond-breaking processes occur in the same step (all the events occur "in concert").

The mechanism for the addition of oxygen to a double bond to form an epoxide is analogous to the mechanism we just saw for formation of a cyclic bromonium ion (Section 4.7) or a cyclic mercurinium ion (Section 4.8).

In a concerted reaction, all the bond-making and bond-breaking processes occur in the same step.

In all three reactions, a lone pair on the electrophile is the nucleophile that adds to the other sp^2 carbon. However, unlike the cyclic bromonium or mercurinium ions, the epoxide is stable enough to isolate because none of the ring atoms has a positive charge.

The common name of an epoxide is obtained by adding "oxide" to the common name of the alkene, assuming that the oxygen atom is where the π bond of an alkene would be. The simplest epoxide is ethylene oxide.

$H_2C=CH_2$
ethylene

H_2C-CH_2 (O)
ethylene oxide

$H_2C=CHCH_3$
propylene

$H_2C-CHCH_3$ (O)
propylene oxide

There are two systematic ways to name epoxides. One method calls the three-membered oxygen-containing ring "oxirane," and gives oxygen the 1-position in the ring. Thus, 2-ethyloxirane has an ethyl substituent at the 2-position of the oxirane ring. Alternatively, an epoxide can be named as an alkane, with an "epoxy" prefix that identifies the carbons to which the oxygen is attached.

$H_2C-CHCH_2CH_3$
2-ethyloxirane
1,2-epoxybutane

$CH_3CH-CHCH_3$
2,3-dimethyloxirane
2,3-epoxybutane

2,2-dimethyloxirane
1,2-epoxy-2-methylpropane

PROBLEM 26 ♦

Draw the structure of the following compounds:

a. 2-propyloxirane
b. cyclohexene oxide
c. 2,2,3,3-tetramethyloxirane
d. 2,3-epoxy-2-methylpentane

PROBLEM 27 ♦

What alkene would you treat with a peroxyacid in order to obtain each of the following epoxides?

a.

b. $H_2C-CHCH_2CH_3$ (O)

4.11 THE ADDITION OF BORANE TO AN ALKENE: HYDROBORATION—OXIDATION

An atom or a molecule does not have to be positively charged to be an electrophile. Borane (BH_3), a neutral molecule, is an electrophile because its boron atom does not have a complete octet: it has only six shared electrons in its valence shell. We have seen that boron forms bonds using sp^2 orbitals (Chapter 1, Problem 34b); thus, like a methyl cation, it has an empty p orbital that can accept electrons.

Because borane is an electrophile, it can react with an alkene. When the addition reaction is over, an aqueous solution of sodium hydroxide and hydrogen peroxide is added to the reaction mixture. The product of the reaction is an alcohol. The overall process—the addition of borane to an alkene, followed by reaction with hydroxide ion and hydrogen peroxide—is called **hydroboration–oxidation**. The reaction was first reported by H. C. Brown in 1959.

Hydroboration–Oxidation

$$\text{RCH}=\text{CHR} \xrightarrow[\text{2. HO}^-,\ \text{H}_2\text{O}_2,\ \text{H}_2\text{O}]{\text{1. BH}_3/\text{THF}} \text{RCH}-\text{CHR}$$

π bond breaks

new σ bond   new σ bond

H   OH

an alcohol

As the following reactions show, the alcohol formed from the hydroboration–oxidation of an alkene has the H and OH groups switched in comparison with the alcohol formed from the acid-catalyzed addition of water (Section 4.5). However, in both reactions *the electrophile adds to the sp^2 carbon that is bonded to the greater number of hydrogens*. In the acid-catalyzed addition of water, H^+ is the electrophile and H_2O is the nucleophile, whereas in hydroboration–oxidation, as we will see, BH_3 is the electrophile (with HO subsequently taking its place) and H^- is the nucleophile.

In the acid-catalyzed addition of water, H^+ is the electrophile; in hydroboration–oxidation, H^- is the nucleophile.

$$\text{CH}_3\text{CH}=\text{CH}_2 \xrightarrow[\text{H}_2\text{O}]{\text{H}_2\text{SO}_4} \text{CH}_3\overset{\underset{\textstyle |}{\text{OH}}}{\text{CH}}\text{CH}_3$$

propene   **2-propanol**

$$\text{CH}_3\text{CH}=\text{CH}_2 \xrightarrow[\text{2. HO}^-,\ \text{H}_2\text{O}_2,\ \text{H}_2\text{O}]{\text{1. BH}_3/\text{THF}} \text{CH}_3\text{CH}_2\text{CH}_2\text{OH}$$

propene   **1-propanol**

Borane and Diborane

Borane exists primarily as a colorless gas called diborane. Diborane is a **dimer**—a molecule formed by the joining of two identical molecules. Because boron is surrounded by only six electrons in borane, it has a strong tendency to acquire an additional electron pair. In the dimer, therefore, two boron atoms share the two electrons in a hydrogen–boron bond by means of unusual half-bonds. These hydrogen–boron bonds are shown as dotted lines to indicate that they consist of fewer than the normal two electrons.

$$2\ \ \underset{\text{borane}}{\text{H—B—H}} \ \rightleftharpoons\ \underset{\text{diborane}}{\text{B}\cdots\text{B}}$$

Diborane (B_2H_6) is a flammable, toxic, and explosive gas. A borane-THF complex—prepared by dissolving diborane in THF—is a more convenient and less dangerous reagent. One of the lone pairs of THF satisfies boron's requirement for an additional two electrons The borane–THF complex is used as the source of BH_3 for hydroboration.

tetrahydrofuran (THF)

$$\underset{\text{diborane}}{\text{B}\cdots\text{B}} \ \rightleftharpoons\ 2\ \underset{\text{borane-THF complex}}{\overset{\text{O}^+}{\underset{}{\text{B}^-}}}$$

To understand why the hydroboration–oxidation of propene forms 1-propanol, we must look at the mechanism of the reaction. As the electrophilic boron accepts the π electrons from the nucleophilic alkene and forms a bond with one sp^2 carbon, it donates a hydride ion to the other sp^2 carbon. The addition of borane to an alkene is another example of a concerted reaction (Section 4.10).

$$CH_3CH=\!\!=\!\!CH_2 \longrightarrow CH_3CH-CH_2$$

nucleophile

H—BH$_2$

electrophile

H   BH$_2$

an alkylborane

Because both the electrophilic boron and the nucleophilic hydride ion are added to the alkene in one step, an intermediate is not formed.

Boron, like the other electrophiles we have looked at, adds to the sp^2 carbon that is bonded to the greater number of hydrogens. We can explain the regioselectivity of boron addition if we examine the two possible transition states, which show that the $C-B$ bond has formed to a greater extent than has the $C-H$ bond. Consequently, the sp^2 carbon that does not become attached to boron has a partial positive charge. Addition of boron to the sp^2 carbon bonded to the greater number of hydrogens forms a more stable transition state because the partial positive charge is on a secondary carbon. In contrast, the partial positive charge is on a primary carbon if boron adds to the other sp^2 carbon. Thus, the addition of boron and the addition of an electrophile such as H^+ take place at the same sp^2 carbon for the same reason: it results in formation of the more stable transition state.

addition of BH$_3$		addition of HBr	

more stable transition state	less stable transition state	more stable transition state	less stable transition state

The alkylborane that is formed in the first step of the reaction reacts with another molecule of alkene to form a dialkylborane, which then reacts with yet another molecule of alkene to form a trialkylborane. In each of these reactions, boron adds to the sp^2 carbon bonded to the greater number of hydrogens and the hydride ion adds to the other sp^2 carbon.

$$CH_3CH=\!\!=\!\!CH_2 \longrightarrow CH_3CH-CH_2-BHR$$

H—BHR

an alkylborane

H

a dialkylborane

$$CH_3CH=\!\!=\!\!CH_2 \longrightarrow CH_3CH-CH_2-BR_2$$

H—BR$_2$

a dialkylborane

H

a trialkylborane

The alkylborane (RBH_2) is a bulkier molecule than BH_3 because R is a larger substituent than H. The dialkylborane with two R groups (R_2BH) is even bulkier than the alkylborane. Thus, there are now two reasons for the alkylborane and the dialkylborane to add to the sp^2 carbon that is bonded to the greater number of hydrogens: first, to achieve the *most stable carbocation-like transition state*, and second, because there is *more room* at this carbon for the bulky group to attach itself.

Steric effects are space-filling effects (recall the discussion of steric strain in Section 2.10). **Steric hindrance** is a steric effect caused by bulky groups at the site of the reaction that make it difficult for the reactants to approach each other. Steric hindrance associated with the alkylborane—and particularly with the dialkylborane—causes the electrophile to add to the sp^2 carbon that is bonded to the greater number of hydrogens because that is the least sterically hindered of the two sp^2 carbons.

When the hydroboration reaction is over, an aqueous solution of sodium hydroxide and hydrogen peroxide (HOOH) is added to the reaction mixture in order to replace boron with an OH group. Because replacing boron with an OH group is an *oxidation reaction* (the number of C—O bonds has increased), the overall reaction is called hydroboration–oxidation.

$$R-\overset{\overset{\displaystyle R}{|}}{\underset{\underset{\displaystyle R}{|}}{B}} \quad \xrightarrow{\text{HO}^-,\ \text{H}_2\text{O}_2,\ \text{H}_2\text{O}} \quad 3\ \ R-OH\ +\ {}^-B(OH)_4$$

MECHANISM FOR THE OXIDATION REACTION

The mechanism for the oxidation reaction shows that:

- A hydrogen peroxide ion (a nucleophile) adds to R_3B (an electrophile).
- A 1,2-alkyl shift displaces a hydroxide ion. These first two steps are repeated two more times, so the three R groups all become OR groups.
- Hydroxide ion (a nucleophile) adds to $(RO)_3B$ (an electrophile).
- An alkoxide ion is eliminated.
- Protonating the alkoxide ion forms the alcohol. The last three steps are repeated two more times, so all three alkoxide ions are expelled from boron and three molecules of alcohol are formed.

We have seen that, in the overall hydroboration–oxidation reaction, 1 mole of BH_3 reacts with 3 moles of alkene to form 3 moles of alcohol. The OH ends up attached to the sp^2 carbon that was bonded to the greater number of hydrogens because it replaces boron, which was the original electrophile in the reaction.

chem place Synthetic Tutorial: Hydroboration-oxidation

Mechanistic Tutorial: Hydroboration-oxidation

$$3\ CH_3CH{=}CH_2\ +\ BH_3\ \xrightarrow{\text{THF}}\ (CH_3CH_2CH_2)_3B\ \xrightarrow[\text{H}_2\text{O}]{\text{HO}^-,\ \text{H}_2\text{O}_2}\ 3\ CH_3CH_2CH_2OH\ +\ {}^-B(OH)_4$$

Because carbocation intermediates are not formed in the hydroboration reaction, carbocation rearrangements do not occur.

PROBLEM 28♦

How many moles of BH_3 are needed to react with 2 moles of 1-pentene?

PROBLEM 29♦

What product would be obtained from hydroboration–oxidation of the following alkenes?

a. 2-methyl-2-butene   **b.** 1-methylcyclohexene

4.12 THE ADDITION OF HYDROGEN TO AN ALKENE

In the presence of a metal catalyst, hydrogen (H_2) adds to the double bond of an alkene to form an alkane. The reaction is a *reduction* reaction because there are more C—H bonds in the product than in the reactant (Section 4.9). The most common metal catalyst is palladium, which is used as a powder adsorbed on charcoal to maximize its surface area; it is referred to as "palladium on carbon." Platinum, used most often as an oxide (PtO_2), is also frequently employed; PtO_2 is called Adams catalyst.

$$CH_3CH{=}CHCH_3 \ + \ H_2 \ \xrightarrow{\text{Pd/C}} \ CH_3CH_2CH_2CH_3$$

2-butene   **butane**

Roger Adams (1889–1971), *born in Boston and a descendant of John Adams, received a Ph.D. from Harvard University and was a professor of chemistry at the University of Illinois from 1916 to 1957. During his career, Adams supervised more than 250 graduate students and had a profound effect on the development of organic chemistry. Among his many accomplishments, he and Sir Alexander Todd (Section 28.0) clarified the structure of tetrahydrocannabinol (THC), the active ingredient in marijuana. Adams's research showed that the test commonly used at that time by the Federal Bureau of Narcotics to detect marijuana was actually detecting an innocuous companion compound.*

1-methylcyclohexene   **methylcyclohexane**

The metal catalyst is required because without it the energy barrier to the reaction would be enormous, since the H—H bond is so strong (Table 3.2). The catalyst decreases the energy of activation by weakening the H—H bond.

The addition of hydrogen is called **hydrogenation**. Because hydrogenation reactions require a catalyst, they are **catalytic hydrogenations**. The metal catalysts described above are insoluble in the reaction mixture and therefore are classified as **heterogeneous catalysts**. When the reaction is over, the heterogeneous catalyst can easily be separated from the reaction mixture by filtration. It can then be recycled, which is fortunate, since metal catalysts tend to be expensive.

The details of the mechanism of catalytic hydrogenation are not completely understood. We know that hydrogen is adsorbed on the surface of the metal and that the alkene complexes with the metal by overlapping its *p* orbitals with vacant orbitals of the metal. All the bond-breaking and bond-forming events occur on the surface of the metal. As the alkane product forms, it diffuses away from the metal surface (Figure 4.5).

hydrogen molecules settle on the surface of the catalyst and react with the metal atoms

the alkene approaches the surface of the catalyst

the π bond between the two carbons is replaced by two C—H σ bonds

▲ **Figure 4.5**
Catalytic hydrogenation of an alkene.

Although it is not an accurate picture of what actually happens, we can think of the reaction as occurring in the following way: both the H—H bond and the π bond break, and the hydrogen radicals add to the carbon radicals.

chem
place Tutorial:
Catalytic hydrogenation of ethene

$$CH_3CH=CHCH_3 \longrightarrow CH_3\overset{\cdot}{C}H-\overset{\cdot}{C}HCH_3 \longrightarrow CH_3CH-CHCH_3$$
$$H—H \qquad\qquad H\cdot \quad \cdot H \qquad\qquad\quad \underset{H}{|} \quad \underset{H}{|}$$

The heat released in a hydrogenation reaction is called the **heat of hydrogenation**. It is customary to give it a positive value. Hydrogenation reactions, however, are exothermic (they have negative $\Delta H°$ values), so *the heat of hydrogenation is the absolute value of the $\Delta H°$ of the reaction; that is, the value of $\Delta H°$ without the negative sign.*

		$\Delta H°$	
	heat of hydrogenation	kcal/mol	kJ/mol

CH₃
|
CH₃C=CHCH₃ + H₂ —Pd/C→ CH₃CHCH₂CH₃ ... 26.9 kcal/mol ... −26.9 ... −113
2-methyl-2-butene

CH₃
|
CH₂=CCH₂CH₃ + H₂ —Pd/C→ CH₃CHCH₂CH₃ ... 28.5 kcal/mol ... −28.5 ... −119
2-methyl-1-butene

CH₃
|
CH₃CHCH=CH₂ + H₂ —Pd/C→ CH₃CHCH₂CH₃ ... 30.3 kcal/mol ... −30.3 ... −127
3-methyl-1-butene

the product of each of the reactions is 2-methylbutane

Because we do not know the precise mechanism of a hydrogenation reaction, we cannot draw a reaction coordinate diagram for it. We can, however, draw a diagram showing the relative energies of the reactants and products (Figure 4.6). The three catalytic hydrogenation reactions shown above all form the same alkane product, so the energy of the *product* is the same for each reaction. The three reactions, however, have different heats of hydrogenation, so the three *reactants* must have different energies. For example, 3-methyl-1-butene releases the most heat, so it must have the most energy to begin with (it must be the *least* stable of the three alkenes). In contrast, 2-methyl-2-butene releases the least heat, so it must have the least energy to begin with (it must be the *most* stable of the three alkenes). Notice that *the greater the stability of a compound, the lower is its energy and the smaller is its heat of hydrogenation.*

The most stable alkene has the smallest heat of hydrogenation.

▲ **Figure 4.6**
The relative energies (stabilities) of three alkenes that can be catalytically hydrogenated to 2-methylbutane.

Trans Fats

While fats are solids at room temperature, oils are liquids because they contain more carbon–carbon double bonds and therefore cannot pack as tightly together (Section 27.1). Oils are said to be polyunsaturated, since they have many double bonds.

COOH

linoleic acid
an 18-carbon fatty acid with two cis double bonds

Some or all of the double bonds in oils can be reduced by catalytic hydrogenation. For example, margarine and shortening are prepared by hydrogenating vegetable oils, such as soybean oil and safflower oil, until they have the desired creamy, solid consistency.

All the double bonds in naturally occurring fats and oils have the cis configuration. The heat used in the hydrogenation process breaks the π bond of these double bonds. Sometimes, instead of becoming hydrogenated, the double bond reforms. If

the sigma bond rotated while the π bond was broken, the double bond can reform in the trans configuration (Section 3.4), forming what is known as a trans fat.

COOH

oleic acid
an 18-carbon fatty acid with one cis double bond
before being heated

COOH

an 18-carbon fatty acid with one trans double bond
after being heated

Trans fats are a health concern because they increase LDL, the so-called "bad" cholesterol (Section 2.15). Epidemiology studies have shown that a 2% increase in the daily intake of trans fats significantly increases the incidence of cardiovascular disease.

PROBLEM-SOLVING STRATEGY

Choosing the Reactant for a Synthesis

What alkene would you start with if you wanted to synthesize methylcyclohexane?

You need to choose an alkene with the same number of carbons, attached in the same way, as those in the desired product. Several alkenes could be used for this synthesis, because the double bond can be located anywhere in the molecule.

CH$_2$ or CH$_3$ or CH$_3$ or CH$_3$ $\xrightarrow[\text{Pd/C}]{\text{H}_2}$ CH$_3$

Now continue on to Problem 30.

PROBLEM 30

What alkene would you start with if you wanted to synthesize:

a. pentane?

b. ethylcyclopentane?

PROBLEM 31

How many different alkenes can be hydrogenated to form:

a. butane?

b. 3-methylpentane

c. hexane?

4.13 THE RELATIVE STABILITIES OF ALKENES

If you look at the structures of the three alkene reactants in Figure 4.6, you will see that the most stable alkene has two alkyl substituents bonded to one of its sp^2 carbons and one alkyl substituent bonded to the other sp^2 carbon, for a total of three alkyl substituents (three methyl groups) bonded to its two sp^2 carbons. The alkene of intermediate stability has a total of two alkyl substituents (a methyl group and an ethyl group) bonded to its sp^2 carbons, and the least stable of the three alkenes has only one alkyl substituent (an isopropyl group) bonded to an sp^2 carbon. Thus, it is apparent that alkyl substituents bonded to the sp^2 carbons of an alkene have a stabilizing effect on the alkene.

relative stabilities of alkyl-substituted alkenes

The greater the number of alkyl groups bonded to the sp^2 carbons of an alkene, the more stable it is.

Alkyl substituents stabilize both alkenes *and* carbocations.

We have seen that alkyl substituents bonded to the sp^2 carbon of a carbocation stabilize the carbocation (Section 4.2). Now we see that alkyl substituents bonded to the sp^2 carbon of an alkene stabilize the alkene. In both cases, stabilization is the result of hyperconjugation (Section 4.2), although hyperconjugation stabilizes carbocations considerably more than it stabilizes alkenes.

We can, therefore, make the following statement: *the more alkyl substituents bonded to the* sp^2 *carbons of an alkene, the greater is its stability.* (Some students find it easier to look at the number of hydrogens bonded to the sp^2 carbons. In terms of hydrogens, the statement is: *the fewer hydrogens bonded to the* sp^2 *carbons of an alkene, the greater is its stability.*)

PROBLEM 32 ♦

The same alkane is obtained from the catalytic hydrogenation of both alkene A and alkene B. The heat of hydrogenation of alkene A is 29.8 kcal/mol (125 kJ/mol), and the heat of hydrogenation of alkene B is 31.4 kcal/mol (131 kJ/mol). Which alkene is more stable?

PROBLEM 33 ♦

a. Which of the following compounds is the most stable?

b. Which is the least stable?
c. Which has the smallest heat of hydrogenation?

Both *trans*-2-butene and *cis*-2-butene have two alkyl groups bonded to their sp^2 carbons, but *trans*-2-butene has a smaller heat of hydrogenation. This means that the trans isomer, in which the large substituents are farther apart, is more stable than the cis isomer, in which the large substituents are closer together.

	heat of hydrogenation	kcal/mol	kJ/mol
		$\Delta H°$	
trans-2-butene	27.6	−27.6	−115
cis-2-butene	28.6	−28.6	−120

When the large substituents are on the same side of the double bond, their electron clouds can interfere with each other, causing steric strain in the molecule (Section 2.10) and making it less stable. When the large substituents are on opposite sides of the double bond, their electron clouds cannot interact, and the molecule has less steric strain and is therefore more stable.

the cis isomer has steric strain

the trans isomer does not have steric strain

cis-2-butene

trans-2-butene

The heat of hydrogenation of *cis*-2-butene, in which the two alkyl substituents are on the *same side* of the double bond, is similar to that of 2-methylpropene, in which the two alkyl substituents are on the *same carbon*. The three dialkyl-substituted alkenes are all *less* stable than a trialkyl-substituted alkene and are all *more* stable than a monoalkyl-substituted alkene.

relative stabilities of dialkyl-substituted alkenes

alkyl substituents are trans	>	alkyl substituents are cis	~	alkyl substituents are on the same sp^2 carbon

PROBLEM 34◆

Rank the following compounds in order of decreasing stability:

  trans-3-hexene, *cis*-3-hexene, *cis*-2,5-dimethyl-3-hexene, *cis*-3,4-dimethyl-3-hexene

4.14 REACTIONS AND SYNTHESIS

This chapter has been concerned with the reactions of alkenes. You have seen why alkenes react, the kinds of reagents with which they react, the mechanisms by which the reactions occur, and the products that are formed. It is important to remember that when you are studying reactions, you are simultaneously studying synthesis. When you learn that compound A reacts with a certain reagent to form compound B, you are learning not only about the reactivity of A, but also about one way that compound B can be synthesized.

$$A \longrightarrow B$$

A reacts; B is synthesized

For example, you have seen that many different reagents can add to alkenes and that compounds such as alkyl halides, vicinal dihalides, halohydrins, alcohols, ethers, epoxides, and alkanes are synthesized as a result.

Although you have seen how alkenes react and have learned about the kinds of compounds that are synthesized when alkenes undergo reactions, you have not yet seen how alkenes are synthesized. You have seen that the reactions of alkenes involve the *addition* of atoms (or groups of atoms) to the two sp^2 carbons of the double bond. Reactions that lead to the synthesis of alkenes are exactly the opposite; they involve the *elimination* of atoms (or groups of atoms) from two adjacent sp^3 carbons.

$$\text{C}=\text{C} + \text{Y}^+ + \text{Z}^- \underset{\substack{\text{synthesis of an alkene} \\ \text{an elimination reaction}}}{\overset{\substack{\text{reaction of an alkene} \\ \text{an addition reaction}}}{\rightleftharpoons}} -\overset{|}{\underset{\text{Y}}{\text{C}}}-\overset{|}{\underset{\text{Z}}{\text{C}}}-$$

You will learn how alkenes are synthesized when you study compounds that undergo elimination reactions. The various reactions that result in the synthesis of alkenes are listed in Appendix IV.

Pesticides: Natural and Synthetic

Long before chemists learned to create compounds that would protect plants from predators, plants were doing the job themselves. Plants had every incentive to synthesize pesticides. When you cannot run, you need to find another way to protect yourself. But which pesticides are more harmful, those synthesized by chemists or those synthesized by plants? Unfortunately, we do not know the answer because although federal laws require all human-made pesticides to be tested for any cancer-causing effects, they do not require testing of plant-made pesticides. Besides, risk evaluations of chemicals are usually done on rats, and something that is carcinogenic in a rat may or may not be carcinogenic in a human. Furthermore, when rats are tested, they are exposed to much greater concentrations of the chemical than would be experienced by a human, and some chemicals are harmful only at high doses. For example, we all need sodium chloride for survival, but high concentrations are poisonous; and although we associate alfalfa sprouts with healthy eating, monkeys fed very large amounts of alfalfa sprouts have been found to develop an immune system disorder.

PROBLEM 35   **SOLVED**

Indicate how each of the following compounds can be synthesized from an alkene:

a. (structure: cyclohexane with Cl and OH on adjacent carbons)

b. (structure: cyclohexane with CH₃ and OH on adjacent carbons)

Solution

a. The only alkene that can be used for this synthesis is cyclohexene. To get the desired substituents on the ring, cyclohexene must react with Cl_2 in an aqueous solution so that water will be the nucleophile.

(reaction scheme: cyclohexene $\xrightarrow[\text{H}_2\text{O}]{\text{Cl}_2}$ 2-chlorocyclohexanol)

b. The alkene that should be used here is 1-methylcyclohexene. To get the substituents in the desired locations, the electrophile must be BH_3, with HO taking boron's place in the subsequent oxidation reaction.

(reaction scheme: 1-methylcyclohexene $\xrightarrow[\text{2. HO}^-,\ \text{H}_2\text{O}_2,\ \text{H}_2\text{O}]{\text{1. BH}_3/\text{THF}}$ 2-methylcyclohexanol)

PROBLEM 36♦

Why should 3-methylcyclohexene not be used as the starting material in Problem 35b?

PROBLEM 37

Indicate how each of the following compounds can be synthesized from an alkene:

a. CH_3CHOCH_3
         |
        CH_3

c. [cyclohexane with CH_2OH substituent]

e. [cyclohexane with CH_3 and Br substituents]

b. [structure with two Br substituents]
        Br
    [chain]
        Br

d. [cyclohexane with CH_3 and OCH_3 substituents]

f. [cyclohexane with $OCH_2CH_2CH_3$ substituent]

SUMMARY

Alkenes undergo **electrophilic addition reactions**. These reactions start with the addition of an *electrophile* to the sp^2 carbon bonded to the greater number of hydrogens; a nucleophile then adds to the other sp^2 carbon.

The addition of hydrogen halides and the acid-catalyzed addition of water and alcohols form **carbocation intermediates**. **Hyperconjugation** causes **tertiary carbocations** to be more stable than **secondary carbocations**, which are more stable than **primary carbocations**. A carbocation will rearrange if it becomes more stable as a result of the rearrangement. **Carbocation rearrangements** occur by **1,2-hydride shifts**, **1,2-methyl shifts**, and **ring expansion**.

Oxymercuration, **alkoxymercuration**, and the addition of Br_2 or Cl_2 form cyclic intermediates. **Epoxidation** and **hydroboration** are **concerted reactions** so they do not form an **intermediate**. Because these reactions do not form a carbocation intermediate, carbocation rearrangements do not occur.

The products of oxymercuration and alkoxymercuration are reduced. **A reduction** reaction increases the number of C—H bonds. **Hydroboration** products are oxidized. **An oxidation** reaction increases the number of C—O, C—N, or C—X bonds (where X denotes a halogen). The reaction of an alkene with a peroxyacid to form an epoxide is another example of an oxidation reaction.

The **Hammond postulate** states that a transition state is more similar in structure to the species to which it is closer in energy; thus, the transition states of endergonic reactions resemble the products, and the transition states of exergonic reactions resemble the reactants. For the reactions in this chapter, we have seen that the more stable product has the more stable transition state and leads to the major product of the reaction. **Regioselectivity** is the preferential formation of one **constitutional isomer** over another.

The addition of H_2 to an alkene in the presence of a metal catalyst is called **catalytic hydrogenation**; it is a reduction reaction. The **heat of hydrogenation** is the heat released in a hydrogenation reaction. The *greater* the *stability* of a compound, the *lower* is its *energy* and the *smaller* is its *heat of hydrogenation*. The more alkyl substituents bonded to the sp^2 carbons of an alkene, the greater is its stability. Alkyl substituents stabilize both alkenes and carbocations by hyperconjugation. **Trans alkenes** are more stable than **cis alkenes** because of steric strain.

Electrophilic addition reactions of alkenes lead to the **synthesis** of **alkyl halides**, **vicinal dihalides**, **halohydrins**, **alcohols**, **ethers**, **epoxides**, and **alkanes**.

SUMMARY OF REACTIONS

As you review the reactions of alkenes, keep in mind the feature that is common to all of them: the first step of each reaction is the addition of an electrophile to the sp^2 carbon that is bonded to the greater number of hydrogens.

1. Electrophilic addition reactions
    a. Addition of hydrogen halides; H^+ is the electrophile (Section 4.1).

$$RCH=CH_2 + HX \longrightarrow RCHCH_3$$
$$\qquad\qquad\qquad\qquad\quad |$$
$$\qquad\qquad\qquad\qquad\quad X$$

HX = HF, HCl, HBr, HI

b. Acid-catalyzed addition of water and alcohols; H$^+$ is the electrophile (Section 4.5 and 4.6).

$$RCH{=}CH_2 \ + \ H_2O \ \underset{}{\overset{H_2SO_4}{\rightleftharpoons}} \ \underset{\overset{|}{OH}}{RCHCH_3}$$

$$RCH{=}CH_2 \ + \ CH_3OH \ \underset{}{\overset{H_2SO_4}{\rightleftharpoons}} \ \underset{\overset{|}{OCH_3}}{RCHCH_3}$$

c. Addition of halogen; Br$^+$ or Cl$^+$ is the electrophile (Section 4.8).

$$RCH{=}CH_2 \ + \ Cl_2 \ \xrightarrow{CH_2Cl_2} \ \underset{\overset{|}{Cl}}{RCHCH_2Cl}$$

$$RCH{=}CH_2 \ + \ Br_2 \ \xrightarrow{CH_2Cl_2} \ \underset{\overset{|}{Br}}{RCHCH_2Br}$$

$$RCH{=}CH_2 \ + \ Br_2 \ \xrightarrow{H_2O} \ \underset{\overset{|}{OH}}{RCHCH_2Br}$$

d. Oxymercuration–reduction and alkoxymercuration–reduction; Hg is the electrophile and the nucleophile (Section 4.9).

$$RCH{=}CH_2 \ \xrightarrow[\text{2. NaBH}_4]{\text{1. Hg(O}_2\text{CCH}_3)_2\text{, H}_2\text{O,THF}} \ \underset{\overset{|}{OH}}{RCHCH_3}$$

$$RCH{=}CH_2 \ \xrightarrow[\text{2. NaBH}_4]{\text{1. Hg(O}_2\text{CCF}_3)_2\text{, CH}_3\text{OH}} \ \underset{\overset{|}{OCH_3}}{RCHCH_3}$$

e. Addition of a peroxyacid: O is the electrophile and the nucleophile (Section 4.10).

$$RCH{=}CH_2 \ + \ \underset{}{\overset{\overset{\displaystyle O}{\|}}{R{-}C}}{-}OOH \ \longrightarrow \ \overset{O}{\overset{\triangle}{RCH{-}CH_2}} \ + \ \underset{}{\overset{\overset{\displaystyle O}{\|}}{R{-}C}}{-}OH$$

f. Hydroboration–oxidation; B is the electrophile and H$^-$ is the nucleophile; B is subsequently replaced by OH (Section 4.11).

$$RCH{=}CH_2 \ \xrightarrow[\text{2. HO}^-\text{, H}_2\text{O}_2\text{, H}_2\text{O}]{\text{1. BH}_3\text{/THF}} \ RCH_2CH_2OH$$

2. Addition of hydrogen (Section 4.12)

$$RCH{=}CH_2 \ + \ H_2 \ \xrightarrow{\text{Pd/C or PtO}_2} \ RCH_2CH_3$$

KEY TERMS

PROBLEMS

38. Give the major product of each of the following reactions:

a. [structure: cyclohexene with CH₂CH₃ and Br substituents] + HBr ⟶

c. [structure: cyclohexane with CH=CH₂] + HBr ⟶

b. CH_2=CCH_2CH_3 (with CH₃ substituent) + HBr ⟶

d. CH_3CH_2CCH=CH_2 (with CH₃ substituents) + HBr ⟶

39. Identify the electrophile and the nucleophile in each of the following reaction steps. Then draw curved arrows to illustrate the bond-making and bond-breaking processes.

a. $CH_3\overset{+}{C}HCH_3$ + :Cl:⁻ ⟶ CH_3CHCH_3 with :Cl:

b. CH_3CH=CH_2 + H—Br ⟶ $CH_3\overset{+}{C}H$—CH_3 + Br⁻

c. CH_3CH=CH_2 + BH_3 ⟶ CH_3CH_2—CH_2BH_2

40. What will be the major product of the reaction of 2-methyl-2-butene with each of the following reagents?

a. HBr
b. a peroxyacid
c. HI
d. Cl_2/CH_2Cl_2
e. ICl

f. H_2/Pd
g. Br_2 + excess NaCl
h. $Hg(O_2CCH_3)_2$, H_2O followed by $NaBH_4$
i. H_2O + trace H_2SO_4
j. Br_2/CH_2Cl_2

k. Br_2/H_2O
l. Br_2/CH_3OH
m. BH_3/THF, followed by H_2O_2, HO^-, H_2O
n. $Hg(O_2CCF_3)_2$ + CH_3OH, followed by $NaBH_4$

41. Give two names for each of the following:

a. [structure with CH_3CH_2, O, C—CHCHCH₃, CH_3CH_2, CH₃]

b. [structure with H_3C, O, C—CHCH₂CH₃, H_3C]

42. a. Which compound is the most stable: 3,4-dimethyl-2-hexene, 2,3-dimethyl-2-hexene, or 4,5-dimethyl-2-hexene?
b. Which would you expect to have the largest heat of hydrogenation?
c. Which would you expect to have the lowest heat of hydrogenation?

43. What reagents are required to synthesize the following alcohols?

44. When 3-methyl-1-butene reacts with HBr, two alkyl halides are formed: 2-bromo-3-methylbutane and 2-bromo-2-methylbutane. Propose a mechanism that explains the formation of these products.

45. Problem 40 in Chapter 3 asked you to give the structures of all alkenes with molecular formula C_6H_{12}. Use those structures to answer the following questions:
a. Which of the compounds is the most stable?
b. Which of the compounds is the least stable?

46. Draw curved arrows to show the flow of electrons responsible for the conversion of reactants into products.

a. $CH_3-\overset{\overset{:\ddot{O}:^-}{|}}{\underset{\underset{CH_3}{|}}{C}}-OCH_3 \longrightarrow CH_3\overset{\overset{:\ddot{O}}{||}}{C}CH_3 + CH_3\ddot{\ddot{O}}:^-$

b. $CH_3C\equiv C-H + :\ddot{N}H_2 \longrightarrow CH_3C\equiv C^- + \ddot{N}H_3$

c. $CH_3CH_2-Br + CH_3\ddot{\ddot{O}}:^- \longrightarrow CH_3CH_2-\ddot{O}CH_3 + Br^-$

47. Give the reagents that would be required to carry out the following syntheses:

48. Give the major product of each of the following reactions:

49. Propose a mechanism for the following reaction. (*Hint:* it is a concerted reaction.)

$$:\bar{C}H_2-\overset{+}{N}\equiv N + CH_2=CH_2 \longrightarrow \triangle + N_2$$
diazomethane

Note: Diazomethane is a gas that must be handled with great care because it is both explosive and toxic.

50. Using any alkene and any other reagents, how would you prepare the following compounds?

a.

b. $CH_3CH_2CH_2\underset{\underset{Cl}{|}}{C}HCH_3$

c. (cyclohexane)CH_2OH

d. $CH_3CH_2\underset{\underset{Br}{|}}{C}H\underset{\underset{OH}{|}}{C}HCH_2CH_3$

e. (cyclohexane)$\underset{\underset{OH}{|}}{C}H_2CHCH_3$

f. $CH_3CH_2\underset{\underset{Br}{|}}{C}H\underset{\underset{Cl}{|}}{C}HCH_2CH_3$

51. a. Identify two alkenes that react with HBr to give 1-bromo-1-methylcyclohexane without undergoing a carbocation rearrangement.
   b. Would both alkenes form the same alkyl halide if DBr were used instead of HBr?

52. For each of the following pairs, indicate which member is the more stable:

a. $CH_3\overset{\overset{\displaystyle CH_3}{|}}{\underset{+}{C}}CH_3$ or $CH_3\overset{+}{C}HCH_2CH_3$

b. $CH_3\overset{+}{C}HCH_3$ or $CH_3\overset{+}{C}HCH_2Cl$

c. or

d. or

e. $CH_3\overset{\overset{\displaystyle CH_3}{|}}{C}=CHCH_2CH_3$ or $CH_3CH=\overset{\overset{\displaystyle CH_3}{|}}{C}CHCH_3$

f. or

53. The second-order rate constant (in units of $M^{-1}s^{-1}$) for acid-catalyzed hydration at 25 °C is given for each of the following alkenes:

$$\underset{H}{\overset{H_3C}{\diagdown}}C=CH_2 \qquad \underset{H}{\overset{H_3C}{\diagdown}}C=C\underset{H}{\overset{CH_3}{\diagup}} \qquad \underset{H}{\overset{H_3C}{\diagdown}}C=C\underset{CH_3}{\overset{H}{\diagup}} \qquad \underset{H}{\overset{H_3C}{\diagdown}}C=C\underset{CH_3}{\overset{CH_3}{\diagup}} \qquad \underset{H_3C}{\overset{H_3C}{\diagdown}}C=C\underset{CH_3}{\overset{CH_3}{\diagup}}$$

4.95×10^{-8} 8.32×10^{-8} 3.51×10^{-8} 2.15×10^{-4} 3.42×10^{-4}

a. Calculate the relative rates of hydration of the alkenes. (*Hint*: Divide each rate constant by the smallest rate constant of the series: 3.51×10^{-8}.)
b. Why does (Z)-2-butene react faster than (E)-2-butene?
c. Why does 2-methyl-2-butene react faster than (Z)-2-butene?
d. Why does 2,3-dimethyl-2-butene react faster than 2-methyl-2-butene?

54. Which compound has the greater dipole moment?

a. $\underset{H}{\overset{Cl}{\diagdown}}C=C\underset{Cl}{\overset{H}{\diagup}}$ or $\underset{H}{\overset{H}{\diagdown}}C=C\underset{Cl}{\overset{H}{\diagup}}$

b. $\underset{H}{\overset{Cl}{\diagdown}}C=C\underset{CH_3}{\overset{H}{\diagup}}$ or $\underset{H}{\overset{Cl}{\diagdown}}C=C\underset{H}{\overset{CH_3}{\diagup}}$

55. A student was about to turn in the products he had obtained from the reaction of HI with 3,3,3-trifluoropropene when he realized that the labels had fallen off his flasks and he did not know which label belonged where. His friend reminded him of the rule that says the electrophile adds to the sp^2 carbon that is bonded to the greater number of hydrogens. In other words, he should put the label 1,1,1-trifluoro-2-iodopropane on the flask containing the most product and label the flask with the least product 1,1,1-trifluoro-3-iodopropane. Should he follow this advice?

56. a. Propose a mechanism for the following reaction (show all curved arrows):

$$CH_3CH_2CH=CH_2 + CH_3OH \xrightarrow{H_2SO_4} CH_3CH_2\underset{\underset{\displaystyle OCH_3}{|}}{C}HCH_3$$

b. Which step is the rate-determining step?
c. What is the electrophile in the first step?
d. What is the nucleophile in the first step?
e. What is the electrophile in the second step?
f. What is the nucleophile in the second step?

57. Propose a mechanism for each of the following reactions:

a. + H_2O $\xrightarrow{H_2SO_4}$

b. + HCl ⟶

58. Give the major products for each of the following reactions:

a. $HOCH_2CH_2CH_2CH=CH_2$ + Br_2 $\xrightarrow{CH_2Cl_2}$

b. $HOCH_2CH_2CH_2CH_2CH=CH_2$ + Br_2 $\xrightarrow{CH_2Cl_2}$

59. a. What product is obtained from the reaction of HCl with 1-butene? With 2-butene?
   b. Which of the two reactions has the greater free energy of activation?
   c. Which of the two alkenes reacts more rapidly with HCl?
   d. Which compound reacts more rapidly with HCl, (Z)-2-butene or (E)-2-butene?

60. What would be the major product of the reaction of each of the following with HBr?

   a.

   b.

   c.

   d.

61. a. How many alkenes could you treat with H_2, Pd/C in order to prepare methylcyclopentane?
   b. Which of the alkenes is the most stable?
   c. Which of the alkenes has the smallest heat of hydrogenation?

62. a. Propose a mechanism for the following reaction:

   b. Is the initially formed carbocation primary, secondary, or tertiary?
   c. Is the rearranged carbocation primary, secondary, or tertiary?
   d. Why does the rearrangement occur?

63. When the following compound is hydrated in the presence of acid, the unreacted alkene is found to have retained the deuterium atoms:

   What does the preceding statement tell you about the mechanism for hydration?

64. Propose a mechanism for the following reaction:

65. a. Dichlorocarbene can be generated by heating chloroform with HO^-. Propose a mechanism for the reaction.

$$CHCl_3 \ + \ HO^- \ \xrightarrow{\Delta} \ Cl_2C: \ + \ H_2O \ + \ Cl^-$$
$$\text{chloroform} \qquad\qquad \text{dichlorocarbene}$$

   b. Dichlorocarbene can also be generated by heating sodium trichloroacetate. Propose a mechanism for the reaction.

$$\xrightarrow{\Delta} \ Cl_2C: \ + \ CO_2 \ + \ Na^+ Cl^-$$

sodium trichloroacetate

5

Stereochemistry

The Arrangement of Atoms in Space:
The Stereochemistry of Addition Reactions

**nonsuperimposable
mirror images**

COMPOUNDS WITH THE SAME MOLECULAR FORMULA BUT DIFFERENT STRUCTURES ARE called **isomers**. Isomers fall into two main classes: *constitutional isomers* and *stereoisomers*. **Constitutional isomers** differ in the way their atoms are connected (Section 2.0). For example, ethanol and dimethyl ether are constitutional isomers; they have the same molecular formula (C_2H_6O), but the oxygen in ethanol is bonded to a carbon and to a hydrogen, whereas the oxygen in dimethyl ether is bonded to two carbons.

constitutional isomers

CH_3CH_2OH and CH_3OCH_3
ethanol   dimethyl ether

$CH_3CH_2CH_2CH_2Cl$ and $CH_3CH_2\overset{\overset{\textstyle Cl}{|}}{C}HCH_3$
1-chlorobutane   2-chlorobutane

$CH_3CH_2CH_2CH_2CH_3$ and $CH_3\overset{\overset{\textstyle CH_3}{|}}{C}HCH_2CH_3$
pentane   isopentane

$CH_3\overset{\overset{\textstyle O}{||}}{C}CH_3$ and $CH_3CH_2\overset{\overset{\textstyle O}{||}}{C}H$
acetone   propionaldehyde

Unlike constitutional isomers, the atoms in stereoisomers are connected in the same way. **Stereoisomers** (also called **configurational isomers**) differ in the way their atoms are arranged in space. Like constitutional isomers, stereoisomers can be separated because they are different compounds; they can interconvert only if bonds are broken (Section 3.4). There are two kinds of stereoisomers: *cis–trans isomers* and isomers that contain *asymmetric centers*.

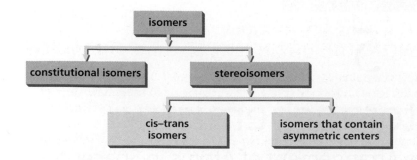

After reviewing cis–trans isomers, we will look at isomers that contain asymmetric centers, the only stereoisomers that you have not seen previously. Then we will go back and look at the reactions you learned in Chapter 4—and for those reactions with products that can have stereoisomers, see what specific stereoisomers are formed.

PROBLEM 1 ◆

a. Draw three constitutional isomers with molecular formula C_3H_8O.
b. How many constitutional isomers can you draw for $C_4H_{10}O$?

5.1   CIS—TRANS ISOMERS RESULT FROM RESTRICTED ROTATION

Cis–trans isomers (also called **geometric isomers**) result from restricted rotation. Restricted rotation can be caused either by a *double bond* or by a *cyclic structure*. We have seen that the restricted rotation about its carbon–carbon double bond causes an alkene such as 2-pentene to have cis and trans isomers (Section 3.4). The **cis isomer** has the hydrogens on the *same side* of the double bond and the **trans isomer** has the hydrogens on *opposite sides* of the double bond. (Remember that *Z* and *E* are used instead of cis and trans for more complex molecules.)

cis-2-pentene

As a result of restricted rotation about the bonds in a ring, cyclic compounds that have two substituents bonded to different carbons also have cis and trans isomers (Section 2.14). The cis isomer has its substituents on the same side of the ring, whereas the trans isomer has its substituents on opposite sides of the ring.

trans-2-pentene

cis-1-bromo-3-chlorocyclobutane   *trans*-1-bromo-3-chlorocyclobutane

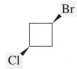

cis-1,4-dimethylcyclohexane   *trans*-1,4-dimethylcyclohexane

---

PROBLEM 2

Draw the cis and trans isomers for the following:

a. 3-hexene
b. 2-methyl-3-heptene
c. 1-bromo-4-chlorocyclohexane
d. 1-ethyl-3-methylcyclobutane

5.2 A CHIRAL OBJECT HAS A NONSUPERIMPOSABLE MIRROR IMAGE

Why can't you put your right shoe on your left foot? Why can't you put your right glove on your left hand? It is because hands, feet, gloves, and shoes have right-handed and left-handed forms. An object with a right-handed and a left-handed form is said to be **chiral** (ky-ral), a word derived from the Greek word *cheir*, which means "hand."

A chiral object has a *nonsuperimposable mirror image*. In other words, its mirror image *is not the same* as an image of the object itself. A hand is chiral because when you look at your right hand in a mirror, you see not a right hand but a left hand (Figure 5.1). In contrast, a chair is not chiral; the reflection of the chair in the mirror looks the same as the chair itself. Objects that are not chiral are said to be **achiral**. An achiral object has a *superimposable mirror image*. Some other achiral objects are a table, a bowl, and a balloon (assuming they are simple and unadorned).

chiral objects

right hand   left hand

achiral objects

◀ **Figure 5.1**
Using a mirror to test for chirality. A chiral object is not the same as its mirror image—they are nonsuperimposable. An achiral object is the same as its mirror image—they are superimposable.

PROBLEM 3 ◆

Which of the following objects are chiral?
a. a mug with DAD written to one side of the handle
b. a mug with MOM written to one side of the handle
c. a mug with DAD written opposite the handle
d. a mug with MOM written opposite the handle

e. a wheelbarrow
f. a remote control device
g. a nail
h. a screw

PROBLEM 4 ◆

a. Name five capital letters that are chiral.
b. Name five capital letters that are achiral.

5.3 AN ASYMMETRIC CENTER IS A CAUSE OF CHIRALITY IN A MOLECULE

Objects are not the only things that can be chiral. Molecules can be chiral too. The usual *cause of chirality in a molecule is an asymmetric center*. (Other features that cause chirality are relatively uncommon and beyond the scope of this book, but you can see one example in Problem 101 at the end of this chapter.)

A molecule with an asymmetric center is chiral.

an asymmetric center

An **asymmetric center** (or chiral center) is an atom bonded to four different groups. Each of the compounds shown below has an asymmetric center indicated by a star. For example, the starred carbon in 4-octanol is an asymmetric center because it is bonded to four different groups (H, OH, CH₂CH₂CH₃, and CH₂CH₂CH₂CH₃). Notice that the atoms immediately bonded to the asymmetric center are not necessarily different from one another; the propyl and butyl groups are different even though the point at which they differ is several atoms away from the asymmetric center. The starred carbon in 2,4-dimethylhexane is an asymmetric center because it too is bonded to four different groups— (methyl, ethyl, isobutyl, and hydrogen).

$$CH_3CH_2CH_2\overset{*}{C}HCH_2CH_2CH_2CH_3$$
$$|$$
$$OH$$
4-octanol

$$CH_3\overset{*}{C}HCH_2CH_3$$
$$|$$
$$Br$$
2-bromobutane

$$CH_3$$
$$|$$
$$CH_3\overset{}{C}HCH_2\overset{*}{C}HCH_2CH_3$$
$$|$$
$$CH_3$$
2,4-dimethylhexane

chem place Tutorial: Identification of asymmetric centers I

Tutorial: Identification of asymmetric centers II

Tutorial: Identification of asymmetric centers III

PROBLEM 5 ♦

Which of the following compounds have an asymmetric center?

a. CH₃CH₂CHCH₃
　　　　　|
　　　　　Cl

b. CH₃CH₂CHCH₃
　　　　　|
　　　　　CH₃

c. CH₃CH₂CCH₂CH₂CH₃
　　　| |
　　 CH₃ Br

d. CH₃CH₂OH

e. CH₃CH₂CHCH₂CH₃
　　　　　　|
　　　　　　Br

f. CH₂=CHCHCH₃
　　　　　　|
　　　　　 NH₂

PROBLEM 6　SOLVED

Tetracycline is called a broad-spectrum antibiotic because it is active against a wide variety of bacteria. How many asymmetric centers does tetracycline have?

Solution　Only sp^3 carbons can be asymmetric centers, because an asymmetric center must have four different groups attached to it. Therefore, we start by locating all the sp^3 carbons in tetracycline. (They are numbered in red.) Tetracycline has nine sp^3 carbons. Four of them (1, 2, 5, and 8) are not asymmetric centers because they are not bonded to four different groups. Tetracycline, therefore, has five asymmetric centers.

tetracycline

5.4   ISOMERS WITH ONE ASYMMETRIC CENTER

A compound with one asymmetric center, such as 2-bromobutane, can exist as two stereoisomers. The two stereoisomers are analogous to a left and a right hand. If we imagine a mirror between the two stereoisomers, we can see they are mirror images of each other. Moreover, they are nonsuperimposable mirror images and thus different molecules.

$$CH_3\overset{*}{C}HCH_2CH_3$$
$$|$$
$$Br$$

2-bromobutane

the two stereoisomers of 2-bromobutane
enantiomers

NOTE TO THE STUDENT

Prove to yourself that the two stereoisomers of 2-bromobutane are not identical by building ball-and-stick models to represent them and trying to superimpose one on the other; use four different-colored balls to represent the four different groups bonded to the asymmetric center. Special Topic IV in the *Study Guide and Solutions Manual* tells you what other models you should build as you go through this chapter.

Molecules that are nonsuperimposable mirror images of each other are called **enantiomers** (from the Greek *enantion*, which means "opposite"). Thus, the two stereo-isomers of 2-bromobutane are enantiomers. A molecule that has a *nonsuperimposable* mirror image, like an object that has a *nonsuperimposable* mirror image, is *chiral*. Therefore, each member of a pair of enantiomers is chiral. Notice that chirality is a property of an entire object or an entire molecule.

A molecule that has a *superimposable* mirror image, like an object that has a *superimposable* mirror image, is *achiral*. To see that the achiral molecule on the right below is superimposable on its mirror image, mentally rotate it clockwise.

a chiral molecule | nonsuperimposable mirror image
enantiomers

an achiral molecule | superimposable mirror image
identical molecules

A chiral molecule has a nonsuperimposable mirror image.

An achiral molecule has a superimposable mirror image.

PROBLEM 7 ◆

Which of the compounds in Problem 5 can exist as enantiomers?

5.5 ASYMMETRIC CENTERS AND STEREOCENTERS

An asymmetric center is also called a **stereocenter** (or a **stereogenic center**), but they do not mean quite the same thing. A stereocenter is an atom at which the interchange of two groups produces a stereoisomer. Thus stereocenters include both (1) *asymmetric centers*, where the interchange of two groups produces an enantiomer, and (2) the sp^2 carbons of an alkene or the sp^3 carbons of a cyclic compound, where the interchange of two groups converts a cis isomer to a trans isomer (or a Z isomer to an E isomer) or vice versa. This means that although *all asymmetric centers are stereocenters*, not all stereocenters are asymmetric centers.

5.6 HOW TO DRAW ENANTIOMERS

Chemists draw enantiomers using either *perspective formulas* or *Fischer projections*. A **perspective formula** shows two of the bonds to the asymmetric center in the plane of the paper, one bond as a solid wedge protruding forward out of the paper, and the fourth bond as a hatched wedge extending behind the paper. The solid wedge and the hatched wedge must be adjacent to one another. When you draw the first enantiomer, the four groups bonded to the asymmetric center can be placed around it in any order. Then draw the second enantiomer by drawing the mirror image of the first.

A solid wedge represents a bond that extends out of the plane of the paper toward the viewer.

A hatched wedge represents a bond that points back from the plane of the paper away from the viewer.

When you draw a perspective formula, make sure that the two bonds in the plane of the paper are adjacent to one another; neither the solid wedge nor the hatched wedge should be drawn between them.

perspective formulas of the enantiomers of 2-bromobutane

A **Fischer projection** is a shortcut for showing the three-dimensional arrangement of groups bonded to an asymmetric center. Devised in the late 1800s by Emil Fischer (Section 21.0), when printing techniques could not handle wedges but only vertical and horizontal lines, it represents an asymmetric center as the point of intersection of two perpendicular lines. Horizontal lines represent the bonds that project out of the plane of the paper toward the viewer, and vertical lines represent the bonds that extend back from the plane of the paper away from the viewer. The carbon chain is usually drawn vertically, with C-1 at the top.

In a Fischer projection, horizontal lines project out of the plane of the paper toward the viewer, and vertical lines extend back from the plane of the paper away from the viewer.

Fischer projections of the enantiomers
of 2-bromobutane

When you draw enantiomers using a Fischer projection, you can put the four atoms or groups bonded to the asymmetric center around that center in any order. Then draw the second enantiomer by interchanging two of the atoms or groups. It does not matter which two you interchange. (Make models to convince yourself that this is true.) It is best to interchange the groups on the two horizontal bonds, because then the enantiomers look like mirror images on your paper.

Whether you are drawing perspective formulas or Fischer projections, interchanging two atoms or groups will produce the other enantiomer. Interchanging two atoms or groups a second time brings you back to the original molecule.

PROBLEM 8

Draw enantiomers for each of the following using:

a. perspective formulas.
b. Fischer projections.

1. CH_3CHCH_2OH (Br)   2. $ClCH_2CH_2CHCH_2CH_3$ (CH_3)   3. $CH_3CHCHCH_3$ (CH_3, OH)

PROBLEM 9   **SOLVED**

Do the following structures represent identical molecules or a pair of enantiomers?

$HC=CH_2$ / C / CH_3CH_2 CH_3 / H and CH_2CH_3 / H C CH_3 / $HC=CH_2$

Solution   Interchanging two atoms or groups attached to an asymmetric center of a perspective formula produces an enantiomer. Interchanging two atoms or groups a second time brings you back to the original molecule. Because groups have to be interchanged twice to get from one structure to the other, the two structures represent identical molecules.

$HC=CH_2$ / C / CH_3CH_2 CH_3 / H →(interchange **vinyl and H**) H / C / CH_3CH_2 CH_3 / $HC=CH_2$ →(interchange **ethyl and H**) CH_2CH_3 / H C CH_3 / $HC=CH_2$

In Section 5.7 you will learn another way to determine if two structures represent identical molecules or enantiomers.

5.7 NAMING ENANTIOMERS BY THE *R,S* SYSTEM

How do we name the different stereoisomers of a compound like 2-bromobutane so that we know which one we are talking about? We need a system of nomenclature that indicates the arrangement of the atoms or groups about the asymmetric center. Chemists use the letters *R* and *S* for this purpose. For any pair of enantiomers with one asymmetric center, one member will have the **R configuration** and the other will have the **S configuration**. The *R,S* system was devised by R. S. Cahn, C. Ingold, and V. Prelog.

We will first look at how we can determine the configuration of a compound if we have a three-dimensional model.

1. **Rank the groups (or atoms) bonded to the asymmetric center in order of priority.** The atomic numbers of the atoms directly attached to the asymmetric center determine the relative priorities. The higher the atomic number, the higher the priority. This should remind you of the way that relative priorities are determined for *E* and *Z* isomers (Section 3.5), because the system of priorities was originally devised for the *R,S* system of nomenclature and was later adopted for the *E,Z* system.

BIOGRAPHY

Born in London, England, **Robert Sidney Cahn (1899–1981)** *received an M.A. from Cambridge University and a doctorate in natural philosophy in France. He edited the* Journal of the Chemical Society *(London) from 1949 to 1963.*

BIOGRAPHY

Sir Christopher Ingold (1893–1970), *born in Ilford, England, was a professor of chemistry at Leeds University (1924–1930) and at University College, London (1930–1970). In 1958 he was knighted by Queen Elizabeth II. (See page 334).*

B I O G R A P H Y

Vladimir Prelog (1906–1998) *was born in Sarajevo, Bosnia. In 1929 he received a Dr. Ing. degree from the Institute of Technology in Prague, Czechoslovakia. He taught at the University of Zagreb from 1935 until 1941, when he fled to Switzerland just ahead of the invading German army. He was a professor at the Swiss Federal Institute of Technology (ETH). For work that contributed to an understanding of how living organisms carry out chemical reactions, he shared the 1975 Nobel Prize in Chemistry with John Cornforth (page 240).*

this has the highest priority

this has the lowest priority

2. Orient the molecule so that the group (or atom) with the lowest priority (4) is directed away from you. Then draw an imaginary arrow from the group (or atom) with the highest priority (1) to the group (or atom) with the next highest priority (2). If the arrow points clockwise, the asymmetric center has the *R* configuration (*R* is for *rectus*, which is Latin for "right"). If the arrow points counterclockwise, the asymmetric center has the *S* configuration (*S* is for *sinister*, which is Latin for "left").

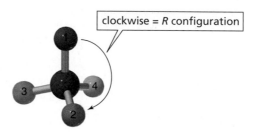

clockwise = *R* configuration

If you forget which direction corresponds to which configuration, imagine driving a car and turning the steering wheel clockwise to make a right turn or counterclockwise to make a left turn.

right turn

left turn

The molecule is oriented so that the group with the lowest priority points away from the viewer. If an arrow drawn from the highest priority group to the next-highest priority group points clockwise, the molecule has the *R* configuration.

PROBLEM 10◆

Which of the following molecular models are identical?

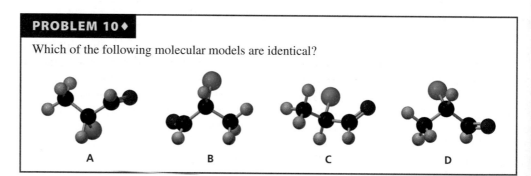

A   B   C   D

If you are able to visualize spatial relationships easily, the above two rules are all you need to determine whether the asymmetric center of a molecule written on a two-dimensional piece of paper has the *R* or the *S* configuration. Mentally rotate the molecule so that the group (or atom) with the lowest priority (4) is directed away from you, then draw an imaginary arrow from the group (or atom) with the highest priority to the group (or atom) with the next highest priority.

If you have trouble visualizing spatial relationships and you do not have access to a model, the following sets of instructions will allow you to determine the configuration about an asymmetric center without having to rotate the molecule mentally.

First, let's look at how you can determine the configuration of a compound drawn as a perspective formula. We will use the enantiomers of 2-bromobutane as an example.

the enantiomers of 2-bromobutane

1. Rank the groups (or atoms) that are bonded to the asymmetric center in order of priority. In our example, bromine has the highest priority (1), the ethyl group has the second highest priority (2), the methyl group is next (3), and hydrogen has the lowest priority (4). (Revisit Section 3.5 if you don't understand how these priorities are assigned.)

2. If the group (or atom) with the lowest priority (4) is bonded by a hatched wedge, draw an arrow from the group (or atom) with the highest priority (1) directly to the group (or atom) with the second highest priority (2). If the arrow points clockwise, the compound has the *R* configuration, and if it points counterclockwise, the compound has the *S* configuration.

the group with the lowest priority is bonded by a hatched wedge

(*S*)-2-bromobutane   **(*R*)-2-bromobutane**

Clockwise specifies *R* if the lowest priority substituent is on a hatched wedge.

Counterclockwise specifies *S* if the lowest priority substituent is on a hatched wedge.

3. If the group with the lowest priority (4) is not bonded by a hatched wedge, interchange group 4 with the group bonded by a hatched wedge. Then proceed as in step 2: Draw an arrow from the group (or atom) with the highest priority (1) to the group (or atom) with the second-highest priority (2). Because you have interchanged two groups, you are now determining the configuration of the *enantiomer* of the original molecule. So if the arrow points clockwise, the enantiomer (with the interchanged groups) has the *R* configuration, which means the original molecule has the *S* configuration. On the other hand, if the arrow points counterclockwise, the enantiomer (with the interchanged groups) has the *S* configuration, which means the original molecule has the *R* configuration.

switch
CH₃ and H

what is its configuration?

this molecule has the *R* configuration; therefore, the molecule had the *S* configuration before the groups were switched

4. If there is a group between group (1) and group (2), make sure the arrow is drawn from (1) to (2) to (3) and **not** from (1) to (3) to (2).

PROBLEM 11 ◆

Assign relative priorities to the groups or atoms within each of the following sets:

a. $—CH_2OH$ $—CH_3$ $—H$ $—CH_2CH_2OH$

b. $—CH=O$ $—OH$ $—CH_3$ $—CH_2OH$

c. $—CH(CH_3)_2$ $—CH_2CH_2Br$ $—Cl$ $—CH_2CH_2CH_2Br$

d. $—CH=CH_2$ $—CH_2CH_3$ ⬡ $—CH_3$

PROBLEM 12 ◆

Indicate whether each of the following structures has the *R* or the *S* configuration:

a.
```
        Br
        |
      .C.''''CH₂CH₃
    H / \
        CH₃
```

b.
```
       H
       |
      .C.''''CH₃
   Br /  \
        COOH
```

c.

d.

Now let's see how to determine the configuration of a compound drawn as a Fischer projection.

1. Rank the groups (or atoms) that are bonded to the asymmetric center in order of priority.

2. Draw an arrow from the group (or atom) with the highest priority (1) to the group (or atom) with the next highest priority (2). If the arrow points clockwise, the enantiomer has the *R* configuration; if it points counterclockwise, the enantiomer has the *S* configuration, *provided that the group with the lowest priority (4) is on a vertical bond.*

$$CH_3CH_2 \overset{\overset{1}{Cl}}{\underset{\underset{4}{H}}{\vert}} CH_2CH_2CH_3 \qquad CH_3CH_2CH_2 \overset{\overset{1}{Cl}}{\underset{\underset{4}{H}}{\vert}} CH_2CH_3$$

     (R)-3-chlorohexane   **(S)-3-chlorohexane**

3. If the group (or atom) with the lowest priority is on a *horizontal bond*, the answer you get from the direction of the arrow will be the opposite of the correct answer. For example, if the arrow points clockwise, suggesting that the asymmetric center has the *R* configuration, it actually has the *S* configuration; if the arrow points counterclockwise, suggesting that the asymmetric center has the *S* configuration, it actually has the *R* configuration. In the following example, the group with the lowest priority is on a horizontal bond, so clockwise signifies the *S* configuration, not the *R* configuration.

Clockwise specifies *R* if the lowest priority substituent is on a vertical bond.

Clockwise specifies *S* if the lowest priority substituent is on a horizontal bond.

$$4\,H \overset{\overset{3}{CH_3}}{\underset{\underset{2}{CH_2CH_3}}{\vert}} \overset{1}{OH} \qquad HO \overset{\overset{3}{CH_3}}{\underset{\underset{2}{CH_2CH_3}}{\vert}} H\,4$$

    (S)-2-butanol   **(R)-2-butanol**

4. If there is a group between group (1) and group (2), make sure the arrow is drawn from (1) to (2) to (3), as in the following structures, and not from (1) to (3) to (2).

$$4\,H \overset{\overset{2}{\overset{O}{\underset{\Vert}{C}}OH}}{\underset{\underset{1}{OH}}{\vert}} CH_3\,3 \qquad 3\,CH_3 \overset{\overset{2}{\overset{O}{\underset{\Vert}{C}}OH}}{\underset{\underset{1}{OH}}{\vert}} H\,4$$

    (S)-lactic acid   **(R)-lactic acid**

NOTE TO THE STUDENT

When comparing two Fischer projections to see if they are the same or different, never rotate one 90° or flip it "front-to-back," because that is a quick way to get a wrong answer. A Fischer projection can be rotated 180° in the plane of the paper, but that is the only way you can move it without risking an incorrect answer.

PROBLEM 13 ◆

Indicate the configuration of the following:

a.   CH(CH₃)₂
    CH₃CH₂──┼──CH₂Br
           CH₃

b.   CH₂CH₂CH₃
    HO──┼──H
        CH₂OH

c.   Br
    CH₃──┼──H
        CH₂CH₃

d.   CH₂CH₂CH₂CH₃
    CH₃──┼──CH₂CH₂CH₃
        CH₂CH₃

PROBLEM-SOLVING STRATEGY

Recognizing Pairs of Enantiomers

Do the structures represent identical molecules or a pair of enantiomers?

The easiest way to find out whether two molecules are enantiomers or identical molecules is to determine their configurations. If one has the *R* configuration and the other has the *S* configuration, they are enantiomers. If they both have the *R* configuration or both have the *S* configuration, they are identical molecules. Because the structure on the left has the *S* configuration and the structure on the right has the *R* configuration, we know that they represent a pair of enantiomers.

Now continue on to Problem 14.

PROBLEM 14 ◆ SOLVED

Do the following structures represent identical molecules or a pair of enantiomers?

Solution to 14a The first structure shown in part **a** has the *R* configuration, and the second structure also has the *R* configuration. Because they both have the same configuration, the structures represent identical molecules.

PROBLEM-SOLVING STRATEGY

Drawing an Enantiomer with a Desired Configuration

(S)-Alanine is a naturally occurring amino acid. Draw its structure using a perspective formula.

$$CH_3CHCOO^-$$
$$|$$
$$^+NH_3$$

alanine

First draw the bonds about the asymmetric center. Remember that the two bonds in the plane of the paper must be adjacent to one another.

Put the group with the lowest priority on the hatched wedge. Put the group with the highest priority on any remaining bond.

Because you have been asked to draw the S enantiomer, draw an arrow counterclockwise from the group with the highest priority to the next available bond and put the group with the next highest priority on that bond.

Put the remaining substituent on the last available bond.

Now continue on to Problem 15.

PROBLEM 15

Draw perspective formulas for the following:
a. (S)-2-chlorobutane
b. (R)-1,2-dibromobutane

5.8 CHIRAL COMPOUNDS ARE OPTICALLY ACTIVE

BIOGRAPHY

*Born in Scotland, **William Nicol** (1768–1851) was a professor at the University of Edinburgh. He developed the first prism that produced plane-polarized light. He also developed methods to produce thin slices of materials for use in microscopic studies.*

Enantiomers share many of the same properties; they have the same boiling points, the same melting points, and the same solubilities. In fact, all the physical properties of enantiomers are the same except those that stem from how groups bonded to the asymmetric center are arranged in space. One property that enantiomers do not share is the way they interact with plane-polarized light.

Normal light, such as that coming from a light bulb or the sun, consists of rays that oscillate in all directions. In contrast, all the rays in a beam of **plane-polarized light** oscillate in a single plane. Plane-polarized light is produced by passing normal light through a polarizer, such as a polarized lens or a Nicol prism. Only light oscillating in a certain plane can pass through.

You can experience the effect of a polarized lens by wearing a pair of polarized sunglasses. Polarized sunglasses allow only light oscillating in a single plane to pass through, which is why they block reflections (glare) more effectively than nonpolarized sunglasses do.

In 1815, the physicist Jean-Baptiste Biot discovered that certain naturally occurring organic substances, such as camphor and oil of turpentine, are able to rotate the **plane of polarization** of plane-polarized light. He noted that some compounds rotated it clockwise and others counterclockwise, while some did not rotate it at all. He proposed that the ability to rotate the plane of polarization of plane-polarized light was attributable to some asymmetry in the molecules. Van't Hoff and Le Bel later determined that the asymmetry was associated with compounds having one or more asymmetric centers.

When plane-polarized light passes through a solution of achiral molecules, the light emerges from the solution with its plane of polarization unchanged. *An achiral compound does not rotate the plane of polarization of plane-polarized light.*

However, when polarized light passes through a solution of a chiral compound, the light emerges with its plane of polarization changed. Thus, *a chiral compound rotates the plane of polarization of plane-polarized light.* A chiral compound can rotate it clockwise or counterclockwise. If one enantiomer rotates it clockwise, its mirror image will rotate it exactly the same amount counterclockwise.

When light is filtered through two polarized lenses at a 90° angle to one another, none of the light passes through.

A compound that rotates the plane of polarization of plane-polarized light is said to be **optically active**. In other words, chiral compounds are optically active, and achiral compounds are **optically inactive**.

If an optically active compound rotates the plane of polarization clockwise, the compound is said to be **dextrorotatory**, indicated in the compound's name by the prefix (+). If it rotates it counterclockwise, it is said to be **levorotatory**, indicated by (−). *Dextro* and *levo* are Latin prefixes for "to the right" and "to the left," respectively. Sometimes lowercase *d* and *l* are used instead of (+) and (−).

Do not confuse (+) and (−) with *R* and *S*. The (+) and (−) symbols indicate the direction in which an optically active compound rotates the plane of polarization of plane-polarized light, whereas *R* and *S* indicate the arrangement of the groups about an asymmetric center. Some compounds with the *R* configuration are (+) and some are (−). Likewise, some molecules with the *S* configuration are (+) and some are (−).

We can tell by looking at the structure of a compound whether it has the *R* or the *S* configuration, but the only way we can tell whether a compound is dextrorotatory (+) or levorotatory (−) is to put the compound in a polarimeter, an instrument that measures the direction and the amount the plane of polarization of plane-polarized light is rotated. For example, (*S*)-lactic acid and (*S*)-sodium lactate both have an *S* configuration, but (*S*)-lactic acid has been found to be dextrorotatory whereas (*S*)-sodium lactate is levorotatory. When we know the direction an optically active compound rotates the plane of polarization, we can incorporate (+) or (−) into its name.

$$
\begin{array}{cc}
CH_3 & CH_3 \\
| & | \\
HO\text{—}C\text{—}H & HO\text{—}C\text{—}H \\
| & | \\
COOH & COO^- \; Na^+ \\
\textbf{(S)-(+)-lactic acid} & \textbf{(S)-(−)-sodium lactate}
\end{array}
$$

PROBLEM 16 ◆

a. Is (*R*)-lactic acid dextrorotatory or levorotatory?
b. Is (*R*)-sodium lactate dextrorotatory or levorotatory?

5.9 HOW SPECIFIC ROTATION IS MEASURED

Figure 5.2 provides a simplified description of how a **polarimeter** functions. The amount of rotation caused by an optically active compound will vary with the wavelength of the light being used, so the light source in a polarimeter must produce monochromatic (single-wavelength) light. Most polarimeters use light from a sodium arc (called the sodium D-line; wavelength = 589 nm; see Section 13.17). In a polarimeter, monochromatic light passes through a polarizer and emerges as plane-polarized light. The polarized light then passes through a sample tube. If the tube is empty, or filled with an optically inactive solvent, the light emerges from it with its plane of polarization unchanged. The light then passes through an analyzer, which is a second polarizer mounted on an eyepiece with a dial marked in degrees. Before the start of an experiment, the user looks through the eyepiece and rotates the analyzer until he or she sees total darkness. At this point the analyzer is at a right angle to the first polarizer, so no light passes through. This analyzer setting corresponds to zero rotation.

The sample to be measured is then placed in the sample tube. If the sample is optically active, it will rotate the plane of polarization. The analyzer, therefore, will no longer block all the light, so some light reaches the user's eye. The user now rotates the analyzer again until no light passes through. The degree to which the analyzer is rotated can be read from the dial and represents the difference between an optically inactive sample and the optically active sample. This value, which is measured in degrees, is called the **observed rotation** (α). It is dependent on the number of optically active molecules that direction of light propagation

| light source | normal light | polarizer | plane-polarized light | sample tube containing a chiral compound | plane-polarized light | analyzer viewer |

▲ **Figure 5.2**
A schematic drawing of a polarimeter.

the light encounters in the sample, which depends in turn on the concentration of the sample and the length of the sample tube. The observed rotation also depends on the temperature and the wavelength of the light source.

Each optically active compound has a characteristic specific rotation. A compound's **specific rotation** is the rotation caused by a solution of 1.0 g of the compound per milliliter of solution in a sample tube 1.0 decimeter long at a specified temperature and wavelength.* The specific rotation can be calculated from the observed rotation using the following formula:

$$[\alpha]^T_\lambda = \frac{\alpha}{l \times c}$$

where $[\alpha]$ is the specific rotation; T is temperature in °C; λ is the wavelength of the incident light (when the sodium D-line is used, λ is indicated as D); α is the observed rotation; l is the length of the sample tube in decimeters; and c is the concentration of the sample in grams per milliliter of solution.

If one enantiomer has a specific rotation of +5.75, the specific rotation of the other enantiomer must be −5.75, because the mirror-image molecule rotates the plane of polarization the same amount but in the opposite direction.

(R)-2-methyl-1-butanol

$[\alpha]^{20\,°C}_D = +5.75$

(S)-2-methyl-1-butanol

$[\alpha]^{20\,°C}_D = -5.75$

The specific rotations of some common compounds are shown in Table 5.1.

Table 5.1 Specific Rotation of Some Naturally Occurring Compounds	
Cholesterol	− 31.5
Cocaine	− 16
Codeine	− 136
Morphine	− 132
Penicillin V	+ 233
Progesterone	+ 172
Sucrose (table sugar)	+ 66.5
Testosterone	+ 109

*Unlike observed rotation, which is measured in degrees, specific rotation has units of $10^{-1}\,deg\,cm^2\,g^{-1}$. In this book, values of specific rotation will be given without units.

A mixture of equal amounts of two enantiomers—such as (R)-($-$)-lactic acid and (S)-($+$)-lactic acid—is called a **racemic mixture** or a **racemate**. Racemic mixtures do not rotate the plane of polarization of plane-polarized light. They are optically inactive because for every molecule in a racemic mixture that rotates the plane of polarization in one direction, there is a mirror-image molecule that rotates the plane in the opposite direction. As a result, the light emerges from a racemic mixture with its plane of polarization unchanged. The symbol ($\pm$) is used to specify a racemic mixture. Thus, ($\pm$)-2-bromobutane indicates a mixture of 50% ($+$)-2-bromobutane and 50% ($-$)-2-bromobutane.

PROBLEM 17♦

The observed rotation of 2.0 g of a compound in 50 mL of solution in a polarimeter tube 20-cm long is $+13.4°$. What is the specific rotation of the compound?

PROBLEM 18♦

(S)-($+$)-Monosodium glutamate (MSG) is a flavor enhancer used in many foods. Some people have an allergic reaction to MSG (headache, chest pain, and an overall feeling of weakness). "Fast food" often contains substantial amounts of MSG, which is widely used in Chinese food as well. (S)-($+$)-MSG has a specific rotation of $+24$.

$$COO^- Na^+$$
$$|$$
$$^-OOCCH_2CH_2 \overset{\displaystyle C}{\underset{\displaystyle \overset{+}{NH_3}}{\diagup}} {}^{\cdots\cdots\!} H$$

(S)-($+$)-monosodium glutamate

a. What is the specific rotation of (R)-($-$)-monosodium glutamate?
b. What is the specific rotation of a racemic mixture of MSG?

5.10 ENANTIOMERIC EXCESS

Whether a particular sample consists of a single enantiomer or a mixture of enantiomers can be determined by its **observed specific rotation**, which is the specific rotation measured for a particular sample. For example, if a sample of (S)-($+$)-2-bromobutane is **enantiomerically pure**—meaning only one enantiomer is present, it will have an *observed specific rotation* of $+23.1$ because the *specific rotation* of (S)-($+$)-2-bromobutane is $+23.1$. If, however, the sample of 2-bromobutane is a racemic mixture, it will have an observed specific rotation of 0. If the observed specific rotation is positive but less than $+23.1$, we will know that the sample is a mixture of enantiomers and that the mixture contains more of the enantiomer with the S configuration than the enantiomer with the R configuration. The **enantiomeric excess (ee)** tells us how much of an excess of one enantiomer is in the mixture. It can be calculated from the observed specific rotation:

$$\text{enantiomeric excess} = \frac{\text{observed specific rotation}}{\text{specific rotation of the pure enantiomer}} \times 100\%$$

For example, if the sample of 2-bromobutane has an observed specific rotation of $+9.2$, the enantiomeric excess is 40%. In other words, the excess of one of the enantiomers comprises 40% of the mixture.

$$\text{enantiomeric excess} = \frac{+9.2}{+23.1} \times 100\% = 40\%$$

If the mixture has a 40% enantiomeric excess, 40% of the mixture is excess S enantiomer and 60% is a racemic mixture. Half of the racemic mixture plus the amount of excess S enantiomer equals the amount of the S enantiomer present in the mixture. Therefore, 70% of the mixture is the S enantiomer [(1/2 × 60) + 40] and 30% is the R enantiomer.

PROBLEM 19◆

(+)-Mandelic acid has a specific rotation of +158. What would be the observed specific rotation of each of the following mixtures?

a. 25% (−)-mandelic acid and 75% (+)-mandelic acid
b. 50% (−)-mandelic acid and 50% (+)-mandelic acid
c. 75% (−)-mandelic acid and 25% (+)-mandelic acid

PROBLEM 20◆

Naproxen, a nonsteroidal anti-inflammatory drug that is the active ingredient in Aleve (page 94), has a specific rotation of +66. One commercial preparation results in a mixture that has a 97% enantiomeric excess.

a. Does naproxen have the *R* or the *S* configuration?
b. What percent of each enantiomer is obtained from the commercial preparation?

PROBLEM 21   SOLVED

A solution prepared by mixing 10 mL of a 0.10 M solution of the *R* enantiomer of a compound and 30 mL of a 0.10 M solution of the *S* enantiomer was found to have an observed specific rotation of +4.8. What is the specific rotation of each of the enantiomers? (*Hint*: mL × M = millimole, abbreviated mmol)

Solution   One (10 mL × 0.10M) mmol of the *R* enantiomer is mixed with 3 (30 mL × 0.10M) mmol of the *S* enantiomer; 1 mmol of the *R* enantiomer plus 1 mmol of the *S* enantiomer will form 2 mmol of a racemic mixture, so there will be 2 mmol of *S* enantiomer left over. Because 2 mmol out of 4 mmol is excess *S* enantiomer (2/4 = 0.50), the solution has a 50% enantiomeric excess.

$$\text{enantiomer excess} = \frac{\text{observed specific rotation}}{\text{specific rotation of the pure enantiomer}} \times 100\%$$

$$50\% = \frac{+4.8}{x} \times 100\%$$

$$\frac{50}{100} = \frac{+4.8}{x}$$

$$\frac{1}{2} = \frac{+4.8}{x}$$

$$x = 2\,(+4.8)$$

$$x = +9.6$$

The *S* enantiomer has a specific rotation of +9.6; the *R* enantiomer has a specific rotation of −9.6.

5.11 ISOMERS WITH MORE THAN ONE ASYMMETRIC CENTER

Many organic compounds have more than one asymmetric center. The more asymmetric centers a compound has, the more stereoisomers it can have. If we know the number of asymmetric centers, we can calculate the *maximum* number of stereoisomers for that compound: *a compound can have a maximum of 2^n stereoisomers, where* n *equals the number of asymmetric centers* (provided it does not also have stereocenters that would cause it to have cis–trans isomers; see Problem 22). For example, 3-chloro-2-butanol has two asymmetric centers. Therefore, it can have a maximum of four ($2^2 = 4$)

stereoisomers. The four stereoisomers are shown below both as perspective formulas and as Fischer projections.

$$CH_3\overset{*}{C}H\overset{*}{C}HCH_3$$
$$\underset{Cl}{|}\ \underset{OH}{|}$$

3-chloro-2-butanol

erythro enantiomers   threo enantiomers

perspective formulas of the stereoisomers of 3-chloro-2-butanol (staggered)

stereoisomers of 3-chloro-2-butanol

erythro enantiomers   threo enantiomers

Fischer projections of the stereoisomers of 3-chloro-2-butanol

The four stereoisomers of 3-chloro-2-butanol consist of two pairs of enantiomers. Stereoisomers **1** and **2** are nonsuperimposable mirror images. They, therefore, are enantiomers. Stereoisomers **3** and **4** are also enantiomers. Stereoisomers **1** and **3** are not identical, and they are not mirror images. Such stereoisomers are called **diastereomers**. *Diastereomers are stereoisomers that are not enantiomers.* Stereoisomers **1** and **4**, **2** and **3**, and **2** and **4** are also pairs of diastereomers. Notice that in a pair of diastereomers, the configuration of one of the asymmetric centers is the same but the configuration of the other asymmetric center is different. (Note that cis–trans isomers are also considered to be diastereomers, because they are stereoisomers that are not enantiomers.)

Enantiomers have *identical physical properties* (except for the way they interact with polarized light) and *identical chemical properties*, so they react at the same rate with a given achiral reagent. (In Section 5.21, we will see that they react at different rates with chiral reagents.)

Diastereomers have *different physical properties*, meaning different melting points, boiling points, solubilities, specific rotations, and so on, and *different chemical properties*, so they react with a given achiral reagent at different rates.

When Fischer projections are drawn for stereoisomers with two adjacent asymmetric centers (such as those for 3-chloro-2-butanol), the enantiomers with similar groups on the same side of the carbon chain are called the **erythro enantiomers** (Section 22.3). Those with similar groups on opposite sides are called the **threo enantiomers**. Therefore, **1** and **2** are the erythro enantiomers of 3-chloro-2-butanol (the hydrogens are on the same side), whereas **3** and **4** are the threo enantiomers. In each of the Fischer projections shown here, the horizontal bonds project out of the paper toward the viewer and the vertical bonds extend behind the paper away from the viewer. Groups can rotate freely about the carbon–carbon single bonds, but Fischer projections show the stereoisomers in their eclipsed conformations.

Because a Fischer projection does not show the three-dimensional structure of the molecule, and because it represents the molecule in a relatively unstable eclipsed conformation, most chemists prefer to use perspective formulas. Perspective formulas (those shown on the top of this page) show the molecule's three-dimensional structure in a stable, staggered conformation, so they provide a more accurate representation of structure.

Diastereomers are stereoisomers that are not enantiomers.

When perspective formulas are drawn to show the stereoisomers in their less stable eclipsed conformations (those shown below), we can easily see that the erythro enantiomers have similar groups on the same side. We will use both perspective formulas and Fischer projections to depict the arrangement of groups bonded to an asymmetric center.

erythro enantiomers   threo enantiomers

perspective formulas of the stereoisomers of 3-chloro-2-butanol (eclipsed)

PROBLEM 22

The following compound has only one asymmetric center. Why then does it have four stereoisomers?

$$CH_3CH_2\overset{*}{C}HCH_2CH=CHCH_3$$
$$|$$
$$Br$$

chem Tutorial:
place   Nonsuperimposable mirror image

PROBLEM 23 ◆

Is the following statement correct?
A compound can have a maximum of 2^n stereoisomers, where n equals the number of stereocenters?

PROBLEM 24 ◆

a. Stereoisomers with two asymmetric centers are called _____ if the configuration of both asymmetric centers in one stereoisomer is the opposite of the configuration of the asymmetric centers in the other stereoisomer.
b. Stereoisomers with two asymmetric centers are called _____ if the configuration of both asymmetric centers in one stereoisomer is the same as the configuration of the asymmetric centers in the other stereoisomer.
c. Stereoisomers with two asymmetric centers are called _____ if one of the asymmetric centers has the same configuration in both stereoisomers and the other asymmetric center has the opposite configuration in the two stereoisomers.

PROBLEM 25 ◆

The stereoisomer of cholesterol found in nature is

cholesterol

a. How many asymmetric centers does cholesterol have?
b. What is the maximum number of stereoisomers that cholesterol can have?

PROBLEM 26

Draw the stereoisomers of the following amino acids. Indicate pairs of enantiomers and pairs of diastereomers.

$$CH_3CHCH_2-CHCOO^-$$
$$|\qquad\quad|$$
$$CH_3\quad {}^+NH_3$$
leucine

$$CH_3CH_2CH-CHCOO^-$$
$$|\qquad\quad|$$
$$CH_3\ {}^+NH_3$$
isoleucine

1-Bromo-2-methylcyclopentane also has two asymmetric centers and four stereoisomers. Because the compound is cyclic, the substituents can be either cis or trans. The cis isomer exists as a pair of enantiomers, and the trans isomer exists as a pair of enantiomers.

cis-**1-bromo-2-methylcyclopentane**   *trans*-**1-bromo-2-methylcyclopentane**

1-Bromo-3-methylcyclobutane does not have any asymmetric centers. The C-1 carbon has a bromine and a hydrogen attached to it, but its other two groups [—$CH_2CH(CH_3)CH_2$—] are identical; C-3 has a methyl group and a hydrogen attached to it, but its other two groups [—$CH_2CH(Br)CH_2$—] are identical. Because the compound does not have a carbon with four different groups attached to it, it has only two stereoisomers, the cis isomer and the trans isomer. The cis and trans isomers do not have enantiomers; they are achiral molecules.

cis-**1-bromo-3-methylcyclobutane**   *trans*-**1-bromo-3-methylcyclobutane**

1-Bromo-3-methylcyclohexane has two asymmetric centers. The carbon that is bonded to a hydrogen and a bromine is also bonded to two different carbon-containing groups (—$CH_2CH(CH_3)CH_2CH_2CH_2$— and —$CH_2CH_2CH_2CH(CH_3)CH_2$—), so it is an asymmetric center. The carbon that is bonded to a hydrogen and a methyl group is also bonded to two different carbon-containing groups, so it too is an asymmetric center.

Because the compound has two asymmetric centers, it has four stereoisomers. Enantiomers can be drawn for the cis isomer, and enantiomers can be drawn for the trans isomer. Each of the stereoisomers is a chiral molecule.

cis-**1-bromo-3-methylcyclohexane**   *trans*-**1-bromo-3-methylcyclohexane**

1-Bromo-4-methylcyclohexane has no asymmetric centers. Therefore, the compound has only one cis isomer and one trans isomer. Each of the stereoisomers is an achiral molecule.

cis-**1-bromo-4-methylcyclohexane**   *trans*-**1-bromo-4-methylcyclohexane**

PROBLEM 27

Draw all possible stereoisomers for each of the following:
a. 2-chloro-3-hexanol
b. 2-bromo-4-chlorohexane
c. 2,3-dichloropentane
d. 1,3-dibromopentane

PROBLEM 28

Draw the stereoisomers of 2-methylcyclohexanol.

PROBLEM 29◆

Of all the possible cyclooctanes that have one chloro substituent and one methyl substituent, which ones do not have any asymmetric centers?

PROBLEM-SOLVING STRATEGY

Drawing Enantiomers and Diastereomers

Draw an enantiomer and a diastereomer for the following:

You can draw an enantiomer in one of two ways. You can change the configuration of all the asymmetric centers by changing all wedges to dashes and all dashes to wedges as in **A**. Or you can draw a mirror image of the compound as in **B**. Notice that since **A** and **B** are each an enantiomer of the given compound, **A** and **B** are identical molecules.

or

A   **B**

You can draw a diastereomer by changing the configuration of only one of the asymmetric centers as in **C**.

C

Now continue on to Problem 30.

PROBLEM 30

Draw a diastereomer for each of the following:

a.

$$\begin{array}{c} CH_3 \\ H\!\!-\!\!\!\vert\!\!-\!\!OH \\ H\!\!-\!\!\!\vert\!\!-\!\!OH \\ CH_3 \end{array}$$

b.

$$\begin{array}{cc} Cl & Cl \\ H^{\text{\tiny|||}}C\!\!-\!\!C\!\!-\!\!H \\ CH_3CH_2 & CH_3 \end{array}$$

c.

$$\begin{array}{cc} H_3C & CH_3 \\ \diagdown & \diagup \\ C\!\!=\!\!C \\ \diagup & \diagdown \\ H & H \end{array}$$

d.

PROBLEM 31◆

Indicate whether each of the structures in the second row is an enantiomer of, a diastereomer of, or identical to the structure in the top row.

A   **B**   **C**   **D**

5.12 MESO COMPOUNDS HAVE ASYMMETRIC CENTERS BUT ARE OPTICALLY INACTIVE

In the examples we have just seen, the compounds with two asymmetric centers had four stereoisomers. However, some compounds with two asymmetric centers have only three stereoisomers. This is why we emphasized in Section 5.11 that the *maximum* number of stereoisomers a compound with n asymmetric centers can have is 2^n (unless it has stereocenters that are not asymmetric centers), instead of stating that a compound with n asymmetric centers has 2^n stereoisomers.

An example of a compound with two asymmetric centers that has only three stereoisomers is 2,3-dibromobutane.

$$CH_3CHCHCH_3$$

Br Br

2,3-dibromobutane

perspective formulas of the stereoisomers of 2,3-dibromobutane (staggered)

The "missing" isomer is the mirror image of **1** because **1** and its mirror image are the same molecule. This can be seen more clearly when the perspective formulas are drawn in eclipsed conformations or when Fischer projections are used.

perspective formulas of the stereoisomers of 2,3-dibromobutane (eclipsed)

Fischer projections of the stereoisomers of 2,3-dibromobutane

It is easy to see from the following perspective formulas that **1** and its mirror image are identical. To convince yourself that the Fischer projection of **1** and its mirror image are identical, rotate the mirror image 180°. (*Remember, you can move Fischer projections only by rotating them 180° in the plane of the paper.*)

superimposable mirror image

superimposable mirror image

Stereoisomer **1** is called a meso compound. Even though a **meso** (mee-zo) **compound** has asymmetric centers, it is achiral. A meso compound does not rotate polarized light because it is superimposable on its mirror image. *Mesos* is the Greek word for "middle."

A meso compound is achiral.

A meso compound can be recognized by the fact that it has two or more asymmetric centers and a plane of symmetry. A **plane of symmetry** cuts the molecule in half so that one half is the mirror image of the other. A molecule with a plane of symmetry does not have an enantiomer. Compare stereoisomer **1**, which has a plane of symmetry and thus no enantiomer, with stereoisomer **2**, which does not have a plane of symmetry and therefore *does* have an enantiomer. *If a compound has a plane of symmetry, it will not be optically active and will not have an enantiomer, even though it has asymmetric centers.*

meso compounds

A meso compound has two or more asymmetric centers and a plane of symmetry.

A chiral compound cannot have a plane of symmetry.

It is easy to recognize when a compound with two asymmetric centers has a stereoisomer that is a meso compound—the four atoms or groups bonded to one asymmetric center are identical to the four atoms or groups bonded to the other asymmetric center. A *compound with the same four atoms or groups bonded to two different asymmetric centers will have three stereoisomers: one will be a meso compound, and the other two will be enantiomers.*

If a compound has a plane of symmetry, it will not be optically active even though it has asymmetric centers.

If a compound with two asymmetric centers has the same four groups bonded to each of the asymmetric centers, one of its stereoisomers will be a meso compound.

In the case of cyclic compounds, the cis isomer will be a meso compound and the trans isomer will be a pair of enantiomers.

In the perspective formula shown above, *cis*-1,2-dibromocyclohexane appears to have a plane of symmetry. Remember, however, that cyclohexane is not a planar hexagon but exists preferentially in the chair conformation, and the chair conformation of *cis*-1,2-dibromocyclohexane does not have a plane of symmetry. Only the much less stable boat conformation of *cis*-1,2-dibromocyclohexane has a plane of symmetry. This issue raises the question of whether *cis*-1,2-dibromocyclohexane is a meso compound. The answer is yes. If a molecule has an achiral conformer (that is, a conformer with a plane of symmetry), the molecule is achiral, even if the achiral conformer is not the most stable conformer. An achiral molecule with two asymmetric centers is a meso compound.

chair conformer   boat conformer

This rule holds for acyclic compounds as well. We have just seen that 2,3-dibromobutane is an achiral meso compound because it has a plane of symmetry. To find its plane of symmetry, however, we had to look at a relatively unstable eclipsed conformation. The more stable staggered conformation does not have a plane of symmetry. 2,3-Dibromobutane is still a meso compound, however, because it has a conformation that has a plane of symmetry.

eclipsed conformer   staggered conformer

PROBLEM-SOLVING STRATEGY

Recognizing whether a Compound has a Stereoisomer that is a Meso Compound

Which of the following compounds has a stereoisomer that is a meso compound?

A   2,3-dimethylbutane
B   3,4-dimethylhexane
C   2-bromo-3-methylpentane
D   1,3-dimethylcyclohexane

E   1,4-dimethylcyclohexane
F   1,2-dimethylcyclohexane
G   3,4-diethylhexane
H   1-bromo-2-methylcyclohexane

Check each compound to see if it has the necessary requirements for having a stereoisomer that is a meso compound. That is, does it have two asymmetric centers, and if so, do they each have the same four substituents attached to them?

Compounds **A**, **E**, and **G** do *not* have a stereoisomer that is a meso compound because they do not have any asymmetric centers.

Compounds **C** and **H** each have two asymmetric centers. They do *not* have a stereoisomer that is a meso compound, however, because each of the asymmetric centers is *not* bonded to the same four substituents.

Compounds **B**, **D**, and **F** have two asymmetric centers, and each asymmetric center is bonded to the same four substituents. Therefore, these compounds have a stereoisomer that is a meso compound.

chem
place Tutorial:
Optical activity

Tutorial:
Identification of stereoisomers
with multiple asymmetric centers

Tutorial:
Plane of symmetry

In the case of the acyclic compound, the isomer that is the meso compound is the one that has a plane of symmetry when the compound is drawn in its eclipsed conformation (**B**). For the cyclic compounds, the cis isomer is the meso compound (**D** and **F**).

B   D   F

Now continue on to Problem 32.

PROBLEM 32 ◆

Which of the following compounds has a stereoisomer that is a meso compound?

A   2,4-dibromohexane
B   2,4-dibromopentane
C   2,4-dimethylpentane

D   1,3-dichlorocyclohexane
E   1,4-dichlorocyclohexane
F   1,2-dichlorocyclobutane

PROBLEM 33   SOLVED

Which of the following compounds are chiral?

Solution   In the top row of compounds, only the third compound is chiral. The first compound has a plane of symmetry, and a chiral molecule does not have a plane of symmetry; the second and fourth compounds do not have any asymmetric centers and each has a plane of symmetry. In the bottom row, the first and third compounds are chiral. The second and fourth compounds each have a plane of symmetry. Thus, only the following compounds are chiral.

PROBLEM 34

Draw all the stereoisomers for each of the following compounds:

a. 1-bromo-2-methylbutane
b. 1-chloro-3-methylpentane
c. 2-methyl-1-propanol
d. 2-bromo-1-butanol
e. 3-chloro-3-methylpentane
f. 3-bromo-2-butanol
g. 3,4-dichlorohexane

h. 2,4-dichloropentane
i. 2,4-dichloroheptane
j. 1,2-dichlorocyclobutane
k. 1,3-dichlorocyclohexane
l. 1,4-dichlorocyclohexane
m. 1-bromo-2-chlorocyclobutane
n. 1-bromo-3-chlorocyclobutane

5.13 HOW TO NAME ISOMERS WITH MORE THAN ONE ASYMMETRIC CENTER

If a compound has more than one asymmetric center, the steps used to determine whether an asymmetric center has the R or the S configuration must be applied to each of the asymmetric centers individually. As an example, let's name one of the stereoisomers of 3-bromo-2-butanol.

a stereoisomer of 3-bromo-2-butanol

First, we will determine the configuration at C-2. The OH group has the highest priority, the C-3 carbon (the C attached to Br, C, H) has the next-highest priority, CH_3 is next, and H has the lowest priority. Because the group with the lowest priority is bonded by a hatched wedge, we can immediately draw an arrow from the group with the highest priority to the group with the next highest priority. That arrow points counterclockwise, so the configuration at C-2 is S.

Now we need to determine the configuration at C-3. Because the group with the lowest priority (H) is not bonded by a hatched wedge, we must put it there by temporarily switching two groups.

The arrow going from **1** (Br, the highest priority group) to **2** (the C attached to O, C, H) to **3** (the methyl group) points counterclockwise, suggesting C-3 has the S configuration. However, because we switched two groups before we drew the arrow, C-3 has the opposite configuration—it has the R configuration. Thus, the isomer is named (2S,3R)-3-bromo-2-butanol.

(2S,3R)-3-bromo-2-butanol

When Fischer projections are used, the procedure is similar. Just apply the steps to each asymmetric center that you learned for a Fischer projection with one asymmetric center. At C-2, the arrow from the group with the highest priority to the group with the next highest priority points clockwise, which would suggest an R configuration. However, the group with the lowest priority is on a horizontal bond, leading us to conclude that C-2 has the S configuration (Section 5.7).

Repeating these steps for C-3 identifies that asymmetric center as having the R configuration. Thus, the isomer is named (2S,3R)-3-bromo-2-butanol.

$$
\begin{array}{c}
\text{CH}_3 \\
\text{H}-\!\!\!\overset{}{\underset{2}{|}}\!\!\!-\text{OH} \\
{}^4\text{H}-\!\!\!\overset{}{\underset{}{|}}\!\!\!-\text{Br}^{1} \\
\boxed{R}\ {}^3\text{CH}_3
\end{array}
$$

(2S,3R)-3-bromo-2-butanol

The four stereoisomers of 3-bromo-2-butanol are named as shown here. Take a few minutes to verify the names.

(2S,3R)-3-bromo-
2-butanol

(2R,3S)-3-bromo-
2-butanol

(2S,3S)-3-bromo-
2-butanol

(2R,3R)-3-bromo-
2-butanol

perspective formulas of the stereoisomers of 3-bromo-2-butanol

(2S,3R)-3-bromo-
2-butanol

(2R,3S)-3-bromo-
2-butanol

(2S,3S)-3-bromo-
2-butanol

(2R,3R)-3-bromo-
2-butanol

Fischer projections of the stereoisomers of 3-bromo-2-butanol

Notice that enantiomers have the opposite configuration at both asymmetric centers, whereas diastereomers have the same configuration at one asymmetric center and the opposite configuration at the other.

PROBLEM 35

Draw and name the four stereoisomers of 1,3-dichloro-2-pentanol using:
a. perspective formulas   **b.** Fischer projections

Tartaric acid has three stereoisomers because each of its two asymmetric centers has the same set of four substituents. The meso compound and the pair of enantiomers are named as shown.

(2R,3S)-tartaric acid
a meso compound

(2R,3R)-tartaric acid
a pair of enantiomers

(2S,3S)-tartaric acid

perspective formulas of the stereoisomers of tartaric acid

(2R,3S)-tartaric acid
a meso compound

(2R,3R)-tartaric acid
a pair of enantiomers

(2S,3S)-tartaric acid

Fischer projections of the stereoisomers of tartaric acid

The physical properties of the three stereoisomers of tartaric acid are listed in Table 5.2. The meso compound and either of the enantiomers are diastereomers. Notice that the physical properties of the enantiomers are the same, whereas the physical properties of the diastereomers are different.

Table 5.2 Physical Properties of the Stereoisomers of Tartaric Acid			
	Melting point, °C	Specific rotation	Solubility, g/100 g H$_2$O at 15 °C
(2R,3R)-(+)-Tartaric acid	171	+11.98	139
(2S,3S)-(−)-Tartaric acid	171	−11.98	139
(2R,3S)-Tartaric acid (meso)	146	0	125
(±)-Tartaric acid	206	0	139

PROBLEM 36◆

Chloramphenicol is a broad-spectrum antibiotic that is particularly useful against typhoid fever. What is the configuration of each of its asymmetric centers?

chloramphenicol

PROBLEM-SOLVING STRATEGY

Drawing a Perspective Formula for a Compound with Two Asymmetric Centers

Draw a perspective formula for (2S,3R)-3-chloro-2-pentanol.

First write a condensed structure for the compound, ignoring the configuration at the asymmetric centers.

3-chloro-2-pentanol

Now draw the bonds about the asymmetric centers. Remember that the solid and hatched wedges must be adjacent.

At each asymmetric center, put the group with the lowest priority on the hatched wedge.

At each asymmetric center, put the group with the highest priority on a bond so that an arrow will point clockwise, if you want the *R* configuration, or counterclockwise, if you want the *S* configuration, to the group with the next highest priority.

$$\underset{S}{\boxed{S}} \quad \underset{R}{\boxed{R}}$$

Put the remaining substituents on the last available bonds.

(2S,3R)-3-chloro-2-pentanol

Now continue on to Problem 37.

PROBLEM 37

Draw a perspective formula for each of the following:

a. (S)-3-chloro-1-pentanol

b. (2R,3R)-2,3-dibromopentane

c. (2S,3R)-3-methyl-2-pentanol

d. (R)-1,2-dibromobutane

PROBLEM 38 ♦

Threonine, an amino acid, has four stereoisomers. The isomer found in nature is (2S,3R)-threonine. Which of the following structures represents the naturally occurring amino acid?

stereosiomers of threonine

PROBLEM 39 ♦

Name the following:

a.

b.

c.

d.

PROBLEM 40

Name the isomers you drew in Problem 28.

5.14 REACTIONS OF COMPOUNDS THAT CONTAIN AN ASYMMETRIC CENTER

When a compound containing an asymmetric center undergoes a reaction, the effect on the configuration of the asymmetric center depends on the reaction. If the reaction does not break any of the four bonds to the asymmetric center, then the relative positions of the groups bonded to the asymmetric center will not change. For example, when (S)-1-chloro-3-methylpentane reacts with hydroxide ion, OH substitutes for Cl. (We will see why OH substitutes for Cl in Section 8.2.) Because the reaction does not break any of the bonds to the asymmetric center, the reactant and product have the same **relative configuration**, meaning the groups maintain their relative positions, so that the CH_3CH_2 group is on the left, the CH_3 group is attached to a solid wedge, and the H is attached to a hatched wedge.

If a reaction does not break a bond to the asymmetric center, the reactant and the product will have the same relative configurations.

(S)-1-chloro-3-methylpentane   **(S)-3-methyl-1-pentanol**

A Word of Warning. Even if the four groups bonded to the asymmetric center maintain their relative positions, an *S* reactant does not always form an *S* product as occurred in the preceding reaction, and an *R* reactant does not always form an *R* product. For example, in the reaction shown below, the groups maintain their relative positions during the reaction; thus the reactant and the product have the same *relative configurations*. Nevertheless, the reactant has the *S* configuration, but the product has the *R* configuration. Although the groups have maintained their relative positions, their relative priorities—as defined by the Cahn–Ingold–Prelog rules—have changed (the vinyl group has the highest priority in the reactant, whereas the propyl group has the highest priority in the product; Section 3.5). The change in relative priorities—not any change in the relative positions of the groups—is what caused the *S* reactant to become an *R* product.

Two compounds with the same relative configuration do not necessarily have the same absolute configuration.

(S)-3-methyl-1-hexene   **(R)-3-methylhexane**

The reactant and product in the preceding example have the same relative configuration, but because the reactant has the *S* configuration and the product has the *R* configuration, they have different absolute configurations. The **absolute configuration** is the compound's *actual* configuration. In other words, the configuration is known in an absolute sense rather than in a relative one. To know the *absolute configuration* of a compound is to know whether it has the *R* or the *S* configuration. To know that two compounds have the same *relative configuration* is to know that the groups attached to the asymmetric center in both compounds have the same relative positions.

We have just seen that if the reaction does not break any of the bonds to the asymmetric center, the reactant and product will have the same relative configuration. However, if the reaction *does break* a bond to the asymmetric center, the product can have the same relative configuration as the reactant, or it can have the opposite relative configuration. Which of the products is actually formed depends on the mechanism of the reaction. Therefore, we cannot predict what the configuration of the product will be unless we know the mechanism of the reaction.

If a reaction does break a bond to the asymmetric center, you cannot predict the configuration of the product unless you know the mechanism of the reaction.

has the same relative configuration as the reactant

has a relative configuration opposite to that of the reactant

---

PROBLEM 41   SOLVED

(S)-$(-)$-2-Methyl-1-butanol can be converted to $(+)$-2-methylbutanoic acid without breaking any of the bonds to the asymmetric center. What is the configuration of $(-)$-2-methylbutanoic acid?

(S)-(–)-2-methyl-1-butanol   **(+)-2-methylbutanoic acid**

Solution   We know that $(+)$-2-methylbutanoic acid has the relative configuration shown because it was formed from (S)-$(-)$-2-methyl-1-butanol without breaking any bonds to the asymmetric center. By looking at $(+)$-2-methylbutanoic acid, we know that it has the S configuration. We can conclude then that $(-)$-2-methylbutanoic acid has the R configuration.

PROBLEM 42 ◆

The stereoisomer of 1-iodo-2-methylbutane with the R configuration rotates the plane of polarization of plane-polarized light clockwise. The reaction shown below results in an alcohol that rotates the plane of polarization counterclockwise. What is the configuration of $(+)$-2-methyl-1-butanol?

5.15 USING REACTIONS THAT DO NOT BREAK BONDS TO AN ASYMMETRIC CENTER TO DETERMINE RELATIVE CONFIGURATIONS

Glyceraldehyde has one asymmetric center and therefore it has two stereoisomers. Their absolute configurations were not known until 1951. Thus, before that time, chemists did not know whether $(+)$-glyceraldehyde had the R or the S configuration, although they had arbitrarily assigned it the R configuration. They had a 50–50 chance of being correct.

(R)-(+)-glyceraldehyde   **(S)-(–)-glyceraldehyde**

The configurations of many organic compounds were originally deduced based on whether they could be synthesized from $(+)$- or from $(-)$-glyceraldehyde, or converted to $(+)$- or to $(-)$-glyceraldehyde, *by means of reactions that do not break any of the bonds to the asymmetric center.* For example, since chemists assumed that the configuration of $(+)$-glyceraldehyde was the one shown above, they could assume that $(-)$-lactic acid had the configuration shown on page 226, because a series of reactions that do not break any bonds to the asymmetric center show that $(-)$-lactic acid and $(+)$-glyceraldehyde have the same relative configuration. Yet, because chemists did not know for sure that $(+)$-glyceraldehyde had the R configuration, the configurations assigned to these molecules were relative configurations, not absolute configurations. They were relative to

(+)-glyceraldehyde and were based on the *assumption* that (+)-glyceraldehyde had the *R* configuration.

$$HgO \qquad \overset{HNO_2}{\underset{H_2O}{\longleftarrow}} \qquad \overset{NaNO_2}{\underset{HBr}{\longrightarrow}} \qquad \overset{Zn}{\underset{HCl}{\longrightarrow}}$$

(+)-glyceraldehyde (–)-glyceric acid (+)-isoserine (–)-3-bromo-2-hydroxypropanoic acid (–)-lactic acid

In 1951, the Dutch chemists J. M. Bijvoet, A. F. Peerdeman, and A. J. van Bommel, using X-ray crystallography (Section 14.23) and a new technique known as anomalous dispersion, determined that the sodium rubidium salt of (+)-tartaric acid had the *R,R* configuration. Because (+)-tartaric acid could be synthesized from (−)-glyceraldehyde, (−)-glyceraldehyde had to be the *S* enantiomer. The assumption, therefore, that (+)-glyceraldehyde had the *R* configuration was correct!

several steps

(−)-glyceraldehyde   (+)-tartaric acid

The work of these chemists immediately provided absolute configurations for all the compounds whose relative configurations had been determined by syntheses from or conversions to (+)-glyceraldehyde. Thus, (−)-lactic acid has the configuration shown above. If (+)-glyceraldehyde had been the *S* enantiomer (that is, if it had the configuration opposite to the one shown above), (−)-lactic acid would also have had the configuration opposite to the one shown.

PROBLEM 43 ◆

What is the absolute configuration of each of the following compounds?

a. (−)-glyceric acid
b. (+)-isoserine

c. (−)-glyceraldehyde
d. (+)-lactic acid

PROBLEM 44 ◆

Which of the following is true?

a. If two compounds have the same relative configuration, they will have the same absolute configuration.
b. If two compounds have the same relative configuration and you know the absolute configuration of either one of them, you can determine the absolute configuration of the other.
c. An *R* reactant always forms an *S* product.

5.16 HOW ENANTIOMERS CAN BE SEPARATED

Enantiomers cannot be separated by the usual separation techniques such as fractional distillation or crystallization because their identical boiling points and solubilities cause them to distill or crystallize simultaneously. Louis Pasteur was the first to succeed in separating a pair of enantiomers. While working with crystals of sodium ammonium tartrate, he noted that the crystals were not identical—some were "right-handed" and some were "left-handed." After painstakingly separating the two kinds of crystals with a pair of tweezers, he found that a solution of the right-handed crystals rotated the plane of polarization of plane-polarized light clockwise, whereas a solution of the left-handed crystals rotated it counterclockwise.

left-handed crystals   right-handed crystals

sodium ammonium tartrate

Crystals of potassium hydrogen tartrate, a naturally occurring salt found in wines. Most fruits produce citric acid, but grapes produce large quantities of tartaric acid instead. Potassium hydrogen tartrate, also called cream of tartar, is used in place of vinegar or lemon juice in some recipes.

Pasteur, only 26 years old at the time and unknown in scientific circles, was concerned about the accuracy of his observations because a few years earlier, the well-known German organic chemist Eilhardt Mitscherlich had reported that crystals of sodium ammonium tartrate were all identical. Pasteur immediately reported his findings to Jean-Baptiste Biot (Section 5.8) and repeated the experiment with Biot present. Biot was convinced that Pasteur had successfully separated the enantiomers of sodium ammonium tartrate. Pasteur's experiment also gave rise to a new chemical term. Tartaric acid is obtained from grapes, so it was also called racemic acid (*racemus* is Latin for "a bunch of grapes"). This is why a mixture of equal amounts of enantiomers came to be known as a **racemic mixture** (Section 5.9). Separation of enantiomers is called the **resolution of a racemic mixture**.

Later, chemists recognized how lucky Pasteur had been. Sodium ammonium tartrate forms asymmetric crystals only under the precise conditions that Pasteur happened to employ. Under other conditions, the symmetrical crystals that had fooled Mitscherlich are formed. But, to quote Pasteur, "Chance favors the prepared mind."

Separating enantiomers by hand, as Pasteur did, is not a universally useful method because few compounds form asymmetric crystals. Until relatively recently, separating enantiomers was a very tedious process. The enantiomers had to be chemically converted to diastereomers, which could be separated because they have different physical properties (Section 5.11). After separation, the individual diastereomers had to be chemically converted back to the original enantiomers.

Fortunately, enantiomers can now be separated relatively easily by a technique called **chromatography**. In this method, the mixture to be separated is dissolved in a solvent and the solution is passed through a column packed with a chiral material that tends to adsorb organic compounds. The two enantiomers can be expected to move through the column at different rates because they will have different affinities for the chiral material—just as a right hand prefers a right-hand glove to a left-hand glove—so one enantiomer will emerge from the column before the other. Because it is now so much easier to separate enantiomers, many drugs are being sold as single enantiomers rather than as racemic mixtures (see page 228).

The chiral material used in chromatography is one example of a **chiral probe**, something capable of distinguishing between enantiomers. A polarimeter is another example of a chiral probe (Section 5.9). In Section 5.21, you will see two kinds of biological molecules—enzymes and receptors—that are chiral probes. You will also see that enzymes that react with one enantiomer but not another can also be used to separate enantiomers.

PROBLEM 45 ◆

Limonene exists as two different stereoisomers. The *R* enantiomer is found in oranges and the *S* enantiomer is found in lemons. Which of the following molecules is found in oranges?

(+)-limonene   (–)-limonene

Chiral Drugs

Until relatively recently, most drugs with one or more asymmetric centers have been marketed as racemic mixtures because of the difficulty of synthesizing single enantiomers and the high cost of separating enantiomers. In 1992, however, the Food and Drug Administration issued a policy statement encouraging drug companies to use recent advances in synthesis and separation techniques to develop single enantiomer drugs. Now one-third of all chiral drugs sold are single enantiomers. Drug companies have been able to extend their patents by marketing a single enantiomer of a drug that was previously available only as a racemate (Section 31.13).

If a drug is sold as a racemate, the FDA requires that both enantiomers be tested because drugs bind to receptors, and since receptors are chiral, the enantiomers of a drug can bind to them differently (Section 5.21). Therefore, enantiomers can have similar or very different physiological properties. Examples are numerous. The *S* isomer of Prozac, an antidepressant, is better at blocking serotonin but is used up faster than the *R* isomer. Testing has shown that (*S*)-(+)-ketamine is four times more potent an anesthetic than (*R*)-(−)-ketamine, and disturbing side effects are apparently associated only with the (*R*)-(−)-enantiomer. Only the *S* isomer of the beta-blocker propranolol shows activity; the *R* isomer is inactive. The activity of ibuprofen, the popular analgesic marketed as Advil, Nuprin, and Motrin, resides primarily in the (*S*)-(+)-enantiomer. Heroin addicts can be maintained with (−)-α-acetylmethadol for a 72-hour period compared to 24 hours with racemic methadone. This means less frequent visits to an outpatient clinic; a single dose can keep an addict stable through an entire weekend (Section 31.3).

Prescribing a single enantiomer spares the patient from having to metabolize the less potent enantiomer and decreases the chance of unwanted drug interactions. One reason that Lipitor is the most popular statin is that it is the only one that is available as a single enantiomer. Drugs that could not be given as racemates because of the toxicity of one of the enantiomers can now be used. For example, (*S*)-penicillamine can be used to treat Wilson's disease even though (*R*)-penicillamine causes blindness.

5.17 NITROGEN AND PHOSPHORUS ATOMS CAN BE ASYMMETRIC CENTERS

Atoms other than carbon can be asymmetric centers. Any atom, such as nitrogen or phosphorus, that has four different groups or atoms attached to it is an asymmetric center. For example, the following pairs of compounds are enantiomers.

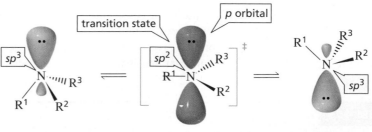

If one of the four "groups" attached to nitrogen is a lone pair, the enantiomers cannot be separated because they interconvert rapidly at room temperature. This rapid interconversion is called **amine inversion**. One way to picture amine inversion is to think of an umbrella that turns inside out in a windstorm.

amine inversion

Amine inversion takes place through a transition state in which the sp^3 nitrogen becomes an sp^2 nitrogen. The three groups bonded to the sp^2 nitrogen are coplanar in the transition state with bond angles of 120°, and the lone pair is in a *p* orbital. The "inverted" and "noninverted" amine molecules are enantiomers, but they cannot be separated because amine inversion is so rapid. The energy required for amine inversion is approximately 6 kcal/mol (or 25 kJ/mol), about twice the amount of energy required for rotation about a carbon–carbon single bond, but still small enough to allow the enantiomers to interconvert rapidly at room temperature. The lone pair is necessary for inversion: quaternary ammonium ions—ions with four bonds to nitrogen and hence no lone pair—do not invert.

PROBLEM 46

Explain why compound A has two stereoisomers, but compounds B and C exist as single compounds.

5.18 THE STEREOCHEMISTRY OF REACTIONS: REGIOSELECTIVE, STEREOSELECTIVE, AND STEREOSPECIFIC REACTIONS

When we looked at the electrophilic addition reactions that alkenes undergo (Chapter 4), we examined the step-by-step process by which each reaction occurs (the mechanism of the reaction), and we determined what products are formed. However, we did not consider the stereochemistry of the reactions.

Stereochemistry is the field of chemistry that deals with the structures of molecules in three dimensions. When we study the stereochemistry of a reaction, we are concerned with the following questions:

1. If the *product* of a reaction can exist as two or more stereoisomers, does the reaction produce a single stereoisomer, a set of particular stereoisomers, or all possible stereoisomers?

2. If the *reactant* can exist as two or more stereoisomers, do all stereoisomers of the reactant form the same stereoisomers of the product, or does each stereoisomer of the reactant form a different stereoisomer or set of stereoisomers of the product?

Before we examine the stereochemistry of electrophilic addition reactions, we need to become familiar with some terms used in describing the stereochemistry of a reaction.

We have seen that a **regioselective** reaction is one in which two *constitutional isomers* can be obtained as products, but more of one is obtained than the other (Section 4.4). In other words, a regioselective reaction selects for a particular constitutional isomer. Recall that a reaction can be *moderately regioselective*, *highly regioselective*, or *completely regioselective* depending on the relative amounts of the constitutional isomers formed in the reaction.

a regioselective reaction

more B is formed than C

> A regioselective reaction forms more of one constitutional isomer than of another.

Stereoselective is a similar term, but it refers to the preferential formation of a *stereoisomer* rather than a *constitutional isomer*. If a reaction that generates a carbon–carbon double bond or an asymmetric center in a product forms one stereoisomer preferentially over another, it is a stereoselective reaction. In other words, it selects for a particular stereoisomer. Depending on the degree of preference for a particular stereoisomer, a reaction can be described as being *moderately stereoselective*, *highly stereoselective*, or *completely stereoselective*.

a stereoselective reaction

A stereoselective reaction forms more of one stereoisomer than of another.

$$\boxed{\text{stereoisomers}}$$
$$A \longrightarrow B \; + \; C$$

more B is formed than C

A reaction is **stereospecific** if the *reactant* can exist as stereoisomers and each stereoisomer of the reactant forms a different stereoisomer or a different set of stereoisomers of the product.

In a stereospecific reaction each stereoisomer forms a different stereoisomeric product or a different set of stereoisomeric products.

stereospecific reactions

$$\boxed{\text{stereoisomers}} \Big\langle \begin{array}{c} A \longrightarrow B \\ C \longrightarrow D \end{array} \Big\rangle \boxed{\text{stereoisomers}}$$

A stereospecific reaction is also stereoselective. A stereoselective reaction is not necessarily stereospecific.

In the preceding reaction, stereoisomer A forms stereoisomer B but does not form D, so the reaction is stereoselective in addition to being stereospecific. Because a stereospecific reaction does not form all possible stereoisomers of the product, *all stereospecific reactions are also stereoselective. However, not all stereoselective reactions are stereospecific*, because there are stereoselective reactions in which the reactant does not have a carbon–carbon double bond or an asymmetric center, so it does not have stereoisomers.

5.19   THE STEREOCHEMISTRY OF ELECTROPHILIC ADDITION REACTIONS OF ALKENES

Now that you are familiar with electrophilic addition reactions *and* with stereoisomers, we can combine the two topics and look at the stereochemistry of electrophilic addition reactions. In other words, we will look at the stereoisomers that are formed in the electrophilic addition reactions that were discussed in Chapter 4.

We have seen that when an alkene reacts with an electrophilic reagent such as HBr, the major product of the addition reaction is the one obtained by adding the electrophile (H^+) to the sp^2 carbon bonded to the greater number of hydrogens and adding the nucleophile (Br^-) to the other sp^2 carbon (Section 4.4). Thus, the major product obtained from the reaction of propene with HBr is 2-bromopropane. This particular product does not have stereoisomers because it does not have an asymmetric center. Therefore, we do not have to be concerned with the stereochemistry of this reaction.

$$CH_3CH{=}CH_2 \xrightarrow{\text{HBr}} CH_3\overset{+}{C}HCH_3 \longrightarrow CH_3CHCH_3$$

propene Br^- $|$
                                                                                          Br

2-bromopropane
no stereoisomers

If, however, the reaction creates a product with an asymmetric center, we need to know which stereoisomers are formed. For example, the reaction of HBr with 1-butene forms 2-bromobutane, a compound with an asymmetric center. But what is the configuration of the product? Do we get the *R* enantiomer, the *S* enantiomer, or both enantiomers?

$$CH_3CH_2CH{=}CH_2 \xrightarrow{\text{HBr}} CH_3CH_2\overset{+}{C}HCH_3 \longrightarrow CH_3CH_2CHCH_3$$

1-butene Br^- $|$
                                                                                          Br

$\boxed{\text{asymmetric center}}$

2-bromobutane

We will begin our discussion of the stereochemistry of electrophilic addition reactions by looking at reactions that form a product with one asymmetric center. Then we will look at reactions that form a product with two asymmetric centers.

Addition Reactions that Form a Product with One Asymmetric Center

When a reactant that does not have an asymmetric center undergoes a reaction that forms a product with *one* asymmetric center, the product will always be a racemic mixture. For example, the reaction of 1-butene with HBr that we just looked at on page 230 forms identical amounts of (*R*)-2-bromobutane and (*S*)-2-bromobutane. Thus, the reaction is not stereoselective because it does not select for a particular stereoisomer. Why is this so?

We can see why a racemic mixture is obtained if we examine the structure of the carbocation formed in the first step of the reaction. The positively charged carbon is sp^2 hybridized, so the three atoms to which it is bonded lie in a plane (Section 1.10). When the bromide ion approaches the positively charged carbon from above the plane, one enantiomer is formed, but when it approaches from below the plane, the other enantiomer is formed. Because the bromide ion has equal access to both sides of the plane, identical amounts of the *R* and *S* enantiomers are formed in the reaction.

PROBLEM 47 ♦

a. Is the reaction of 2-butene with HBr regioselective?

b. Is it stereoselective?

c. Is it stereospecific?

d. Is the reaction of 1-butene with HBr regioselective?

e. Is it stereoselective?

f. Is it stereospecific?

chem place Tutorial: Common terms in stereochemistry

PROBLEM 48

What stereoisomers are obtained from each of the following reactions?

a. $CH_3CH_2CH_2CH{=}CH_2$ $\xrightarrow{\text{HCl}}$

b. (structure) $\xrightarrow[\text{H}_2\text{O}]{\text{H}_2\text{SO}_4}$

c. (structure) $\xrightarrow[\text{CH}_3\text{OH}]{\text{H}_2\text{SO}_4}$

d. (structure) $\xrightarrow{\text{HBr}}$

If an addition reaction creates an asymmetric center in a compound that already has an asymmetric center (and the reactant is a single enantiomer of that compound), a pair of diastereomers will be formed. For example, let's look at the reaction shown on page 232, where R, R′ and R″ signify different groups. Because none of the bonds to the asymmetric center in the reactant is broken during the addition of HBr, the configuration of this asymmetric center does not change. When the electrophilic addition reaction creates the new asymmetric center, the bromide ion can approach the planar carbocation intermediate from either the top or the bottom, so two stereoisomers result. The stereoisomers are diastereomers because one of the asymmetric centers has the same configuration in both stereoisomers and the other has opposite configurations.

Because the products of the preceding reaction are diastereomers, the transition states that lead to them are also diastereomeric. The two transition states, therefore, will not have the same stability, so different amounts of the two diastereomers will be formed. Thus, the reaction is stereoselective—it forms more of one stereoisomer than of the other. The reaction is also stereospecific; the alkene with an asymmetric center in the *R* configuration forms a different pair of diastereomers than the alkene with an asymmetric center in the *S* configuration.

Addition Reactions that Form Products with Two Asymmetric Centers

When a reactant that does not have an asymmetric center undergoes a reaction that forms a product with *two* asymmetric centers, the stereoisomers that are formed depend on the mechanism of the reaction.

Addition Reactions That Form a Carbocation Intermediate. If an addition reaction that forms a carbocation intermediate results in a product with two new asymmetric centers, four stereoisomers are obtained.

perspective formulas of the stereoisomers of the product

Fischer projections of the stereoisomers of the product

In the first step of the reaction, the proton can approach the plane containing the double-bonded carbons of the alkene from either above or below to form the carbocation. Once the carbocation is formed, the chloride ion can approach the positively charged carbon from above or below. As a result, four stereoisomers are obtained as products: the addition of the proton and the chloride ion can be described as above-above (both adding from above), above-below, below-above, or below-below. When two substituents add to the same side of a double bond, the addition is called **syn addition**. When two substituents add to opposite sides of a double bond, the addition is called **anti addition**. Both syn and anti additions occur in alkene addition reactions that form a carbocation intermediate. Equal amounts of the four stereoisomers are obtained so the reaction is not stereoselective and, because the four stereoisomers formed by the cis alkene are identical to the four stereoisomers formed by the trans alkene, the reaction is also not stereospecific.

The Stereochemistry of Hydrogen Addition. We have seen that in a catalytic hydrogenation reaction, the alkene sits on the surface of a metal catalyst on which H_2 has been adsorbed (Section 4.12). As a result, both hydrogen atoms add to the same side of the double bond, so the addition of H_2 to an alkene is a syn addition reaction.

addition of H_2 is a syn addition

If addition of H_2 to an alkene forms a product with two asymmetric centers, then only two of the four possible stereoisomers are obtained because only syn addition can occur. (The other two stereoisomers would have to come from anti addition.) One of the two stereoisomers results from addition of both hydrogens from above the plane of the double bond, and the other results from addition of both hydrogens from below the plane, because the alkene can sit on the metal catalyst with either side facing up. The particular pair of stereoisomers that is formed depends on whether the reactant is a *cis* alkene or a *trans* alkene. Syn addition of H_2 to a *cis* alkene forms only the erythro enantiomers. (In Section 5.11, we saw that the erythro enantiomers are the ones with identical groups on the same side of the carbon chain in the eclipsed conformers.)

If each of the two asymmetric centers in the product is bonded to the same four substituents, a meso compound will be formed instead of the erythro enantiomers.

In contrast, syn addition of H_2 to a *trans* alkene forms only the threo enantiomers. Thus, the addition of hydrogen is a stereospecific reaction—the products obtained from addition to the cis isomer are different from the products obtained from addition to the trans isomer. It is also a stereoselective reaction because all possible stereoisomers are not formed.

If the reactant is a cyclic compound, the addition of H_2 will form the cis enantiomers since the two hydrogens add to the same side of the double bond.

1-isopropyl-2-methyl-cyclopentene

Each of the two asymmetric centers in the product of the following reaction is bonded to the same four substituents. Therefore, syn addition forms a meso compound.

1,2-dimethyl-cyclopentene

Cyclic Alkenes

Cyclic alkenes with fewer than seven carbons in the ring, such as cyclopentene and cyclohexene, exist only in the cis configuration because they do not have enough carbons to form a trans double bond. Therefore, it is not necessary to use the cis designation with their names. Cyclic alkenes with seven or more carbons in the ring can form both cis and trans isomers, so the configuration of the compound must be specified in its name.

cyclopentene   cyclohexene   *cis*-cyclooctene   *trans*-cyclooctene

---

PROBLEM 49

a. What stereoisomers are formed in the following reaction?

b. What stereoisomer is formed in greater yield?

The Stereochemistry of Peroxyacid Addition. The addition of a peroxyacid to an alkene to form an epoxide is a concerted reaction: the oxygen atom adds to the two sp^2 carbons at the same time (Section 4.10). Therefore, it must be a syn addition.

an alkene   an epoxide

addition of peroxyacid is a syn addition

The oxygen can add from above or from below the plane containing the double bond. Therefore, addition of a peroxyacid to an alkene forms two stereoisomers. Syn addition to a cis alkene forms the cis enantiomers. Because only syn addition occurs, the reaction is stereoselective. (If you turn the stereoisomer on the right upside down, you can see that it is the mirror image of the isomer on the left.)

cis-2-pentene

Syn addition to a trans alkene forms the trans enantiomers.

trans-2-pentene

Addition of a peroxyacid to *cis*-2-butene forms a meso compound since each of the two asymmetric centers is attached to the same four groups (Section 5.12).

cis-2-butene

PROBLEM 50 ◆

a. What alkene would be required to synthesize the following compounds?

b. What other epoxide would be formed?

The Stereochemistry of Hydroboration—Oxidation. The addition of borane to an alkene is also a concerted reaction (Section 4.11). The boron and the hydride ion add to the two sp^2 carbons of the double bond at the same time. Because the two species add simultaneously, they must add to the same side of the double bond. Thus, the addition of borane to an alkene, like the addition of hydrogen and the addition of a peroxyacid, is a syn addition.

addition of borane is a syn addition

When the resulting alkylborane is oxidized by reaction with hydrogen peroxide and hydroxide ion, the OH group ends up in the same position as the boron group it replaces. Consequently, the overall reaction, called hydroboration–oxidation, amounts to a syn addition of water to a carbon–carbon double bond.

an alkyl borane   an alcohol

hydroboration–oxidation is a syn addition of water

Because only syn addition occurs, hydroboration–oxidation is stereoselective—only two of the four possible stereoisomers are formed. As we saw when we looked at the addition of H_2 or a peroxyacid, if the reactant is cyclic, syn addition results in the formation of only the pair of enantiomers that has the added groups on the same side of the ring.

PROBLEM 51 ◆

What stereoisomers would be obtained from hydroboration–oxidation of the following compounds?

a. cyclohexene

b. 1-ethylcyclohexene

c. *cis*-2-butene

d. (Z)-3,4-dimethyl-3-hexene

Addition Reactions that Form a Cyclic Bromonium Ion Intermediate. If two asymmetric centers are created as the result of an addition reaction that forms a bromonium ion intermediate, only one pair of enantiomers will be formed. The addition of Br_2 to the cis alkene forms only the threo enantiomers.

If you have trouble determining the configuration of a product, make a model.

Similarly, the addition of Br_2 to the trans alkene forms only the erythro enantiomers. Because the cis and trans isomers form different products, the reaction is stereospecific as well as stereoselective.

Because the addition of Br_2 to the cis alkene forms the threo enantiomers, we know that anti addition must have occurred, since we have just seen that syn addition would have formed the erythro enantiomers. The addition of Br_2 is anti because the reaction intermediate is a cyclic bromonium ion (Section 4.8). Once the bromonium ion is formed, the bridged bromine atom blocks that side of the ion. As a result, the negatively charged bromide ion must approach from the opposite side (following either the green arrows *or* the red arrows as shown on page 237). Thus, the two bromine atoms add to opposite sides of the double bond. Because only anti addition of Br_2 can occur, only two of the four possible stereoisomers are obtained.

addition of Br$_2$ is an anti addition

chem Tutorial:
place Review halogenation

If the two asymmetric centers in the product each have the same four substituents, the erythro isomers are identical and constitute a meso compound. Therefore, addition of Br$_2$ to *trans*-2-butene forms a meso compound.

Because only anti addition occurs, addition of Br$_2$ to cyclohexene forms only the enantiomers that have the bromines on opposite sides of the ring.

A summary of the stereochemistry of the products obtained from electrophilic addition reactions to alkenes is given in Table 5.3.

Table 5.3	Stereochemistry of Alkene Addition Reactions		
Reaction		**Type of addition**	**Stereoisomers formed**
Addition reactions that create one asymmetric center in the product			1. If the reactant does not have an asymmetric center, a racemic mixture will be obtained.
			2. If the reactant has an asymmetric center, unequal amounts of a pair of diastereomers will be obtained.
Addition reactions that create two asymmetric centers in the product			
	Addition of reagents that form a carbocation intermediate	syn and anti	Four stereoisomers will be obtained (the cis and trans isomers form the same products).
	Addition of H$_2$	syn	cis ⟶ erythro or cis enantiomers*
	Addition of borane		trans ⟶ threo or trans enantiomers
	Addition of a peroxyacid		
	Addition of Br$_2$, Br$_2$ + H$_2$O, Br$_2$ + ROH (any reaction that forms a cyclic bromonium ion intermediate)	anti	cis ⟶ threo or trans enantiomers
			trans ⟶ erythro or cis enantiomers*

* If the two asymmetric centers have the same substituents, a meso compound will be obtained instead of the pair of erythro enantiomers.

PROBLEM 52

Reaction of 2-ethyl-1-pentene with Br_2, with H_2 + Pd/C, or with BH_3/THF followed by aqueous HO^- + H_2O_2 leads to a racemic mixture. Explain why a racemic mixture is obtained in each case.

PROBLEM 53

How could you prove, using a sample of *trans*-2-butene, that addition of Br_2 forms a cyclic bromonium ion intermediate rather than a carbocation intermediate?

One way to remember what stereoisomers are obtained from a reaction that creates a product with two asymmetric centers is the mnemonic **CIS-SYN-(ERYTHRO or CIS)**. (The third term is "erythro" if the product is acyclic, and "cis" if it is cyclic.) The three terms are easy to remember because they all mean "on the same side." You can change any two of the terms but you cannot change just one. For example, **TRANS-ANTI-(ERYTHRO or CIS)**, **TRANS-SYN-(THREO or TRANS)**, and **CIS-ANTI-(THREO or TRANS)**, are allowed, but **TRANS-SYN- (ERYTHRO or CIS)** is not allowed. Thus, if you have a cis reactant that undergoes addition of Br_2 (which is anti), the threo products are obtained if the products are acyclic and the trans products are obtained if the product is cyclic. This mnemonic will work for all reactions that have products with structures that can be described by erythro and threo or cis and trans.

PROBLEM-SOLVING STRATEGY

Predicting the Stereoisomers Obtained from Addition Reactions of Alkenes

What stereoisomers are obtained from the following reactions:

a. 1-butene + HCl

c. *cis*-3-heptene + Br_2

b. cyclohexene + HBr

d. *trans*-3-hexene + Br_2

Start by drawing the product without regard to its configuration to check whether the reaction has created any asymmetric centers. Then determine the configurations of the products, paying attention to the configuration (if any) of the reactant, how many asymmetric centers are formed, and the mechanism of the reaction. Let's start with part **a**.

a. $CH_3CH_2\overset{\displaystyle |}{\underset{\displaystyle Cl}{C}}HCH_3$

The product has one asymmetric center, so equal amounts of the *R* and *S* enantiomers will be obtained.

b.

The product does not have an asymmetric center, so it has no stereoisomers.

c. $CH_3CH_2\overset{\displaystyle |}{\underset{\displaystyle Br}{C}}H\overset{\displaystyle |}{\underset{\displaystyle Br}{C}}HCH_2CH_2CH_3$

Two asymmetric centers have been created in the product. Because the reactant is cis and addition of Br_2 is anti, the threo enantiomers are formed.

d. CH₃CH₂CHCHCH₂CH₃
         | |
         Br Br

Two asymmetric centers have been created in the product. Because the reactant is trans and addition of Br₂ is anti, one would expect the erythro enantiomers. However, the two asymmetric centers are bonded to the same four groups, so the erythro product is a meso compound. Thus, only one stereoisomer is formed.

Now continue on to Problem 54.

PROBLEM 54

What stereoisomers are obtained from the following reactions:

a. *trans*-2-butene + HBr
b. (Z)-3-methyl-2-pentene + HBr
c. (E)-3-methyl-2-pentene + HBr
d. *cis*-3-hexene + HBr
e. *cis*-2-pentene + Br₂
f. 1-hexene + Br₂

PROBLEM 55

When Br₂ adds to an alkene that has different substituents on each of the two sp^2 carbons, such as *cis*-2-heptene, identical amounts of the two threo enantiomers are obtained even though Br⁻ is more likely to attack the less sterically hindered carbon atom of the bromonium ion. Explain why identical amounts of the two threo enantiomers are obtained.

PROBLEM 56

a. What products would be obtained from the addition of Br₂ to cyclohexene if the solvent were H₂O instead of CH₂Cl₂?
b. Propose a mechanism for the reaction.

PROBLEM 57

What stereoisomers would you expect to obtain from each of the following reactions?

a. What is the major product obtained from the reaction of propene and Br_2 plus excess Cl^-?
b. Indicate the relative amounts of the stereoisomers obtained.

B I O G R A P H Y

For studies on the stereochemistry of enzyme-catalyzed reactions, **Sir John Cornforth** *received the Nobel Prize in Chemistry in 1975 (sharing it with Vladimir Prelog, page 202). Born in Australia in 1917, Cornforth studied at the University of Sydney and received a Ph.D. from Oxford. His major research was carried out in laboratories at Britain's Medical Research Council and at Shell Research Ltd. He was declared "Australian of the Year" in 1975 and was knighted in 1977.*

5.20 THE STEREOCHEMISTRY OF ENZYME-CATALYZED REACTIONS

The chemistry associated with living organisms is called **biochemistry**. When you study biochemistry, you study the structures and functions of the molecules found in the biological world and the reactions involved in the synthesis and degradation of these molecules. Because the compounds in living organisms are organic compounds, it is not surprising that many of the reactions encountered in organic chemistry also occur in biological systems. Living cells do not contain molecules such as Cl_2, HBr, or BH_3, so you would not expect to find the addition of such reagents to alkenes in biological systems. However, living cells do contain water and acid catalysts, so some alkenes found in biological systems undergo the acid-catalyzed addition of water (Section 4.5).

Reactions that occur in biological systems are catalyzed by proteins called **enzymes**. When an enzyme catalyzes a reaction that forms a product with an asymmetric center, only one stereoisomer is formed because enzyme-catalyzed reactions are completely stereoselective. For example, the enzyme fumarase catalyzes the addition of water to fumarate to form malate, a compound with one asymmetric center.

However, the reaction forms only (*S*)-malate; the *R* enantiomer is not formed.

An enzyme-catalyzed reaction forms only one stereoisomer because an enzyme's binding site can restrict delivery of the reagents to only one side of the reactant's functional group.

Enzyme-catalyzed reactions are also stereospecific; an enzyme typically catalyzes the reaction of only one stereoisomer. For example, fumarase catalyzes the addition of water to fumarate (the trans isomer) but not to maleate (the cis isomer).

Frank H. Westheimer (1912–2007) *did fundamental work on the stereochemistry of enzyme-catalyzed reactions. Born in Baltimore, he received his graduate training at Harvard University, served on the faculty of the University of Chicago, and subsequently returned to Harvard as a professor of chemistry.*

An enzyme is able to differentiate between the two stereoisomers because only one of them has the structure that allows it to fit into the enzyme's binding site where the reaction takes place.

Chiral Catalysts

The problem of having to separate enantiomers can be avoided if a synthesis is carried out that forms one of the enantiomers preferentially. **Chiral catalysts** are being developed that will synthesize one enantiomer in great excess over the other. For example, the catalytic hydrogenation of 2-ethyl-1-pentene forms equal amounts of two enantiomers because H_2 can be delivered equally easily to both faces of the double bond (Section 5.19).

$$CH_3CH_2\underset{CH_3CH_2CH_2}{\overset{|}{C}}{=}CH_2 \xrightarrow[\text{Pd/C}]{H_2}$$

(R)-3-methylhexane + (S)-3-methylhexane

    50%   50%

If, however, the metal catalyst is complexed to a chiral organic molecule, H_2 will be delivered to only one face of the double bond. One such chiral catalyst—using Ru(II) as the metal and BINAP (2,2′-bis(diphenylphosphino)-1,1′-binaphthyl) as the chiral molecule—has been used to synthesize (S)-naproxen, the active ingredient in Aleve and in several other over-the-counter nonsteroidal anti-inflammatory drugs (Section 2.9), in greater than 98% enantiomeric excess.

$$\xrightarrow[\text{(R)-BINAP–Ru(II)}]{H_2}$$

(S)-naproxen
>98% ee

PROBLEM 59 ◆

What minimum percent of naproxen is obtained as the *S* enantiomer in the above synthesis?

5.21 ENANTIOMERS CAN BE DISTINGUISHED BY BIOLOGICAL MOLECULES

Enzymes and receptors can tell the difference between enantiomers because enzymes and receptors are proteins, and proteins are chiral molecules.

Enzymes

When enantiomers react with *achiral* reagents, both enantiomers react at the same rate because they have the same chemical properties. Thus, hydroxide ion (an achiral reagent) reacts with (R)-2-bromobutane at the same rate that it reacts with (S)-2-bromobutane.

Because an enzyme is a *chiral reagent*, not only can it distinguish between cis–trans isomers, such as maleate and fumarate (Section 5.20), it can also distinguish between enantiomers and catalyze the reaction of only one of them.

Chemists can use an enzyme's specificity for a particular enantiomer to separate enantiomers. For example, the enzyme D-amino acid oxidase catalyzes only the oxidation of the *R* enantiomer and leaves the *S* enantiomer unchanged. The product of the enzyme-catalyzed reaction can be easily separated from the unreacted enantiomer.

An achiral reagent reacts identically with both enantiomers. A sock, which is achiral, fits on either foot.

A chiral reagent reacts differently with each enantiomer. A shoe, which is chiral, fits on only one foot.

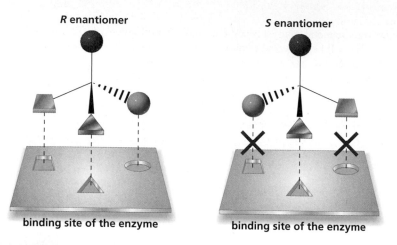

R enantiomer + *S* enantiomer → oxidized *R* enantiomer + unreacted *S* enantiomer

An enzyme is able to differentiate between enantiomers and between cis and trans isomers, as we saw in Section 5.20, because its binding site is chiral. The enzyme will therefore bind only the stereoisomer whose substituents are in the correct positions to interact with substituents in the chiral binding site. In Figure 5.3 the enzyme binds the *R* enantiomer but not the *S* enantiomer. The latter does not have its substituents in the proper positions, so they cannot bind efficiently to the enzyme. Like a right-handed glove, which fits only the right hand, an enzyme forms only one stereoisomer and reacts with only one stereoisomer (Section 5.20).

▶ **Figure 5.3**
Schematic diagram showing why only one enantiomer is bound by a enzyme. One enantiomer fits into the binding site and one does not.

R enantiomer   *S* enantiomer

binding site of the enzyme   binding site of the enzyme

PROBLEM 60 ◆

a. What would be the product of the reaction of fumarate and H_2O if H_2SO_4 were used as a catalyst instead of fumarase?

b. What would be the product of the reaction of maleate and H_2O if H_2SO_4 were used as a catalyst instead of fumarase?

Receptors

A **receptor** is a protein that binds a particular molecule. Because a receptor is chiral, it will bind one enantiomer better than the other, just like an enzyme binds one enantiomer better than another.

The fact that a receptor typically recognizes only one enantiomer means that enantiomers can have different physiological properties. For example, receptors located on the exteriors of nerve cells in the nose are able to perceive and differentiate the estimated 10,000 smells to which the cells are exposed. The reason that (R)-$(-)$-carvone (found in spearmint oil) and (S)-$(+)$-carvone (the main constituent of caraway seed oil) have such different odors is that each enantiomer fits into a different receptor.

(R)-(−)-carvone
spearmint oil

$[\alpha]_D^{20\,°C} = -62.5$

(S)-(+)-carvone
caraway seed oil

$[\alpha]_D^{20\,°C} = +62.5$

Many drugs exert their physiological activity by binding to cell-surface receptors. If the drug has an asymmetric center, the receptor can bind one of the enantiomers preferentially. Thus, enantiomers of a drug can have the same physiological activities, different degrees of the same activity, or very different activities, depending on the drug.

The Enantiomers of Thalidomide

Thalidomide was developed in West Germany and was first marketed (as Contergan) in 1957 for insomnia, tension, and morning sickness during pregnancy. At that time it was available in more than 40 countries but had not been approved for use in the United States because Frances O. Kelsey, a physician for the Food and Drug Administration (FDA), had insisted upon additional tests to explain a British study that had found nervous system side effects.

The dextrorotatory isomer has stronger sedative properties but the commercial drug was a racemic mixture. No one knew that the levorotatory isomer was a teratogen—a compound that causes congenital deformations—until women who had been given the drug during the first three months of pregnancy gave

birth to babies with a wide variety of defects, with deformed limbs being the most common. By the time the danger was recognized and the drug withdrawn from the market on November 27, 1961, about 10,000 children had been damaged. It was eventually determined that the dextrorotatory isomer also has mild teratogenic activity and that each of the enantiomers can racemize (interconvert) in the body. Thus, it is not clear whether the birth defects would have been less severe if the women had been given the dextrorotatory isomer only. Because thalidomide damaged fast growing cells in the developing fetus, it has recently has been approved—with restrictions and with tight controls—for the eradication of certain kinds of cancer cells.

thalidomide

PROBLEM 61 ♦

Would the nitrogen be attached to the asymmetric center in (*R*)-thalidomide by a solid wedge or by a hatched wedge?

SUMMARY

Stereochemistry is the field of chemistry that deals with the structures of molecules in three dimensions. Compounds with the same molecular formula but different structures are called **isomers**; they fall into two classes: constitutional isomers and stereoisomers. **Constitutional isomers** differ in the way their atoms are connected. **Stereoisomers** differ in the way their atoms are arranged in space. There are two kinds of stereoisomers: **cis–trans isomers** and isomers that contain **asymmetric centers**.

A **chiral** molecule has a nonsuperimposable mirror image. An **achiral** molecule has a superimposable mirror image. The feature that is most often the cause of chirality is an asymmetric center. An **asymmetric center** is an atom (most often a carbon) bonded to four different atoms or groups.

Nonsuperimposable mirror-image molecules are called **enantiomers. Diastereomers** are stereoisomers that are not

enantiomers. Enantiomers have identical physical and chemical properties; diastereomers have different physical and chemical properties. An achiral reagent reacts identically with both enantiomers; a chiral reagent reacts differently with each enantiomer. A **racemic mixture** is a mixture of equal amounts of two enantiomers.

The letters *R* and *S* indicate the **configuration** about an asymmetric center. If one member of a pair of stereoisomers has the *R* and the other has the *S* configuration, they are enantiomers; if they both have the *R* or both have the *S* configuration, they are identical molecules.

Chiral compounds are **optically active**, meaning that they rotate the plane of polarization of plane-polarized light; achiral compounds are **optically inactive**. If one enantiomer rotates the plane of polarization clockwise (+), its mirror image will rotate it the same amount counterclockwise (−). Each optically active compound has a characteristic **specific**

rotation. A **racemic mixture**, indicated by ±, is optically inactive. A **meso compound** has two or more asymmetric centers and a plane of symmetry; it is optically inactive. A compound with the same four groups bonded to two different asymmetric centers will have three stereoisomers, a meso compound and a pair of enantiomers.

If a reaction does not break any bonds to the asymmetric center, the reactant and product will have the same **relative configuration**—their substituents will have the same relative positions. The **absolute configuration** is the actual configuration. If a reaction does break a bond to the asymmetric center, the configuration of the product will depend on the mechanism of the reaction.

A **regioselective** reaction selects for a particular constitutional isomer; a **stereoselective** reaction selects for a particular stereoisomer. A reaction is **stereospecific** if the reactant can exist as stereoisomers and each stereoisomer forms a different or different set of stereoisomers. When a reactant that does not have an asymmetric center forms a product with one asymmetric center, the product will be a racemic mixture.

In **syn addition** the substituents add to the same side of a double bond; in **anti addition** they add to the opposite sides. Both syn and anti addition occur in electrophilic addition reactions that form a carbocation intermediate. Addition of H_2 to an alkene is a syn addition reaction; addition of a peroxyacid is a syn addition of an oxygen atom; hydroboration–oxidation is overall a syn addition of water. Addition of Br_2 is an anti addition reaction. An enzyme-catalyzed reaction forms only one stereoisomer; an enzyme typically catalyzes the reaction of only one stereoisomer.

KEY TERMS

absolute configuration (p. 224)
achiral (p. 197)
amine inversion (p. 228)
anti addition (p. 232)
asymmetric center (p. 198)
biochemistry (p. 240)
chiral (p. 197)
chiral catalyst (p. 241)
chiral probe (p. 227)
cis isomer (p. 196)
cis–trans isomers (p. 196)
chromatography (p. 227)
configurational isomers (p. 195)
constitutional isomers (p. 195)
dextrorotatory (p. 208)
diastereomer (p. 212)
enantiomers (p. 199)
enantiomerically pure (p. 210)

enantiomeric excess (ee) (p. 210)
enzyme (p. 240)
erythro enantiomers (p. 212)
Fischer projection (p. 200)
geometric isomers (p. 196)
isomers (p. 195)
levorotatory (p. 208)
meso compound (p. 216)
observed rotation (p. 208)
observed specific rotation (p. 210)
optically active (p. 208)
optically inactive (p. 208)
perspective formula (p. 200)
plane of polarization (p. 207)
plane of symmetry (p. 216)
plane-polarized light (p. 206)
polarimeter (p. 208)
racemate (p. 210)

racemic mixture (p. 210)
receptor (p. 242)
R configuration (p. 201)
regioselective (p. 229)
relative configuration (p. 224)
resolution of a racemic mixture (p. 227)
S configuration (p. 201)
specific rotation (p. 209)
stereocenter (p. 200)
stereochemistry (p. 229)
stereogenic center (p. 200)
stereoisomers (p. 195)
stereoselective (p. 229)
stereospecific (p. 230)
syn addition (p. 232)
threo enantiomers (p. 212)
trans isomer (p. 196)

PROBLEMS

62. Disregarding stereoisomers, give the structures of all compounds with molecular formula C_5H_{10}. Which ones can exist as stereoisomers?

63. Draw all possible stereoisomers for each of the following. Indicate if no stereoisomers are possible.

a. 1-bromo-2-chlorocyclohexane
b. 2-bromo-4-methylpentane
c. 1,2-dichlorocyclohexane
d. 2-bromo-4-chloropentane
e. 3-heptene
f. 1-bromo-4-chlorocyclohexane

g. 1,2-dimethylcyclopropane
h. 4-bromo-2-pentene
i. 3,3-dimethylpentane
j. 3-chloro-1-butene
k. 1-bromo-2-chlorocyclobutane
l. 1-bromo-3-chlorocyclobutane

64. Which of the following has an asymmetric center?

$$CHBr_2Cl \qquad BHFCl \qquad CH_3CHCl_2 \qquad CHFBrCl \qquad BeHCl$$

65. Name each of the following compounds using R,S and E,Z (Section 3.5) designations where necessary:

a.

HC=CH₂
|
CH₃CH₂ — C ʷʷ CH₃
|
H

b.

F   I
  \   /
   C = C
  /   \
Cl   Br

c.

CH₃
|
HO —— H
H —— Cl
|
CH₂CH₃

d.

$$
\begin{array}{c}
F \quad\quad H \\
C=C \\
Cl \quad\quad Br
\end{array}
$$

e.

f.

$$
\begin{array}{c}
\quad\quad\quad\quad CH_3 \\
BrCH_2CH_2 \quad\quad CH_2CH_2CHCH_3 \\
C=C \\
Br \quad\quad CH_3
\end{array}
$$

g.

$$
\begin{array}{c}
CH_2OH \\
HO-\!\!\!\!-CH_3 \\
CH_2CH_2CH_2OH
\end{array}
$$

h.

$$
\begin{array}{c}
CH_3CH_2 \quad\quad Br \\
C-C\!\!-CH_3 \\
H \quad\quad\quad CH_2Br \\
HO
\end{array}
$$

i.

$$
\begin{array}{c}
\quad\quad CH_3 \\
CH_3CH \quad\quad CH_2CH_2CH_2CH_3 \\
C=C \\
H_3C \quad\quad CH_2CH_2Cl
\end{array}
$$

66. Mevacor is used clinically to lower serum cholesterol levels. How many asymmetric centers does Mevacor have?

Mevacor®

67. Indicate whether each of the following pairs of compounds are identical or are enantiomers, diastereomers, or constitutional isomers:

a.

and

b.

and

c.

and

d.

and

e.

$$
\begin{array}{c}
CH_3CH_2 \quad\quad Br \\
C-C\!\!-CH_3 \\
H \quad\quad\quad CH(CH_3)_2 \\
HO
\end{array}
$$

and

$$
\begin{array}{c}
CH_3CH_2 \quad\quad CH_3 \\
C-C\!\!-CH(CH_3)_2 \\
HO \quad\quad\quad Br \\
H
\end{array}
$$

f.

and

g.

$$
\begin{array}{c}
H \quad\quad CH_3 \\
C=C \\
CH_3 \quad\quad Br
\end{array}
$$

and

$$
\begin{array}{c}
H \quad\quad Br \\
C=C \\
CH_3 \quad\quad CH_3
\end{array}
$$

h.

$$
\begin{array}{c}
Br \quad\quad CH_3 \\
C=C \\
H \quad\quad CH_3
\end{array}
$$

and

$$
\begin{array}{c}
H \quad\quad CH_3 \\
C=C \\
Br \quad\quad CH_3
\end{array}
$$

68. a. Give the product or products that would be obtained from the reaction of *cis*-2-butene and *trans*-2-butene with each of the following reagents. If a product can exist as stereoisomers, show which stereoisomers are obtained.

  1. HCl
  2. BH$_3$/THF followed by HO$^-$, H$_2$O$_2$, H$_2$O
  3. a peroxyacid
  4. Br$_2$ in CH$_2$Cl$_2$

  5. Br$_2$ + H$_2$O
  6. H$_2$ + Pd/C
  7. H$_2$O + H$_2$SO$_4$
  8. CH$_3$OH + H$_2$SO$_4$

  b. With which reagents do the two alkenes react to give different products?

69. Which of the following are optically active?

70. For many centuries, the Chinese have used extracts from a group of herbs known as ephedra to treat asthma. A compound named ephedrine that has been isolated from these herbs was found to be a potent dilator of air passages in the lungs.

a. How many stereoisomers are possible for ephedrine?

b. The stereoisomer shown below is the one that is pharmacologically active. What is the configuration of each of the asymmetric centers?

ephedrine

71. Which of the following compounds have an achiral stereoisomer?

a. 2,3-dichlorobutane
b. 2,3-dichloropentane
c. 2,3-dichloro-2,3-dimethylbutane
d. 1,3-dichlorocyclopentane
e. 1,3-dibromocyclobutane

f. 2,4-dibromopentane
g. 2,3-dibromopentane
h. 1,4-dimethylcyclohexane
i. 1,2-dimethylcyclopentane
j. 1,2-dimethylcyclobutane

72. Indicate whether each of the following pairs of compounds are identical or are enantiomers, diastereomers, or constitutional isomers:

73. Give the products, including their configurations, obtained from the reaction of 1-ethylcyclohexene with the following reagents:

a. HBr
b. H_2, Pd/C

c. BH_3/THF followed by HO^-, H_2O_2, H_2O
d. Br_2/CH_2Cl_2

74. Citrate synthase, one of the enzymes in the series of enzyme-catalyzed reactions known as the citric acid cycle (Section 26.10), catalyzes the synthesis of citric acid from oxaloacetic acid and acetyl-CoA. If the synthesis is carried out with acetyl-CoA that contains radioactive carbon (^{14}C) in the indicated position (Section 1.1), the isomer shown here is obtained.

$$HOOCCH_2CCOOH + {}^{14}CH_3CSCoA \xrightarrow{\text{citrate synthase}}$$

oxaloacetic acid   acetyl-CoA

citric acid

a. Which stereoisomer of citric acid is synthesized, R or S?

b. Why is the other stereoisomer not obtained?

c. If the acetyl-CoA used in the synthesis does not contain ^{14}C (Section 1.1), will the product of the reaction be chiral or achiral?

75. Give the products of the following reactions. If the products can exist as stereoisomers, show which stereoisomers are obtained.

a. cis-2-pentene + HCl
b. trans-2-pentene + HCl
c. 1-ethylcyclohexene + H_2O + H_2SO_4
d. 2,3-dimethyl-3-hexene + H_2, Pd/C
e. 1,2-dimethylcyclohexene + HCl

f. 1,2-dideuteriocyclohexene + H_2, Pd/C
g. 3,3-dimethyl-1-pentene + Br_2/CH_2Cl_2
h. (E)-3,4-dimethyl-3-heptene + H_2, Pd/C
i. (Z)-3,4-dimethyl-3-heptene + H_2, Pd/C
j. 1-chloro-2-ethylcyclohexene + H_2, Pd/C

76. Indicate whether each of the following pairs of compounds are identical or are enantiomers, diastereomers, or constitutional isomers:

a.

$$HC=CH_2$$
C with CH₃, CH₃CH₂, H

and

$$CH_2CH_3$$
C with H, CH₃, HC=CH₂

e.

cyclohexane with CH₃

and

cyclopentane with CH₂CH₃

b.

$$CH_2OH$$
H—CH₃
$$CH_2CH_3$$

and

$$CH_2CH_3$$
CH₃—H
$$CH_2OH$$

f.

cyclohexane with Cl, Cl

and

cyclohexane with Cl, Cl

c.

$$CH_3$$
HO—H
H—Cl
$$CH_3$$

and

$$CH_3$$
H—OH
Cl—H
$$CH_3$$

g.

cyclohexane with Cl, Cl

and

cyclohexane with Cl, Cl

d.

$$CH_3$$
HO—H
H—Cl
$$CH_2CH_3$$

and

$$CH_2CH_3$$
HO—H
H—Cl
$$CH_3$$

h.

cyclohexane with Cl, Cl

and

cyclohexane with Cl, Cl

77. The specific rotation of (R)-(+)-glyceraldehyde is +8.7. If the observed specific rotation of a mixture of (R)-glyceraldehyde and (S)-glyceraldehyde is +1.4, what percent of glyceraldehyde is present as the R enantiomer?

78. Indicate whether each of the following structures is (R)-2-chlorobutane or (S)-2-chlorobutane. (Use models, if necessary.)

a.

$$Cl$$
C with CH₃CH₂, CH₃, H

c. (structure with Cl)

e.

Cl, H₃C—H, H—CH₃, H

b.

$$CH_3$$
H—Cl
$$CH_2CH_3$$

d. (structure with Cl)

f.

CH₃, H—H, H—Cl, CH₃

79. A solution of an unknown compound (3.0 g of the compound in 20 mL of solution), when placed in a polarimeter tube 2.0 dm long, was found to rotate the plane of polarized light 1.8° in a counterclockwise direction. What is the specific rotation of the compound?

80. Butaclamol is a potent antipsychotic that has been used clinically in the treatment of schizophrenia. How many asymmetric centers does it have?

Butaclamol®

81. Explain how R and S are related to (+) and (−).

82. Give the products of the following reactions. If the products can exist as stereoisomers, show which stereoisomers are obtained.

  a. cis-2-pentene + Br_2/CH_2Cl_2
  b. trans-2-pentene + Br_2/CH_2Cl_2
  c. 1-butene + HCl
  d. methylcyclohexene + HBr
  e. trans-3-hexene + Br_2/CH_2Cl_2
  f. cis-3-hexene + Br_2/CH_2Cl_2

  g. 3,3-dimethyl-1-pentene + HBr
  h. cis-2-butene + HBr
  i. (Z)-2,3-dichloro-2-butene + H_2, Pd/C
  j. (E)-2,3-dichloro-2-butene + H_2, Pd/C
  k. (Z)-3,4-dimethyl-3-hexene + H_2, Pd/C
  l. (E)-3,4-dimethyl-3-hexene + H_2, Pd/C

83. a. Draw all possible stereoisomers for the following.

$$HOCH_2CH-CH-CHCH_2OH$$
$$OH \quad OH \quad OH$$

  b. Which isomers are optically inactive (will not rotate the plane of polarization of plane-polarized light)?

84. Indicate the configuration of the asymmetric centers in the following molecules:

a.

b.

c.

85. a. Draw all the isomers with molecular formula C_6H_{12} that contain a cyclobutane ring. (*Hint*: There are seven.)
   b. Name the compounds without specifying the configuration of any asymmetric centers.
   c. Identify:

   1. constitutional isomers
   2. stereoisomers
   3. cis–trans isomers
   4. chiral compounds

   5. achiral compounds
   6. meso compounds
   7. enantiomers
   8. diastereomers

86. A compound has a specific rotation of -39.0. A solution of the compound (0.187 g/mL) has an observed rotation of $-6.52°$ when placed in a polarimeter tube 10 cm long. What is the percent of each enantiomer in the solution?

87. Indicate whether each of the following pairs of compounds are identical or are enantiomers, diastereomers, or constitutional isomers:

a.   and

c.   and

b.   and

d.   and

88. Draw structures for each of the following molecules:
   a. (*S*)-1-bromo-1-chlorobutane
   b. (2*R*,3*R*)-2,3-dichloropentane
   c. an achiral isomer of 1,2-dimethylcyclohexane
   d. a chiral isomer of 1,2-dibromocyclobutane
   e. two achiral isomers of 3,4,5-trimethylheptane

89. Explain why the enantiomers of 1,2-dimethylaziridine can be separated, even though one of the "groups" attached to nitrogen is a lone pair.

enantiomers of 1,2-dimethylaziridine

90. Of the possible products shown for the following reaction, are there any that would not be formed?

91. A sample of (*S*)-(+)-lactic acid was found to have an optical purity of 72%. How much *R* isomer is present in the sample?

92. Indicate whether each of the structures in the second row is an enantiomer of, a diastereomer of, or is identical to the structure in the top row.

$$
\begin{array}{c}
CH_3 \\
H{-}\!\!\!-\!\!\!-Br \\
H{-}\!\!\!-\!\!\!-CH_3 \\
CH_2CH_3
\end{array}
$$

A B C D E

93. Give the products of the following reactions including their configurations:

$$
\begin{array}{c}
\text{HBr} \\
\xleftarrow{\quad} \\
\text{Br}_2\text{, CH}_3\text{OH} \\
\xleftarrow{\quad} \\
\text{H}_2\text{O, H}_2\text{SO}_4 \\
\xleftarrow{\quad} \\
\text{H}_2 \\
\text{Pd/C}
\end{array}
\quad
\begin{array}{c}
H \quad CH_3 \\
C{=}C \\
H_3C \quad CH(CH_3)_2
\end{array}
\quad
\begin{array}{c}
\text{Br}_2\text{, CH}_2\text{Cl}_2 \\
\xrightarrow{\quad} \\
\text{1. BH}_3\text{/THF} \\
\text{2. H}_2\text{O}_2\text{, HO}^- \\
\xrightarrow{\quad} \\
\text{Br}_2\text{, H}_2\text{O} \\
\xrightarrow{\quad}
\end{array}
$$

94. a. Using the wedge-and-dash notation, draw the nine stereoisomers of 1,2,3,4,5,6-hexachlorocyclohexane.
 b. From the nine stereoisomers, identify one pair of enantiomers.
 c. Draw the most stable conformation of the most stable stereoisomer.

95. Tamiflu is used for the prevention and treatment of flu. What is the configuration of each of its asymmetric centers?

Tamiflu®

96. A student decided that the configuration of the asymmetric centers in a sugar such as D-glucose could be determined rapidly by simply assigning the R configuration to an asymmetric center with an OH group on the right and the S configuration to an asymmetric center with an OH group on the left. Is he correct? (We will see in Chapter 21 that the "D" in D-glucose means the OH group on the bottommost asymmetric center is on the right.)

$$
\begin{array}{c}
HC{=}O \\
H{-}\!\!\!-OH \\
HO{-}\!\!\!-H \\
H{-}\!\!\!-OH \\
H{-}\!\!\!-OH \\
CH_2OH
\end{array}
$$

D-glucose

97. When fumarate reacts with D_2O in the presence of the enzyme fumarase, only one isomer of the product is formed, as shown below. Is the enzyme catalyzing a syn or an anti addition of D_2O?

$$
\begin{array}{c}
{}^-OOC \quad H \\
C{=}C \\
H \quad COO^-
\end{array}
\quad + \ D_2O \xrightarrow{\text{fumarase}}
\begin{array}{c}
COO^- \\
DO{-}\!\!\!-H \\
D{-}\!\!\!-H \\
COO^-
\end{array}
$$

fumarate

98. When (S)-(+)-1-chloro-2-methylbutane reacts with chlorine, one of the products is (−)-1,4-dichloro-2-methylbutane. Does this product have the R or the S configuration?

99. Indicate the configuration of the asymmetric centers in the following molecules:

a.   **b.**   **c.**

100. **a.** Draw the two chair conformers for each of the stereoisomers of *trans*-1-*tert*-butyl-3-methylcyclohexane.
b. For each pair, indicate which conformer is more stable.

101. **a.** Do the following compounds have any asymmetric centers?
1. $CH_2\!\!=\!\!C\!\!=\!\!CH_2$
2. $CH_3CH\!\!=\!\!C\!\!=\!\!CHCH_3$
b. Are the compounds chiral? (*Hint*: Make models.)

102. Is the following compound optically active?

6

The Reactions of Alkynes •

An Introduction to Multistep Synthesis

1-butyne + **2 HCl** ⟶ **2,2-dichlorobutane**

AN **ALKYNE** IS A HYDROCARBON THAT CONTAINS A CARBON–CARBON TRIPLE BOND. Because of its triple bond, an alkyne has four fewer hydrogens than an alkane with the same number of carbons. Therefore, while the general molecular formula for an acyclic (noncyclic) alkane is C_nH_{2n+2}, the general molecular formula for an acyclic alkyne is C_nH_{2n-2} and that for a cyclic alkyne is C_nH_{2n-4}.

Only a few alkynes are found in nature. Examples include capillin, which has fungicidal activity, and ichthyothereol, a convulsant used by the indigenous people of the Amazon for poisoned arrowheads. A class of naturally occurring compounds called enediynes has been found to have powerful antibiotic and anticancer properties. All enediynes have a nine- or ten-membered ring that contains two triple bonds separated by a double bond. Chemists are currently studying these compounds to see which of them might be developed into successful drugs.

The few drugs now on the market that contain alkyne functional groups are not naturally occurring compounds; they exist only because chemists have been able to synthesize them. Their trade names are shown on page 252, in green. Trade names are always capitalized; only the company that holds the patent for a product can use the product's trade name for commercial purposes (Section 31.1).

Parsal® Sinovial®
parsalmide
an analgesic

Eudatin® Supirdyl®
pargyline
an antihypertensive

Norquen® Ovastol®
mestranol
a component in oral contraceptives

PROBLEM 1 ◆

What is the molecular formula for a cyclic hydrocarbon with 14 carbons and two triple bonds?

6.1 THE NOMENCLATURE OF ALKYNES

The systematic name of an alkyne is obtained by replacing the "ane" ending of the alkane name with "yne." Analogous to the way compounds with other functional groups are named (Sections 2.6, 2.7, 3.2), the longest continuous chain containing the functional group, in this case the carbon–carbon triple bond, is numbered in the direction that gives the alkyne functional group suffix as low a number as possible. If the triple bond is at the end of the chain, the alkyne is classified as a **terminal alkyne**. Alkynes with triple bonds located elsewhere along the chain are called **internal alkynes**. For example, 1-butyne is a terminal alkyne, whereas 2-pentyne is an internal alkyne.

	HC≡CH	$\overset{4}{C}H_3\overset{3}{C}H_2\overset{2}{C}≡\overset{1}{C}H$	$\overset{1}{C}H_3\overset{2}{C}≡\overset{3}{C}\overset{4}{C}H_2\overset{5}{C}H_3$	$\overset{4}{C}H_3\overset{3}{C}H\overset{2}{C}≡\overset{1}{C}CH_3$
Systematic:	ethyne	1-butyne	2-pentyne	4-methyl-2-hexyne
Common:	acetylene	ethylacetylene	ethylmethylacetylene	sec-butylmethyl-acetylene
		a terminal alkyne	an internal alkyne	

(4-methyl-2-hexyne structure has $\overset{5}{C}H_2\overset{6}{C}H_3$ branch)

1-hexyne
a terminal alkyne

In common nomenclature, alkynes are named as *substituted acetylenes*. The common name is obtained by stating the names of the alkyl groups, in alphabetical order, that have replaced the hydrogens of acetylene. Acetylene, the common name for the smallest alkyne, may be familiar to you because of the oxyacetylene torch used to cut steel. It is an unfortunate common name for an alkyne because its "ene" ending is characteristic of a double bond rather than a triple bond.

If counting from either direction leads to the same number for the functional group suffix, the correct systematic name is the one that contains the lowest substituent number. If the compound contains more than one substituent, the substituents are listed in alphabetical order.

3-hexyne
an internal alkyne

$\overset{1}{C}H_3\overset{2}{C}H\overset{3}{C}H\overset{4}{C}≡\overset{5}{C}\overset{6}{C}H_2\overset{7}{C}H_2\overset{8}{C}H_3$
(Cl on C2, Br on C3)

3-bromo-2-chloro-4-octyne
not **6-bromo-7-chloro-4-octyne**
because 2 < 6

$\overset{6}{C}H_3\overset{5}{C}H\overset{4}{C}≡\overset{3}{C}\overset{2}{C}H_2\overset{1}{C}H_2Br$
(CH₃ on C5)

1-bromo-5-methyl-3-hexyne
not **6-bromo-2-methyl-3-hexyne**
because 1 < 2

A substituent receives the lowest possible number only if there is no functional group suffix or if counting from either direction leads to the same number for the functional group suffix.

PROBLEM 2 ◆

Draw the structure for each of the following:

a. 1-chloro-3-hexyne
b. cyclooctyne
c. isopropylacetylene

d. *sec*-butylisobutylacetylene
e. 4,4-dimethyl-1-pentyne
f. dimethylacetylene

PROBLEM 3

Draw the structures and give the common and systematic names for the seven alkynes with molecular formula C_6H_{10}.

PROBLEM 4 ◆

Give the systematic name for each of the following:

a. $BrCH_2CH_2C{\equiv}CCH_3$

b. $CH_3CH_2CHC{\equiv}CCH_2CHCH_3$
           | |
           Br   Cl

c. $CH_3OCH_2C{\equiv}CCH_2CH_3$

d. $CH_3CH_2CHC{\equiv}CH$
           |
           $CH_2CH_2CH_3$

PROBLEM 5 ◆

Give the systematic name for each of the following:

a.   b.   c.

6.2 HOW TO NAME A COMPOUND THAT HAS MORE THAN ONE FUNCTIONAL GROUP

We have seen how compounds with two alcohol groups (Section 2.6) and two double bonds (Section 3.2) are named. Similar rules are followed for naming compounds with two triple bonds, using the ending "diyne."

$CH_2{=}C{=}CH_2$

systematic: propadiene
common: allene

$\overset{6}{C}H_3\overset{5}{C}H{=}\overset{4}{C}H\overset{3}{C}H_2\overset{2}{C}{=}\overset{1}{C}H_2$ with CH_3 on carbon 2

2-methyl-1,4-hexadiene
or
2-methylhexa-1,4-diene

$CH_3\overset{|}{C}HC{\equiv}CCH_2C{\equiv}CH$ with CH_3

6-methyl-1,4-heptadiyne
or
6-methylhepta-1,4-diyne

To name an alkene in which the second functional group is not another double bond but, like the alkene functional group, is identified by a functional group suffix, find the longest continuous chain containing both functional groups and put both suffixes at the end of the name. The "ene" ending should be first, with the terminal "e" omitted to avoid two adjacent vowels. The number indicating the location of the first-stated functional group is usually placed before the name of the parent chain. The number indicating the location of the second-stated functional group is placed immediately before the suffix for that functional group. If the two functional groups are a *double bond* and a *triple bond*, the chain is numbered in the direction that produces a name containing the lower number. Thus, in the following examples, the lower number is given to the alkyne suffix in the compound on the left and to the alkene suffix in the compound on the right.

> When the functional groups are a double bond and a triple bond, the chain is numbered in the direction that produces the name containing the lowest possible number, regardless of which functional group gets the lower number.

$\overset{7}{C}H_3\overset{6}{C}H{=}\overset{5}{C}H\overset{4}{C}H_2\overset{3}{C}H_2\overset{2}{C}{\equiv}\overset{1}{C}H$

5-hepten-1-yne
not **2-hepten-6-yne**
because 1 < 2

$\overset{1}{C}H_2{=}\overset{2}{C}H\overset{3}{C}H_2\overset{4}{C}H_2\overset{5}{C}{\equiv}\overset{6}{C}CH_3$

1-hepten-5-yne
not **6-hepten-2-yne**
because 1 < 2

$CH_2CH_2CH_2CH_3$
$\overset{1}{C}H_2{=}\overset{2}{C}H\overset{3}{C}HC{\equiv}\overset{5}{C}CH_3$
           $\overset{4}{}$ $\overset{6}{}$

3-butyl-1-hexen-4-yne

the longest continuous chain has eight carbons, but the 8-carbon chain does not contain both functional groups; therefore, the compound is named as a hexenyne because the longest continuous chain containing both functional groups has six carbons

If the same low number is obtained in both directions, the chain is numbered in the direction that gives the double bond the lower number.

If there is a tie between a double bond and a triple bond, the double bond gets the lower number.

$$\overset{1}{C}H_3\overset{2}{C}H=\overset{3}{C}H\overset{4}{C}\equiv\overset{5}{C}\overset{6}{C}H_3 \qquad \overset{6}{H}C\equiv\overset{5}{C}\overset{4}{C}H_2\overset{3}{C}H_2\overset{2}{C}H=\overset{1}{C}H_2$$

2-hexen-4-yne   1-hexen-5-yne
not 4-hexen-2-yne   *not* 5-hexen-1-yne

If the second functional group suffix has a higher priority than the alkene suffix, the chain is numbered in the direction that assigns the lower number to the functional group with the higher-priority suffix. (The relative priorities of the functional group suffixes are shown in Table 6.1.) The highest priority functional group is assumed to be at the 1-position in cyclic compounds.

Table 6.1   Priorities of Functional Group Suffixes

highest priority — C=O > OH > NH$_2$ > C=C = C≡C — lowest priority

the double bond is given priority over a triple bond only when there is a tie

A chain is numbered to give the lowest possible number to the functional group with the higher priority.

CH$_2$=CHCH$_2$OH
2-propen-1-ol
not 1-propen-3-ol

CH$_3$C(CH$_3$)=CHCH$_2$CH$_2$OH
4-methyl-3-penten-1-ol

CH$_2$=CHCH$_2$CH$_2$CH$_2$CH(NH$_2$)CH$_3$
6-hepten-2-amine

CH$_3$CH$_2$CH=CHCH(OH)CH$_3$
3-hexen-2-ol

6-methyl-2-cyclohexenol

3-cyclohexenamine

PROBLEM 6 ♦

Give the systematic name for each of the following:

a. CH$_2$=CHCH$_2$C≡CCH$_2$CH$_3$

b. CH$_3$CH=CC(CH$_3$)CH$_2$CH=CH$_2$

c. CH$_3$CH$_2$CH=CC(CH=CH$_2$)CH$_2$CH$_2$C≡CH

d. HOCH$_2$CH$_2$C≡CH

e. CH$_3$CH=CHCH=CHCH=CH$_2$

f. CH$_3$CH=CCH$_3$CH$_2$CH(CH$_3$)CH$_2$OH

How a Banana Slug Knows What to Eat

Many species of mushrooms synthesize 1-octen-3-ol, which is a repellent that drives off predatory slugs. Such mushrooms can be recognized by small bite marks on their caps, where the slug started to nibble before the volatile compound was released. Humans are not put off by the release of this compound because to humans 1-octen-3-ol smells like a mushroom. 1-Octen-3-ol also has antibacterial properties that may protect the mushroom from organisms that would otherwise invade the wound made by the slug. Not surprisingly, the species of mushroom that banana slugs commonly eat cannot synthesize 1-octen-3-ol.

1-octen-3-ol

PROBLEM 7♦

Name the following:

a.   b.   c.

6.3 THE PHYSICAL PROPERTIES OF UNSATURATED HYDROCARBONS

All hydrocarbons have similar physical properties. In other words, alkenes and alkynes have physical properties similar to those of alkanes (Section 2.9). All are insoluble in water and soluble in nonpolar solvents such as benzene or diethyl ether. They are less dense than water and, like all other homologous series, have boiling points that increase with increasing molecular weight (Table 6.2). Alkynes are more linear than alkenes, and a triple bond is more polarizable than a double bond (Section 2.9). These two features cause alkynes to have stronger van der Waals interactions. As a result, an alkyne has a higher boiling point than an alkene containing the same number of carbons.

Table 6.2 Boiling Points of the Smallest Hydrocarbons					
	bp (°C)		**bp (°C)**		**bp (°C)**
CH_3CH_3 ethane	−88.6	$H_2C{=}CH_2$ ethene	−104	$HC{\equiv}CH$ ethyne	−84
$CH_3CH_2CH_3$ propane	−42.1	$CH_3CH{=}CH_2$ propene	−47	$CH_3C{\equiv}CH$ propyne	−23
$CH_3CH_2CH_2CH_3$ butane	−0.5	$CH_3CH_2CH{=}CH_2$ 1-butene	−6.5	$CH_3CH_2C{\equiv}CH$ 1-butyne	8
$CH_3(CH_2)_3CH_3$ pentane	36.1	$CH_3CH_2CH_2CH{=}CH_2$ 1-pentene	30	$CH_3CH_2CH_2C{\equiv}CH$ 1-pentyne	39
$CH_3(CH_2)_4CH_3$ hexane	68.7	$CH_3CH_2CH_2CH_2CH{=}CH_2$ 1-hexene	63.5	$CH_3CH_2CH_2CH_2C{\equiv}CH$ 1-hexyne	71
		$CH_3CH{=}CHCH_3$ cis-2-butene	3.7	$CH_3C{\equiv}CCH_3$ 2-butyne	27
		$CH_3CH{=}CHCH_3$ trans-2-butene	0.9	$CH_3CH_2C{\equiv}CCH_3$ 2-pentyne	55

Internal alkenes have higher boiling points than terminal alkenes. Similarly, internal alkynes have higher boiling points than terminal alkynes. Notice that the boiling point of *cis*-2-butene is slightly higher than that of *trans*-2-butene because the cis isomer has a small dipole moment, whereas the dipole moment of the trans isomer is zero (Section 3.4).

PROBLEM 8♦

What is the smallest alkane, the smallest alkene, and the smallest alkyne in Table 6.2 that are liquids at room temperature?

6.4 THE STRUCTURE OF ALKYNES

The structure of ethyne was discussed in Section 1.9, where we saw that each carbon is *sp* hybridized, so each has two *sp* orbitals and two *p* orbitals. One *sp* orbital overlaps the *s* orbital of a hydrogen, and the other overlaps an *sp* orbital of the other carbon. (Remember that the small lobes of the *sp* orbitals are not shown.) Because the *sp* orbitals are oriented as far from each other as possible to minimize electron repulsion, ethyne is a linear molecule with bond angles of 180°.

Alkynes have structures similar to that of ethyne. Recall that the triple bond is formed by each of the two *p* orbitals on one *sp* carbon overlapping the parallel *p* orbital on the other *sp* carbon to form two π bonds (Figure 6.1). The electrostatic potential maps for ethyne (displayed above) and 2-butyne (displayed below) show that the end result can be thought of as a cylinder of electrons wrapped around the σ bond.

A triple bond is composed of a σ bond and two π bonds.

▶ **Figure 6.1**
(a) Each of the two π bonds of a triple bond is formed by side-to-side overlap of a *p* orbital of one carbon with a parallel *p* orbital of the adjacent carbon.
(b) The electrostatic potential map for 2-butyne.

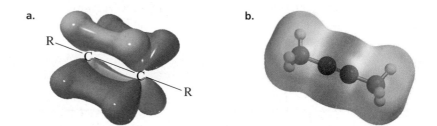

We have seen that a carbon–carbon triple bond is shorter and stronger than a carbon–carbon double bond, which in turn, is shorter and stronger than a carbon–carbon single bond. We have also seen that a π bond is weaker than a σ bond (Section 1.14). The relatively weak π bonds allow alkynes to react easily.

Alkyl groups stabilize alkynes, just as they stabilize alkenes, by hyperconjugation (Section 4.2). Internal alkynes, therefore, are more stable than terminal alkynes. We now have seen that *alkyl groups stabilize alkenes, alkynes,* and *carbocations.*

PROBLEM 9 ◆

What orbitals are used to form the carbon–carbon σ bond between the highlighted carbons?

a. $CH_3CH=CHCH_3$ **d.** $CH_3C≡CCH_3$ **g.** $CH_3CH=CHCH_2CH_3$

b. $CH_3CH=CHCH_3$ **e.** $CH_3C≡CCH_3$ **h.** $CH_3C≡CCH_2CH_3$

c. $CH_3CH=C=CH_2$ **f.** $CH_2=CHCH=CH_2$ **i.** $CH_2=CHC≡CH$

6.5 HOW ALKYNES REACT

With a cloud of electrons completely surrounding the σ bond, an alkyne is an electron-rich molecule. In other words, it is a nucleophile. It will therefore react with an electrophile.

MECHANISM FOR THE ELECTROPHILIC ADDITION REACTION

- The relatively weak π bond breaks because the π electrons are attracted to the electrophilic proton.
- The positively charged carbocation intermediate reacts rapidly with the negatively charged chloride ion.

Thus alkynes, like alkenes, undergo electrophilic addition reactions. We will see that the same electrophilic reagents that add to alkenes also add to alkynes and that—again like alkenes—electrophilic addition to a *terminal* alkyne is regioselective. The addition reactions of alkynes, however, have a feature that the corresponding reactions of alkenes do not have: because the product of the addition of an electrophilic reagent to an alkyne is an alkene, a second electrophilic addition reaction can occur if excess hydrogen halide is present.

$$
CH_3C{\equiv}CCH_3 \xrightarrow{\text{HCl}} \underset{\displaystyle \overset{|}{Cl}}{CH_3C}{=}CHCH_3 \xrightarrow{\text{HCl}} \underset{\displaystyle \underset{Cl}{|}}{\overset{\displaystyle \overset{Cl}{|}}{CH_3CCH_2CH_3}}
$$

a second electrophilic addition reaction occurs

An alkyne is *less* reactive than an alkene in electrophilic addition reactions. This might at first seem surprising because an alkyne is less stable than an alkene (Figure 6.2). However, reactivity depends on $\Delta G^{\ddagger}$, which in turn depends on the stability of the reactant *and* the stability of the transition state (Section 3.7). For an alkyne to be both less stable and less reactive than an alkene, two conditions must hold: the transition state for the rate-limiting step (the first step) of an electrophilic addition reaction for an alkyne must be less stable than the transition state for the first step of an electrophilic addition reaction for an alkene, *and* the difference in the stabilities of the transition states must be greater than the difference in the stabilities of the reactants so that $\Delta G^{\ddagger}_{\text{alkyne}} > \Delta G^{\ddagger}_{\text{alkene}}$ (Figure 6.2).

Alkynes are less reactive than alkenes in electrophilic addition reactions.

◀ **Figure 6.2**
Comparison of the free energies of activation for the addition of an electrophile to an alkyne and to an alkene. Because an alkyne is less reactive than an alkene toward electrophilic addition, we know that the $\Delta G^{\ddagger}$ for the reaction of an alkyne is greater than the $\Delta G^{\ddagger}$ for the reaction of an alkene.

Why is the transition state for the first step of an electrophilic addition reaction for an alkyne less stable than that for an alkene? The Hammond postulate predicts that the structure of the transition state for the first step of the reaction will resemble the structure of the carbocation intermediate, which is the product of the first step (Section 4.3). The carbocation that is formed when a proton adds to an alkyne is a vinylic cation, whereas the carbocation that is formed when a proton adds to an alkene is an alkyl cation. A **vinylic cation** has a positive charge on a vinylic carbon. A vinylic cation is less stable than a *similarly substituted* alkyl cation. In other words, a primary vinylic cation is less stable than a primary alkyl cation, and a secondary vinylic cation is less stable than a secondary alkyl cation.

relative stabilities of carbocations

Why is a vinylic cation less stable than a similarly substituted alkyl cation? For one thing, a vinyl cation has a positive charge on an *sp* carbon, which is more electronegative than the *sp²* carbon of an alkyl cation and is therefore less able to bear a positive charge (Section 1.21). Moreover, hyperconjugation is less effective in stabilizing a charge on a vinylic cation than on an alkyl cation (Section 4.2).

> ### PROBLEM 10 ♦
>
> Under what circumstances can you assume that the less stable of two compounds will be the more reactive compound?

6.6 THE ADDITION OF HYDROGEN HALIDES AND THE ADDITION OF HALOGENS TO AN ALKYNE

If the alkyne is a *terminal* alkyne, the electrophilic addition reaction is regioselective: the H^+ will add to the *sp* carbon that is bonded to the hydrogen.

The electrophile adds to the *sp* carbon of a terminal alkyne that is bonded to the hydrogen.

The electrophile adds to the sp carbon that is bonded to the hydrogen because the secondary vinylic cation that results is more stable than the primary vinylic cation that would be formed if the H^+ added to the other sp carbon (Section 6.5).

The addition of a hydrogen halide to an alkyne can be stopped after the addition of one equivalent of hydrogen halide because, although an alkyne is less reactive than an alkene, an alkyne is more reactive than the halo-substituted alkene that is the product of the first addition reaction. The halo-substituted alkene is less reactive because a halogen substituent withdraws electrons inductively (through the σ bond), thereby decreasing the nucleophilic character of the double bond.

Although the addition of a hydrogen halide to an alkyne can be stopped after the addition of one equivalent of hydrogen halide, a second electrophilic addition reaction will take place if excess hydrogen halide is present. The product of the second addition reaction is a **geminal dihalide,** a molecule with two halogens on the same carbon. "Geminal" comes from *geminus,* which is Latin for "twin."

When the second equivalent of hydrogen halide adds to the double bond, the electrophile (H^+) adds to the sp^2 carbon bonded to the greater number of hydrogens—as predicted by the rule that governs electrophilic addition reactions (Section 4.4). The carbocation that results is more stable than the carbocation that would have been formed if H^+ had added to the other sp^2 carbon because bromine can share the positive charge with carbon by overlapping one of its orbitals that contains a lone pair with the empty $2p$ orbital of the positively charged carbon.

In describing the mechanism for addition of a hydrogen halide, we have shown the intermediate as a vinylic cation. This mechanism may not be completely correct. A secondary vinylic cation is about as stable as a primary carbocation, and generally primary carbocations are too unstable to be formed. Some chemists, therefore, think that a **π-complex** rather than a vinylic cation is formed as an intermediate.

$$\underset{\textbf{a } \pi\textbf{-complex}}{\overset{\overset{\overset{\delta-\ Cl}{|}}{\underset{}{\overset{\delta+\ H}{\diagup \ \diagdown}}}}{HC\equiv CH}}$$

Support for the intermediate's being a π-complex comes from the observation that many (but not all) alkyne addition reactions are stereoselective. For example, the addition of HCl to 2-butyne forms only (Z)-2-chloro-2-butene, which means that only anti addition of H and Cl occurs. Clearly, the nature of the intermediate in alkyne addition reactions is not completely understood.

$$CH_3C\equiv CCH_3 \xrightarrow{\textbf{HCl}} \underset{\textbf{(Z)-2-chloro-2-butene}}{\underset{H_3C}{\overset{H}{\diagdown}}C=C\underset{Cl}{\overset{CH_3}{\diagup}}}$$

anti addition

2-butyne

Addition of a hydrogen halide to an *internal* alkyne forms two geminal dihalides because the initial addition of the proton can occur with equal ease to either of the *sp* carbons.

$$\underset{\substack{\textbf{2-pentyne}\\\textbf{an internal alkyne}}}{CH_3CH_2C\equiv CCH_3} + \underset{\textbf{excess}}{HCl} \longrightarrow \underset{\textbf{2,2-dichloropentane}}{CH_3CH_2CH_2\overset{\overset{Cl}{|}}{\underset{\underset{Cl}{|}}{C}}CH_3} + \underset{\textbf{3,3-dichloropentane}}{CH_3CH_2\overset{\overset{Cl}{|}}{\underset{\underset{Cl}{|}}{C}}CH_2CH_3}$$

Notice, however, that if the same group is attached to each of the *sp* carbons of the internal alkyne, only one geminal dihalide will be formed.

$$\underset{\substack{\textbf{3-hexyne}\\\textbf{a symmetrical}\\\textbf{internal alkyne}}}{CH_3CH_2C\equiv CCH_2CH_3} + \underset{\textbf{excess}}{HBr} \longrightarrow \underset{\textbf{3,3-dibromohexane}}{CH_3CH_2CH_2\overset{\overset{Br}{|}}{\underset{\underset{Br}{|}}{C}}CH_2CH_3}$$

The halogens Cl_2 and Br_2 also add to alkynes. In the presence of excess halogen, a second addition reaction occurs. Typically, the solvent is CH_2Cl_2.

$$CH_3CH_2C{\equiv}CCH_3 \xrightarrow[CH_2Cl_2]{Cl_2} CH_3CH_2\overset{Cl}{\underset{Cl}{C}}{=}CCH_3 \xrightarrow[CH_2Cl_2]{Cl_2} CH_3CH_2\overset{Cl\ Cl}{\underset{Cl\ Cl}{C-C}}CH_3$$

$$CH_3C{\equiv}CH \xrightarrow[CH_2Cl_2]{Br_2} CH_3\overset{Br}{\underset{Br}{C}}{=}CH \xrightarrow[CH_2Cl_2]{Br_2} CH_3\overset{Br\ Br}{\underset{Br\ Br}{C-CH}}$$

PROBLEM 11 ◆

Give the major product of each of the following reactions:

a. $HC{\equiv}CCH_3 \xrightarrow{HBr}$

b. $HC{\equiv}CCH_3 \xrightarrow{\text{excess} \atop HBr}$

c. $CH_3C{\equiv}CCH_3 \xrightarrow[CH_2Cl_2]{Br_2}$

d. $HC{\equiv}CCH_3 \xrightarrow[CH_2Cl_2]{\text{excess } Br_2}$

e. $CH_3C{\equiv}CCH_3 \xrightarrow{\text{excess} \atop HBr}$

f. $CH_3C{\equiv}CCH_2CH_3 \xrightarrow{\text{excess} \atop HBr}$

PROBLEM 12 ◆

From what you know about the stereochemistry of alkene addition reactions, predict the configuration of the product that would be obtained from the reaction of 2-butyne with one equivalent of Br_2 in CH_2Cl_2.

---

chem place Tutorial: Addition of HCl to an alkyne

6.7 THE ADDITION OF WATER TO AN ALKYNE

In Section 4.5, we saw that alkenes undergo the acid-catalyzed addition of water. The product of the reaction is an alcohol.

$$\underset{\textbf{1-butene}}{CH_3CH_2CH{=}CH_2} + H_2O \xrightarrow{H_2SO_4} \underset{\textbf{2-butanol}}{CH_3CH_2\underset{OH\ \ H}{CH-CH_2}}$$

Alkynes also undergo the acid-catalyzed addition of water. The initial product of the reaction is an *enol*. An **enol** is a compound with a carbon–carbon double bond and an OH group bonded to one of the sp^2 carbons. (The suffix "ene" signifies the double bond, and "ol" the OH group. When the two suffixes are joined, the second *e* of "ene" is dropped to avoid two consecutive vowels, but the word is pronounced as if the second *e* were still there: "ene-ol.")

$$CH_3C{\equiv}CCH_3 + H_2O \xrightarrow{H_2SO_4} \underset{\textbf{an enol}}{CH_3\overset{OH}{C}{=}CHCH_3} \rightleftharpoons \underset{\textbf{a ketone}}{CH_3\overset{O}{C}{-}CH_2CH_3}$$

The enol immediately rearranges to a *ketone*, a compound with the general structure shown below. A carbon doubly bonded to an oxygen is called a **carbonyl** ("car-bo-neel") **group**. A **ketone** ("key-tone") is a compound that has two alkyl groups bonded to a carbonyl group; an **aldehyde** is a compound that has at least one hydrogen bonded to a carbonyl group.

$$\underset{\textbf{a carbonyl group}}{\overset{O}{\underset{}{C}}} \qquad \underset{\textbf{a ketone}}{\overset{O}{\underset{R\ \ \ R}{C}}} \qquad \underset{\textbf{an aldehyde}}{\overset{O}{\underset{R\ \ \ H}{C}}}$$

A ketone and an enol differ only in the location of a double bond and a hydrogen. A ketone and its corresponding enol are called **keto–enol tautomers. Tautomers** ("taw-toe-mers") are isomers that are in rapid equilibrium. Interconversion of the tautomers is called **tautomerization.** We will examine the mechanism for keto-enol interconversion in Chapter 19. For now, the important thing to remember is that the keto and enol tautomers come to equilibrium in solution, and the keto tautomer, because it is usually much more stable than the enol tautomer, predominates.

$$
\underset{\text{keto tautomer}}{RCH_2-\overset{\overset{\textstyle O}{\|}}{C}-R} \;\rightleftharpoons\; \underset{\text{enol tautomer}}{RCH=\overset{\overset{\textstyle OH}{|}}{C}-R}
$$
$$\text{tautomerization}$$

The addition of water to an internal alkyne that has the same group attached to each of the *sp* carbons forms a single ketone as a product. But if the two groups are not identical, two ketones are formed because the initial addition of the proton can occur to either of the *sp* carbons.

$$
\underset{\substack{\text{a symmetrical} \\ \text{internal alkyne}}}{CH_3CH_2C\equiv CCH_2CH_3} + H_2O \xrightarrow{H_2SO_4} CH_3CH_2\overset{\overset{\textstyle O}{\|}}{C}CH_2CH_2CH_3
$$

$$
\underset{\substack{\text{an unsymmetrical} \\ \text{internal alkyne}}}{CH_3C\equiv CCH_2CH_3} + H_2O \xrightarrow{H_2SO_4} CH_3\overset{\overset{\textstyle O}{\|}}{C}CH_2CH_2CH_3 + CH_3CH_2\overset{\overset{\textstyle O}{\|}}{C}CH_2CH_3
$$

Terminal alkynes are less reactive than internal alkynes toward the addition of water. The addition of water to a terminal alkyne will occur if mercuric ion (Hg^{2+}) is added to the acidic mixture. The mercuric ion is a catalyst—it increases the rate of the addition reaction.

$$
CH_3CH_2C\equiv CH + H_2O \xrightarrow[HgSO_4]{H_2SO_4} \underset{\text{an enol}}{CH_3CH_2\overset{\overset{\textstyle OH}{|}}{C}=CH_2} \rightleftharpoons \underset{\text{a ketone}}{CH_3CH_2\overset{\overset{\textstyle O}{\|}}{C}-CH_3}
$$

The mechanism for the *mercuric-ion-catalyzed hydration* of an alkyne is shown below. The intermediate formed in the first step should remind you of the cyclic bromonium and mercurinium ions formed as intermediates in electrophilic addition reactions of alkenes (Sections 4.8 and 4.9).

MECHANISM FOR THE MERCURIC-ION-CATALYZED HYDRATION OF AN ALKYNE

- Reaction of the alkyne with mercuric ion (Hg^{2+}) forms a cyclic mercurinium ion. (Two of the electrons in mercury's filled 5*d* atomic orbital are shown.)

- Water attacks the more substituted carbon of the cyclic intermediate (Section 4.8).
- The protonated OH group, which is a very strong acid, loses a proton to form a mercuric enol, which immediately rearranges to a mercuric ketone.
- Loss of the mercuric ion forms an enol, which rearranges to a ketone.

Notice that the overall addition of water follows the general rule for electrophilic addition reactions: the electrophile (H^+) adds to the *sp* carbon bonded to the greater number of hydrogens.

chem place Tutorial: Mercuric-ion-catalyzed hydration of an alkyne

Tutorial: Alkynes: Common terms

PROBLEM 13◆

What ketones would be formed from the acid-catalyzed hydration of 3-heptyne?

PROBLEM 14◆

Which alkyne would be the best one to use for the synthesis of each of the following ketones?

a. CH_3CCH_3 **b.** $CH_3CH_2CCH_2CH_2CH_3$ **c.** $CH_3C{-}$⟨ ⟩

PROBLEM 15◆

Draw all the enol tautomers for each of the ketones in Problem 14.

BH₃

6.8 THE ADDITION OF BORANE TO AN ALKYNE: HYDROBORATION–OXIDATION

Borane adds to alkynes in the same way it adds to alkenes. That is, boron is the electrophile and H^- is the nucleophile, and one mole of BH_3 reacts with three moles of alkyne to form one mole of boron-substituted alkene (Section 4.11). When the addition reaction is over, aqueous sodium hydroxide and hydrogen peroxide are added to the reaction mixture. The end result, as in the case of alkenes, is replacement of the boron by an OH group. The enol that is formed immediately rearranges to a ketone.

$$3\ CH_3C{\equiv}CCH_3\ +\ BH_3\ \xrightarrow{THF}\ \underset{\text{boron-substituted alkene}}{\overset{H_3C\qquad CH_3}{\underset{H\qquad B-R}{C{=}C}}}\ \xrightarrow[H_2O]{HO^-,\ H_2O_2}\ 3\ \underset{\text{an enol}}{\overset{H_3C\qquad CH_3}{\underset{H\qquad OH}{C{=}C}}}\ \rightleftharpoons\ 3\ \underset{\text{a ketone}}{CH_3CH_2\overset{O}{\overset{\|}{C}}CH_3}$$

The addition of borane to a terminal alkyne exhibits the same regioselectivity seen in borane addition to an alkene. Boron, with its electron-seeking empty orbital, adds preferentially to the *sp* carbon bonded to the hydrogen. Thus, the reaction follows the general rule for electrophilic addition reactions: the electrophile (BH_3) adds to the *sp* carbon bonded to the greater number of hydrogens. Since the boron-containing group is subsequently replaced by an OH group, hydroboration–oxidation of a terminal alkyne produces an *aldehyde* (the carbonyl group *is* on the terminal carbon), whereas the mercuric-ion-catalyzed addition of water to a terminal alkyne produces a *ketone* (the carbonyl group is *not* on the terminal carbon).

$$CH_3C{\equiv}CH$$

$$\xrightarrow[\text{2. HO}^-, \text{H}_2\text{O}_2, \text{H}_2\text{O}]{\text{1. BH}_3/\text{THF}} CH_3CH{=}\overset{\text{OH}}{\underset{|}{C}}H \rightleftharpoons CH_3CH_2\overset{\text{O}}{\overset{\|}{C}}H$$
an aldehyde

$$\xrightarrow[\text{HgSO}_4]{\text{H}_2\text{O}, \text{H}_2\text{SO}_4} CH_3\overset{\text{OH}}{\underset{|}{C}}{=}CH_2 \rightleftharpoons CH_3\overset{\text{O}}{\overset{\|}{C}}CH_3$$
a ketone

Hydroboration–oxidation of a terminal alkyne forms an aldehyde.

Mercuric-ion catalyzed addition of water to a terminal alkyne forms a ketone.

PROBLEM 16

For each of the following alkynes, give the products of (1) the acid catalyzed addition of water (mercuric ion is added for part a) and (2) hydroboration–oxidation:

a. 1-butyne   **b.** 2-butyne   **c.** 2-pentyne

PROBLEM 17 ♦

There is only one alkyne that forms an aldehyde when it undergoes the mercuric-ion-catalyzed addition of water. Identify the alkyne.

6.9 THE ADDITION OF HYDROGEN TO AN ALKYNE

Alkynes undergo catalytic hydrogenation just as alkenes do (Section 4.12). The initial product is an alkene, but it is difficult to stop the reaction at that stage because of hydrogen's strong tendency to add to alkenes in the presence of these efficient metal catalysts. The final product of the hydrogenation reaction, therefore, is an alkane.

$$CH_3CH_2C{\equiv}CH \xrightarrow[\text{Pd/C}]{\text{H}_2} CH_3CH_2CH{=}CH_2 \xrightarrow[\text{Pd/C}]{\text{H}_2} CH_3CH_2CH_2CH_3$$
alkyne   **alkene**   **alkane**

an alkyne is converted to an alkane

The reaction can be stopped at the alkene stage if a "poisoned" (partially deactivated) metal catalyst is used. The most commonly used partially deactivated metal catalyst is called Lindlar catalyst, which is prepared by precipitating palladium on calcium carbonate and treating it with lead(II) acetate and quinoline. This treatment modifies the surface of the palladium, making it much more effective at catalyzing the addition of hydrogen to a triple bond than to a double bond.

$$CH_3CH_2C{\equiv}CH + H_2 \xrightarrow[\text{catalyst}]{\text{Lindlar}} CH_3CH_2CH{=}CH_2$$

Because the alkyne sits on the surface of the metal catalyst and the hydrogens are delivered to the triple bond from the surface of the catalyst, both hydrogens are delivered to the same side of the double bond. In other words, only syn addition of hydrogen occurs (Section 5.19). Syn addition of hydrogen to an internal alkyne forms a *cis alkene*.

BIOGRAPHY

Herbert H. M. Lindlar *was born in Switzerland in 1909 and received a Ph.D. from the University of Bern. He worked at Hoffmann–La Roche and Co. in Basel, Switzerland, and authored many patents. His last patent was a procedure for isolating xylose, a carbohydrate, from the waste produced in paper mills.*

$$(CH_3COO^-)_2Pb^{2+}$$
lead(II) acetate

syn addition has occurred

$$CH_3CH_2C{\equiv}CCH_3 + H_2 \xrightarrow[\text{catalyst}]{\text{Lindlar}} \underset{CH_3CH_2}{\overset{H}{}}C{=}C\underset{CH_3}{\overset{H}{}}$$
2-pentyne   *cis*-**2-pentene**

quinoline

Internal alkynes can be converted to *trans alkenes* using sodium (or lithium) in liquid ammonia. The reaction stops at the alkene stage because sodium (or lithium) reacts more rapidly with triple bonds than with double bonds. Ammonia is a gas at room temperature (bp $= -33\ °C$), so it is kept in the liquid state by use of a dry ice/acetone mixture, which has a temperature of $-78\ °C$.

$$CH_3C\equiv CCH_3 \xrightarrow[\substack{-78\ °C}]{\substack{Na\ or\ Li \\ NH_3\ (liq)}}$$

2-butyne

trans-2-butene

MECHANISM FOR CONVERSION OF AN ALKYNE TO A TRANS ALKENE

The steps in the mechanism for the conversion of an internal alkyne to a trans alkene are:

- The single electron from the *s* orbital of sodium (or lithium) is transferred to an *sp* carbon of the alkyne to form a **radical anion**—a species with a negative charge and an unpaired electron. Notice that the transfer of a single electron is represented by an arrow head with a single barb. (Recall that sodium and lithium have a strong tendency to lose the single electron in their outer-shell *s* orbital; Section 1.3.)

- The radical anion is such a strong base that it can remove a proton from ammonia. This results in the formation of a **vinylic radical**—the radical's unpaired electron is on a vinylic carbon.

- Another single-electron transfer from sodium (or lithium) to the vinylic radical forms a vinylic anion.

- The vinylic anion is also a strong base; it removes a proton from another molecule of ammonia. The product is a trans alkene.

Both the radical anion and the vinylic anion can have either the cis or the trans configuration. The cis and trans radical anions are in equilibrium, and so are the cis and trans vinylic anions. In each case the equilibrium favors the trans isomer. In the trans radical anion, the non-bonded electrons are as far apart as possible, making it more stable than the cis isomer. In the trans vinylic anion, the relatively bulky alkyl groups are as far from each other as possible, so it is more stable than the cis isomer. (Section 4.13). The greater stability of the trans isomers causes the product to be a trans alkene.

| trans radical anion more stable | cis radical anion less stable because of electron repulsion | trans vinylic anion more stable | cis vinylic anion less stable because of steric strain |

chem place Tutorial: Hydrogenation/lindlar catalyst

Tutorial: Synthesis of trans alkenes using Na/NH₃ (liq)

PROBLEM 18◆

Describe the alkyne you would start with and the reagents you would use if you wanted to synthesize:

a. pentane   **b.** *cis*-2-butene   **c.** *trans*-2-pentene   **d.** 1-hexene

6.10 A HYDROGEN BONDED TO AN *sp* CARBON IS "ACIDIC"

We have seen that the hybridization of an atom affects the acidity of a hydrogen bonded to it because the electronegativity of an atom depends on its hybridization. For example, an *sp* carbon is more electronegative than an sp^2 carbon, which is more electronegative than an sp^3 carbon (Section 1.21).

relative electronegativities of carbon atoms

$$\boxed{\begin{matrix}\text{most}\\\text{electronegative}\end{matrix}} \quad sp \;>\; sp^2 \;>\; sp^3 \quad \boxed{\begin{matrix}\text{least}\\\text{electronegative}\end{matrix}}$$

> An *sp* carbon is more electronegative than an sp^2 carbon, which is more electronegative than an sp^3 carbon.

Because the most acidic compound is the one with its hydrogen attached to the most electronegative atom (when the atoms are the same size), ethyne is a stronger acid than ethene, and ethene is a stronger acid than ethane.

$HC{\equiv}CH$	$H_2C{=}CH_2$	CH_3CH_3
ethyne	ethene	ethane
$pK_a = 25$	$pK_a = 44$	$pK_a > 60$

In order to remove a proton from an acid (in a reaction that strongly favors products), the base that removes the proton must be stronger than the base that is generated as a result of removing the proton (Section 1.20). In other words, you must start with a stronger base than the base that will be formed. Because NH_3 is a weaker acid ($pK_a = 36$) than a terminal alkyne ($pK_a = 25$), the conjugate base of NH_3 ($^-NH_2$) is a stronger base than the carbanion—called an acetylide ion—that is formed when a hydrogen is removed from the *sp* carbon of a terminal alkyne. Therefore, an amide ion ($^-NH_2$) can be used to remove a proton from a terminal alkyne to prepare an **acetylide ion**.

$$RC{\equiv}CH \;+\; {}^-NH_2 \;\rightleftharpoons\; RC{\equiv}C^- \;+\; NH_3$$

$\boxed{\text{stronger acid}}$	amide ion	acetylide ion	NH_3
	$\boxed{\text{stronger base}}$	weaker base	weaker acid

> The stronger the acid, the weaker its conjugate base.

In contrast, if hydroxide ion were used as the base, the reaction would strongly favor the reactants because hydroxide ion is a much weaker base than the acetylide ion that would be formed.

$$RC{\equiv}CH \;+\; HO^- \;\rightleftharpoons\; RC{\equiv}C^- \;+\; H_2O$$

weaker acid	hydroxide anion	acetylide anion	H_2O
	weaker base	$\boxed{\text{stronger base}}$	$\boxed{\text{stronger acid}}$

> To remove a proton from an acid in a reaction that favors products, the base that removes the proton must be stronger than the base that is formed.

An amide ion ($^-NH_2$) cannot remove a hydrogen bonded to an sp^2 or an sp^3 carbon. Only a hydrogen bonded to an *sp* carbon is sufficiently acidic to be removed by an amide ion. Consequently, a hydrogen bonded to an *sp* carbon sometimes is referred to as an "acidic" hydrogen. The "acidic" property of terminal alkynes is one way their reactivity differs from that of alkenes. Be careful not to misinterpret what is meant when we say that a hydrogen bonded to an *sp* carbon is "acidic." It is more acidic than most other carbon-bound hydrogens, but it is much less acidic than a hydrogen of a water molecule, and water is only a very weakly acidic compound ($pK_a = 15.7$).

relative acid strengths

$\boxed{\begin{matrix}\text{strongest}\\\text{acid}\end{matrix}}$ HF	>	H_2O	>	$HC{\equiv}CH$	>	NH_3	>	$H_2C{=}CH_2$	>	CH_3CH_3 $\boxed{\begin{matrix}\text{weakest}\\\text{acid}\end{matrix}}$
$pK_a = 3.2$		$pK_a = 15.7$		$pK_a = 25$		$pK_a = 36$		$pK_a = 44$		$pK_a > 60$

Sodium Amide and Sodium in Ammonia

Take care not to confuse the compound sodium amide (Na^+ $^-NH_2$), also called sodamide, with a mixture of sodium (Na) in liquid ammonia. Sodium amide is the strong base used to remove a proton from a terminal alkyne. Sodium in ammonia is the source of electrons and protons, respectively, used to convert an internal alkyne to a trans alkene (Section 6.9).

PROBLEM 19◆

Any base whose conjugate acid has a pK_a greater than _____ can remove a proton from a terminal alkyne to form an acetylide ion (in a reaction that favors products).

PROBLEM 20◆

Explain why sodium amide cannot be used to form a carbanion from an alkane in a reaction that favors products.

PROBLEM-SOLVING STRATEGY

Comparing the Acidities of Compounds

a. List the following compounds in order of decreasing acidity:

$$CH_3CH_2\overset{+}{N}H_3 \qquad CH_3CH{=}\overset{+}{N}H_2 \qquad CH_3C{\equiv}\overset{+}{N}H$$

To compare the acidities of a group of compounds, first look at how the compounds differ. These three compounds differ in the hybridization of the nitrogen to which the acidic hydrogen is attached. Now, recall what you know about hybridization and acidity. You know that the hybridization of an atom affects its electronegativity (sp is more electronegative than sp^2, and sp^2 is more electronegative than sp^3). You also know that the more electronegative the atom to which a hydrogen is attached, the more acidic the hydrogen. Now you can answer the question.

relative acidities $\quad CH_3C{\equiv}\overset{+}{N}H \;>\; CH_3CH{=}\overset{+}{N}H_2 \;>\; CH_3CH_2\overset{+}{N}H_3$

b. Draw the conjugate bases of the above compounds and list them in order of decreasing basicity.

To obtain the structures of the conjugate bases, remove a proton from each of the compounds. The stronger the acid, the weaker its conjugate base, so using the relative acid strengths obtained in part **a**, we find that the order of decreasing basicity is:

relative basicities $\quad CH_3CH_2NH_2 \;>\; CH_3CH{=}NH \;>\; CH_3C{\equiv}N$

Now continue on to Problem 21.

PROBLEM 21◆

List the following in order of decreasing basicity:

a. $\quad CH_3CH_2CH{=}\overset{-}{C}H \qquad CH_3CH_2C{\equiv}C^- \qquad CH_3CH_2CH_2\overset{-}{C}H_2$

b. $\quad CH_3CH_2O^- \qquad F^- \qquad CH_3C{\equiv}C^- \qquad ^-NH_2$

PROBLEM 22 **SOLVED**

Which carbocation in each of the following pairs is more stable?

a. $CH_3\overset{+}{C}H_2$ or $H_2C{=}\overset{+}{C}H$ **b.** $H_2C{=}\overset{+}{C}H$ or $HC{\equiv}\overset{+}{C}$

Solution to 22a A double-bonded (sp^2) carbon is more electronegative than a single-bonded (sp^3) carbon. Therefore, a double-bonded carbon with a positive charge would be less stable than a single-bonded carbon with a positive charge. Thus, the ethyl carbocation is more stable.

6.11 SYNTHESIS USING ACETYLIDE IONS

Reactions that form carbon–carbon bonds are important in the synthesis of organic compounds because, without such reactions, we could not convert molecules with small carbon skeletons into molecules with larger carbon skeletons. Instead, the product of a reaction would always have the same number of carbons as the starting material.

One reaction that forms a carbon–carbon bond is the reaction of an acetylide ion with an alkyl halide. Only primary alkyl halides or methyl halides should be used in this reaction.

$$CH_3CH_2C\equiv C^- \ + \ CH_3CH_2CH_2Br \ \longrightarrow \ CH_3CH_2C\equiv CCH_2CH_2CH_3 \ + \ Br^-$$
3-heptyne

The mechanism for this reaction is well understood. Bromine is more electronegative than carbon, and as a result, the electrons in the C—Br bond are not shared equally by the two atoms. There is a partial positive charge on carbon and a partial negative charge on bromine.

$$CH_3CH_2C\equiv \ddot{C}^- \ + \ CH_3CH_2CH_2 \overset{\delta+}{-} \overset{\delta-}{Br} \ \longrightarrow \ CH_3CH_2C\equiv CCH_2CH_2CH_3 \ + \ Br^-$$

The negatively charged acetylide ion (a nucleophile) is attracted to the partially positively charged carbon (an electrophile) of the alkyl halide. As the electrons of the acetylide ion approach the carbon to form the new C—C bond, they push out the bromine and its bonding electrons because carbon can bond to no more than four atoms at a time.

The reaction above is an example of an *alkylation reaction.* An **alkylation reaction** attaches an alkyl group to a species. The mechanism for this and similar reactions will be discussed in greater detail in Chapter 8. At that time we will also see why the reaction works best with primary alkyl halides and methyl halides.

We can convert terminal alkynes into internal alkynes of any desired chain length, simply by choosing an alkyl halide of the appropriate structure. Just count the number of carbons in the terminal alkyne and the number of carbons in the product to see how many carbons are needed in the alkyl halide.

$$CH_3CH_2CH_2C\equiv CH \ \xrightarrow{\text{NaNH}_2} \ CH_3CH_2CH_2C\equiv C^- \ \xrightarrow{\text{CH}_3\text{CH}_2\text{Br}} \ CH_3CH_2CH_2C\equiv CCH_2CH_3$$
1-pentyne   3-heptyne

PROBLEM 23 **SOLVED**

A chemist wants to synthesize 3-heptyne but cannot find any 1-pentyne, the starting material used in the synthesis shown above. How else can 3-heptyne be synthesized?

Solution The *sp* carbons of 3-heptyne are bonded to an *ethyl* group and to a *propyl* group. Therefore to produce 3-heptyne, the acetylide ion of 1-pentyne can react with an *ethyl halide* or the acetylide ion of 1-butyne can react with a *propyl halide.* Since 1-pentyne is not available, the chemist should use 1-butyne and a propyl halide.

$$CH_3CH_2C\equiv CH \ \xrightarrow[\text{2. CH}_3\text{CH}_2\text{CH}_2\text{Cl}]{\text{1. NaNH}_2} \ CH_3CH_2C\equiv CCH_2CH_2CH_3$$
1-butyne   3-heptyne

(Remember that the numbers 1 and 2 in front of the reagents above and below the reaction arrow indicate two sequential reactions; the second reagent is not added until reaction with the first reagent is completely over.)

6.12 DESIGNING A SYNTHESIS I: AN INTRODUCTION TO MULTISTEP SYNTHESIS

For each reaction that has been presented so far, we have seen *why* the reaction occurs, *how* it occurs, and the *products* that are formed. A good way for you to review these reactions is to design syntheses, because when you design a synthesis, you have to be able to recall many of the reactions you have learned.

Synthetic chemists consider time, cost, and yield in designing syntheses. In the interest of time, a well-designed synthesis will consist of as few steps (sequential reactions) as possible, and each of those steps will be a reaction that is easy to carry out. If two chemists in a pharmaceutical company were each asked to prepare a new drug, and one synthesized the drug in three simple steps while the other used six difficult steps, which chemist would not get a raise? The costs of the starting materials are also taken into consideration in designing a synthesis. Moreover, each step in the synthesis should provide the greatest possible yield of the desired product. The more reactant needed to synthesize 1 gram of product, the more expensive the product is to produce. Sometimes, a synthesis involving several steps is preferred because the starting materials are inexpensive, the reactions are easy to carry out, and the yield of each step is high. Such a synthesis is better than one with fewer steps if those steps require expensive starting materials and consist of reactions that are more difficult to run or give lower yields. At this point in your chemical education, however, you are not yet familiar with the costs of different chemicals or the difficulty of carrying out specific reactions. So, for the time being, when you design a synthesis, just focus on finding the route with the fewest steps.

The following examples will give you an idea of the type of thinking required to design a successful synthesis. Problems of this kind will appear repeatedly throughout the book, because working them is a good way to learn organic chemistry.

Example 1. Starting with 1-butyne, how could you make the ketone shown below? You can use any organic or inorganic reagents.

$$CH_3CH_2C\equiv CH \xrightarrow{?} CH_3CH_2\overset{\overset{\displaystyle O}{\|}}{C}CH_2CH_2CH_3$$
1-butyne

Many chemists find that the easiest way to design a synthesis is to work backward. Instead of looking at the starting material and deciding how to do the first step of the synthesis, look at the product and decide how to do the last step.

The product of the synthesis is a ketone. At this point, the only reactions that you know that form a ketone are the acid-catalyzed addition of water to an alkyne and the hydroboration–oxidation of an alkyne. We will use the acid-catalyzed addition of water because it is an easier reaction to carry out. (As the number of reactions that you know increases, you may find it helpful to consult Appendix IV when designing syntheses; it lists the methods that can be used to synthesize each functional group.) If the alkyne used in the reaction has identical substituents on both *sp* carbons, only one ketone will be obtained. Thus, 3-hexyne is the alkyne that should be used for the synthesis of the desired ketone.

Appendix IV lists the methods that can be used to synthesize each functional group.

$$CH_3CH_2C\equiv CCH_2CH_3 \xrightarrow[H_2SO_4]{H_2O} CH_3CH_2\overset{\overset{\displaystyle OH}{|}}{C}=CHCH_2CH_3 \rightleftharpoons CH_3CH_2\overset{\overset{\displaystyle O}{\|}}{C}CH_2CH_2CH_3$$
3-hexyne

3-Hexyne can be obtained from the starting material (1-butyne) by removing the proton from its *sp* carbon, followed by alkylation. To produce the desired six-carbon product, a two-carbon alkyl halide must be used in the alkylation reaction.

$$CH_3CH_2C\equiv CH \xrightarrow[\text{2. } CH_3CH_2Br]{\text{1. } NaNH_2} CH_3CH_2C\equiv CCH_2CH_3$$
1-butyne   **3-hexyne**

Designing a synthesis by working backward from product to reactant is not simply a technique taught to organic chemistry students. It is used so frequently by experienced synthetic chemists that it has been given a name—**retrosynthetic analysis**. Chemists use open arrows when they write retrosynthetic analyses, to indicate they are working backward. Typically, the reagents needed to carry out each step are not specified until the reaction is written in the forward direction. For example, the ketone synthesis discussed on page 268 can be arrived at by the following retrosynthetic analysis.

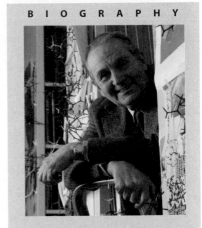

retrosynthetic analysis

$$\underset{\underset{\text{CH}_3\text{CH}_2\overset{\displaystyle O}{\overset{\|}{C}}\text{CH}_2\text{CH}_2\text{CH}_3}{}}{} \implies \text{CH}_3\text{CH}_2\text{C}\equiv\text{CCH}_2\text{CH}_3 \implies \text{CH}_3\text{CH}_2\text{C}\equiv\text{CH}$$

Once the complete sequence of reactions has been worked out by retrosynthetic analysis, the synthetic scheme can be written by reversing the steps and including the reagents required for each step.

Elias James Corey *coined the term* retrosynthetic analysis. *He was born in Massachusetts in 1928 and is a professor of chemistry at Harvard University. He received the Nobel Prize in Chemistry in 1990 for his contribution to synthetic organic chemistry.*

synthesis

$$\text{CH}_3\text{CH}_2\text{C}\equiv\text{CH} \xrightarrow[\text{2. CH}_3\text{CH}_2\text{Br}]{\text{1. NaNH}_2} \text{CH}_3\text{CH}_2\text{C}\equiv\text{CCH}_2\text{CH}_3 \xrightarrow[\text{H}_2\text{SO}_4]{\text{H}_2\text{O}} \text{CH}_3\text{CH}_2\overset{\displaystyle O}{\overset{\|}{C}}\text{CH}_2\text{CH}_2\text{CH}_3$$

Example 2. Starting with ethyne, how could you make 2-bromopentane?

$$\text{HC}\equiv\text{CH} \xrightarrow{?} \underset{\underset{\text{Br}}{|}}{\text{CH}_3\text{CH}_2\text{CH}_2\text{CHCH}_3}$$

ethyne

2-bromopentane

The desired product can be prepared from 1-pentene, which can be prepared from 1-pentyne. 1-Pentyne can be prepared from ethyne and an alkyl halide with three carbons.

retrosynthetic analysis

$$\underset{\underset{\text{Br}}{|}}{\text{CH}_3\text{CH}_2\text{CH}_2\text{CHCH}_3} \implies \text{CH}_3\text{CH}_2\text{CH}_2\text{CH}=\text{CH}_2 \implies \text{CH}_3\text{CH}_2\text{CH}_2\text{C}\equiv\text{CH} \implies \text{HC}\equiv\text{CH}$$

Now we can write the synthetic scheme:

synthesis

$$\text{HC}\equiv\text{CH} \xrightarrow[\text{2. CH}_3\text{CH}_2\text{CH}_2\text{Br}]{\text{1. NaNH}_2} \text{CH}_3\text{CH}_2\text{CH}_2\text{C}\equiv\text{CH} \xrightarrow[\substack{\text{Lindlar}\\\text{catalyst}}]{\text{H}_2} \text{CH}_3\text{CH}_2\text{CH}_2\text{CH}=\text{CH}_2 \xrightarrow{\text{HBr}} \underset{\underset{\text{Br}}{|}}{\text{CH}_3\text{CH}_2\text{CH}_2\text{CHCH}_3}$$

Example 3. How could 2,6-dimethylheptane be prepared from an alkyne and an alkyl halide? (The prime in R′ signifies that R and R′ can be different alkyl groups.)

$$\text{RC}\equiv\text{CH} + \text{R}'\text{Br} \xrightarrow{?} \underset{\underset{\text{CH}_3}{|}\qquad\quad\underset{\text{CH}_3}{|}}{\text{CH}_3\text{CHCH}_2\text{CH}_2\text{CH}_2\text{CHCH}_3}$$

2,6-dimethylheptane

2,6-Dimethyl-3-heptyne is the only alkyne that will form the desired alkane upon hydrogenation. This alkyne can be dissected in two different ways: the alkyne could be prepared from the reaction of an acetylide ion with a primary alkyl halide (isobutyl bromide) or from the reaction of an acetylide ion with a secondary alkyl halide (isopropyl bromide).

retrosynthetic analysis

$$CH_3CHCH_2CH_2CH_2CHCH_3 \Longrightarrow CH_3CHCH_2C\equiv CCHCH_3$$
$$\quad\ |\qquad\qquad\qquad |\qquad\qquad\qquad\quad |\qquad\qquad |$$
$$\quad\ CH_3\qquad\qquad\ CH_3\qquad\qquad\quad CH_3\qquad\quad CH_3$$

$$CH_3CHCH_2Br + HC\equiv CCHCH_3 \quad or \quad CH_3CHBr + HC\equiv CCH_2CHCH_3$$
$$\quad\ |\qquad\qquad\qquad\qquad |\qquad\qquad\qquad\qquad |\qquad\qquad\qquad\qquad\ |$$
$$\quad\ CH_3\qquad\qquad\qquad CH_3\qquad\qquad\qquad CH_3\qquad\qquad\qquad\ CH_3$$

Because we know that the reaction of an acetylide ion with an alkyl halide works best with primary alkyl halides and methyl halides, we know how to proceed:

synthesis

$$CH_3CHC\equiv CH \xrightarrow[\text{2. } CH_3CHCH_2Br]{\text{1. } NaNH_2} CH_3CHC\equiv CCH_2CHCH_3 \xrightarrow[\text{Pd/C}]{H_2} CH_3CHCH_2CH_2CH_2CHCH_3$$
$$\quad |\qquad\qquad\qquad\qquad\qquad\qquad\qquad\ |\qquad\qquad |\qquad\qquad\qquad\qquad\qquad\ |\qquad\qquad\qquad |$$
$$\quad CH_3\qquad\qquad\qquad CH_3\qquad\qquad\ CH_3\qquad CH_3\qquad\qquad\qquad\ CH_3\qquad\qquad\ CH_3$$

Example 4. How could you carry out the following synthesis using the given starting material?

An alcohol can be prepared from an alkene, and an alkene can be prepared from an alkyne.

retrosynthetic analysis

You can use either of the two methods you know for converting an alkyne into an alkene, because the desired alkene does not have cis–trans isomers. Hydroboration–oxidation must be used to convert the alkene into the desired alcohol because acid-catalyzed addition of water would form a different alcohol.

synthesis

Example 5. How could you prepare (*E*)-2-pentene from ethyne?

$$HC\equiv CH \xrightarrow{\ ?\ }$$

(*E*)-2-pentene

A trans alkene can be prepared from the reaction of an internal alkyne with sodium and liquid ammonia. The alkyne needed to synthesize the desired alkene can be prepared from 1-butyne and a methyl halide. 1-Butyne can be prepared from ethyne and an ethyl halide.

retrosynthetic analysis

$$CH_3CH_2 \quad H \atop C=C \atop H \quad CH_3 \implies CH_3CH_2C{\equiv}CCH_3 \implies CH_3CH_2C{\equiv}CH \implies HC{\equiv}CH$$

synthesis

$$HC{\equiv}CH \xrightarrow[\text{2. } CH_3CH_2Br]{\text{1. } NaNH_2} CH_3CH_2C{\equiv}CH \xrightarrow[\text{2. } CH_3Br]{\text{1. } NaNH_2} CH_3CH_2C{\equiv}CCH_3 \xrightarrow[-78\,°C]{Na/NH_3\,(liq)} \begin{matrix} CH_3CH_2 & H \\ C=C \\ H & CH_3 \end{matrix}$$

Example 6. How could you prepare *cis*-2,3-diethyloxirane from ethyne?

$$HC{\equiv}CH \xrightarrow{\text{?}} \begin{matrix} O \\ H^{\text{''''}}\,C{-}C\,^{\text{''''}}H \\ CH_3CH_2 \quad CH_2CH_3 \end{matrix}$$
cis-2,3-diethyloxirane

A cis epoxide can be prepared from a cis alkene and a peroxyacid. The cis alkene that should be used is *cis*-3-hexene, which can be obtained from 3-hexyne. 3-Hexyne can be prepared from 1-butyne and an ethyl halide, and 1-butyne can be prepared from ethyne and an ethyl halide.

retrosynthetic analysis

$$\begin{matrix} O \\ H^{\text{''''}}\,C{-}C\,^{\text{''''}}H \\ CH_3CH_2 \quad CH_2CH_3 \end{matrix} \implies \begin{matrix} H \quad H \\ C=C \\ CH_3CH_2 \quad CH_2CH_3 \end{matrix} \implies CH_3CH_2C{\equiv}CCH_2CH_3 \implies CH_3CH_2C{\equiv}CH \implies HC{\equiv}CH$$

The alkyne must be converted to the alkene using H_2 and Lindlar catalyst so that the desired cis alkene is formed.

synthesis

$$HC{\equiv}CH \xrightarrow[\text{2. } CH_3CH_2Br]{\text{1. } NaNH_2} CH_3CH_2C{\equiv}CH \xrightarrow[\text{2. } CH_3CH_2Br]{\text{1. } NaNH_2} CH_3CH_2C{\equiv}CCH_2CH_3 \xrightarrow[\substack{\text{Lindlar} \\ \text{catalyst}}]{H_2} \begin{matrix} H \quad H \\ C=C \\ CH_3CH_2 \quad CH_2CH_3 \end{matrix}$$

$$\xrightarrow[]{\substack{O \\ \parallel \\ CH_3COOH}} \begin{matrix} O \\ H^{\text{''''}}\,C{-}C\,^{\text{''''}}H \\ CH_3CH_2 \quad CH_2CH_3 \end{matrix}$$

Example 7. How could you prepare 3,3-dibromohexane from reagents that contain no more than two carbon atoms?

$$\text{reagents with no more than 2 carbon atoms} \xrightarrow{\text{?}} \begin{matrix} Br \\ | \\ CH_3CH_2CCH_2CH_2CH_3 \\ | \\ Br \end{matrix}$$
3,3-dibromohexane

A geminal dibromide can be prepared from an alkyne. 3-Hexyne is the alkyne of choice because it will form one geminal dibromide, whereas 2-hexyne would form two different geminal dibromides. 3-Hexyne can be prepared from 1-butyne and ethyl bromide, and 1-butyne can be prepared from ethyne and ethyl bromide.

retrosynthetic analysis

$$CH_3CH_2\overset{\displaystyle Br}{\underset{\displaystyle Br}{C}}CH_2CH_2CH_3 \implies CH_3CH_2C\equiv CCH_2CH_3 \implies CH_3CH_2C\equiv CH \implies HC\equiv CH$$

synthesis

$$HC\equiv CH \xrightarrow[\text{2. CH}_3\text{CH}_2\text{Br}]{\text{1. NaNH}_2} CH_3CH_2C\equiv CH \xrightarrow[\text{2. CH}_3\text{CH}_2\text{Br}]{\text{1. NaNH}_2} CH_3CH_2C\equiv CCH_2CH_3 \xrightarrow{\textbf{excess HBr}} CH_3CH_2\overset{\displaystyle Br}{\underset{\displaystyle Br}{C}}CH_2CH_2CH_3$$

Green Chemistry: Aiming for Sustainability

Chemical innovations have improved the quality of virtually every aspect of life: food, shelter, medicine, transportation, communication, and the availability of new materials. This improvement, however, has come with a price—the damage that the development and disposal of chemicals has inflicted on the environment.

Chemists now are focused on sustainability, which is defined as "meeting the needs of the current generation without sacrificing the ability to meet the needs of future generations." One way to achieve sustainability is through the use of green chemistry.

Green chemistry is pollution prevention at the molecular level: it involves the design of chemical products and processes so that the generation of polluting substances is reduced or eliminated. For example, chemists are now designing products not only for function but also for biodegradability. They are designing syntheses that use and generate substances that cause little or no toxicity to health or to the environment. Green chemical syntheses can be cost effective since they reduce the cost for such things as waste disposal, regulatory compliance, and liability. Applying the principles of green chemistry can help us achieve a sustainable future.

chem place Tutorial:
Retrosynthesis using alkynes as reagents

PROBLEM 24

Starting with acetylene, how could the following compounds be synthesized?

a. $CH_3CH_2CH_2C\equiv CH$

b. $CH_3CH=CH_2$

c.
$$\overset{\displaystyle H_3C}{}\overset{\displaystyle }{C}=\overset{\displaystyle CH_3}{\underset{\displaystyle H}{C}}\underset{\displaystyle H}{}$$

d. $CH_3CH_2CH_2CH_2\overset{\displaystyle O}{\overset{\|}{C}}H$

e. $CH_3\underset{\displaystyle Br}{CH}CH_3$

f. $CH_3\overset{\displaystyle Cl}{\underset{\displaystyle Cl}{C}}CH_3$

SUMMARY

An **alkyne** is a hydrocarbon that contains a carbon–carbon triple bond. A triple bond can be thought of as a cylinder of electrons wrapped around the σ bond. The functional group suffix of an alkyne is "yne." A **terminal alkyne** has the triple bond at the end of the chain; an **internal alkyne** has the triple bond located elsewhere along the chain. Internal alkynes, with two alkyl substituents bonded to the sp carbons, are more stable than terminal alkynes. We now have seen that alkyl groups stabilize carbocations, alkenes, and alkynes.

Alkynes, like alkenes, undergo electrophilic addition reactions. The same reagents that add to alkenes also add to alkynes. Even though an alkyne is less stable than an alkene, it is less reactive because a **vinylic cation** is less stable than a similarly substituted alkyl cation. Electrophilic addition to a terminal alkyne is regioselective; the electrophile adds to the sp carbon that is bonded to the hydrogen because the intermediate formed—a secondary vinylic cation—is more stable than a primary vinylic cation. If excess reagent is available, alkynes undergo a second addition reaction with hydrogen halides and halogens because the product of the first reaction is an alkene.

When an alkyne undergoes the acid-catalyzed addition of water, the product of the reaction is an enol. The enol immediately rearranges to a ketone. A **ketone** is a compound that has two alkyl groups bonded to a **carbonyl** (C=O) **group**. An **aldehyde** is a compound that has at least one hydrogen bonded to a carbonyl group. The ketone and enol are called **keto–enol tautomers**; they differ in the location of a double bond and a hydrogen. Interconversion of the tautomers is called **tautomerization**. The keto tautomer predominates at equilibrium. Terminal alkynes add water if a mercuric ion catalyst is added to the acidic mixture. In hydroboration–oxidation, H^+ is not the electrophile, $H:^-$ is the nucleophile. Consequently, the mercuric-ion-catalyzed addition of water to a terminal alkyne produces a *ketone*, whereas hydroboration–oxidation of a terminal alkyne produces an *aldehyde*.

Alkynes, like alkenes, undergo catalytic hydrogenation to form an alkane. Addition of hydrogen to an alkyne in the presence of Lindlar catalyst forms *an alkene*; if it is an internal alkyne, a *cis alkene* is formed. Sodium in liquid ammonia converts an internal alkyne to a *trans alkene*.

The electronegativities of carbon atoms decrease in the order: $sp > sp^2 > sp^3$. Therefore, ethyne is a stronger acid than ethene, and ethene is a stronger acid than ethane. An amide ion can remove a hydrogen bonded to an *sp* carbon of a terminal alkyne because it is a stronger base than the **acetylide ion** that is formed. An acetylide ion can undergo an alkylation reaction with a methyl halide or a primary alkyl halide to form an internal alkyne. An **alkylation reaction** attaches an alkyl group to a species.

Designing a synthesis by working backward is called **retrosynthetic analysis**. Chemists use open arrows to indicate they are working backward. The reagents needed to carry out each step are not included until the reaction is written in the forward direction.

SUMMARY OF REACTIONS

1. Electrophilic addition reactions
   a. Addition of hydrogen halides (H^+ is the electrophile; Section 6.6)

$$HX \ = \ HF, HCl, HBr, HI$$

   b. Addition of halogens (Section 6.6)

   c. Acid-catalyzed addition of water/hydroboration–oxidation (Sections 6.7 and 6.8)

2. Addition of hydrogen (Section 6.9)

$$RC \equiv CR' + 2 H_2 \xrightarrow{\text{Pd/C}} RCH_2CH_2R'$$
an alkane

$$R-C \equiv C-R' + H_2 \xrightarrow[\text{catalyst}]{\text{Lindlar}} \overset{H}{\underset{R}{C}} = \overset{H}{\underset{R'}{C}}$$
a cis alkene

$$R-C \equiv C-R' \xrightarrow[\substack{NH_3 \text{ (liq)} \\ -78\ °C}]{\text{Na or Li}} \overset{R}{\underset{H}{C}} = \overset{H}{\underset{R'}{C}}$$
a trans alkene

3. Removal of a proton from a terminal alkyne, followed by alkylation (Sections 6.10 and 6.11)

$$RC \equiv CH \xrightarrow{NaNH_2} RC \equiv C^- \xrightarrow{R'CH_2Br} RC \equiv CCH_2R'$$

KEY TERMS

acetylide ion (p. 265)
aldehyde (p. 260)
alkylation reaction (p. 267)
alkyne (p. 251)
carbonyl group (p. 260)
enol (p. 260)

geminal dihalide (p. 258)
internal alkyne (p. 252)
keto–enol tautomers (p. 261)
ketone (p. 260)
π-complex (p. 259)
radical anion (p. 264)

retrosynthetic analysis (p. 269)
tautomerization (p. 261)
tautomers (p. 261)
terminal alkyne (p. 252)
vinylic cation (p. 257)
vinylic radical (p. 264)

PROBLEMS

25. Give the major product obtained from reaction of each of the following with excess HCl:

a. $CH_3CH_2C \equiv CH$ **b.** $CH_3CH_2C \equiv CCH_2CH_3$ **c.** $CH_3CH_2C \equiv CCH_2CH_2CH_3$

26. Draw a structure for each of the following:

a. 2-hexyne
b. 5-ethyl-3-octyne
c. methylacetylene
d. vinylacetylene

e. methoxyethyne
f. *sec*-butyl-*tert*-butylacetylene
g. 1-bromo-1-pentyne
h. 5-methyl-3-cyclohexenol

i. diethylacetylene
j. di-*tert*-butylacetylene
k. cyclopentylacetylene
l. 5,6-dimethyl-2-heptyne

27. Identify the electrophile and the nucleophile in each of the following reaction steps. Then draw curved arrows to illustrate the bond-making and bond-breaking processes.

$$CH_3CH_2\overset{+}{C}=CH_2 \quad + \quad :\ddot{\underset{\cdot\cdot}{Cl}}:^- \longrightarrow CH_3CH_2C=CH_2$$
$$\underset{:\ddot{\underset{\cdot\cdot}{Cl}}:}{\overset{|}{}}$$

$$CH_3C \equiv CH \quad + \quad H-Br \longrightarrow CH_3\overset{+}{C}=CH_2 \quad + \quad :\ddot{\underset{\cdot\cdot}{Br}}:^-$$

$$CH_3C \equiv C-H \quad + \quad :\ddot{N}H_2 \longrightarrow CH_3C \equiv C:^- \quad + \quad \dot{N}H_3$$

28. Give the systematic name for each of the following:

a. $CH_3C{\equiv}CCH_2CHCH_3$
   $\qquad\qquad\qquad\quad |$
   $\qquad\qquad\qquad\; Br$

b. $CH_3C{\equiv}CCH_2CHCH_3$
   $\qquad\qquad\qquad\quad |$
   $\qquad\qquad\qquad\; CH_2CH_2CH_3$

c. $CH_3C{\equiv}CCH_2CCH_3$ with CH_3 above and CH_3 below the central C

d. $CH_3CHCH_2C{\equiv}CCHCH_3$
   $\qquad\; |\qquad\qquad\qquad |$
   $\qquad\; Cl\qquad\qquad\qquad CH_3$

e. (cyclooctadiene ring structure)

f. (cyclohexadiene with two CH₃ groups)

29. What reagents could be used to carry out the following syntheses?

RCH_2CH_3
$RCH{=}CH_2$
$\quad Br$
$\quad |$
$RCCH_3$
$\quad |$
$\quad Br$
$RC{=}CH_2$
$\quad |$
$\quad Br$

center: $RC{\equiv}CH$

$RCH-CH_2$ (epoxide, O bridge) *peroxyacid*
$RCHCH_3$
$\quad |$
$\quad Br$
O
$||$
$RCCH_3$
O
$||$
RCH_2CH

(handwritten: H_2 Pt, Na in NH₃, HBr, HO gp)

30. A student was given the structural formulas of several compounds and was asked to give them systematic names. How many did she name correctly? Correct those that are misnamed.

a. 4-ethyl-2-pentyne   b. 1-bromo-4-heptyne   c. 2-methyl-3-hexyne   d. 3-pentyne

31. Draw the structures and give the common and systematic names for alkynes with molecular formula C_7H_{12}.

32. Explain why the following reaction results in the product that is shown:

$$CH_3CH_2CH_2C{\equiv}CH \xrightarrow[\text{H}_2\text{O}]{\text{Br}_2} CH_3CH_2CH_2\overset{\overset{\displaystyle O}{||}}{C}CH_2Br$$

33. How could the following compounds be synthesized, starting with a hydrocarbon that has the same number of carbons as the desired product?

a. $CH_3CH_2CH_2CH_2\overset{\overset{\displaystyle O}{||}}{C}H$

b. $CH_3CH_2CH_2CH_2OH$

c. $CH_3CH_2CH_2\overset{\overset{\displaystyle O}{||}}{C}CH_2CH_2CH_2CH_3$

34. What reagents would you use for the following syntheses?

a. (Z)-3-hexene from 3-hexyne   b. (E)-3-hexene from 3-hexyne   c. hexane from 3-hexyne

35. Give the systematic name for each of the following:

a. $CH_3C{\equiv}CCH_2CH_2CH_2CH{=}CH_2$

b. $\underset{\underset{H}{|}}{HOCH_2CH_2}C{=}C\underset{\underset{H}{|}}{CH_2CH_3}$

c. $CH_3CH_2C{\equiv}CCH_2CH_2C{\equiv}CH$

d. (cyclohexadiene with Cl)

e. (cycloheptatriene with CH₃)

36. What is the molecular formula of a hydrocarbon that has 1 triple bond, 2 double bonds, 1 ring, and 32 carbons?

37. What will be the major product of the reaction of 1 mol of propyne with each of the following reagents?

a. HBr (1 mol)
b. HBr (2 mol)
c. Br_2 (1 mol)/CH_2Cl_2
d. Br_2 (2 mol)/CH_2Cl_2
e. aqueous H_2SO_4, $HgSO_4$

f. borane in THF followed by H_2O_2/HO^-/H_2O
g. excess H_2, Pd/C
h. H_2/Lindlar catalyst
i. sodium in liquid ammonia at $-78\,°C$

j. sodium amide
k. product of part **j** followed by 1-chloropropane

38. Answer Problem 37 **a–i** using 2-butyne as the starting material instead of propyne.

39. Give the products of the following reactions.

a. ═══⟍⟋ + Cl_2 excess $\xrightarrow{CH_2Cl_2}$

e. ─═══⟋ + H_2 $\xrightarrow{Pd/C}$

b. ═══⟍⟋ + Cl_2 $\xrightarrow{CH_2Cl_2}$

f. ─═══⟋ + H_2 $\xrightarrow{\text{Lindlar catalyst}}$

c. ═══⟍⟋ + H_2O $\xrightarrow{H_2SO_4}$

g. ─═══⟋ $\xrightarrow[\substack{NH_3 \text{ (liq)} \\ -78\,°C}]{Na}$

d. ═══⟍⟋ + $\xrightarrow[\text{2. HO}^-,\ H_2O_2,\ H_2O]{\text{1. BH}_3/\text{THF}}$

40. a. Starting with 3-methyl-1-butyne, how could you prepare the following alcohols?
1. 2-methyl-2-butanol   **2.** 3-methyl-1-butanol
b. In each case, a second alcohol would also be obtained. What alcohol would it be?

41. How many of the following names are correct? Correct the incorrect names.
a. 4-heptyne
b. 2-ethyl-3-hexyne
c. 4-chloro-2-pentyne
d. 2,3-dimethyl-5-octyne
e. 4,4-dimethyl-2-pentyne
f. 2,5-dimethyl-3-hexyne

42. Which of the following pairs are keto–enol tautomers?

a. $CH_3CH_2CH{=}CHCH_2OH$ and $CH_3CH_2CH_2CH_2\overset{\displaystyle O}{\overset{\|}{C}}H$

b. $CH_3\overset{OH}{\underset{|}{C}}HCH_3$ and $CH_3\overset{O}{\overset{\|}{C}}CH_3$

c. $CH_3CH_2CH{=}CHOH$ and $CH_3CH_2CH_2\overset{O}{\overset{\|}{C}}H$

d. $CH_3CH_2CH_2CH{=}CHOH$ and $CH_3CH_2CH_2\overset{\displaystyle O}{\overset{\|}{C}}CH_3$

e. $CH_3CH_2CH_2\overset{OH}{\underset{|}{C}}{=}CH_2$ and $CH_3CH_2CH_2\overset{O}{\overset{\|}{C}}CH_3$

43. Using ethyne as the starting material, how can the following compounds be prepared?

a. $CH_3\overset{O}{\overset{\|}{C}}H$

b. $CH_3CH_2\underset{\underset{Br}{|}}{C}HCH_2Br$

c. $CH_3\overset{O}{\overset{\|}{C}}CH_3$

d. ⟋⟍═⟋

e. ⟍⟋═⟍⟋

f. ⟋⟍⟋⟍

44. Give the stereoisomers obtained when 2-butyne undergoes each of the following reaction sequences:
a. 1. H_2/Lindlar catalyst 2. Br_2/CH_2Cl_2 **b.** 1. Na/NH_3(liq), −78 °C 2. Br_2/CH_2Cl_2 **c.** 1. Cl_2/CH_2Cl_2 2. Br_2/CH_2Cl_2

45. Draw the keto tautomer for each of the following:

a. $CH_3CH{=}\overset{OH}{\underset{|}{C}}CH_3$

b. $CH_3CH_2CH_2\overset{OH}{\underset{|}{C}}{=}CH_2$

c. ⬡—OH

d. ⬡=CHOH

46. Show how each of the following compounds could be prepared using the given starting material, any necessary inorganic reagents, and any necessary organic compound that has no more than four carbons:

a. $HC{\equiv}CH$ ⟶ $CH_3CH_2CH_2CH_2\overset{\displaystyle O}{\overset{\|}{C}}CH_3$

b. $HC{\equiv}CH$ ⟶ $CH_3CH_2\underset{\underset{Br}{|}}{C}HCH_3$

c. $HC{\equiv}CH$ ⟶ $CH_3CH_2CH_2\underset{\underset{OH}{|}}{C}HCH_3$

d. ⬡—C≡CH ⟶ ⬡—$CH_2\overset{O}{\overset{\|}{C}}H$

e. ⬡—C≡CH ⟶ ⬡—$\overset{O}{\overset{\|}{C}}CH_3$

f. ⬡—C≡CCH₃ ⟶ $\overset{H\qquad H}{\underset{\underset{\displaystyle ⬡}{}\qquad CH_3}{C{=}C}}$

47. A chemist was planning to synthesize 3-octyne by adding 1-bromobutane to the product obtained from the reaction of 1-butyne with sodium amide. Unfortunately, however, he had forgotten to order 1-butyne. How else can he prepare 3-octyne?

48. a. Explain why a single pure product is obtained from hydroboration–oxidation of 2-butyne, whereas two products are obtained from hydroboration–oxidation of 2-pentyne.
  b. Name two other internal alkynes that will yield only one product on hydroboration–oxidation.

49. Give the configurations of the products obtained from the following reactions:

  a. $CH_3CH_2C{\equiv}CCH_2CH_3$ $\xrightarrow[\text{2. D}_2,\text{ Pd/C}]{\text{1. Na, NH}_3\text{(liq), }-78\ ^\circ\text{C}}$

  b. $CH_3CH_2C{\equiv}CCH_2CH_3$ $\xrightarrow[\text{2. D}_2,\text{ Pd/C}]{\text{1. H}_2\text{/Lindlar catalyst}}$

50. α-Farnesene is a dodecatetraene found in the waxy coating of apple skins. What is its systematic name? Include E and Z where necessary to indicate the configuration of the double bonds.

α-farnesene

51. Show how the following compounds could be synthesized starting with acetylene:
  a. *cis*-2-octene   **b.** *trans*-3-heptene   **c.** 4-bromo-3-hexanol

52. In Section 6.5 it was stated that hyperconjugation is less effective in stabilizing the charge on a vinylic cation than the charge on an alkyl cation. Why do you think this is so?

7

Delocalized Electrons and Their Effect on Stability, Reactivity, and pK_a • More about Molecular Orbital Theory

benzene   **cyclohexane**

ELECTRONS THAT ARE RESTRICTED TO A PARTICULAR REGION ARE CALLED **LOCALIZED electrons**. Localized electrons either belong to a single atom or are shared by two atoms.

$$CH_3\!-\!\ddot{N}H_2 \qquad CH_3\!-\!CH\!=\!CH_2$$

localized electrons   localized electrons

Many organic compounds contain *delocalized* electrons. **Delocalized electrons** are shared by three or more atoms. You were first introduced to delocalized electrons in Section 1.23, where you saw that the two electrons represented by the π bond of the COO^- group are shared by three atoms—the carbon and both oxygens. The dashed lines in the chemical structure indicate that the two electrons are delocalized over three atoms.

$$CH_3C\underset{\ddot{\underset{..}{O}}:^{\delta-}}{\overset{\ddot{\overset{..}{O}}:^{\delta-}}{\Big\langle}}$$

delocalized electrons

In this chapter, you will learn how to recognize compounds that contain delocalized electrons and how to draw structures that represent the electron distribution in molecules with delocalized electrons. You will also be introduced to some of the special characteristics of compounds that have delocalized electrons. You will then be able to understand some of the wide-ranging effects that delocalized electrons have on the reactions and properties of organic compounds. We begin by looking at benzene, a compound whose properties chemists could not explain until they recognized that electrons in organic molecules could be delocalized.

7.1 DELOCALIZED ELECTRONS EXPLAIN BENZENE'S STRUCTURE

Because they did not know about delocalized electrons, early organic chemists were puzzled by benzene's structure. They knew that benzene had a molecular formula of C_6H_6, that it was an unusually stable compound, and that it did not undergo the addition reactions characteristic of alkenes (Section 3.6). They also knew that when a different atom was substituted for any one of its hydrogens, only one product was obtained, and when the substituted product underwent a second substitution, three products were obtained.

$$C_6H_6 \xrightarrow[\text{with an X}]{\text{replace a hydrogen}} C_6H_5X \xrightarrow[\text{with an X}]{\text{replace a hydrogen}} C_6H_4X_2 + C_6H_4X_2 + C_6H_4X_2$$

one monosubstituted compound · three disubstituted compounds

What kind of structure might we predict for benzene if we knew only what the early chemists knew? The molecular formula (C_6H_6) tells us that benzene has eight fewer hydrogens than an acyclic alkane with six carbons ($C_nH_{2n+2} = C_6H_{14}$). Benzene, therefore, has a degree of unsaturation of four. In other words, the total number of rings and π bonds in benzene is four (Section 3.1).

Because only one product is obtained regardless of which of the six hydrogens of benzene is replaced with another atom, we know that all the hydrogens must be identical. Two structures that fit these requirements are shown here:

For every two hydrogens that are missing from the general molecular formula, C_nH_{2n+2}, a hydrocarbon has either a π bond or a ring.

$$CH_3C{\equiv}C{-}C{\equiv}CCH_3$$

shorter double bond
longer single bond

Neither of these structures is consistent with the observation that three compounds are obtained if a second hydrogen is replaced with another atom. The acyclic structure yields two disubstituted products.

$$CH_3C{\equiv}C{-}C{\equiv}CCH_3 \xrightarrow[\text{with Br's}]{\text{replace 2 H's}} CH_3C{\equiv}C{-}C{\equiv}CCHBr \quad \text{and} \quad BrCH_2C{\equiv}C{-}C{\equiv}CCH_2Br$$
$$\qquad\qquad\qquad\qquad\qquad\qquad\qquad\qquad\qquad\qquad\quad |$$
$$\qquad\qquad\qquad\qquad\qquad\qquad\qquad\qquad\qquad\qquad Br$$

The cyclic structure, with alternating single and slightly shorter double bonds, yields four disubstituted products—a 1,3-disubstituted product, a 1,4-disubstituted product, and two 1,2-disubstituted products—because the two substituents can be placed either on two adjacent carbons joined by a single bond or on two adjacent carbons joined by a double bond.

replace 2 H's with Br's

1,3-disubstituted product   1,4-disubstituted product   1,2-disubstituted product   1,2-disubstituted product

In 1865, the German chemist Friedrich Kekulé suggested a way of resolving this dilemma. He proposed that benzene was not a single compound, but a mixture of two compounds in rapid equilibrium.

Kekulé structures of benzene

Kekulé's proposal explained why only three disubstituted products are obtained when a monosubstituted benzene undergoes a second substitution. According to Kekulé, there actually *are* four disubstituted products, but the two 1,2-disubstituted products interconvert too rapidly to be distinguished and separated from each other.

The Kekulé structures of benzene account for the molecular formula of benzene and for the number of isomers obtained as a result of monosubstitution or disubstitution. However, they fail to account for the unusual stability of benzene that prevents its double bonds from undergoing the addition reactions characteristic of alkenes.

That benzene has a six-membered ring was confirmed in 1901, when Paul Sabatier found that catalytic hydrogenation of benzene produced cyclohexane. This, however, still did not solve the puzzle of benzene's structure.

Controversy over the structure of benzene continued until the 1930s, when the new techniques of X-ray and electron diffraction (Section 14.23) produced a surprising result: they showed that *benzene is a planar molecule and that the six carbon–carbon bonds all have the same length.* The length of each carbon–carbon bond is 1.39 Å, which is shorter than a carbon–carbon single bond (1.54 Å) but longer than a carbon–carbon double bond (1.33 Å; Section 1.14). In other words, benzene does not have alternating single and double bonds.

If the carbon–carbon bonds in benzene all have the same length, they must also have the same number of electrons between the carbons. This can be so, however, only if the π electrons are delocalized around the ring, rather than each pair of π electrons being localized between two carbons. To better understand the concept of delocalized electrons, we will now take a close look at the bonding in benzene.

PROBLEM 1♦

a. How many monosubstituted products would each of the following compounds have? (Notice that each compound has the same molecular formula as benzene.)

   1. HC≡CC≡CCH$_2$CH$_3$ **2.** CH$_2$=CHC≡CCH=CH$_2$

b. How many disubstituted products would each of the preceding compounds have? (Do not include stereoisomers.)

c. How many disubstituted products would each of the compounds have if stereoisomers are included?

Friedrich August Kekulé von Stradonitz (1829–1896) was born in Germany. He entered the University of Giessen to study architecture but switched to chemistry after taking a course in the subject. He was a professor of chemistry at the University of Heidelberg, at the University of Ghent in Belgium, and then at the University of Bonn. In 1890, he gave an extemporaneous speech at the twenty-fifth-anniversary celebration of his first paper on the cyclic structure of benzene. In this speech, he claimed that he had arrived at the Kekulé structures as a result of dozing off in front of a fire while working on a textbook. He dreamed of chains of carbon atoms twisting and turning in a snakelike motion, when suddenly the head of one snake seized hold of its own tail and formed a spinning ring. Recently, the veracity of his snake story has been questioned by those who point out that there is no written record of the dream from the time he experienced it in 1861 until the time he related it in 1890. Others counter that dreams are not the kind of evidence one publishes in scientific papers, although it is not uncommon for scientists to report creative ideas emerging from their subconscious at moments when they were not thinking about science. Also, Kekulé warned against publishing dreams when he said, "Let us learn to dream, and perhaps then we shall learn the truth. But let us also beware not to publish our dreams until

they have been examined by the wakened mind." In 1895, he was made a nobleman by Emperor William II of Germany. This allowed him to add "von Stradonitz" to his name. Kekulé's students received three of the first five Nobel Prizes in Chemistry: van't Hoff in 1901 (page 207), Fischer in 1902 (page 952), and Baeyer in 1905 (page 102).

Friedrich August Kekulé von Stradonitz

PROBLEM 2

Between 1865 and 1890, other possible structures were proposed for benzene, two of which are shown here:

Dewar benzene

Ladenburg benzene

Considering what nineteenth-century chemists knew about benzene, which is a better proposal for benzene's structure, Dewar benzene or Ladenburg benzene? Why?

7.2 THE BONDING IN BENZENE

Each of benzene's six carbons is sp^2 hybridized. An sp^2 carbon has bond angles of 120° —identical to the size of the angles of a planar hexagon. Thus, benzene is a planar molecule. Each of the carbons in benzene uses two sp^2 orbitals to bond to two other carbons; the third sp^2 orbital of each carbon overlaps the s orbital of a hydrogen (Figure 7.1a). Each carbon also has a p orbital at right angles to the sp^2 orbitals. Because benzene is planar, the six p orbitals are parallel (Figure 7.1b). The p orbitals are close enough for side-to-side overlap, so each p orbital overlaps the p orbitals on *both* adjacent carbons. As a result, the overlapping p orbitals form a continuous doughnut-shaped cloud of electrons above, and another doughnut-shaped cloud of electrons below, the plane of the benzene ring (Figure 7.1c). The electrostatic potential map (Figure 7.1d) shows that all the carbon–carbon bonds have the same electron density.

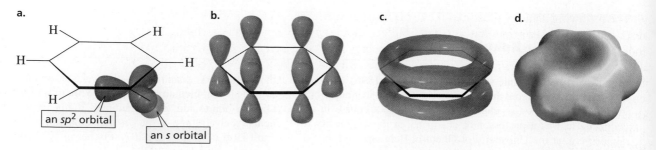

▲ **Figure 7.1**
(a) The carbon–carbon and carbon–hydrogen σ bonds in benzene. (b) The p orbital on each carbon can overlap two adjacent p orbitals. (c) The clouds of electrons above and below the plane of the benzene ring. (d) The electrostatic potential map for benzene.

Each of the six π electrons, therefore, is localized neither on a single carbon nor in a bond between two carbons (as in an alkene). Instead, each π electron is shared by all six carbons. In other words, the six π electrons are delocalized—they roam freely within the doughnut-shaped clouds that lie over and under the planar ring of carbons. Benzene is often drawn as a hexagon containing either dashed lines or a circle to symbolize the six delocalized π electrons.

This type of representation makes it clear that there are no double bonds in benzene. We see now that Kekulé's structure was very nearly correct. The actual structure of benzene is a Kekulé structure with delocalized electrons.

7.3 RESONANCE CONTRIBUTORS AND THE RESONANCE HYBRID

A disadvantage of using dashed lines (or a circle) to represent delocalized electrons is that they do not tell us how many π electrons they represent. For example, the dashed lines inside the hexagon shown above indicate that the π electrons are shared equally by all six carbons and that all the carbon–carbon bonds have the same length, but they do not show how many π electrons are in the ring. Consequently, chemists prefer to use structures that portray the electrons as localized (and show the numbers of electrons), even though the electrons in the compound's actual structure are delocalized. The *approximate* structure with localized electrons is called a **resonance contributor**, a **resonance structure**, or a **contributing resonance structure**. The *actual* structure with delocalized electrons is called a **resonance hybrid**. Notice that it is easy to see that there are six π electrons in the ring of each resonance contributor of benzene.

Electron delocalization is shown by double-headed arrows (⟷). Equilibrium is shown by two arrows pointing in opposite directions (⇌).

Resonance contributors are shown with a double-headed arrow between them. The double-headed arrow does *not* mean that the structures are in equilibrium with one another. Rather, it indicates that the actual structure lies somewhere between the structures of the resonance contributors. Resonance contributors are merely a convenient way to show the π electrons; they do not represent any real electron distribution.

The following analogy illustrates the difference between resonance contributors and the resonance hybrid. Imagine that you are trying to describe to a friend what a rhinoceros looks like. You might tell your friend that a rhinoceros looks like a cross between a unicorn and a dragon. Like resonance contributors, the unicorn and the dragon do not really exist. Furthermore, like resonance contributors, they are not in equilibrium: a rhinoceros does not change back and forth between the two forms, looking like a unicorn one instant and a dragon the next. The unicorn and dragon are simply ways to describe what the actual animal—the rhinoceros—looks like. *Resonance contributors, like unicorns and dragons, are imaginary, not real. Only the resonance hybrid, like the rhinoceros, is real.*

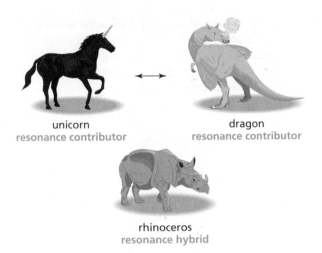

unicorn
resonance contributor

dragon
resonance contributor

rhinoceros
resonance hybrid

Electron delocalization is most effective if all the atoms sharing the delocalized electrons lie in or close to the same plane, so that their p orbitals can maximally overlap. For example, cyclooctatetraene is not planar; its sp^2 carbons have bond angles of 120°, whereas a planar eight-membered ring would have bond angles of 135° (another factor that causes cyclooctatetraene to be nonplanar will be discussed in Section 15.6). Because the ring is not planar, a p orbital can overlap with one adjacent p orbital, but it can have little overlap with the other adjacent p orbital. Therefore, the eight π electrons are not delocalized over the entire cyclooctatetraene ring, and its carbon–carbon bonds do not all have the same length.

7.4 HOW TO DRAW RESONANCE CONTRIBUTORS

We have seen that an organic compound with delocalized electrons is generally represented as a structure with localized electrons to let us know how many π electrons it has. For example, nitroethane is represented as having a nitrogen–oxygen double bond and a nitrogen–oxygen single bond.

$$CH_3CH_2-\overset{+}{N}\overset{\displaystyle :\ddot{O}}{\underset{\displaystyle :\ddot{O}:^-}{\diagup\!\!\diagup}}$$

nitroethane

However, the two nitrogen–oxygen bonds in nitroethane actually have the same bond length. A more accurate description of the molecule's structure is obtained by drawing the two resonance contributors. Both resonance contributors show the compound with a nitrogen–oxygen double bond and a nitrogen–oxygen single bond, but they indicate that the electrons are delocalized by depicting the double bond in one contributor as a single bond in the other.

The resonance hybrid, in contrast, shows that the two π electrons are shared by three atoms. The resonance hybrid also shows that the two nitrogen–oxygen bonds are identical and that the negative charge is shared equally by both oxygens. Thus, we need to visualize and mentally average both resonance contributors to appreciate what the actual molecule—the resonance hybrid—looks like.

Delocalized electrons result from a *p* orbital overlapping the *p* orbitals of more than one adjacent atom.

Rules for Drawing Resonance Contributors

To draw a set of resonance contributors, we draw a Lewis structure for the molecule—it becomes our first resonance contributor—and then we move the electrons, following the rules listed below, to generate the next resonance contributor.

1. Only electrons move. Atoms never move.
2. Only π electrons (electrons in π bonds) and lone-pair electrons can move. (Never move σ electrons.)
3. The total number of electrons in the molecule does not change. Therefore, each of the resonance contributors for a particular compound must have the same net charge. If one has a net charge of 0, all the others must also have net charges of 0. (A net charge of 0 does not necessarily mean that there is no charge on any of the atoms: a molecule with a positive charge on one atom and a negative charge on another atom has a net charge of 0.)

Notice, as you study the following resonance contributors and practice drawing them yourself, that the electrons (π electrons or lone pairs) are always moved toward an sp^2 or an sp hybridized atom. Remember that an sp^2 carbon is either a positively charged carbon or a double-bonded carbon (Sections 1.8 and 1.10), and an sp carbon is generally a triple-bonded carbon (Section 1.9). Electrons cannot be moved toward an sp^3 carbon because an sp^3 carbon has a complete octet, and therefore cannot accommodate any more electrons.

To draw resonance contributors, move only *π* electrons or lone pairs toward an *sp²* (or *sp*) carbon.

The carbocation below has delocalized electrons. To draw its resonance contributor, we *move the π electrons toward an sp^2 carbon.* The curved arrow shows you how to draw the second contributor. Remember the tail of the curved arrow shows where the electrons start from, and the head shows where the electrons are going. The resonance hybrid shows that the positive charge is shared by two carbons.

Let's compare this carbocation with a similar compound in which all the electrons are localized. The π electrons in the compound shown below cannot move, because the carbon they would move toward is an sp^3 carbon, and sp^3 carbons cannot accept electrons.

an sp^3 carbon
cannot accept electrons

$$CH_2=CH-CH_2\overset{+}{C}HCH_3$$

localized electrons

In the next example, π electrons again move toward an sp^2 carbon. The resonance hybrid shows that the positive charge is shared by three carbons.

an sp^2 carbon

$$CH_3CH=CH-CH=CH-\overset{+}{C}H_2 \longleftrightarrow CH_3CH=CH-\overset{+}{C}H-CH=CH_2 \longleftrightarrow CH_3\overset{+}{C}H-CH=CH-CH=CH_2$$

resonance contributors

$$CH_3\overset{\delta+}{CH}=CH=CH=CH=CH_2$$

resonance hybrid

The resonance contributor for the next compound is obtained by *moving lone-pair electrons toward an sp^2 carbon*. The sp^2 carbon can accommodate the new electrons by breaking a π bond. The lone-pair electrons in the example on the right below are not delocalized because if they were, they would have to move toward an sp^3 carbon.

an sp^2 carbon   resonance contributors

an sp^3 carbon
cannot accept
electrons

resonance hybrid

In the next example, *lone-pair electrons move toward an sp carbon.*

$$CH_3\overset{..}{\overset{-}{C}}H-C\equiv CH \longleftrightarrow CH_3CH=C=\overset{..}{C}H$$

The resonance contributor for the next compound is obtained by *moving π electrons toward an sp carbon.*

$$CH_2=CH-C\equiv N \longleftrightarrow \overset{+}{C}H_2-CH=C=\overset{..}{\overset{-}{N}}$$

PROBLEM 3

a. Which of the following compounds have delocalized electrons?

1. $CH_2=CHCH_2CH=CH_2$

2. $CH_3CH=CHCH=CH\overset{+}{C}H_2$

3. $CH_3CH_2\overset{..}{N}HCH_2CH=CH_2$

4. (pyrrole structure with N–H)

5. (cyclohexene ring with O)

6. (cyclohexadiene ring with $-CH_2\overset{..}{N}H_2$)

7. (cyclohexadiene ring with $-\overset{..}{N}H_2$)

b. Draw the resonance contributors for the compounds that have delocalized electrons.

chem Tutorial:
place Drawing resonance contributors

Tutorial:
Localized and delocalized
electrons

Peptide Bonds

Every third bond in a protein chain is a peptide bond. A resonance contributor can be drawn for a peptide bond by moving the lone pair on nitrogen toward the sp^2 carbon.

Because of the partial double-bond character of the peptide bond, the carbon and nitrogen atoms and the two atoms bonded to each of them are held rigidly in a plane, as represented below by the blue and green boxes. This planarity affects the way proteins can fold, so it has important implications for the three-dimensional shape of these biological molecules (Section 23.14).

peptide bond

a segment of a protein

7.5 THE PREDICTED STABILITIES OF RESONANCE CONTRIBUTORS

All resonance contributors do not necessarily contribute equally to the resonance hybrid. The degree to which each resonance contributor contributes depends on its predicted stability. Because resonance contributors are not real, their stabilities cannot be measured. Therefore, the stabilities of resonance contributors have to be predicted based on molecular features found in real molecules. *The greater the predicted stability of a resonance contributor, the more it contributes to the structure of the resonance hybrid; and the more it contributes to the structure of the resonance hybrid, the more similar the contributor is to the real molecule.* The examples that follow illustrate these points.

The greater the predicted stability of a resonance contributor, the more it contributes to the structure of the resonance hybrid.

The two resonance contributors for a carboxylic acid are shown below, labeled **A** and **B**. Structure **B** has two features that make it less stable than structure **A**: one of the oxygens has a positive charge—not a comfortable situation for an electronegative atom—and the structure has separated charges. A molecule with **separated charges** has a positive charge and a negative charge that can be neutralized by the movement of electrons. Resonance contributors with separated charges are relatively unstable (relatively high in energy) because energy is required to keep opposite charges separated. Structure **A**, therefore, is predicted to be more stable than structure **B**. Consequently, **A** makes a greater contribution to the resonance hybrid, so the resonance hybrid looks more like **A** than like **B**.

separated charges

A   B

a carboxylic acid

The two resonance contributors for a carboxylate ion are shown next.

C   D

a carboxylate ion

Structures **C** and **D** are predicted to be equally stable and therefore are expected to contribute equally to the resonance hybrid.

When electrons can be moved in more than one direction, the most stable resonance contributor is obtained by moving them *toward* the more electronegative atom. For instance, structure **G** in the next example results from moving the π electrons (red arrows) toward oxygen—the most electronegative atom in the molecule, while structure **E** results from moving the π electrons (blue arrows) away from oxygen.

an incomplete octet

E

resonance contributor obtained by moving π electrons away from the most electronegative atom

an insignificant resonance contributor

F

an incomplete octet

G

resonance contributor obtained by moving π electrons toward the most electronegative atom

We can predict that structure **G** will make only a small contribution to the resonance hybrid because it has separated charges, as well as an atom with an incomplete octet. Structure **E** also has separated charges and an atom with an incomplete octet, but its predicted stability is even less than that of structure **G** because it has a positive charge on the electronegative oxygen atom. Its contribution to the resonance hybrid is so insignificant that we do not need to include it as one of the resonance contributors. The resonance hybrid, therefore, looks very much like structure **F**.

The only time you need to show a resonance contributor obtained by moving electrons *away* from the most electronegative atom is when that is the only way the electrons can be moved. In other words, movement of electrons away from the most electronegative atom is better than no movement at all, because electron delocalization makes a molecule more stable (as we will see in Section 7.6). For example, the only resonance contributor that can be drawn for the following molecule requires movement of the electrons away from oxygen:

H   **I**

Structure **I** is predicted to be relatively unstable because it has separated charges and its most electronegative atom is the atom with the positive charge. Therefore, the structure of the resonance hybrid is similar to structure **H**, with only a small contribution from structure **I**.

Let's now see which of the resonance contributors shown below has a greater predicted stability. Structure **J** has a negative charge on carbon, and structure **K** has a negative charge on oxygen. Oxygen is more electronegative than carbon, so oxygen can accommodate the negative charge better. Consequently, structure **K** is predicted to be more stable than structure **J**. The resonance hybrid, therefore, more closely resembles structure **K**; that is, the resonance hybrid has a greater concentration of negative charge on the oxygen than on the carbon.

J   **K**

We can summarize the features that decrease the predicted stability of a resonance contributor as follows:

1. an atom with an incomplete octet
2. a negative charge that is not on the most electronegative atom or a positive charge that is not on the least electronegative (most electropositive) atom
3. charge separation

When we compare the relative stabilities of resonance contributors, an atom with an incomplete octet (feature 1) generally makes a structure more unstable than does either feature 2 or feature 3.

NOTE TO THE STUDENT

Special Topic V in the *Study Guide and Solutions Manual* will give you additional practice drawing resonance contributors and determining their relative predicted stabilities.

PROBLEM 4   SOLVED

Draw resonance contributors for each of the following species and rank the contributors in order of decreasing contribution to the hybrid:

a.

b.

c.

d.

e.

f. $CH_3\overset{+}{C}H$—CH=$CHCH_3$

Solution to 4a   Structure **A** is more stable than structure **B** because the positive charge is on a tertiary carbon in **A** and on a secondary carbon in **B** (Section 4.2).

PROBLEM 5

Draw the resonance hybrid for each of the species in Problem 4.

7.6 DELOCALIZATION ENERGY IS THE ADDITIONAL STABILITY DELOCALIZED ELECTRONS GIVE TO A COMPOUND

The delocalization energy is a measure of how much more stable a compound with delocalized electrons is than it would be if its electrons were localized.

A resonance hybrid is more stable than any of its resonance contributors is predicted to be.

Delocalized electrons stabilize a compound. The extra stability a compound gains from having delocalized electrons is called the **delocalization energy**. Electron delocalization is also called **resonance**, so delocalization energy is also called **resonance energy** or **resonance stabilization energy**. Knowing that delocalized electrons increase the stability of a molecule, we can conclude that *a resonance hybrid is more stable than any of its resonance contributors is predicted to be.*

The delocalization energy associated with a compound that has delocalized electrons depends on the number *and* predicted stability of the resonance contributors: *the greater the number of relatively stable resonance contributors, the greater is the delocalization energy.** For example, the delocalization energy of a carboxylate ion with two relatively stable resonance contributors is significantly greater than the delocalization energy of a carboxylic acid with only one relatively stable resonance contributor (page 286).

relatively stable   relatively stable

---

*In cyclic systems, there is another factor that profoundly influences the predicted stability of resonance contributors. We will discuss this factor in Sections 15.2, 15.6, and 15.7.

Notice that it is the number of *relatively stable* resonance contributors—not the total number of resonance contributors—that is important in determining the delocalization energy. For example, the delocalization energy of a carboxylate ion with two relatively stable resonance contributors (page 288) is greater than the delocalization energy of the compound in the following example (also see page 291) because even though the latter has three resonance contributors, only one of them is relatively stable:

$$\bar{C}H_2-CH{=}CH-\overset{+}{C}H_2 \quad\longleftrightarrow\quad CH_2{=}CH-CH{=}CH_2 \quad\longleftrightarrow\quad \overset{+}{C}H_2-CH{=}CH-\bar{C}H_2$$

| relatively unstable | relatively stable | relatively unstable |

The greater the number of relatively stable resonance contributors, the greater is the delocalization energy.

The more nearly equivalent the resonance contributors are in structure, the greater is the delocalization energy. The carbonate dianion is particularly stable because it has three equivalent resonance contributors.

The more nearly equivalent the resonance contributors are in structure, the greater is the delocalization energy.

We can now summarize what we know about resonance contributors:

1. The greater the predicted stability of a resonance contributor, the more it contributes to the resonance hybrid.
2. The greater the number of relatively stable resonance contributors, the greater is the delocalization energy.
3. The more nearly equivalent the resonance contributors, the greater is the delocalization energy.

PROBLEM 6♦

a. Predict the relative bond lengths of the three carbon–oxygen bonds in the carbonate ion (CO_3^{2-}).
b. What would you expect the charge to be on each oxygen?

PROBLEM-SOLVING STRATEGY

Determining Relative Stabilities

Which carbocation is more stable?

$$CH_3CH{=}CH-\overset{+}{C}H_2 \quad\text{or}\quad \overset{\overset{\displaystyle CH_3}{|}}{CH_3C}{=}CH-\overset{+}{C}H_2$$

Start by drawing the resonance contributors for each carbocation.

$$CH_3CH{=}CH-\overset{+}{C}H_2 \longleftrightarrow CH_3\overset{+}{C}H-CH{=}CH_2 \qquad \overset{\overset{\displaystyle CH_3}{|}}{CH_3C}{=}CH-\overset{+}{C}H_2 \longleftrightarrow \overset{\overset{\displaystyle CH_3}{|}}{CH_3\underset{+}{C}}-CH{=}CH_2$$

Now look at how the two sets of resonance contributors differ and think about how those differences affect the relative stabilities of the two resonance hybrids.

Each carbocation has two resonance contributors. The positive charge of the carbocation on the left is shared by a primary carbon and a secondary carbon. The positive charge of the carbocation on the right is shared by a primary carbon and a tertiary carbon. Because a tertiary carbon is more stable than a secondary carbon (Section 4.2), the carbocation on the right is more stable.

Now continue on to Problem 7.

PROBLEM 7♦

Which species is more stable?

a. $\overset{\overset{\displaystyle CH_2}{\parallel}}{CH_3CH_2\overset{+}{C}CH_2}$ or $CH_3CH_2CH={\overset{+}{C}HCH_2}$

b. $\overset{\overset{\displaystyle O}{\parallel}}{CH_3\underset{}{\overset{}{C}}}{}_{\displaystyle CH=CH_2}$ or $\overset{\overset{\displaystyle O}{\parallel}}{CH_3\underset{}{\overset{}{C}}}{}_{\displaystyle CH=CHCH_3}$

c. $CH_3\overset{\overset{\displaystyle O^-}{|}}{CHCH}=CH_2$ or $CH_3\overset{\overset{\displaystyle O^-}{|}}{C}=CHCH_3$

d. $\overset{\overset{\displaystyle +NH_2}{\parallel}}{CH_3\underset{NH_2}{\overset{}{C}}}$ or $\overset{\overset{\displaystyle +OH}{\parallel}}{CH_3\underset{NH_2}{\overset{}{C}}}$

PROBLEM 8♦

Which species has the greatest delocalization energy?

$$\overset{\overset{\displaystyle O}{\parallel}}{\underset{H \qquad O^-}{C}} \qquad \overset{\overset{\displaystyle O}{\parallel}}{\underset{^-O \qquad O^-}{C}} \qquad \overset{\overset{\displaystyle O}{\parallel}}{\underset{H \qquad OH}{C}}$$

7.7 EXAMPLES THAT SHOW HOW DELOCALIZED ELECTRONS AFFECT STABILITY

We will now look at two examples that illustrate the extra stability a molecule acquires as a result of having delocalized electrons.

Stability of Dienes

Dienes are hydrocarbons with two double bonds. **Isolated dienes** have isolated double bonds: **isolated double bonds** are separated by more than one single bond. **Conjugated dienes** have conjugated double bonds: **conjugated double bonds** are separated by one single bond.

double bonds are separated by more than one single bond

double bonds are separated by one single bond

$CH_2=CH-CH_2-CH=CH_2$
an isolated diene

$CH_3CH=CH-CH=CHCH_3$
a conjugated diene

We saw in Section 4.11 that the relative stabilities of alkenes can be determined by their $-\Delta H°$ values for catalytic hydrogenation (that is, by their heats of hydrogenation). Remember that the most stable alkene has the smallest heat of hydrogenation; it gives off the least heat when it is hydrogenated because it has less energy to begin with.

The heat of hydrogenation of 1,3-pentadiene (a conjugated diene) is smaller than that of 1,4-pentadiene (an isolated diene). We can conclude, therefore, that conjugated dienes are more stable than isolated dienes.

The most stable alkene has the smallest heat of hydrogenation.

| | Heat of hydrogenation | $\Delta H°$ | |
		(kcal/mol)	(kJ/mol)
$CH_2{=}CH{-}CH_2{-}CH{=}CH_2$ + $2\ H_2$ $\xrightarrow{\text{Pd/C}}$ $CH_3CH_2CH_2CH_2CH_3$	60.2	−60.2	−252
1,4-pentadiene an isolated diene			
$CH_2{=}CH{-}CH{=}CHCH_3$ + $2\ H_2$ $\xrightarrow{\text{Pd/C}}$ $CH_3CH_2CH_2CH_2CH_3$	54.1	−54.1	−226
1,3-pentadiene a conjugated diene			

Why is a conjugated diene more stable than an isolated diene? Two factors contribute to the difference. The first is *electron delocalization*. The π electrons in each of the double bonds of an isolated diene are *localized* between two carbons. In contrast, the π electrons in a conjugated diene are *delocalized*. As we discovered in Section 7.6, electron delocalization stabilizes a molecule. The resonance hybrid shows that the single bond in a conjugated diene such as 1,3-butadiene is not a pure single bond, but has partial double-bond character as a result of electron delocalization. Notice that because the compound does not have an electronegative atom that would determine the direction in which the electrons move, they can move both to the left (blue arrows) and to the right (red arrows).

An increase in delocalization energy means an increase in stability.

$$\bar{C}H_2{-}CH{=}CH{-}\overset{+}{C}H_2 \longleftrightarrow CH_2{=}CH{-}CH{=}CH_2 \longleftrightarrow \overset{+}{C}H_2{-}CH{=}CH{-}\bar{C}H_2$$
resonance contributors

delocalized electrons

$$CH_2{=\!=\!=}CH{=\!=\!=}CH{=\!=\!=}CH_2$$
1,3-butadiene
resonance hybrid

The *hybridization of the orbitals* forming the carbon–carbon single bonds also causes a conjugated diene to be more stable than an isolated diene. The carbon–carbon single bond in 1,3-pentadiene is formed from the overlap of an sp^2 orbital with another sp^2 orbital, whereas the carbon–carbon single bonds in 1,4-pentadiene are formed from the overlap of an sp^3 orbital with an sp^2 orbital.

single bond formed by sp^2–sp^2 overlap

single bonds formed by sp^3–sp^2 overlap

$$CH_2{=}CH{-}CH{=}CH{-}CH_3 \qquad CH_2{=}CH{-}CH_2{-}CH{=}CH_2$$
1,3-pentadiene   **1,4-pentadiene**

In Section 1.14, we saw that the length and strength of a σ bond depend on how close the electrons in the bonding orbital are to the nucleus: *the closer the electrons are to the nucleus, the shorter and stronger is the σ bond.* Because a $2s$ electron is closer, on average, to the nucleus than is a $2p$ electron, a bond formed by sp^2–sp^2 overlap is shorter and stronger than one formed by sp^3–sp^2 overlap (Table 7.1). (An sp^2 orbital has 33.3% s character, whereas an sp^3 orbital has only 25% s character.) Thus, a conjugated diene has one stronger single bond than an isolated diene, and stronger bonds cause a compound to be more stable.

Table 7.1	Dependence of the Length of a Carbon–Carbon Single Bond on the Hybridization of the Orbitals Used in Its Formation	
Compound	**Hybridization**	**Bond length (Å)**
H$_3$C—CH$_3$	sp^3–sp^3	1.54
H$_3$C—C(H)=CH$_2$	sp^3–sp^2	1.50
H$_2$C=C(H)—C(H)=CH$_2$	sp^2–sp^2	1.47
H$_3$C—C≡CH	sp^3–sp	1.46
H$_2$C=C(H)—C≡CH	sp^2–sp	1.43
HC≡C—C≡CH	sp–sp	1.37

Allenes are compounds that have **cumulated double bonds**. These are double bonds that are adjacent to one another. The cumulated double bonds give allenes an unusual geometry because the central carbon is sp hybrdized. One of its p orbitals overlaps a p orbital of an adjacent sp^2 carbon. Its second p orbital overlaps a p orbital of the other sp^2 carbon (Figure 7.2a).

a.   **b.**

▲ **Figure 7.2**
(a) Double bonds are formed by p orbital–p orbital overlap. The two p orbitals on the central carbon are perpendicular, causing allene to be a nonplanar molecule. (b) 2,3-Pentadiene has a nonsuperimposable mirror image. It is therefore a chiral molecule, even though it does not have an asymmetric center.

The two p orbitals of the central carbon are perpendicular. Therefore, the plane containing one H—C—H group is perpendicular to the plane containing the other H—C—H group. Thus, a substituted allene such as 2,3-pentadiene has a nonsuperimposable mirror image (Figure 7.2b), so it is a chiral molecule, even though it does not have any asymmetric centers. (See Problem 101 on page 250.)

PROBLEM 9◆

The heat of hydrogenation of 2,3-pentadiene, a cumulated diene, is 70.5 kcal/mol. What are the relative stabilities of cumulated, conjugated, and isolated dienes?

PROBLEM 10◆

Name the following dienes and rank them in order of increasing stability. (Alkyl groups stabilize dienes in the same way that they stabilize alkenes; see Section 4.12.)

CH$_3$CH=CHCH=CHCH$_3$ CH$_2$=CHCH$_2$CH=CH$_2$

CH$_3$C(CH$_3$)=CHCH=C(CH$_3$)CH$_3$ CH$_3$CH=CHCH=CH$_2$

Stability of Allylic and Benzylic Cations

We now look at two classes of carbocations that have delocalized electrons and are there-fore more stable than similar carbocations with localized electrons. An **allylic cation** is a carbocation with a positive charge on an allylic carbon; an **allylic carbon** is a carbon adjacent to an sp^2 carbon of an alkene (Section 3.2). A **benzylic cation** is a carbocation with a positive charge on a benzylic carbon; a **benzylic carbon** is a carbon adjacent to an sp^2 carbon of a benzene ring.

an allylic carbon

a benzylic carbon

$CH_2\!\!=\!\!CH\overset{+}{C}HR$

an allylic cation

$\overset{+}{C}HR$

a benzylic cation

The *allyl cation* is an unsubstituted allylic cation, and the *benzyl cation* is an unsubstituted benzylic cation.

$CH_2\!\!=\!\!CH\overset{+}{C}H_2$

the allyl cation

$\overset{+}{C}H_2$

the benzyl cation

allyl cation

An allylic cation has two resonance contributors. The positive charge is not localized on a single carbon, but is shared by two carbons.

$$RCH\!\!=\!\!CH\!\!-\!\!\overset{+}{C}H_2 \longleftrightarrow R\overset{+}{C}H\!\!-\!\!CH\!\!=\!\!CH_2$$

an allylic cation

A benzylic cation has five resonance contributors. Notice that the positive charge is shared by four carbons.

$\overset{+}{C}HR \longleftrightarrow \overset{+}{=}CHR \longleftrightarrow +\overset{}{=}CHR \longleftrightarrow \overset{}{=}CHR \longleftrightarrow \overset{+}{C}HR$

a benzylic cation

benzyl cation

Because the allyl and benzyl cations have delocalized electrons, they are more stable than other primary carbocations. (Indeed, they have about the same stability as secondary alkyl carbocations.) We can add the benzyl and allyl cations to the list of carbocations whose relative stabilities were shown in Sections 4.2 and 6.5.

relative stabilities of carbocations

| most stable | $R\!-\!\overset{+}{\underset{R}{\overset{R}{C}}}$ | > | $\overset{+}{=}CH_2$ | ≈ | $CH_2\!\!=\!\!CH\overset{+}{C}H_2$ | ≈ | $R\!-\!\overset{+}{\underset{H}{\overset{R}{C}}}$ | > | $R\!-\!\overset{+}{\underset{H}{\overset{H}{C}}}$ | > | $H\!-\!\overset{+}{\underset{H}{\overset{H}{C}}}$ | > | $CH_2\!\!=\!\!\overset{+}{C}H$ | least stable |

a tertiary carbocation | benzyl cation | allyl cation | a secondary carbocation | a primary carbocation | methyl cation | vinyl cation

Not all allylic and benzylic cations have the same stability. Just as a tertiary alkyl carbocation is more stable than a secondary alkyl carbocation, a tertiary allylic cation is more stable than a secondary allylic cation, which in turn is more stable than the (primary) allyl cation. Similarly, a tertiary benzylic cation is more stable than a secondary benzylic cation, which is more stable than the (primary) benzyl cation.

relative stabilities

Notice that it is the *primary* benzyl and the *primary* allyl cations that have about the same stability as *secondary* alkyl carbocations. Secondary benzylic and allylic cations, as well as tertiary benzylic and allylic cations, are even more stable than primary benzyl and allyl cations.

PROBLEM 11◆

Which carbocation in each of the following pairs is more stable?

a. [structure] or [structure]   c. [structure] or [structure]

b. CH₃OĊH₂ or CH₃NHĊH₂

7.8 A MOLECULAR ORBITAL DESCRIPTION OF STABILITY

Take a few minutes to review Section 1.6.

See Special Topic VI in the *Study Guide and Solutions Manual* for additional information on molecular orbital theory.

So far in our discussion we have used resonance contributors to show why compounds are stabilized by electron delocalization. The stabilization of compounds by electron delocalization can also be explained by molecular orbital (MO) theory.

We saw in Section 1.5 that the two lobes of a *p* orbital have opposite phases. We also saw that when two in-phase *p* orbitals overlap, a covalent bond is formed, and when two out-of-phase *p* orbitals overlap, they cancel each other and produce a node between the two nuclei (Section 1.6).

Let's review how the *π* molecular orbitals of ethene are constructed. An MO description of ethene is shown in Figure 7.3. The two *p* orbitals can be either in-phase or out-of-phase. (The different phases are indicated by different colors.) Notice that the number of orbitals is conserved—the number of molecular orbitals equals the number of atomic orbitals that produced them. Thus, the two atomic *p* orbitals of ethene overlap to produce two *π* molecular orbitals. Side-to-side overlap of in-phase *p* orbitals (lobes of the same color) produces a *π* **bonding molecular orbital** designated ψ₁ (the Greek letter psi). The bonding molecular orbital is lower in energy than the *p* atomic orbitals, and it encompasses both carbons. In other words, each electron in the bonding molecular orbital spreads over both carbons.

Side-to-side overlap of out-of-phase *p* orbitals produces a *π** **antibonding molecular orbital**, ψ₂, which is higher in energy than the *p* atomic orbitals. The antibonding molecular orbital has a node between the lobes of opposite phases. Recall that the overlap of in-phase orbitals holds atoms together; it is a bonding interaction. In contrast, the overlap of out-of-phase orbitals pulls atoms apart; it is an antibonding interaction.

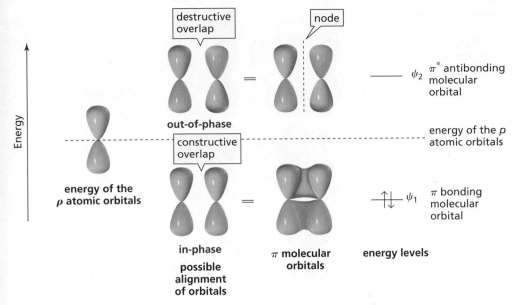

◀ **Figure 7.3**
The distribution of electrons in ethene. Overlapping of in-phase *p* orbitals produces a bonding molecular orbital that is lower in energy than the *p* atomic orbitals. Overlapping of out-of-phase *p* orbitals produces an antibonding molecular orbital that is higher in energy than the *p* atomic orbitals.

The π electrons are placed in molecular orbitals according to the same rules that govern the placement of electrons in atomic orbitals (Section 1.2): the aufbau principle (orbitals are filled in order of increasing energy), the Pauli exclusion principle (each orbital can hold two electrons of opposite spin), and Hund's rule (an electron will occupy an empty degenerate orbital before it will pair up with an electron that is already present in an orbital).

1,3-Butadiene and 1,4-Pentadiene

The two π electrons in 1,3-butadiene are delocalized over four carbons (Section 7.7). In other words, there are four carbons in the π system.

$$\overset{..}{C}H_2 - CH = CH - \overset{+}{C}H_2 \longleftrightarrow CH_2 = CH - CH = CH_2 \longleftrightarrow \overset{+}{C}H_2 - CH = CH - \overset{..}{C}H_2$$

1,3-butadiene
resonance contributors

$$CH_2 = CH = CH = CH_2$$
resonance hybrid

A molecular orbital description of 1,3-butadiene is shown in Figure 7.4. Each of the four carbons contributes one *p* atomic orbital, and the four *p* atomic orbitals combine to produce four π molecular orbitals: ψ_1, ψ_2, ψ_3, and ψ_4, in order of increasing energy. Thus, we see that a molecular orbital results from the **linear combination of atomic orbitals (LCAO)**. Half of the MOs are π bonding MOs (ψ_1 and ψ_2), and the other half are π^* antibonding MOs (ψ_3 and ψ_4). The energies of the bonding and antibonding MOs are symmetrically distributed above and below the energy of the *p* atomic orbitals.

Notice that as the MOs increase in energy, the number of nodes within them increases and the number of bonding interactions decreases. The lowest-energy MO (ψ_1) has only the node that bisects the *p* orbitals (it has no nodes between the nuclei because all the blue lobes overlap on one face of the molecule and all the green lobes overlap on the other face) and three bonding interactions; ψ_2 has one node between the nuclei and two bonding interactions (for a net result of one bonding interaction); ψ_3 has two nodes between the nuclei and one bonding interaction (for a net result of one antibonding interaction); and ψ_4 has three nodes between the nuclei—three antibonding interactions—and no bonding interactions. The four π electrons of 1,3-butadiene reside in ψ_1 and ψ_2.

1,3-Butadiene's lowest-energy MO (ψ_1) is particularly stable because it has three bonding interactions and its two electrons are delocalized over all four nuclei, encompassing all the carbons in the π system. The MO next in energy (ψ_2) is also a bonding MO because

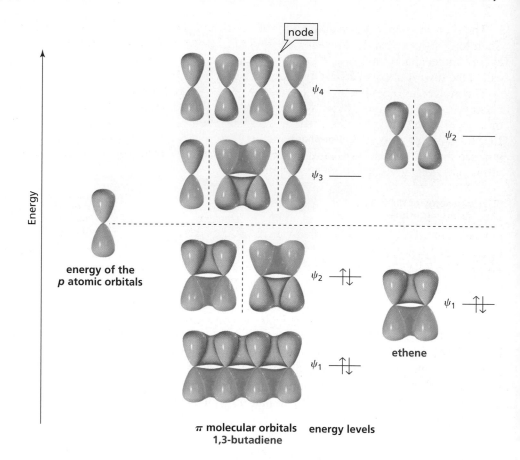

► **Figure 7.4**
Four *p* atomic orbitals overlap to produce four molecular orbitals in 1,3-butadiene, and two *p* atomic orbitals overlap to produce two molecular orbitals in ethene. In both compounds, the bonding MOs are filled and the antibonding MOs are empty.

it has one more bonding interaction than antibonding interaction; it is not as strongly bonding or as low in energy as ψ_1. These two bonding MOs show that the greatest π electron density in a compound with two double bonds joined by one single bond is between C-1 and C-2 and between C-3 and C-4, but there is some π electron density between C-2 and C-3—just as the resonance contributors show. They also show why 1,3-butadiene is most stable in a planar conformation: if 1,3-butadiene weren't planar, there would be little or no overlap between C-2 and C-3. Overall, ψ_3 is an antibonding MO: it has one more antibonding interaction than bonding interaction, but it is not as strongly antibonding as ψ_4; which has no bonding interactions and three antibonding interactions.

Both ψ_1 and ψ_3 are **symmetric molecular orbitals;** they have a plane of symmetry, so one half is the mirror image of the other half. In contrast, both ψ_2 and ψ_4 are **antisymmetric**; they do not have a plane of symmetry (but would have one, if one half of the MO were turned upside down). Notice that as the MOs increase in energy, they alternate from symmetric to antisymmetric.

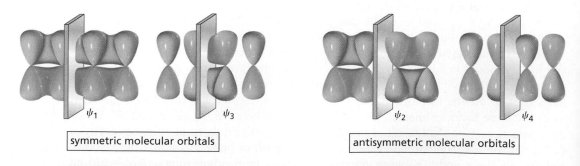

The energies of the MOs of 1,3-butadiene and ethene are compared in Figure 7.4. Notice that the average energy of the electrons in 1,3-butadiene is lower than the electrons in ethene. This lower energy is the delocalization energy. In other words, 1,3-butadiene is stabilized by electron delocalization.

The highest-energy molecular orbital of 1,3-butadiene that contains electrons is ψ_2. Therefore, ψ_2 is called the **highest occupied molecular orbital (HOMO)**. The lowest-energy molecular orbital of 1,3-butadiene that does not contain electrons is ψ_3; ψ_3 is called the **lowest unoccupied molecular orbital (LUMO)**.

The molecular orbital description of 1,3-butadiene shown in Figure 7.4 represents the electronic configuration of the molecule in its *ground state*. If the molecule absorbs light of an appropriate wavelength, the light will promote an electron from its HOMO to its LUMO (from ψ_2 to ψ_3). The molecule will then be in an *excited* state (Section 1.2). We will see that the excitation of an electron from the HOMO to the LUMO is the basis of ultraviolet and visible spectroscopy (Section 13.17).

HOMO = the highest occupied
molecular orbital

LUMO = the lowest unoccupied
molecular orbital

PROBLEM 12◆

What is the total number of nodes in the ψ_3 and ψ_4 molecular orbitals of 1,3-butadiene?

PROBLEM 13◆

Answer the following questions for the π molecular orbitals of 1,3-butadiene:
a. Which are the bonding MOs, and which are the antibonding MOs?
b. Which MOs are symmetric, and which are antisymmetric?
c. Which MO is the HOMO, and which is the LUMO in the ground state?
d. Which MO is the HOMO, and which is the LUMO in the excited state?
e. What is the relationship between the HOMO and the LUMO and symmetric and antisymmetric orbitals?

Now let's look at the π molecular orbitals of 1,4-pentadiene.

$CH_2{=}CHCH_2CH{=}CH_2$
1,4-pentadiene

the CH$_2$ group causes
the π electrons to be
isolated

the π electrons are
conjugated

lowest energy
π molecular orbital of
1,4-pentadiene

lowest energy
π molecular orbital of
1,3-butadiene

1,4-Pentadiene, like 1,3-butadiene, has four π electrons. However, unlike the delocalized π electrons in 1,3-butadiene, the two pairs of π electrons in 1,4-pentadiene are completely separate from one another. In other words, the electrons are localized. The molecular orbitals of 1,4-pentadiene have the same energy as those of ethene, a compound with one pair of localized π electrons. Thus, molecular orbital theory and resonance contributors are two different ways to show that the π electrons in 1,3-butadiene are delocalized and that electron delocalization stabilizes a molecule.

1,3,5-Hexatriene and Benzene

1,3,5-Hexatriene, with six carbons, has six p atomic orbitals.

$CH_2{=}CH{-}CH{=}CH{-}CH{=}CH_2$
1,3,5-hexatriene

$CH_2{=\!=\!=}CH{=\!=\!=}CH{=\!=\!=}CH{=\!=\!=}CH{=\!=\!=}CH_2$
resonance hybrid of
1,3,5-hexatriene

The six p atomic orbitals combine to produce six π molecular orbitals: ψ_1, ψ_2, ψ_3, ψ_4, ψ_5, and ψ_6 (Figure 7.5). Half of the MOs (ψ_1, ψ_2, and ψ_3) are bonding and the other half (ψ_4, ψ_5, and ψ_6) are antibonding. 1,3,5-Hexatriene's six π electrons occupy the three bonding MOs (ψ_1, ψ_2, and ψ_3), and two of the electrons (those in ψ_1) are delocalized over all six carbons. Thus, molecular orbital theory and resonance contributors are two different ways of showing that the π electrons in 1,3,5-hexatriene are delocalized. Notice in Figure 7.5 that as the MOs increase in energy, the number of nodes increases, the number of bonding interactions decreases, and the MOs alternate from symmetric to antisymmetric.

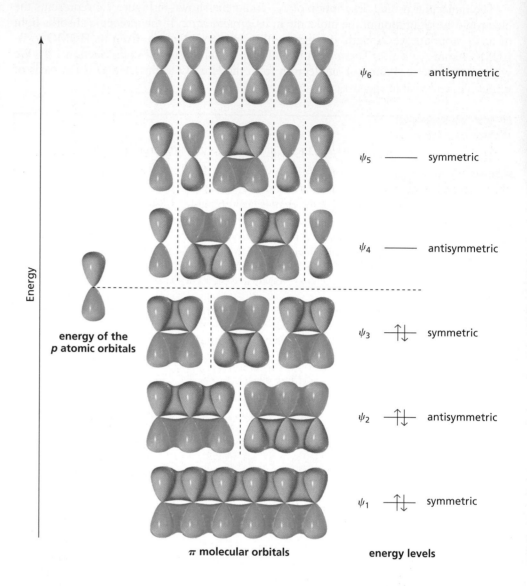

▶ **Figure 7.5**
Six *p* atomic orbitals overlap to produce the six π molecular orbitals of 1,3,5-hexatriene. The six π electrons occupy the three bonding molecular orbitals $\psi_1, \psi_2,$ and ψ_3.

π molecular orbitals   energy levels

PROBLEM 14 ◆

Answer the following questions for the π molecular orbitals of 1,3,5-hexatriene:
a. Which are the bonding MOs, and which are the antibonding MOs?
b. Which MOs are symmetric, and which are antisymmetric?
c. Which MO is the HOMO, and which is the LUMO in the ground state?
d. Which MO is the HOMO, and which is the LUMO in the excited state?
e. What is the relationship between the HOMO and the LUMO and symmetric and antisymmetric orbitals?

Like 1,3,5-hexatriene, benzene has a six-carbon π system. The six-carbon π system in benzene, however, is cyclic. The six *p* atomic orbitals combine to produce six π molecular orbitals (Figure 7.6). Three of the MOs are bonding ($\psi_1, \psi_2,$ and ψ_3) and three are antibonding ($\psi_4, \psi_5,$ and ψ_6). Benzene's six π electrons occupy the three lowest-energy MOs (the bonding MOs). The method used to determine the relative energies of the MOs of compounds with cyclic π systems is described in Section 15.7.

p atomic orbitals of benzene

energy levels

◀ **Figure 7.6**
Benzene has six π molecular orbitals, three bonding (ψ_1, ψ_2, ψ_3) and three antibonding (ψ_4, ψ_5, ψ_6). The six π electrons occupy the three bonding molecular orbitals.

Figure 7.7 shows that there are *six* bonding interactions in the lowest-energy MO (ψ_1) of benzene—one more than in the lowest-energy MO of 1,3,5-hexatriene (Figure 7.5). In other words, when the three double bonds of benzene are arranged in a ring, the molecule's stability increases. The other two bonding MOs of benzene (ψ_2 and ψ_3) are degenerate: ψ_2 has four bonding interactions and two antibonding interactions, for a net of two bonding interactions, and ψ_3 also has two bonding interactions. Thus, ψ_2 and ψ_3 are bonding MOs, but they are not as strongly bonding as ψ_1.

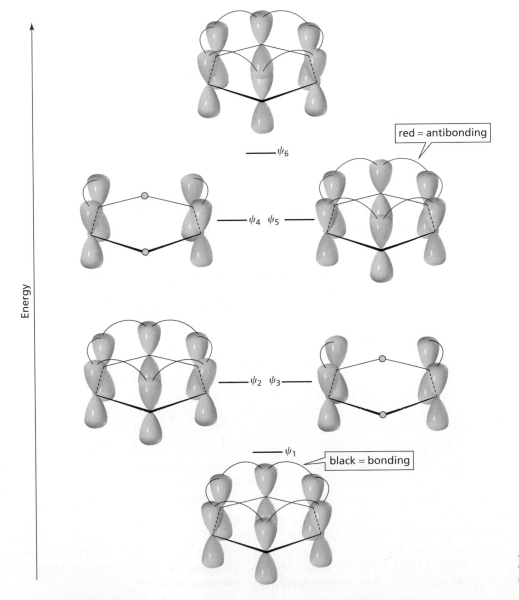

red = antibonding

black = bonding

◀ **Figure 7.7**
As the energy of the π molecular orbitals increases, the net number of bonding interactions decreases.

The energy levels of the MOs of ethene, 1,3-butadiene, 1,3,5-hexatriene, and benzene are compared in Figure 7.8. You can see that benzene is a particularly stable molecule. Compounds such as benzene that are unusually stable because of large delocalization energies are called **aromatic compounds**. The structural features that make a compound aromatic will be discussed in Section 15.2. Benzene's large delocalization energy is what prevents it from undergoing the addition reactions characteristic of alkenes, one of the observations that puzzled nineteenth-century chemists (Section 7.1).

▶ **Figure 7.8**
A comparison of the energy levels of the π molecular orbitals of ethene, 1,3-butadiene, 1,3,5-hexatriene, and benzene.

PROBLEM 15 ◆

How many bonding interactions are there in the ψ_1 and ψ_2 molecular orbitals of the following compounds?

a. 1,3-butadiene   **b.** 1,3,5,7-octatetraene

7.9 HOW DELOCALIZED ELECTRONS AFFECT pK_a VALUES

We have seen that a carboxylic acid is a much stronger acid than an alcohol. For example, the pK_a of acetic acid is 4.76, whereas the pK_a of ethanol is 15.9 (Section 1.18). We know, then, that the conjugate base of a carboxylic acid is considerably weaker—and therefore more stable—than the conjugate base of an alcohol. (Recall that the stronger the acid, the weaker and more stable is its conjugate base.)

$$
\begin{array}{cc}
\underset{\substack{\text{acetic acid}\\ \text{p}K_a = 4.76}}{\overset{\displaystyle\overset{O}{\underset{}{\|}}}{CH_3 \overset{C}{} OH}}
&
\underset{\substack{\text{ethanol}\\ \text{p}K_a = 15.9}}{CH_3CH_2OH}
\end{array}
$$

The difference in stability of the two conjugate bases is attributable to two factors. First, the carboxylate ion has a double-bonded oxygen atom that replaces two hydrogens of the alkoxide ion. Inductive electron withdrawal by this oxygen stabilizes the ion by decreasing the electron density of the negatively charged oxygen (Section 1.21).

A nearby electronegative atom stabilizes an anion by inductive electron withdrawal.

$$
\begin{array}{cc}
\underset{\text{a carboxylate ion}}{\overset{\displaystyle\overset{O}{\|}}{CH_3 \overset{C}{} O^-}}
&
\underset{\text{an alkoxide ion}}{CH_3CH_2O^-}
\end{array}
$$

The other factor responsible for the increased stability of the carboxylate ion is its *greater delocalization energy* relative to that of its conjugate acid. The carboxylate ion has greater delocalization energy because the ion has two equivalent resonance contributors that are predicted to be relatively stable, whereas the carboxylic acid has only one (Section 7.6). Therefore, loss of a proton from a carboxylic acid is accompanied by increased delocalization energy—in other words, an increase in stability.

resonance contributors of a carboxylic acid

resonance contributors of a carboxylate ion

acetic acid

acetate ion

In contrast, all the electrons in an alcohol, such as ethanol, and its conjugate base are localized, so loss of a proton from an alcohol is not accompanied by an increase in delocalization energy.

$$CH_3CH_2OH \rightleftharpoons CH_3CH_2O^- + H^+$$

ethanol   ethoxide ion

The same two factors responsible for the greater acidity of a carboxylic acid compared with an alcohol cause phenol to be more acidic than an alcohol such as cyclohexanol: stabilization of phenol's conjugate base both by inductive *electron withdrawal* and by an increase in *delocalization energy*.

phenol
pK_a = 10

cyclohexanol
pK_a = 16

CH_3CH_2OH

ethanol
pK_a = 16

The OH group of phenol is attached to an sp^2 carbon, which is more electronegative than the sp^3 carbon to which the OH group of cyclohexanol is attached (Section 1.21). The greater *inductive electron withdrawal* by the more electronegative sp^2 carbon stabilizes the conjugate base by decreasing the electron density of its negatively charged oxygen. While both phenol and the phenolate ion have delocalized electrons, the delocalization energy of the phenolate ion is greater than that of phenol because three of phenol's resonance contributors have separated charges as well as a positive charge on an oxygen. The loss of a proton from phenol, therefore, is accompanied by an increase in delocalization energy.

phenol

phenolate ion

phenol   **phenolate ion**

In contrast, the conjugate base of cyclohexanol does not have any delocalized electrons to stabilize it.

cyclohexanol   **cyclohexanolate ion**

Phenol is a weaker acid than a carboxylic acid because electron withdrawal from the oxygen in the phenolate ion is not as great as in the carboxylate ion. In addition, the increased delocalization energy resulting from loss of a proton is not as great in a phenolate ion as in a carboxylate ion, where the negative charge is shared equally by two oxygens.

The same two factors can be invoked to explain why protonated aniline is a stronger acid than protonated cyclohexylamine.

protonated aniline
pK_a = 4.60

protonated cyclohexylamine
pK_a = 11.2

First, aniline's nitrogen is attached to an sp^2 carbon, whereas cyclohexylamine's nitrogen is attached to a less electronegative sp^3 carbon. Second, the nitrogen atom of protonated aniline lacks a lone pair that can be delocalized. However, when the nitrogen loses a proton, the lone pair that formerly held the proton can be delocalized. Loss of a proton, therefore, is accompanied by an increase in delocalization energy.

protonated aniline

aniline

protonated aniline	aniline

In contrast, cyclohexylamine does not have any delocalized electrons to stabilize it.

protonated cyclohexylamine	cyclohexylamine $+$ H$^+$

We can now add phenol and protonated aniline to the list of organic compounds whose approximate pK_a values you should know (Table 7.2). They are also listed inside the back cover for easy reference.

Table 7.2	Approximate pK_a Values		
pK_a < 0	**pK_a ≈ 5**	**pK_a ≈ 10**	**pK_a ≈ 15**
$\overset{+}{R\underset{H}{O}H}$	$\underset{R}{\overset{O}{\underset{}{\parallel}}}\overset{}{\underset{OH}{C}}$	$R\overset{+}{N}H_3$	ROH
$\overset{+OH}{\underset{R}{\overset{\parallel}{C}}\underset{OH}{}}$	$\overset{+}{N}H_3$ (phenyl)	OH (phenyl)	H$_2$O
H$_3$O$^+$			

PROBLEM-SOLVING STRATEGY

Determining Relative Acidities

Which is a stronger acid?

$$CH_3CH_2OH \quad \text{or} \quad CH_2{=}CHOH$$
ethyl alcohol   **vinyl alcohol**

The strength of an acid depends on the stability of its conjugate base. Bases are stabilized by electron-withdrawing substituents and by electron delocalization. So you can answer the question by comparing the stabilities of the two conjugate bases and remembering that the more stable base will have the more acidic conjugate acid.

localized electrons   delocalized electrons

$$CH_3CH_2\!-\!\ddot{O}\!:^- \qquad CH_2\!=\!CH\!-\!\ddot{O}\!:^- \longleftrightarrow {}^-\!\ddot{C}H_2\!-\!CH\!=\!\ddot{O}\!:$$

All the electrons in ethanol's conjugate base are localized. However, vinyl alcohol's conjugate base is stabilized by electron delocalization. In addition, it is stabilized by its oxygen's being attached to an sp^2 carbon, which is more electronegative than the sp^3 carbon that the oxygen in ethanol is attached to. Therefore, vinyl alcohol is the stronger acid.

Now continue on to Problem 16.

chem place Tutorial: Acidity and electron delocalization

PROBLEM 16 ◆

Which is a stronger acid?

a.

O (double bond to C), H—C—CH$_2$OH   or   O (double bond to C), CH$_3$—C—OH

c. $CH_3CH_2CH_2\overset{+}{N}H_3$ or $CH_3CH\!=\!CH\overset{+}{N}H_3$

b. $CH_3CH\!=\!CHCH_2OH$ or $CH_3CH\!=\!CHOH$

PROBLEM 17 ◆

Which is a stronger base?
a. ethylamine or aniline
b. ethylamine or ethoxide ion $(CH_3CH_2O^-)$
c. phenolate ion or ethoxide ion

PROBLEM 18 ◆

Rank the following compounds in order of decreasing acid strength:

⬡—OH   ⬡—CH$_2$OH   ⬡—COOH

PROBLEM 19   **SOLVED**

Which of the following would you predict to be the stronger acid?

⬡—COOH   or   O (double bond to N$^+$), $^-$O—N$^+$⬡—COOH

Solution   The nitro-substituted compound is the stronger acid because the nitro substituent withdraws electrons both inductively (through the σ bonds) and by resonance (through the π bonds). Withdrawal of electrons through π bonds is called **resonance electron withdrawal**. We have seen that electron-withdrawing substituents increase the acidity of a compound by stabilizing its conjugate base.

withdrawing electrons by resonance

PROBLEM 20♦

A methoxy substituent attached to a benzene ring withdraws electrons inductively (through the σ bonds) because oxygen is more electronegative than carbon. The group also donates electrons through the π bonds—called **resonance electron donation**.

From the pK_a values of the unsubstituted and methoxy-substituted carboxylic acids, predict which is a more important effect, inductive electron withdrawal or resonance electron donation.

$pK_a = 4.20$ $pK_a = 4.47$

7.10 DELOCALIZED ELECTRONS CAN AFFECT THE PRODUCT OF A REACTION

Our ability to predict the product of an organic reaction often depends on recognizing when organic molecules have delocalized electrons. For example, the alkene in the following reaction has the same number of hydrogens on both of its sp^2 carbons:

Therefore, the rule that tells us to add the electrophile to the sp^2 carbon bonded to the greater number of hydrogens predicts that approximately equal amounts of the two products shown above will be formed. When the reaction is carried out, however, only one of the products is obtained.

The rule leads us to an incorrect prediction of the reaction product because it does not take electron delocalization into consideration. It presumes that both carbocation intermediates are equally stable since they are both secondary carbocations. The rule does not take into account the fact that one intermediate is a secondary alkyl carbocation and the other is a secondary benzylic cation. Because the secondary benzylic cation is stabilized by electron delocalization, it is formed more readily. The difference in the rates of formation of the two carbocations is sufficient to cause only one product to be obtained.

a secondary benzylic cation   a secondary alkyl carbocation

This example serves as a warning. The rule describing the sp^2 carbon to which the electrophile becomes attached cannot be used for reactions involving carbocations that can be stabilized by electron delocalization. In such cases, you must look at the relative stabilities of the individual carbocations to predict the major product of the reaction.

PROBLEM 21♦

What is the major product obtained from the addition of HBr to the following compound?

$$\langle\ \rangle\!\!-\!CH_2CH\!=\!CH_2$$

PROBLEM 22   **SOLVED**

Predict the sites on each of the following compounds where protonation can occur.

a. $CH_3CH\!=\!CHOCH_3 \ + \ H^+$ **b.** (structure) $-N\langle\ \rangle \ + \ H^+$

Solution to 22a   The resonance contributors reveal that there are two sites that can be protonated: the lone pair on oxygen and the lone pair on carbon.

sites of protonation

$$CH_3\overset{\frown}{CH}\!=\!CH\overset{\frown}{-}\overset{..}{\overset{..}{O}}CH_3 \ \longleftrightarrow \ CH_3\overset{-}{\overset{..}{C}}H\!-\!CH\!=\!\overset{+}{\overset{..}{O}}CH_3 \qquad CH_3CH\!=\!CH\overset{..}{\overset{..}{O}}CH_3$$

resonance contributors

For the next example of how delocalized electrons can affect the product of a reaction, we will compare the products formed when *isolated dienes* (dienes that have only localized electrons) undergo electrophilic addition reactions to the products formed when *conjugated dienes* (dienes that have delocalized electrons) undergo the same reactions.

$$CH_2\!=\!CHCH_2CH_2CH\!=\!CH_2 \qquad CH_3CH\!=\!CH\!-\!CH\!=\!CHCH_3$$
an isolated diene   **a conjugated diene**

Reactions of Isolated Dienes

The reactions of *dienes with isolated double bonds* are just like the reactions of alkenes. If an excess of the electrophilic reagent is present, two independent electrophilic addition reactions will occur. In each reaction, *the electrophile adds to the sp^2 carbon that is bonded to the greater number of hydrogens.*

$$CH_2\!=\!CHCH_2CH_2CH\!=\!CH_2 \ + \ HBr \ \longrightarrow \ CH_3CHCH_2CH_2CHCH_3$$
1,5-hexadiene   **excess** $\ \ \ |\qquad\qquad\quad|$
$\qquad\qquad\qquad\qquad\qquad\qquad\qquad\qquad\qquad\qquad\qquad\qquad Br\qquad\qquad\ \ Br$

The reaction proceeds exactly as we would predict from our knowledge of the mechanism for the reaction of alkenes with electrophilic reagents.

MECHANISM FOR THE REACTION OF AN ISOLATED DIENE WITH EXCESS HBr

$$CH_2\!=\!CHCH_2CH_2CH\!=\!CH_2 \ + \ H\!-\!\overset{..}{\underset{..}{Br}}\text{:} \ \longrightarrow \ CH_3\overset{+}{C}HCH_2CH_2CH\!=\!CH_2 \ \longrightarrow \ CH_3CHCH_2CH_2CH\!=\!CH_2$$
$$+\text{:}\overset{..}{\underset{..}{Br}}\text{:}^- \qquad\qquad\qquad\qquad\qquad\qquad | \quad Br$$
$$\qquad\qquad\qquad\qquad\qquad\qquad\qquad\qquad\qquad\qquad\qquad\qquad\qquad\qquad\qquad\qquad\quad \downarrow H\!-\!\overset{..}{\underset{..}{Br}}\text{:}$$

$$CH_3CHCH_2CH_2CHCH_3 \ \longleftarrow \ CH_3CHCH_2CH_2\overset{+}{C}HCH_3$$
$$| \qquad\qquad\quad | \qquad\qquad\qquad\qquad\qquad | \qquad\qquad +\text{:}\overset{..}{\underset{..}{Br}}\text{:}^-$$
$$Br\qquad\qquad Br \qquad\qquad\qquad\qquad\qquad Br$$

- The electrophile (H^+) adds to the electron-rich double bond in a manner that produces the more stable carbocation (Section 4.4).
- The bromide ion adds to the carbocation.

- Because there is an excess of the electrophilic reagent, there is enough reagent to add to the other double bond; the H^+ adds in a manner that produces the more stable carbocation (Section 4.4).
- The bromide ion adds to the carbocation.

If there is only enough electrophilic reagent to add to one of the double bonds, it will add preferentially to the more reactive double bond. For example, in the following reaction, addition of HCl to the double bond on the left forms a secondary carbocation, whereas addition of HCl to the double bond on the right forms a tertiary carbocation. Because the tertiary carbocation is formed faster (Section 4.4), the major product of the reaction will be 5-chloro-5-methyl-1-hexene in the presence of a limited amount of HCl.

$$CH_2{=}CHCH_2CH_2\overset{\overset{\displaystyle CH_3}{|}}{C}{=}CH_2 \ + \ HCl \ \longrightarrow \ CH_2{=}CHCH_2CH_2\overset{\overset{\displaystyle CH_3}{|}}{\underset{\underset{\displaystyle Cl}{|}}{C}}CH_3$$

2-methyl-1,5-hexadiene   **1 mol**
1 mol

5-chloro-5-methyl-1-hexene
major product

PROBLEM 23

Give the major product of each of the following reactions, assuming that one equivalent of each reagent is used in each reaction.

a. $CH_2{=}CHCH_2CH_2CH{=}\overset{\overset{\displaystyle CH_3}{|}}{C}CH_3 \xrightarrow{\text{HBr}}$

c. $\xrightarrow{\text{HCl}}$

b. $HC{\equiv}CCH_2CH_2CH{=}CH_2 \xrightarrow{\text{Cl}_2}$

PROBLEM 24♦

Which of the double bonds in zingiberene, the compound responsible for the aroma of ginger, is the most reactive in an electrophilic addition reaction?

zingiberene

Reactions of Conjugated Dienes

When a diene with *conjugated double bonds*, such as 1,3-butadiene, reacts with a limited amount of electrophilic reagent, so that addition can occur at only one of the double bonds, two addition products are formed. One is a **1,2-addition product**, which is a result of addition at the 1- and 2-positions. The other is a **1,4-addition product**, the result of addition at the 1- and 4-positions. **1,2-Addition** is called **direct addition**, and **1,4-addition** is called **conjugate addition**.

$$\overset{1}{C}H_2{=}\overset{2}{C}H{-}\overset{3}{C}H{=}\overset{4}{C}H_2 \ + \ Cl_2 \ \longrightarrow \ CH_2{-}CH{-}CH{=}CH_2 \ + \ CH_2{-}CH{=}CH{-}CH_2$$

1,3-butadiene   **1 mol**
1 mol

3,4-dichloro-1-butene   **1,4-dichloro-2-butene**
1,2-addition product   **1,4-addition product**

$$CH_2{=}CH{-}CH{=}CH_2 \ + \ HBr \ \longrightarrow \ CH_3CH{-}CH{=}CH_2 \ + \ CH_3{-}CH{=}CH{-}CH_2$$

1,3-butadiene   **1 mol**
1 mol

3-bromo-1-butene   **1-bromo-2-butene**
1,2-addition product   **1,4-addition product**

On the basis of your knowledge of how electrophilic reagents add to double bonds, you would expect the 1,2-addition product. However, the 1,4-addition product is surprising, because not only did the reagent not add to adjacent carbons, but a double bond has changed its position. The double bond in the 1,4-product is between the 2- and 3-positions, whereas the reactant had a single bond in this position.

When we talk about addition at the 1- and 2-positions or at the 1- and 4-positions, the numbers refer to the four carbons of the conjugated system. Thus, the carbon in the 1-position is one of the sp^2 carbons at the end of the conjugated system—it is not necessarily the first carbon in the molecule.

> **An isolated diene undergoes only 1,2-addition.**
>
> **A conjugated diene undergoes both 1,2- and 1,4-addition.**

$$\underset{\text{the conjugated system}}{R-\overset{1}{C}H=\overset{2}{C}H-\overset{3}{C}H=\overset{4}{C}H-R}$$

For example, the 1- and 4-positions in the conjugated system are actually the 2- and 5-positions of 2,4-hexadiene.

$$CH_3CH=CH-CH=CHCH_3 \xrightarrow{\textbf{Br}_2} \underset{\substack{\text{4,5-dibromo-2-hexene} \\ \textbf{1,2-addition product}}}{CH_3CH-\underset{Br}{\overset{|}{C}H}-\underset{Br}{\overset{|}{C}H}=CHCH_3} + \underset{\substack{\text{2,5-dibromo-3-hexene} \\ \textbf{1,4-addition product}}}{CH_3CH-CH=CH-\underset{Br}{\overset{|}{C}HCH_3}}$$

2,4-hexadiene

To understand why an electrophilic addition reaction to a conjugated diene forms both 1,2-addition and 1,4-addition products, we need to look at the mechanism of the reaction.

MECHANISM FOR THE REACTION OF A CONJUGATED DIENE WITH HBr

- The proton adds to C-1, forming an allylic cation. The allylic cation has delocalized electrons; therefore, the positive charge is shared by two carbons.
- The resonance contributors of the allylic cation show that the positive charge is shared by C-2 and C-4. Consequently, the bromide ion can add to either C-2 or C-4 to form the 1,2-addition product or the 1,4-addition product, respectively.

Notice that in the first step of the reaction, adding to C-1 is the same as adding to C-4 because 1,3-butadiene is symmetrical. The proton does not add to C-2 or to C-3 because doing so would form a primary carbocation. The primary carbocation would not have delocalized electrons. Thus, it would not be as stable as the allylic cation, which has delocalized electrons.

As we look at more examples, notice that the first step in all electrophilic additions to conjugated dienes is addition of the electrophile to one of the sp^2 carbons at the end of the conjugated system. This is the only way to form a carbocation that is stabilized by electron delocalization. If the electrophile were to add to one of the internal sp^2 carbons, the resulting carbocation would not have delocalized electrons.

$$CH_3\overset{\delta+}{-}CH\text{===}CH\overset{\delta+}{\text{===}}CH_2$$

PROBLEM 25 ♦

Give the products of the following reactions, assuming that one equivalent of each reagent is used in each reaction:

a. $CH_3CH\text{=}CH\text{—}CH\text{=}CHCH_3$ $\xrightarrow{Cl_2}$ **c.** ⬠ $\xrightarrow{Br_2}$

b. $CH_3CH\text{=}\underset{\underset{CH_3}{|}}{C}\text{—}\overset{\overset{CH_3}{|}}{C}\text{=}CHCH_3$ $\xrightarrow{HBr}$

PROBLEM 26

What stereoisomers are obtained from the reactions shown on pages 305 and 306. (*Hint:* Review Section 5.19.)

If the conjugated diene is not symmetrical, the major products of the reaction are those obtained by adding the electrophile to whichever sp^2 carbon at the end of the conjugated system results in formation of the more stable carbocation. For example, in the following reaction, the proton adds preferentially to C-1 because the positive charge on the resulting carbocation is shared by a tertiary allylic and a primary allylic carbon. Adding the proton to C-4 would form a carbocation in which the positive charge is shared by a secondary allylic and a primary allylic carbon. Because addition to C-1 forms the more stable carbocation, 3-bromo-3-methyl-1-butene and 1-bromo-3-methyl-2-butene are the major products of the reaction.

$$\overset{1}{CH_2}\text{=}\underset{\underset{2\text{-methyl-1,3-butadiene}}{}}{\overset{\overset{CH_3}{|}}{C}}\text{—}CH\text{=}\overset{4}{CH_2} + HBr \longrightarrow CH_3\text{—}\underset{\underset{Br}{|}}{\overset{\overset{CH_3}{|}}{C}}\text{—}CH\text{=}CH_2 + CH_3\text{—}\overset{\overset{CH_3}{|}}{C}\text{=}CH\text{—}\underset{\underset{Br}{|}}{CH_2}$$

3-bromo-3-methyl-
1-butene   1-bromo-3-methyl-
2-butene

$$CH_3\overset{+}{\underset{}{C}}\text{—}CH\text{=}CH_2 \longleftrightarrow CH_3\overset{\overset{CH_3}{|}}{C}\text{=}CH\text{—}\overset{+}{CH_2} \qquad CH_2\text{=}\overset{\overset{CH_3}{|}}{C}\text{—}\overset{+}{CHCH_3} \longleftrightarrow \overset{+}{CH_2}\text{—}\overset{\overset{CH_3}{|}}{C}\text{=}CHCH_3$$

carbocation formed by adding H⁺ to C-1   **carbocation formed by adding H⁺ to C-4**

PROBLEM 27

What products would be obtained from the reaction of 1,3,5-hexatriene with one equivalent of HBr? Disregard stereoisomers.

PROBLEM 28

Give the products of the following reactions, disregarding stereoisomers. (One equivalent of each reagent is used in each reaction.)

a. $CH_3CH\text{=}CH\text{—}\underset{\underset{CH_3}{|}}{C}\text{=}CH_2$ $\xrightarrow{Cl_2}$ **b.** $CH_3CH\text{=}CH\text{—}\underset{\underset{CH_3}{|}}{C}\text{=}CHCH_3$ $\xrightarrow{HBr}$

7.11 THERMODYNAMIC VERSUS KINETIC CONTROL OF REACTIONS

When a conjugated diene undergoes an electrophilic addition reaction, two factors—the temperature at which the reaction is carried out and the structure of the reactant—determine whether the 1,2-addition product or the 1,4-addition product will be the major product of the reaction.

When a reaction produces more than one product, *the most rapidly formed product* is called the **kinetic product**, and *the most stable product* is called the **thermodynamic product**. Reactions that produce the kinetic product as the major product are said to be **kinetically controlled**. Reactions that produce the thermodynamic product as the major product are said to be **thermodynamically controlled**.

In many organic reactions, the most stable product is also the one that is formed most rapidly. In other words, the kinetic product and the thermodynamic product are one and the same. Electrophilic addition to 1,3-butadiene is an example of a reaction in which the kinetic product and the thermodynamic product are *not* the same: the 1,2-addition product is the kinetic product, and the 1,4-addition product is the thermodynamic product.

> The kinetic product is the product that is formed most rapidly.

> The thermodynamic product is the most stable product.

$$CH_2=CHCH=CH_2 \ + \ HBr \ \longrightarrow \ \underset{\underset{Br}{|}}{CH_3CHCH=CH_2} \ + \ \underset{\underset{Br}{|}}{CH_3CH=CHCH_2}$$

1,3-butadiene

1,2-addition product **1,4-addition product**
kinetic product **thermodynamic product**

For a reaction in which the kinetic and thermodynamic products are not the same, the product that predominates depends on the conditions under which the reaction is carried out. If the reaction is carried out under conditions that are sufficiently mild (low in temperature) to cause the reaction to be *irreversible*, the major product will be the *kinetic product*. For example, when addition of HBr to 1,3-butadiene is carried out at −80 °C, the major product is the *1,2-addition product*, the product that is formed more rapidly.

> The kinetic product predominates when the reaction is irreversible.

$$CH_2=CHCH=CH_2 \ + \ HBr \ \xrightarrow{-80 \ °C} \ \underset{\underset{Br}{|}}{CH_3CHCH=CH_2} \ + \ \underset{\underset{Br}{|}}{CH_3CH=CHCH_2}$$

1,2-addition product **1,4-addition product**
80% **20%**

If, on the other hand, the reaction is carried out under conditions that are sufficiently vigorous (high in temperature) to cause the reaction to be *reversible*, the major product will be the *thermodynamic product*. Therefore, when the same reaction is carried out at 45 °C, the major product is the *1,4-addition product*—the product that is more stable.

> The thermodynamic product predominates when the reaction is reversible.

$$CH_2=CHCH=CH_2 \ + \ HBr \ \underset{}{\overset{45 \ °C}{\rightleftharpoons}} \ \underset{\underset{Br}{|}}{CH_3CHCH=CH_2} \ + \ \underset{\underset{Br}{|}}{CH_3CH=CHCH_2}$$

1,2-addition product **1,4-addition product**
15% **85%**

A reaction coordinate diagram helps explain why different products predominate under different reaction conditions (Figure 7.9). The first step of the addition reaction is the same whether the 1,2-addition product or the 1,4-addition product is ultimately formed: a proton adds to C-1. The second step of the reaction is the one that determines whether the nucleophile (Br⁻) adds to C-2 or C-4.

◀ **Figure 7.9**
A reaction coordinate diagram for the addition of HBr to 1,3-butadiene.

At low temperatures ($-80\ ^\circ$C), there is enough energy for the reactants to overcome the energy barrier for the first step of the reaction, and there is enough energy for the intermediate formed in the first step to form the two addition products. However, there is not enough energy for the reverse reaction to occur: the products cannot overcome the large energy barriers separating them from the intermediate. Consequently, the relative amounts of the two products obtained at $-80\ ^\circ$C reflect the relative energy barriers for the second step of the reaction. The energy barrier to formation of the 1,2-addition product is lower than the energy barrier to formation of the 1,4-addition product, so the major product is the 1,2-addition product.

In contrast, at 45 $^\circ$C, there is enough energy for one or more of the products to revert back to the intermediate. The intermediate is called a **common intermediate** because it is an intermediate that both products have in common. Even if both products can revert back to the common intermediate, it is easier for the 1,2-addition product to do so. Each time the 1,2-addition product reverts back to the common intermediate, the common intermediate can reform the 1,2-addition product or form the 1,4-addition product. Thus, the ability to revert to a common intermediate allows the products to interconvert. When two products can interconvert, their relative amounts at equilibrium depend on their relative stabilities.

Thus, a reaction that is *irreversible* under the conditions employed in the experiment is *kinetically controlled*. When a reaction is under *kinetic control*, the relative amounts of the products *depend on the rates* at which they are formed.

When sufficient energy is available to make the reaction *reversible, it is thermodynamically controlled*. When a reaction is under *thermodynamic control*, the relative amounts of the products *depend on their stabilities*.

For each reaction that is irreversible under mild conditions and reversible under more vigorous conditions, there is a temperature at which the change from irreversible to reversible occurs. The temperature at which a reaction changes from being kinetically controlled to being thermodynamically controlled depends on the reactants. For example, the reaction of 1,3-butadiene with HCl remains under kinetic control at 45 °C, even though addition of HBr to 1,3-butadiene is under thermodynamic control at that temperature. Because a C—Cl bond is stronger than a C—Br bond (Table 3.2), a higher temperature is required for the products containing a C—Cl bond to undergo the reverse reaction. (Remember, thermodynamic control is achieved only when there is sufficient energy to reverse one or both of the reactions.)

For the reaction of 1,3-butadiene with HBr, why is the 1,4-addition product more stable? We saw in Section 4.13 that the relative stability of an alkene is determined by the number of alkyl groups bonded to its sp^2 carbons: the greater the number of alkyl groups, the more stable is the alkene. The two products formed from the reaction of 1,3-butadiene with one equivalent of HBr have different stabilities since the 1,2-addition product has one alkyl group bonded to its sp^2 carbons, whereas the 1,4-product has two alkyl groups bonded to its sp^2 carbons. The 1,4-addition product, therefore, is more stable. Thus, it is the thermodynamic product.

$$CH_3CHCH{=}CH_2 \qquad\qquad CH_3CH{=}CHCH_2$$
$$\quad\;\mid \qquad\qquad\qquad\qquad\qquad\qquad \mid$$
$$\quad\;Br \qquad\qquad\qquad\qquad\qquad\qquad Br$$

1,2-addition product   **1,4-addition product**
kinetic product   **thermodynamic product**

The next question we need to answer is, why is the 1,2-addition product formed faster? For many years, chemists thought it was because the transition state for formation of the 1,2-addition product resembles the resonance contributor in which the positive charge is on a secondary allylic carbon. In contrast, the transition state for formation of the 1,4-addition product resembles the resonance contributor in which the positive charge is on a less stable primary allylic carbon.

transition state for formation of the 1,2-addition product   **transition state for formation of the 1,4-addition product**

If this explanation were correct, the kinetically controlled reaction of 1,3-pentadiene with DCl would form equal amounts of the 1,2- and 1,4-addition products, because their transition states would both have the same stability (both would have a partial positive charge on a secondary allylic carbon). However, the kinetically controlled reaction of 1,3-pentadiene forms essentially the same relative amounts of the two addition products as are formed by the kinetically controlled reaction of 1,3-butadiene. Why is the 1,2-addition product formed faster in both reactions?

1,3 pentadiene

1,2-addition product
78%

1,4-addition product
22%

The answer is that after D^+ adds to the double bond, the chloride ion can form a bond with C-2 faster than it can form a bond with C-4 simply because it is closer to C-2 than to C-4. So it is a *proximity effect* that causes the 1,2-addition product to be formed faster. A **proximity effect** is an effect caused by one species being close to another.

secondary allylic cation

$$CH_2-\overset{2}{\underset{\underset{D}{|}}{CH}}-CH=CHCH_3 \quad \longleftrightarrow \quad CH_2-CH=CH-\overset{4}{\underset{\underset{D}{|}}{CH}}CH_3$$

Cl⁻   Cl⁻

Cl⁻ is closer to C-2 than to C-4

PROBLEM 29◆

a. Why does deuterium add to C-1 rather than to C-4 in the preceding reaction?
b. Why was DCl rather than HCl used in the reaction?

PROBLEM 30◆

a. When HBr adds to a conjugated diene, what is the rate-determining step?
b. When HBr adds to a conjugated diene, what is the product-determining step?

Because the greater proximity of the nucleophile to C-2 contributes to the faster rate of formation of the 1,2-addition product, the 1,2-addition product is the kinetic product for the reactions of essentially all conjugated dienes. Do *not* assume, however, that the 1,4-addition product is *always* the thermodynamic product. The structure of the conjugated diene is what ultimately determines the thermodynamic product. For example, the 1,2-addition product is both the kinetic product and the thermodynamic product in the following reaction, because not only is it formed faster, it is also more stable than the 1,4-product.

why more stable?

$$\underset{\text{4-methyl-1,3-pentadiene}}{CH_2=CHCH=\overset{\overset{\displaystyle CH_3}{|}}{C}CH_3} \; + \; HBr \; \longrightarrow \; \underset{\substack{\text{4-bromo-2-methyl-2-pentene}\\\text{1,2-addition product}\\\text{kinetic product}\\\text{thermodynamic product}}}{CH_3\underset{\underset{Br}{|}}{C}HCH=\overset{\overset{\displaystyle CH_3}{|}}{C}CH_3} \; + \; \underset{\substack{\text{4-bromo-4-methyl-2-pentene}\\\text{1,4-addition product}}}{CH_3CH=CH\underset{\underset{Br}{|}}{\overset{\overset{\displaystyle CH_3}{|}}{C}}CH_3}$$

The 1,2- and 1,4-addition products obtained from the next reaction have the same stability because both have the same number of alkyl groups bonded to their sp^2 carbons. Thus, neither is the thermodynamic product, but the 1,2-addition product is still the kinetic product.

$$\underset{\text{2,4-hexadiene}}{CH_3CH=CHCH=CHCH_3} \; \xrightarrow{\text{HCl}} \; \underset{\substack{\text{4-chloro-2-hexene}\\\text{1,2-addition product}\\\text{kinetic product}}}{CH_3CH_2\underset{\underset{Cl}{|}}{C}HCH=CHCH_3} \; + \; \underset{\substack{\text{2-chloro-3-hexene}\\\text{1,4-addition product}}}{CH_3CH_2CH=CH\underset{\underset{Cl}{|}}{C}HCH_3}$$

the products have the same stability

chem Tutorial:
place Thermodynamic product versus
kinetic product

PROBLEM 31   **SOLVED**

For each of the following reactions, give the major 1,2- and 1,4-addition products and indicate which is the kinetic product and which is the thermodynamic product:

  a.
        +   HCl   ⟶

  c.
        +   HCl   ⟶

  b.
        +   HCl   ⟶

Solution to 31a   First we need to determine which of the sp^2 carbons at the ends of the conjugated system gets the proton. The proton will be more apt to add to the sp^2 carbon indicated below because the resulting carbocation shares its positive charge with a tertiary allylic and a secondary allylic carbon. If the proton were to add to the sp^2 carbon at the other end of the conjugated system, the carbocation that would be formed would be less stable because its positive charge would be shared by a primary allylic and a secondary allylic carbon. Therefore, 3-chloro-3-methylcyclohexene is the 1,2-addition product and 3-chloro-1-methylcyclohexene is the 1,4-addition product. 3-Chloro-3-methylcyclohexene is the kinetic product because of the chloride ion's proximity to C-2, and 3-chloro-1-methylcyclohexene is the thermodynamic product because its more highly substituted double bond makes it more stable.

H⁺ adds here

HCl ⟶   ⟷   ⟶

+ Cl⁻

**3-chloro-3-
methylcyclohexene
kinetic
product**

**3-chloro-1-
methylcyclohexene
thermodynamic
product**

7.12 THE DIELS—ALDER REACTION IS A 1,4-ADDITION REACTION

Reactions that create new carbon–carbon bonds are very important to synthetic organic chemists because it is only through such reactions that small carbon skeletons can be converted into larger ones (Section 6.11). The Diels–Alder reaction is a particularly important reaction because it creates *two* new carbon–carbon bonds and in the process forms a cyclic molecule. In recognition of the importance of this reaction to synthetic organic chemistry, Otto Diels and Kurt Alder shared the Nobel Prize in Chemistry in 1950.

In a **Diels–Alder reaction**, a conjugated diene reacts with a compound containing a carbon–carbon double bond. The latter compound is called a **dienophile** because it "loves a diene." (Recall that Δ signifies heat.)

$$CH_2=CH-CH=CH_2 \quad + \quad CH_2=CH-R \quad \xrightarrow{\Delta}$$
   conjugated diene   **dienophile**

Although this reaction may not look like any reaction you have seen before, it is simply the 1,4-addition of an electrophile and a nucleophile to a conjugated diene. However, unlike the other 1,4-addition reactions you have seen—where the electrophile adds to the diene in the first step and the nucleophile adds to the carbocation in the second step—the Diels–Alder reaction is a **concerted reaction**: the addition of the electrophile and the nucleophile occurs in a single step. The reaction looks odd at first glance because the electrophile and the nucleophile that add to the conjugated diene are the adjacent sp^2 carbons of a double bond. As with other 1,4-addition reactions, the double bond in the product is between C-2 and C-3 of what was the conjugated diene.

conjugated diene	dienophile	transition state	
four π electrons	two π electrons	six π electrons	

nucleophile / electrophile → transition state ‡ → new σ bond / new double bond / new σ bond

The Diels–Alder reaction is a pericyclic reaction. A **pericyclic reaction** is a reaction that takes place in one step by a cyclic shift of electrons. It is also a cycloaddition reaction. A **cycloaddition reaction** is a reaction in which two reactants form a cyclic product. More precisely, the Diels–Alder reaction is a **[4 + 2] cycloaddition reaction** because, of the six π electrons that participate in the cyclic transition state, *four* come from the conjugated diene and *two* come from the dienophile. The reactivity of the dienophile is increased if one or more electron-withdrawing groups are attached to its sp^2 carbons.

nucleophile / electron-withdrawing group

a 1,4-addition reaction to 1,3-butadiene

An electron-withdrawing group, such as a carbonyl group (C=O) or a cyano (C≡N) group, withdraws electrons from the dienophile's double bond. This puts a partial positive charge on one of its sp^2 carbons. The partially positively charged sp^2 carbon is the electrophile that is attacked by the π electrons of the conjugated diene. Thus, the electon-withdrawing groups makes the dienophile a better electrophile (Figure 7.10). The other sp^2 carbon of the dienophile is the nucleophile that adds to C-4 of the diene.

resonance contributors of the dienophile

resonance hybrid

> The Diels–Alder reaction is a 1,4-addition of a dienophile to a conjugated diene.

◀ **Figure 7.10**
By comparing these electrostatic potential maps, you can see that an electron-withdrawing substituent decreases the electron density of the carbon–carbon double bond.

A Molecular Orbital Description of the Diels–Alder Reaction

The two new σ bonds formed in a Diels–Alder reaction result from a transfer of electron density between the reactants. Molecular orbital theory provides insight into this process. In a cycloaddition reaction, the orbitals of one reactant must overlap the orbitals of the second reactant. Because the new σ bonds in the product are formed by donation of electron density from one reactant to the other, we must consider the HOMO of one reactant and the LUMO of the other, because only an empty orbital can accept electrons. It does not matter whether we envision the overlap as between the HOMO of the dienophile and the LUMO of the diene or vice versa. We just need to consider the HOMO of one and the LUMO of the other.

To construct the HOMO and LUMO needed to illustrate the transfer of electrons, we need to look back at Figures 7.3 and 7.4. They show that the HOMO of the diene and the LUMO of the dienophile are both antisymmetric (Figure 7.11a) and that the LUMO of the diene and the HOMO of the dienophile are both symmetric (Figure 7.11b).

▶ **Figure 7.11**
The new σ bonds formed in a Diels–Alder reaction result from overlap of in-phase orbitals.
(a) Overlap of the HOMO of the diene and the LUMO of the dienophile.
(b) Overlap of the HOMO of the dienophile and the LUMO of the diene.

Pericyclic reactions, such as the Diels–Alder reaction, can be described by a theory called the *conservation of orbital symmetry*. This simple theory says that pericyclic reactions occur as a result of the overlap of in-phase orbitals. The phase of the orbitals in Figure 7.11 is indicated by their color. Thus, each new σ bond formed in a Diels–Alder reaction must be created by the overlap of orbitals of the same color. Because two new σ bonds are formed, we need to have four orbitals in the correct place and with the correct symmetry (color). The figure shows that, regardless of which pair of HOMO and LUMO we choose, the overlapping orbitals have the same color. In other words, a Diels–Alder reaction occurs with relative ease. The Diels–Alder reaction and other cycloaddition reactions will be discussed in greater detail in Section 30.4.

A wide variety of cyclic compounds can be obtained by varying the structures of the conjugated diene and the dienophile. Notice that compounds containing carbon–carbon triple bonds can also be used as dienophiles in Diels–Alder reactions to prepare compounds with two isolated double bonds.

If the dienophile has two carbon–carbon double bonds, two successive Diels–Alder reactions can occur if excess diene is available.

PROBLEM 32

Explain why a [2 + 2] cycloaddition reaction will not occur without the absorption of light. Recall that unless molecules absorb light, they have a ground-state electronic configuration; that is, the electrons are in the available orbitals with the lowest energy.

chem Tutorial:
place Diels–Alder reaction

Tutorial:
Molecular orbital

PROBLEM 33♦

Give the products of each of the following reactions:

a. $CH_2{=}CH{-}CH{=}CH_2$ + $CH_3\overset{O}{\overset{\|}{C}}{-}C{\equiv}C{-}\overset{O}{\overset{\|}{C}}CH_3$ $\xrightarrow{\Delta}$

b. $CH_2{=}CH{-}CH{=}CH_2$ + $HC{\equiv}C{-}C{\equiv}N$ $\xrightarrow{\Delta}$

c.

d.

Predicting the Product When Both Reagents Are Unsymmetrically Substituted

In each of the preceding Diels–Alder reactions, only one product is formed (disregarding stereoisomers) because at least one of the reacting molecules is symmetrically substituted. If both the diene and the dienophile are unsymmetrically substituted, however, two products are possible. The products are constitutional isomers.

Two products are possible because the reactants can align in two different ways.

The product that will be formed (or will be formed in greater yield) depends on the charge distribution in each of the reactants. To determine the charge distribution, we need to draw resonance contributors. In the reaction presented above, the methoxy group of the diene is capable of *donating electrons by resonance* (see Problem 20). As a result, the terminal carbon atom bears a partial negative charge. The carbonyl group of the dienophile, on the other hand, *withdraws electrons by resonance* (see Problem 19), so its terminal carbon has a partial positive charge.

resonance contributors of the diene

resonance contributors of the dienophile

The partially positively charged carbon atom of the dienophile will bond preferentially to the partially negatively charged carbon of the diene. Therefore, 2-methoxy-3-cyclohexenecarbaldehyde will be the major product.

PROBLEM 34◆

What would be the major product if the methoxy substituent in the preceding reaction were bonded to C-2 of the diene rather than to C-1?

PROBLEM 35

Write a general rule that can be used to predict the major product of a Diels–Alder reaction depending on the location of a resonance electron donating substituent on the diene.

PROBLEM 36◆

Give the products of each of the following reactions:

a. CH_2=CH—CH=CH—CH_3 + HC≡C—C≡N: $\xrightarrow{\Delta}$

b. CH_2=CH—$\underset{\underset{CH_3}{|}}{C}$=$CH_2$ + HC≡C—C≡N $\xrightarrow{\Delta}$

p orbitals of both adjacent carbons. The six π electrons are shared by all six carbons. Thus, benzene is a planar molecule with six delocalized π electrons.

Chemists use **resonance contributors**—structures with localized electrons—to approximate the structure of a compound that has delocalized electrons: the **resonance hybrid**. To draw resonance contributors, move only π electrons or lone-pair electrons toward an sp^2 or sp hybridized atom. The total number of electrons and the number of paired and unpaired electrons do not change.

The greater the predicted stability of the resonance contributor, the more it contributes to the structure of the hybrid and the more similar its structure is to the real molecule. The predicted stability is decreased by (1) an atom with an incomplete octet, (2) a negative (positive) charge not on the most electronegative (electropositive) atom, or (3) charge separation. A resonance hybrid is more stable than the predicted stability of any of its resonance contributors.

The extra stability a compound gains from having delocalized electrons is called **delocalization energy**, **resonance energy**, or **resonance stabilization**. It tells us how much more stable a compound with delocalized electrons is than it would be if its electrons were localized. The greater the number of relatively stable resonance contributors and the more nearly equivalent they are, the greater is the delocalization energy of the compound. Allylic and benzylic cations have delocalized electrons, so they are more stable than similarly substituted carbocations with localized electrons. Compounds such as benzene that are unusually stable because of large delocalization energies are called **aromatic compounds**.

Conjugated double bonds are separated by one single bond. **Isolated double bonds** are separated by more than one single bond. Because dienes with conjugated double bonds have delocalized electrons, they are more stable than dienes with isolated double bonds. The most stable alkene has the smallest heat of hydrogenation.

A molecular orbital results from the **linear combination of atomic orbitals** (LCAO). The number of orbitals is conserved; in other words, the number of molecular orbitals equals the number of atomic orbitals that produced them. Side-to-side overlap of in-phase *p* orbitals produces a **bonding molecular orbital**, which is more stable than the atomic orbitals. Side-to-side overlap of out-of-phase *p* orbitals produces an **antibonding molecular orbital**, which is less stable than the atomic orbitals. The **highest occupied molecular orbital (HOMO)** is the highest-energy MO that contains electrons. The **lowest unoccupied molecular orbital (LUMO)** is the lowest-energy MO that does not contain electrons.

As the MOs increase in energy, the number of nodes increases, the number of bonding interactions decreases, and the orbitals alternate from **symmetric** to **antisymmetric**. Molecular orbital theory and resonance contributors both show that electrons are delocalized and that electron delocalization makes a molecule more stable.

Electron delocalization can affect the pK_a of a compound. A carboxylic acid and a phenol are more acidic than an alcohol, and a protonated aniline is more acidic than a protonated amine because electron withdrawal stabilizes their conjugate bases and the loss of a proton is accompanied by an increase in delocalization energy. Donation of electrons through π bonds is called **resonance electron donation**; withdrawal of electrons through π bonds is called **resonance electron withdrawal**.

Electron delocalization can affect the nature of the product formed in a reaction. An isolated diene, like an alkene, undergoes only 1,2-addition. If there is only enough electrophilic reagent to add to one of the double bonds, it will add preferentially to the one that forms the more stable carbocation. A conjugated diene reacts with a limited amount of electrophilic reagent to form a **1,2-addition product** and a **1,4-addition product**. The first step is addition of the electrophile to one of the sp^2 carbons at the end of the conjugated system.

When a reaction produces more than one product, the product formed most rapidly is the **kinetic product**; the most stable product is the **thermodynamic product**. If the reaction is carried out under mild conditions so that it is irreversible, the major product will be the kinetic product; if the reaction is carried out under more vigorous conditions so that it is reversible, the major product will be the thermodynamic product. When a reaction is **kinetically controlled**, the relative amounts of the products depend on the rates at which they are formed; when a reaction is **thermodynamically controlled**, the relative amounts of the products depend on their stabilities. A **common intermediate** is an intermediate that both products have in common. In electrophilic addition to a conjugated diene, the 1,2-product is always the kinetic product; either the 1,2- or the 1,4-product can be the thermodynamic product, depending on the structures of the products.

In a **Diels–Alder reaction**, a **conjugated diene** reacts with a **dienophile** to form a cyclic compound; in this concerted **[4 + 2]** cycloaddition reaction, two new σ bonds are formed at the expense of two π bonds. The conjugated diene must be in an **s-cis conformation**. The reactivity of the **dienophile** is increased by electron-withdrawing groups attached to the sp^2 carbons. In the molecular orbital description of the reaction, the **HOMO** of one reactant and the **LUMO** of the other are used to show the transfer of electrons between the molecules. According to the conservation of orbital symmetry, **pericyclic reactions** occur as a result of the overlap of in-phase orbitals. If both the diene and the dienophile are unsymmetrically substituted, two products are possible because the reactants can be aligned in two different ways. The Diels–Alder reaction is a syn addition reaction. In **bridged bicyclic compounds**, a substituent can be **endo** or **exo**; endo is favored if the dienophile's substituent has π electrons.

SUMMARY OF REACTIONS

1. In the presence of excess electrophilic reagent, both double bonds of an *isolated diene* will undergo electrophilic addition.

$$CH_2=CHCH_2CH_2\overset{\overset{\displaystyle CH_3}{|}}{C}=CH_2 \;+\; HBr \underset{\textbf{excess}}{\longrightarrow} CH_3\overset{}{C}HCH_2CH_2\overset{\overset{\displaystyle CH_3}{|}}{\underset{\underset{\displaystyle Br}{|}}{C}}CH_3$$

In the presence of only one equivalent of electrophilic reagent, only the most reactive double bond of an *isolated diene* will undergo electrophilic addition (Section 7.10).

$$CH_2=CHCH_2CH_2\overset{\overset{\displaystyle CH_3}{|}}{C}=CH_2 \;+\; HBr \longrightarrow CH_2=CHCH_2CH_2\overset{\overset{\displaystyle CH_3}{|}}{\underset{\underset{\displaystyle Br}{|}}{C}}CH_3$$

2. Conjugated dienes undergo 1,2- and 1,4-addition in the presence of one equivalent of an electrophilic reagent (Section 7.10).

$$RCH=CHCH=CHR \;+\; HBr \longrightarrow RCH_2\overset{}{\underset{\underset{\displaystyle Br}{|}}{C}}HCH=CHR \;+\; RCH_2CH=CH\overset{}{\underset{\underset{\displaystyle Br}{|}}{C}}HR$$

$$\textbf{1,2-addition product} \qquad\qquad \textbf{1,4-addition product}$$

3. Conjugated dienes undergo 1,4-addition with a dienophile (a Diels–Alder reaction) (Section 7.12).

$$CH_2=CH-CH=CH_2 \;+\; CH_2=CH\overset{\overset{\displaystyle O}{\|}}{\underset{}{C}}{\diagdown}R \longrightarrow$$

KEY TERMS

1,2-addition (p. 307)
1,4-addition (p. 307)
1,2-addition product (p. 307)
1,4-addition product (p. 307)
allene (p. 292)
allylic carbon (p. 293)
allylic cation (p. 293)
antibonding molecular orbital (p. 294)
antisymmetric molecular orbital (p. 296)
aromatic compounds (p. 300)
benzylic carbon (p. 293)
benzylic cation (p. 293)
bonding molecular orbital (p. 294)
bridged bicyclic compound (p. 319)
common intermediate (p. 311)
concerted reaction (p. 310)
conjugate addition (p. 307)
conjugated dienes (p. 290)
conjugated double bonds (p. 290)
contributing resonance structure (p. 282)

cumulated double bonds (p. 292)
cycloaddition reaction (p. 315)
[4 + 2] cycloaddition reaction (p. 315)
delocalization energy (p. 288)
delocalized electrons (p. 278)
Diels–Alder reaction (p. 314)
diene (p. 290)
dienophile (p. 314)
direct addition (p. 307)
electron delocalization (p. 288)
endo (p. 319)
exo (p. 319)
highest occupied molecular orbital
    (HOMO) (p. 297)
isolated diene (p. 278)
isolated double bonds (p. 290)
kinetically controlled (p. 310)
kinetic product (p. 310)
linear combination of atomic orbitals
    (LCAO) (p. 295)

localized electrons (p. 278)
lowest unoccupied molecular orbital
    (LUMO) (p. 297)
pericyclic reaction (p. 315)
proximity effect (p. 313)
resonance (p. 288)
resonance contributor (p. 282)
resonance electron donation (p. 282)
resonance electron withdrawal (p. 304)
resonance energy (p. 288)
resonance hybrid (p. 282)
resonance stabilization energy (p. 288)
resonance structure (p. 282)
s-cis conformation (p. 319)
separated charges (p. 286)
s-trans conformation (p. 319)
symmetric molecular orbital (p. 296)
thermodynamically controlled (p. 310)
thermodynamic product (p. 310)

PROBLEMS

41. Which of the following have delocalized electrons?

a.

CH_2=CH C(=O) CH_3

b. CH_3CH=$CHOCH_2CH_3$

c. $CH_3\overset{+}{C}HCH_2CH$=$CH_2$

d.

e.

f. $CH_3\overset{+}{C}CH_2CH$=CH_2 (with CH_3 on the C)

g. CH_2=$CHCH_2CH$=CH_2

h. $CH_3CH_2NHCH_2CH$=$CHCH_3$

i.

j.

k.

l. $CH_3CH_2\overset{+}{C}HCH$=$CH_2$

m. CH_3CH_2NHCH=$CHCH_3$

n.

42. a. Draw resonance contributors for the following species, showing all the lone pairs:
   1. CH_2N_2 2. N_2O 3. NO_2^-
   b. For each species, indicate the most stable resonance contributor.

43. Give the major product of each of the following reactions, assuming the presence of one equivalent of each reagent:

a.

$+$ HBr $\longrightarrow$

b.

$+$ HBr $\longrightarrow$

44. Draw resonance contributors for the following ions:

a.

b.

c.

d.

45. Give all the products of the following reaction.

$+$ HO^-

46. Are the following pairs of structures resonance contributors or different compounds?

a.

CH_3 C(=O) CH_2CH_3 and CH_3 C(OH)= CH_2CH_3

b. $CH_3\overset{+}{C}HCH$=$CHCH_3$ and CH_3CH=$CHCH_2\overset{+}{C}H_2$

c. CH_3CH=$CH\overset{+}{C}HCH$=CH_2 and $CH_3\overset{+}{C}HCH$=$CHCH$=CH_2

d.

and

e.

and

47. a. How many linear dienes have molecular formula C_6H_{10}? (Disregard cis–trans isomers.)
   b. How many of the linear dienes in part a are conjugated dienes?
   c. How many are isolated dienes?

48. a. Draw resonance contributors for the following species. Do not include structures that are so unstable that their contributions to the resonance hybrid would be negligible. Indicate which are major contributors and which are minor contributors to the resonance hybrid.

   1. $CH_3CH=CHOCH_3$

   2.

   3.

   4.

   5.

   6. $CH_3CH=CH\overset{+}{C}H_2$

   7.

   8.

   9. $CH_3CH=CHCH=CH\overset{+}{C}H_2$

   10.

   11. $CH_3\overset{\cdot\cdot}{\overset{-}{C}}HCN$

   12.

   13.

   14.

   15.

   b. Do any of the species have resonance contributors that all contribute equally to the resonance hybrid?

49. Which compound would you expect to have the greater heat of hydrogenation, 1,2-pentadiene or 1,4-pentadiene?

50. Which resonance contributor makes the greater contribution to the resonance hybrid?

   a. $CH_3\overset{+}{C}HCH=CH_2$ or $CH_3CH=CH\overset{+}{C}H_2$

   b. or

   c. or

   d. or

51. a. Which oxygen atom has the greater electron density?

   b. Which compound has the greater electron density on its nitrogen atom?

c. Which compound has the greater electron density on its oxygen atom?

or

52. Which compound is a stronger base?

53. The triphenylmethyl cation is so stable that a salt such as triphenylmethyl chloride can be isolated and stored. Why is this carbocation so stable?

triphenylmethyl chloride

54. Which compound is a stronger acid?

or

55. Which can lose a proton more readily, a methyl group bonded to cyclohexane or a methyl group bonded to benzene?

or

56. Draw the resonance contributors for the following anion, and rank them in order of decreasing stability:

$$CH_3CH_2\ddot{O} \quad \overset{\displaystyle :\ddot{O}}{\underset{}{\overset{\|}{C}}} \quad \overset{}{\underset{}{CH-C\equiv N:}}$$

57. Rank the following compounds in order of decreasing acidity:

58. Which species in each pair is more stable?

a.

or

c.

or

b.

or

d.

or

59. Which species in each of the pairs in Problem 58 is the stronger base?

60. Why is the delocalization energy of pyrrole (21 kcal/mol) greater than that of furan (16 kcal/mol)?

pyrrole   furan

61. Rank the following compounds in order of decreasing acidity of the indicated hydrogen:

62. Answer the following questions for the π molecular orbitals of 1,3,5,7-octatetraene:
  a. How many π MOs does the compound have?
  b. Which are the bonding MOs, and which are the antibonding MOs?
  c. Which MOs are symmetric, and which are antisymmetric?
  d. Which MO is the HOMO, and which is the LUMO in the ground state?
  e. Which MO is the HOMO, and which is the LUMO in the excited state?
  f. What is the relationship between HOMO and LUMO and symmetric and antisymmetric orbitals?
  g. How many nodes does the highest-energy π molecular orbital of 1,3,5,7-octatetraene have between the nuclei?

63. A student treated 1,3-cyclohexadiene with Br_2 and obtained two products (disregarding stereoisomers). His lab partner treated 1,3-cyclohexadiene with HBr and was surprised to find that he obtained only one product (disregarding stereoisomers). Account for these results.

64. How could the following compounds be synthesized using a Diels–Alder reaction?
  a.
  c.
  b. CO$_2$CH$_3$
  d.

65. a. How could each of the following compounds be prepared from a hydrocarbon in a single step?

  1.   **2.**   **3.**

  b. What other organic compound would be obtained from each synthesis?

66. a. Give the products obtained from the reaction of 1 mol HBr with 1 mol 1,3,5-hexatriene.
  b. Which product(s) will predominate if the reaction is under kinetic control?
  c. Which product(s) will predominate if the reaction is under thermodynamic control?

67. How would the following substituents affect the rate of a Diels–Alder reaction?
  a. an electron-donating substituent in the diene
  b. an electron-donating substituent in the dienophile
  c. an electron-withdrawing substituent in the diene

68. Give the major products obtained from the reaction of one equivalent of HCl with the following compounds. For each reaction, indicate the kinetic and thermodynamic products.
  a. 2,3-dimethyl-1,3-pentadiene
  b. 2,4-dimethyl-1,3-pentadiene

69. The acid dissociation constant (K_a) for loss of a proton from cyclohexanol is 1×10^{-16}.

   a. Draw an energy diagram for loss of a proton from cyclohexanol.

b. Draw the resonance contributors for phenol.

c. Draw the resonance contributors for the phenolate ion.

d. On the same plot with the energy diagram for loss of a proton from cyclohexanol, draw an energy diagram for loss of a proton from phenol.

e. Which has a greater K_a, cyclohexanol or phenol?

f. Which is a stronger acid, cyclohexanol or phenol?

70. Protonated cyclohexylamine has a $K_a = 1 \times 10^{-11}$. Using the same sequence of steps as in Problem 69, determine which is a stronger base, cyclohexylamine or aniline.

71. Give the product or products that would be obtained from each of the following reactions:

a.

b.

c.

72. What two sets of a conjugated diene and a dienophile could be used to prepare the following compound?

73. a. Which dienophile in each pair is more reactive in a Diels–Alder reaction?

   1. $CH_2{=}CHCH$ or $CH_2{=}CHCH_2CH$ **2.** $CH_2{=}CHCH$ or $CH_2{=}CHCH_3$

   b. Which diene is more reactive in a Diels–Alder reaction?

$$CH_2{=}CHCH{=}CHOCH_3 \quad \text{or} \quad CH_2{=}CHCH{=}CHCH_2OCH_3$$

74. Cyclopentadiene can react with itself in a Diels–Alder reaction. Draw the endo and exo products.

75. Which diene and which dienophile could be used to prepare each of the following?

a.

c.

b.

d.

76. a. Give the products of the following reaction:

+ Br₂ ⟶

b. How many stereoisomers of each product could be obtained?

77. As many as 18 different Diels–Alder products could be obtained by heating a mixture of 1,3-butadiene and 2-methyl-1,3-butadiene. Identify the products.

78. On a single graph, draw the reaction coordinate for the addition of one equivalent of HBr to 2-methyl-1,3-pentadiene and one equivalent of HBr to 2-methyl-1,4-pentadiene. Which reaction is faster?

79. While attempting to recrystallize maleic anhydride, a student dissolved it in freshly distilled cyclopentadiene rather than in freshly distilled cyclopentane. Was his recrystallization successful?

O≼–O–≽O

maleic anhydride

80. The following equilibrium is driven to the right if the reaction is carried out in the presence of maleic anhydride (see Problem 79):

What is the function of maleic anhydride?

81. In 1935, J. Bredt, a German chemist, proposed that a bicycloalkene could not have a double bond at a bridgehead carbon unless one of the rings contains at least eight carbons. This is known as Bredt's rule. Explain why there cannot be a double bond at this position.

bridgehead
carbon

82. The experiment shown below and discussed in Section 7.11, showed that the proximity of the chloride ion to C-2 in the transition state caused the 1,2-addition product to be formed faster than the 1,4-addition product:

CH_2=CHCH=CHCH₃ + DCl $\xrightarrow{\text{–78 °C}}$ CH₂CHCH=CHCH₃ + CH₂CH=CHCHCH₃
    | | | |
    D Cl   D   Cl

a. Why was it important for the investigators to know that the reaction was being carried out under kinetic control?
b. How could the investigators determine that the reaction was being carried out under kinetic control?

83. A student wanted to know whether the greater proximity of the nucleophile to the C-2 carbon in the transition state is what causes the 1,2-addition product to be formed faster when 1,3-butadiene reacts with HCl. Therefore, she decided to investigate the reaction of 2-methyl-1,3-cyclohexadiene with HCl. Her friend told her that she should use 1-methyl-1,3-cyclohexadiene instead. Should she follow her friend's advice?

Substitution and Elimination Reactions

The first three chapters in Part 3 discuss the reactions of compounds that have an electron-withdrawing atom or group—a potential leaving group—bonded to an sp^3 hybridized carbon. These compounds can undergo substitution reactions, elimination reactions, or both. The fourth chapter in Part 3 introduces you to organometallic compounds, a class of nucleophiles that can participate in substitution reactions. The last chapter in Part 3 discusses the reactions of alkanes, compounds that do not have a leaving group but that can undergo a radical substitution reaction under extreme conditions.

CHAPTER 8
Substitution Reactions of Alkyl Halides

Chapter 8 discusses the substitution reactions of alkyl halides. Of the different compounds that undergo substitution and elimination reactions, alkyl halides are examined first because they have relatively good leaving groups. The chapter also describes the kinds of compounds that biological organisms use in place of alkyl halides, since alkyl halides are not readily available in nature.

CHAPTER 9
Elimination Reactions of Alkyl Halides • Competition Between Substitution and Elimination

Chapter 9 covers the elimination reactions of alkyl halides. Because many alkyl halides can undergo both substitution and elimination reactions, this chapter also discusses the factors that determine whether a given alkyl halide will undergo a substitution reaction, an elimination reaction, or both substitution and elimination reactions.

CHAPTER 10
Reactions of Alcohols, Amines, Ethers, Epoxides, and Sulfur-Containing Compounds

Chapter 10 discusses compounds other than alkyl halides that undergo substitution and elimination reactions. There you will see that because alcohols and ethers have relatively poor leaving groups compared with the leaving groups of alkyl halides, alcohols and ethers must be activated before they can be substituted or eliminated. Several methods commonly used to activate leaving groups will be examined. The chapter also looks at the reactions of epoxides, which show how ring strain affects leaving ability. Amines have such poor leaving groups that they cannot undergo substitution and elimination reactions. However, quaternary ammonium ions, which have much better leaving groups than amines, do undergo elimination reactions. The chapter also compares the reactions of thiols and sulfides with those of alcohols and ethers.

CHAPTER 11
Organometallic Compounds

Organometallic compounds are very important to synthetic organic chemists. These compounds contain a carbon–metal bond. Because the metal is less electronegative than carbon, organometallic compounds are used as a source of nucleophilic alkyl groups. They are also used in reactions that form new carbon–carbon single bonds as well as new carbon–carbon double bonds.

CHAPTER 12
Radicals • Reactions of Alkanes

Chapter 12 discusses the substitution reactions of alkanes, hydrocarbons that contain only single bonds. In previous chapters, we have seen that when a compound reacts, the weakest bond in the molecule breaks first. Alkanes, however, have only strong bonds. Therefore, conditions vigorous enough to generate radicals are required for alkanes to react. The chapter also looks at radical substitution reactions and radical addition reactions of alkenes. It concludes with a discussion of some radical reactions that occur in the biological world.

8

Substitution Reactions of Alkyl Halides

AN ELECTRONEGATIVE ATOM OR AN ELECTRON-WITHDRAWING GROUP ATTACHED TO AN sp^3 carbon creates a polar bond. A compound with such a bond can undergo substitution reactions and/or elimination reactions.

$$\overset{\delta+}{RCH_2}\text{—}\overset{\delta-}{X}$$

An electronegative atom or an electron-withdrawing group

a polar bond

In a **substitution reaction**, the electronegative atom or electron-withdrawing group is replaced by another atom or group. In an **elimination reaction**, the electronegative atom or electron-withdrawing group is eliminated, along with a hydrogen from an adjacent carbon. The atom or group that is *substituted* or *eliminated* in these reactions is called a **leaving group**.

$$RCH_2CH_2X \;+\; Y^-$$

a substitution reaction → $RCH_2CH_2Y \;+\; X^-$

an elimination reaction → $RCH{=}CH_2 \;+\; HY \;+\; X^-$

the leaving group

This chapter focuses on the substitution reactions of alkyl halides—compounds in which the leaving group is a halide ion (F^-, Cl^-, Br^-, or I^-). The nomenclature of alkyl halides was discussed in Section 2.4.

alkyl halides

R—F	R—Cl	R—Br	R—I
an alkyl fluoride	**an alkyl chloride**	**an alkyl bromide**	**an alkyl iodide**

In Chapter 9, we will discuss the elimination reactions of alkyl halides and the factors that determine whether substitution or elimination will prevail when an alkyl halide undergoes a reaction.

Alkyl halides are a good family of compounds with which to start the study of substitution and elimination reactions because they have relatively good leaving groups; that is, the halide ions are easily displaced. After studying the reactions of alkyl halides, you will be prepared to look, in Chapter 10, at the substitution and elimination reactions of compounds with poor leaving groups—those that are more difficult to displace.

Substitution reactions are important in organic chemistry because they make it possible to convert readily available alkyl halides into a wide variety of other compounds. Substitution reactions are also important in the cells of plants and animals. We will see, however, that because alkyl halides are insoluble in water, and cells exist in predominantly aqueous environments, biological systems use compounds in which the group that is replaced is more polar than a halogen and, therefore, more soluble in water.

Survival Compounds

For a long time chemists thought that only a few organic compounds containing halogen atoms (organohalides) occurred in nature. Now, however, over 5000 naturally occurring organohalides are known. Several marine organisms, including sponges, corals, and algae, synthesize organohalides that they use to deter predators. For example, red algae synthesize a toxic, foul-tasting organohalide that keeps predators from eating them. One predator that is not deterred, however, is a mollusk called a sea hare. After

consuming red algae, a sea hare converts the algae's organohalide into a structurally similar compound it uses for its own defense. Unlike other mollusks, a sea hare does not have a shell. Its method of defense is to surround itself with a slimy substance that contains the organohalide, thereby protecting itself from carnivorous fish.

Humans synthesize organohalides to defend against infection. The human immune system has an enzyme that kills invading bacteria by halogenating them.

synthesized by red algae

synthesized by the sea hare

a sea hare

8.1   THE MECHANISM FOR AN S$_N$2 REACTION

You will see that there are two different mechanisms by which a substitution reaction can take place. As you would expect, each of these mechanisms involves the *reaction of a nucleophile with an electrophile*. In both mechanisms, the atom or group that replaces the leaving group is a nucleophile. The substitution reactions therefore are more precisely called **nucleophilic substitution reactions**.

Perhaps you have been wondering how the mechanism for a reaction is determined. Remember that a mechanism describes the step-by-step process by which reactants are converted into products. It is a theory that fits the accumulated experimental evidence pertaining to the reaction. We can learn a great deal about a reaction's mechanism by studying its **kinetics**—the factors that affect the rate of the reaction.

The rate of the reaction of bromomethane with hydroxide ion—a nucleophilic substitution reaction—depends on the concentrations of both reagents. If the concentration of bromomethane in the reaction mixture is doubled, the rate of the reaction doubles. Likewise,

**Edward Davies Hughes
(1906–1963)**, *born in northern
Wales, earned a Ph.D. from the
University of Wales and a
D.Sc. from the University of
London, where he worked with
Sir Christopher Ingold. He was
a professor of chemistry at
University College, London.*

if the concentration of the nucleophile (hydroxide ion) is doubled, the rate of the reaction doubles. If the concentrations of both reactants are doubled, the rate of the reaction quadruples.

$$CH_3Br \ + \ HO^- \ \longrightarrow \ CH_3OH \ + \ Br^-$$
bromomethane   methanol

Because we know the relationship between the rate of the reaction and the concentration of the reactants, we can write a rate law for the reaction (Section 3.8):

rate ∝ [alkyl halide][nucleophile]

The proportionality sign (∝) can be replaced by an equals sign and a proportionality constant (k).

The proportionality constant is called a **rate constant**. The magnitude of the rate constant for a particular reaction indicates how difficult it is for the reactants to overcome the energy barrier of the reaction—how hard it is to reach the transition state. The larger the rate constant, the lower is the energy barrier and, therefore, the easier it is for the reactants to reach the transition state (see Figure 8.3 on page 337).

rate = k [alkyl halide][nucleophile]

the rate constant

The **rate law** tells us which molecules are involved in the transition state of the rate-determining step of the reaction. From the rate law for the reaction of bromomethane with hydroxide ion, for example, we know that *both* bromomethane and hydroxide ion are involved in the rate-determining transition state. Because the rate of this reaction depends linearly on the concentration of each of the two reactants, the reaction is a **second-order reaction**.

PROBLEM 1♦

How is the rate of the reaction affected if the concentration of bromomethane is changed from 1.00 M to 0.50 M?

Sir Christopher Ingold (1893–1970),
*in addition to determining the
mechanism for the S_N2 reaction,
was a member of the group that
developed the system of nomenclature for enantiomers (see
page 201). He also participated
in developing resonance theory.*

The reaction of bromomethane with hydroxide ion is an example of an **S_N2 reaction**, where "S" stands for substitution, "N" for nucleophilic, and "2" for bimolecular. **Bimolecular** means that two molecules are involved in the transition state of the rate-determining step. In 1937, Edward Hughes and Christopher Ingold proposed a mechanism for an S_N2 reaction. They based their mechanism on the following three pieces of *experimental evidence*:

1. The rate of the substitution reaction depends on the concentration of the alkyl halide *and* on the concentration of the nucleophile, indicating that both reactants are involved in the transition state of the rate-determining step.

2. As the hydrogens of bromomethane are successively replaced with methyl groups, the rate of the substitution reaction with a given nucleophile becomes progressively slower (Table 8.1).

3. The substitution reaction of an alkyl halide in which the halogen is bonded to an asymmetric center leads to the formation of only one stereoisomer, and the configuration of the asymmetric center in the product is inverted relative to its configuration in the reacting alkyl halide.

Hughes and Ingold proposed that an S_N2 reaction is a *concerted* reaction (that is, it takes place in a single step), so no intermediates are formed. The nucleophile attacks the electrophilic carbon that bears the leaving group, and displaces the leaving group.

Table 8.1 Relative Rates of S$_N$2 Reactions for Several Alkyl Halides

$$R-Br \ + \ Cl^- \ \xrightarrow{S_N2} \ R-Cl \ + \ Br^-$$

Alkyl halide	Class of alkyl halide	Relative rate
CH$_3$—Br	methyl	1200
CH$_3$CH$_2$—Br	primary	40
CH$_3$CH$_2$CH$_2$—Br	primary	16
CH$_3$CH—Br \ | \ CH$_3$	secondary	1
CH$_3$ | CH$_3$C—Br | CH$_3$	tertiary	too slow to measure

MECHANISM FOR THE S$_N$2 REACTION OF AN ALKYL HALIDE

An S$_N$2 reaction is a one-step reaction.

A productive collision is one that leads to the formation of the product. A productive collision in an S$_N$2 reaction requires the nucleophile to hit the carbon on the side opposite the side bonded to the leaving group. Therefore, the carbon is said to undergo **back-side attack**. Why must the nucleophile attack from the back side? The simplest explanation is that the leaving group blocks the approach of the nucleophile to the front side of the molecule.

Molecular orbital theory also explains back-side attack. Recall from Section 7.12 that to form a bond, the LUMO (lowest unoccupied molecular orbital) of one species must interact with the HOMO (highest occupied molecular orbital) of the other. When the nucleophile approaches the alkyl halide, the filled nonbonding molecular orbital (the HOMO) of the nucleophile must interact with the empty σ^* antibonding molecular orbital (the LUMO) associated with the C—Br bond. Figure 8.1a shows that in a back-side attack, a bonding interaction occurs between the nucleophile and the larger lobe of σ^*. Compare this with what happens when the nucleophile approaches the front side of the carbon (Figure 8.1b): Both a bonding and an antibonding interaction occur, and the two cancel each other, so no bond forms. Consequently, a nucleophile always approaches an sp^3 carbon from its back side. (We saw back-side attack previously in the reaction of a bromide ion with a cyclic bromonium ion; Section 5.19.)

How does Hughes and Ingold's mechanism account for the three pieces of experimental evidence? The mechanism shows that the alkyl halide and the nucleophile come together in the transition state of the one-step reaction. Therefore, increasing the concentration of either of them makes their collision more probable. Thus, the reaction will follow second-order kinetics, exactly as observed.

A nucleophile attacks the back side of the carbon that is bonded to the leaving group.

transition state

▶ **Figure 8.1**
(a) Back-side attack results in a bonding interaction between the HOMO (the filled nonbonding orbital) of the nucleophile and the LUMO (the empty σ^* antibonding orbital) of C—Br.
(b) Front-side attack results in both a bonding and an antibonding interaction that cancel each other out.

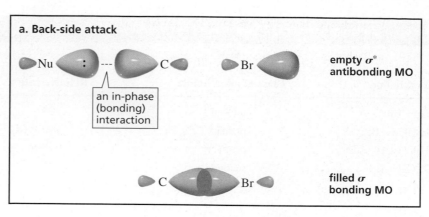

a. **Back-side attack**

an in-phase (bonding) interaction

empty σ^* antibonding MO

filled σ bonding MO

b. **Front-side attack**

an out-of-phase (antibonding) interaction

an in-phase (bonding) interaction

empty σ^* antibonding MO

filled σ bonding MO

Viktor Meyer (1848–1897) *was born in Germany. To prevent him from becoming an actor, his parents persuaded him to enter the University of Heidelberg, where he earned a Ph.D. in 1867 at the age of 18. Meyer was a professor of chemistry at the Universities of Stuttgart and Heidelberg. He coined the term* stereochemistry *for the study of molecular shapes and was the first to describe the effect of steric hindrance on a reaction.*

Bulky substituents attached to the carbon that undergoes back-side attack will decrease the nucleophile's access to the carbon's back side and will therefore decrease the rate of the reaction (Figure 8.2). This explains why substituting methyl groups for the hydrogens in bromomethane progressively slows the rate of the substitution reaction (Table 8.1).

▲ **Figure 8.2**
The approach of HO^- to a methyl halide, a primary alkyl halide, a secondary alkyl halide, and a tertiary alkyl halide. Increasing the bulk of the substituents bonded to the carbon that is undergoing nucleophilic attack decreases access to the back side of the carbon, thereby decreasing the rate of the S_N2 reaction.

Steric effects are effects caused by the fact that groups occupy a certain volume of space (Section 2.10). A steric effect that decreases reactivity is called **steric hindrance**. Steric hindrance occurs when groups are in the way at a reaction site. Steric hindrance causes alkyl halides to have the following relative reactivities in an S_N2 reaction because, *generally*, primary alkyl halides are less sterically hindered than secondary alkyl halides, which, in turn, are less sterically hindered than tertiary alkyl halides:

The relative lack of steric hindrance causes methyl halides and primary alkyl halides to be the most reactive alkyl halides in S_N2 reactions.

relative reactivities of alkyl halides in an S_N2 reaction

| most reactive | methyl halide > 1° alkyl halide > 2° alkyl halide > 3° alkyl halide | too unreactive to undergo an S_N2 reaction |

Tertiary alkyl halides cannot undergo S_N2 reactions.

The three alkyl groups of a tertiary alkyl halide make it impossible for the nucleophile to come within bonding distance of the tertiary carbon, so tertiary alkyl halides are unable to undergo S_N2 reactions.

The reaction coordinate diagrams for the S$_N$2 reaction of *unhindered* bromomethane (Figure 8.3a) and for the S$_N$2 reaction of a *sterically hindered* secondary alkyl bromide (Figure 8.3b) show that steric hindrance raises the energy of the transition state, slowing the reaction.

▲ Figure 8.3
Reaction coordinate diagrams for (a) the S$_N$2 reaction of bromomethane with hydroxide ion; (b) an S$_N$2 reaction of a sterically hindered secondary alkyl bromide with hydroxide ion.

PROBLEM 2◆

Does increasing the energy barrier for an S$_N$2 reaction increase or decrease the magnitude of the rate constant for the reaction?

The rate of an S$_N$2 reaction depends not only on the *number* of alkyl groups attached to the carbon that is undergoing nucleophilic attack, but also on their size. For example, while bromoethane and 1-bromopropane are both primary alkyl halides, bromoethane is more than twice as reactive in an S$_N$2 reaction (Table 8.1) because the bulkier alkyl group on the carbon undergoing nucleophilic attack in 1-bromopropane provides more steric hindrance to back-side attack. Also, although 1-bromo-2,2-dimethylpropane is a primary alkyl halide, it undergoes S$_N$2 reactions very slowly because its single alkyl group is unusually bulky.

$$CH_3CCH_2Br$$ with CH_3 above and CH_3 below the central C
1-bromo-2,2-dimethylpropane

Now we will look at the third piece of experimental evidence used by Hughes and Ingold to arrive at their proposed mechanism. Figure 8.4 shows that as the nucleophile approaches the back side of the carbon of bromomethane, the C—H bonds begin to move away from the nucleophile and its attacking electrons. By the time the transition state is reached, the C—H bonds are all in the same plane and the carbon is pentacoordinate (fully bonded to three atoms and partially bonded to two) rather than tetrahedral. As the nucleophile gets closer to the carbon and the bromine moves farther away from it, the C—H bonds continue to move in the same direction. Eventually, the bond between carbon and the nucleophile is fully formed, and the bond between carbon and bromine is completely broken, so the carbon is once again tetrahedral.

three bonds are in the same plane

▲ Figure 8.4
An S$_N$2 reaction between hydroxide ion and bromomethane.

chem Tutorial:
place S_N2

Tutorial:
S_N2: a concerted reaction

Tutorial:
Steric hindrance in the S_N2 reaction

The carbon at which substitution occurs has inverted its configuration during the course of the reaction, just like an umbrella tends to invert in a windstorm. This **inversion of configuration** is called a *Walden inversion*, after Paul Walden, who first discovered that the configuration of a compound becomes inverted during the course of an S_N2 reaction.

Because an S_N2 reaction takes place with inversion of configuration, only one substitution product is formed when an alkyl halide whose halogen atom is bonded to an asymmetric center undergoes an S_N2 reaction. The configuration of that product is inverted relative to the configuration of the alkyl halide. For example, the substitution product obtained from the reaction of hydroxide ion with (*R*)-2-bromopentane is (*S*)-2-pentanol. Thus, the mechanism proposed by Hughes and Ingold also accounts for the observed configuration of the product.

To draw the inverted product of an S_N2 reaction, draw the mirror image of the reactant and replace the halogen with the nucleophile.

the configuration of the product is inverted relative to the configuration of the reactant

$$CH_3CH_2 \overset{CH_3}{\underset{Br}{C}} H \quad + \quad HO^- \quad \longrightarrow \quad H \overset{CH_3}{\underset{HO}{C}} CH_2CH_3 \quad + \quad Br^-$$

(*R*)-2-bromobutane (*S*)-2-butanol

PROBLEM 3 ◆

Arrange the following alkyl bromides in order of decreasing reactivity in an S_N2 reaction: 1-bromo-2-methylbutane, 1-bromo-3-methylbutane, 2-bromo-2-methylbutane, and 1-bromopentane.

PROBLEM 4 ◆   **SOLVED**

Determine the product that would be formed from the S_N2 reaction of

a. 2-bromobutane and hydroxide ion.
b. (*R*)-2-bromobutane and hydroxide ion.
c. (*S*)-3-chlorohexane and hydroxide ion.
d. 3-iodopentane and hydroxide ion.

Solution to 4a   The product is 2-butanol. Because the reaction is an S_N2 reaction, we know that the configuration of the product is inverted relative to the configuration of the reactant. The configuration of the reactant is not specified, however, so we cannot specify the configuration of the product.

the configuration is not specified

$$CH_3CHCH_2CH_3 \quad + \quad HO^- \quad \longrightarrow \quad CH_3CHCH_2CH_3 \quad + \quad Br^-$$
$$\underset{Br}{|} \qquad\qquad\qquad\qquad\qquad\qquad \underset{OH}{|}$$

Paul Walden (1863–1957) *was born in Cesis, Latvia, the son of a farmer. His parents died when he was a child, and he supported himself at Riga University and St. Petersburg University by working as a tutor. Walden received a Ph.D. from the University of Leipzig and returned to Latvia to become a professor of chemistry at Riga University. Following the Russian Revolution, he went back to Germany to be a professor at the University of Rostock and, later, at the University of Tübingen.*

8.2 FACTORS THAT AFFECT S_N2 REACTIONS

We will now look at how the nature of the leaving group and the nucleophile affect the S_N2 reaction.

The Leaving Group in an S_N2 Reaction

If an alkyl iodide, an alkyl bromide, an alkyl chloride, and an alkyl fluoride all having the same alkyl group were allowed to react with the same nucleophile under the same conditions, we would find that the alkyl iodide is the most reactive and the alkyl fluoride is the least reactive.

				relative rates of reaction
HO$^-$ + RCH$_2$I	$\longrightarrow$	RCH$_2$OH +	I$^-$	30,000
HO$^-$ + RCH$_2$Br	$\longrightarrow$	RCH$_2$OH +	Br$^-$	10,000
HO$^-$ + RCH$_2$Cl	$\longrightarrow$	RCH$_2$OH +	Cl$^-$	200
HO$^-$ + RCH$_2$F	$\longrightarrow$	RCH$_2$OH +	F$^-$	1

The only difference between these four reactions is the nature of the leaving group. From the relative reaction rates, we can see that iodide ion is the best leaving group and fluoride ion is the worst. This brings us to an important rule in organic chemistry that you will encounter frequently: *the weaker the basicity of a group, the better is its leaving propensity*. The reason leaving propensity depends on basicity (even though the former is a kinetic concept and the latter a thermodynamic concept) is that *weak bases are stable bases*; they readily bear the electrons they formerly shared with a proton. Therefore, they do not share their electrons well. Thus a weak base is not bonded as strongly to the carbon as a strong base would be, and a weaker bond is more readily broken.

We have seen that iodide ion is the weakest base of the halide ions and fluoride ion is the strongest (Section 1.21). Therefore, alkyl iodides are the most reactive of the alkyl halides and alkyl fluorides are the least reactive. In fact, the fluoride ion is such a strong base that alkyl fluorides essentially do not undergo S$_N$2 reactions.

relative reactivities of alkyl halides in an S$_N$2 reaction

$$\boxed{\text{most reactive}} \Rrightarrow \text{RI} > \text{RBr} > \text{RCl} > \text{RF} \Lleftarrow \boxed{\begin{array}{l}\text{too unreactive}\\\text{to undergo an}\\\text{S}_N\text{2 reaction}\end{array}}$$

The weaker the base, the better it is as a leaving group.

Stable bases are weak bases.

At the beginning of this chapter, we saw that it is the polar carbon–halogen bond that causes alkyl halides to undergo substitution reactions. Carbon and iodine, however, have the same electronegativity. (See Table 1.3 on page 10.) Why, then, does an alkyl iodide undergo a substitution reaction? We know that larger atoms are more polarizable than smaller atoms. (Recall from Section 2.9 that polarizability is a measure of how easily an atom's electron cloud can be distorted.) The high polarizability of the large iodine atom causes the C—I bond to react as if it were polar, even though, on the basis of the electronegativity of the carbon and iodine atoms, the bond is nonpolar.

The Nucleophile in an S$_N$2 Reaction

When we talk about atoms or molecules that have lone-pair electrons, sometimes we call them bases and sometimes we call them nucleophiles. What is the difference between a base and a nucleophile?

Basicity is a measure of how well a compound (a **base**) shares its lone pair with a proton. The stronger the base, the better it shares its electrons. Basicity is measured by an *equilibrium constant* (the acid dissociation constant, K_a) that indicates the tendency of the conjugate acid of the base to lose a proton (Section 1.17).

Nucleophilicity is a measure of how readily a compound (a **nucleophile**) is able to attack an electron-deficient atom. Nucleophilicity is measured by a *rate constant* (k). In the case of an S$_N$2 reaction, nucleophilicity is a measure of how readily the nucleophile attacks an sp^3 carbon bonded to a leaving group. Because the nucleophile attacks the sp^3 carbon in the rate-determining step of the reaction, the rate of the reaction will depend on the strength of the nucleophile: the better the nucleophile, the faster will be the rate of the S$_N$2 reaction.

In general, *stronger bases are better nucleophiles*. For example, a species with a negative charge is a stronger base *and* a better nucleophile than a species that has the same attacking atom but that is neutral. Thus, HO$^-$ is a stronger base and a better nucleophile than H_2O. Notice that bases are described as being strong or weak; nucleophiles are described as being good or poor.

stronger base, better nucleophile		weaker base, poorer nucleophile
HO^-	>	H_2O
CH_3O^-	>	CH_3OH
$^-NH_2$	>	NH_3
$CH_3CH_2NH^-$	>	$CH_3CH_2NH_2$

If hydrogens are attached to the second-row elements, the resulting compounds have the following relative acidities (Section 1.20):

relative acid strengths

weakest acid ⟶ NH_3 < H_2O < HF

Because the weakest acid has the strongest conjugate base (Section 1.20), the conjugate bases have the following relative base strengths *and* relative nucleophilicities:

relative base strengths and relative nucleophilicities

strongest base ⟶ $^-NH_2$ > HO^- > F^-

best nucleophile

Notice that the amide anion is the strongest base, as well as the best nucleophile.

If, however, the attacking atoms of the nucleophiles are *very different in size*, another factor comes into play: the polarizability of the atom. Because the electrons are farther away in the larger atom, they are not held as tightly and can, therefore, move more freely toward a positive charge. As a result, the electrons are able to overlap the orbital of carbon from farther away, as shown in Figure 8.5. This results in a greater degree of bonding in the transition state, which makes the transition state more stable.

▶ **Figure 8.5**
An iodide ion is larger and more polarizable than a fluoride ion. Therefore, when an iodide ion attacks a carbon, the relatively loosely held electrons of the ion can overlap the orbital of carbon from farther away. The tightly bound electrons of the fluoride ion cannot start to overlap the orbital of carbon until the reactants are closer together.

Now the question becomes, does the greater polarizability that helps the larger atoms to be better nucleophiles make up for the decreased basicity that causes them to be poorer nucleophiles? The answer depends on the solvent.

If the reaction is carried out in an **aprotic polar solvent**—meaning the solvent molecules *do not have* a hydrogen bonded to an oxygen or to a nitrogen—the direct relationship between basicity and nucleophilicity is maintained: the stronger bases are still the best nucleophiles. In other words, the greater polarizability of the larger atoms does not make up for their decreased basicity. *Therefore iodide ion is the poorest nucleophile of the* *halide ions in an aprotic polar solvent.* If, however, the reaction is carried out in a **protic solvent**—meaning the solvent molecules *have* a hydrogen bonded to an oxygen or to a nitrogen—the relationship between basicity and nucleophilicity becomes inverted. The largest atom is the best nucleophile even though it is the weakest base. *Therefore, iodide ion is the best nucleophile of the halide ions in a protic solvent.* (For a list of protic and aprotic solvents, see Table 8.7 on page 361.)

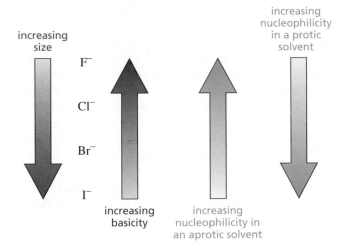

An aprotic solvent does not contain a hydrogen bonded to either an oxygen or a nitrogen.

A protic solvent contains a hydrogen bonded to an oxygen or a nitrogen.

PROBLEM 5 ♦

Indicate whether each of the following solvents is protic or aprotic:

a. chloroform (CHCl$_3$) **c.** acetic acid (CH$_3$COOH)
b. diethyl ether (CH$_3$CH$_2$OCH$_2$CH$_3$) **d.** hexane [CH$_3$(CH$_2$)$_4$CH$_3$]

Nucleophilicity Is Affected by the Solvent

Why, in a protic solvent, is the smallest atom the poorest nucleophile even though it is the strongest base? *How does a protic solvent make strong bases less nucleophilic?* When a negatively charged species is placed in a protic solvent, the ion becomes solvated (Section 2.9). Protic solvents are hydrogen bond donors, so the solvent molecules arrange themselves with their partially positively charged hydrogens pointing toward the negatively charged species. The interaction between the ion and the dipole of the protic solvent is called an **ion–dipole interaction**.

Because the solvent shields the nucleophile, at least one of the ion–dipole interactions must be broken before the nucleophile can participate in an S$_N$2 reaction. Weak bases interact weakly with protic solvents, whereas strong bases interact more strongly because they are better at sharing their electrons. It is easier, therefore, to break the ion–dipole interactions between an iodide ion (a weak base) and the solvent than between a fluoride ion (a stronger base) and the solvent. As a result, in a protic solvent, an iodide ion, even though it is a weaker base, is a better nucleophile than a fluoride ion (Table 8.2).

Table 8.2   Relative Nucleophilicity toward CH₃I in Methanol

$$RS^- > I^- > ^-C{\equiv}N > CH_3O^- > Br^- > NH_3 > Cl^- > F^- > CH_3OH$$

increasing nucleophilicity

Fluoride ion would be a better nucleophile in a *nonpolar solvent* than in a polar solvent because there would be no ion–dipole interactions between the ion and the nonpolar solvent; but ionic compounds are insoluble in most nonpolar solvents. They can, however, dissolve in aprotic polar solvents, such as dimethylformamide (DMF) or dimethylsulfoxide (DMSO). An **aprotic polar solvent** is not a hydrogen bond donor because it does not have a hydrogen attached to an oxygen or to a nitrogen, so there are no positively charged hydrogens to form ion–dipole interactions. The molecules of an aprotic polar solvent have a partial negative charge on their surface that can solvate cations, but the partial positive charge is on the *inside* of the molecule, and therefore less accessible. Fluoride ion, therefore, is a good nucleophile in DMSO and a poor nucleophile in water. Fluoride ion is also a good nucleophile in the gas phase, where there are no solvent molecules.

the δ– is on the surface of the molecule

the δ+ is not very accessible

N,N-dimethylformamide (DMF)   **dimethylsulfoxide (DMSO)**

DMSO can solvate a cation better than it can solvate an anion

---

PROBLEM 6 ♦

a. Which is a stronger base, RO⁻ or RS⁻?
b. Which is a better nucleophile in an aqueous solution?
c. Which is a better nucleophile in DMSO?

PROBLEM 7 ♦

Which is a better nucleophile?

a. Br⁻ or Cl⁻ in H₂O   **e.** HO⁻ or ⁻NH₂ in H₂O

b. Br⁻ or Cl⁻ in DMSO   **f.** HO⁻ or ⁻NH₂ in DMSO

c. CH₃O⁻ or CH₃OH in H₂O   **g.** I⁻ or Br⁻ in H₂O

d. CH₃O⁻ or CH₃OH in DMSO   **h.** I⁻ or Br⁻ in DMSO

Nucleophilicity Is Affected by Steric Effects

Base strength is relatively unaffected by steric effects because a base removes a relatively unhindered proton. The strength of a base depends only on how well the base shares its electrons with a proton. Thus, *tert*-butoxide ion, in spite of its bulkier substituents, is a stronger base than ethoxide ion since *tert*-butanol (pK_a = 18) is a weaker acid than ethanol (pK_a = 15.9).

$$CH_3CH_2O^-$$

$$\underset{\overset{|}{CH_3}}{\overset{\overset{CH_3}{|}}{CH_3CO^-}}$$

ethoxide ion
better nucleophile

tert-butoxide ion
stronger base

ethoxide ion

tert-butoxide ion

Steric effects, on the other hand, do affect nucleophilicity. A bulky nucleophile cannot approach the back side of a carbon as easily as a less sterically hindered nucleophile can. Thus, *tert*-butoxide ion, with its three methyl groups, is a poorer nucleophile than ethoxide ion, even though *tert*-butoxide ion is a stronger base.

PROBLEM 8   **SOLVED**

List the following species in order of *decreasing* nucleophilicity in an aqueous solution:

$$\text{⬡}—O^- \quad CH_3OH \quad HO^- \quad CH_3\overset{\overset{O}{\|}}{C}O^- \quad CH_3S^-$$

Solution   Let's first divide the nucleophiles into groups. There is one nucleophile with a negatively charged sulfur, three with negatively charged oxygens, and one with a neutral oxygen. We know that in the polar aqueous solvent, the compound with the negatively charged sulfur is the most nucleophilic because sulfur is larger than oxygen. We also know that the poorest nucleophile is the one with the neutral oxygen atom. To complete the problem, we need to rank the three nucleophiles with negatively charged oxygens, which we can do by looking at the pK_a values of their conjugate acids. A carboxylic acid is a stronger acid than phenol, which is a stronger acid than water (Section 7.9). Because water is the weakest acid, its conjugate base is the strongest base and the best nucleophile. Thus, the relative nucleophilicities are:

$$CH_3S^- \quad > \quad HO^- \quad > \quad \text{⬡}—O^- \quad > \quad CH_3\overset{\overset{O}{\|}}{C}O^- \quad > \quad CH_3OH$$

PROBLEM 9 ◆

For each of the following pairs of S_N2 reactions, indicate which occurs faster:
a. $CH_3CH_2Br + H_2O$ or $CH_3CH_2Br + HO^-$
b. $\underset{\overset{|}{CH_3}}{CH_3CHCH_2Br} + HO^-$ or $\underset{\overset{|}{CH_3}}{CH_3CH_2CHBr} + HO^-$
c. $CH_3CH_2Cl + CH_3O^-$ or $CH_3CH_2Cl + CH_3S^-$
         (in ethanol)
d. $CH_3CH_2Cl + I^-$ or $CH_3CH_2Br + I^-$

8.3 THE REVERSIBILITY OF AN S_N2 REACTION DEPENDS ON THE BASICITIES OF THE LEAVING GROUPS IN THE FORWARD AND REVERSE DIRECTIONS

Many different kinds of nucleophiles can react with alkyl halides. Therefore, a wide range of organic compounds can be synthesized by means of S_N2 reactions. Notice that the second-to-last reaction on page 344 is the reaction of an alkyl halide with an acetylide ion. This is the reaction we looked at in Section 6.11 that is used to create longer carbon chains.

$$CH_3CH_2Cl + HO^- \longrightarrow CH_3CH_2OH + Cl^-$$
an alcohol

$$CH_3CH_2Br + HS^- \longrightarrow CH_3CH_2SH + Br^-$$
a thiol

$$CH_3CH_2I + RO^- \longrightarrow CH_3CH_2OR + I^-$$
an ether

$$CH_3CH_2Br + RS^- \longrightarrow CH_3CH_2SR + Br^-$$
a thioether

$$CH_3CH_2Cl + {}^-NH_2 \longrightarrow CH_3CH_2NH_2 + Cl^-$$
a primary amine

$$CH_3CH_2Br + {}^-C\equiv CR \longrightarrow CH_3CH_2C\equiv CR + Br^-$$
an alkyne

$$CH_3CH_2I + {}^-C\equiv N \longrightarrow CH_3CH_2C\equiv N + I^-$$
a nitrile

It may seem that the reverse of each of these reactions satisfies the requirements for a nucleophilic substitution reaction. For example, the reverse of the first reaction would be the reaction of chloride ion (a nucleophile) with ethanol (with an HO⁻ leaving group). But ethanol and chloride ion do *not* react.

Why does a nucleophilic substitution reaction take place in one direction, but not in the other? We can answer this question by comparing the leaving propensity of Cl⁻ in the forward direction and the leaving propensity of HO⁻ in the reverse direction. To compare leaving propensities means comparing basicities. Because HCl is a much stronger acid than H₂O (Table 8.3), Cl⁻ is a much weaker base than HO⁻; and because it is a weaker base, Cl⁻ is a better leaving group. Consequently, HO⁻ can displace Cl⁻ in the forward reaction, but Cl⁻ cannot displace HO⁻ in the reverse reaction. This is shown graphically in Figure 8.6a: the free energy of activation in the forward direction is much smaller than the free energy of activation in the reverse direction. Thus, an S_N2 reaction proceeds in the direction that allows the stronger base to displace the weaker base (the better leaving group).

▲ **Figure 8.6**
(a) A reaction coordinate diagram for an irreversible S_N2 reaction.
(b) A reaction coordinate diagram for a reversible S_N2 reaction.

If the difference between the basicities of the nucleophile and the leaving group is not very large, the reaction will be reversible (Figure 8.6b). For example, in the reaction of bromoethane with iodide ion, Br⁻ is the leaving group in one direction and I⁻ is the leaving group in the other direction. The reaction is reversible because the pK_a values of the conjugate acids of the two leaving groups are similar (pK_a of HBr = −9; pK_a of HI = −10; see Table 8.3).

Table 8.3   The Acidities of the Conjugate Acids of Some Leaving Groups

Acid	pK$_a$	Conjugate base (leaving group)
HI	−10.0	I$^-$
HBr	−9.0	Br$^-$
HCl	−7.0	Cl$^-$
⬡—SO$_3$H	−6.5	⬡—SO$_3^-$
H$_2$SO$_4$	−5.0	HSO$_4^-$
CH$_3$$\overset{+}{\text{O}}H_2$	−2.5	CH$_3$OH
H$_3$O$^+$	−1.7	H$_2$O
HF	3.2	F$^-$
$\overset{\text{O}}{\overset{\|}{\text{CH}_3\text{COH}}}$	4.8	$\overset{\text{O}}{\overset{\|}{\text{CH}_3\text{CO}^-}}$
H$_2$S	7.0	HS$^-$
HC≡N	9.1	$^-$C≡N
$\overset{+}{\text{N}}$H$_4$	9.4	NH$_3$
CH$_3$CH$_2$SH	10.5	CH$_3$CH$_2$S$^-$
(CH$_3$)$_3$$\overset{+}{\text{N}}$H	10.8	(CH$_3$)$_3$N
CH$_3$OH	15.5	CH$_3$O$^-$
H$_2$O	15.7	HO$^-$
HC≡CH	25	HC≡C$^-$
H$_2$	35	H$^-$
NH$_3$	36	$^-$NH$_2$

An S$_N$2 reaction proceeds in the direction that allows the stronger base to displace the weaker base.

$$\text{CH}_3\text{CH}_2\text{Br} + \text{I}^- \rightleftharpoons \text{CH}_3\text{CH}_2\text{I} + \text{Br}^-$$

an S$_N$2 reaction is reversible when the basicities of the leaving groups are similar

We have seen that a reversible reaction can be driven toward the desired products by removing one of the products as it is formed (Le Châtelier's principle; Section 3.7). Thus, if the concentration of product C is decreased, A and B will react to form more C and D to maintain the value of the equilibrium constant.

$$\text{A} + \text{B} \rightleftharpoons \text{C} + \text{D}$$

$$K_{eq} = \frac{[\text{C}][\text{D}]}{[\text{A}][\text{B}]}$$

For example, the reaction of chloroethane with methanol is reversible because the difference between the basicities of the nucleophile and the leaving group is not very large. However, if the reaction is carried out in a neutral solution, the protonated product will lose a proton (Section 1.25), disturbing the equilibrium and driving the reaction toward the products.

$$\text{CH}_3\text{CH}_2\text{Cl} + \text{CH}_3\text{OH} \rightleftharpoons \underset{\text{H} + \text{Cl}^-}{\text{CH}_3\text{CH}_2\overset{+}{\text{O}}\text{CH}_3} \xrightarrow{\text{fast}} \text{CH}_3\text{CH}_2\text{OCH}_3 + \text{H}^+$$

If an equilibrium is disturbed, the system will adjust to offset the disturbance.

Eradicating Termites

Alkyl halides can be very toxic to biological organisms. For example, bromomethane is used to kill termites and other pests. Bromomethane works by methylating the NH_2 and SH groups of enzymes, thereby destroying the enzymes' ability to catalyze necessary biological reactions. Unfortunately, bromomethane has been found to deplete the ozone layer (Section 12.12), so its production has recently been banned in developed countries, and developing countries will have until 2015 to phase out its use.

PROBLEM 10

Check to see whether the pK_a values listed in Table 8.3 predict correctly the direction of each of the reactions on page 344.

PROBLEM 11 ♦

What is the product of the reaction of bromoethane with each of the following nucleophiles?
a. $CH_3CH_2CH_2O^-$
b. $CH_3C{\equiv}C^-$
c. $(CH_3)_3N$
d. $CH_3CH_2S^-$

PROBLEM 12   SOLVED

The reaction of chloromethane with hydroxide ion at 30 °C has a $\Delta G°$ value of $-21.7\,kcal/mol$. What is the equilibrium constant for the reaction?

Solution   The equation needed to calculate K_{eq} from the change in free energy is given in Section 3.7.

$$\ln K_{eq} = \frac{-\Delta G°}{RT}$$

$$\ln K_{eq} = \frac{-(-21.7\ \text{kcal mol}^{-1})}{0.001986\ \text{kcal mol}^{-1}\,\text{K}^{-1} \times 303\ \text{K}} = \frac{21.7}{0.60}$$

$$\ln K_{eq} = 36.1$$

$$K_{eq} = 4.8 \times 10^{15}$$

As expected, this highly exergonic reaction (Figure 8.6a) has a very large equilibrium constant.

PROBLEM 13   SOLVED

What product is obtained when ethylamine reacts with excess methyl iodide in a basic solution of potassium carbonate?

$$CH_3CH_2\ddot{N}H_2 \;+\; CH_3{-}I \xrightarrow{\;\textbf{K}_2\textbf{CO}_3\;} \;?$$
excess

Solution   Methyl iodide and ethylamine undergo an S_N2 reaction. The product of the reaction is a secondary amine that is predominantly in its basic (neutral) form since the reaction is carried out in a basic solution. The secondary amine can undergo an S_N2 reaction with another equivalent of methyl iodide, forming a tertiary amine. The tertiary amine can react with methyl iodide in yet another S_N2 reaction. The final product of the reaction is a quaternary ammonium iodide.

$$CH_3CH_2\ddot{N}H_2 + CH_3{-}I \longrightarrow CH_3CH_2\overset{+}{N}H_2CH_3 \quad \underset{I^-}{} \xrightarrow{\;\textbf{K}_2\textbf{CO}_3\;} CH_3CH_2\ddot{N}HCH_3$$

$$\Big\downarrow CH_3{-}I$$

$$\underset{CH_3\ \ I^-}{\overset{\overset{\displaystyle CH_3}{\displaystyle |{+}}}{CH_3CH_2\overset{}{N}CH_3}} \xleftarrow{\;CH_3{-}I\;} \underset{CH_3}{CH_3CH_2\ddot{N}CH_3} \xrightleftharpoons{\;\textbf{K}_2\textbf{CO}_3\;} \underset{CH_3\ \ I^-}{CH_3CH_2\overset{+}{N}HCH_3}$$

The reaction of an amine with sufficient methyl iodide to convert the amine into a quaternary ammonium iodide is called **exhaustive methylation**.

PROBLEM 14

a. Explain why the reaction of an alkyl halide with ammonia gives a low yield of primary amine.

b. Explain why a much better yield of primary amine is obtained from the reaction of an alkyl halide with azide ion ($^-N_3$), followed by catalytic hydrogenation. (*Hint*: An alkyl azide is not nucleophilic.)

$$CH_3CH_2CH_2Br \xrightarrow{\ ^-N_3\ } CH_3CH_2CH_2N{=}\overset{+}{N}{=}N^- \xrightarrow[Pd/C]{H_2} CH_3CH_2CH_2NH_2 + N_2$$
an alkyl azide

Why Carbon Instead of Silicon?

There are two reasons living organisms are composed primarily of carbon, oxygen, hydrogen, and nitrogen: the *fitness* of these elements for specific roles in life processes and their *availability* in the environment. Of the two reasons, we can see that fitness was more important than availability because carbon rather than silicon became the fundamental building block of living organisms, even though silicon, which is just below carbon in the periodic table, is more than 140 times more abundant than carbon in the Earth's crust.

Why are hydrogen, carbon, oxygen, and nitrogen so well suited for the roles they play in living organisms? First and foremost, they are among the smallest atoms that form covalent bonds, and carbon, oxygen, and nitrogen can also form multiple bonds. Because the atoms are small and can form multiple bonds, they form strong bonds that give rise to stable molecules. The compounds that make up living organisms must be stable and, therefore, slow to react if the organisms are to survive.

Silicon has almost twice the diameter of carbon, so silicon forms longer and weaker bonds. Consequently, an S_N2 reaction at silicon would occur much more rapidly than an S_N2 reaction at carbon. Moreover, silicon has another problem. The end product of carbon metabolism is CO_2. The analogous product of silicon metabolism would be SiO_2. But unlike carbon that is doubly bonded to oxygen in CO_2, silicon is only singly bonded to oxygen in SiO_2. Therefore, silicon dioxide molecules polymerize to form quartz (sand). It is hard to imagine that life could exist, much less proliferate, if animals exhaled sand instead of CO_2!

Abundance (atoms/100 atoms)

Element	In living organisms	In Earth's crust
H	49	0.22
C	25	0.19
O	25	47
N	0.3	0.1
Si	0.03	28

8.4 THE MECHANISM FOR AN S_N1 REACTION

Given our understanding of S_N2 reactions, we would expect the rate of the reaction of 2-bromo-2-methylpropane with water to be very slow because water is a poor nucleophile and the alkyl halide is sterically hindered to attack by a nucleophile. It turns out, however, that the reaction is surprisingly fast. In fact, it is over 1 million times faster than the reaction of bromomethane (a compound with no steric hindrance) with water (Table 8.4). Clearly, the reaction must be taking place by a mechanism different from that of an S_N2 reaction.

$$
\begin{array}{c}
\qquad CH_3 \qquad\qquad\qquad\qquad CH_3 \\
\qquad | \qquad\qquad\qquad\qquad\qquad | \\
CH_3C{-}Br \ + \ H_2O \ \longrightarrow \ CH_3C{-}OH \ + \ HBr \\
\qquad | \qquad\qquad\qquad\qquad\qquad | \\
\qquad CH_3 \qquad\qquad\qquad\qquad CH_3
\end{array}
$$

2-bromo-2-methylpropane   **2-methyl-2-propanol**

We have seen that in order to determine the mechanism of a reaction, we need to find out what factors affect the rate of the reaction, and we need to know the configuration of the products of the reaction. Finding that doubling the concentration of the alkyl halide doubles the rate of the reaction, but changing the concentration of the nucleophile has no effect on the rate of the reaction, allows us to write a rate law for the reaction:

rate = k[**alkyl halide**]

Table 8.4	Relative Rates of S_N1 Reactions for Several Alkyl Bromides (solvent is H_2O, nucleophile is H_2O)	
Alkyl bromide	**Class of alkyl bromide**	**Relative rate**
$\begin{array}{c}CH_3\\ |\\ CH_3C\!-\!Br\\ |\\ CH_3\end{array}$	tertiary	1,200,000
$\begin{array}{c}CH_3CH\!-\!Br\\ |\\ CH_3\end{array}$	secondary	11.6
$CH_3CH_2\!-\!Br$	primary	1.00*
$CH_3\!-\!Br$	methyl	1.05*

*Although the rate of the S_N1 reaction of this compound with water is 0, a small rate is observed as a result of an S_N2 reaction.

The rate of the reaction depends linearly on the concentration of only one reactant. Thus, the reaction is a **first-order reaction** (Section 3.7).

Because the rate law for the reaction of 2-bromo-2-methylpropane with water differs from the rate law for the reaction of bromomethane with hydroxide ion (Section 8.1), the two reactions must have different mechanisms. We have seen that the reaction between bromomethane and hydroxide ion is an S_N2 reaction. The reaction between 2-bromo-2-methylpropane and water is an **S_N1 reaction**, where "S" stands for substitution, "N" stands for nucleophilic, and "1" stands for unimolecular. **Unimolecular** means that only one molecule is involved in the transition state of the rate-determining step. The mechanism for an S_N1 reaction is based on the following experimental evidence:

1. The rate law shows that the rate of the reaction depends only on the concentration of the alkyl halide, which means that only the alkyl halide is involved in the transition state of the rate-determining step.

2. When the methyl groups of 2-bromo-2-methylpropane are successively replaced by hydrogens, the rate of the S_N1 reaction decreases progressively (Table 8.4). This is the opposite of the pattern of reactivity exhibited by alkyl halides in S_N2 reactions (Table 8.1).

3. The substitution reaction of an alkyl halide in which the halogen is bonded to an asymmetric center forms two stereoisomers: one with the same relative configuration as that of the reacting alkyl halide, and the other with the inverted configuration compared to that of the alkyl halide.

Unlike an S_N2 reaction, where the leaving group departs and the nucleophile approaches *at the same time*, the leaving group in an S_N1 reaction departs *before* the nucleophile approaches.

MECHANISM FOR THE S_N1 REACTION OF AN ALKYL HALIDE

- In the first step of the mechanism, the carbon–halogen bond breaks and the previously shared pair of electrons stays with the halogen. As a result, a carbocation intermediate is formed.

- In the second step, the nucleophile reacts rapidly with the carbocation (an electrophile) to form a protonated alcohol.

- Whether the alcohol product will exist in its protonated (acidic) form or neutral (basic) form depends on the pH of the solution. At pH = 7, the alcohol will exist predominantly in its neutral form (Section 1.25).

An S$_N$1 reaction is a two-step reaction.

Because the rate of an S$_N$1 reaction depends only on the concentration of the alkyl halide, the first step must be the slow (rate-determining) step. The nucleophile is not involved in the rate-determining step, so its concentration has no effect on the rate of the reaction. If you look at the reaction coordinate diagram in Figure 8.7, you will see why increasing the rate of the second step will not make an S$_N$1 reaction go any faster.

◀ **Figure 8.7**
A reaction coordinate diagram for an S$_N$1 reaction.

How does the mechanism for an S$_N$1 reaction account for the three pieces of experimental evidence? First, because the alkyl halide is the only species that participates in the rate-determining step, the mechanism agrees with the observation that the rate of the reaction depends only on the concentration of the alkyl halide; it does not depend on the concentration of the nucleophile.

Second, the mechanism shows that a carbocation is formed in the rate-determining step. We know that a tertiary carbocation is more stable and is therefore formed more easily than a secondary carbocation, which in turn is more stable and formed more easily than a primary carbocation (Section 4.2). Tertiary alkyl halides, therefore, are more reactive than secondary alkyl halides, which are more reactive than primary alkyl halides. This relative order of reactivity agrees with the observation that the rate of an S$_N$1 reaction decreases as the methyl groups of 2-bromo-2-methylpropane are successively replaced by hydrogens (Table 8.4).

Carbocation stability: 3° > 2° > 1°

relative reactivities of alkyl halides in an S$_N$1 reaction

| most reactive | 3° alkyl halide > 2° alkyl halide > 1° alkyl halide | too unreactive to undergo an S$_N$1 reaction |

In reality, primary carbocations and methyl cations are so unstable that primary alkyl halides and methyl halides do not undergo S$_N$1 reactions. (The very slow reactions reported for bromoethane and bromomethane in Table 8.4 are S$_N$2 reactions.)

Third, the positively charged carbon of the carbocation intermediate is sp^2 hybridized, which means the three bonds connected to it are in the same plane. In the second step of the S$_N$1 reaction, the nucleophile can approach the carbocation from either side of the plane.

Primary alkyl halides and methyl halides cannot undergo S$_N$1 reactions.

If the nucleophile adds to the side of the carbon from which the leaving group departed (labeled b in the depiction above), the product will have the same relative configuration as that of the reacting alkyl halide. If, however, the nucleophile adds to the opposite side of the carbon (labeled a in the depiction above), the product will have the inverted configuration relative to the configuration of the alkyl halide. We can now understand why an S_N1 reaction of an alkyl halide in which the leaving group is attached to an asymmetric center forms two stereoisomers: addition of the nucleophile to one side of the planar carbocation forms one stereoisomer, and addition to the other side produces the other stereoisomer.

if the leaving group in an S_N1 reaction is attached to an asymmetric center, a pair of enantiomers will be formed as products

chem Tutorial:
place S_N1

Tutorial:
S_N1 racemization-inversion

Tutorial:
S_N1 racemization-retention

PROBLEM 15◆

Arrange the following alkyl bromides in order of decreasing reactivity in an S_N1 reaction: 2-bromopropane, 1-bromopropane, 2-bromo-2-methylpropane, bromomethane.

PROBLEM 16

Explain why the rates given in Table 8.4 for the S_N2 reactions of bromoethane and bromomethane are so slow.

8.5 FACTORS THAT AFFECT S_N1 REACTIONS

We will now look at how the nature of the leaving group and the nucleophile affect S_N1 reactions, and we will see that these reactions can undergo carbocation rearrangements.

The Leaving Group in S_N1 Reactions

Because the rate-determining step of an S_N1 reaction is the dissociation of the alkyl halide to form a carbocation, two factors affect the rate of the reaction: (1) the ease with which the leaving group dissociates from the carbon, and (2) the stability of the carbocation that is formed. In the preceding section, we saw how carbocation stability affects the rate of the reaction. But how do we rank the relative reactivity of a series of alkyl halides with different leaving groups that dissociate to form the same carbocation?

As in the case of an S$_N$2 reaction, there is a direct relationship between basicity and leaving propensity in an S$_N$1 reaction: the weaker the base, the less tightly it is bonded to the carbon and the more easily the carbon–halogen bond can be broken. As a result, an alkyl iodide is the most reactive and an alkyl fluoride is the least reactive of the alkyl halides in both S$_N$1 and S$_N$2 reactions.

relative reactivities of alkyl halides in an S$_N$1 reaction

$$\boxed{\text{most reactive}} > RI > RBr > RCl > RF < \boxed{\text{least reactive}}$$

The Nucleophile in S$_N$1 Reactions

We have seen that the rate-determining step of an S$_N$1 reaction is formation of the carbocation. Because the nucleophile does not participate until *after* the rate-determining step, the reactivity of the nucleophile has no effect on the rate of an S$_N$1 reaction (Figure 8.7).

In most S$_N$1 reactions, the solvent is the nucleophile. For example, the relative rates given in Table 8.4 are for the reactions of alkyl halides with water in water. Water serves as both the nucleophile and the solvent. Reaction with a solvent is called **solvolysis**. Thus, the relative rates in Table 8.4 are for the solvolysis of the indicated alkyl bromides in water.

Carbocation Rearrangements

In Section 4.7, we saw that a carbocation will rearrange if it becomes more stable in the process. If the carbocation formed in an S$_N$1 reaction rearranges, S$_N$1 and S$_N$2 reactions of the same alkyl halide can produce different constitutional isomers as products, since a carbocation is not formed in an S$_N$2 reaction and therefore the carbon skeleton cannot rearrange. For example, in the following reaction, the product obtained from an S$_N$1 reaction is different from the product obtained from an S$_N$2 reaction. When the reaction is carried out under conditions that favor an S$_N$1 reaction, the secondary carbocation formed initially undergoes a 1,2-hydride shift to form a more stable tertiary carbocation; this changes the carbon skeleton of the reactant. In Sections 8.9 and 8.10, you will see that we can exercise some control over whether an S$_N$1 or an S$_N$2 reaction takes place by selecting appropriate reaction conditions.

> When a reaction forms a carbocation intermediate, always check for the possibility of a carbocation rearrangement.

PROBLEM 17 ♦

Arrange the following alkyl halides in order of decreasing reactivity in an S$_N$1 reaction: 2-bromopentane, 2-chloropentane, 1-chloropentane, 3-bromo-3-methylpentane.

chem Tutorial:
place Carbocation rearrangements

PROBLEM 18◆

Which of the following alkyl halides form a substitution product in an S_N1 reaction that is different from the substitution product formed in an S_N2 reaction?

A

B

C

D

E

F

PROBLEM 19◆

Two substitution products result from the reaction of 3-chloro-3-methyl-1-butene with sodium acetate ($CH_3COO^-Na^+$) in acetic acid under conditions that favor an S_N1 reaction. Identify the products.

8.6 MORE ABOUT THE STEREOCHEMISTRY OF S_N2 AND S_N1 REACTIONS

We have seen that when an alkyl halide with a leaving group attached to an asymmetric center undergoes an S_N2 reaction, the product has an inverted configuration, but when it undergoes an S_N1 reaction, the product is a pair of enantiomers. Let's now look at some examples of the stereoisomers formed in S_N2 and S_N1 reactions.

The Stereochemistry of S_N2 Reactions

The reaction of 2-bromopropane with hydroxide ion forms a substitution product without any asymmetric centers. The product, therefore, has no stereoisomers.

$$CH_3CHCH_3 + HO^- \longrightarrow CH_3CHCH_3 + Br^-$$

2-bromopropane (Br)   **2-propanol** (OH)

The reaction of 2-bromobutane with hydroxide ion forms a substitution product with an asymmetric center. The product, therefore, has stereoisomers.

asymmetric center   asymmetric center

$$CH_3CHCH_2CH_3 + HO^- \longrightarrow CH_3CHCH_2CH_3 + Br^-$$

2-bromobutane (Br)   **2-butanol** (OH)

However we cannot predict which stereoisomers of the product will be formed unless we know the configuration of the reactant *and* whether the reaction is an S_N2 or an S_N1 reaction.

For example, when (S)-2-bromobutane undergoes an S_N2 reaction, we know that the product will be (R)-2-butanol, because in an S_N2 reaction, the incoming nucleophile attacks the back side of the carbon that is attached to the halogen (Section 8.2). Therefore, the configuration of the product will be inverted relative to that of the reactant. (Recall that an S_N2 reaction takes place with *inversion of configuration.*)

An S_N2 reaction takes place with inversion of configuration.

the configuration is inverted
relative to that of the reactant

CH$_2$CH$_3$
|
C""""H
H$_3$C   Br

(S)-2-bromobutane

+ HO⁻   —S$_N$2 conditions→

CH$_2$CH$_3$
|
H""""C
HO   CH$_3$

(R)-2-butanol

+ Br⁻

If the leaving group is attached to an asymmetric center, an S$_N$2 reaction forms the stereoisomer with the inverted configuration.

The Stereochemistry of S$_N$1 Reactions

In contrast to the S$_N$2 reaction, the S$_N$1 reaction of (S)-2-bromobutane forms two substitution products: one with the same relative configuration as the reactant and the other with the inverted configuration because, in an S$_N$1 reaction, the nucleophile can attack either side of the planar carbocation intermediate (Section 8.4).

CH$_2$CH$_3$
|
C""""H
H$_3$C   Br

(S)-2-bromobutane

+ H$_2$O   —S$_N$1 conditions→

product with the inverted configuration

CH$_2$CH$_3$
|
H""""C
HO   CH$_3$

(R)-2-butanol

+

product with the retained configuration

CH$_2$CH$_3$
|
C""""H
H$_3$C   OH

(S)-2-butanol

+ HBr

If the leaving group is attached to an asymmetric center, an S$_N$1 reaction forms a pair of enantiomers.

Although you might expect that equal amounts of both products should be formed in an S$_N$1 reaction, a greater amount of the product with the inverted configuration is obtained in most cases. Typically, 50 to 70% of the product of an S$_N$1 reaction is the inverted product. If the reaction leads to equal amounts of the two stereoisomers, the reaction is said to take place with **complete racemization**. When more of one of the products is formed, the reaction is said to take place with **partial racemization**.

Saul Winstein was the first to explain why a greater amount of inverted product is generally formed in an S$_N$1 reaction. He postulated that dissociation of the alkyl halide initially results in the formation of an **intimate ion pair**. In an intimate ion pair, the bond between the carbon and the leaving group has broken, but the cation and anion remain next to each other. When they move slightly father apart, they become a *solvent-separated ion pair*, meaning an ion pair with one or more solvent molecules between the cation and the anion. As the ions separate further, they become dissociated ions.

An S$_N$1 reaction takes place with racemization.

solvent

R—X   ⟶   R⁺ X⁻   ⟶   R⁺ [solvent] X⁻   ⟶   R⁺ [solvent] X⁻
undissociated   **intimate**   **solvent-separated**   **dissociated ions**
molecule   **ion pair**   **ion pair**

The nucleophile can attack any of these four species. If the nucleophile attacks only the completely dissociated carbocation, the product will be completely racemized. If the nucleophile attacks the carbocation of either the intimate ion pair or the solvent-separated ion pair, the leaving group will be in position to partially block the approach of the nucleophile to that side of the carbocation. As a result, more of the product with the inverted configuration will be formed.

CH$_2$CH$_3$
|
H$_2$O →   C⁺   ← H$_2$O
H$_3$C   H

Br⁻ has diffused away, giving H$_2$O equal access to both sides of the carbocation

CH$_2$CH$_3$
|
H$_2$O →   C⁺ Br⁻   ✕ H$_2$O
H$_3$C   H

Br⁻ has not diffused away, so it blocks the approach of H$_2$O to one side of the carbocation

BIOGRAPHY

Saul Winstein (1912–1969) *was born in Montreal, Canada. He received a Ph.D. from the California Institute of Technology and was a professor of chemistry at the University of California, Los Angeles, from 1942 until his death.*

(Notice that if the nucleophile attacks the undissociated molecule, the reaction will be an S_N2 reaction and all of the product will have the inverted configuration.)

The difference between the products obtained from an S_N1 reaction and from an S_N2 reaction is a little easier to visualize in the case of cyclic compounds. For example, when *cis*-1-bromo-4-methylcyclohexane undergoes an S_N2 reaction, only the trans product is obtained because the carbon bonded to the leaving group is attacked by the nucleophile only on its back side.

$$CH_3 \blacktriangleright \bigcirc \blacktriangleleft Br \ + \ HO^- \xrightarrow{\text{S_N2 conditions}} CH_3 \blacktriangleright \bigcirc \cdots OH \ + \ Br^-$$

cis-1-bromo-4-methylcyclohexane   **trans-4-methylcyclohexanol**

However, when *cis*-1-bromo-4-methylcyclohexane undergoes an S_N1 reaction, both the cis and the trans products are formed because the nucleophile can approach the carbocation intermediate from either side.

$$CH_3 \blacktriangleright \bigcirc \blacktriangleleft Br \ + \ H_2O \xrightarrow{\text{S_N1 conditions}} CH_3 \blacktriangleright \bigcirc \cdots OH \ + \ CH_3 \blacktriangleright \bigcirc \blacktriangleleft OH \ + \ HBr$$

cis-1-bromo-4-methylcyclohexane   **trans-4-methylcyclohexanol**   **cis-4-methylcyclohexanol**

PROBLEM 20

Give the substitution products that will be formed from the following reactions if:
a. the reaction is carried out under conditions that favor an S_N2 reaction.
b. the reaction is carried out under conditions that favor an S_N1 reaction.
   1. *trans*-1-iodo-4-ethylcyclohexane + sodium methoxide/methanol
   2. *cis*-1-chloro-3-methylcyclobutane + sodium hydroxide/water

---

8.7 BENZYLIC HALIDES, ALLYLIC HALIDES, VINYLIC HALIDES, AND ARYL HALIDES

Up to this point, our discussion of substitution reactions has been limited to methyl halides and primary, secondary, and tertiary alkyl halides. But what about benzylic, allylic, vinylic, and aryl halides?

Let's first consider benzylic and allylic halides. Unless they are tertiary, these halides readily undergo S_N2 reactions. Tertiary benzylic and tertiary allylic halides, like other tertiary halides, are unreactive in S_N2 reactions because of steric hindrance.

Benzylic and allylic halides undergo S_N1 and S_N2 reactions.

$$\bigcirc\!\!\!-CH_2Cl \ + \ CH_3O^- \xrightarrow{\text{S_N2 conditions}} \bigcirc\!\!\!-CH_2OCH_3 \ + \ Cl^-$$
benzyl chloride   **benzyl methyl ether**

$$CH_3CH{=}CHCH_2Br \ + \ HO^- \xrightarrow{\text{S_N2 conditions}} CH_3CH{=}CHCH_2OH \ + \ Br^-$$
1-bromo-2-butene   **2-buten-1-ol**
an allylic halide

Benzylic and allylic halides readily undergo S_N1 reactions as well because they form relatively stable carbocations. While primary alkyl halides (such as CH_3CH_2Br and $CH_3CH_2CH_2Br$) cannot undergo S_N1 reactions because their carbocations are too unstable, primary benzylic and primary allylic halides readily undergo S_N1 reactions because their carbocations are stabilized by electron delocalization (Section 7.7).

$$\text{C}_6\text{H}_5\text{--CH}_2\text{Cl} \xrightleftharpoons{\textbf{S}_{\textbf{N}}\textbf{1}} \text{C}_6\text{H}_5\text{--}\overset{+}{\text{CH}}_2 + \text{Cl}^- \xrightarrow{\textbf{CH}_3\textbf{OH}} \text{C}_6\text{H}_5\text{--CH}_2\text{OCH}_3 + \text{H}^+$$

$$\text{CH}_2\text{=CHCH}_2\text{Br} \xrightleftharpoons{\textbf{S}_{\textbf{N}}\textbf{1}} \text{CH}_2\text{=CH}\overset{+}{\text{CH}}_2 + \text{Br}^- \longleftrightarrow \overset{+}{\text{CH}}_2\text{CH=CH}_2 \xrightarrow{\textbf{H}_2\textbf{O}} \text{CH}_2\text{=CHCH}_2\text{OH} + \text{H}^+$$

If the two resonance contributors of the allylic carbocation intermediate are not symmetrical as they are in the above example, two substitution products will be formed. This is another example of how electron delocalization can affect the nature of the products formed in a reaction (Section 7.10).

$$\text{CH}_3\text{CH=CHCH}_2\text{Br} \xrightleftharpoons{\textbf{S}_{\textbf{N}}\textbf{1}} \text{CH}_3\text{CH=CH}\overset{+}{\text{CH}}_2 \longleftrightarrow \text{CH}_3\overset{+}{\text{CH}}\text{CH=CH}_2 + \text{Br}^-$$

$$\downarrow \textbf{H}_2\textbf{O} \qquad\qquad\qquad \downarrow \textbf{H}_2\textbf{O}$$

$$\text{CH}_3\text{CH=CHCH}_2\text{OH} \qquad\qquad \text{CH}_3\text{CHCH=CH}_2$$
$$+\ \text{H}^+ \qquad\qquad\qquad\quad |\text{OH} + \text{H}^+$$

Vinylic halides and aryl halides (compounds in which the halogen is attached to an aromatic ring such as benzene) do not undergo S_N2 or S_N1 reactions. They do not undergo S_N2 reactions because, as the nucleophile approaches the back side of the sp^2 carbon, it is repelled by the π electron cloud of the double bond or the aromatic ring.

a nucleophile is repelled by the π electron cloud

a vinylic halide　　　**an aryl halide**

There are two reasons vinylic halides and aryl halides do not undergo S_N1 reactions. First, vinylic and aryl cations are even more unstable than primary carbocations (Section 6.5) because the positive charge is on an sp carbon. Since sp carbons are more electronegative than the sp^2 carbons that carry the positive charge of alkyl carbocations, sp carbons are more resistant to becoming positively charged. Second, we have seen that sp^2 carbons form stronger σ bonds than do sp^3 carbons (Section 1.14). As a result, when a halogen is bonded to an sp^2 carbon, it is harder to break the carbon–halogen bond.

sp^2 carbon　　　sp carbon

$$\text{RCH=CH--Cl} \ \xcancel{\longrightarrow} \ \text{RCH=}\overset{+}{\text{CH}} + \text{Cl}^-$$

vinylic cation
too unstable to be formed

sp^2 carbon　　　sp carbon

aryl cation
too unstable to be formed

Vinylic and aryl halides do not undergo S_N1 or S_N2 reactions.

PROBLEM-SOLVING STRATEGY

Predicting Relative Reactivities

Which alkyl halide would you expect to be more reactive in an S_N1 solvolysis reaction?

When asked to determine the relative reactivities of two compounds, we need to compare the $\Delta G^{\ddagger}$ values of their rate-determining steps. The faster-reacting compound will have the *smaller* $\Delta G^{\ddagger}$ value, that is, the smaller difference between its free energy and the free energy of its rate-determining transition state. Both alkyl halides have approximately the same stability, so the difference in their reaction rates will be due primarily to the difference in the stabilities of the transition states for their rate-determining steps. The rate-determining step is carbocation formation, and the transition state will resemble the carbocation more than it will resemble the reactant (Section 4.3). Therefore, the compound that forms the more stable carbocation will be the one that has the faster rate of solvolysis. Unlike the carbocation formed by the compound on the left that does not have delocalized electrons, the carbocation formed by the compound on the right is stabilized by electron delocalization. Thus, the compound on the right will undergo solvolysis more rapidly.

Now continue on to Problems 21–22.

PROBLEM 21

Which alkyl halide would be expected to be more reactive in an S_N1 solvolysis reaction?

PROBLEM 22 ♦

Which alkyl halide would you expect to be more reactive in an S_N2 reaction with a given nucleophile? In each case, you can assume that both alkyl halides have the same stability.

PROBLEM 23 ♦

For pairs **a–f** in Problem 22, which compound would be more reactive in an S_N1 reaction?

PROBLEM 24

Give the products obtained from the following reaction and show their configurations:
a. under conditions that favor an S_N2 reaction.
b. under conditions that favor an S_N1 reaction.

8.8 COMPETITION BETWEEN S$_N$2 AND S$_N$1 REACTIONS

The characteristics of S$_N$2 and S$_N$1 reactions are compared in Table 8.5. Remember that the "2" in "S$_N$2" and the "1" in "S$_N$1" refer to the molecularity of the reaction (the number of molecules involved in the transition state of the rate-determining step), and *not* to the number of steps in the mechanism. In fact, the opposite is true: an S$_N$2 reaction proceeds by a *one*-step concerted mechanism, and an S$_N$1 reaction proceeds by a *two*-step mechanism with a carbocation intermediate.

Table 8.5   Comparison of S$_N$2 and S$_N$1 Reactions

S$_N$2	S$_N$1
A one-step mechanism	A stepwise mechanism with a carbocation intermediate
A bimolecular rate-determining step	A unimolecular rate-determining step
No carbocation rearrangements — *just one product*	Carbocation rearrangements — *nucleophile comes to where...*
The better the nucleophile, the faster the rate of the reaction.	The strength of the nucleophile does not affect the rate of the reaction.
Reactivity order: methyl > 1° > 2° > 3° (No reaction with tertiary.)	Reactivity order: 3° > 2° > 1° > methyl (No reaction with primary or methyl.)
Product has the inverted configuration relative to that of the reactant.	Products have both the retained and the inverted configurations relative to that of the reactant.
Leaving group: I$^-$ > Br$^-$ > Cl$^-$ > F$^-$	Leaving group: I$^-$ > Br$^-$ > Cl$^-$ > F$^-$

We have seen that *methyl halides and primary alkyl halides undergo only* S$_N$2 *reactions* because methyl cations and primary carbocations, which would have to be formed in an S$_N$1 reaction, are too unstable to be formed. *Tertiary alkyl halides undergo only* S$_N$1 *reactions* because steric hindrance makes them unreactive in S$_N$2 reactions. *Secondary alkyl halides as well as benzylic and allylic halides (unless they are tertiary) can undergo both* S$_N$1 *and* S$_N$2 *reactions* because they form relatively stable carbocations and the steric hindrance associated with these alkyl halides is generally not very great. *Vinylic and aryl halides do not undergo either* S$_N$1 *or* S$_N$2 *reactions*. These results are summarized in Table 8.6.

Table 8.6   Summary of the Reactivity of Alkyl Halides in Nucleophilic Substitution Reactions

Methyl and 1° alkyl halides	S$_N$2 only
Vinylic and aryl halides	Neither S$_N$1 nor S$_N$2
2° alkyl halides	S$_N$1 and S$_N$2
1° and 2° benzylic and 1° and 2° allylic halides	S$_N$1 and S$_N$2
3° alkyl halides	S$_N$1 only
3° benzylic and 3° allylic halides	S$_N$1 only

When an alkyl halide can undergo *both* S$_N$1 *and* S$_N$2 reactions, both take place simultaneously. The conditions under which the reaction is carried out determine which of the reactions predominates. Therefore, we have some control over which reaction takes place.

What conditions favor an S$_N$2 reaction? This is an important question to synthetic chemists because an S$_N$2 reaction forms a single substitution product, whereas an S$_N$1 reaction can form more than one substitution product if the reactant is an allyl halide or has an asymmetric center. An S$_N$1 reaction is further complicated by carbocation rearrangements. In other words, an S$_N$2 reaction is a synthetic chemist's friend, but an S$_N$1 reaction can be a synthetic chemist's nightmare.

When the *structure* of the alkyl halide allows it to undergo both S_N2 and S_N1 reactions, three conditions determine which reaction will predominate: (1) the *concentration* of the nucleophile, (2) the *reactivity* of the nucleophile, and (3) the *solvent* in which the reaction is carried out. To understand how the concentration and the reactivity of the nucleophile affect whether an S_N2 or an S_N1 reaction predominates, we must examine the rate laws for the two reactions (Sections 8.1 and 8.4). The rate constants have been given subscripts that indicate the reaction order.

a second-order reaction

Rate law for an S_N2 reaction $= k_2$ [alkyl halide] [nucleophile]

Rate law for an S_N1 reaction $= k_1$ [alkyl halide]

a first-order reaction

The rate law for the reaction of an alkyl halide that can undergo both S_N2 and S_N1 reactions simultaneously is the sum of the individual rate laws.

$$\text{rate} \;=\; k_2[\text{alkyl halide}][\text{nucleophile}] \;+\; k_1[\text{alkyl halide}]$$

contribution to the rate by an S_N2 reaction

contribution to the rate by an S_N1 reaction

From the rate law, you can see that increasing the *concentration* of the nucleophile increases the rate of an S_N2 reaction but has no effect on the rate of an S_N1 reaction. Therefore, when both reactions occur simultaneously, increasing the concentration of the nucleophile increases the fraction of the reaction that takes place by an S_N2 pathway. The slow (and only) step of an S_N2 reaction is attack of the nucleophile on the alkyl halide. Increasing the *reactivity* of the nucleophile increases the rate of an S_N2 reaction by increasing the value of the rate constant (k_2), because a more reactive nucleophile is better able to displace the leaving group. The slow step of an S_N1 reaction is the dissociation of the alkyl halide. The carbocation formed in the slow step reacts rapidly in a second step with any nucleophile present in the reaction mixture. Increasing the rate of the fast step does not affect the rate of the prior slow, carbocation-forming step. This means that increasing the reactivity of the nucleophile has no effect on the rate of an S_N1 reaction. A good nucleophile, therefore, favors an S_N2 reaction over an S_N1 reaction. A poor nucleophile favors an S_N1 reaction, not by increasing the rate of the S_N1 reaction itself, but by decreasing the rate of the competing S_N2 reaction. In summary:

- An S_N2 reaction is favored by a high concentration of a good nucleophile.
- An S_N1 reaction is favored by a poor nucleophile.

Look back at the S_N1 reactions in previous sections and notice that every one of them has a poor nucleophile (H_2O, CH_3OH), whereas all the S_N2 reactions have good nucleophiles (HO^-, CH_3O^-). In other words, a poor nucleophile encourages an S_N1 reaction, and a good nucleophile encourages an S_N2 reaction. In Section 8.9, we will look at the third factor that influences whether an S_N2 or an S_N1 reaction will predominate—the solvent in which the reaction is carried out.

PROBLEM-SOLVING STRATEGY

Predicting Whether a Substitution Reaction Is an S_N1 or an S_N2 Reaction

This problem will give you practice determining whether a substitution reaction will take place by an S_N1 or an S_N2 pathway. (Keep in mind that good nucleophiles encourage S_N2 reactions, whereas poor nucleophiles encourage S_N1 reactions.)

Give the configuration(s) of the substitution product(s) that will be formed from the reactions of the following secondary alkyl halides with the indicated nucleophile:

Because a high concentration of a good nucleophile is used, we can predict that the reaction is an S$_N$2 reaction. Therefore, the product will have the inverted configuration relative to the configuration of the reactant. (An easy way to draw the inverted product is to draw the mirror image of the reacting alkyl halide and then put the nucleophile in the same location as the leaving group.)

b. $H_3C-\underset{Br}{\overset{CH_2CH_3}{C}}\cdots H$ + CH_3OH ⟶ $H_3C-\underset{OCH_3}{\overset{CH_2CH_3}{C}}\cdots H$ + $H\cdots\underset{CH_3O}{\overset{CH_2CH_3}{C}}-CH_3$

Because a poor nucleophile is used, we can predict that the S$_N$1 reaction predominates. Therefore, we will obtain two substitution products, one with the retained configuration and one with the inverted configuration, relative to the configuration of the reactant.

c. $CH_3CH_2\underset{I}{CH}CH_2CH_3$ + CH_3OH ⟶ $CH_3CH_2\underset{OCH_3}{CH}CH_2CH_3$

The poor nucleophile allows us to predict that the reaction is an S$_N$1 reaction. However, the product does not have an asymmetric center, so it does not have stereoisomers. Therefore, only one substitution product will be formed. (The same substitution product would have been obtained if the reaction had been an S$_N$2 reaction.)

d. $CH_3CH_2\underset{Cl}{CH}CH_3$ + $\underset{\textbf{high concentration}}{HO^-}$ ⟶ $CH_3CH_2\underset{OH}{CH}CH_3$

Because a high concentration of a good nucleophile is employed, we can predict that the reaction is an S$_N$2 reaction. Therefore, the product will have the inverted configuration relative to the configuration of the reactant. But since the configuration of the reactant is not indicated, we do not know the configuration of the product.

e. $CH_3CH_2\underset{I}{CH}CH_3$ + H_2O ⟶ $H_3C-\underset{OH}{\overset{CH_2CH_3}{C}}\cdots H$ + $H\cdots\underset{HO}{\overset{CH_2CH_3}{C}}-CH_3$

Because the nucleophile is poor, we can predict that the reaction is an S$_N$1 reaction. Therefore, both stereoisomers will be formed, regardless of the configuration of the reactant.

Now continue on to Problem 25.

PROBLEM 25

Give the configuration(s) of the substitution product(s) that will be formed from the reactions of the following secondary alkyl halides with the indicated nucleophile:

a. $H_3C-\underset{Br}{\overset{CH_2CH_3}{C}}\cdots H$ + $\underset{\textbf{high concentration}}{CH_3CH_2CH_2O^-}$ ⟶

b. $H_3C-\underset{Cl}{\overset{CH_2CH_2CH_3}{C}}\cdots H$ + $\underset{\textbf{high concentration}}{NH_3}$ ⟶

c.   cyclohexane with CH$_3$ and Cl + $\underset{\textbf{high concentration}}{CH_3O^-}$ ⟶

d.   cyclohexane with CH$_3$ and Cl + CH_3OH ⟶

e. $H\cdots\underset{Br}{\overset{CH_2CH_3}{C}}-CH_3$ + $\underset{\textbf{high concentration}}{CH_3O^-}$ ⟶

f. $H\cdots\underset{Br}{\overset{CH_2CH_3}{C}}-CH_3$ + CH_3OH ⟶

PROBLEM 26◆

Which of the following reactions will go faster if the concentration of the nucleophile is increased?

A   + CH₃O⁻ ⟶ + Br⁻

B   + CH₃S⁻ ⟶ + Br⁻

C   + ⟶ + Br⁻

PROBLEM 27   SOLVED

The rate law for the substitution reaction of 2-bromobutane and HO^- in 75% ethanol and 25% water at 30°C is

$$\text{rate} = 3.20 \times 10^{-5}[\text{2-bromobutane}][HO^-] + 1.5 \times 10^{-6}[\text{2-bromobutane}]$$

What percentage of the reaction takes place by an S_N2 pathway under the following conditions?

a. $[HO^-] = 1.00\,M$ **b.** $[HO^-] = 0.001\,M$

Solution to 27a

$$\text{percentage by } S_N2 = \frac{\text{amount by } S_N2}{\text{amount by } S_N2 + \text{amount by } S_N1} \times 100$$

$$= \frac{3.20 \times 10^{-5}[\text{2-bromobutane}](1.00) \times 100}{3.20 \times 10^{-5}[\text{2-bromobutane}](1.00) + 1.5 \times 10^{-6}[\text{2-bromobutane}]}$$

$$= \frac{3.20 \times 10^{-5}}{3.20 \times 10^{-5} + 0.15 \times 10^{-5}} \times 100 = \frac{3.20 \times 10^{-5}}{3.35 \times 10^{-5}} \times 100$$

$$= 96\%$$

chem Tutorial:
place S_N2 promoting factors

Tutorial:
Common terms

8.9   THE ROLE OF THE SOLVENT IN S_N2 AND S_N1 REACTIONS

The solvent in which a nucleophilic substitution reaction is carried out also influences whether an S_N2 or an S_N1 reaction will predominate. Before we can understand how a particular solvent favors one reaction over another, we must understand how solvents stabilize organic molecules.

The **dielectric constant** of a solvent is a measure of how well the solvent can insulate opposite charges from one another. Solvent molecules insulate a charge by clustering around it, so that the positive poles of solvent molecules surround negative charges while the negative poles of solvent molecules surround positive charges. Recall that the interaction between a solvent and an ion or a molecule dissolved in that solvent is called *solvation* (Section 2.9). When an ion interacts with a polar solvent, the charge is no longer localized solely on the ion, but is spread out to the surrounding solvent molecules. Spreading out the charge stabilizes the charged species.

ion–dipole interactions between a negatively charged species and water

ion–dipole interactions between a positively charged species and water

Polar solvents have high dielectric constants and thus are very good at insulating (solvating) charges. Nonpolar solvents have low dielectric constants and are poor insulators. The dielectric constants of some common solvents are listed in Table 8.7 where they are divided into two groups: protic solvents and aprotic solvents. Recall that **protic solvents** contain a hydrogen bonded to an oxygen or to a nitrogen. **Aprotic solvents** do not have a hydrogen bonded to an oxygen or to a nitrogen.

Table 8.7	The Dielectric Constants of Some Common Solvents			
Solvent	**Structure**	**Abbreviation**	**Dielectric constant** (ε, at 25 °C)	**Boiling point** (°C)
Protic solvents				
Water	H_2O	—	79	100
Formic acid	HCOOH	—	59	100.6
Methanol	CH_3OH	MeOH	33	64.7
Ethanol	CH_3CH_2OH	EtOH	25	78.3
tert-Butyl alcohol	$(CH_3)_3COH$	*tert*-BuOH	11	82.3
Acetic acid	CH_3COOH	HOAc	6	117.9
Aprotic solvents				
Dimethyl sulfoxide	$(CH_3)_2SO$	DMSO	47	189
Acetonitrile	CH_3CN	MeCN	38	81.6
Dimethylformamide	$(CH_3)_2NCHO$	DMF	37	153
Hexamethylphosphoric acid triamide	$[(CH_3)_2N]_3PO$	HMPA	30	233
Acetone	$(CH_3)_2CO$	Me$_2$CO	21	56.3
Dichloromethane	CH_2Cl_2	—	9.1	40
Tetrahydrofuran		THF	7.6	66
Ethyl acetate	$CH_3COOCH_2CH_3$	EtOAc	6	77.1
Diethyl ether	$CH_3CH_2OCH_2CH_3$	Et$_2$O	4.3	34.6
Toluene		—	2.4	110.6
Hexane	$CH_3(CH_2)_4CH_3$	—	1.9	68.7

Stabilization of charges by solvent interaction plays an important role in organic reactions. For example, when an alkyl halide undergoes an S$_N$1 reaction, the first step is dissociation of the carbon–halogen bond to form a carbocation and a halide ion. Energy is required to break the bond, but with no bonds being formed, where does the energy come from? If the reaction is carried out in a polar solvent, the ions that are produced are solvated. The energy associated with a single ion–dipole interaction is small, but the additive effect of all the ion–dipole interactions that take place when a solvent stabilizes a charged species represents a great deal of energy. These ion–dipole interactions provide much of the energy necessary for dissociation of the carbon–halogen bond. So, in an S_N1 reaction, the alkyl halide does not fall apart spontaneously, but instead, polar solvent molecules pull it apart. An S_N1 reaction, therefore, cannot take place in a nonpolar solvent. It also cannot take place in the gas phase, where there are no solvent molecules and, consequently, no solvation effects.

Solvation Effects

The tremendous amount of energy provided by solvation can be appreciated by considering the energy required to break the crystal lattice of sodium chloride (table salt) (Figure 1.1). In the absence of a solvent, sodium chloride must be heated to more than 800 °C to overcome the forces that hold the oppositely charged ions together. However, sodium chloride readily dissolves in water at room temperature because solvation of the Na^+ and Cl^- ions by water provides the energy necessary to separate the ions.

How a Solvent Affects Reaction Rates in General

One simple rule describes how a change in solvent will affect the rate of most chemical reactions: *increasing the polarity of the solvent will decrease the rate of the reaction if one or more reactants in the rate-determining step are charged and will increase the rate of the reaction if none of the reactants in the rate-determining step is charged.*

Now let's see why this rule is true. The rate of a reaction depends on the difference between the free energy of the reactants and the free energy of the transition state for the rate-determining step of the reaction. We can, therefore, predict how changing the polarity of the solvent will affect the rate of a reaction simply by looking at the charge on the reactants of the rate-determining step and the charge on the transition state of the rate-determining step, to see which of these species will be more stabilized by a polar solvent.

The greater or more concentrated the charge on a molecule, the stronger will be its interactions with a polar solvent and the more the charge will be stabilized. Therefore, if the size or concentration of the charge on the reactants is greater than that on the transition state, a polar solvent will stabilize the reactants more than it will stabilize the transition state, increasing the difference in energy ($\Delta G^{\ddagger}$) between them. Consequently, *increasing the polarity of the solvent will decrease the rate of the reaction*, as shown in Figure 8.8.

Increasing the polarity of the solvent will decrease the rate of the reaction if one or more reactants in the rate-determining step are charged.

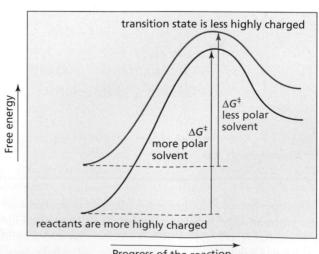

▶ **Figure 8.8**
A reaction coordinate diagram for a reaction in which the charge on the reactants is greater than the charge on the transition state.

On the other hand, if the size or concentration of the charge on the transition state is greater than that on the reactants, a polar solvent will stabilize the transition state more than it will stabilize the reactants. Therefore, *increasing the polarity of the solvent* will decrease the difference in energy ($\Delta G^{\ddagger}$) between the transition state and the reactants, which *will increase the rate of the reaction*, as shown in Figure 8.9.

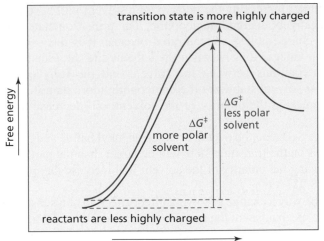

Increasing the polarity of the solvent will increase the rate of the reaction if none of the reactants in the rate-determining step is charged.

◀ **Figure 8.9**
A reaction coordinate diagram for a reaction in which the charge on the transition state is greater than the charge on the reactants.

How a Solvent Affects the Rate of an S$_N$1 Reaction

Now let's look at specific kinds of reactions, beginning with an S$_N$1 reaction of an alkyl halide. The alkyl halide, which is the only reactant in the rate-determining step of an S$_N$1 reaction, is a neutral molecule with a small dipole moment. The rate-determining transition state has greater partial charges because as the carbon–halogen bond breaks, the carbon becomes more positive and the halogen becomes more negative. Since the partial charges on the transition state are greater than the partial charges on the reactant, increasing the polarity of the solvent will stabilize the transition state more than the reactant and will increase the rate of the S$_N$1 reaction (Figure 8.9 and Table 8.8).

rate-determining step of an S$_N$1 reaction

Table 8.8	The Effect of the Polarity of the Solvent on the Rate of Reaction of 2-Bromo-2-methylpropane in an S$_N$1 Reaction
Solvent	**Relative rate**
100% water	1200
80% water / 20% ethanol	400
50% water / 50% ethanol	60
20% water / 80% ethanol	10
100% ethanol	1

We will see in Chapter 10 that compounds other than alkyl halides can undergo S$_N$1 reactions. As long as the compound undergoing an S$_N$1 reaction is neutral, increasing the polarity of the solvent will *increase* the rate of the S$_N$1 reaction because the polar solvent will stabilize the dispersed charges on the transition state more than it will stabilize the relatively neutral reactant (Figure 8.9). If, however, the compound undergoing an S$_N$1 reaction is charged, increasing the polarity of the solvent will *decrease* the rate of the reaction because the more polar solvent will stabilize the full charge on the reactant to a greater extent than it will stabilize the dispersed charge on the transition state (Figure 8.8).

How a Solvent Affects the Rate of an S$_N$2 Reaction

The way in which a change in the polarity of the solvent affects the rate of an S$_N$2 reaction depends on whether the reactants are charged or neutral, just as in an S$_N$1 reaction.

Most S$_N$2 reactions of alkyl halides occur between a neutral alkyl halide and a charged nucleophile. Increasing the polarity of a solvent will have a strong stabilizing effect on the negatively charged nucleophile. The transition state also has a negative charge, but that charge is less concentrated because it is dispersed over two atoms. Consequently, the interactions between the solvent and the transition state are not as strong as the interactions between the solvent and the fully charged nucleophile. Therefore, a polar solvent stabilizes the nucleophile more than it stabilizes the transition state, so increasing the polarity of the solvent will decrease the rate of the reaction (Figure 8.8).

If, however, the S$_N$2 reaction occurs between an alkyl halide and a neutral nucleophile, the partial charges on the transition state will be larger than the partial charges on the reactants, so increasing the polarity of the solvent will increase the rate of the substitution reaction (Figure 8.9).

In summary, the way a change in solvent affects the rate of a substitution reaction does not depend on the mechanism of the reaction. It depends *only* on whether a reactant in the rate-determining step is charged. *If a reactant in the rate-determining step is charged, increasing the polarity of the solvent will decrease the rate of the reaction. If none of the reactants in the rate-determining step is charged, increasing the polarity of the solvent will increase the rate of the reaction.*

When we discussed the solvation of charged species by a polar solvent, the polar solvents we considered were hydrogen bond donors (protic polar solvents) such as water and alcohols. Some polar solvents—for example, *N,N*-dimethylformamide (DMF), dimethyl sulfoxide (DMSO), and hexamethylphosphoric acid triamide (HMPA)—are not hydrogen bond donors; they are aprotic polar solvents (Table 8.7).

Because a polar solvent decreases the rate of an S$_N$2 reaction when the nucleophile is negatively charged, we would like to carry out such a reaction in a nonpolar solvent. However, negatively charged nucleophiles generally will not dissolve in nonpolar solvents. Instead, an aprotic polar solvent is used. Because aprotic polar solvents are not hydrogen bond donors, they are less effective than polar protic solvents at solvating negative charges; indeed, we have seen that they solvate negative charges very poorly (Section 8.3). Thus, the rate of an S$_N$2 reaction with a negatively charged nucleophile will be greater in an aprotic polar solvent than in a protic polar solvent. Consequently, an aprotic polar solvent is the solvent of choice for an S$_N$2 reaction in which the nucleophile is negatively charged, whereas a protic polar solvent is used if the nucleophile is a neutral molecule.

We have now seen that when an alkyl halide can undergo both S$_N$2 and S$_N$1 reactions, the S$_N$2 reaction will be favored by a high concentration of a good (negatively charged) nucleophile in an aprotic polar solvent, whereas the S$_N$1 reaction will be favored by a poor (neutral) nucleophile in a protic polar solvent.

An S$_N$2 reaction of an alkyl halide is favored by a high concentration of a good nucleophile in an aprotic polar solvent.

An S$_N$1 reaction of an alkyl halide is favored by a poor nucleophile in a protic polar solvent.

Environmental Adaptation

The microorganism *Xanthobacter* has learned to use alkyl halides that reach the ground as industrial pollutants as a source of carbon. The microorganism synthesizes an enzyme that uses the alkyl halide as a starting material to produce other carbon-containing compounds that it needs. This enzyme has several nonpolar groups at its active site (the pocket in the enzyme where the reaction it catalyzes takes place). The first step of the enzyme-catalyzed reaction is an S$_N$2 reaction with a charged nucleophile. The nonpolar groups on the surface of the enzyme provide the nonpolar environment needed to increase the rate of the reaction.

PROBLEM 28 ◆

Although amines are neutral molecules, they are good nucleophiles. Would an S_N2 reaction between an amine and an alkyl halide be faster in a protic polar solvent or in an aprotic polar solvent?

PROBLEM 29 ◆

How will the rate of each of the following S_N2 reactions change if it is carried out in a more polar solvent?

a. $CH_3CH_2CH_2CH_2Br + HO^- \longrightarrow CH_3CH_2CH_2CH_2OH + Br^-$

b. $CH_3\overset{+}{S}CH_3 + NH_3 \longrightarrow CH_3\overset{+}{N}H_3 + CH_3SCH_3$
$|$
CH_3

c. $CH_3CH_2I + NH_3 \longrightarrow CH_3CH_2\overset{+}{N}H_3\ I^-$

PROBLEM 30 ◆

Which reaction in each of the following pairs will take place more rapidly?

a. $CH_3Br + HO^- \longrightarrow CH_3OH + Br^-$

$CH_3Br + H_2O \longrightarrow CH_3OH + HBr$

b. $CH_3I + HO^- \longrightarrow CH_3OH + I^-$

$CH_3Cl + HO^- \longrightarrow CH_3OH + Cl^-$

c. $CH_3Br + NH_3 \longrightarrow CH_3\overset{+}{N}H_3 + Br^-$

$CH_3Br + H_2O \longrightarrow CH_3OH + Br^-$

d. $CH_3Br + HO^- \xrightarrow{\text{DMSO}} CH_3OH + Br^-$

$CH_3Br + HO^- \xrightarrow{\text{EtOH}} CH_3OH + Br^-$

e. $CH_3Br + NH_3 \xrightarrow{\text{Et}_2\text{O}} CH_3\overset{+}{N}H_3 + Br^-$

$CH_3Br + NH_3 \xrightarrow{\text{EtOH}} CH_3\overset{+}{N}H_3 + Br^-$

PROBLEM 31   SOLVED

Most of the pK_a values given throughout this text are values determined in water. How would the pK_a values of the following classes of compounds change if they were determined in a solvent less polar than water such as 50% water/50% dioxane: carboxylic acids, alcohols, phenols, ammonium ions ($R\overset{+}{N}H_3$), and anilinium ions ($C_6H_5\overset{+}{N}H_3$)?

Solution A pK_a is the negative logarithm of an equilibrium constant, K_a (Section 1.17). Because we are determining how changing the polarity of a solvent affects an equilibrium constant, we must look at how changing the polarity of the solvent affects the stability of the reactants and products (Section 3.7).

$$K_a = \frac{[B^-]\,[H^+]}{[HB]} \qquad K_a = \frac{[B]\,[H^+]}{[HB^+]}$$

$$\boxed{\text{a neutral acid}} \qquad \boxed{\text{a positively charged acid}}$$

Carboxylic acids, alcohols, and phenols are neutral in their acidic forms (HB) and charged in their basic forms (B$^-$). A polar protic solvent will stabilize B$^-$ and H$^+$ more than it will stabilize HB, thereby increasing K_a. Therefore, K_a will be larger in water than in a less polar solvent, so the pK_a values of carboxylic acids, alcohols, and phenols will be higher (they will be weaker acids) in a less polar solvent.

Ammonium ions and anilinium ions are charged in their acidic forms (HB^+) and neutral in their basic forms (B). A polar solvent will stabilize HB^+ and H^+ more than it will stabilize B. Because HB^+ is stabilized slightly more than H^+, K_a will be smaller in water than in a less polar solvent, so the pK_a values of ammonium ions and anilinium ions will be lower (they will be stronger acids) in a less polar solvent.

PROBLEM 32 ♦

Would you expect acetate ion ($CH_3CO_2^-$) to be a more reactive nucleophile in an S_N2 reaction with an alkyl halide carried out in methanol or in dimethyl sulfoxide?

PROBLEM 33 ♦

Under which of the following reaction conditions would (R)-2-chlorobutane form the most (R)-2-butanol: HO^- in 50% water and 50% ethanol or HO^- in 100% ethanol?

8.10 INTERMOLECULAR VERSUS INTRAMOLECULAR REACTIONS

A molecule with two functional groups is called a **bifunctional molecule**. If the two functional groups are able to react with each other, two kinds of reactions can occur. As an example, let's look at a molecule with two functional groups that can react in an S_N2 reaction: a strong nucleophile and an alkyl halide. The nucleophilic alkoxide ion of one molecule can displace the bromide ion of a second molecule. Such a reaction is called an intermolecular reaction. *Inter* is Latin for "between": an **intermolecular reaction** takes place between two molecules. If the product of this reaction subsequently reacts with a third bifunctional molecule (and then a fourth, and so on), a polymer will be formed. A polymer is a large molecule formed by linking together repeating units of small molecules (Chapter 29).

an intermolecular reaction

Alternatively, the nucleophilic alkoxide ion of a molecule can displace the bromide ion of the same molecule, thereby forming a cyclic compound. Such a reaction is called an intramolecular reaction. *Intra* is Latin for "within": an **intramolecular reaction** takes place within a single molecule.

an intramolecular reaction

Which reaction is more likely to occur, the intermolecular reaction or the intramolecular reaction? The answer depends on the *concentration* of the bifunctional molecule and the *size of the ring* that would be formed in the intramolecular reaction.

The intramolecular reaction has an advantage: the reacting groups are tethered together, so they do not have to diffuse through the solvent to find a group with which to react. Therefore, a low concentration of reactant favors an intramolecular reaction because the two functional groups have a better chance of finding each other if they are in the same molecule. A high concentration of reactant helps compensate for the advantage gained by tethering, increasing the likelihood of intermolecular reactions.

How much of an advantage an intramolecular reaction has over an intermolecular reaction depends on the size of the ring that is formed—that is, on the length of the tether. If the intramolecular reaction forms a five- or six-membered ring, it will be highly favored over the intermolecular reaction because five- and six-membered rings are stable and, therefore, easily formed.

Three- and four-membered rings are strained, which makes them less stable than five- and six-membered rings and so less easily formed. The higher activation energy for three- and four-membered ring formation cancels some of the advantage gained by tethering.

Three-membered ring compounds are generally formed more easily than four-membered ring compounds. For a cyclic ether of any size to form, the nucleophilic oxygen atom must be oriented so that it can attack the back side of the carbon bonded to the halogen. Rotation about a C—C bond can produce conformations in which the groups point away from one another and are not able to react. The molecule that forms a three-membered ring ether has only one C—C bond that can rotate, whereas the molecule that forms a four-membered ring has two C—C bonds that can rotate. Therefore, the molecule that forms the three-membered rings is more apt to have its reacting groups in the conformation required for reaction.

The likelihood of the reacting groups finding each other decreases sharply when the groups are in compounds that would form seven-membered and larger rings. Therefore, the intramolecular reaction becomes less favored as the ring size increases beyond six members.

PROBLEM 34 ◆

Which compound in each pair, after removing a proton from the OH group, would form a cyclic ether more rapidly?

a. HO‿‿‿‿Br   or   HO‿‿‿Br

b. HO‿‿Br   or   HO‿‿‿Br

c. HO‿‿‿‿Br   or   HO‿‿‿‿Br

PROBLEM-SOLVING STRATEGY

Investigating How Stereochemistry Affects Reactivity

Which of the following compounds will form an epoxide as a result of reacting with sodium hydroxide?

cis-2-bromocyclohexanol   *trans*-2-bromocyclohexanol

Hydroxide ion will remove a proton from the OH group, forming a strong nucleophile that can react with the alkyl halide in an S_N2 reaction to form an epoxide. An S_N2 reaction requires back-side attack. Only when the alkoxide ion and Br are on opposite sides of the cyclohexane ring will the alkoxide ion be able to attack the back side of the carbon that is attached to Br. Therefore, only *trans*-2-bromocyclohexanol will be able to form an epoxide.

Now continue on to Problem 35.

PROBLEM 35 ◆

Give the products of the following reactions:

a.

c. $BrCH_2CH_2CH_2CH_2CH_2OH$ $\xrightarrow{\text{NaOH}}$

d. $CH_3CH_2\overset{\overset{\displaystyle CH_3}{|}}{\underset{\underset{\displaystyle OH}{|}}{C}}CH_2Cl$ $\xrightarrow{\text{NaOH}}$

b.

e. $CH_3CH_2CH_2CH=CH_2$ $\xrightarrow[\text{2. NaOH}]{\text{1. Cl}_2\text{, H}_2\text{O}}$

8.11 BIOLOGICAL METHYLATING REAGENTS HAVE GOOD LEAVING GROUPS

If an organic chemist wanted to put a methyl group on a nucleophile, methyl iodide would most likely be used as the methylating agent. Of the methyl halides, methyl iodide has the most easily displaced leaving group because I^- is the weakest base of the halide ions. In addition, methyl iodide is a liquid at room temperature, so it is easier to handle than methyl bromide or methyl chloride that are gases at room temperature. The reaction would be a simple S_N2 reaction.

Methyl halides, however, are not available in a living cell. Because they are only slightly soluble in water, they are not found in the predominantly aqueous environments of biological systems. Instead, biological systems use *S*-adenosylmethionine (SAM; also called AdoMet), a water soluble compound, as a methylating agent. (A less common biological methylating agent is discussed in Section 25.24.) Although it looks much more complicated than methyl iodide, SAM performs the same function: it transfers a methyl group to a nucleophile. Notice that the methyl group of SAM is attached to a positively charged sulfur, which can readily accept the electrons left behind when the methyl group is transferred. In other words, the methyl group is attached to a very good leaving group, allowing biological methylation to take place at a reasonable rate.

S-adenosylmethionine
SAM
AdoMet

S-adenosylhomocysteine
SAH

A specific example of a methylation reaction that takes place in biological systems is the conversion of noradrenaline (norepinephrine) to adrenaline (epinephrine). The reaction uses SAM to provide the methyl group. Noradrenaline and adrenaline are hormones that control glycogen metabolism; they are released into the bloodstream in response to stress. Adrenaline is more potent than noradrenaline.

norepinephrine
noradrenaline

epinephrine
adrenaline

The conversion of phosphatidylethanolamine, a component of cell membranes, into phosphatidylcholine, another component of cell membranes, requires three methylations by three equivalents of SAM. (Biological cell membranes are discussed in Section 27.4.)

phosphatidylethanolamine

phosphatidylcholine

S-Adenosylmethionine: A Natural Antidepressant

Marketed under the name SAMe (pronounced Sammy), S-adenosylmethionine is sold in many health food and drug stores as a treatment for depression and arthritis. Although SAMe has been used clinically in Europe for more than two decades, it has not been rigorously evaluated in the United States and therefore has not been approved by the FDA. It can be sold, however, because the FDA does not prohibit the sale of most naturally occurring substances as long as the marketer does not make therapeutic claims. SAMe has also been found to be effective in the treatment of liver diseases, such as diseases caused by alcohol and the hepatitis C virus. The attenuation of liver injuries is accompanied by increased levels of glutathione in the liver. Glutathione is an important biological antioxidant (Section 23.9). SAM is required for the biosynthesis of cysteine, an amino acid that, in turn, is required for the synthesis of glutathione.

SUMMARY

Alkyl halides undergo two kinds of **nucleophilic substitution reactions**: S_N2 and S_N1. In both reactions, a nucleophile substitutes for a halogen. An S_N2 reaction is bimolecular: two molecules are involved in the transition state of the rate-limiting step. An S_N1 reaction is unimolecular; one molecule is involved in the transition state of the rate-limiting step.

The rate of an **S_N2 reaction** depends on the concentration of both the alkyl halide and the nucleophile. An S_N2 reaction has a one-step mechanism: the nucleophile attacks the back side of the carbon that is attached to the halogen. The reaction proceeds in the direction that allows the stronger base to displace the weaker base; it is reversible only if the difference between the basicities of the nucleophile and the leaving group is small. The rate of an S_N2 reaction is affected by steric hindrance: the bulkier the groups at the back side of the carbon undergoing attack, the slower is the reaction. Tertiary alkyl halides, therefore, cannot undergo S_N2 reactions. An S_N2 reaction takes place with **inversion of configuration**.

The rate of an **S_N1 reaction** depends only on the concentration of the alkyl halide. The halogen departs in the first step, forming a carbocation that is attacked by a nucleophile in the second step. Consequently, carbocation rearrangements can occur. The rate of an S_N1 reaction depends on the ease of carbocation formation. Tertiary alkyl halides, therefore, are more reactive than secondary alkyl halides because tertiary carbocations are more stable than secondary carbocations. Primary carbocations are so unstable that primary alkyl halides cannot undergo S_N1 reactions. An S_N1 reaction is accompanied by racemization. Most S_N1 reactions are **solvolysis** reactions: the solvent is the nucleophile.

The rates of both S_N2 and S_N1 reactions are influenced by the nature of the leaving group. Weak bases are the best leaving groups because weak bases form the weakest bonds. Thus, the weaker the basicity of the leaving group, the faster the reaction will occur. Therefore, the relative reactivities of alkyl halides that differ only in the halogen atom are RI > RBr > RCl > RF in both S_N2 and S_N1 reactions.

Basicity is a measure of how well a compound shares its lone pair with a proton. **Nucleophilicity** is a measure of how readily a species is able to attack an electron-deficient atom. In general, the stronger base is a better nucleophile. However, if the attacking atoms are very different in size, the relationship between basicity and nucleophilicity depends on the solvent. Only in protic solvents are basicity and nucleophilicity reversed: the smaller stronger bases are poorer nucleophiles because of **ion–dipole interactions** between the ion and the solvent.

Methyl halides and primary alkyl halides undergo only S_N2 reactions; tertiary alkyl halides undergo only S_N1 reactions; vinylic and aryl halides undergo neither S_N2 nor S_N1 reactions; and secondary alkyl halides and benzylic and allylic halides (unless they are tertiary) undergo both S_N1 and S_N2 reactions. When the structure of the alkyl halide allows it to undergo both S_N2 and S_N1 reactions, the S_N2 reaction is favored by a high concentration of a good nucleophile in an aprotic polar solvent, whereas the S_N1 reaction is favored by a poor nucleophile in a protic polar solvent.

Protic solvents (H_2O, ROH) have a hydrogen attached to an O or an N; **aprotic solvents** (DMF, DMSO) do not have a hydrogen attached to an O or an N. The **dielectric constant** of a solvent tells how well the solvent insulates opposite charges from one another. Increasing the polarity of the solvent will decrease the rate of the reaction if one or more reactants in the rate-determining step are charged and will increase the rate of the reaction if none of the reactants in the rate-determining step is charged.

If the two functional groups of a **bifunctional molecule** can react with each other, both **intermolecular** and **intramolecular reactions** can occur. The reaction that is more likely to occur depends on the concentration of the bifunctional molecule and the size of the ring that would be formed in the intramolecular reaction.

SUMMARY OF REACTIONS

1. S_N2 reaction: a one-step mechanism

$$\overset{\cdot\cdot}{Nu}^- \ + \ -\overset{|}{\underset{|}{C}}-X \ \longrightarrow \ -\overset{|}{\underset{|}{C}}-Nu \ + \ X^-$$

Relative reactivities of alkyl halides: $CH_3X > 1° > 2° > 3°$.
Only the inverted product is formed.

2. S_N1 reaction: a two-step mechanism with a carbocation intermediate

$$-\overset{|}{\underset{|}{C}}-X \ \longrightarrow \ -\overset{|}{\underset{|}{C}}{}^+ \ \overset{\overset{\cdot\cdot}{Nu}^-}{\longrightarrow} \ -\overset{|}{\underset{|}{C}}-Nu$$
$$+ \ X^-$$

Relative reactivities of alkyl halides: $3° > 2° > 1° > CH_3X$
Both the inverted and noninverted products are formed.

KEY TERMS

aprotic polar solvent (p. 340)
aprotic solvent (p. 361)
back-side attack (p. 335)
base (p. 339)
basicity (p. 339)
bifunctional molecule (p. 366)
bimolecular (p. 334)
complete racemization (p. 353)
dielectric constant (p. 360)
elimination reaction (p. 332)
exhaustive methylation (p. 346)
first-order reaction (p. 348)

intermolecular reaction (p. 366)
intimate ion pair (p. 353)
intramolecular reaction (p. 366)
inversion of configuration (p. 338)
ion–dipole interaction (p. 341)
kinetics (p. 333)
leaving group (p. 332)
nucleophile (p. 339)
nucleophilicity (p. 339)
nucleophilic substitution
    reaction (p. 333)
partial racemization (p. 353)

protic solvent (p. 361)
rate constant (p. 334)
rate law (p. 334)
second-order reaction (p. 334)
S_N1 reaction (p. 348)
S_N2 reaction (p. 334)
solvolysis (p. 351)
steric effects (p. 336)
steric hindrance (p. 336)
substitution reaction (p. 332)
unimolecular (p. 348)

PROBLEMS

36. Give the product of the reaction of bromomethane with each of the following nucleophiles:
   a. HO^- **b.** $^-NH_2$ **c.** CH_3SH **d.** HS^- **e.** CH_3O^- **f.** CH_3NH_2

37. Indicate how each of the factors listed below affects
   a. an S_N1 reaction.
   b. an S_N2 reaction.
      1. the structure of the alkyl halide   **3.** the concentration of the nucleophile
      2. the reactivity of the nucleophile   **4.** the solvent

38. Which is a better nucleophile in methanol?
   a. H_2O or HO^- **b.** NH_3 or H_2O **c.** H_2O or H_2S **d.** HO^- or HS^- **e.** I^- or Br^- **f.** Cl^- or Br^-

39. Indicate which member of each pair in Problem 38 is a better leaving group.

40. What nucleophiles could be used to react with 1-iodobutane to prepare the following compounds?

a. OH   d. SH

b. O⁻   e. S   g. N

c. N–H   f. O–C(=O)   h.

41. Starting with cyclohexene, how could the following compounds be prepared?
a. methoxycyclohexane   **b.** dicyclohexyl ether   **c.** cyclohexylmethylamine

42. Rank the following compounds in order of *decreasing* nucleophilicity:

a. CH_3CO^- (with O double bond), $CH_3CH_2S^-$, $CH_3CH_2O^-$ in methanol   c. H_2O and NH_3 in methanol

b. —O⁻ and —O⁻ in DMSO   d. Br^-, Cl^-, I^- in methanol

43. The pK_a of acetic acid in water is 4.76 (Section 1.18). What effect would a decrease in the polarity of the solvent have on the pK_a? Why?

44. a. Identify the products that form when 2-bromo-2-methylpropane is dissolved in a mixture of 80% ethanol and 20% water.
    b. Explain why the same products are obtained when 2-chloro-2-methylpropane is dissolved in a mixture of 80% ethanol and 20% water.

45. For each of the following reactions, give the substitution products; if the products can exist as stereoisomers, show what stereoisomers are obtained:
a. (*R*)-2-bromopentane + high concentration of CH_3O^- **d.** *trans*-1-chloro-2-methylcyclohexane + CH_3OH
b. (*R*)-2-bromopentane + CH_3OH **e.** 3-bromo-2-methylpentane + CH_3OH
c. *trans*-1-chloro-2-methylcyclohexane + high concentration of CH_3O^- **f.** 3-bromo-3-methylpentane + CH_3OH

46. Give the products obtained from the solvolysis of each of the following compounds in ethanol:

a. Br   b. –CH_2Br c. Br

47. Would you expect methoxide ion to be a better nucleophile if it were dissolved in CH_3OH or if it were dissolved in DMSO? Why?

48. Which reaction in each of the following pairs will take place more rapidly?

a. Cl $\xrightarrow{CH_3S^-}$ S + Cl^- c. Cl $\xrightarrow{H_2O}$ OH + HCl

Cl $\xrightarrow{(CH_3)_2CHS^-}$ S + Cl^-

Cl $\xrightarrow{H_2O}$ OH + HCl

b. Cl $\xrightarrow{HO^-}$ OH + Cl^- d. $(CH_3)_3CBr \xrightarrow{H_2O} (CH_3)_3COH$ + HBr

O Cl $\xrightarrow{HO^-}$ O OH + Cl^- $(CH_3)_3CBr \xrightarrow{CH_3CH_2OH} (CH_3)_3COCH_2CH_3$ + HBr

49. The reaction of an alkyl chloride with potassium iodide is generally carried out in acetone to maximize the amount of alkyl iodide that is formed. Why does the solvent increase the yield of alkyl iodide? (*Hint:* Potassium iodide is soluble in acetone, but potassium chloride is not.)

50. In Section 8.11, we saw that *S*-adenosylmethionine (SAM) methylates the nitrogen atom of noradrenaline to form adrenaline, a more potent hormone. If SAM methylates an OH group on the benzene ring instead, it completely destroys noradrenaline's activity. Give the mechanism for the methylation of the OH group by SAM.

noradrenaline   + SAM → a biologically inactive compound   + SAH

51. *tert*-Butyl chloride undergoes solvolysis in both acetic acid and formic acid.

Solvolysis occurs 5000 times faster in one of the acids than in the other. In which solvent is solvolysis faster? Explain your answer. (*Hint*: See Table 8.3.)

52. For each of the following reactions, give the substitution products; if the products can exist as stereoisomers, show what stereoisomers are obtained:
  a. (2S,3S)-2-chloro-3-methylpentane + high concentration of CH_3O^-
  b. (2S,3R)-2-chloro-3-methylpentane + high concentration of CH_3O^-
  c. (2R,3S)-2-chloro-3-methylpentane + high concentration of CH_3O^-
  d. (2R,3R)-2-chloro-3-methylpentane + high concentration of CH_3O^-
  e. 3-chloro-2,2-dimethylpentane + CH_3CH_2OH
  f. benzyl bromide + CH_3CH_2OH

53. Give the substitution products obtained when each of the following compounds is added to a solution of sodium acetate in acetic acid.
  a. 2-chloro-2-methyl-3-hexene   **b.** 3-bromo-1-methylcyclohexene

54. Show how each of the following compounds can be synthesized from the given starting materials.

  a. $CH_3CH_2CH_2Br$ $\longrightarrow$ $CH_3CH_2CH_2CH_2CH_3$

  b. $CH_3CH_2CH_2Br$ $\longrightarrow$ $CH_3CH_2CH_2\overset{\overset{\displaystyle O}{\|}}{C}CH_3$

  c. $CH_3CH_2CH_2Br$ $\longrightarrow$ $CH_3CH_2CH_2CH_2\overset{\overset{\displaystyle O}{\|}}{C}H$

  d. $CH_3CH_2CH_2Br$ $\longrightarrow$ $CH_3CH_2\overset{O}{\overset{\displaystyle /\backslash}{CH-CH_2}}$

55. In which solvent would the equilibrium for the following S_N2 reaction lie farther to the right, ethanol or diethyl ether?

$$CH_3SCH_3 + CH_3Br \rightleftharpoons CH_3\overset{\overset{\displaystyle CH_3}{|}}{\underset{+}{S}}CH_3 + Br^-$$

56. The rate of reaction of methyl iodide with quinuclidine was measured in nitrobenzene, and then the rate of reaction of methyl iodide with triethylamine was measured in the same solvent. The concentration of the reagents was the same in both experiments.
  a. Which reaction had the larger rate constant?
  b. The same experiment was done using isopropyl iodide instead of methyl iodide. Which reaction had the larger rate constant?
  c. Which alkyl halide has the larger $k_{triethylamine}/k_{quinuclidine}$ ratio?

quinuclidine

$$\overset{\overset{\displaystyle CH_2CH_3}{|}}{CH_3CH_2NCH_2CH_3}$$
triethylamine

57. Only one bromoether (disregarding stereoisomers) is obtained from the reaction of the following alkyl dihalide with methanol. Give the structure of the ether.

58. When equivalent amounts of methyl bromide and sodium iodide are dissolved in methanol, the concentration of iodide ion quickly decreases and then slowly returns to its original concentration. Account for this observation.

59. The rate constant of an intramolecular reaction depends on the size of the ring (n) that is formed. Explain the relative rates of formation of the cyclic secondary ammonium ions.

$$Br-(CH_2)_{\overline{n-1}}NH_2 \longrightarrow (\overline{CH_2})_{n-1} \,^+NH_2 + Br^-$$

n =	3	4	5	6	7	10
relative rate:	1×10^{-1}	2×10^{-3}	100	1.7	3×10^{-3}	1×10^{-8}

60. For each of the following reactions, give the substitution products, assuming that all the reactions are carried out under S_N2 conditions; if the products can exist as stereoisomers, show what stereoisomers are formed:
a. (3S,4S)-3-bromo-4-methylhexane + CH_3O^-
b. (3S,4R)-3-bromo-4-methylhexane + CH_3O^-
c. (3R,4R)-3-bromo-4-methylhexane + CH_3O^-
d. (3R,4S)-3-bromo-4-methylhexane + CH_3O^-

61. Explain why tetrahydrofuran can solvate a positively charged species better than diethyl ether can.

tetrahydrofuran $CH_3CH_2OCH_2CH_3$
                    diethyl ether

62. Propose a mechanism for each of the following reactions:

a.

b.

63. Which of the following will react faster in an S_N1 reaction, *cis*-1-bromo-4-*tert*-butylcyclohexane or *trans*-1-bromo-4-*tert*-butylcyclohexane?

64. Alkyl halides have been used as insecticides since the discovery of DDT in 1939. DDT was the first compound to be found that had a high toxicity to insects and a relatively low toxicity to mammals. In 1972, DDT was banned in the United States because it is a long-lasting compound and its widespread use was resulting in the accumulation of substantial concentrations in wildlife. Chlordane is an alkyl halide insecticide used to protect wooden buildings from termites. Chlordane can be synthesized from two reactants in a one-step reaction. One of the reactants is hexachlorocyclopentadiene. What is the other reactant? (*Hint*: See Section 7.12.)

chlordane

65. Explain why the following alkyl halide does not undergo a substitution reaction, regardless of the conditions under which the reaction is run.

9

Elimination Reactions of Alkyl Halides · Competition between Substitution and Elimination

CH₃CH₂CHCH₂CH₃
    |
    Cl
        CH₃O⁻

$$H_3C \quad\quad H$$
$$C=C$$
$$H \quad\quad CH_2CH_3$$

$$H_3C \quad\quad CH_2CH_3$$
$$C=C$$
$$H \quad\quad H$$

IN ADDITION TO UNDERGOING THE NUCLEOPHILIC SUBSTITUTION REACTIONS DESCRIBED in Chapter 8, alkyl halides also undergo elimination reactions. In an **elimination reaction**, atoms or groups are removed from a reactant. For example, when an alkyl halide undergoes an elimination reaction, the halogen (X) is removed from one carbon and a hydrogen is removed from an adjacent carbon. A double bond is formed between the two carbons from which the atoms are eliminated. Therefore, *the product of an elimination reaction is an alkene.*

CH₃CH₂CH₂X + Y⁻

    substitution → CH₃CH₂CH₂Y + X⁻

    elimination → CH₃CH=CH₂ + HY + X⁻

new double bond

We will start this chapter by looking at the elimination reactions of alkyl halides. Then we will examine the factors that determine whether a given alkyl halide will undergo a substitution reaction, an elimination reaction, or both substitution and elimination reactions.

The product of an elimination reaction is an alkene.

Investigating Naturally Occurring Organohalides

Like many other natural products—that is, compounds produced in nature—certain organohalides found in marine organisms have interesting and potent biological activity. Cyclocinamide A, one such organohalide, comes from a creature called an orange-encrusting sponge. This compound, as well as a host of analogs, has impressive antitumor properties that are currently being exploited in the development of new anticancer drugs.

Jasplankinolide, another organohalide found in a sponge, modulates the formation and depolymerization of actin mi-crotubules. Microtubules are found in all cells and are used for motile events, such as transportation of vesicles, migration, and cell division. Jasplankinolide is therefore being used to further our understanding of these processes. Notice that cyclocinamide A has four asymmetric centers and jas-plankinolide has six. In view of the great diversity of marine life, the ocean probably contains many compounds with useful medicinal properties waiting to be discovered by scientists.

cyclocinamide A

jasplankinolide

9.1 THE E2 REACTION

Just as there are two nucleophilic substitution reactions, S_N1 and S_N2, there are two important elimination reactions, E1 and E2. The following reaction is an example of an **E2 reaction**; "E" stands for *elimination* and "2" stands for *bimolecular* (Section 8.2).

$$CH_3-\underset{\underset{Br}{|}}{\overset{\overset{CH_3}{|}}{C}}-CH_3 + HO^- \longrightarrow CH_2=\underset{}{\overset{\overset{CH_3}{|}}{C}}-CH_3 + H_2O + Br^-$$

2-bromo-2-methylpropane   **2-methylpropene**

The rate of an E2 reaction depends linearly on the concentrations of both the alkyl halide and hydroxide ion. It is therefore a second-order reaction.

> **rate = k[alkyl halide][base]**

The rate law tells us that both the alkyl halide and hydroxide ion are involved in the transition state of the rate-determining step. The following mechanism—which portrays an E2 reaction as a concerted one-step reaction—agrees with the observed second-order kinetics:

MECHANISM FOR THE E2 REACTION

a proton is removed

a double bond is formed

Br⁻ is eliminated

$$\longrightarrow CH_2=\overset{\overset{CH_3}{|}}{C}-CH_3 + H_2O + Br^-$$

- The base (hydroxide ion) removes a proton from a carbon that is adjacent to the carbon bonded to the halogen. As the proton is removed, the electrons that it shared with carbon move toward the adjacent carbon that is bonded to the halogen. As these electrons move toward the carbon, the halogen leaves, taking its bonding electrons with it.

When the reaction is over, the electrons that were originally bonded to the hydrogen in the reactant have formed a π bond in the product. Removal of a proton and a halide ion is called **dehydrohalogenation**.

The carbon to which the halogen is attached is called the **α-carbon**. A carbon adjacent to the α-carbon is called a **β-carbon**. Because the elimination reaction is initiated by removing a proton from a β-carbon, an E2 reaction is sometimes called a **β-elimination reaction**. It is also called a **1,2-elimination reaction** because the atoms being removed are on adjacent carbons.

(handwritten) = the carbon to which the halogen is attached

a base ⟶ B: H | α-carbon | RCH—CHR ⟶ RCH=CHR + BH + Br⁻

β-carbon *(handwritten)* = carbon adjacent to the α-carbon

Br

(handwritten margin note) ✱ an E2 rxn is sometimes called a β-elimination reaction b/c t/ elim. r xn is initiated by removing a proton from a β-carbon.

In a series of alkyl halides that have the same alkyl group, alkyl iodides are the most reactive and alkyl fluorides the least reactive in E2 reactions because weaker bases are better leaving groups (Section 8.3).

(margin box) The weaker the base, the better a leaving group it is. *(handwritten)* E2

relative reactivities of alkyl halides in an E2 reaction

most reactive ⟶ RI > RBr > RCl > RF ⟵ least reactive

9.2 AN E2 REACTION IS REGIOSELECTIVE

An alkyl halide such as 2-bromopropane has two β-carbons from which a proton can be removed in an E2 reaction. Because the two β-carbons are identical, the proton can be removed equally easily from either one.

β-carbons

$$CH_3CHCH_3 \ + \ CH_3O^- \ \longrightarrow \ CH_3CH{=}CH_2 \ + \ CH_3OH \ + \ Br^-$$
|
Br   **propene**

2-bromopropane

In (contrast,) 2-bromobutane has two structurally different β-carbons from which a proton can be removed. Therefore when 2-bromobutane reacts with a base, two elimination products are formed: 2-butene (80%) and 1-butene (20%). This E2 reaction is *regioselective* because more of one constitutional isomer is formed than of the other.

β-carbons   *(handwritten)* regioselective   *(handwritten)* 2 elimination pdts. are formed: could form   could form

$$CH_3CHCH_2CH_3 \ + \ CH_3O^- \ \xrightarrow{CH_3OH} \ CH_3CH{=}CHCH_3 \ + \ CH_2{=}CHCH_2CH_3 \ + \ CH_3OH \ + \ Br^-$$
|
Br   **2-butene**   **1-butene**
2-bromobutane   **80%**   **20%**
                                      (mixture of *E* and *Z*) *(handwritten)* constitutional

(handwritten) base

What factors dictate which of the two alkenes will be formed in greater yield? In other words, what causes regioselectivity in an E2 reaction? We can answer that question by looking at the reaction coordinate diagram in Figure 9.1.

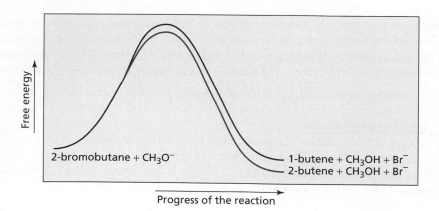

► **Figure 9.1**
A reaction coordinate diagram for the E2 reaction of 2-bromobutane and methoxide ion.

In the transition state leading to an alkene, the C—H and C—Br bonds are partially broken and the double bond is partially formed (the partially broken and partially formed bonds are indicated below by dashed lines), giving the transition state an alkene-like structure. Any factors that stabilize the alkene will also stabilize the alkene-like transition state, allowing the alkene to be formed faster.

transition state leading to 2-butene

more stable

transition state leading to 1-butene

less stable

The difference in the rate of formation of the two alkenes is not very great. Consequently, they are both formed, but the *more stable* of the two alkenes will generally be the major product of the reaction. We have seen that the stability of an alkene depends on the number of alkyl substituents bonded to its sp^2 carbons: the greater the number of alkyl substituents, the more stable is the alkene (Section 4.12). Therefore, 2-butene, with a total of two methyl substituents bonded to its sp^2 carbons, is more stable than 1-butene, with one ethyl substituent. Thus, 2-butene is formed faster than 1-butene.

The following reaction also forms two elimination products. Because 2-methyl-2-butene is the more substituted alkene (it has a greater number of alkyl substituents bonded to its sp^2 carbons), it is the more stable of the two alkenes and, therefore, is the major product of the elimination reaction.

The major product of an E2 reaction is generally the most stable alkene.

2-bromo-2-methylbutane

2-methyl-2-butene
70%

2-methyl-1-butene
30%

Alexander M. Zaitsev, a nineteenth-century Russian chemist, devised a shortcut to predict the more substituted alkene product. He pointed out *that the more substituted alkene is obtained when a hydrogen is removed from the β-carbon* that is bonded to the fewest hydrogens. This is called Zaitsev's rule. In 2-chloropentane, for example, one β-carbon is bonded to three hydrogens, and the other β-carbon is bonded to two hydrogens. According to **Zaitsev's rule**, the more substituted alkene will be the one formed by removing a proton from the β-carbon bonded to two hydrogens. Therefore, 2-pentene (a disubstituted alkene) is the major product, and 1-pentene (a monosubstituted alkene) is the minor product.

2 β-hydrogens | 3 β-hydrogens

$$\underset{\text{2-chloropentane}}{CH_3CH_2CH_2\overset{\displaystyle Cl}{\underset{\displaystyle |}{C}}HCH_3} + HO^- \longrightarrow \underset{\substack{\text{2-pentene}\\67\%\\\text{(mixture of } E \text{ and } Z)}}{\overset{\text{disubstituted}}{CH_3CH_2CH=CHCH_3}} + \underset{\substack{\text{1-pentene}\\33\%}}{\overset{\text{monosubstituted}}{CH_3CH_2CH_2CH=CH_2}}$$

Because elimination from a tertiary alkyl halide typically leads to a more substituted alkene than does elimination from a secondary alkyl halide, and elimination from a secondary alkyl halide generally leads to a more substituted alkene than does elimination from a primary alkyl halide, the relative reactivities of alkyl halides in an E2 reaction are as follows:

relative reactivities of alkyl halides in an E2 reaction

tertiary alkyl halide > secondary alkyl halide > primary alkyl halide

$$\underset{\displaystyle \underset{Br}{\overset{\displaystyle R}{RCH_2C}}}{} \qquad \underset{\displaystyle \underset{Br}{RCH_2CHR}}{} \qquad RCH_2CH_2Br$$

$$\downarrow \qquad\qquad\qquad \downarrow \qquad\qquad\qquad \downarrow$$

$$\overset{\displaystyle R}{\underset{}{RCH=CR}} \qquad RCH=CHR \qquad RCH=CH_2$$

| three alkyl substituents | two alkyl substituents | one alkyl substituent |

3° → most substituted alkene (handwritten)

PROBLEM 1 ♦

What would be the major elimination product obtained from the reaction of each of the following alkyl halides with hydroxide ion?

a. $CH_3\overset{\displaystyle CH_3}{\underset{\displaystyle I}{C}}CH_2CH_3$ **b.** $CH_3\overset{\displaystyle CH_3}{\underset{\displaystyle Br}{C}}HCHCH_3$ **c.** $CH_3CH_2\overset{\displaystyle CH_3}{\underset{\displaystyle CH_3}{C}}-\underset{\displaystyle Br}{C}HCH_3$

Keep in mind that the major product of an E2 reaction is the *more stable alkene*, and Zaitsev's rule is just a shortcut to determine which of the possible alkene products is the *more substituted alkene*. The more substituted alkene is not, however, always the more stable alkene. In each of the following reactions, the major product is the conjugated alkene because it is the more stable alkene, even though it is not the more substituted alkene.

Zaitsev's rule leads to the most substituted alkene.

$$\underset{\text{4-chloro-5-methyl-1-hexene}}{CH_2=CHCH_2\overset{\displaystyle CH_3}{\underset{\displaystyle Cl}{C}}HCHCH_3} \xrightarrow{HO^-} \underset{\substack{\text{5-methyl-1,3-hexadiene}\\\textbf{a conjugated diene}\\\textbf{major product}}}{CH_2=CHCH=\overset{\displaystyle CH_3}{CHCHCH_3}} + \underset{\substack{\text{5-methyl-1,4-hexadiene}\\\textbf{an isolated diene}\\\textbf{minor product}}}{CH_2=CHCH_2CH=\overset{\displaystyle CH_3}{CCH_3}} + H_2O + Cl^-$$

conjugated (handwritten)

$$\underset{\substack{\text{2-bromo-3-methyl-}\\\text{1-phenylbutane}}}{\text{C}_6\text{H}_5-CH_2\overset{\displaystyle CH_3}{\underset{\displaystyle Br}{C}}HCHCH_3} \xrightarrow{HO^-} \underset{\substack{\text{3-methyl-1-phenyl-1-butene}\\\textbf{the double bond is}\\\textbf{conjugated with the}\\\textbf{benzene ring}\\\textbf{major product}}}{\text{C}_6\text{H}_5-CH=\overset{\displaystyle CH_3}{CHCHCH_3}} + \underset{\substack{\text{3-methyl-1-phenyl-2-butene}\\\textbf{the double bond is}\\\textbf{not conjugated with the}\\\textbf{benzene ring}\\\textbf{minor product}}}{\text{C}_6\text{H}_5-CH_2CH=\overset{\displaystyle CH_3}{CCH_3}} + H_2O + Br^-$$

conjugated (handwritten)

conjugated
π's most
stable

> **The most stable alkene is generally (but not always) the most substituted alkene.**

Zaitsev's rule cannot be used to predict the major products of the foregoing reactions because it does not take account of the fact that conjugated double bonds are more stable than isolated double bonds (Section 7.7). Therefore, if the alkyl halide has a double bond or a benzene ring, do not use Zaitsev's rule to predict the most stable (major) product of an elimination reaction.

In some elimination reactions, the more stable alkene is not the major product. For example, if the base in an E2 reaction is bulky and the approach to the alkyl halide is sterically hindered, the base will preferentially remove the most accessible hydrogen. In the following reaction, it is easier for the bulky *tert*-butoxide ion to remove one of the more exposed terminal hydrogens, which leads to formation of the less substituted alkene. Because the less substituted alkene is more easily formed, it is the major product of the reaction. The data in Table 9.1 show that the percentage of the less substituted alkene increases as the size of the base increases.

If the alkyl halide is not sterically hindered and the base is only moderately hindered, the more stable product will be the major product, in accordance with the general rule. For example, the major product of the following reaction is 2-butene. In other words, it takes a lot of steric hindrance for the less stable product to be the major product.

Table 9.1   Effect of the Steric Properties of the Base on the Distribution of Products in an E2 Reaction

Base	More substituted alkene	Less substituted alkene
$CH_3CH_2O^-$	79%	21%
$CH_3\overset{\underset{\textstyle CH_3}{\vert}}{\underset{\underset{\textstyle CH_3}{\vert}}{C}}O^-$	27%	73%
$CH_3\overset{\underset{\textstyle CH_3}{\vert}}{\underset{\underset{\textstyle CH_2CH_3}{\vert}}{C}}O^-$	19%	81%
$CH_3CH_2\overset{\underset{\textstyle CH_2CH_3}{\vert}}{\underset{\underset{\textstyle CH_2CH_3}{\vert}}{C}}O^-$	8%	92%

PROBLEM 2 ♦

Which of the alkyl halides in each pair is more reactive in an E2 reaction?

PROBLEM 3

Draw a reaction coordinate diagram for the E2 reaction of 2-bromo-2,3-dimethylbutane with sodium *tert*-butoxide.

Although the major product of an E2 reaction of alkyl chlorides, alkyl bromides, and alkyl iodides is normally the more substituted alkene, the major product of the E2 reaction of alkyl fluorides is the less substituted alkene.

$$CH_3\overset{\underset{\displaystyle |}{F}}{C}HCH_2CH_2CH_3 \; + \; CH_3O^- \; \xrightarrow{CH_3OH} \; CH_3CH{=}CHCH_2CH_3 \; + \; CH_2{=}CHCH_2CH_2CH_3 \; + \; CH_3OH \; + \; F^-$$

| 2-fluoropentane | methoxide ion | | 2-pentene 30% (mixture of *E* and *Z*) | 1-pentene 70% | | |

Why do alkyl fluorides give a different major product? When a hydrogen and a chlorine, bromine, or iodine are eliminated from an alkyl halide, the halogen starts to leave as soon as the base begins to remove the proton. Consequently, a negative charge does not build up on the carbon that is losing the proton. Thus, the transition state resembles an alkene rather than a carbanion (see page 378). The fluoride ion, however, is the strongest base of the halide ions and therefore the poorest leaving group. So when a base begins to remove a proton from an alkyl fluoride, the fluoride ion does not have as strong a propensity to leave as another halide ion would have. As a result, negative charge develops on the carbon that is losing the proton, causing the transition state to resemble a carbanion rather than an alkene. To determine which of the carbanion-like transition states is more stable, we need to see which carbanion would be more stable.

carbanion-like transition state

$$\overset{\delta^-}{O}CH_3$$
H
$$\overset{\delta^-}{C}H_2CHCH_2CH_2CH_3$$
F

transition state leading to 1-pentene more stable

$$\overset{\delta^-}{O}CH_3$$
H
$$CH_3CHCHCH_2CH_3 \; {\scriptstyle\delta^-}$$
F

transition state leading to 2-pentene less stable

We have seen that carbocations, because they are positively charged, are *stabilized* by electron-donating alkyl groups. Thus, tertiary carbocations are the most stable, and methyl cations are the least stable (Section 4.2).

relative stabilities of carbocations

most stable $\;$ R—C⁺ (with R, R) $\;>\;$ R—C⁺ (with R, H) $\;>\;$ R—C⁺ (with H, H) $\;>\;$ H—C⁺ (with H, H) $\;$ least stable

| tertiary carbocation | secondary carbocation | primary carbocation | methyl cation |

Carbanions, on the other hand, are negatively charged, so they are *destabilized* by electron-donating alkyl groups. Therefore, methyl anions are the most stable and tertiary carbanions are the least stable. (The difference in solvation energies also contributes to this trend.)

relative stabilities of carbanions

Carbocation stability: **3° > 2° > 1°**

Carbanion stability: **1° > 2° > 3°**

$$\boxed{\text{least stable}} \; R-\overset{R}{\underset{R}{C:}} \; < \; R-\overset{R}{\underset{H}{C:}} \; < \; R-\overset{H}{\underset{H}{C:}} \; < \; H-\overset{H}{\underset{H}{C:}} \; \boxed{\text{most stable}}$$

tertiary carbanion   secondary carbanion   primary carbanion   methyl anion

The developing negative charge in the transition state leading to 1-pentene is on a primary carbon (see page 381), which is more stable than the transition state leading to 2-pentene, in which the developing negative charge is on a secondary carbon. Because the transition state leading to 1-pentene is more stable, 1-pentene is formed more rapidly and is the major product of the E2 reaction.

The data in Table 9.2 show that as the halide ion increases in basicity (and so decreases in leaving propensity), the yield of the more substituted alkene product decreases. However, the more substituted alkene remains the major elimination product in all cases, except when the halogen is fluorine.

Table 9.2   Products Obtained from the E2 Reaction of CH_3O^- and 2-Halohexanes

$$\overset{X}{\underset{|}{CH_3CHCH_2CH_2CH_2CH_3}} \; + \; CH_3O^- \; \longrightarrow \; CH_3CH=CHCH_2CH_2CH_3 \; + \; CH_2=CHCH_2CH_2CH_2CH_3$$

2-hexene
(mixture of *E* and *Z*)   1-hexene

Leaving group	Conjugate acid	pK_a	More substituted product	Less substituted product
X = I	HI	−10	81%	19%
X = Br	HBr	−9	72%	28%
X = Cl	HCl	−7	67%	33%
X = F	HF	3.2	30%	70%

We can summarize by saying that *the major product of an E2 elimination reaction is the more stable alkene* except *if the reactants are sterically hindered or the leaving group is poor* (for example, a fluoride ion), in which case the major product will be the less stable alkene. In Section 9.6, you will see that the more stable alkene is not always the major product in the case of certain cyclic compounds.

PROBLEM 4♦

Give the major elimination product obtained from an E2 reaction of each of the following alkyl halides with hydroxide ion:

a. $\overset{}{CH_3CHCH_2CH_3}$
   $\underset{Cl}{|}$

b. $\overset{CH_3}{CH_3CHCHCH_2CH_3}$
   $\underset{Cl}{|}$

c. $CH_3CHCH_2CH=CH_2$
   $\underset{Cl}{|}$

d. $\overset{}{CH_3CHCH_2CH_3}$
   $\underset{F}{|}$

e. (cyclohexene ring with Br substituent)

f. $\overset{CH_3}{CH_3CHCHCH_2CH_3}$
   $\underset{F}{|}$

PROBLEM 5♦

Which alkyl halide in each pair would you expect to be more reactive in an E2 reaction?

a. [structure] or [structure]   **c.** [structure] or [structure]

chem Tutorial:
place E2 dehydrohalogenation

b. [structure] or [structure]   **d.** [structure] or [structure]

9.3 THE E1 REACTION

The second kind of elimination reaction that alkyl halides can undergo is an E1 reaction. The following reaction is an example of an **E1 reaction**; "E" stands for *elimination* and "1" stands for *unimolecular*.

$$CH_3\text{—}\underset{\underset{Br}{|}}{\overset{\overset{CH_3}{|}}{C}}\text{—}CH_3 + H_2O \longrightarrow CH_2{=}\underset{}{\overset{\overset{CH_3}{|}}{C}}\text{—}CH_3 + H_3O^+ + Br^-$$

2-bromo-2-methylpropane   **2-methylpropene**

An E1 reaction is a first-order elimination reaction because the rate of the reaction depends linearly only on the concentration of the alkyl halide.

rate = *k*[alkyl halide]

We therefore know that only the alkyl halide takes part in the rate-determining step of the reaction. Therefore, an E1 reaction must have at least two steps. The following mechanism agrees with the observed first-order kinetics. Because the first step is the rate-determining step, an increase in the concentration of the base—which participates in the second step of the reaction only—has no effect on the rate of the reaction.

MECHANISM FOR THE E1 REACTION

$$CH_3\text{—}\underset{\underset{Br}{|}}{\overset{\overset{CH_3}{|}}{C}}\text{—}CH_3 \underset{slow}{\rightleftharpoons} CH_2\text{—}\underset{+}{\overset{\overset{CH_3}{|}}{C}}\text{—}CH_3 \xrightarrow{fast} CH_2{=}\overset{\overset{CH_3}{|}}{C}\text{—}CH_3 + H_3O^+$$

the alkyl halide dissociates, forming a carbocation

H₂Ö: + Br⁻

the base removes a proton from a β-carbon

- The alkyl halide dissociates, forming a carbocation.
- The base forms the elimination product by removing a proton from a carbon that is adjacent to the positively charged carbon (that is, from a β-carbon).

We have seen that the pK_a of a compound such as ethane that has hydrogens attached only to sp^3 carbons is > 60 (Section 6.10). How, then, can a weak base like water remove a proton from an sp^3 carbon in the second step of the reaction? First of all, the pK_a is greatly reduced by the adjacent positively charged carbon that can accept the electrons left behind when the proton is removed. Second, the β-carbon shares the positive charge as a result of hyperconjugation. Hyperconjugation drains electron density from the C—H bond, thereby weakening it. Recall that hyperconjugation—where the σ electrons of a bond attached to a carbon adjacent to the positively charged carbon spread into the empty p orbital—is responsible for the greater stability of a tertiary carbocation compared with a secondary carbocation (Section 4.2).

When more than one alkene can be formed, the E1 reaction, like the E2 reaction is regioselective. The major product is generally the *more substituted alkene*.

$$CH_3CH_2\overset{\overset{\displaystyle CH_3}{|}}{\underset{\underset{\displaystyle Cl}{|}}{C}}CH_3 \;+\; H_2O \longrightarrow CH_3CH{=}\overset{\overset{\displaystyle CH_3}{|}}{C}CH_3 \;+\; CH_3CH_2\overset{\overset{\displaystyle CH_3}{|}}{C}{=}CH_2 \;+\; H_3O^+ \;+\; Cl^-$$

2-chloro-2-methylbutane

2-methyl-2-butene
major product

2-methyl-1-butene
minor product

The more substituted alkene is the major product because its greater stability causes the transition state leading to its formation to be more stable (Figure 9.2). Thus, it is formed more rapidly. The more substituted alkene is formed by removing the hydrogen from the β-carbon bonded to the fewest hydrogens, in accordance with Zaitsev's rule.

▶ **Figure 9.2**
A reaction coordinate diagram for the E1 reaction of 2-chloro-2-methylbutane. The major product is the more substituted alkene because its greater stability causes the transition state leading to its formation to be more stable.

Because the first step of an E1 reaction is the rate-determining step, the rate of an E1 reaction depends both on the ease with which the carbocation is formed *and* on how readily the leaving group leaves. The more stable the carbocation, the more easily it is formed, because more stable carbocations have more stable transition states leading to their formation. Therefore, the relative reactivities of a series of alkyl halides that all have the same leaving group parallel the relative stabilities of the carbocations. Tertiary benzylic and tertiary allylic halides are the most reactive alkyl halides because their carbocations—the most stable carbocations in the sequence shown below—are the easiest to form (Section 7.7).

relative reactivities of alkyl halides in an E1 reaction = relative stabilities of carbocations

3° benzylic ≈ 3° allylic > 2° benzylic ≈ 2° allylic ≈ 3° > 1° benzylic ≈ 1° allylic ≈ 2° > 1° > vinyl

most
stable

least
stable

Notice that tertiary alkyl halides are more reactive than secondary alkyl halides, which, in turn, are more reactive than primary alkyl halides, in both E1 and E2 reactions (Section 9.2).

We have seen that the weakest bases are the best leaving groups (Section 9.1). There-fore, for series of alkyl halides with the same alkyl group, alkyl iodides are the most reactive and alkyl fluorides the least reactive in E1 reactions.

relative reactivities of alkyl halides in an E1 reaction

$$\boxed{\text{most reactive}} \Longrightarrow RI > RBr > RCl > RF \Longleftarrow \boxed{\text{least reactive}}$$

Thus for *both* E2 and E1 reactions:

- the major product is generally the most stable alkene.
- tertiary alkyl halides are the most reactive and primary alkyl halides are the least reactive.
- for alkyl halides with the same alkyl group, alkyl iodides are the most reactive and alkyl fluorides are the least reactive.

Because the E1 reaction forms a carbocation intermediate, the carbon skeleton can rearrange before the proton is lost, if rearrangement leads to a more stable carbocation. For example, the secondary carbocation that is formed initially in the following reaction undergoes a 1,2-methyl shift to become a more stable tertiary benzylic cation. This cation undergoes deprotonation to form the alkene.

In the next reaction, the secondary carbocation formed initially undergoes a 1,2-hydride shift to become a more stable secondary allylic cation:

PROBLEM 6 ◆

Four alkenes are formed from the E1 reaction of 3-bromo-2,3-dimethylpentane. Give the structures of the alkenes, and rank them according to the amounts that would be formed.

PROBLEM 7 ◆

If 2-fluoropentane were to undergo an E1 reaction, would you expect the major product to be the one predicted by Zaitsev's rule? Explain.

PROBLEM 8 ◆

Which of the following compounds would react faster in an
a. E1 reaction?   **b.** E2 reaction?   **c.** S_N1 reaction?   **d.** S_N2 reaction?

A

B

PROBLEM-SOLVING STRATEGY

Proposing a Mechanism

Propose a mechanism for the following reaction:

Because the reagent used in the reaction is an acid, we start by protonating the molecule. We need to protonate it at the position that allows the most stable carbocation to be formed. Protonating the CH_2 group forms a tertiary allylic carbocation in which the positive charge is delocalized over two other carbons. Electron delocalization and a 1,2-methyl shift result in a carbocation with the desired carbon skeleton. Loss of a proton gives the final product.

Now continue on to Problem 9.

chem Tutorial:
place Mechanism for E1 reaction

PROBLEM 9

Propose a mechanism for the following reaction:

9.4 COMPETITION BETWEEN E2 AND E1 REACTIONS

Primary alkyl halides undergo only E2 reactions; they cannot undergo E1 reactions because primary carbocations are too unstable to be formed. *Secondary* and *tertiary* alkyl halides undergo both E2 and E1 reactions (Table 9.3).

Table 9.3   Summary of the Reactivity of Alkyl Halides in Elimination Reactions

Primary alkyl halide	E2 only
Secondary alkyl halide	E1 and E2
Tertiary alkyl halide	E1 and E2

S$_N$2 and E2 reactions of alkyl halides are favored by a high concentration of a good nucleophile in an aprotic polar solvent.

For those alkyl halides that can undergo both E2 and E1 reactions, the E2 reaction is favored by the same factors that favor an S$_N$2 reaction and the E1 reaction is favored by the same factors that favor an S$_N$1 reaction. Thus, *an E2 reaction is favored by a high concentration of a strong base and an aprotic polar solvent (such as DMSO or DMF), whereas an E1 reaction is favored by a weak base and a protic polar solvent (such as H$_2$O or ROH).* How the solvent favors one reaction over another was discussed in Section 8.9.

S$_N$1 and E1 reactions of alkyl halides are favored by a poor nucleophile in a protic polar solvent.

Notice that a tertiary alkyl halide and a strong base were chosen to illustrate the E2 reaction in Section 9.1, whereas a tertiary alkyl halide and a weak base were used to illustrate the E1 reaction in Section 9.3.

PROBLEM 10♦

For each of the following reactions, (1) decide which kind of elimination reaction will occur, E2 or E1, and (2) give the major elimination product of each reaction, disregarding stereoisomers:

a. $CH_3CH_2CHCH_3$ $\xrightarrow[\text{DMSO}]{CH_3O^-}$
   |
   Br

b. $CH_3CH_2CHCH_3$ $\xrightarrow{CH_3OH}$
   |
   Br

c. $CH_3\overset{CH_3}{\underset{Cl}{\overset{|}{\underset{|}{C}}}}CH_3$ $\xrightarrow{H_2O}$

d. $CH_3\overset{CH_3}{\underset{Cl}{\overset{|}{\underset{|}{C}}}}CH_3$ $\xrightarrow[\text{DMF}]{HO^-}$

e. $CH_3\overset{CH_3}{\underset{CH_3}{\overset{|}{\underset{|}{C}}}}-\overset{}{\underset{Br}{\overset{}{\underset{|}{C}}}}HCH_3$ $\xrightarrow{CH_3CH_2OH}$

f. $CH_3\overset{CH_3}{\underset{CH_3}{\overset{|}{\underset{|}{C}}}}-\overset{}{\underset{Br}{\overset{}{\underset{|}{C}}}}HCH_3$ $\xrightarrow[\text{DMSO}]{CH_3CH_2O^-}$

PROBLEM 11♦

The rate law for the reaction of HO^- with *tert*-butyl bromide to form an elimination product in 75% ethanol/25% water at 30 °C is the sum of the rate laws for the E2 and E1 reactions:

rate $= 7.1 \times 10^{-5}$ [*tert*-butyl bromide] [HO^-] $+ 1.5 \times 10^{-5}$ [*tert*-butyl bromide]

What percentage of the reaction takes place by the E2 pathway when the following conditions exist?

a. [HO^-] = 5.0 M   b. [HO^-] = 0.0025 M

9.5 E2 AND E1 REACTIONS ARE STEREOSELECTIVE

We have seen that E2 and E1 reactions are regioselective: more of one constitutional isomer is formed than the other. For example, the major product formed from either the E2 *or* the E1 reaction of 2-bromopentane is 2-pentene (Sections 9.1 and 9.3). Now we will see that E2 and E1 reactions also are stereoselective.

$$CH_3CH_2CH_2\overset{Br}{\underset{}{\overset{|}{C}}}HCH_3 \xrightarrow[CH_3CH_2OH]{CH_3CH_2O^-} CH_3CH_2CH{=}CHCH_3 \ + \ CH_3CH_2CH_2CH{=}CH_2$$

2-bromopentane   2-pentene   1-pentene
                                  72%   28%
                          (mixture of *E* and *Z*)

The Stereoisomers Formed in an E2 Reaction

An E2 reaction removes two groups from adjacent carbons. It is a concerted reaction because the two groups are eliminated in the same step. The bonds to the groups to be eliminated (identified as H and X in the example below) must be in the same plane because the sp^3 orbital of the carbon bonded to H and the sp^3 orbital of the carbon bonded to X become overlapping *p* orbitals in the alkene product. Therefore, the orbitals must overlap in the transition state. For the overlap to be optimal, the orbitals must be parallel (that is, in the same plane).

There are two ways in which the C—H and C—X bonds can be in the same plane. They can either be parallel to one another on the same side of the molecule—an arrangement called **syn-periplanar**—or they can be parallel to one another on opposite sides of the molecule—an arrangement called **anti-periplanar**.

substituents are syn-periplanar   substituents are anti-periplanar
an eclipsed conformation   **a staggered conformation**

If an elimination reaction removes two substituents from the same side of the C—C bond, it is called a **syn elimination**. If the substituents are removed from opposite sides of the C—C bond, the reaction is called an **anti elimination**. Both types of elimination can occur, but syn elimination is much slower, so anti elimination is highly favored in an E2 reaction. One reason anti elimination is favored is that syn elimination requires the molecule to be in an eclipsed conformation, whereas anti elimination requires it to be in a more stable, staggered conformation.

Sawhorse projections, which show the C—C bond from an oblique angle, reveal another reason that anti elimination is favored. In syn elimination, the electrons of the departing hydrogen move to the *front* side of the carbon bonded to X, whereas in anti elimination, the electrons move to the *back* side of the carbon bonded to X.

We have seen that displacement reactions occur through back-side attack because in that way they achieve the best overlap of the interacting orbitals (Section 8.1). Finally, in anti elimination, the electron-rich base is spared the repulsion it experiences when it is on the same side of the molecule as the electron-rich departing halide ion.

Because of the factors that favor anti elimination, an E2 reaction is *stereoselective;* which means that more of one stereoisomer is formed than the other. For example, the 2-pentene obtained as the major product from the elimination reaction of 2-bromopentane on page 387 can exist as a pair of stereoisomers, and more (*E*)-2-pentene is formed than (*Z*)-2-pentene.

We can make the following general statement about the stereoselectivity of E2 reactions: if the reactant has *two hydrogens* bonded to the carbon from which a hydrogen is to be removed, both the *E* and *Z* products will be formed, because the reactant has two conformers in which the groups to be eliminated are anti.

Anti elimination predominates in an E2 reaction.

The alkene with the *bulkiest groups on opposite sides of the double bond* will be formed in greater yield because it is the more stable alkene, so it will have the more stable transition state leading to its formation (Figure 9.3). Remember that the alkene with the bulkiest groups on the *same* side of the double bond is less stable because the electron clouds of the large substituents can interfere with each other, causing steric strain (Section 4.13).

interacting electron clouds cause steric strain

(E)-2-pentene

(Z)-2-pentene

When two hydrogens are bonded to the β-carbon, the major product of an E2 reaction is the alkene with the bulkiest substituents on opposite sides of the double bond.

◄ Figure 9.3
A reaction coordinate diagram for the E2 reaction of 2-bromopentane and ethoxide ion. The more stable alkene has the more stable transition state and therefore is formed more rapidly.

Thus, the following elimination reaction leads predominantly to the *E* isomer because this stereoisomer has the methyl group (the bulkier group on one sp^2 carbon) opposite the *tert*-butyl group (the bulkier group on the other sp^2 carbon).

CH₃CH₂—C—C—CH₃ →

3-bromo-2,2,3-trimethyl-pentane

(E)-3,4,4-trimethyl-2-pentene
major product

(Z)-3,4,4-trimethyl-2-pentene
minor product

On the other hand, if the β-carbon from which a hydrogen is to be removed is bonded to only *one hydrogen*, there is only one conformer in which the groups to be eliminated are anti. Therefore, only one alkene product can be formed. The particular stereoisomer formed depends on the configuration of the reactant. For example, anti elimination of HBr from (2S,3S)-2-bromo-3-phenylbutane forms the *E* isomer, whereas anti elimination of HBr from (2S,3R)-2-bromo-3-phenylbutane forms the *Z* isomer. Notice that the groups that are not eliminated retain their relative positions. (If you have trouble understanding how to decide which product is formed, see the answer to Problem 43d in the *Study Guide and Solutions Manual*.)

(2S,3S)-2-bromo-3-phenylbutane

(E)-2-phenyl-2-butene   MAJOR

(2S,3R)-2-bromo-3-phenylbutane

(Z)-2-phenyl-2-butene

When only one hydrogen is bonded to the β-carbon, the major product of an E2 reaction depends on the structure of the alkyl halide.

Molecular models can be helpful whenever complex stereochemistry is involved.

PROBLEM 12♦

a. For each of the following alkyl halides, give the structure of the major product that would be obtained from an E2 reaction, indicating its configuration:

1. $CH_3CH_2\overset{\overset{\displaystyle Br}{|}}{C}H\overset{\overset{\displaystyle CH_3}{|}}{C}HCH_3$ 2. $CH_3CH_2\overset{}{C}HCH_2CH=CH_2$ with Cl below   3. $CH_3CH_2CHCH_2$—⟨benzene ring⟩ with Cl below

b. Does the product obtained depend on whether you start with the R or S enantiomer of the reactant?

The Stereoisomers Formed in an E1 Reaction

An E1 reaction, like an E2 reaction, is stereoselective; both the E and Z products will be formed, and the major product will be the one with the *bulkiest groups on opposite sides of the double bond*. Let's see why this is so.

We have seen that an E1 reaction takes place in two steps. The leaving group leaves in the first step, and a proton is lost from an adjacent carbon in the second step, following Zaitsev's rule for forming the more stable alkene. The carbocation created in the first step is planar, so the electrons from a departing proton can move toward the positively charged carbon from *either side*. Therefore, both syn and anti elimination can occur.

Because both syn and anti elimination can occur in an E1 reaction, both the E and Z products are formed, regardless of whether the β-carbon from which the proton is removed is bonded to one or to two hydrogens. The major product is the one with the bulkiest groups on opposite sides of the double bond, because that is the more stable alkene.

The major stereoisomer obtained in an E1 reaction is the alkene in which the bulkiest substituents are on opposite sides of the double bond.

In contrast, we just saw that an E2 reaction forms both the E and Z products only if the β-carbon from which the proton is removed is bonded to two hydrogens. If the β-carbon is bonded to only one hydrogen, an E2 reaction forms only one product because anti elimination is favored.

PROBLEM 13♦   SOLVED

For each of the following alkyl halides, determine the major product formed when it undergoes an E1 reaction:

a. $CH_3CH_2CH_2CH_2\overset{}{C}HCH_3$ with Br below

b. $CH_3CH_2CH_2\overset{\overset{\displaystyle CH_3}{|}}{C}CH_3$ with Cl below

c. $CH_3CH_2CH_2\overset{\overset{\displaystyle CH_3}{|}}{C}HCHCH_2CH_3$ with I below

d. ⟨cyclohexane ring with Cl and CH₃ on top carbon⟩

Solution to 13a   First, we need to consider the regiochemistry of the reaction: more 2-hexene will be formed than 1-hexene because 2-hexene is more stable.

$$CH_3CH_2CH_2CH_2CHCH_3 \quad \xrightarrow{E1} \quad CH_3CH_2CH_2CH{=}CHCH_3 \quad + \quad CH_3CH_2CH_2CH_2CH{=}CH_2$$

$$\underset{\displaystyle Br}{\mid}$$

2-hexene   **1-hexene**

Next, we need to consider the stereochemistry of the reaction: of the 2-hexene that is formed, more will be (*E*)-2-hexene than (*Z*)-2-hexene, because (*E*)-2-hexene is more stable. Thus, (*E*)-2-hexene is the major product of the reaction.

(*E*)-2-hexene

(*Z*)-2-hexene

chem Tutorial:
place   E2 regiochemistry

Tutorial:
E2 stereochemistry

Tutorial:
Common terms in E1 and E2
reactions

9.6 ELIMINATION FROM SUBSTITUTED CYCLOHEXANES

Elimination from substituted cyclohexanes follows the same stereochemical rules as elimination from open-chain compounds.

E2 Reactions of Substituted Cyclohexanes

We just saw that to achieve the anti-periplanar geometry favored in an E2 reaction, the two groups being eliminated must be parallel (Section 9.5). For two groups on a cyclohexane ring to be parallel, they both must be *in axial positions*.

groups to be eliminated must both be in axial positions

In an E2 reaction of a substituted cyclohexane, the groups being eliminated must both be in axial positions.

The more stable conformer of chlorocyclohexane does not undergo an E2 reaction, because the chloro substituent is in an equatorial position. (Recall from Section 2.13 that the more stable conformer of a monosubstituted cyclohexane is the one in which the substituent is in an equatorial position because there is more room for a substituent in that position.) The less stable conformer, with the chloro substituent in the axial position, readily undergoes an E2 reaction.

more stable   **less stable**

↓ HO⁻
↓ E2 conditions

k' ↓ HO⁻
    ↓ E2 conditions

no reaction $+ \ H_2O \ + \ Cl^-$

Because only one of the two conformers undergoes an E2 reaction, the rate constant for the elimination reaction is given by $k'K_{eq}$, where $K_{eq} = $ [reactive conformer]/[unreactive conformer]. Therefore, the reaction is faster if K_{eq} is large.

$$K_{eq} = \frac{\text{[more stable conformer]}}{\text{[less stable conformer]}} \qquad K_{eq} = \frac{\text{[less stable conformer]}}{\text{[more stable conformer]}}$$

large number — [more stable conformer]

small number — [less stable conformer]

small number — [less stable conformer]

large number — [more stable conformer]

for a reaction that takes place through the more stable conformer

for a reaction that takes place through the less stable conformer

Most molecules are in the more stable conformer at any given time. Therefore, K_{eq} will be large if elimination takes place by way of the more stable conformer, and it will be small if elimination takes place by way of the less stable conformer. Now let's look at two examples.

Neomenthyl chloride undergoes an E2 reaction with ethoxide ion about 200 times faster than menthyl chloride does. The conformer of neomenthyl chloride that undergoes elimination is the *more* stable conformer because when the Cl and H are in the required axial positions, the methyl and isopropyl groups are in equatorial positions.

neomenthyl chloride
more stable

less stable

$CH_3CH_2O^- $ | **E2 conditions**

+ CH_3CH_2OH + Cl^-

In contrast, the conformer of menthyl chloride that undergoes elimination is the *less* stable conformer because when the Cl and H are in the required axial positions, the methyl and isopropyl groups are also in axial positions.

menthyl chloride
more stable

less stable

$CH_3CH_2O^- $ | **E2 conditions**

+ CH_3CH_2OH + Cl^-

Notice that when menthyl chloride (above) or *trans*-1-chloro-2-methylcyclohexane (below) undergoes an E2 reaction, the hydrogen that is eliminated is not removed from the β-carbon bonded to the fewest hydrogens. This may seem like a violation of Zaitsev's rule, but the rule states that when there is *more than one* β-carbon from which a hydrogen *can be removed*, the hydrogen is removed from the β-carbon bonded to the fewest hydrogens. The hydrogen that is removed has to be in an axial position, and menthyl chloride and *trans*-1-chloro-2-methylcyclohexane both have only one β-carbon with a hydrogen in an axial position. Therefore, that hydrogen is the one that is removed, even though it is not bonded to the β-carbon with the fewest hydrogens.

PROBLEM 14♦

Why do *cis*-1-bromo-2-ethylcyclohexane and *trans*-1-bromo-2-ethylcyclohexane form different major products when they undergo an E2 reaction?

PROBLEM 15♦

Which isomer reacts more rapidly in an E2 reaction, *cis*-1-bromo-4-*tert*-butylcyclohexane or *trans*-1-bromo-4-*tert*-butylcyclohexane? Explain your answer.

E1 Reactions of Substituted Cyclohexanes

When a substituted cyclohexane undergoes an E1 reaction, the two groups that are eliminated do not both have to be in axial positions because the elimination reaction is not concerted. In the following reaction, a carbocation is formed in the first step. It then loses a proton from the adjacent carbon that is bonded to the fewest hydrogens—in other words, Zaitsev's rule is followed.

Stamps issued in honor of English Nobel laureates:
(a) Sir Derek Barton for conformational analysis, 1969;
(b) Sir Walter Haworth for the synthesis of vitamin C, 1937;
(c) A. J. P. Martin and Richard L. M. Synge for chromatography, 1952;
(d) William H. Bragg and William L. Bragg for crystallography, 1915.
(The Braggs are one of six father–son pairs who both received Nobel Prizes.)

Because a carbocation is formed in an E1 reaction, you must check for the possibility of a carbocation rearrangement before you use Zaitsev's rule to determine the elimination product. In the following reaction, the initially formed secondary carbocation undergoes a 1,2-hydride shift to form a more stable tertiary carbocation.

secondary carbocation

1,2-hydride shift

tertiary carbocation

An E1 reaction includes both syn and anti elimination.

Table 9.4 summarizes the stereochemical outcomes of substitution and elimination reactions.

Table 9.4	Stereochemistry of Substitution and Elimination Reactions
Reaction	**Products**
S$_N$1	Both stereoisomers (R and S) are formed (more inverted than retained).
E1	Both E and Z stereoisomers are formed (more of the stereoisomer with the bulkiest groups on opposite sides of the double bond).
S$_N$2	Only the inverted product is formed.
E2	Both E and Z stereoisomers are formed (more of the stereoisomer with the bulkiest groups on opposite sides of the double bond) unless the β-carbon of the reactant is bonded to only one hydrogen, in which case only one stereoisomer is formed; its configuration depends on the configuration of the reactant.

PROBLEM 16

Give the substitution and elimination products for the following reactions, showing the configuration of each product:

a. (S)-2-chlorohexane $\xrightarrow[\text{S}_N\text{2/E2 conditions}]{\text{CH}_3\text{O}^-}$

b. (S)-2-chlorohexane $\xrightarrow[\text{S}_N\text{1/E1 conditions}]{\text{CH}_3\text{OH}}$

c. trans-1-chloro-2-methylcyclohexane $\xrightarrow[\text{S}_N\text{2/E2 conditions}]{\text{CH}_3\text{O}^-}$

d. trans-1-chloro-2-methylcyclohexane $\xrightarrow[\text{S}_N\text{1/E1 conditions}]{\text{CH}_3\text{OH}}$

e. $\xrightarrow[\text{S}_N\text{2/E2 conditions}]{\text{CH}_3\text{O}^-}$

f. $\xrightarrow[\text{S}_N\text{1/E1 conditions}]{\text{CH}_3\text{OH}}$

chem Tutorial:
place E2 elimination from cyclic compounds

9.7 A KINETIC ISOTOPE EFFECT CAN HELP DETERMINE A MECHANISM

We have seen that a mechanism is a model that accounts for all the experimental evidence that has accumulated concerning a reaction. For example, the mechanisms of the S_N1, S_N2, E1, and E2 reactions are based on the rate law of each reaction, the relative reactivities of specific reactants, and the structures of specific products.

Another kind of experimental evidence that is helpful in determining the mechanism of a reaction is the **deuterium kinetic isotope effect**—the ratio of the rate constant observed for a compound containing hydrogen to the rate constant observed for an identical compound in which one or more of the hydrogens has been replaced by deuterium, an isotope of hydrogen. Recall that the nucleus of a deuterium atom has one proton and one neutron, whereas the nucleus of a hydrogen atom contains only a proton (Section 1.1).

$$\textbf{deuterium kinetic isotope effect} = \frac{k_H}{k_D} = \frac{\textbf{rate constant for H-containing reactant}}{\textbf{rate constant for D-containing reactant}}$$

The chemical properties of deuterium and hydrogen are similar; however, a C—D bond is about 1.2 kcal/mol (5 kJ/mol) stronger than a C—H bond. Therefore, a C—D bond is more difficult to break than a corresponding C—H bond.

When the rate constant (k_H) for elimination of HBr from 1-bromo-2-phenylethane is compared with the rate constant (k_D) for elimination of DBr from 2-bromo-1,1-dideuterio-1-phenylethane (determined under identical conditions), k_H is found to be 7.1 times greater than k_D. The deuterium kinetic isotope effect for this reaction, therefore, is 7.1. The difference in the reaction rates is due to the difference in energy required to break a C—H bond compared with a C—D bond.

1-bromo-2-phenylethane

2-bromo-1,1-dideuterio-1-phenylethane

Because the deuterium kinetic isotope effect is greater than 1.0 for this reaction, indicating that the change from hydrogen to deuterium affects the rate of the reaction, we know that the C—H (or C—D) bond must be broken in the rate-determining step, a fact consistent with the mechanism proposed for an E2 reaction.

PROBLEM 17♦

List the following compounds in order of decreasing reactivity in an E2 reaction:

> **PROBLEM 18♦**
>
> If the two reactions described in this section were E1 elimination reactions, what value would you expect to obtain for the deuterium kinetic isotope effect?

9.8 COMPETITION BETWEEN SUBSTITUTION AND ELIMINATION

(We have seen that alkyl halides can undergo four types of reactions: S_N2, S_N1, E2, and E1.) As a result, you may feel a bit overwhelmed when you are asked to predict the products of the reaction of a given alkyl halide and a nucleophile/base. Let's therefore pause to organize what we know about the reactions of alkyl halides to make it a little easier for you to predict their products. (Notice, in the following discussion, that HO^- is called a *nucleophile* in a substitution reaction (because it attacks a carbon) and a *base* in an elimination reaction (because it removes a proton).)

To predict the products of an alkyl halide reaction, the first thing you must decide is whether the reaction conditions favor S_N2/E2 or S_N1/E1 reactions. (Recall that the conditions that favor an S_N2 reaction also favor an E2 reaction, and the conditions that favor an S_N1 reaction also favor an E1 reaction.)

Look back at the S_N1/E1 reactions in previous sections and notice that they all have poor nucleophiles/weak bases (H_2O, CH_3OH), whereas the S_N2/E2 reactions have good nucleophiles/strong bases (HO^-, CH_3O^-, NH_3). In other words, a good nucleophile/strong base encourages S_N2/E2 reactions, and a poor nucleophile/weak base encourages S_N1/E1 reactions by discouraging S_N2/E2 reactions.

Having decided whether the reaction conditions favor S_N2/E2 reactions or S_N1/E1 reactions, you must next decide whether the alkyl halide will form the substitution product, the elimination product, or both substitution and elimination products. The relative amounts of substitution and elimination products depend on whether the alkyl halide is primary, secondary, or tertiary, and on the nature of the nucleophile/base. This question is discussed next and is summarized in Table 9.6 on page 399.

> An S_N2/E2 reaction of an alkyl halide is favored by a high concentration of a good nucleophile/strong base.
>
> An S_N1/E1 reaction of an alkyl halide is favored by a poor nucleophile/weak base.

S_N2/E2 Conditions

Let's first consider conditions that lead to S_N2/E2 reactions: a high concentration of a good nucleophile/strong base. A negatively charged species can act as a nucleophile and attack the back side of the α-carbon to form the substitution product, or it can act as a base and remove a hydrogen from a β-carbon, leading to the elimination product. Thus, the two reactions compete with each other. In fact, they both occur and occur for the same reason: the electron-withdrawing halogen gives the carbon to which it is bonded a partial positive charge.

$$CH_3-CH_2-Br \longrightarrow CH_3CH_2OH + Br^-$$
$$HO^-$$
substitution product

$$CH_2-CH_2-Br \longrightarrow CH_2=CH_2 + H_2O + Br^-$$
$$H \quad HO^-$$
elimination product

The relative reactivities of alkyl halides in S_N2 and E2 reactions are shown in Table 9.5. Because a *primary* alkyl halide is the most reactive in an S_N2 reaction (because the back side of the α-carbon is relatively unhindered; Section 8.1) and the least reactive in an E2 reaction (Section 9.2), a primary alkyl halide forms principally the substitution product in a reaction carried out under conditions that favor $S_N2/E2$ reactions. In other words, substitution wins the competition.

a primary alkyl halide

propyl bromide $+ CH_3O^- \xrightarrow{CH_3OH}$ methyl propyl ether **90%** $+$ propene **10%** $+ CH_3OH + Br^-$

Primary alkyl halides undergo primarily substitution under $S_N2/E2$ conditions.

Table 9.5	Relative Reactivities of Alkyl Halides		
In an S_N2 reaction:	$1° > 2° > 3°$	In an S_N1 reaction:	$3° > 2° > 1°$
In an E2 reaction:	$3° > 2° > 1°$	In an E1 reaction:	$3° > 2° > 1°$

However, if either the primary alkyl halide or the nucleophile/base is sterically hindered, the nucleophile will have difficulty getting to the back side of the α-carbon. As a result, elimination will win the competition.

the primary alkyl halide is sterically hindered

1-bromo-2-methyl-propane $+ CH_3O^- \xrightarrow{CH_3OH}$ 1-methoxy-2-methylpropane **40%** $+$ 2-methylpropene **60%** $+ CH_3OH + Br^-$

the nucleophile is sterically hindered

1-bromopentane $+ \times O^- \xrightarrow{(CH_3)_3COH}$ 1-*tert*-butoxypentane **15%** $+$ 1-pentene **85%** $+ \times OH + Br^-$

A *secondary* alkyl halide forms both substitution and elimination products under $S_N2/E2$ conditions. The relative amounts of the two products depend on the strength and bulk of the nucleophile/base. *The stronger and bulkier the base, the greater the percentage of the elimination product.* For example, acetic acid is a stronger acid ($pK_a = 4.76$) than ethanol ($pK_a = 15.9$), which means that acetate ion is a weaker base than ethoxide ion. The elimination product is the main product formed from the reaction of 2-chloropropane with the strongly basic ethoxide ion, whereas no elimination product is formed with the weakly basic acetate ion. The percentage of elimination product produced would be increased further if the bulky *tert*-butoxide ion were used instead of ethoxide ion (Section 8.2).

a secondary alkyl halide / a strong base favors the elimination product

2-chloropropane $+$ ethoxide ion $\xrightarrow{CH_3CH_2OH}$ 2-ethoxypropane **25%** $+$ propene **75%** $+ \quad OH + Cl^-$

2-chloropropane $+$ acetate ion $\xrightarrow{\text{acetic acid}}$ isopropyl acetate **100%** $+ Cl^-$

a weak base favors the substitution product

The relative amounts of substitution and elimination products are also affected by temperature; higher temperatures favor elimination because of the greater $\Delta S°$ value for the elimination reaction since an elimination reaction forms more product molecules than does a substitution reaction (Section 3.7).

2-propanol
47%

propene
53%

a higher temperature favors elimination

Strong and bulky bases and high temperatures favor elimination over substitution.

2-propanol
29%

propene
71%

A *tertiary* alkyl halide is the least reactive of the alkyl halides in an S_N2 reaction and the most reactive in an E2 reaction (Table 9.5). Consequently, only the elimination product is formed when a tertiary alkyl halide reacts with a nucleophile/base under S_N2/E2 conditions.

a tertiary alkyl halide

Tertiary alkyl halides undergo only elimination under S_N2/E2 conditions.

2-bromo-2-methyl-propane

2-methylpropene
100%

PROBLEM 19♦

In what way would you expect the ratio of substitution product to elimination product formed from the reaction of propyl bromide wtih CH_3O^- in methanol to change if the nucleophile were changed to CH_3S^-?

PROBLEM 20♦

Explain why only a substitution product and no elimination product is obtained when the following compound is treated with sodium methoxide:

S_N1/E1 Conditions

Now let's look at what happens when conditions (a poor nucleophile/weak base) favor S_N1/E1 reactions. In S_N1/E1 reactions, the alkyl halide dissociates to form a carbocation, which can then either combine with the nucleophile to form the substitution product or lose a proton to form the elimination product.

Alkyl halides have the same order of reactivity in S_N1 reactions as they do in E1 reactions, because both reactions have the same rate-determining step—dissociation of the alkyl halide to form a carbocation (Table 9.5). This means that all alkyl halides that react under S_N1/E1 conditions will give both substitution and elimination products. Remember that primary alkyl halides do not undergo S_N1/E1 reactions because primary carbocations are too unstable to be formed. Fortunately, S_N1/E1 reactions of tertiary alkyl halides favor the substitution product, because the elimination product is the only product obtained under S_N2/E2 conditions.

Primary alkyl halides do not form carbocations; therefore, they cannot undergo S_N1 and E1 reactions.

$$\underset{\underset{CH_3}{|}}{\overset{\overset{CH_3}{|}}{CH_3\overset{|}{C}Br}} + CH_3CH_2OH \xrightarrow{\textbf{S}_\textbf{N}\textbf{1}} \underset{\underset{CH_3}{|}}{\overset{\overset{CH_3}{|}}{CH_3\overset{|}{C}OCH_2CH_3}} + \underset{}{\overset{\overset{CH_3}{|}}{CH_3\overset{|}{C}=CH_2}}$$

$$\textbf{81\%}\textbf{19\%}$$

$$\underset{\underset{CH_3}{|}}{\overset{\overset{CH_3}{|}}{CH_3\overset{|}{C}Br}} + CH_3CH_2O^- \xrightarrow{\textbf{S}_\textbf{N}\textbf{2}} \overset{\overset{CH_3}{|}}{CH_3\overset{|}{C}=CH_2}$$

$$\textbf{100\%}$$

Table 9.6 summarizes the products obtained when alkyl halides react with nucleophiles/bases under S_N2/E2 and under S_N1/E1 conditions.

Table 9.6   Summary of the Products Expected in Substitution and Elimination Reactions

Class of alkyl halide	S_N2 versus E2	S_N1 versus E1
Primary alkyl halide	Primarily substitution, unless there is steric hindrance in the alkyl halide or nucleophile, in which case elimination is favored	Cannot undergo S_N1/E1 reactions
Secondary alkyl halide	Both substitution and elimination; the stronger and bulkier the base and the higher the temperature, the greater the percentage of elimination	Both substitution and elimination
Tertiary alkyl halide	Only elimination	Both substitution and elimination

PROBLEM 21 ♦

a. Which reacts faster in an S_N2 reaction?

$$CH_3CH_2CH_2Br \quad \text{or} \quad \underset{\underset{Br}{|}}{CH_3CH_2CHCH_3}$$

b. Which reacts faster in an E1 reaction?

or

c. Which reacts faster in an S_N1 reaction?

$$\underset{\underset{Br}{|}}{\overset{\overset{CH_3}{|}}{CH_3CHCHCH_3}} \quad \text{or} \quad \underset{\underset{Br}{|}}{\overset{\overset{CH_3}{|}}{CH_3CH_2CCH_3}}$$

d. Which reacts faster in an E2 reaction?

or

chem
place   Tutorial:
         E2 promoting factors

PROBLEM 22♦

Indicate whether the specified alkyl halides will give primarily substitution products, only elimination products, both substitution and elimination products, or no products when they are treated with the following:

a. methanol under $S_N1/E1$ conditions
b. sodium methoxide under $S_N2/E2$ conditions

   1. 1-bromobutane   **3.** 2-bromobutane
   2. 1-bromo-2-methylpropane   **4.** 2-bromo-2-methylpropane

PROBLEM 23♦

a. Explain why 1-bromo-2,2-dimethylpropane has difficulty undergoing both S_N2 and S_N1 reactions.
b. Can it undergo E2 and E1 reactions?

9.9 SUBSTITUTION AND ELIMINATION REACTIONS IN SYNTHESIS

When substitution or elimination reactions are used in synthesis, care must be taken to choose reactants and reaction conditions that will maximize the yield of the desired product.

Using Substitution Reactions to Synthesize Compounds

In Section 8.3, you saw that nucleophilic substitution reactions of alkyl halides can lead to a wide variety of organic compounds. For example, ethers are synthesized by the reaction of an alkyl halide with an alkoxide ion. This reaction, discovered by Alexander Williamson in 1850, is still considered one of the best ways to synthesize an ether.

Williamson ether synthesis

$$\underset{\text{alkyl halide}}{R-Br} \;+\; \underset{\text{alkoxide ion}}{R-O^-} \;\longrightarrow\; \underset{\text{ether}}{R-O-R} \;+\; Br^-$$

The alkoxide ion (RO^-) for the **Williamson ether synthesis** is prepared by using sodium metal or sodium hydride (NaH) to remove a proton from an alcohol.

$$ROH \;+\; Na \;\longrightarrow\; RO^- \;+\; Na^+ \;+\; \tfrac{1}{2}H_2$$

$$ROH \;+\; NaH \;\longrightarrow\; RO^- \;+\; Na^+ \;+\; H_2$$

The Williamson ether synthesis is a nucleophilic substitution reaction. It requires a high concentration of a good nucleophile, which indicates that it is an S_N2 reaction. If you want to synthesize an ether such as butyl propyl ether, you have a choice of starting materials: you can use either a propyl halide and butoxide ion or a butyl halide and propoxide ion.

$$\underset{\text{propyl bromide}}{CH_3CH_2CH_2Br} \;+\; \underset{\text{butoxide ion}}{CH_3CH_2CH_2CH_2O^-} \;\longrightarrow\; \underset{\text{butyl propyl ether}}{CH_3CH_2CH_2OCH_2CH_2CH_2CH_3} \;+\; Br^-$$

$$\underset{\text{butyl bromide}}{CH_3CH_2CH_2CH_2Br} \;+\; \underset{\text{propoxide ion}}{CH_3CH_2CH_2O^-} \;\longrightarrow\; \underset{\text{butyl propyl ether}}{CH_3CH_2CH_2CH_2OCH_2CH_2CH_3} \;+\; Br^-$$

However, if you want to synthesize *tert*-butyl ethyl ether, the starting materials must be an ethyl halide and *tert*-butoxide ion. If you used a *tert*-butyl halide and ethoxide ion as reactants, you would not obtain any ether because the reaction of a tertiary alkyl halide under $S_N2/E2$ conditions forms only the elimination product. Consequently, a Williamson ether synthesis should be designed in such a way that the *less hindered alkyl group* is provided by the *alkyl halide* and the *more hindered alkyl group* comes from the *alkoxide ion*.

$$CH_3CH_2Br + \underset{\text{\textit{tert}-butoxide ion}}{\overset{CH_3}{\underset{CH_3}{CH_3\overset{|}{\underset{|}{C}}O^-}}} \longrightarrow \underset{\text{\textit{tert}-butyl ethyl ether}}{\overset{CH_3}{\underset{CH_3}{CH_3CH_2O\overset{|}{\underset{|}{C}}CH_3}}} + \underset{\text{ethene}}{CH_2{=}CH_2} + \overset{CH_3}{\underset{CH_3}{CH_3\overset{|}{\underset{|}{C}}OH}} + Br^-$$

ethyl bromide

$$\underset{\text{ethoxide ion}}{CH_3CH_2O^-} + \underset{\text{\textit{tert}-butyl bromide}}{\overset{CH_3}{\underset{CH_3}{CH_3\overset{|}{\underset{|}{C}}Br}}} \longrightarrow \underset{\text{2-methylpropene}}{\overset{CH_3}{CH_2{=}\overset{|}{C}CH_3}} + CH_3CH_2OH + Br^-$$

In ether synthesis, the less hindered group should be provided by the alkyl halide.

We saw in Section 6.11 that alkynes can be synthesized by the reaction of an acetylide anion with an alkyl halide.

$$CH_3CH_2C{\equiv}C^- + CH_3CH_2CH_2Br \longrightarrow CH_3CH_2C{\equiv}CCH_2CH_2CH_3 + Br^-$$

Now that you know that this is an S_N2 reaction (the alkyl halide reacts with a high concentration of a good nucleophile), you can understand why you were told that it is best to use primary alkyl halides and methyl halides in the reaction. These alkyl halides are the only ones that form primarily the desired substitution product. A tertiary alkyl halide would form only the elimination product, and a secondary alkyl halide would form mainly the elimination product because the acetylide ion is a very strong base.

PROBLEM 24♦

What other organic product will be formed when the alkyl halide used in the synthesis of butyl propyl ether is

a. propyl bromide?   **b.** butyl bromide?

PROBLEM 25

How could the following ethers be prepared using an alkyl halide and an alcohol?

a. $CH_3CH_2\overset{CH_3}{\overset{|}{C}}HOCH_2CH_2CH_3$ **c.** $CH_3CH_2OCH_2\overset{CH_3}{\overset{|}{C}}HCH_2CH_2CH_3$

b. ⬡—OCH_3 **d.** ⬡—CH_2O—⬡

Using Elimination Reactions to Synthesize Compounds

If you want to synthesize an alkene, you should choose the most hindered alkyl halide possible in order to maximize the elimination product and minimize the substitution product. For example, 2-bromopropane would be a better starting material than 1-bromopropane for the synthesis of propene because the secondary alkyl halide would give a higher yield of the desired elimination product and a lower yield of the competing substitution product. The percentage of alkene could be further increased by using a sterically hindered base such as *tert*-butoxide ion instead of hydroxide ion.

$$\underset{\text{2-bromopropane}}{\overset{Br}{CH_3\overset{|}{C}HCH_3}} + HO^- \longrightarrow \underset{\text{major product}}{CH_3CH{=}CH_2} + \underset{\text{minor product}}{\overset{OH}{CH_3\overset{|}{C}HCH_3}} + H_2O + Br^-$$

$$\underset{\text{1-bromopropane}}{CH_3CH_2CH_2Br} + HO^- \longrightarrow \underset{\text{minor product}}{CH_3CH{=}CH_2} + \underset{\text{major product}}{CH_3CH_2CH_2OH} + H_2O + Br^-$$

To synthesize 2-methyl-2-butene from 2-bromo-2-methylbutane, you would use $S_N2/E2$ conditions (a high concentration of CH_3O^- in an aprotic polar solvent) because a tertiary alkyl halide gives *only* the elimination product under those conditions.

If $S_N1/E1$ conditions were used (a low concentration of CH_3O^- in a protic polar solvent), both elimination and substitution products would be obtained.

$$\begin{array}{ccc}
& & \overset{CH_3}{\underset{}{\overset{|}{CH_3C}}}\!=\!CHCH_3 + CH_3OH + Br^- \\
\end{array}$$

$$\underset{\substack{| \\ Br \\ \text{2-bromo-2-methylbutane}}}{\overset{CH_3}{\overset{|}{CH_3CCH_2CH_3}}} + CH_3O^- \xrightarrow[\text{conditions}]{S_N2/E2} \quad\text{and}\quad \xrightarrow[\text{conditions}]{S_N1/E1}$$

$$\overset{CH_3}{\overset{|}{CH_3C}}\!=\!\underset{\text{2-methyl-2-butene}}{CHCH_3} + \underset{\substack{| \\ OCH_3 \\ \text{2-methoxy-2-methylbutane}}}{\overset{CH_3}{\overset{|}{CH_3CCH_2CH_3}}} + H_2O + Br^-$$

PROBLEM 26◆

Identify the three products formed when 2-bromo-2-methylpropane is dissolved in a mixture of 80% ethanol and 20% water.

PROBLEM 27

a. What products (including stereoisomers, if applicable) would be formed from the reaction of 3-bromo-2-methylpentane with HO^- under $S_N2/E2$ conditions and under $S_N1/E1$ conditions?
b. Answer the same question for 3-bromo-3-methylpentane.

If two halogens are on the same carbon (geminal dihalides) or on adjacent carbons (vicinal dihalides), two consecutive E2 reactions will form a triple bond. This is how alkynes are commonly synthesized.

$$\underset{\substack{| \\ Br \\ \text{a geminal dibromide}}}{\overset{\substack{Br \\ |}}{RCH_2CR}} \xrightarrow{^-NH_2} \underset{\substack{| \\ Br \\ \text{a vinylic bromide}}}{RCH\!=\!CR} \xrightarrow{^-NH_2} \underset{\text{an alkyne}}{RC\!\equiv\!CR} + 2\,NH_3 + 2\,Br^-$$

$$\underset{\substack{| \; | \\ Cl \; Cl \\ \text{a vinylic dichloride}}}{RCHCHR} \xrightarrow{^-NH_2} \underset{\substack{| \\ Cl \\ \text{a vinylic chloride}}}{RCH\!=\!CR} \xrightarrow{^-NH_2} \underset{\text{an alkyne}}{RC\!\equiv\!CR} + 2\,NH_3 + 2\,Cl^-$$

The vinylic halide intermediates in the preceding reactions are relatively unreactive. Consequently, a very strong base, such as $^-NH_2$, is needed for the second elimination reaction. If a weaker base, such as HO^-, is used at room temperature, the reaction will stop at the vinylic halide and no alkyne will be formed.

Because a vicinal dihalide is formed from the reaction of an alkene with Br_2 or Cl_2, you have just learned how to convert a double bond into a triple bond.

$$\underset{\text{2-butene}}{CH_3CH\!=\!CHCH_3} \xrightarrow[CH_2Cl_2]{Br_2} \underset{\substack{| \; | \\ Br \; Br}}{CH_3CHCHCH_3} \xrightarrow{^-NH_2} \underset{\substack{| \\ Br}}{CH_3CH\!=\!CCH_3} \xrightarrow{^-NH_2} \underset{\text{2-butyne}}{CH_3C\!\equiv\!CCH_3} + 2\,NH_3 + 2\,Br^-$$

PROBLEM 28

Why isn't a cumulated diene formed in the preceding reaction?

PROBLEM 29

What product will be obtained when the following compound undergoes two successive elimination reactions?

$$\underset{\substack{| \quad\quad | \\ Cl \quad\quad Cl}}{\overset{\substack{CH_3 \quad\quad CH_3 \\ | \quad\quad |}}{CH_3CHCHCH_2CHCHCH_3}} + \underset{\text{excess}}{HO^-} \longrightarrow$$

9.10 DESIGNING A SYNTHESIS II: APPROACHING THE PROBLEM

When you are asked to design a synthesis, one way to approach the task is to think about the starting material you have been given and ask yourself if there is an obvious series of reactions beginning with the starting material that can get you on the road to the **target molecule** (the desired product). Sometimes this is the best way to approach a *simple* synthesis. The following examples will give you practice employing this strategy.

Example 1. Using the given starting material, how could you prepare the target molecule?

$$\text{(cyclopentene)} \xrightarrow{?} \text{(cyclopentane)}-C\equiv N$$

Adding HBr to the alkene would form a compound with a leaving group that can be replaced by a nucleophile. Because $^-C\equiv N$ is a relatively weak base (the pK_a of $HC\equiv N$ is 9.1), the desired substitution reaction will be favored over the competing elimination reaction.

synthesis

$$\text{(cyclopentene)} \xrightarrow{\text{HBr}} \text{(cyclopentane)}-Br \xrightarrow{\ ^-C\equiv N\ } \text{(cyclopentane)}-C\equiv N$$

target molecule

Example 2. Starting with 1-bromo-1-methylcyclohexane, how could you prepare *trans*-2-methylcyclohexanol?

$$\text{(cyclohexane with CH}_3\text{ and Br)} \xrightarrow{?} \text{(cyclohexane with CH}_3\text{ and OH)}$$

The elimination reaction should be carried out under E2 conditions because under these conditions tertiary alkyl halides undergo only elimination, so there will be no competing substitution product. Because hydroboration–oxidation overall results in the syn addition of water, the target molecule (as well as its enantiomer) is obtained.

synthesis

$$\text{(cyclohexane, CH}_3, Br)} \xrightarrow[\substack{\text{CH}_3\text{CH}_2\text{O}^- \\ \text{CH}_3\text{CH}_2\text{OH}}]{\substack{\text{high} \\ \text{concentration}}} \text{(methylcyclohexene)} \xrightarrow[\text{2. H}_2\text{O}_2,\ \text{HO}^-,\ \text{H}_2\text{O}]{\text{1. BH}_3/\text{THF}} \text{(CH}_3, \text{OH)} + \text{(CH}_3, \text{OH)}$$

target molecule

As you saw in Section 6.12, working backward can be a useful way to design a synthesis, particularly when the starting material does not clearly indicate how to proceed. Look at the target molecule and ask yourself how it could be prepared. Once you have an answer, look at the precursor you have identified for the target molecule and ask yourself how that precursor could be prepared. Keep working backward one step at a time, until you get to a readily available starting material. We learned that this technique is called *retrosynthetic analysis*. (Section 6.12).

Example 3. How could you prepare ethyl methyl ketone from 1-bromobutane?

$$\text{CH}_3\text{CH}_2\text{CH}_2\text{CH}_2\text{Br} \xrightarrow{?} \text{CH}_3\text{CH}_2\overset{\overset{\text{O}}{\|}}{\text{C}}\text{CH}_3$$

At this point in your study of organic chemistry, you know only two ways to synthesize a ketone: (1) the addition of water to an alkyne (Section 6.7) and (2) hydroboration–oxidation of an alkyne (Section 6.8). The alkyne can be prepared from two successive E2 reactions of a vicinal dihalide, which in turn can be synthesized from an alkene. The desired alkene can be prepared from the given starting material by an elimination reaction.

retrosynthetic analysis

$$CH_3CH_2\overset{\overset{\text{O}}{\|}}{C}CH_3 \Longrightarrow CH_3CH_2C{\equiv}CH \Longrightarrow CH_3CH_2\underset{\underset{\text{Br}}{|}}{CH}CH_2Br \Longrightarrow CH_3CH_2CH{=}CH_2 \Longrightarrow CH_3CH_2CH_2CH_2Br$$

target molecule

open arrow indicates you are working backwards

Now you can write the reaction sequence in the forward direction, along with the reagents needed to carry out each reaction. Notice that a bulky base is used in the elimination reaction in order to maximize the amount of elimination product.

synthesis

$$CH_3CH_2CH_2CH_2Br \xrightarrow[\substack{\textbf{\textit{tert}-BuOH}}]{\substack{\text{high}\\\text{concentration}\\\textbf{\textit{tert}-BuO}^-}} CH_3CH_2CH{=}CH_2 \xrightarrow[\textbf{CH}_2\textbf{Cl}_2]{\textbf{Br}_2} CH_3CH_2\underset{\underset{\text{Br}}{|}}{CH}CH_2Br \xrightarrow{\textbf{2 }\overset{-}{\textbf{NH}}_2} CH_3CH_2C{\equiv}CH$$

$$\xrightarrow[\textbf{HgSO}_4]{\substack{\textbf{H}_2\textbf{SO}_4 \ \ \ \\ \ \ \ \textbf{H}_2\textbf{O}}} \ \underset{\textbf{target molecule}}{CH_3CH_2\overset{\overset{\text{O}}{\|}}{C}CH_3}$$

Example 4. How could the following cyclic ether be prepared from the given starting material?

$$BrCH_2CH_2CH_2CH{=}CH_2 \xrightarrow{\ ?\ } \ \text{[cyclic ether with CH}_3\text{]}$$

To prepare a cyclic ether, the alkyl halide and alcohol required for ether synthesis must both be part of the same molecule. Since the target ether has a five-membered ring, the carbons bearing the two reacting groups must be separated by two additional carbons. Addition of water to the given starting material will create the required bifunctional compound, which after deprotonation will form the cyclic ether *via* an intramolecular reaction.

retrosynthetic analysis

$$\text{[cyclic ether]}_{\text{CH}_3} \Longrightarrow BrCH_2CH_2CH_2\underset{\underset{\text{OH}}{|}}{CH}CH_3 \Longrightarrow BrCH_2CH_2CH_2CH{=}CH_2$$

target molecule

synthesis

$$BrCH_2CH_2CH_2CH{=}CH_2 \xrightarrow[\textbf{H}_2\textbf{O}]{\textbf{H}_2\textbf{SO}_4} BrCH_2CH_2CH_2\underset{\underset{\text{OH}}{|}}{CH}CH_3 \xrightarrow{\textbf{Na}} \text{[cyclic ether]}_{\text{CH}_3}$$

target molecule

PROBLEM 30

How could you have prepared the target molecule in the preceding synthesis using 4-penten-1-ol as the starting material? Which synthesis would give you a higher yield of the target molecule?

PROBLEM 31

For each of the following target molecules, design a multistep synthesis to show how it could be prepared from the given starting material:

a.

b.

c.

d.

chem Tutorial:
place Retrosynthetic analysis

SUMMARY

In addition to undergoing nucleophilic substitution reactions, alkyl halides undergo β-elimination reactions, in which the halogen is removed from one carbon, a hydrogen is removed from an adjacent carbon, and a double bond is formed between the two carbons from which the atoms were eliminated. The product of an **elimination reaction** is therefore an alkene. Removal of a proton and a halide ion is called **dehydrohalogenation**. There are two important β-elimination reactions, E1 and E2.

An **E2 reaction** is a concerted, one-step reaction; the proton and halide ion are removed in the same step, so no intermediate is formed. In an **E1 reaction**, the alkyl halide dissociates, forming a carbocation intermediate. In a second step, a base removes a proton from a carbon that is adjacent to the positively charged carbon. Because the E1 reaction forms a carbocation intermediate, the carbon skeleton can rearrange before the proton is lost.

Primary alkyl halides undergo only E2 elimination reactions. Secondary and tertiary alkyl halides undergo both E2 and E1 reactions. For alkyl halides that can undergo both E2 and E1 reactions, the E2 reaction is favored by the same factors that favor an S_N2 reaction—a high concentration of a strong base and an aprotic polar solvent—and the E1 reaction is favored by the same factors that favor an S_N1 reaction—a weak base and a protic polar solvent.

An E2 reaction is regioselective; the major product is the more stable alkene, unless the reactants are sterically hindered or the leaving group is poor. The more stable alkene is generally (but not always) the more substituted alkene. The more substituted alkene is predicted by Zaitsev's rule: it is the alkene formed when a hydrogen is removed from the β-carbon bonded to the fewest hydrogens. Alkyl substitution increases the stability of a carbocation and decreases the stability of a carbanion.

An E2 reaction is also stereoselective: **anti elimination** is favored. If the β-carbon has two hydrogens, both E and Z products will be formed, but the one with the bulkiest groups on opposite sides of the double bond will be formed in greater yield because it is more stable. If the β-carbon has only one hydrogen, only one alkene is formed, since there is only one conformer in which the groups to be eliminated are anti. The two groups eliminated from a six-membered ring must both be in axial positions; elimination is more rapid when H and X are diaxial in the more stable conformer.

An E1 reaction is regioselective: the major product is the more stable alkene, which is generally the more substituted alkene. An E1 reaction is stereoselective: the major product is the alkene with the bulkiest groups on opposite sides of the double bond. The carbocation formed in the first step can undergo both syn and anti elimination; therefore, the two groups eliminated from a six-membered ring do not both have to be in axial positions.

Predicting which products are formed when an alkyl halide undergoes a reaction begins with determining whether the conditions favor $S_N2/E2$ or $S_N1/E1$ reactions. When $S_N2/E2$ reactions are favored, primary alkyl halides form primarily substitution products unless the nucleophile/base is sterically hindered, in which case elimination products predominate. Secondary alkyl halides form both substitution and elimination products; the stronger and bulkier the base and the higher the temperature, the greater is the percentage of the elimination product. Tertiary alkyl halides form only elimination products. When $S_N1/E1$ conditions are favored, secondary and tertiary alkyl halides form both substitution and elimination products; primary alkyl halides do not undergo $S_N1/E1$ reactions.

The **Williamson ether synthesis** involves the reaction of an alkyl halide with an alkoxide ion. If two halogens are on the same or adjacent carbons, two consecutive E2 dehydrohalogenations form a triple bond.

SUMMARY OF REACTIONS

1. E2 reaction: a one-step mechanism

$$\ddot{B} \;+\; -\overset{|}{\underset{|}{C}}\!-\!\overset{|}{\underset{|}{C}}\!-\!X \;\longrightarrow\; \overset{}{\underset{}{}}C{=}C\overset{}{\underset{}{}} \;+\; {}^{+}BH \;+\; X^{-}$$

Relative reactivities of alkyl halides: $3° > 2° > 1°$

Anti elimination: both E and Z stereoisomers are formed. The isomer with the bulkiest groups on opposite sides of the double bond will be formed in greater yield. If the β-carbon from which the hydrogen is removed is bonded to only one hydrogen, only one elimination product is formed. Its configuration depends on the configuration of the reactant.

2. E1 reaction: a two-step mechanism with a carbocation intermediate

$$-\overset{|}{\underset{H}{C}}\!-\!\overset{|}{\underset{|}{C}}\!-\!X \;\longrightarrow\; -\overset{|}{\underset{H}{C}}\!-\!\overset{|}{\underset{}{C}}{}^{+} \;\longrightarrow\; \overset{}{\underset{}{}}C{=}C\overset{}{\underset{}{}} \;+\; {}^{+}BH$$

$$\ddot{B} \;+\; X^{-}$$

Relative reactivities of alkyl halides: $3° > 2° > 1°$

Anti and syn elimination: both E and Z stereoisomers are formed. The isomer with the bulkiest groups on opposite sides of the double bond will be formed in greater yield.

Competing S_N2 and E2 Reactions
Primary alkyl halides: primarily substitution
Secondary alkyl halides: substitution and elimination
Tertiary alkyl halides: only elimination

Competing S_N1 and E1 Reactions
Primary alkyl halides: cannot undergo S_N1 or E1 reactions
Secondary alkyl halides: substitution and elimination
Tertiary alkyl halides: substitution and elimination

KEY TERMS

anti elimination (p. 388)
anti-periplanar (p. 387)
α-carbon (p. 377)
β-carbon (p. 377)
dehydrohalogenation (p. 377)
deuterium kinetic isotope effect (p. 395)

elimination reaction (p. 375)
β-elimination reaction (p. 377)
E1 reaction (p. 383)
E2 reaction (p. 376)
1,2-elimination reaction (p. 377)
sawhorse projection (p. 388)

syn elimination (p. 388)
syn-periplanar (p. 387)
target molecule (p. 403)
Williamson ether synthesis (p. 400)
Zaitsev's rule (p. 378)

PROBLEMS

32. Give the major product obtained when each of the following alkyl halides undergoes an E2 reaction:

a. CH$_3$CHCH$_2$CH$_3$
    |
    Br

c. CH$_3$CHCH$_2$CH$_3$
    |
    Cl

e. CH$_3$CHCH$_2$CH$_2$CH$_3$
    |
    Cl

b. [cyclohexane ring with Cl substituent]

d. [cyclohexane ring with CH$_2$Cl substituent]

f. [cyclohexane ring with CH$_3$ and Cl substituents on same carbon]

33. Give the major product obtained when each alkyl halide in Problem 32 undergoes an E1 reaction.

34. a. Indicate how each of the following factors affects an E1 reaction:
    1. the structure of the alkyl halide
    2. the strength of the base
    3. the concentration of the base
    4. the solvent
  b. Indicate how each of the same factors affects an E2 reaction.

35. Which species in each pair is more stable?

a. $CH_3\overset{-}{C}HCH_2CH_3$ or $CH_3CH_2CH_2\overset{-}{C}H_2$

b. $CH_3\overset{+}{C}HCH_2CH_3$ or $CH_3CH_2CH_2\overset{+}{C}H_2$

c. $\overset{+}{C}H_2CH_2CH=CH_2$ or $CH_3\overset{+}{C}HCH=CH_2$

d. $\overset{-}{C}H_2CH_2CH=CH_2$ or $CH_3\overset{-}{C}HCH=CH_2$

e. $CH_3CHCH=CH_2$ or $CH_3CH_2C=CH_2$
    $\quad\quad\ |$ $\quad\quad\quad\quad\quad\quad |$
    $\quad\quad CH_3$ $\quad\quad\quad\quad\quad CH_3$

f. $CH_3CH\overset{-}{C}HCH_3$ or $CH_3\overset{-}{C}CH_2CH_3$
    $\quad\ |$ $\quad\quad\quad\quad\quad\ |$
    $\quad CH_3$ $\quad\quad\quad\quad CH_3$

g. $CH_3CH\overset{+}{C}HCH_3$ or $CH_3\overset{+}{C}CH_2CH_3$
    $\quad\ |$ $\quad\quad\quad\quad\quad\ |$
    $\quad CH_3$ $\quad\quad\quad\quad CH_3$

36. A chemist wanted to synthesize the anesthetic 2-ethoxy-2-methylpropane. He used ethoxide ion and 2-chloro-2-methylpropane for his synthesis and ended up with no ether. What was the product of his synthesis? What reagents should he have used?

37. Which reactant in each of the following pairs will undergo an elimination reaction more rapidly? Explain your choice.

a. $(CH_3)_3CCl \xrightarrow[\text{H}_2\text{O}]{\text{HO}^-}$ or $(CH_3)_3CBr \xrightarrow[\text{H}_2\text{O}]{\text{HO}^-}$

b. $\xrightarrow[\text{CH}_3\text{OH}]{\text{CH}_3\text{O}^-}$ or $\xrightarrow[\text{CH}_3\text{OH}]{\text{CH}_3\text{O}^-}$

38. For each of the following reactions, give the major elimination product; if the product can exist as stereoisomers, indicate which stereoisomer is obtained in greater yield.
 a. (*R*)-2-bromohexane + high concentration of HO⁻
 b. (*R*)-2-bromohexane + H₂O
 c. *trans*-1-chloro-2-methylcyclohexane + high concentration of CH₃O⁻
 d. *trans*-1-chloro-2-methylcyclohexane + CH₃OH
 e. 3-bromo-3-methylpentane + high concentration of HO⁻
 f. 3-bromo-3-methylpentane + H₂O

39. a. Which reacts faster in an E2 reaction, 3-bromocyclohexene or bromocyclohexane?
 b. Which reacts faster in an E1 reaction?

40. Starting with an alkyl halide, how could the following compounds be prepared?
 a. 2-methoxybutane   **b.** 1-methoxybutane   **c.** butylmethylamine

41. Indicate which of the compounds in each pair will give a higher substitution-product to elimination-product ratio when it reacts with isopropyl bromide:
 a. ethoxide ion or *tert*-butoxide ion   **c.** Cl⁻ or Br⁻
 b. ⁻OCN or ⁻SC̈N   **d.** CH₃S⁻ or CH₃O⁻

42. Rank the following compounds in order of decreasing reactivity in an E2 reaction:

43. For each of the following alkyl halides, indicate what stereoisomer would be obtained in greatest yield from the reaction of the alkyl halide with a high concentration of hydroxide ion.
 a. 3-bromo-2,2,3-trimethylpentane   **c.** 3-bromo-2,3-dimethylpentane
 b. 4-bromo-2,2,3,3-tetramethylpentane   **d.** 3-bromo-3,4-dimethylhexane

44. When 2-bromo-2,3-dimethylbutane reacts with a base under E2 conditions, two alkenes (2,3-dimethyl-1-butene and 2,3-dimethyl-2-butene) are formed.
 a. Which of the bases shown below would give the highest percentage of the 1-alkene?
 b. Which would give the highest percentage of the 2-alkene?

$$CH_3 \quad\quad\quad CH_2CH_3 \quad\quad\quad\quad\quad\quad\quad CH_3$$
$$| \quad\quad\quad\quad\quad | \quad\quad\quad\quad\quad\quad\quad\quad\quad |$$
$$CH_3\overset{}{C}O^- \quad CH_3CH_2\overset{}{C}O^- \quad CH_3CH_2O^- \quad CH_3CH_2\overset{}{C}O^-$$
$$| \quad\quad\quad\quad\quad | \quad\quad\quad\quad\quad\quad\quad\quad\quad |$$
$$CH_3 \quad\quad\quad CH_2CH_3 \quad\quad\quad\quad\quad\quad\quad CH_3$$
$$\quad\text{A} \quad\quad\quad\quad\quad \text{B} \quad\quad\quad\quad\quad \text{C} \quad\quad\quad\quad\quad \text{D}$$

45. a. Give the structures of the products obtained from the reaction of each enantiomer of *cis*-1-chloro-2-isopropylcyclopentane with a high concentration of sodium methoxide in methanol.
  b. Are all the products optically active?
  c. How would the products differ if the starting material were the trans isomer? Are all these products optically active?
  d. Will the cis enantiomers or the trans enantiomers form substitution products more rapidly?
  e. Will the cis enantiomers or the trans enantiomers form elimination products more rapidly?

46. When the following compound undergoes solvolysis in ethanol, three products are obtained. Propose a mechanism to account for the formation of these products.

47. *cis*-1-Bromo-4-*tert*-butylcyclohexane and *trans*-1-bromo-4-*tert*-butylcyclohexane both react with sodium ethoxide in ethanol to give 4-*tert*-butylcyclohexene. Explain why the cis isomer reacts much more rapidly than the trans isomer.

48. For each of the following reactions, give the elimination products; if the products can exist as stereoisomers, indicate which stereoisomers are obtained.
  a. (2*S*,3*S*)-2-chloro-3-methylpentane + high concentration of CH_3O^-
  b. (2*S*,3*R*)-2-chloro-3-methylpentane + high concentration of CH_3O^-
  c. (2*R*,3*S*)-2-chloro-3-methylpentane + high concentration of CH_3O^-
  d. (2*R*,3*R*)-2-chloro-3-methylpentane + high concentration of CH_3O^-
  e. 3-chloro-3-ethyl-2,2-dimethylpentane + high concentration of $CH_3CH_2O^-$

49. Give the major elimination product that would be obtained from each of the following reactants under $S_N2/E2$:

a.

b.

50. Which of the following hexachlorocyclohexanes is the least reactive in an E2 reaction?

51. Explain why the rate of the reaction of 1-bromo-2-butene with ethanol is increased if silver nitrate is added to the reaction mixture.

52. Give the products for each of the following reactions carried out under $S_N2/E2$ conditions. If the products can exist as stereoisomers, show which stereoisomers are formed.
  a. (3*S*,4*S*)-3-bromo-4-methylhexane + CH_3O^-
  b. (3*R*,4*R*)-3-bromo-4-methylhexane + CH_3O^-
  c. (3*S*,4*R*)-3-bromo-4-methylhexane + CH_3O^-
  d. (3*R*,4*S*)-3-bromo-4-methylhexane + CH_3O^-

53. Two elimination products are obtained from the following E2 reaction:

$$CH_3CH_2CHDCH_2Br \xrightarrow{HO^-}$$

  a. What are the elimination products?
  b. Which is formed in greater yield? Explain.

54. How could you prepare the following compounds from the given starting materials?

  a. $CH_3CH_2CH_2CH_2Br \longrightarrow CH_3CH_2\overset{\overset{\displaystyle O}{\|}}{C}CH_2CH_2CH_3$ **b.** $BrCH_2CH_2CH_2CH_2Br \longrightarrow$

55. *cis*-4-Bromocyclohexanol and *trans*-4-bromocyclohexanol form the same elimination product but a different substitution product when they react with HO⁻.

cis-4-bromocyclohexanol

trans-4-bromocyclohexanol

a. Why do they form the same elimination product?
b. Explain, by showing the mechanisms, why different substitution products are obtained.
c. How many stereoisomers does each of the elimination and substitution reactions form?

56. Three substitution products and three elimination products are obtained from the following reaction:

Account for the formation of these products.

57. Only one product is formed when the following stereoisomer of 2-chloro-1,3-dimethylcyclohexane reacts with methoxide ion in a solvent that encourages S_N2/E2 reactions:

When the same compound reacts with methoxide ion in a solvent that favors S_N1/E1 reactions, 12 products are formed. Identify the products that are formed under the two sets of conditions.

58. For each of the following compounds, give the product that will be formed in an E2 reaction and indicate the configuration of the product:
a. (1*S*,2*S*)-1-bromo-1,2-diphenylpropane   b. (1*S*,2*R*)-1-bromo-1,2-diphenylpropane

10

Reactions of Alcohols, Ethers, Epoxides, Amines, and Sulfur-Containing Compounds

CH$_3$OH

CH$_3$OCH$_3$

CH$_3$SH

$$\begin{array}{c} CH_3 \\ \overset{+}{|} \\ CH_3CH_2NCH_3 \\ | \\ CH_3 \end{array}$$

$$\overset{\quad O \quad}{H_2C - CH_2}$$

WE HAVE SEEN THAT ALKYL HALIDES UNDERGO SUBSTITUTION AND ELIMINATION reactions because of their electron-withdrawing halogen atoms (Chapters 8 and 9). Compounds with other electron-withdrawing groups also undergo substitution and elimination reactions. The relative reactivity of these compounds depends on the electron-withdrawing group.

Alcohols and ethers have electron-withdrawing groups (HO$^-$, RO$^-$) that are much stronger bases than the halide ion leaving groups of alkyl halides. Because they are stronger bases, they are poorer leaving groups and therefore much harder to displace. Consequently, alcohols and ethers are less reactive than alkyl halides in substitution and elimination reactions. We will see that because of their strongly basic leaving groups, alcohols and ethers have to be "activated" before they can undergo a substitution or an elimination reaction. The leaving groups of quaternary ammonium ions are a little less basic; they will undergo elimination reactions as long as a strong base is present and the reaction is heated. In contrast, sulfonate esters and **sulfonium ions** have weakly basic leaving groups, so they undergo substitution reactions with ease.

The weaker the base, the more easily it can be displaced.

The stronger the acid, the weaker is its conjugate base.

pK_a HX $= -10$ to 3.2
pK_a R$_3$NH$^+$ $= \sim 10$
pK_a H$_2$O $= \sim 15$
pK_a ROH $= \sim 15$

R—X

R—O—H

R—O—R

$$\begin{array}{c} R \\ \overset{+}{|} \\ R-N-R \\ | \\ R \ HO^- \end{array}$$

$$\begin{array}{c} O \\ \| \\ R-O-S-R \\ \| \\ O \end{array}$$

$$\begin{array}{c} R \\ \overset{+}{|} \\ R-S-R \end{array}$$

an alkyl halide
X = F, Cl, Br, I

an alcohol

an ether

a quaternary ammonium
hydroxide ion

a sulfonate ester

a sulfonium salt

10.1 NUCLEOPHILIC SUBSTITUTION REACTIONS OF ALCOHOLS: FORMING ALKYL HALIDES

An **alcohol** has a strongly basic leaving group (HO^-) that cannot be displaced by a nucleophile. Therefore, an alcohol cannot undergo a nucleophilic substitution reaction.

(poor)

a strongly basic leaving group

$$CH_3-\overset{..}{O}H \ + \ Br^- \quad \xrightarrow{\quad\times\quad} \quad CH_3-Br \ + \ HO^-$$
strong base

However, if the alcohol's OH group is converted into a group that is a weaker base (and therefore a better leaving group), a nucleophilic substitution reaction can occur. One way to convert an OH group into a weaker base is to protonate it by adding acid to the solution. Protonation changes the leaving group from HO^- to H_2O, which is a weak enough base to be displaced by a nucleophile. The substitution reaction is slow and requires heat (except in the case of tertiary alcohols) if it is to take place in a reasonable period of time.

strongly basic

a weakly basic leaving group

$$CH_3-\overset{..}{O}H \ + \ HBr \ \rightleftharpoons \ CH_3-\overset{H}{\overset{|}{\overset{+}{O}}}H \ \xrightarrow{\Delta} \ CH_3-Br \ + \ H_2O$$
weak base

Br^-

poor leaving group

good leaving group

Because the OH group of the alcohol has to be protonated before it can be displaced by a nucleophile, only weakly basic nucleophiles (I^-, Br^-, Cl^-) can be used in the substitution reaction. Moderately and strongly basic nucleophiles (NH_3, RNH_2, CH_3O^-) cannot be used because they too would be protonated in the acidic solution and, once protonated would no longer be nucleophiles ($^+NH_4$, RNH_3^+) or would be poor nucleophiles (CH_3OH).

PROBLEM 1♦

because they no longer have a LP of e's

Why are NH_3 and CH_3NH_2 no longer nucleophiles when they are protonated?

Primary, secondary, and tertiary alcohols all undergo nucleophilic substitution reactions with HI, HBr, and HCl to form alkyl halides.

$$CH_3CH_2CH_2OH \ + \ HI \ \xrightarrow{\Delta} \ CH_3CH_2CH_2I \ + \ H_2O$$
1-propanol
a primary alcohol

1-iodopropane

OH

Br

$$\text{cyclohexanol} + HBr \xrightarrow{\Delta} \text{bromocyclohexane} + H_2O$$
cyclohexanol
a secondary alcohol

bromocyclohexane

$$\overset{CH_3}{\underset{OH}{CH_3\overset{|}{\underset{|}{C}}CH_2CH_3}} \ + \ HBr \ \longrightarrow \ \overset{CH_3}{\underset{Br}{CH_3\overset{|}{\underset{|}{C}}CH_2CH_3}} \ + \ H_2O$$
2-methyl-2-butanol
a tertiary alcohol

2-bromo-2-methylbutane

The mechanism of the substitution reaction depends on the structure of the alcohol. Secondary and tertiary alcohols undergo S_N1 reactions.

MECHANISM FOR THE S_N1 REACTION OF AN ALCOHOL

An acid protonates the most basic atom in a molecule.

- An acid always reacts with an organic molecule in the same way: it protonates the most basic atom in the reactant.
- Weakly basic water is the leaving group that is expelled, forming a carbocation.
- The carbocation has two possible fates: it can combine with a nucleophile and form a substitution product, or it can lose a proton and form an elimination product.

Secondary and tertiary alcohols undergo S_N1 reactions with hydrogen halides.

Although the reaction can form both a substitution product and an elimination product, little elimination product is actually obtained because the alkene formed in an elimination reaction can undergo a subsequent addition reaction with HBr to form more of the substitution product (Section 4.1).

Tertiary alcohols undergo substitution reactions with hydrogen halides faster than secondary alcohols do, because tertiary carbocations are easier to form than secondary carbocations. (Recall that alkyl groups stabilize carbocations by hyperconjugation; Section 4.2) Thus, the reaction of a tertiary alcohol with a hydrogen halide proceeds readily at room temperature, whereas the reaction of a secondary alcohol with a hydrogen halide has to be heated to have the reaction occur at the same rate.

Carbocation stability: 3° > 2° > 1°

Primary alcohols cannot undergo S_N1 reactions because primary carbocations are too unstable to be formed (Section 8.4). Therefore, when a primary alcohol reacts with a hydrogen halide, it must do so by an S_N2 reaction.

MECHANISM FOR THE S_N2 REACTION OF AN ALCOHOL

Primary alcohols undergo S_N2 reactions with hydrogen halides.

- The acid protonates the most basic atom in the reactant.
- The nucleophile hits the back side of the carbon and displaces the leaving group.

Only a substitution product is obtained. No elimination product is formed because the halide ion, although a good nucleophile, is a weak base, and a strong base is required to remove a hydrogen from a β-carbon in an E2 reaction (Section 9.4). (Remember that a β-carbon is the carbon adjacent to the carbon that is attached to the leaving group.)

When HCl is used instead of HBr or HI, the S$_N$2 reaction is slower because Cl$^-$ is a poorer nucleophile than Br$^-$ or I$^-$ in a solution that contains protic polar alcohol and water molecules (Section 8.2). The rate of the reaction can be increased, however, by using ZnCl$_2$ as a catalyst.

$$CH_3CH_2CH_2OH \ + \ HCl \ \xrightarrow[\Delta]{ZnCl_2} \ CH_3CH_2CH_2Cl \ + \ H_2O$$

ZnCl$_2$ is a Lewis acid that complexes strongly with oxygen's lone-pair electrons. This interaction weakens the C—O bond, thereby creating a better leaving group.

$$CH_3CH_2CH_2\ddot{O}H \ + \ ZnCl \longrightarrow CH_3CH_2CH_2\!-\!\overset{\overset{\displaystyle ZnCl}{|}}{\underset{\underset{\displaystyle :\ddot{C}l:^-}{}}{\overset{+}{\ddot{O}}H}} \longrightarrow CH_3CH_2CH_2Cl \ + \ HOZnCl$$

The Lucas Test

The Lucas test determines whether an alcohol is primary, secondary, or tertiary by taking advantage of the relative rates at which the three classes of alcohols react with HCl/ZnCl$_2$. The alcohol is added to a mixture of HCl and ZnCl$_2$, known as Lucas reagent. Low-molecular-weight alcohols are soluble in Lucas reagent, but the alkyl halide products are not, so they cause the solution to turn cloudy. If the alcohol is tertiary, the solution turns cloudy immediately. If the alcohol is secondary, the solution turns cloudy in about one to five minutes. A solution of a primary alcohol turns cloudy only if the solution is heated. Because the test relies on the complete solubility of the alcohol in Lucas reagent, it is limited to alcohols with fewer than six carbons.

BIOGRAPHY

Howard J. Lucas (1885–1963) *was born in Ohio and earned B.S. and M.S. degrees from Ohio State University. He published a description of the Lucas test in 1930. He was a professor of chemistry at the California Institute of Technology.*

PROBLEM 2   SOLVED

Using the pK_a values of the conjugate acids of the leaving groups (the pK_a of HBr is -9; the pK_a of H$_2$O is 15.7; the pK_a of H$_3$O$^+$ is -1.7), explain the difference in reactivity in substitution reactions between:

a. CH$_3$Br and CH$_3$OH   **b.** CH$_3\overset{+}{O}$H$_2$ and CH$_3$OH

Solution to 2a   The conjugate acid of the leaving group of CH$_3$Br is HBr; the conjugate acid of the leaving group of CH$_3$OH is H$_2$O. Because HBr is a much stronger acid (p$K_a = -9$) than H$_2$O (p$K_a = 15.7$), Br$^-$ is a much weaker base than HO$^-$. (Recall that the stronger the acid, the weaker its conjugate base.) Therefore, Br$^-$ is a much better leaving group than HO$^-$, causing CH$_3$Br to be much more reactive than CH$_3$OH.

PROBLEM 3   SOLVED

Show how 1-butanol can be converted into the following compounds:

a. ![structure]   **c.** ![structure]

b. ![structure]   **d.** ![structure]

Solution to 3a   Because the OH group of 1-butanol is too basic to allow the alcohol to undergo a sustitution reaction, the alcohol must first be converted into an alkyl halide. The alkyl halide has a leaving group that can be substituted by CH$_3$O$^-$, the nucleophile required to obtain the desired product.

$$\text{OH} \xrightarrow[\Delta]{HBr} \text{Br} \xrightarrow{CH_3O^-} \text{O}$$

PROBLEM 4 ♦

The observed relative reactivities of primary, secondary, and tertiary alcohols with a hydrogen halide are 3° > 2° > 1°. If secondary alcohols underwent an S_N2 reaction rather than an S_N1 reaction with a hydrogen halide, what would be the relative reactivities of the three classes of alcohols?

Because the reaction of a secondary or a tertiary alcohol with a hydrogen halide is an S_N1 reaction, a carbocation is formed as an intermediate. Therefore, we must check for the possibility of a carbocation rearrangement when determining the product of the substitution reaction. Remember that a carbocation rearrangement will occur if it leads to formation of a more stable carbocation (Section 4.7). For example, the major product of the following reaction is 2-bromo-2-methylbutane, because a 1,2-hydride shift converts the initially formed secondary carbocation into a more stable tertiary carbocation.

$$\begin{array}{ccc}
\underset{\substack{| \\ OH}}{\overset{\substack{CH_3 \\ |}}{CH_3CHCHCH_3}} + HBr & \rightleftharpoons & \underset{\substack{| \\ {}^+OH \\ H}}{\overset{\substack{CH_3 \\ |}}{CH_3CHCHCH_3}} & \rightleftharpoons & \underset{\substack{+ \\ \boxed{\text{secondary carbocation}}}}{\overset{\substack{CH_3 \\ |}}{CH_3CHCHCH_3}} + H_2O & \xrightarrow{\substack{\textbf{1,2-hydride} \\ \textbf{shift}}} & \underset{\substack{+ \\ \boxed{\text{tertiary carbocation}}}}{\overset{\substack{CH_3 \\ |}}{CH_3CCH_2CH_3}}
\end{array}$$

3-methyl-2-butanol

$\Big\downarrow Br^-$

$\underset{\substack{| \\ Br}}{\overset{\substack{CH_3 \\ |}}{CH_3CHCHCH_3}}$

2-bromo-3-methyl-butane
minor product

$\Big\downarrow Br^-$

$\underset{\substack{| \\ Br}}{\overset{\substack{CH_3 \\ |}}{CH_3CCH_2CH_3}}$

2-bromo-2-methyl-butane
major product

Grain Alcohol and Wood Alcohol

When ethanol is ingested, it acts on the central nervous system. Moderate amounts affect judgment and lower inhibitions. Higher amounts interfere with motor coordination and cause slurred speech and amnesia. Still higher amounts cause nausea and loss of consciousness. Ingesting very large amounts of ethanol interferes with spontaneous respiration and can be fatal.

The ethanol in alcoholic beverages is produced by the fermentation of glucose, generally obtained from grapes or from grains such as corn, rye, and wheat (which is why ethanol is also known as grain alcohol). Grains are cooked in the presence of malt (sprouted barley) to convert much of their starch into glucose. Yeast enzymes are added to convert the glucose into ethanol and carbon dioxide (Section 26.8).

The kind of beverage produced (white or red wine, beer, scotch, bourbon, champagne) depends on the plant species providing the glucose, whether the CO_2 formed in the fermenta-

tion is allowed to escape, whether other substances are added, and how the beverage is purified (by sedimentation, for wines; by distillation, for scotch and bourbon).

The tax imposed on liquor would make ethanol a prohibitively expensive laboratory reagent. Laboratory alcohol, therefore, is not taxed because ethanol is needed in a wide variety of commercial processes. Although this alcohol is not taxed, it is carefully regulated by the federal government to make certain that it is not used for the preparation of alcoholic beverages. Denatured alcohol—ethanol that has been made undrinkable by the addition of a denaturant such as benzene or methanol—is not taxed, but the added impurities make it unfit for many laboratory uses.

Methanol, also known as wood alcohol because at one time it was obtained by heating wood in the absence of oxygen, is highly toxic. Ingesting even very small amounts can cause blindness, and ingesting as little as an ounce has been fatal.

$$C_6H_{12}O_6 \xrightarrow{\textbf{yeast enzymes}} 2\ CH_3CH_2OH + 2\ CO_2$$

glucose　　　　　　　　　　**ethanol**

PROBLEM 5◆

Give the major product of each of the following reactions:

a. $CH_3CH_2CHCH_3$ + HBr $\xrightarrow{\Delta}$
　　　　　|
　　　　OH

c. 　　　　CH_3
　　　　　|
　　CH_3C—$CHCH_3$ + HBr $\xrightarrow{\Delta}$
　　　　|　　|
　　　CH_3 OH

b. 　CH_3
　　　\
　　　　—OH + HCl $\longrightarrow$
　（cyclopentane ring）

d. 　　　CH_3 OH
　　　　　|　|
　（cyclohexane ring）$CHCH_3$ + HCl $\xrightarrow{\Delta}$

10.2 OTHER METHODS USED TO CONVERT ALCOHOLS INTO ALKYL HALIDES

Alcohols are inexpensive and readily available compounds, but they do not undergo nucleophilic substitution because the HO^- group is too basic to be displaced by a nucleophile (Section 10.1). Chemists, therefore, need ways to convert readily available but unreactive alcohols into reactive alkyl halides that can be used as starting materials for the preparation of many organic compounds (Section 8.3).

$$R-OH \xrightarrow[\Delta]{HX} R-X \quad (X = Cl, Br, I)$$

- $\xrightarrow{^-OCH_3}$ $R-OCH_3$
- $\xrightarrow{^-C\equiv CCH_3}$ $R-C\equiv CCH_3$
- $\xrightarrow{^-C\equiv N}$ $R-C\equiv N$

alcohol / alkyl halide

We have just seen that an alcohol can be converted into an alkyl halide by treating it with a hydrogen halide. However, better yields are obtained and carbocation rearrangements can be avoided if a phosphorus trihalide (PCl_3, PBr_3, or PI_3)* or thionyl chloride ($SOCl_2$) is used instead.

$$CH_3CH_2OH + PBr_3 \xrightarrow{pyridine} CH_3CH_2Br$$

$$CH_3CH_2OH + PCl_3 \xrightarrow{pyridine} CH_3CH_2Cl$$

$$CH_3CH_2OH + SOCl_2 \xrightarrow{pyridine} CH_3CH_2Cl$$

These reagents all act in the same way: they convert the alcohol into an intermediate with a leaving group that is readily displaced by a halide ion. For example, phosphorus tribromide converts the OH group of an alcohol into a bromophosphite group that can be easily displaced by a bromide ion.

$CH_3CH_2-\ddot{O}H$ + $P-Br$ (Br, Br) phosphorus tribromide $\rightleftharpoons$ $CH_3CH_2-\overset{+}{\ddot{O}}PBr_2$ (H) $\rightleftharpoons$ $CH_3CH_2-\ddot{O}PBr_2$ $\longrightarrow$ CH_3CH_2Br + $^-OPBr_2$

a bromophosphite group

---

*Because of its instability, PI_3 is generated in situ (in the reaction mixture) from the reaction of phosphorus with iodine.

Thionyl chloride converts an OH group into a chlorosulfite group that can be displaced by Cl⁻.

Pyridine is generally used as the solvent in these reactions because it is a poor nucleophile but is sufficiently basic to remove a proton from the intermediate so that it does not revert to starting materials.

The foregoing reactions work well for primary and secondary alcohols, but tertiary alcohols give poor yields because the intermediate formed by a tertiary alcohol is sterically hindered to attack by the halide ion.

Table 10.1 summarizes some of the methods commonly used to convert alcohols into alkyl halides.

Table 10.1 Commonly Used Methods for Converting Alcohols into Alkyl Halides

$$ ROH + HBr \xrightarrow{\Delta} RBr $$

$$ ROH + HI \xrightarrow{\Delta} RI $$

$$ ROH + HCl \xrightarrow[\Delta]{ZnCl_2} RCl $$

$$ ROH + PBr_3 \xrightarrow[\text{pyridine}]{} RBr $$

$$ ROH + PCl_3 \xrightarrow[\text{pyridine}]{} RCl $$

$$ ROH + SOCl_2 \xrightarrow[\text{pyridine}]{} RCl $$

10.3 CONVERTING AN ALCOHOL INTO A SULFONATE ESTER

Besides converting it into an alkyl halide, another way you can activate an alcohol for subsequent reaction with a nucleophile is by converting it into a sulfonate ester. A **sulfonate ester** is formed when an alcohol reacts with a sulfonyl chloride. (Notice that sulfur, which is in the third row of the periodic table, has an expanded valence shell—it is surrounded by 12 electrons.)

The reaction is a nucleophilic substitution reaction: the alcohol displaces the chloride ion. Pyridine is used both as the solvent and to remove a proton from the intermediate.

Several sulfonyl chlorides are available to activate OH groups. The most common one is *para*-toluenesulfonyl chloride.

Once the alcohol has been activated by being converted into a sulfonate ester, the appropriate nucleophile is added, generally under conditions that favor S_N2 reactions. (Notice that in all cases, the added nucleophile is a *much* better nucleophile than the chloride ion that also is present in the solution.) The reactions take place readily at room temperature because the sulfonate ester has an excellent leaving group. Sulfonate esters react with a wide variety of nucleophiles, so they can be used to synthesize a wide variety of compounds.

Sulfonate esters have excellent leaving groups because a sulfonic acid is a very strong acid ($pK_a = -6.5$); its conjugate base is particularly stable (weak) due to delocalization of its negative charge over three oxygens. (Recall from Section 7.6 that electron delocalization stabilizes a species.) The leaving group of a sulfonate ester is about a 100 times better a leaving group than chloride ion.

resonance contributors

para-Toluenesulfonyl chloride is called tosyl chloride and abbreviated TsCl; the product of the reaction of *para*-toluenesulfonyl chloride and an alcohol is called an **alkyl tosylate** and is abbreviated ROTs. The leaving group, therefore, is ⁻OTs.

The product of the reaction of trifluoromethanesulfonyl chloride and an alcohol is called an **alkyl triflate** and is abbreviated ROTf.

$$CH_3CH_2CH_2OTs + {}^-C\equiv N \longrightarrow CH_3CH_2CH_2C\equiv N + {}^-OTs$$
an alkyl tosylate

$$CH_3CH_2CH_2OTf + CH_3NH_2 \longrightarrow CH_3CH_2CH_2\overset{+}{N}H_2CH_3 + {}^-OTf$$
an alkyl triflate

The Inability to Perform an S$_N$2 Reaction Causes a Severe Clinical Disorder

In the human body, an enzyme called HGPRT catalyzes the S$_N$2 reaction shown below. The pyrophosphate group is an excellent leaving group because the electrons released when the group departs, like the electrons released when a sulfonate group departs, are stabilized by electron delocalization.

Clinically, a severe deficiency in HGPRT that makes it impossible to carry out the S$_N$2 reaction causes Lesch-Nyhan syndrome. This congenital defect, which occurs only in males, has tragic symptoms—crippling arthritis and severe malfunctions in the nervous system such as mental retardation, highly aggressive behavior, and self-mutilation. Children with this syndrome have such a compulsive urge to bite their fingers that they have to be restrained. Fortunately, HGPRT deficiencies in fetal cells can be detected by amniocentesis.

PROBLEM 6   SOLVED

Explain why the ether obtained by treating an optically active alcohol with PBr$_3$ followed by sodium methoxide has the same configuration as the alcohol, whereas the ether obtained by treating the alcohol with tosyl chloride followed by sodium methoxide has a configuration opposite that of the alcohol.

1. PBr$_3$/pyridine
2. CH$_3$O$^-$

same configuration as the alcohol

1. TsCl/pyridine
2. CH$_3$O$^-$

configuration opposite to that of the alcohol

Solution   Conversion of the alcohol to the ether by way of the alkyl halide requires two successive S_N2 reactions: (1) attack of Br^- on the bromophosphite and (2) attack of CH_3O^- on the alkyl halide. Each S_N2 reaction takes place with inversion of configuration, so the final product has the same configuration as the starting material. In contrast, conversion of the alcohol to the ether by way of the alkyl tosylate requires only one S_N2 reaction: attack of CH_3O^- on the alkyl tosylate. Therefore, the final product and the starting material have opposite configurations.

PROBLEM 7

Show how 1-propanol can be converted into the following compounds by means of a sulfonate ester:

a. $CH_3CH_2CH_2SCH_2CH_3$

b. $CH_3CH_2CH_2OCH_2CHCH_3$
        |
        CH_3

---

chem Tutorial:
place   Leaving groups

10.4 ELIMINATION REACTIONS OF ALCOHOLS: DEHYDRATION

An alcohol can undergo an elimination reaction by losing an OH from one carbon and an H from an adjacent carbon. The product of the reaction is an alkene. Overall, this amounts to the elimination of a molecule of water. Loss of water from a molecule is called **dehydration**. Dehydration of an alcohol requires an acid catalyst and heat. Sulfuric acid (H_2SO_4) and phosphoric acid (H_3PO_4) are the most commonly used acid catalysts. Recall that a catalyst increases the rate of a reaction but is not consumed during the course of a reaction (Section 4.5).

acid-catalyzed dehydration

$$CH_3CH_2CHCH_3 \xrightleftharpoons[\Delta]{H_2SO_4} CH_3CH=CHCH_3 + H_2O$$
$$\quad\quad | $$
$$\quad\quad OH$$

The mechanism for acid-catalyzed dehydration depends on the structure of the alcohol; dehydrations of secondary and tertiary alcohols are E1 reactions.

MECHANISM FOR THE E1 DEHYDRATION OF AN ALCOHOL

Dehydration of secondary and tertiary alcohols are E1 reactions.

- The acid protonates the most basic atom in the reactant. As we saw earlier, protonation converts the very poor leaving group (HO^-) into a good leaving group (H_2O).
- Water departs, leaving behind a carbocation.
- A base in the reaction mixture (water is the base that is present in the highest concentration) removes a proton from a β-carbon (a carbon adjacent to the positively charged carbon), forming an alkene and regenerating the acid catalyst. Notice that the dehydration reaction is an E1 reaction of a protonated alcohol.

When acid-catalyzed dehydration leads to more than one elimination product, the major product will be the more substituted alkene—the one obtained by removing a proton from the β-carbon bonded to the fewest hydrogens (Section 9.2). The more substituted alkene is the major product because it is the more stable alkene, so it has the more stable transition state leading to its formation (Figure 10.1).

▶ **Figure 10.1**
The reaction coordinate diagram for the dehydration of a protonated alcohol. The major product is the more substituted alkene because the transition state leading to its formation is more stable, allowing that alkene to be formed more rapidly.

Notice that the acid-catalyzed dehydration of an alcohol is the reverse of the acid-catalyzed addition of water to an alkene (Section 4.5).

To prevent the alkene formed in the dehydration reaction from adding water and reforming the alcohol, the alkene is removed by distillation as it is formed, because it has a much lower boiling point than the alcohol (Section 2.9). Removing a product displaces the reaction to the right. (See Le Châtelier's principle, Section 3.7.)

Because the rate-determining step in the dehydration of a secondary or a tertiary alcohol is formation of a carbocation intermediate, the rate of dehydration reflects the ease with which the carbocation is formed: tertiary alcohols are the easiest to dehydrate because tertiary carbocations are more stable and are therefore more easily formed than secondary and primary carbocations (Section 4.2). In order to undergo dehydration, tertiary alcohols must be heated to about 50 °C in 5% H_2SO_4, secondary alcohols must be heated to about 100 °C in 75% H_2SO_4, and primary alcohols can be dehydrated only under extreme conditions (170 °C in 95% H_2SO_4) and by a different mechanism because primary carbocations are too unstable to be formed (Section 8.5).

relative ease of dehydration

Dehydration of secondary and tertiary alcohols involves the formation of a carbocation intermediate, so be sure to check the structure of the carbocation for the possibility of rearrangement. Remember that a carbocation will rearrange if rearrangement produces a more stable carbocation (Section 4.7). For example, the secondary carbocation formed initially in the following reaction rearranges to a more stable tertiary carbocation:

The following reaction provides an example of a **ring-expansion rearrangement**. Both the carbocation formed initially and the carbocation to which it rearranges are secondary carbocations, but the rearranged carbocation is more stable because rearrangement to a larger ring relieves the strain of the four-membered ring (Section 2.11). The rearranged secondary carbocation can rearrange by a 1,2-hydride shift to an even more stable tertiary carbocation. (B: is any base present in the solution.)

PROBLEM 8◆

Which of the following alcohols would dehydrate the most rapidly when heated with acid?

PROBLEM 9◆

What product would be formed if the four-membered ring alcohol shown above were heated with an equivalent amount of HBr rather than with a catalytic amount of H_2SO_4?

While the dehydration of a tertiary or a secondary alcohol is an E1 reaction, the dehydration of a primary alcohol is an E2 reaction, because primary carbocations are too unstable to be formed. Any base (B:) in the reaction mixture (ROH, ROR, H_2O, HSO_4^-)

can remove the proton in the elimination reaction. An ether is also obtained; it is the product of a competing S_N2 reaction, since primary alcohols are the ones most likely to form substitution products in S_N2/E2 reactions (Section 9.8).

MECHANISM FOR THE E2 DEHYDRATION OF AN ALCOHOL AND FOR THE COMPETING S_N2 REACTION

$$CH_3CH_2\overset{..}{\underset{..}{O}}H \;+\; H{-}OSO_3H \;\rightleftharpoons\; CH_2{-}CH_2{-}\overset{+}{O}H \;\xrightarrow{\;E2\;}\; CH_2{=}CH_2 \;+\; H_2O \;+\; HB^+$$

protonation of the most basic atom

removal of a proton from a β-carbon

$+\; HSO_4^-$

elimination product

Dehydration of a primary alcohol is an E2 reaction.

$$CH_3CH_2\overset{..}{\underset{..}{O}}H \;+\; CH_3CH_2{-}\overset{+}{O}H \;\xrightarrow{\;S_N2\;}\; CH_3CH_2\overset{+}{O}CH_2CH_3 \;\longrightarrow\; CH_3CH_2OCH_2CH_3 \;+\; H_3O^+$$

back-side attack by the nucleophile

$H_2\overset{..}{\underset{..}{O}}{:}$

substitution product

Although the dehydration of a primary alcohol is an E2 reaction and therefore does not form a carbocation intermediate, the product obtained in most cases is identical to the product that would be obtained if a carbocation had been formed in an E1 reaction and then had rearranged. For example, we would expect 1-butene to be the product of the E2 dehydration of 1-butanol. However, we find that the product is actually 2-butene, which would have been the product if an E1 reaction had occurred and the initially formed primary carbocation intermediate had rearranged to a more stable secondary carbocation. 2-Butene is the product of the reaction, not because an E1 reaction occurs, but because, after the E2 product (1-butene) forms, a proton from the acidic solution adds to the double bond, adding to the sp^2 carbon bonded to the greater number of hydrogens (in accordance with the rule that governs electrophilic addition reactions; Section 4.4) to form a carbocation. Loss of a proton from the carbocation—from the β-carbon bonded to the fewest hydrogens (in accordance with Zaitsev's rule)—forms 2-butene, the final product of the reaction.

$$CH_3CH_2CH_2CH_2OH \;\underset{\Delta}{\overset{H_2SO_4}{\rightleftharpoons}}\; CH_3CH_2CH{=}CH_2 \;\underset{}{\overset{H^+}{\rightleftharpoons}}\; CH_3CH_2\overset{+}{C}HCH_3 \;\rightleftharpoons\; CH_3CH{=}CHCH_3 \;+\; H^+$$

1-butanol   **1-butene**   **2-butene**

$+\; H_2O$

PROBLEM 10

Heating an alcohol with sulfuric acid is a good way to prepare a symmetrical ether such as diethyl ether.

a. Explain why it is not a good way to prepare an unsymmetrical ether such as ethyl propyl ether.

b. How would you synthesize ethyl propyl ether?

The stereochemical outcome of the E1 dehydration of an alcohol is identical to the stereochemical outcome of the E1 dehydrohalogenation of an alkyl halide. That is, both the E and Z stereoisomers are obtained as products, but the major product is the stereoisomer in which the bulkier group on each of the sp^2 carbons are on opposite sides of the double bond. Because that stereoisomer is more stable, it is formed more rapidly (Section 9.5).

$$CH_3CH_2\underset{\underset{OH}{|}}{C}HCH_3 \; \xrightleftharpoons[\Delta]{H_2SO_4} \; CH_3CH_2\overset{+}{C}HCH_3 + H_2O \longrightarrow$$

2-butanol

trans-2-butene
74%

cis-2-butene
23%

$+ \; CH_3CH_2CH=CH_2 \; + \; H^+$

1-butene
3%

We can summarize what we have learned about the mechanisms by which alcohols undergo substitution and elimination reactions: they react by S_N1 and E1 pathways, unless they cannot. In other words, 3° and 2° alcohols undergo S_N1 and E1 reactions; 1° alcohols, because they cannot form primary carbocations, have to undergo S_N2 and E2 reactions.

The relatively harsh conditions (acid and heat) required for alcohol dehydration, and the structural changes resulting from carbocation rearrangements, may result in low yields of the desired alkene. Dehydration, however, can be carried out under milder conditions by using phosphorus oxychloride ($POCl_3$) and pyridine.

> **Alcohols undergo $S_N1/E1$ reactions unless they would have to form a primary carbocation, in which case they undergo $S_N2/E2$ reactions.**

$$CH_3CH_2\underset{\underset{OH}{|}}{C}HCH_3 \; \xrightarrow[\text{pyridine, 0 °C}]{POCl_3} \; CH_3CH=CHCH_3$$

Reaction with $POCl_3$ converts the OH group of the alcohol into $OPOCl_2$, a good leaving group. The basic reaction conditions favor an E2 reaction, so a carbocation is not formed and carbocation rearrangements do not occur. Pyridine serves as a base to remove the proton in the elimination reaction and to prevent the buildup of HCl, which would add to the alkene.

phosphorus
oxychloride

$+ \; Cl^-$

$\longrightarrow \quad CH_2=CHCH_3$

$2 \; \overset{\;}{\underset{H}{N^+}} \; + \; {}^-OPOCl_2$

Biological Dehydrations

Dehydration reactions occur in many important biological processes. Instead of being catalyzed by strong acids, which would not be available to a cell, they are catalyzed by enzymes. Fumarase, for example, is the enzyme that catalyzes the dehydration of malate in the citric acid cycle. The citric acid cycle is a series of reactions that oxidize compounds derived from carbohydrates, fatty acids, and amino acids (Section 26.10).

fumarase

$+ \; H_2O$

malate   fumarate

Enolase, another enzyme, catalyzes the dehydration of α-phosphoglycerate in glycolysis. Glycolysis is a series of reactions that prepare glucose for entry into the citric acid cycle (Section 26.7).

enolase

$+ \; H_2O$

α-phosphoglycerate   phosphoenolpyruvate

chem Tutorial:
place Alkene synthesis by dehydration I

Tutorial:
Alkene synthesis by dehydration II

PROBLEM 11♦

What alcohol would you treat with phosphorus oxychloride and pyridine to form each of the following alkenes?

a. $CH_3CH_2C(CH_3)=CH_2$

c. $CH_3CH=CHCH_2CH_3$

b. [cyclohexene with CH_3]

d. [cyclohexane with $=CH_2$]

PROBLEM-SOLVING STRATEGY

Proposing a Mechanism

Propose a mechanism for the following reaction:

[structure: 7-membered ring with H₃C, CH₃, CH₃, and ÖH substituents] $\xrightarrow[\Delta]{H_2SO_4}$ [structure: 6-membered ring with CH₂, CH₃, H₃C, CH₃ substituents]

Even the most complicated-looking mechanism can be reasoned out if you proceed one step at a time, keeping in mind the structure of the final product. The oxygen is the only basic atom in the reactant, so that is where protonation occurs. Loss of water forms a tertiary carbocation.

[structure: 7-membered ring with H₃C, CH₃, CH₃, and protonated ÖH₂⁺ group] $\longrightarrow$ [structure: 7-membered ring carbocation with H₃C, CH₃, CH₃] $+$ $H_2\ddot{O}:$

Because the reactant contains a seven-membered ring and the final product has a six-membered ring, a ring-contraction rearrangement must occur. When doing a *ring-contraction* (or a ring-expansion) *rearrangement*, you may find it helpful to label the equivalent carbons in the reactant and product, as shown below. Of the two possible pathways for ring contraction, one leads to a tertiary carbocation and the other leads to a primary carbocation. The correct pathway must be the one that leads to the tertiary carbocation, since that carbocation has the same arrangement of atoms as the product and the primary carbocation would be too unstable to form.

[structure: 7-membered ring with H₃C, CH₃, CH₃, labeled carbons 2 and 1] $\longrightarrow$ [structure: 6-membered ring tertiary carbocation, H₃C, CH₃, CH₃, labeled 2 and 1] | tertiary carbocation |

[structure: 7-membered ring with H₃C, CH₃, CH₃, labeled carbon 2] $\xmapsto{\times}$ [structure: 6-membered ring primary carbocation, H₃C, CH₃, CH₃, CH₂⁺] | primary carbocation |

The final product can now be obtained by removing a proton from the rearranged carbocation.

$H_2\ddot{O}:$ H—CH_2 [structure with labeled 2, CH₃, H₃C, labeled 1, 6-membered ring] $\longrightarrow$ [structure: 6-membered ring with CH₂, CH₃, H₃C, labeled 2 and 1] $+$ $H_3\ddot{O}^+$

Now continue on to Problem 12.

PROBLEM 12

Propose a mechanism for each of the following reactions:

a.

$$\underset{\underset{\text{OH}}{\overset{\overset{\displaystyle CH_3}{|}}{\underset{|}{\overset{-CH_3}{}}}}{\bigcirc} \quad \xrightarrow[\Delta]{H_2SO_4} \quad$$

b.

$$\underset{CH_2OH}{\bigcirc} \quad \xrightarrow[\Delta]{H_2SO_4} \quad \underset{CH_3}{\bigcirc}$$

c.

$$\triangle\!\!-\!\!\underset{\underset{CH_3}{|}}{\overset{\overset{CH_3}{|}}{C}}\!-\!OH \quad + \quad HBr \quad \longrightarrow \quad \underset{CH_3}{\overset{\overset{CH_3}{|}\!-\!Br}{\square}}$$

PROBLEM 13 ◆

Give the major product formed when each of the following alcohols is heated in the presence of H_2SO_4:

a. $CH_3CH_2\underset{\underset{CH_3}{|}}{\overset{\overset{CH_3}{|}}{C}}-\underset{\underset{CH_3}{|}}{\overset{}{CH}}CH_3$
   $OH\ CH_3$

b. $\underset{\square}{\overset{\overset{OH}{|}}{}}\!\!CHCH_2CH_3$

c. $\underset{\bigcirc}{\overset{OH}{\diagdown}}$

d. $\underset{CH_2OH}{\bigcirc}$

e. $CH_3CH_2\underset{\underset{OH}{|}}{\overset{}{CH}}-\underset{\underset{CH_3}{|}}{\overset{\overset{CH_3}{|}}{C}}CH_3$

f. $CH_3CH_2CH_2CH_2CH_2OH$

PROBLEM 14

When the following compound is heated in the presence of H_2SO_4:

a. What constitutional isomer is produced in greatest yield?
b. What stereoisomer is produced in greater yield?

10.5 OXIDATION OF ALCOHOLS

A reagent often used to oxidize alcohols is chromic acid (H_2CrO_4), which is formed when chromium trioxide (CrO_3) or sodium dichromate ($Na_2Cr_2O_7$) is dissolved in aqueous acid. *Secondary alcohols* are oxidized to *ketones*. These reactions are easily recognized as oxidations because the number of C—H bonds in the reactant decreases and the number of C—O bonds increases (Section 4.9).

secondary alcohols   ketones

$$CH_3CH_2\underset{\underset{\displaystyle OH}{|}}{C}HCH_3 \xrightarrow{H_2CrO_4} CH_3CH_2\overset{\overset{\displaystyle O}{\|}}{C}CH_3$$

$$\xrightarrow[H_2SO_4]{CrO_3}$$

Secondary alcohols are oxidized to ketones.

$$\xrightarrow[H_2SO_4]{Na_2Cr_2O_7}$$

Primary alcohols are initially oxidized to aldehydes by these reagents. The reaction, however, does not stop at the aldehyde. Instead, the aldehyde is further oxidized (the number of C—O bonds increases) to a carboxylic acid.

$$CH_3CH_2CH_2CH_2OH \xrightarrow{H_2CrO_4} \left[CH_3CH_2CH_2\overset{\overset{\displaystyle O}{\|}}{C}H \right] \xrightarrow[\text{oxidation}]{\text{further}} CH_3CH_2CH_2\overset{\overset{\displaystyle O}{\|}}{C}OH$$

pyridinium chlorochromate PCC

a primary alcohol   **an aldehyde**   **a carboxylic acid**

The oxidation of a primary alcohol will stop at the aldehyde if pyridinium chlorochromate (PCC) is used as the oxidizing agent in a solvent such as dichloromethane (CH_2Cl_2). We will see why this reaction stops at the aldehyde in Section 20.4.

Primary alcohols are oxidized to carboxylic acids and aldehydes.

$$CH_3CH_2CH_2CH_2OH \xrightarrow[CH_2Cl_2]{PCC} CH_3CH_2CH_2\overset{\overset{\displaystyle O}{\|}}{C}H$$

a primary alcohol   **an aldehyde**

Notice that in the oxidation of both a primary and a secondary alcohol, a hydrogen is removed from the carbon to which the OH is attached. The carbon bearing the OH group in a tertiary alcohol is not bonded to a hydrogen, so its OH group cannot be oxidized to a carbonyl C=O group.

$$CH_3-\underset{\underset{\displaystyle CH_3}{|}}{\overset{\overset{\displaystyle CH_3}{|}}{C}}-OH$$

cannot be oxidized to a carbonyl group

a tertiary alcohol

Notice that both an S_N2 and an E2 reaction are involved in the overall oxidation reaction.

MECHANISM FOR ALCOHOL OXIDATION BY CHROMIC ACID

- An oxygen of chromic acid is protonated in the acidic solution.
- The alcohol molecule displaces a molecule of water in an S_N2 reaction on chromium.

- A base present in the reaction mixture (H_2O, ROH) removes a proton from the strongly acidic species.
- A base removes a proton from the chromate ester in an E2 reaction, thereby forming the carbonyl compound.

Blood Alcohol Content

As blood passes through the arteries in our lungs, an equilibrium is established between alcohol in the blood and alcohol in the breath. Therefore, if the concentration of one is known, the concentration of the other can be estimated.

The test that law enforcement agencies use to approximate a person's blood alcohol level is based on the oxidation of breath ethanol. An oxidizing agent impregnated onto an inert material is enclosed within a sealed glass tube. When the test is to be administered, the ends of the tube are broken off and replaced with a mouthpiece at one end and a balloon-type bag at the other. The person being tested blows into the mouthpiece until the bag is filled with air.

glass tube containing sodium dichromate–sulfuric acid coated on silica gel particles

person breathes into mouthpiece

as person blows into the tube, the plastic bag becomes inflated

Any ethanol in the breath is oxidized as it passes through the column. When ethanol is oxidized, the red-orange dichromate ion is reduced to green chromic ion (Cr^{3+}). The greater the concentration of alcohol in the breath, the farther the green color spreads through the tube.

$$CH_3CH_2OH \;+\; Cr_2O_7^{2-} \xrightarrow{\text{HCl}} CH_3\overset{\displaystyle O}{\overset{\|}{C}}OH \;+\; Cr^{3+}$$

red orange   **green**

If the person fails this test—determined by the extent to which the green color spreads through the tube—a more accurate Breathalyzer™ test is administered. The Breathalyzer test also depends on the oxidation of breath ethanol, but it provides more accurate results because it is quantitative. In the test, a known volume of breath is bubbled through an acidic solution of sodium dichromate, and the concentration of the green chromic ion is measured precisely with a spectrophotometer (Section 13.18).

PROBLEM 15 ◆

Give the product formed from the reaction of each of the following compounds with an acidic solution of sodium dichromate:

a. 3-pentanol
b. 1-pentanol
c. 2-methyl-2-pentanol

d. 2,4-hexanediol
e. cyclohexanol
f. 1,4-butanediol

chem place Tutorial: Oxidation/Reduction

Tutorial: Oxidation reactions of alcohols

PROBLEM 16

Propose a mechanism for the chromic acid oxidation of 1-propanol to propanal.

10.6 NUCLEOPHILIC SUBSTITUTION REACTIONS OF ETHERS

The OR group of an **ether** and the OH group of an alcohol have nearly the same basicity, because the conjugate acids of these two groups have similar pK_a values. (The pK_a of CH_3OH is 15.5, and the pK_a of H_2O is 15.7.) Both groups are strong bases, so both are very poor leaving groups. Consequently, ethers, like alcohols, need to be activated before they can undergo a nucleophilic substitution reaction.

$$R-\overset{..}{\underset{..}{O}}-H \qquad R-\overset{..}{\underset{..}{O}}-R$$

an alcohol   **an ether**

Ethers, like alcohols, can be activated by protonation. Ethers, therefore, can undergo nucleophilic substitution reactions with HBr or HI. (HCl cannot be used because Cl^- is too poor a nucleophile.) As with alcohols, the reaction of ethers with hydrogen halides is slow. The reaction mixture must be heated to cause the reaction to occur at a reasonable rate.

$$R-\ddot{O}-R' \;+\; HI \;\rightleftharpoons\; R-\overset{H}{\underset{I^-}{\overset{+}{O}}}-R' \;\xrightarrow{\Delta}\; R-I \;+\; R'-\ddot{O}H$$

poor leaving group

good leaving group

What happens *after* the ether is protonated depends on the structure of the ether. If departure of ROH creates a relatively stable carbocation (such as a tertiary carbocation), an S_N1 reaction occurs.

MECHANISM FOR ETHER CLEAVAGE: AN S_N1 REACTION

addition of a nucleophile

$$\underset{\overset{|}{CH_3}}{\overset{\overset{|}{CH_3}}{CH_3C}}-\ddot{O}CH_3 \;+\; H-I \;\rightleftharpoons\; \underset{\overset{|}{CH_3}}{\overset{\overset{|}{CH_3}}{CH_3C}}\overset{H}{\underset{+}{\ddot{O}}}CH_3 \;\xrightarrow{S_N1}\; \underset{\overset{|}{CH_3}}{\overset{\overset{|}{CH_3}}{CH_3C^+}} \;\longrightarrow\; \underset{\overset{|}{CH_3}}{\overset{\overset{|}{CH_3}}{CH_3C}}-\ddot{I}$$

protonation

carbocation formation

$+\; CH_3\ddot{O}H$

• Protonation converts the very basic RO^- leaving group into the less basic ROH leaving group.
• The leaving group departs.
• The halide ion combines with the carbocation.

However, if departure of the leaving group would create an unstable carbocation (such as a methyl, vinyl, aryl, or primary carbocation), the leaving group cannot depart. It has to be displaced by the halide ion. In other words, an S_N2 reaction occurs.

MECHANISM FOR ETHER CLEAVAGE: AN S_N2 REACTION

$$CH_3-\ddot{O}-CH_2CH_2CH_3 \;+\; H-I \;\rightleftharpoons\; CH_3-\overset{H}{\underset{+}{\ddot{O}}}-CH_2CH_2CH_3 \;\xrightarrow{S_N2}\; CH_3-\ddot{I} \;+\; CH_3CH_2CH_2-\ddot{O}H$$

protonation

nucleophile attacks the less sterically hindered carbon

• Protonation converts the very basic RO^- leaving group into the less basic ROH leaving group.
• The halide ion preferentially attacks the less sterically hindered of the two alkyl groups.

Ethers are cleaved by an S_N1 pathway unless the instability of the carbocation requires an S_N2 pathway.

In summary, ethers are cleaved by an S_N1 pathway unless the instability of the carbocation causes the reaction to follow an S_N2 pathway.

Ether cleavage forms only a substitution product because the bases in the reaction mixture (halide ions and H_2O) are too weak to remove a proton in an E2 reaction, and any alkene formed in an E1 reaction would undergo electrophilic addition with HBr or HI to form the same alkyl halide as would be obtained from the substitution reaction.

Many of the reagents used to activate alcohols so they can undergo nucleophilic substitution (such as $SOCl_2$ or PCl_3) cannot be used to activate ethers. When an alcohol reacts with an activating agent such as a sulfonyl chloride, a proton dissociates from the intermediate in the second step of the reaction and a stable sulfonate ester results.

$$ROH \;+\; \underset{O}{\overset{O}{\underset{\|}{R'-S}}}-Cl \;\longrightarrow\; \underset{\underset{H}{\overset{|}{O}}}{\overset{O}{\underset{\|}{R'-S}}}-\overset{+}{O}R \;\rightleftharpoons\; \underset{O}{\overset{O}{\underset{\|}{R'-S}}}-OR \;+\; H^+$$

an alcohol

$+\; Cl^-$

a sulfonate ester

However, when an ether reacts with a sulfonyl chloride, the oxygen atom does not have a proton that can dissociate. The alkyl group (R) cannot dissociate, so a stable sulfonate ester cannot be formed. Instead, the more stable starting materials are re-formed.

$$ROR \quad + \quad R'-\overset{\overset{O}{\|}}{\underset{\underset{O}{\|}}{S}}-Cl \quad \rightleftharpoons \quad R'-\overset{\overset{O}{\|}}{\underset{\underset{O}{\|}}{S}}-\overset{+}{\underset{R}{O}}R \quad + \quad Cl^-$$

an ether

Because the only reagents that react with ethers are hydrogen halides, ethers are frequently used as solvents. Some common ether solvents are shown in Table 10.2.

Table 10.2	Some Ethers Are Used as Solvents

| diethyl ether "ether" | tetrahydrofuran THF | tetrahydropyran THP | 1,4-dioxane | 1,2-dimethoxyethane DME | *tert*-butyl methyl ether MTBE |

Anesthetics

Because diethyl ether (commonly known as ether) is a short-lived muscle relaxant, it was at one time widely used as an *inhalation anesthetic*. However, it takes effect slowly and has a slow and unpleasant recovery period, so other compounds, such as enflurane, isoflurane, and halothane, have replaced it as an anesthetic. Even so, diethyl ether is still used where trained anesthesiologists are scarce because it is the safest anesthetic for an untrained person to administer. Anesthetics interact with the nonpolar molecules of cell membranes, causing the membranes to swell, which interferes with their permeability.

| "ether" | isoflurane | enflurane | halothane |

Sodium pentothal (also called thiopental sodium) is commonly used as an *intravenous anesthetic*. The onset of anesthe-

sia and the loss of consciousness occur within seconds of its administration. Care must be taken when administering sodium pentothal because the dose for effective anesthesia is 75% of the lethal dose. Because of this high level of toxicity, it cannot be used as the sole anesthetic but instead is generally used to induce anesthesia before an inhalation anesthetic is administered. Propofol (also called diprivan), in contrast, has all the properties of the "perfect anesthetic": it can be administered as the sole anesthetic by intravenous drip, and it has a rapid and pleasant induction period and a wide margin of safety. Furthermore, recovery from the drug is also rapid and pleasant.

sodium pentothal   propofol diprivan

Amputation of a leg without anesthetic in 1528.

A painting showing the first use of anesthesia (ether) during surgery in 1846 at Massachusetts General Hospital by surgeon John Collins Warren.

PROBLEM 17 SOLVED

Explain why methyl propyl ether forms both methyl iodide and propyl iodide when it is heated with excess HI.

Solution We have just seen that the S_N2 reaction of methyl propyl ether with an equivalent amount of HI forms methyl iodide and propyl alcohol because the methyl group is less sterically hindered to attack by the iodide ion. When there is excess HI, the alcohol product of this first reaction can react with HI in another S_N2 reaction (Section 10.1). Thus, the products are two alkyl iodides.

PROBLEM 18♦

Can HF be used to cleave ethers? Explain.

PROBLEM 19 SOLVED

Give the major products obtained from heating each of the following ethers with one equivalent of HI:

a.

b.

c.

d.

e.

f.

Solution to 19a The reaction takes place by an S_N2 pathway because neither alkyl group will form a relatively stable carbocation. Iodide ion attacks the carbon of the ethyl group because otherwise it would have to attack a vinyl carbon, and vinyl carbons are generally not attacked by nucleophiles (Section 8.7). Thus, the major products are ethyl iodide and an enol that immediately rearranges to an aldehyde (Section 6.7).

10.7 NUCLEOPHILIC SUBSTITUTION REACTIONS OF EPOXIDES

We have seen that an alkene can be converted into an **epoxide** by a peroxyacid (Section 4.10)

NUCLEOPHILIC SUBSTITUTION: NEUTRAL OR BASIC CONDITIONS

> picks up a proton from the solvent or from added acid

$$CH_3CH-CH_2 + CH_3\ddot{O}:^- \longrightarrow CH_3CHCH_2OCH_3 \xrightarrow[\text{or}]{\text{CH}_3\text{OH}} CH_3CHCH_2OCH_3$$

- The C—O bond does not begin to break until the carbon is attacked by the nucleophile. The nucleophile is more likely to attack the *less substituted* carbon because it is less sterically hindered.
- The alkoxide ion picks up a proton from the solvent or from an acid added after the reaction is over.

Thus, the site of nucleophilic attack on an unsymmetrical epoxide under neutral or basic conditions (when the epoxide *is not* protonated) is different from the site of nucleophilic attack under acidic conditions (when the epoxide *is* protonated).

$$CH_3CH-CH_2$$

> site of nucleophilic attack under acidic conditions

> site of nucleophilic attack under basic or neutral conditions

Under acidic conditions, the nucleophile preferentially attacks the most substituted ring carbon.

Under basic conditions, the nucleophile preferentially attacks the less sterically hindered ring carbon.

Epoxides are useful reagents because they can react with a wide variety of nucleophiles, leading to the formation of a wide variety of products.

$$H_2C-C\underset{CH_3}{\overset{CH_3}{|}} + CH_3C\equiv C^- \longrightarrow CH_3C\equiv CCH_2\underset{CH_3}{\overset{O^-}{C}}CH_3 \xrightarrow{HCl} CH_3C\equiv CCH_2\underset{CH_3}{\overset{OH}{C}}CH_3$$

$$CH_3CH-CH_2 + CH_3NH_2 \longrightarrow CH_3CHCH_2\overset{+}{N}H_2CH_3 \longrightarrow CH_3CHCH_2NHCH_3$$

Epoxides also are important in biological processes, because they are reactive enough to be attacked by nucleophiles under the conditions found in living systems (Section 15.20).

Notice that the reaction of cyclohexene oxide with a nucleophile leads to trans products because the S_N2 reaction involves back-side attack. The reaction forms two new asymmetric centers, so back-side attack forms two stereoisomers.

$$+ CH_3O^- \longrightarrow \quad OCH_3 \quad + \quad OCH_3 \quad \xrightarrow{HCl} \quad OH \quad OCH_3 \quad + \quad OCH_3 \quad OH$$

chem Tutorial:
place Ring opening of epoxides

PROBLEM 20◆

Give the major product of each of the following reactions:

a. $H_2C-C\underset{CH_3}{\overset{CH_3}{|}} \xrightarrow[\text{CH}_3\text{OH}]{\text{HCl}}$

b. $H_2C-C\underset{CH_3}{\overset{CH_3}{|}} \xrightarrow[\text{CH}_3\text{OH}]{\text{CH}_3\text{O}^-}$

c. $H-C\underset{H_3C}{-}C\underset{CH_3}{-}CH_3 \xrightarrow[\text{CH}_3\text{OH}]{\text{HCl}}$

d. $H-C\underset{H_3C}{-}C\underset{CH_3}{-}CH_3 \xrightarrow[\text{CH}_3\text{OH}]{\text{CH}_3\text{O}^-}$

> **PROBLEM 21◆**
>
> Would you expect the reactivity of a five-membered ring ether such as tetrahydrofuran (Table 10.2) to be more similar to the reactivity of an epoxide or to the reactivity of a noncyclic ether?

10.8 AMINES DO NOT UNDERGO SUBSTITUTION OR ELIMINATION REACTIONS

We have seen that alcohols and ethers are much less reactive than alkyl halides in substitution and elimination reactions. **Amines** are even *less reactive*. The relative reactivities of an alkyl fluoride (the least reactive of the alkyl halides because it has the poorest leaving group), an alcohol, an ether, and an amine can be appreciated by comparing the pK_a values of the conjugate acids of their leaving groups, recalling that the weaker the acid, the stronger its conjugate base and the poorer the base is as a leaving group. The leaving group of an amine ($^-NH_2$) is such a strong base that amines cannot undergo substitution or elimination reactions.

relative reactivities

The stronger the base, the poorer it is as a leaving group.

most reactive	RCH_2F	>	RCH_2OH	>	RCH_2OR	>	RCH_2NH_2	least reactive
	HF		H_2O		ROH		NH_3	
	$pK_a = 3.2$		$pK_a = 15.7$		$pK_a \sim 16$		$pK_a = 36$	

Protonation of the amino group makes it a better leaving group, but not nearly as good as a protonated alcohol, which is 13 pK_a units more acidic than a protonated amine.

$$CH_3CH_2\overset{+}{O}H_2 \quad > \quad CH_3CH_2\overset{+}{N}H_3$$
$$pK_a = -2.4 \qquad\qquad pK_a = 11.2$$

Therefore, unlike the leaving group of a protonated alcohol, the leaving group of a protonated amine cannot be replaced by a halide ion (Section 10.1). Protonated amino groups also cannot be replaced by strongly basic nucleophiles, such as HO^-, because the nucleophile would react immediately with the acidic hydrogen of the $^+NH_3$ group and thereby be converted to water, which is a poor nucleophile.

$$CH_3CH_2\overset{+}{N}H_3 \quad + \quad HO^- \quad \rightleftharpoons \quad CH_3CH_2NH_2 \quad + \quad H_2O$$

Although amines cannot undergo substitution or elimination reactions, they are extremely important organic compounds. The lone pair on the nitrogen atom allows an amine to act as both a base and as a nucleophile.

Amines are the most common organic bases. We have seen that protonated amines have pK_a values of about 11 (Section 1.18) and that protonated anilines have pK_a values of about 5 (Section 7.9). Neutral amines have very high pK_a values. For example, the pK_a of methylamine is 40.

$CH_3CH_2CH_2\overset{+}{N}H_3$	$CH_3\overset{+}{N}H_2$ $\mid$ CH_3	$CH_3CH_2\overset{+}{N}H$ $\mid$ CH_2CH_3 (with CH_2CH_3)	benzene-$\overset{+}{N}H_3$	CH_3-benzene-$\overset{+}{N}H_3$	CH_3NH_2
$pK_a = 10.8$	$pK_a = 10.9$	$pK_a = 11.1$	$pK_a = 4.58$	$pK_a = 5.07$	$pK_a = 40$

Amines react as nucleophiles in a wide variety of reactions. For example, they react as nucleophiles with alkyl halides in S_N2 reactions.

an S_N2 reaction

$$CH_3CH_2Br \quad + \quad CH_3NH_2 \quad \longrightarrow \quad CH_3CH_2\overset{+}{N}H_2CH_3 \quad + \quad Br^-$$

We will see that they also react as nucleophiles with a wide variety of carbonyl compounds (Sections 17.8–17.10 and 18.8).

 Alkaloids

Alkaloids are amines found in the leaves, bark, roots, or seeds of many plants. Examples include caffeine (found in tea leaves, coffee beans, and cola nuts), nicotine (found in tobacco leaves), and cocaine (obtained from the coca bush in the rainforest areas of Colombia, Peru, and Bolivia). Ephedrine, a bronchodilator, is an alkaloid obtained from *Ephedra sinica*, a plant found in China. Morphine is an alkaloid obtained from opium, a milky fluid exuded by a species of poppy (Section 31.3).

ephedrine

caffeine   nicotine   cocaine   morphine

PROBLEM 22

Why can a halide ion such as Br^- be a nucleophile in an S_N2 reaction with a protonated primary alcohol, but not with a protonated primary amine?

10.9 QUATERNARY AMMONIUM HYDROXIDES UNDERGO ELIMINATION REACTIONS

The leaving group of a **quaternary ammonium ion** has about the same leaving tendency as a protonated amino group, but it does not have an acidic hydrogen that would protonate a basic reactant. A quaternary ammonium ion therefore can undergo an elimination reaction with a strong base. The reaction of a quaternary ammonium ion with hydroxide ion is known as a **Hofmann elimination reaction**. The leaving group in a Hofmann elimination reaction is a tertiary amine. Because a tertiary amine is a relatively poor leaving group, the reaction requires heat.

$$CH_3CH_2CH_2\overset{\overset{CH_3}{|}}{\underset{\underset{CH_3}{|}}{N}}CH_3 \quad HO^- \xrightarrow{\Delta} \quad CH_3CH{=}CH_2 \; + \; \overset{\overset{CH_3}{|}}{\underset{\underset{CH_3}{|}}{:N}}CH_3 \; + \; H_2O$$

A Hofmann elimination reaction is an E2 reaction, which, as you recall, is a concerted, one-step reaction: the proton and the tertiary amine are removed in the same step (Section 9.1). Very little substitution product is formed.

MECHANISM FOR THE HOFMANN ELIMINATION

$$CH_3CH{-}CH_2{-}\overset{\overset{CH_3}{|}}{\underset{\underset{CH_3}{|}}{N}}CH_3 \longrightarrow CH_3CH{=}CH_2 \; + \; \overset{\overset{CH_3}{|}}{\underset{\underset{CH_3}{|}}{:N}}CH_3 \; + \; H_2O$$

$$HO\overset{..}{\underset{..}{:}}$$

August Wilhelm von Hofmann (1818–1892) *was born in Germany. He initially studied law but then switched to chemistry. He founded the German Chemical Society and was a key figure in the development of the German dye industry. Hofmann taught at the Royal College of Chemistry in London for 20 years and then returned to Germany to teach at the University of Berlin. Married four times (and left a widower three times), he had 11 children.*

The tertiary amine is attached to the α-carbon, so the adjacent carbon, from which the proton is removed, is the β-carbon. If the quaternary ammonium ion has more than one β-carbon, the major alkene product is the one obtained by removing a proton from the β-carbon bonded to the *greater number* of hydrogens. In the following reaction, the major alkene product is obtained by removing a proton from the β-carbon bonded to three hydrogens, and the minor alkene product results from removing a proton from the β-carbon bonded to two hydrogens.

In a Hofmann elimination reaction, the proton is removed from the β-carbon bonded to the most hydrogens.

$$\boxed{β\text{-carbon}} \quad \boxed{β\text{-carbon}}$$

$$CH_3CHCH_2CH_2CH_3 \xrightarrow{\Delta} CH_2=CHCH_2CH_2CH_3 + CH_3CH=CHCH_2CH_3 + CH_3\overset{+}{N}CH_3 + H_2O$$

CH₃NCH₃   1-pentene   2-pentene   CH₃
 CH₃ HO⁻   **major product**   **minor product**   **trimethylamine**

PROBLEM 23 ♦

Give the major products of the following reaction:

$$CH_3CHCH_2\overset{+}{N}CH_2CH_2CH_3 \xrightarrow{\Delta}$$

with CH₃ above and CH₃ CH₃ HO⁻ below

PROBLEM 24 ♦

What are the minor products in the preceding Hofmann elimination reaction?

PROBLEM 25 ♦

What is the difference between the reaction that occurs when isopropyltrimethylammonium hydroxide is heated and the reaction that occurs when 2-bromopropane is treated with hydroxide ion?

We have seen that in an E2 reaction of an alkyl chloride, alkyl bromide, or alkyl iodide, the proton is removed from the β-carbon bonded to the *fewest* hydrogens (*Zaitsev's rule*; see Section 9.2). Now, however, we see that in an E2 reaction of a quaternary ammonium ion, the proton is removed from the β-carbon bonded to the *most* hydrogens (*anti-Zaitsev elimination*).

Quaternary amines violate Zaitsev's rule for the same reason that alkyl fluorides violate it (Section 9.2). Alkyl halides, other than alkyl fluorides, have relatively good leaving groups that immediately start to depart when hydroxide ion starts to remove the proton, forming a transition state with an *alkene-like* structure. The proton is removed from the β-carbon bonded to the *fewest hydrogens* in order to achieve the most stable *alkene-like* transition state.

Quaternary ammonium ions and alkyl fluorides have poorer (more basic) leaving groups that do not start to leave when hydroxide ion starts to remove a proton. Therefore, a partial negative charge builds up on the carbon from which the proton is being removed, giving the transition state a *carbanion-like* structure (Section 9.2). The proton is removed from the β-carbon bonded to the *most hydrogens* in order to achieve the most stable *carbanion-like* transition state. (Recall that primary carbanions are more stable than secondary carbanions, which are more stable than tertiary carbanions.) Steric factors also favor anti-Zaitsev elimination. Because the Hofmann elimination reaction occurs in an anti-Zaitsev manner, anti-Zaitsev elimination is also known as *Hofmann elimination.*

PROBLEM 26◆

Give the major products of each of the following reactions:

a. $\xrightarrow{\Delta}$ **b.**   H₃C—N⁺(CH₃)₃   HO⁻ $\xrightarrow{\Delta}$ **c.** $\xrightarrow{\Delta}$

A Useful Bad-Tasting Compound

Bitrex, a quaternary ammonium salt, is nontoxic and one of the most bitter-tasting substances known. It is used to encourage deer to look elsewhere for food; it is put on the backs of animals to keep them from biting one another and on children's fingers to persuade them to stop sucking their thumbs or biting their fingernails; and it is added to toxic substances to keep them from being ingested accidentally.

For a quaternary ammonium ion to undergo an elimination reaction, the counterion must be hydroxide ion, because a strong base is needed to remove the proton from the β-carbon. Halide ions are weak bases, so quaternary ammonium *halides* cannot undergo Hofmann elimination reactions. However, a quaternary ammonium *halide* can be converted into a quaternary ammonium *hydroxide* by treatment with silver oxide and water. The silver halide precipitates, and the halide ion is replaced by hydroxide ion. The compound can now undergo an elimination reaction.

$$2\ \underset{\underset{R}{|}}{\overset{\overset{R}{|}}{R-\overset{+}{N}-R}}\ I^- \ +\ Ag_2O\ +\ H_2O\ \longrightarrow\ 2\ \underset{\underset{R}{|}}{\overset{\overset{R}{|}}{R-\overset{+}{N}-R}}\ HO^-\ +\ 2\ AgI\downarrow$$

PROBLEM 27   **SOLVED**

Describe a synthesis for each of the following compounds, using the given starting material and any necessary reagents:

a. $CH_3CH_2CH_2CH_2NH_2 \longrightarrow CH_3CH_2CH=CH_2$

b. $CH_3CH_2CH_2\underset{\underset{Br}{|}}{C}HCH_3 \longrightarrow CH_3CH_2CH_2CH=CH_2$

c. $\longrightarrow CH_2=CH-CH=CH_2$

Solution to 27a   Although an amine cannot undergo an elimination reaction, a quaternary ammonium hydroxide can. The amine, therefore, must first be converted into a quaternary ammonium iodide by reacting with excess methyl iodide (see Problem 13 on p. 346).

Treatment with aqueous silver oxide forms the quaternary ammonium hydroxide. Heat is required for the elimination reaction.

$$CH_3CH_2CH_2CH_2NH_2 \xrightarrow[\text{K}_2\text{CO}_3]{\text{CH}_3\text{I} \atop \text{excess}} CH_3CH_2CH_2CH_2\overset{+}{N}(CH_3)_3 \xrightarrow[\text{H}_2\text{O}]{\text{Ag}_2\text{O}} CH_3CH_2CH_2CH_2\overset{+}{N}(CH_3)_3 \xrightarrow{\Delta} CH_3CH_2CH{=}CH_2 + H_2O$$
$$\qquad\qquad\qquad\qquad\qquad\qquad\qquad I^- \qquad\qquad\qquad\qquad\qquad\qquad HO^-$$

Early organic chemists used the Hofmann elimination reaction as the last step of a process known as a Hofmann degradation—a method used to identify amines. In a *Hofmann degradation*, an amine is methylated with excess methyl iodide, treated with silver oxide to convert the quaternary ammonium iodide to a quaternary ammonium hydroxide, and then heated to allow it to undergo a Hofmann elimination. Once the alkene is identified, working backward gives the structure of the amine.

> **PROBLEM 28◆**
>
> Identify the amine in each case:
> **a.** 4-Methyl-2-pentene is obtained from the Hofmann degradation of a primary amine.
> **b.** 2-Methyl-1-3-butadiene is obtained from two successive Hofmann degradations of a secondary amine.

10.10 PHASE-TRANSFER CATALYSIS

A problem that often arises in the laboratory is finding a solvent that will dissolve all the reactants needed for a given reaction. For example, if we want cyanide ion to react with 1-bromohexane, we must find a way of mixing sodium cyanide, an ionic compound soluble only in water, with the alkyl halide, which is insoluble in water. If we mix an aqueous solution of sodium cyanide with a solution of the alkyl halide in a nonpolar solvent, there will be two distinct phases—an aqueous phase and a nonpolar phase—because the two solutions are immiscible. How, then, can a reaction between sodium cyanide and 1-bromohexane take place?

$$CH_3CH_2CH_2CH_2CH_2CH_2Br + {}^-C{\equiv}N \xrightarrow{?} CH_3CH_2CH_2CH_2CH_2CH_2C{\equiv}N + Br^-$$
1-bromohexane

The two compounds will be able to react with each other if a catalytic amount of a **phase-transfer catalyst** is added to the reaction mixture.

phase-transfer
catalyst

$$CH_3CH_2CH_2CH_2CH_2CH_2Br + {}^-C{\equiv}N \xrightarrow{\text{R}_4\overset{+}{\text{N}} \text{HSO}_4{}^-} CH_3CH_2CH_2CH_2CH_2CH_2C{\equiv}N + Br^-$$

Quaternary ammonium salts are the most common phase-transfer catalysts. Because of their nonpolar alkyl groups, they are soluble in nonpolar solvents, and because of their charge, they are also soluble in water. Consequently, they can act as an intermediary between the two immiscible phases.

phase-transfer catalysts

$HSO_4{}^-$

$HSO_4{}^-$

$HSO_4{}^-$

tetrabutylammonium hydrogen sulfate

hexadecyltrimethylammonium hydrogen sulfate

benzyltriethylammonium hydrogen sulfate

When a phase-transfer catalyst such as tetrabutylammonium hydrogen sulfate passes into the nonpolar, organic phase, it must carry a counterion with it to balance its positive charge.

The counterion can be either its original counterion (hydrogen sulfate) or another ion that is present in the solution (in the example under discussion, it could be cyanide ion or Br^-). Because there is more cyanide ion than hydrogen sulfate or Br^- in the aqueous phase, the accompanying ion is more often going to be a cyanide ion. Once a cyanide ion has been carried into the organic phase, it can react with the alkyl halide. (When hydrogen sulfate or Br^- is transported into the organic phase, each is unreactive because each is a weak base and a poor nucleophile.) The quaternary ammonium ion will then pass back into the aqueous phase, carrying with it either hydrogen sulfate or bromide ion as a counterion. The reaction continues with the phase-transfer catalyst shuttling back and forth between the two phases. **Phase-transfer catalysis** has been successfully used in a wide variety of organic reactions.

Crown Ethers Can be Used as Phase-Transfer Catalysts

Crown ethers are cyclic compounds containing several ether linkages around a central cavity. A crown ether specifically binds certain metal ions or organic molecules, depending on the cavity's size. The crown ether is called the "host," and the species it binds is called the "guest." Because the ether linkages are chemically inert, the crown ether can bind the guest without reacting with it. The *crown–guest complex* is called an **inclusion compound**. Crown ethers are named [X]-crown-Y, where X is the total number of atoms in the ring and Y is the number of oxygen atoms in the ring. [15]-Crown-5 selectively binds Na^+ because that crown ether has a cavity diameter of 1.7 to 2.2 Å and Na^+ has an ionic diameter of 1.80 Å. Binding occurs through interaction of the positively charged ion with the lone-pair electrons of the oxygen atoms that point into the cavity.

Na^+
guest

**host
[15]-crown-5
ionic diameter = 1.80 Å
cavity diameter = 1.7–2.2 Å**

inclusion compound

Li^+ bound in [12]-crown-4 Na^+ bound in [15]-crown-5 K^+ bound in [18]-crown-6

[18]-Crown-6 has a high affinity for K^+, with an ionic diameter of 2.66 Å. Crown ethers are soluble in nonpolar solvents because the outside of the crown is composed primarily of C—H bonds. Therefore, the counterion of the potassium salt also will be in the nonpolar solvent, where it will be a powerful nucleophile because it will not be solvated.

[18]-crown-6 + KF ⟶ **K$^+$** **F$^-$**

powerful nucleophile

In this way, nucleophilic substitution reactions with alkyl halides, which are soluble only in nonpolar solvents, can readily take place.

The ability of a host to bind only certain guests is an example of **molecular recognition**, the recognition of one molecule for another as a result of specific interactions. Molecular recognition explains how enzymes recognize their substrates, how antibodies recognize antigens, how drugs recognize receptors, and many other biochemical processes. Only recently have chemists been able to design and synthesize organic molecules that exhibit molecular recognition, although the specificity of these synthetic compounds for their guests is generally less highly developed than the specificity exhibited by biological molecules.

Cl + K$^+$I$^-$ $\xrightarrow[\text{acetonitrile}]{\text{[18]-crown-6}}$ I

Br + O$^-$K$^+$ $\xrightarrow[\text{acetonitrile}]{\text{[18]-crown-6}}$

An Unusual Antibiotic

An antibiotic is a compound that interferes with the growth of microorganisms. Nonactin is a naturally occurring antibiotic that owes its biological activity to its ability to disrupt the carefully maintained levels of electrolytes inside and outside a cell. Normal cell function requires gradients between the concentrations of potassium and sodium ions inside the cell and those outside the cell. To achieve these gradients, potassium ions are pumped in and sodium ions are pumped out.

Nonactin disrupts one of these gradients by acting like a crown ether. Nonactin's diameter is such that it specifically binds potassium ions. (The eight oxygen atoms that point into the cavity and interact with K^+ are highlighted below.) The outside of nonactin is nonpolar, so it can easily transport K^+ ions out of the cell through the nonpolar cell membrane. The consequent decrease in the concentration of K^+ within the cell causes the bacterium to die.

nonactin

10.11 THIOLS, SULFIDES, AND SULFONIUM SALTS

Thiols are sulfur analogs of alcohols. They used to be called mercaptans because they form strong complexes with heavy metal cations such as arsenic and mercury (they capture mercury).

$$2 \text{ CH}_3\text{CH}_2\ddot{\text{S}}\text{H} + \text{Hg}^{2+} \longrightarrow \text{CH}_3\text{CH}_2\ddot{\text{S}}-\text{Hg}-\ddot{\text{S}}\text{CH}_2\text{CH}_3 + 2 \text{ H}^+$$

a thiol   **mercuric ion**

Thiols are named by adding the suffix "thiol" to the name of the parent hydrocarbon. If there is a second functional group in the molecule that is identified with a suffix, the SH group can be indicated by its substituent name, "mercapto." Like other substituent names, it is placed before the name of the parent hydrocarbon.

$$CH_3$$
$$|$$
CH_3CH_2SH   CH_3CH_2CH_2SH   CH_3CHCH_2CH_2SH   HSCH_2CH_2OH
ethanethiol   **1-propanethiol**   **3-methyl-1-butanethiol**   **2-mercaptoethanol**

Low-molecular-weight thiols are noted for their strong and pungent odors, such as the odors associated with onions, garlic, and skunks. Natural gas is completely odorless and can cause deadly explosions if a leak goes undetected. Therefore, a small amount of a thiol is added to natural gas to give it an odor so that gas leaks can be detected.

Sulfur atoms are larger than oxygen atoms, so the negative charge of the thiolate ion is spread over a larger volume of space than the charge of an alkoxide ion, causing the thiolate ion to be more stable. (Recall that the more stable the base, the stronger is its conjugate acid; Section 1.18.) Thiols, therefore, are stronger acids ($pK_a = 10$) than alcohols, and thiolate ions are weaker bases than alkoxide ions. The larger thiolate ions are less well solvated than alkoxide ions, so in protic solvents thiolate ions are better nucleophiles than alkoxide ions (Section 8.2).

$$CH_3-\ddot{S}\colon^- + CH_3CH_2-Br \xrightarrow{\text{CH}_3\text{OH}} CH_3-\ddot{S}-CH_2CH_3 + Br^-$$

Because sulfur is not as electronegative as oxygen, thiols are not good at hydrogen bonding. Consequently, they have weaker intermolecular attractions and, therefore, considerably lower boiling points than alcohols (Section 2.9). For example, the boiling point of CH_3CH_2OH is 78 °C, whereas the boiling point of CH_3CH_2SH is 37 °C.

The sulfur analogs of ethers are called **sulfides** or **thioethers**. Sulfur is an excellent nucleophile because its electron cloud is polarizable (Section 8.2). As a result, sulfides react readily with alkyl halides to form **sulfonium salts**, whereas ethers do not react with alkyl halides because oxygen is not as nucleophilic as sulfur and cannot accommodate a charge as well as sulfur can.

$$CH_3-\ddot{S}-CH_3 + CH_3-I \longrightarrow CH_3-\overset{+}{\underset{\ddot{}}{S}}-CH_3 \; I^-$$
$$\text{(with } CH_3 \text{ above S)}$$

dimethyl sulfide   **trimethylsulfonium iodide**
                              a sulfonium salt

Because it has a weakly basic leaving group, a sulfonium ion readily undergoes nucleophilic substitution reactions. Like other S_N2 reactions, the reaction works best if the group undergoing nucleophilic attack is a methyl group or a primary alkyl group. In Section 8.11, we saw that SAM, a biological methylating agent, is a sulfonium salt.

$$HO\colon^- + CH_3-\overset{+CH_3}{\underset{\ddot{}}{S}}-CH_3 \longrightarrow CH_3-\ddot{O}H + CH_3-\ddot{S}-CH_3$$

PROBLEM 29

Using an alkyl halide and a thiol as starting materials, how would you prepare the following compounds?

$$CH_3 \qquad\qquad\qquad CH_3$$
$$| \qquad\qquad\qquad\qquad |$$
a. CH_3SCCH_3 **c.** $CH_2{=}CHCHSCH_2CH_3$
$$|$$
$$CH_3$$

b.

d.

Mustard—A Chemical Warfare Agent

Chemical warfare occurred for the first time in 1915, when Germany released chlorine gas against French and British forces in the battle of Ypres. For the remainder of World War I, both sides used a variety of chemical agents as weapons. One of the more common was mustard, a reagent that produces blisters over the surface of the body. Mustard is a very reactive compound because its highly nucleophilic sulfur atom easily displaces a chloride ion by an intramolecular S_N2 reaction, forming a cyclic sulfonium salt that reacts rapidly with a nucleophile. The sulfonium salt is particularly reactive because of its strained three-membered ring and the excellent (positively charged) leaving group.

The blistering caused by mustard results from the high local concentrations of HCl produced when mustard comes into contact with water—or any other nucleophile—on skin or in lung tissue. Autopsies of soldiers killed by mustard in World War I—estimated to be about 400,000 in number—revealed that they had extremely low white blood cell counts and defects in bone marrow development, indicating profound effects on rapidly dividing cells. An international treaty in the 1980s banned the use of mustard and required that all stockpiles be destroyed.

Alkylating Agents as Cancer Drugs

The discovery that mustard had a profound effect on rapidly dividing cells suggested that it might be an effective antitumor agent. Therefore, chemists started looking for less reactive mustards that might be used clinically.

Because mustard forms a three-membered ring that can react rapidly with nucleophiles, its clinical reactivity is thought to be due to its ability to alkylate groups on the surface of DNA. Alkylating DNA can destroy it. Since cancer is characterized by the uncontrolled growth and proliferation of cells, a drug that destroys DNA can destroy tumors. The cancer drugs shown below are all biological alkyating agents—they attach an alkyl group to a nucleophile under physiological conditions.

Melphalan

Cyclophosphamide

Chloroambucil

Carmustine

PROBLEM 30◆

Why is Melphalan a good alkyating agent?

PROBLEM 31◆

The following three nitrogen mustards were studied for possible clinical use. One is used clinically, one was found to be too unreactive, and one was found to be too insoluble in water to be injected intravenously. Which is which? (*Hint:* Draw resonance contributors.)

PROBLEM 32

Mechlorethamine, the drug in Problem 31 that is in clinical use, is highly reactive and can be administered only by physicians who are experienced in its use. Explain why Cyclophosphamide, Carmustine, and Chloroambucil are less reactive alkylating agents.

SUMMARY

The leaving groups of **alcohols** and **ethers** are stronger bases than halide ions are, so alcohols and ethers are less reactive than alkyl halides and have to be "activated" before they can undergo a substitution or an elimination reaction. There are several ways to activate an alcohol, but only one way to activate an ether. **Epoxides** do not have to be activated, because ring strain increases their reactivity. **Sulfonate esters** and **sulfonium salts** have weakly basic leaving groups, so they undergo substitution reactions with ease.

Primary, secondary, and tertiary alcohols undergo nucleophilic substitution reactions with HI, HBr, and HCl to form alkyl halides. These are S_N1 reactions in the case of tertiary and secondary alcohols and S_N2 reactions in the case of primary alcohols. An alcohol can also be converted into an alkyl halide by phosphorus trihalides or thionyl chloride. These reagents convert the alcohol into an intermediate that has a leaving group easily displaced by a halide ion.

Converting an alcohol to a **sulfonate ester** is another way to activate an alcohol for subsequent reaction with a nucleophile. Because a sulfonic acid is a strong acid, its conjugate base is weak. Activating an alcohol by converting it to a sulfonate ester followed by reaction with a nucleophile forms a substitution product with a configuration opposite to that of the alcohol, whereas activating an alcohol by converting it to an alkyl halide followed by reaction with a nucleophile forms a substitution product with the same configuration as the alcohol.

An alcohol undergoes an elimination reaction if it is heated with an acid catalyst. **Dehydration** (elimination of a water molecule) is an E1 reaction in the case of secondary and tertiary alcohols and an E2 reaction in the case of primary alcohols. Tertiary alcohols are the easiest to dehydrate, and primary alcohols are the hardest. The major product is the more substituted alkene. If the alkene has stereoisomers, the stereoisomer in which the bulkiest groups are on opposite sides of the double bond predominates. E1 reactions form carbocation intermediates, so carbocation and **ring-expansion** (or **ring-contraction**) **rearrangements** can occur.

Chromic acid oxidizes secondary alcohols to ketones and primary alcohols to carboxylic acids. PCC oxidizes primary alcohols to aldehydes.

Ethers can undergo nucleophilic substitution reactions with HBr or HI; if departure of the leaving group creates a relatively stable carbocation, an S_N1 reaction occurs; otherwise, an S_N2 reaction occurs.

Epoxides undergo nucleophilic substitution reactions. Under basic conditions, the least sterically hindered carbon is attacked; under acidic conditions, the most substituted carbon is attacked.

Amines cannot undergo substitution or elimination reactions because their leaving groups ($^-NH_2, ^-NHR, ^-NR_2$) are very strong bases. Quaternary ammonium ions can undergo an E2 reaction known as a Hofmann elimination reaction with HO^- if they are heated. Hydroxide ion removes a proton from the β-carbon bonded to the most hydrogens.

Thiols are sulfur analogs of alcohols. They are stronger acids and have lower boiling points than alcohols. Thiolate ions are weaker bases and better nucleophiles in protic solvents than alkoxide ions. Sulfur analogs of ethers are called **sulfides** or **thioethers**. Sulfides react with alkyl halides to form **sulfonium salts**.

SUMMARY OF REACTIONS

1. Converting an *alcohol* into an *alkyl halide* (Sections 10.1 and 10.2)

$$ROH + HBr \xrightarrow{\Delta} RBr$$

$$ROH + HI \xrightarrow{\Delta} RI$$

$$ROH + HCl \xrightarrow{\Delta} RCl$$

relative rate: tertiary > secondary > primary

$$ROH + PBr_3 \xrightarrow{\text{pyridine}} RBr$$

$$ROH + PCl_3 \xrightarrow{\text{pyridine}} RCl$$

$$ROH + SOCl_2 \xrightarrow{\text{pyridine}} RCl$$

only for primary and secondary alcohols

2. Converting an alcohol into a *sulfonate ester* (Section 10.3)

$$ROH + Cl-\overset{\overset{O}{\|}}{\underset{\underset{O}{\|}}{S}}-R' \xrightarrow{\text{pyridine}} RO-\overset{\overset{O}{\|}}{\underset{\underset{O}{\|}}{S}}-R' + HCl$$

3. Converting an *activated alcohol* (an alkyl halide or a sulfonate ester) into a *compound with a new group bonded to the sp*^{3} *carbon* (Section 10.3)

$$RBr + Y^- \longrightarrow RY + Br^-$$

$$RO-\overset{\overset{O}{\|}}{\underset{\underset{O}{\|}}{S}}-R' + Y^- \longrightarrow RY + {}^-O-\overset{\overset{O}{\|}}{\underset{\underset{O}{\|}}{S}}-R'$$

4. Elimination reactions of alcohols: dehydration (Section 10.4)

$$-\overset{\overset{\big|}{}}{\underset{\underset{H}{\big|}}{C}}-\overset{\overset{\big|}{}}{\underset{\underset{OH}{\big|}}{C}}- \underset{\Delta}{\overset{H_2SO_4}{\rightleftharpoons}} \quad C=C \quad + H_2O$$

$$-\overset{\overset{\big|}{}}{\underset{\underset{H}{\big|}}{C}}-\overset{\overset{\big|}{}}{\underset{\underset{OH}{\big|}}{C}}- \xrightarrow[\text{pyridine, 0 °C}]{POCl_3} \quad C=C \quad + H_2O$$

relative rate: tertiary > secondary > primary

5. Oxidation of alcohols (Section 10.5)

primary alcohols $RCH_2OH \xrightarrow{H_2CrO_4} \left[\overset{\overset{O}{\|}}{RCH}\right] \xrightarrow[\text{oxidation}]{\text{further}} \overset{\overset{O}{\|}}{RCOH}$

$RCH_2OH \xrightarrow[CH_2Cl_2]{PCC} \overset{\overset{O}{\|}}{RCH}$

secondary alcohols $\overset{OH}{\underset{\big|}{RCHR}} \xrightarrow[H_2SO_4]{Na_2Cr_2O_7} \overset{\overset{O}{\|}}{RCR}$

6. Nucleophilic substitution reactions of ethers (Section 10.6)

$$ROR' + HX \xrightarrow{\Delta} ROH + R'X$$

HX = HBr or HI

7. Nucleophilic substitution reactions of *epoxides* (Section 10.7)

$$H_3C \underset{H_3C}{\overset{O}{\diagdown}} C - CH_2 \xrightarrow[\text{CH}_3\text{OH}]{\text{HCl}} CH_3\underset{CH_3}{\overset{OCH_3}{\vert}}CCH_2OH$$

under acidic conditions, the nucleophile attacks the more substituted ring carbon

$$H_3C \underset{H_3C}{\overset{O}{\diagdown}} C - CH_2 \xrightarrow[\text{CH}_3\text{OH}]{\text{CH}_3\text{O}^-} CH_3\underset{CH_3}{\overset{OH}{\vert}}CCH_2OCH_3$$

under neutral or basic conditions, the nucleophile attacks the less sterically hindered ring carbon

8. Elimination reactions of *quaternary ammonium hydroxides*; the proton is removed from the β-carbon bonded to the most hydrogens (Section 10.9).

$$RCH_2CH_2\underset{\underset{\text{CH}_3}{\vert}}{\overset{\overset{\text{CH}_3}{\vert}}{\overset{+}{N}}}CH_3 \quad\underset{HO^-}{} \xrightarrow[\text{elimination}]{\Delta \atop \text{Hofmann}} RCH = CH_2 + \underset{\underset{\text{CH}_3}{\vert}}{\overset{\overset{\text{CH}_3}{\vert}}{N}}CH_3 + H_2O$$

9. Reactions of thiols, sulfides, and sulfonium salts (Section 10.11)

$$2\,RSH + Hg^{2+} \longrightarrow RS-Hg-SR + 2\,H^+$$

$$RS^- + R'-Br \longrightarrow RSR' + Br^-$$

$$R-S-R + R'I \longrightarrow R-\underset{+}{\overset{\overset{R'}{\vert}}{S}}-R \quad I^-$$

$$R-\underset{+}{\overset{\overset{R}{\vert}}{S}}-R + Y^- \longrightarrow RY + R-S-R$$

KEY TERMS

alcohol (p. 411)
alkaloid (p. 435)
alkyl tosylate (p. 417)
alkyl triflate (p. 418)
crown ether (p. 439)
dehydration (p. 419)
epoxide (p. 430)

ether (p. 427)
Hofmann elimination reaction (p. 435)
inclusion compound (p. 439)
molecular recognition (p. 440)
phase-transfer catalysis (p. 438)
phase-transfer catalyst (p. 438)
quaternary ammonium ion (p. 435)

ring-expansion rearrangement (p. 421)
sulfide (p. 441)
sulfonate ester (p. 416)
sulfonium salt (p. 410)
thioether (p. 441)
thiol (p. 440)

PROBLEMS

33. Give the product of each of the following reactions:

a. $CH_3CH_2CH_2OH \xrightarrow[\text{2. } CH_3\overset{O}{\overset{\|}{C}}O^-]{\text{1. methanesulfonyl chloride}}$

b. $CH_3CH_2CH_2CH_2OH + PBr_3 \xrightarrow[\text{pyridine}]{}$

c. $CH_3\underset{\underset{\text{CH}_3}{\vert}}{CH}CH_2CH_2OH \xrightarrow[\text{2. }\bigcirc\!-O^-]{\text{1. } p\text{-toluenesulfonyl chloride}}$

d. $CH_3CH_2CH - C\underset{O}{\overset{CH_3}{\diagup}}\overset{}{\underset{CH_3}{\diagdown}} + CH_3OH \xrightarrow{\text{HCl}}$

e. $CH_3CH_2CH - C\underset{O}{\overset{CH_3}{\diagup}}\overset{}{\underset{CH_3}{\diagdown}} + CH_3OH \xrightarrow{CH_3O^-}$

f. $CH_3CH_2CH_2CH_2OH \xrightarrow[\Delta]{H_2SO_4}$

g. $CH_3\underset{\underset{\text{CH}_3}{\vert}}{CH}CH_2CH_2OH \xrightarrow[\text{pyridine}]{SOCl_2}$

34. Indicate which alcohol in each pair will undergo dehydration more rapidly when heated with H_2SO_4.

a. (structure: benzyl CH_2OH) or (structure: CH_2CH_2OH)

d. (structure: cyclohexyl with OH) or (structure: phenyl with OH)

b. (cyclohexanol) or (cyclohexenol)

e. (structure: phenyl-CH_2CH_2-OH) or (structure: phenyl with OH)

c. (structure: cyclohexyl CH_3/OH) or (structure: cyclohexyl CH_3/OH)

35. Identify **A-D**.

(cyclohexene) $\xrightarrow[H_2O]{Br_2}$ **A** $\xrightarrow{HO^-}$ **B** $\longrightarrow$ **C** + **D**

36. Starting with (*R*)-1-deuterio-1-propanol, how could you prepare:
  a. (*S*)-1-deuterio-1-propanol?   **b.** (*S*)-1-deuterio-1-methoxypropane?   **c.** (*R*)-1-deuterio-1-methoxypropane?

37. What alkenes would you expect to be obtained from the acid-catalyzed dehydration of 1-hexanol?

38. Give the major product(s) of each of the following reactions:

a. $CH_3\overset{CH_3}{\underset{CH_3}{C}}OCH_2CH_3$ + HBr $\xrightarrow{\Delta}$

f. (spiro epoxide cyclohexane) $\xrightarrow[CH_3OH]{CH_3O^-}$

b. $CH_3\overset{}{\underset{CH_3}{CH}}CH_2OCH_3$ + HI $\xrightarrow{\Delta}$

g. CH_3-(cyclohexyl)-OH $\xrightarrow[\text{2. NaC}\equiv\text{N}]{\text{1. TsCl/pyridine}}$

c. $CH_3CH_2\overset{CH_3}{\underset{OH}{CH}}\overset{}{\underset{CH_3}{C}}CH_3$ $\xrightarrow[\Delta]{H_2SO_4}$

h. (cyclohexyl with OH and CH_3) $\xrightarrow{H_2CrO_4}$

d. (cyclohexyl)CH_2CH_2OH $\xrightarrow{H_2CrO_4}$

i. $CH_3\overset{}{\underset{CH_3}{CH}}CH_2\overset{CH_3}{\underset{CH_3}{\overset{+}{N}}}CH_2CH_3$ $\xrightarrow{\Delta}$ HO^-

e. (spiro epoxide cyclohexane) $\xrightarrow[CH_3OH]{HCl}$

39. When heated with H_2SO_4, both 3,3-dimethyl-2-butanol and 2,3-dimethyl-2-butanol are dehydrated to form 2,3-dimethyl-2-butene. Which alcohol dehydrates more rapidly?

40. An unknown alcohol with a molecular formula of $C_7H_{14}O$ was oxidized to an aldehyde with PCC. When an acidic solution of the alcohol was distilled, two alkenes were formed. The alkene formed in greater yield was determined to be 1-methylcyclohexene. The other alcohol formed the original unknown alcohol when treated with BH_3/THF followed by H_2O_2, HO^-, H_2O. Identify the unknown alcohol.

41. Explain why the acid-catalyzed dehydration of an alcohol is a reversible reaction, whereas the base-promoted dehydrohalogenation of an alkyl halide is an irreversible reaction.

42. Propose a mechanism for the following reaction:

$CH_3\overset{O}{\overset{\diagup\diagdown}{CHCH}}-CH_2$ + CH_3O^- $\xrightarrow{CH_3OH}$ $CH_3\overset{O}{\overset{\diagup\diagdown}{CH}}-CHCH_2OCH_3$ + Cl^-
$\quad\underset{Cl}{|}$

43. A Hofmann degradation of a primary amine forms 2-methyl-3-butene. Identify the amine.

44. Explain why (*S*)-2-butanol forms a racemic mixture when it is heated in sulfuric acid.

45. Using the given starting material, any necessary inorganic reagents, and any carbon-containing compounds with no more than two carbons, indicate how the following syntheses could be carried out:

a.

b. $CH_3CH_2CH_2CH_2Br \longrightarrow CH_3CH_2CH_2\overset{\overset{\displaystyle O}{\|}}{C}OH$

46. When piperidine undergoes the series of reactions indicated below, 1,4-pentadiene is obtained as the product. When the four different methyl-substituted piperidines undergo the same series of reactions, each forms a different diene: 1,5-hexadiene, 1,4-pentadiene, 2-methyl-1,4-pentadiene, and 3-methyl-1,4-pentadiene. Which methyl-substituted piperidine yields which diene?

47. When 3-methyl-2-butanol is heated with concentrated HBr, a rearranged product is obtained. When 2-methyl-1-propanol reacts under the same conditions, a rearranged product is not obtained. Explain.

48. When the following seven-membered ring alcohol is dehydrated, three alkenes are formed. Propose a mechanism for their formation.

49. How could you synthesize isopropyl propyl ether, using isopropyl alcohol as the only carbon-containing reagent?

50. Ethylene oxide reacts readily with HO$^-$ because of the strain in the three-membered ring. Explain why cyclopropane, a compound with approximately the same amount of strain, does not react with HO$^-$.

51. Which of the following ethers would be obtained in greatest yield directly from alcohols?

52. Propose a mechanism for each of the following reactions:

53. Triethylene glycol is one of the products obtained from the reaction of ethylene oxide and hydroxide ion. Propose a mechanism for its formation.

$$H_2\overset{O}{\overset{\diagup\diagdown}{C-CH_2}} + HO^- \longrightarrow HOCH_2CH_2OCH_2CH_2OCH_2CH_2OH$$

triethylene glycol

54. Give the major product expected from the reaction of 2-ethyloxirane with each of the following reagents:
   a. 0.1 M HCl   **b.** CH$_3$OH/HCl   **c.** 0.1 M NaOH   **d.** CH$_3$OH/CH$_3$O$^-$

55. a. Propose a mechanism for the following reaction:

b. A small amount of a product containing a six-membered ring is also formed. Give the structure of that product.
c. Why is so little six-membered ring product formed?

56. When ethyl ether is heated with excess HI for several hours, the only organic product obtained is ethyl iodide. Explain why ethyl alcohol is not obtained as a product.

57. Propose a mechanism for the following reaction:

58. An ion with a positively charged nitrogen atom in a three-membered ring is called an aziridinium ion. The following aziridinium ion reacts with sodium methoxide to form compounds A and B:

an aziridinium ion

If a small amount of aqueous Br_2 is added to A, the reddish color of Br_2 persists, but the color disappears when Br_2 is added to B. When the aziridinium ion reacts with methanol, only A is formed. Identify A and B.

59. Propose a mechanism for each of the following reactions:

a.

b.

c.

60. Which of the following reactions occurs most rapidly? Why?

61. The following reaction takes place several times faster than the rate of reaction of 2-chlorobutane with HO^-.

$$(CH_3CH_2)_2\ddot{N}-CH_2CHCH_2CH_3 \xrightarrow{HO^-} (CH_3CH_2)_2\ddot{N}-CHCH_2CH_3$$
$$\underset{Cl}{|} \qquad\qquad\qquad \underset{CH_2OH}{|}$$

a. Explain the enhanced reaction rate.
b. Explain why the OH group in the product is not bonded to the carbon that was bonded to the Cl group in the reactant.

62. A vicinal diol has OH groups on adjacent carbons. The dehydration of a vicinal diol is accompanied by a rearrangement called the pinacol rearrangement. Propose a mechanism for this reaction.

63. Although 2-methyl-1,2-propanediol is an unsymmetrical vicinal diol, only one product is obtained when it is dehydrated in an acidic solution.
  a. What is this product?
  b. Why is only one product formed?

64. What product is obtained when the following vicinal diol is heated in an acidic solution?

65. Two stereoisomers are obtained from the reaction of cyclopentene oxide and dimethylamine. The *R,R*-isomer is used in the manufacture of eclanamine, an antidepressant. What other isomer is obtained?

R,R-**isomer**   **eclanamine**

66. Propose a mechanism for each of the following reactions:

a.

b.

67. Triethylenemelamine (TEM) is an antitumor agent. Its activity is due to its ability to cross-link DNA.

triethylenemelamine (TEM)

  a. Explain why it can be used only under slightly acidic conditions.
  b. Explain why it can cross-link DNA.

11

Organometallic Compounds

CH₃Cl   **CH₃Li**

ALKYL HALIDES, ALCOHOLS, AND ETHERS ALL CONTAIN A CARBON THAT IS BONDED to a *more* electronegative atom. The carbon, therefore, is *electrophilic* and reacts with a nucleophile.

A carbon is an electrophile if it is attached to a more electronegative atom.

But what if you wanted a carbon to react with an electrophile? For that, you would need a compound with a nucleophilic carbon. To be *nucleophilic*, carbon would have to be bonded to a *less* electronegative atom.

A carbon is a nucleophile if it is attached to a less electronegative atom.

Because metals are less electronegative than carbon (Table 11.1), one way to create a nucleophilic carbon is to bond the carbon to a metal. A compound that contains a carbon–metal bond is called an **organometallic compound**. The electrostatic potential maps on the top of this page show that the carbon attached to the halogen in the alkyl halide is an electrophile (it is blue-green), whereas the carbon attached to the metal in the organometallic compound is a nucleophile (it is red).

Many metals can be attached to carbon to form an organometallic compound.

$$\overset{\delta-}{C}—\overset{\delta+}{Mg} \qquad \overset{\delta-}{C}—\overset{\delta+}{Li} \qquad \overset{\delta-}{C}—\overset{\delta+}{Cu} \qquad \overset{\delta-}{C}—\overset{\delta+}{Cd} \qquad \overset{\delta-}{C}—\overset{\delta+}{Pd}$$

$$\overset{\delta-}{C}—\overset{\delta+}{Zn} \qquad \overset{\delta-}{C}—\overset{\delta+}{Al} \qquad \overset{\delta-}{C}—\overset{\delta+}{Pb} \qquad \overset{\delta-}{C}—\overset{\delta+}{Hg} \qquad \overset{\delta-}{C}—\overset{\delta+}{Ru}$$

Table 11.1   The Electronegativities of Some of the Elements[a]

IA	IIA			IB	IIB	IIIA	IVA	VA	VIA	VIIA
H 2.1										
Li 1.0	Be 1.5					B 2.0	C 2.5	N 3.0	O 3.5	F 4.0
Na 0.9	Mg 1.2					Al 1.5	Si 1.8	P 2.1	S 2.5	Cl 3.0
K 0.8	Ca 1.0	Co 1.7	Ni 1.7	Cu 1.8	Zn 1.7	Ga 1.8	Ge 2.0			Br 2.8
		Rh 2.4	Pd 2.4	Ag 1.8	Cd 1.5		Sn 1.7			I 2.5
					Hg 1.5		Pb 1.6			

[a]From the scale devised by Linus Pauling

The name of an organometallic compound usually begins with the name of the alkyl group, followed by the name of the metal.

CH_3CH_2MgBr	$CH_3CH_2CH_2CH_2Li$	$(CH_3CH_2CH_2)_2Cd$	$(CH_3CH_2)_4Pb$
ethylmagnesium bromide	**butyllithium**	**dipropylcadmium**	**tetraethyllead**

11.1 ORGANOLITHIUM AND ORGANOMAGNESIUM COMPOUNDS

Two of the most common organometallic compounds are *organolithium compounds* and *organomagnesium compounds*. **Organolithium compounds** are prepared by adding lithium to an alkyl halide in a nonpolar solvent such as hexane.

$$CH_3CH_2CH_2CH_2Br + 2\,Li \xrightarrow{\text{hexane}} CH_3CH_2CH_2CH_2Li + LiBr$$
1-bromobutane   **butyllithium**

chlorobenzene $+ 2\,Li \xrightarrow{\text{hexane}}$ phenyllithium $-Li + LiCl$

chlorobenzene   **phenyllithium**

Organomagnesium compounds, commonly called **Grignard reagents** after their discoverer, are prepared by adding an alkyl halide to magnesium shavings being stirred in ether—usually diethyl ether or tetrahydrofuran (THF)—under anhydrous conditions. The reaction inserts magnesium between the carbon and the halogen.

cyclohexyl $-Br + Mg \xrightarrow{\text{diethyl ether}}$ cyclohexyl $-MgBr$

cyclohexyl bromide   **cyclohexylmagnesium bromide**

$$CH_2{=}CHBr + Mg \xrightarrow{\text{THF}} CH_2{=}CHMgBr$$
vinyl bromide   **vinylmagnesium bromide**

**Francois Auguste Victor Grignard
(1871–1935)** *was born in France,
the son of a sailmaker. He received
a Ph.D. from the University of
Lyons in 1901. His synthesis of the
first Grignard reagent was
announced in 1900. During the
next five years, some 200 papers
were published about Grignard
reagents. Grignard was a professor
of chemistry at the University of
Nancy and later at the University
of Lyons. He received the Nobel
Prize in Chemistry in 1912.
During World War I, he was
drafted into the French army,
where he developed a method to
detect war gases.*

The solvent plays a crucial role in the formation of a Grignard reagent. The magnesium atom in a Grignard reagent is surrounded by only four electrons, so it needs two more pairs of electrons to form an octet. Solvent molecules provide these electrons; they share their electrons with the metal. Sharing electrons with a metal is called *coordination.* Coordination of the solvent molecules with the magnesium atom allows the Grignard reagent to dissolve in the solvent and prevents it from coating the magnesium shavings, which would make them unreactive.

Because carbon is more electronegative than the metal (Li or Mg) to which it is attached, organolithium and organomagnesium compounds react as if they were carbanions.

$$CH_3CH_2MgBr \qquad \text{reacts as if it were} \qquad CH_3\overset{..}{C}H_2 \; \overset{+}{M}gBr$$
ethylmagnesium bromide

$$\text{⬡—Li} \qquad \text{reacts as if it were} \qquad \text{⬡}{:}^- \; Li^+$$
phenyllithium

Alkyl halides, vinylic halides, and aryl halides can all be used to form organolithium and organomagnesium compounds. Alkyl bromides are the alkyl halides most often used to form organometallic compounds because they react more readily than alkyl chlorides and are less expensive than alkyl iodides.

11.2 THE REACTION OF ORGANOLITHIUM COMPOUNDS AND GRIGNARD REAGENTS WITH ELECTROPHILES

The nucleophilic carbon of an organometallic compound reacts with an electrophile. For example, in the following reactions, the organolithium reagent and the Grignard reagent each react with an epoxide in a nucleophilic substitution reaction.

$$CH_3{-}Li \; + \; CH_3CH{-}CHCH_3 \; \longrightarrow \; \underset{\underset{CH_3}{|}}{CH_3CHCHCH_3} \; + \; Li^+ \; \xrightarrow{HCl} \; \underset{\underset{CH_3}{|}}{\overset{OH}{CH_3CHCHCH_3}}$$

nucleophile   electrophile

$$CH_3CH_2{-}MgBr \; + \; H_2C{-}CH_2 \; \longrightarrow \; CH_3CH_2CH_2CH_2O^- \; \xrightarrow{HCl} \; CH_3CH_2CH_2CH_2OH$$
$$+ \; Mg^{2+} \; + \; Br^-$$

Notice that when an organometallic compound reacts with ethylene oxide, a primary alcohol containing two more carbons than the organometallic compound is formed.

PROBLEM 1 ♦

What alcohols would be formed from the reaction of ethylene oxide with the following Grignard reagents?

a. $CH_3CH_2CH_2MgBr$ **b.** ⬡—CH_2MgBr **c.** ⬡—MgCl

PROBLEM 2

How could the following compounds be prepared, using cyclohexene as a starting material?

a. ⬡—CH_2CH_3 **b.** ⬡$\overset{CH_3}{\underset{Br}{|}}$ **c.** ⬡—⬡

Organomagnesium and organolithium compounds are such strong bases that they will react immediately with any acid present in the reaction mixture, even with very weak acids such as water and alcohols. When this happens, the organometallic compound is converted into an alkane. If D_2O is used instead of H_2O, a deuterated compound will be obtained.

$$CH_3CH_2\underset{\underset{Br}{|}}{C}HCH_3 \xrightarrow[\text{THF}]{\text{Mg}} CH_3CH_2\underset{\underset{MgBr}{|}}{C}HCH_3 \xrightarrow{\substack{H_2O \nearrow \\ \\ D_2O \searrow}} \begin{array}{l} CH_3CH_2CH_2CH_3 \\ \\ CH_3CH_2\underset{\underset{D}{|}}{C}HCH_3 \end{array}$$

This means that Grignard reagents and organolithium compounds cannot be prepared from compounds that contain acidic groups (OH, NH_2, NHR, SH, $C\equiv CH$, or $COOH$ groups). Because even trace amounts of moisture can destroy an organometallic compound, it is important that all reagents are dry when organometallic compounds are being synthesized and when they react with other reagents.

PROBLEM 3   SOLVED

Using any necessary reagents, show how the following compounds could be prepared using ethylene oxide as one of the reactants:

a. $CH_3CH_2CH_2CH_2OH$

b. $CH_3CH_2CH_2CH_2Br$

c. $CH_3CH_2CH_2CH_2D$

d. $CH_3CH_2CH_2CH_2CH_2CH_2OH$

Solution

a. $CH_3CH_2Br \xrightarrow[\text{Et}_2O]{\text{Mg}} CH_3CH_2MgBr \xrightarrow[\text{2.HCl}]{1. \; \triangle\!\!\!\!O} CH_3CH_2CH_2CH_2OH$

b. product of a $\xrightarrow{\text{PBr}_3} CH_3CH_2CH_2CH_2Br$

c. product of b $\xrightarrow[\text{Et}_2O]{\text{Mg}} CH_3CH_2CH_2CH_2MgBr \xrightarrow{\text{D}_2\text{O}} CH_3CH_2CH_2CH_2D$

d. the same reaction sequence as in part a, but with butyl bromide in the first step.

PROBLEM 4◆

Which of the following reactions will occur? (For the pK_a values necessary to do this problem, see Appendix II. Recall that a strong acid reacts to give a weak acid; see Section 1.20.)

$$CH_3MgBr + H_2O \longrightarrow CH_4 + HOMgBr$$

$$CH_3MgBr + CH_3OH \longrightarrow CH_4 + CH_3OMgBr$$

$$CH_3MgBr + NH_3 \longrightarrow CH_4 + H_2NMgBr$$

$$CH_3MgBr + CH_3NH_2 \longrightarrow CH_4 + CH_3NMgBr$$

$$CH_3MgBr + HC\equiv CH \longrightarrow CH_4 + HC\equiv CMgBr$$

11.3 TRANSMETALLATION

The reactivity of an organometallic compound toward an electrophile depends on the polarity of the carbon–metal bond: the greater the polarity of the bond, the more reactive the compound is as a nucleophile. The polarity of the bond depends on the difference in electronegativity between the metal and carbon (Table 11.1). For example, magnesium has an electronegativity of 1.2, compared with 2.5 for carbon. This large difference in electronegativity makes the carbon–magnesium bond highly polar (it is about 52% ionic). Lithium (1.0) is even less electronegative than magnesium (1.2). Thus, the carbon–lithium bond is more polar than the carbon–magnesium bond, so an organolithium reagent is a more reactive nucleophilic reagent than a Grignard reagent.

Transmetallation occurs if the metal can be transferred to a more electronegative metal.

An organometallic compound will undergo **transmetallation** (metal exchange) if it is added to a metal halide whose metal is more electronegative than the metal in the organometallic compound. In other words, metal exchange will occur if the alkyl group can be transferred to a metal with an electronegativity closer to that of carbon, thereby forming a less polar carbon–metal bond. For example, cadmium is more electronegative (1.5) than magnesium (1.2). Consequently, a carbon–cadmium bond is less polar than a carbon–magnesium bond, so metal exchange occurs.

$$2\ CH_3CH_2MgCl\ +\ CdCl_2\ \longrightarrow\ (CH_3CH_2)_2Cd\ +\ 2\ MgCl_2$$
ethylmagnesium   diethylcadmium
chloride

(handwritten: (3+/greater+/ difference in EN))
(handwritten: the greater +/ polarity of +/ c–metal bond, +/ more reactive is the organometallic compound)

PROBLEM 5♦

(handwritten: 2.5−1.0=1.5   C−Na   C−Li;   2.5−0.9=(1.6) ← more reactive)

Which is more reactive, an organolithium compound or an organosodium compound?

PROBLEM 6♦

What organometallic compound will be formed from the reaction of methylmagnesium chloride and SiCl₄? (*Hint:* See Table 11.1.)

(handwritten: 4 CH₃MgCl + SiCl₄ → (CH₃)₄Si + 4 MgCl₂   bc Si is more EN than Mg, transmetallation will occur)

11.4 COUPLING REACTIONS

Coupling reactions join two CH-containing groups.

New carbon–carbon bonds can be made using an organometallic reagent in which the metal ion is a *transition metal*. Transition metals are indicated by purple in the periodic table at the back of this book. The reactions are called **coupling reactions** because two CH-containing groups (any two alkyl, aryl, or vinylic groups) are joined (coupled) together.

The first organometallic compounds used in coupling reactions were **Gilman reagents**, also called **dialkyl lithium cuprates**. They are prepared by the reaction of an organolithium compound with cuprous iodide in diethyl ether or THF.

B I O G R A P H Y

Henry Gilman (1893–1986), *born in Boston, received his B.A. and Ph.D. degrees from Harvard University. He joined the faculty at Iowa State University in 1919 and remained there for his entire career. He published over 1000 research papers, more than half of them after he lost almost all of his sight as the result of a detached retina and glaucoma in 1947. His wife, Ruth, acted as his eyes for 40 years.*

$$2\ CH_3Li\ +\ CuI\ \xrightarrow{\ THF\ }\ (CH_3)_2CuLi\ +\ LiI$$
an organolithium   a dialkyl lithium cuprate
reagent   a Gilman reagent

Gilman reagents are very useful to synthetic chemists. When a Gilman reagent reacts with an alkyl halide (with the exception of alkyl fluorides, which do not undergo this reaction), one of the alkyl groups of the Gilman reagent replaces the halogen. This means that an alkane can be formed from two alkyl halides—one alkyl halide is used to form the Gilman reagent, which then reacts with the second alkyl halide. The precise mechanism of the reaction is unknown but is thought to involve radicals.

(handwritten: replaces   one of them)

$$CH_3CH_2CH_2CH_2Br\ +\ (CH_3CH_2CH_2)_2CuLi\ \xrightarrow{\ THF\ }\ CH_3CH_2CH_2CH_2CH_2CH_2CH_3\ +\ CH_3CH_2CH_2Cu\ +\ LiBr$$
heptane

(handwritten: one alkane formed from 2 alkyl halides)

Gilman reagents can react with primary, secondary, vinylic, and aryl halides. Thus, they can be used to prepare compounds that cannot be prepared by nucleophilic substitution reactions. For example, S$_N$2 reactions with Grignard reagents or organolithium compounds cannot be used to prepare the following compounds because vinylic and aryl halides cannot undergo nucleophilic attack (Section 8.7):

*Gilman reagents replace halogens & couple 2 compounds together if it weren't before.

Coupling Reactions   455

Gilman reagents can even replace halogens in compounds that contain other functional groups.

$$CH_3CH(Br)\overset{O}{\underset{}{C}}CH_3 + (CH_3)_2CuLi \xrightarrow{\text{THF}} CH_3CH(CH_3)\overset{O}{\underset{}{C}}CH_3 + CH_3Cu + LiBr$$

(cyclopentene with Cl and CH₃) + $(CH_2{=}C(CH_3){-})_2CuLi \xrightarrow{\text{THF}}$ (cyclopentene with C(=CH₂) and CH₃) + $CH_2{=}\overset{CH_3}{\underset{}{C}}Cu$ + LiCl

The configuration of a vinylic halide is maintained when it reacts with a Gilman reagent. In other words, a trans vinylic halide will form a trans alkene, and a cis vinylic halide will form a cis alkene.

trans: CH_3—CH=CH—Br + $(CH_3)_2CuLi \longrightarrow$ CH_3—CH=CH—CH_3 (trans)

config. is maintained! (w/ a Gilman reagent)

cis: CH_3—CH=CH—Br + $(CH_3)_2CuLi \longrightarrow$ CH_3—CH=CH—CH_3 (cis)

PROBLEM 7

What alkyl halide would be required to react with $(CH_2{=}CH)_2CuLi$ in order to form each of the following compounds?

a. (structure) b. (structure) c. (structure) d. (structure)

chem place Tutorial: Orgnometallic compounds

PROBLEM 8

Explain why tertiary alkyl halides cannot be used in coupling reactions with Gilman reagents.

Tutorial: Common terms

PROBLEM 9

Muscalure is the sex attractant of the common housefly. Flies are lured to traps filled with fly bait containing muscalure and an insecticide. Eating the bait is fatal.

$$CH_3(CH_2)_7\overset{}{\underset{H}{C}}{=}\overset{}{\underset{H}{C}}(CH_2)_{12}CH_3$$

muscalure

How could you synthesize muscalure using the following reagents?

$$CH_3(CH_2)_7\overset{}{\underset{H}{C}}{=}\overset{}{\underset{H}{C}}(CH_2)_8Br \quad \text{and} \quad CH_3(CH_2)_4Br$$

11.5 PALLADIUM-CATALYZED COUPLING REACTIONS

In recent years, many new methods of using transition metals to carry out coupling reactions have been developed. These methods have greatly expanded the synthetic chemist's arsenal of reactions for forming carbon–carbon bonds. A wide variety of transition metals are used in these reactions. We will look at two reactions that use a palladium catalyst: the *Suzuki reaction* and the *Heck reaction*. The two reactions have several features in common:

• They both replace a halogen of a vinylic halide or an aryl halide* with a carbon-containing group. (We will see that the carbon-containing group is donated by an organoborane in a Suzuki reaction and by an alkene in a Heck reaction.)

$$\begin{array}{ccc} \diagdown & \diagup & \\ C=C & \longrightarrow & C=C \\ \diagup & \diagdown & \\ & Br & R \end{array}$$

a vinylic halide

$$\text{Ar—I} \longrightarrow \text{Ar—R}$$

an aryl halide

• The first step in both reactions is insertion of palladium between the carbon and halogen to form an **organopalladium compound**.

$$\text{R—X} + \text{Pd} \longrightarrow \text{R—Pd—X}$$

an organopalladium compound

If the organopalladium compound has a β-hydrogen, it will rapidly undergo an elimination reaction and the coupling reaction will not occur. This explains why the reactions are carried out on vinylic and aryl halides—they cannot undergo an elimination reaction under the conditions used to carry out the coupling reactions.

$$\boxed{\beta\text{-hydrogens}}$$
$$\text{R—CH}_2\text{CH}_2\text{—Pd—X} \xrightarrow{\ \beta\text{-elimination}\ } \text{R—CH=CH}_2$$

• The reactions can be carried out even if the reactants have other functional groups.
• The reactions are stereospecific: The configuration of the double bond in a vinylic halide is retained in the product.
• The reactions give high yields of products (80–98%).

The Suzuki Reaction

The **Suzuki reaction** couples a vinylic halide or an aryl halide with an **organoborane** in a basic solution. The organoborane can be either an **alkylborane**, an **alkenylborane**, or an **arylborane**. (Palladium can be coordinated with a variety of groups known as ligands; they are indicated as L.) The general reaction can be written as follows:

$$\text{R—X} \quad + \quad \begin{array}{c} \\ R'\text{—B} \end{array}\begin{array}{c} \diagup OR \\ \diagdown OR \end{array} \quad \xrightarrow[\text{HO}^-]{\text{PdL}_2} \quad \text{R—R}'$$

a vinylic halide or an aryl halide   **an organoborane** $\boxed{\text{new C—C bond}}$

---

*Vinylic and aryl bromides and iodides work best. The reactions can also be carried out with vinylic and aryl triflates (Section 10.3).

Specific examples of the Suzuki reaction are shown below.

easy

an alkylborane

an alkenylborane

an arylborane

When the reactant is a vinylic halide, the configuration of the vinyl group will be retained in the product. When alkenylboranes are used, the new double bond in the product will be trans because alkenylboranes have a *trans (E) configuration* (see below). The mechanism for the Suzuki reaction is shown below.

In a Suzuki reaction, the R group of an organoborane replaces the halogen.

MECHANISM FOR THE SUZUKI REACTION

$$R-X \xrightarrow{PdL_2} R-Pd-X \longrightarrow R-Pd-R' \longrightarrow R-R'$$

palladium

last step: reductive elimin - 2 groups are eliminated from t/ metal.

1st step: called oxidative addition (2 new groups are added to t/ metal)

- Palladium is inserted between the carbon and the halogen.

- Carbon is more electronegative than boron. Therefore, R′ is a nucleophile—it attacks palladium in an S_N2 reaction, and the halide ion is displaced. This is a transmetallation reaction—the alkyl group is transferred from boron to palladium. (As we saw in Section 11.3, transmetallation will occur if an organometallic compound is added to a metal halide whose metal is more electronegative than the metal in the organometallic compound. Palladium is more electronegative than boron; see Table 11.1.)

- The last step is the reverse of the first step: Palladium is eliminated and a new C—C bond is formed. (The base regenerates the palladium catalyst.)

The insertion of a metal between two atoms is called **oxidative addition**—two new groups are added to the metal. **Reductive elimination** eliminates two groups from the metal. Thus, the first step in a Suzuki reaction is an *oxidative addition*, and the last step is a *reductive elimination*.

Oxidative addition: two groups are added to the metal

Reductive elimination: two groups are eliminated from the metal

The alkylborane or alkenylborane used in a Suzuki reaction is prepared by hydroboration of an alkene or an alkyne, respectively. We saw in Sections 4.11 and 6.8 that boron adds to the multiply-bonded carbon that is bonded to the greater number of hydrogens. Remember that hydroboration involves syn addition—the B and the H are added to the same side of the double bond (Section 5.19). Therefore, an alkenylborane will have a *trans configuration*.

$$RCH{=}CH_2 \quad + \quad H{-}B\overset{OR}{\underset{OR}{}} \quad \longrightarrow \quad RCH_2CH_2{-}B\overset{OR}{\underset{OR}{}}$$

an alkylborane

$$RCH{\equiv}CH \quad + \quad H{-}B\overset{OR}{\underset{OR}{}} \quad \longrightarrow \quad \underset{H}{\overset{R}{C}}{=}\underset{B(OR)_2}{\overset{H}{C}}$$

trans

an alkenylborane

An arylborane is prepared from an organolithium compound.

$$\text{Ph-Li} \quad + \quad B(OR)_3 \quad \longrightarrow \quad \text{Ph-}B(OR)_2 \quad + \quad LiOR$$

PROBLEM 10♦

Give the products of the following reactions:

a. Br—C₆H₄—B(OR)₂ + alkyl-Br ⟶

b. (3-NO₂)C₆H₄—B(OR)₂ + alkyl-I ⟶

PROBLEM 11♦

What alkyl halides would you use to synthesize the following compounds, using the organoborane shown?

$$\text{pentenyl-}B\overset{OR}{\underset{OR}{}}$$

a. **b.** **c.**

PROBLEM 12♦

What hydrocarbon would you use to prepare the organoborane of Problem 11?

The Heck Reaction (substitution)

The **Heck reaction** couples a vinylic halide or an aryl halide with an *alkene* in the presence of a base such as triethylamine. The alkene is generally ethene or a monosubstituted alkene. The Heck reaction is a substitution reaction: a vinylic hydrogen of the alkene is replaced by the R group of the aryl or vinylic halide. The general reaction can be written as follows:

H is substituted by R   R is trans to Z

$$R{-}X \quad + \quad \underset{\text{alkene}}{\overset{H}{\underset{Z}{}}} \quad \xrightarrow[\text{(CH}_3\text{CH}_2)_3\text{N}]{\text{PdL}_2} \quad \underset{Z}{\overset{R}{}}$$

a vinylic halide
or
an aryl halide

trans

new C—C bond

Specific examples of the Heck reaction are shown below.

[handwritten: you can use // same conditions]
[handwritten: new!]
[handwritten: (both are for t Heck subst. rxn)]

the new C-C bond is trans to the substituent

[handwritten: new]

When the reactant is a vinylic halide, the configuration of the vinyl group will be retained in the product. The new C—C bond will be *trans* to the substituent (Z) on the vinylic halide. The mechanism for the Heck reaction is shown below.

In a Heck reaction, the R group of the halide replaces a vinyl hydrogen of an alkene.

MECHANISM FOR THE HECK REACTION

[handwritten: oxidative addition]
[handwritten: β-elim. rxn]

$$R-X \xrightarrow{PdL_2} R-Pd-X \longrightarrow R \cdots \xrightarrow{\beta\text{-elimination}} R \cdots Z + HB^+$$

- The first step is an oxidative addition: palladium is inserted between the carbon and the halogen.
- Because carbon is more electronegative than palladium, R is a nucleophile. It adds to the sp^2 carbon of the alkene, breaking the π bond; the electrons of the π bond add to palladium.
- The last step is a β-elimination reaction; a hydrogen is removed from a β-carbon, and Pd—X is eliminated. (The base regenerates the palladium catalyst.)

The nucleophilic R group can add to either sp^2 carbon of the alkene. Therefore, if the alkene is not symmetrical, the reaction will lead to a high yield of a single product only in the following situations:

- If one of the sp^2 carbons is sterically hindered to nucleophilic attack.
- If one of the sp^2 carbons is bonded to a group that can withdraw electrons by resonance (such as C=O or C=N), the other sp^2 carbon will have a partial positive charge that will make it more susceptible to nucleophilic attack.

PROBLEM 13◆

Give the products of the following reactions:

a.

b.

PROBLEM 14♦

Give the products of the following reactions:

a. [structure: 2-methyl-1-bromobut-2-ene] + [structure: methyl vinyl ketone] $\xrightarrow[\text{(CH}_3\text{CH}_2)_3\text{N}]{\text{PdL}_2}$

b. [structure: 2-methylbut-2-ene with Br] + [structure: methyl vinyl ketone] $\xrightarrow[\text{(CH}_3\text{CH}_2)_3\text{N}]{\text{PdL}_2}$

PROBLEM 15♦

Identify two pairs of an alkyl bromide and an alkene that could be used in a Heck reaction to prepare the following compound:

[structure: 4-acetyl-4'-methoxystilbene with OCH₃]

PROBLEM 16

Show how the Suzuki and Heck reactions can be used to prepare the following compounds:

a. [structure: (E)-1-phenyl-1-butene]   **b.** [structure: butylbenzene]

11.6 ALKENE METATHESIS

Alkene metathesis, also called **olefin metathesis**, is a reaction that breaks the strongest bond in an alkene (the double bond) and then rejoins the fragments. When the fragments are joined, the new double bond is formed between two carbons that were not previously bonded. *Metathesis* is a Greek word that means "transposition."

$$\underset{\text{2 carbons}}{\boxed{\text{join these}}} \quad \begin{array}{c} \text{R—CH}{=}\text{CH}_2 \\ \text{R—CH}{=}\text{CH}_2 \end{array} \quad \underset{\text{2 carbons}}{\boxed{\text{join these}}} \quad \xrightarrow{\text{metathesis}} \quad \begin{array}{c} \text{R} \\ | \\ \text{CH} \\ \| \\ \text{CH} \\ | \\ \text{R} \end{array} \quad + \quad \begin{array}{c} \text{CH}_2 \\ \| \\ \text{CH}_2 \end{array}$$

There are two ways in which the fragments can be joined to give a double bond between carbons that were not previously bonded. If the fragments are joined as shown above, two new alkene products are obtained. If, however, the fragments are joined as shown below, the starting material is re-formed, and it can undergo anther round of metathesis.

$$\underset{\text{2 carbons}}{\boxed{\text{join these}}} \quad \begin{array}{c} \text{R—CH}{=}\text{CH}_2 \\ \text{CH}_2{=}\text{CH—R} \end{array} \quad \underset{\text{2 carbons}}{\boxed{\text{join these}}} \quad \xrightarrow{\text{metathesis}} \quad \begin{array}{c} \text{R} \\ | \\ \text{CH} \\ \| \\ \text{CH}_2 \end{array} \quad + \quad \begin{array}{c} \text{CH}_2 \\ \| \\ \text{CH} \\ | \\ \text{R} \end{array}$$

Terminal alkenes give the best yield of a single alkene product because one of the new alkene products will be ethene. Ethene is a gas and therefore will be removed from the reaction mixture as it is formed. This will force the equilibrium that exists between the two pathways for joining the fragments toward ethene and the other new alkene.

Alkene metathesis requires a transition metal catalyst. A large variety of alkenes can undergo metathesis if the catalyst is one that does not affect other functional groups that might be in the starting material. Grubbs catalysts—catalysts that contain ruthenium—have been found to be the most useful. The ligands (L) in the Grubbs catalyst shown below are not identified because there are several generations of Grubbs catalysts, each with different ligands.

$$\underset{\textbf{Grubbs catalyst}}{\overset{Cl}{\underset{Cl}{\overset{L}{\underset{L}{|}}}Ru=CH-C_6H_5}}$$

An example of alkene metathesis is shown below. If both *E* and *Z* isomers are possible for the product of metathesis, both will be formed.

$$2\ CH_3CH_2CH=CH_2 \xrightarrow[\textbf{catalyst}]{\textbf{Grubbs}} \underset{\textbf{both } E \textbf{ and } Z}{CH_3CH_2CH=CHCH_2CH_3}\ +\ CH_2=CH_2$$

If the reactant is a diene, **ring-closing metathesis** will occur.

$$\xrightarrow[\textbf{catalyst}]{\textbf{Grubbs}} \qquad +\ CH_2=CH_2$$

Metathesis starts by breaking the π bond of the alkene and transferring a fragment to the metal. The mechanism for this initial phase of the reaction is shown below.

MECHANISM FOR METATHESIS

Grubbs catalyst is written as $M=CH-C_6H_5$

- The Grubbs catalyst and the alkene undergo a [2 + 2] cycloaddition reaction. This reaction forms two different metallocyclobutane intermediates because the metal can bond to either the less substituted or the more substituted sp^2 carbon of the alkene.

- Each of the metallocyclobutane intermediates undergoes a ring-opening reaction. Two different metal-containing intermediates are formed (I and II).

Each of the metal-containing intermediates reacts with the starting alkene to form a new alkene. The mechanism on page 462 shows how, overall, two molecules of the starting alkene are converted to two new alkenes. Notice that the mechanism for formation of the two alkenes is the same as the mechanism shown on page 461 for formation of the two metal-containing intermediates.

MECHANISM FOR METATHESIS (continued)

- Each metallocyclobutane intermediate undergoes a [2 + 2] cycloaddition reaction followed by a ring-opening reaction.
- The metal can bond to the alkene in two different ways. Only if the metal in I bonds to the *more substituted sp²* carbon is a new alkene product formed. If the metal bonds to the less substituted *sp²* carbon, the starting alkene will be re-formed.
- Only if the metal in II bonds to the *less substituted sp²* carbon is a new alkene product formed. If the metal bonds to the more substituted *sp²* carbon, the starting alkene will be re-formed.

Notice that the product of the reaction of metal-containing intermediate I is metal-containing intermediate II, and the product of the reaction of metal-containing intermediate II is metal-containing intermediate I. Each of the newly formed metal-containing intermediates can now react with another molecule of the alkene starting material.

PROBLEM 17

What products would be obtained from metathesis of each of the following alkenes?

a. $CH_2\!=\!\overset{\displaystyle CH_3}{\underset{\displaystyle CH_2CH_3}{C}}$

b. $=\!CH_2$

c. $CH_3CH_2CH\!=\!CH_2$

PROBLEM 18

Give the product of ring-closing metathesis for each of the following compounds:

a.   b.   c.

PROBLEM 19 ◆

What alkene will undergo metathesis to form each of the following compounds?

a.   b.   c.

Two different alkenes can be used as the starting materials for metathesis.

$$CH_3CH\!=\!CHCH_3 \ + \ CH_3CH_2CH\!=\!CHCH_2CH_3 \longrightarrow 2 \ CH_3CH\!=\!CHCH_2CH_3$$

Zare kept

Alkynes can also undergo metathesis. The preferred catalysts for alkyne metathesis are Schrock catalysts—catalysts that contain molybdenum or tungsten as the transition metal.

Schrock catalyst

$$CH_3CH_2C{\equiv}CH \xrightarrow{\text{Schrock catalyst}} CH_3CH_2C{\equiv}CCH_2CH_3 \ + \ HC{\equiv}CH$$

PROBLEM 20

What is the maximum yield of 2-pentene that can be formed in the reaction shown on the bottom of page 462?

PROBLEM 21 ◆

What products would be obtained from metathesis of the following alkyne?

$$\text{(benzene ring)}-C{\equiv}C-\text{(benzene ring)}-CH_3$$

SUMMARY

The carbon attached to the halogen in an alkyl halide is an electrophile, whereas the carbon attached to the metal in an organometallic compound is a nucleophile. **Organomagnesium compounds (Grignard reagents)** and **organolithium compounds** are the most common **organometallic compounds**—compounds that contain a carbon–metal bond. They cannot be prepared from compounds that contain acidic groups. The greater the polarity of the carbon–metal bond, the more reactive the organometallic compound is as a nucleophile.

New carbon–carbon bonds can be made using organometallic compounds that contain a transition metal. The reactions are called **coupling reactions** because two carbon-containing groups are joined together. **Gilman reagents** were the first organometallic compounds used in coupling reactions.

The **Suzuki** and **Heck reactions** are coupling reactions that require a palladium catalyst. The first step of both reactions is the same—the palladium is inserted between the carbon and the halogen, a reaction called **oxidative addition**. The second step of the Suzuki reaction is an S_N2 transmetallation reaction; the second step of the Heck reaction is a [2 + 2] cycloaddition reaction. The last step of the Suzuki reaction is a **reductive elimination**; the last step of the Heck reaction is a β-elimination.

Alkene metathesis (or **olefin metathesis**) breaks the double bond of an alkene and then rejoins the fragments. When the fragments are joined, the new double bond is formed between two carbons that were not previously bonded. Terminal alkenes give the best yield of a single alkene product because one of products is ethene. Alkynes also undergo metathesis. *—Shrock catalyst!*

SUMMARY OF REACTIONS

1. Formation of an *organolithium* or *organomagnesium* compound and its reaction with an *epoxide* (Sections 11.1, 11.2)

$$RBr \xrightarrow[\text{diethyl ether}]{\textbf{Mg}} RMgBr$$

a Grignard reagent

$$RMgBr \ + \ \underset{\text{O}}{H_2C{-}CH_2} \longrightarrow RCH_2CH_2O^- \xrightarrow{\textbf{HCl}} RCH_2CH_2OH$$

product alcohol contains two more carbons than the Grignard reagent

2. Coupling Reactions
   a. Coupling of an alkyl halide and a *Gilman reagent* (Section 11.4)

$$2 \ R'Li \ + \ CuI \xrightarrow{\textbf{THF}} R'_2CuLi \ + \ LiI$$

a Gilman reagent

$$R{-}X \ + \ R'_2CuLi \xrightarrow{\textbf{THF}} R{-}R' \ + \ R'Cu \ + \ LiX$$

$X = $ **Cl, Br, or I**

$R = $ **primary, secondary, vinylic, aryl**

b. Coupling of a *vinylic* or an *aryl halide* with an *organoborane*: the Suzuki reaction (Section 11.5)

$$R-X \; + \; R'-B(OR)_2 \xrightarrow[HO^-]{PdL_2} R-R'$$

$$R-X \; + \; \text{(aryl)}-B(OR)_2 \xrightarrow[HO^-]{PdL_2} \text{(aryl)}-R$$

X = Br, I

R = vinylic, aryl

c. Coupling of a *vinylic* or an *aryl halide* with an *alkene*: the Heck reaction (Section 11.5)

$$R-X \; + \; \diagup\!\!\diagup Z \xrightarrow[(CH_3CH_2)_3N]{PdL_2} R\diagup\!\!\diagup Z$$

the product is a trans alkene

$$R-X \; + \; \text{(benzene)} \xrightarrow[(CH_3CH_2)_3N]{PdL_2} \text{(aryl)}-R$$

X = Br, I

R = vinylic, aryl

3. Alkene metathesis (Section 11.6)
a. starting material is an alkene

$$2\,R-CH=CH_2 \xrightarrow{\text{Grubbs catalyst}} R-CH=CH-R \; + \; CH_2=CH_2$$

The reaction works best with a terminal alkene

b. starting material is a diene

$$\xrightarrow{\text{Grubbs catalyst}} \text{(cyclopentene)} \; + \; CH_2=CH_2$$

c. starting material is an alkyne

$$RC\equiv CH \xrightarrow{\text{Schrock catalyst}} RC\equiv CR \; + \; HC\equiv CH$$

KEY TERMS

PROBLEMS

22. Give the products of the following reactions:

a. [benzene ring with I] + [propene] $\xrightarrow[\text{(CH}_3\text{CH}_2)_3\text{N}]{\text{PdL}_2}$

d. [benzene ring with I] + [cyclohexene] $\xrightarrow[\text{(CH}_3\text{CH}_2)_3\text{N}]{\text{PdL}_2}$

b. [benzene ring]—CH$_2$MgBr $\xrightarrow[\text{2. HCl, H}_2\text{O}]{\text{1. ethylene oxide}}$

e. [benzene ring with Br] + [propyl]—B(OR)$_2$ $\xrightarrow[\text{HO}^-]{\text{PdL}_2}$

c. [cyclohexene with Cl] $\xrightarrow{\text{(CH}_3\text{CH}_2\text{CH}_2)_2\text{CuLi}}$

f. CH$_3$C≡CH $\xrightarrow[\text{2. } \text{Br, PdL}_2, \text{HO}^-]{\text{1. HB(OR)}_2}$

23. Which of the following alkyl halides could be successfully used to form a Grignard reagent?

HO~~~Br (**A**)   Br~~~OH with O (**B**)   N~~~Br (**C**)   Br~~~NH$_2$ (**D**)

24. Identify A through H.

CH$_3$Br $\xrightarrow[\text{B}]{\text{A}}$ C $\xrightarrow[\text{2. E}]{\text{1. D}}$ CH$_3$CH$_2$CH$_2$OH $\xrightarrow[\substack{\text{2. G}\\\text{3. H}}]{\text{1. F}}$ CH$_3$CH$_2$CH$_2$OCH$_2$CH$_2$OH

25. Using the given starting material, any necessary inorganic reagents, and any carbon-containing compounds with no more that two carbons, indicate how each of the following compounds can be prepared:

a. [benzene with Br] → [benzene with CH$_2$CH$_2$OH]

d. [benzene with Br] → [benzene-CH=CH-C≡N]

b. CH$_3$CHCH$_2$OH → CH$_3$CHCH$_2$CH$_2$CH$_2$OH
         | |
        CH$_3$ CH$_3$

e. [epoxide on cyclohexane] → [cyclohexene with CH$_3$]

c. CH$_3$CH$_2$C≡CH → CH$_3$CH$_2$C≡CCH$_2$CH$_2$OH

26. What alkyl halide would be needed to react with lithium divinylcuprate [(CH$_2$=CH)$_2$CuLi] for the synthesis of each of the following compounds?

a. [cyclohexane with vinyl]   **b.** [cyclohexane with allyl]   **c.** [branched alkene]   **d.** [branched diene]

27. What vinylic halide would need to be coupled with styrene (C$_6$H$_5$-CH=CH$_2$) for the synthesis of each of the following compounds via a Heck reaction?

a. [benzene-CH=CH with methyl diene]   **b.** [benzene diene with methyl]   **c.** [benzene diene with ethyl]

28. Give the products of the following reactions:

a. (phenyl)–Br + (styrene) $\xrightarrow[\text{(CH}_3\text{CH}_2)_3\text{N}]{\text{PdL}_2}$

c. (phenyl)–Br + (methyl vinyl ketone) $\xrightarrow[\text{(CH}_3\text{CH}_2)_3\text{N}]{\text{PdL}_2}$

b. (phenyl)–I + $\diagup\diagdown\diagup$B(OR)$_2$ $\xrightarrow[\text{HO}^-]{\text{PdL}_2}$

d. (phenyl)–I $\xrightarrow{\begin{array}{l}\text{1. Li}\\ \text{2. B(OR)}_3\\ \text{3. CH}_2\text{=CHBr, PdL}_2\text{, HO}^-\end{array}}$

29. Using the given starting material, any necessary inorganic reagents, and any carbon-containing compounds with no more that two carbons, indicate how each of the following compounds can be prepared:

a. $CH_3CH_2CH_2CH_2Br \longrightarrow CH_3CH_2CH_2CH_2CH_2\overset{\overset{\displaystyle O}{\|}}{C}H$

b. $CH_3CH=CHCH_3 \longrightarrow CH_3CH=\underset{\underset{\displaystyle CH_3}{|}}{C}CH_2CH_3$

c. $CH_3CH=CHCH_3 \longrightarrow CH_3\underset{\underset{\displaystyle CH_3}{|}}{C}H\overset{\overset{\displaystyle O}{\|}}{C}CH_3$

30. Dimerization is a side reaction that occurs during the preparation of a Grignard reagent. Propose a mechanism that accounts for the formation of the dimer.

(cyclohexyl)–Br $\xrightarrow{\text{Mg}}$ (cyclohexyl)–MgBr + (bicyclohexyl)

a dimer

31. A student added an equivalent of 3,4-epoxy-4-methylcyclohexanol to an ether solution of methyl magnesium bromide and then added dilute hydrochloric acid. He expected that the product would be 1,2-dimethyl-1,4-cyclohexanediol. He did not get any of the expected product. What product did he get?

3,4-epoxy-4-methyl-cyclohexanol

1,2-dimethyl-1,4-cyclohexanediol

32. Using the given starting material, any necessary inorganic reagents, and any carbon-containing compounds with no more that two carbons, indicate how each of the following compounds can be prepared:

a. (cyclohexene) $\longrightarrow$ (3-methylcyclohexene with CH$_3$)

c. $CH_3CH_2CH=CH_2 \longrightarrow CH_3CH_2CH_2CH_2CH_2CH_2CH_2CH_3$

b. (cyclohexane–OH) $\longrightarrow$ (cyclohexane–CH$_2$CH$_2$OH)

d. (CH$_3$)$_2$CHCH(OH)CH$_3$ type with OH $\longrightarrow$ same with D

33. a. Which of the following compounds cannot be prepared by a Heck reaction?

     A   B   C

 b. For those compounds that can be prepared by a Heck reaction, what starting materials are required?

34. Bombykol is the sex pheromone of the silkworm moth.

bombykol

Show how bombykol can be synthesized from the following compounds.

HO⎯⎯⎯⎯⎯⎯≡ + ⎯⎯⎯⎯

                Br

          ⎯⎯⎯⎯⎯OH

     bombykol

35. A dibromide loses only one bromine when it reacts with sodium hydroxide. The dibromide forms toluene (C_6H_5-CH_3) when it reacts with magnesium shavings in ether followed by treatment with dilute acid. Give possible structures for the dibromide.

36. What starting material is required in order to synthesize each of the following compounds by ring-closing metathesis?

a.   **b.**   **c.**

12

Radicals • Reactions of Alkanes

vitamin C

vitamin E

WE HAVE SEEN THAT THERE ARE THREE CLASSES OF HYDROCARBONS: *ALKANES*, WHICH contain only single bonds; *alkenes*, which contain double bonds; and *alkynes*, which contain triple bonds. Because **alkanes** do not contain any double or triple bonds, they are called **saturated hydrocarbons**, meaning they are saturated with hydrogen. A few examples of alkanes are

CH₃CH₂CH₂CH₃
butane

CH₂CH₃

ethylcyclopentane

4-ethyl-3,3-dimethyldecane

CH₃

CH₃

trans-1,3-dimethyl-cyclohexane

12.1 ALKANES ARE UNREACTIVE COMPOUNDS

The double and triple bonds of alkenes and alkynes are composed of strong σ bonds and weaker π bonds. We have seen that the reactivity of *alkenes* and *alkynes* is the result of an electrophile being attracted to the cloud of electrons that constitutes the π bond (Sections 3.6 and 6.5).

Alkanes have only strong σ bonds. In addition, the electrons in the C—H and C—C σ bonds are shared equally by the bonding atoms, so none of the atoms in an alkane has any significant charge. This means that they are neither nucleophiles nor electrophiles, so neither electrophiles nor nucleophiles are attracted to them. Alkanes, therefore, are relatively unreactive compounds. The failure of alkanes to undergo reactions prompted early organic chemists to call them *paraffins*, from the Latin *parum affinis*, which means "little affinity" (for other compounds).

Natural Gas and Petroleum

Alkanes are widespread both on Earth and on other planets. The atmospheres of Jupiter, Saturn, Uranus, and Neptune contain large quantities of methane (CH_4), the smallest alkane, an odorless and flammable gas. In fact, the blue colors of Uranus and Neptune are the result of methane in their atmospheres. Alkanes on Earth are found in natural gas and petroleum, which are formed by the decomposition of plant and animal material that have been buried for long periods of time in the Earth's crust, where oxygen is scarce. Natural gas and petroleum, therefore, are known as *fossil fuels*.

Natural gas is approximately 75% methane. The remaining 25% is composed of other small alkanes such as ethane, propane, and butane. In the 1950s, natural gas replaced coal as the main energy source for domestic and industrial heating in many parts of the United States.

- natural gas
- gasoline
- kerosene, jet fuel
- heating oil, diesel oil
- lubricants
- asphalt, tar
- heating element

Petroleum is a complex mixture of alkanes and cycloalkanes that can be separated into fractions by distillation. The fraction that boils off at the lowest temperature (hydrocarbons containing three and four carbons) is a gas that can be liquefied under pressure. This gas is used as a fuel for cigarette lighters, camp stoves, and barbecues. The fraction that boils at somewhat higher temperatures (hydrocarbons containing 5 to 11 carbons) is gasoline; the next fraction (9 to 16 carbons) includes kerosene and jet fuel. The fraction with 15 to 25 carbons is used for heating oil and diesel oil, and the highest-boiling fraction is used for lubricants and greases. After distillation, a nonvolatile residue called asphalt or tar is left behind.

The 5- to 11-carbon fraction that is used for gasoline is, in fact, a poor fuel for internal combustion engines and requires a process known as catalytic cracking to become a high-performance gasoline. Catalytic cracking converts straight-chain hydrocarbons that are poor fuels into branched-chain compounds that are high-performance fuels (Section 2.2). Originally, cracking (also called pyrolysis) required heating the gasoline to very high temperatures in order to obtain hydrocarbons with three to five carbons. Modern cracking methods use catalysts to accomplish the same thing at much lower temperatures.

Fossil Fuels: A Problematic Energy Source

Modern society faces three major problems as a consequence of our dependence on fossil fuels for energy. First, these fuels are a nonrenewable resource and the world's supply is continually decreasing. Second, a group of Middle Eastern and South American countries controls a large portion of the world's supply of petroleum. These countries have formed a cartel called the *Organization of Petroleum Exporting Countries* (*OPEC*) that controls both the supply and the price of crude oil. Political instability in any OPEC country can seriously affect the world's oil supply.

Third, burning fossil fuels—particularly coal—increases the concentration of CO_2 in the atmosphere; burning coal increases the concentration of both CO_2 and SO_2. Scientists have established experimentally that atmospheric SO_2 causes "acid rain," a

threat to the Earth's plants and, therefore, to our food and oxygen supplies (Section 1.17).

Since 1958, the concentration of atmospheric CO_2 at Mauna Loa, Hawaii, has been periodically measured. The concentration has increased 20% since the first measurements were taken, causing scientists to predict an increase in the Earth's temperature as a result of the absorption of infrared radiation by CO_2 (the *greenhouse effect*). A steady increase in the temperature of the Earth would have devastating consequences, including the formation of new deserts, massive crop failure, and the melting of glaciers with a concomitant rise in sea level. Clearly, what we need is a renewable, nonpolitical, nonpolluting, and economically affordable source of energy.

12.2 THE CHLORINATION AND BROMINATION OF ALKANES

Alkanes react with chlorine (Cl_2) or bromine (Br_2) to form alkyl chlorides or alkyl bromides. These **halogenation reactions** take place only at high temperatures or in the presence of light. (Irradiation with light is symbolized by $h\nu$.) They are the only reactions that alkanes undergo (without a metal catalyst being involved), with the exception of **combustion** (burning), a reaction with oxygen that takes place at high temperatures and converts alkanes to carbon dioxide and water.

$$CH_4 \;+\; Cl_2 \;\xrightarrow[\substack{\text{or} \\ h\nu}]{\Delta}\; \underset{\text{chloromethane}}{CH_3Cl} \;+\; HCl$$

$$CH_3CH_3 \;+\; Br_2 \;\xrightarrow[\substack{\text{or} \\ h\nu}]{\Delta}\; \underset{\text{bromoethane}}{CH_3CH_2Br} \;+\; HBr$$

When a bond breaks so that both of its electrons stay with one of the atoms, the process is called **heterolytic bond cleavage** or **heterolysis**. When a bond breaks so that each of the atoms retains one of the bonding electrons, the process is called **homolytic bond cleavage**, or **homolysis**. Notice that an arrowhead with one barb—sometimes called a fishhook—signifies the movement of one electron, whereas an arrowhead with two barbs signifies the movement of two electrons (Section 3.6).

The mechanism for the halogenation of an alkane is well understood. As an example, let's look at the mechanism for the monochlorination of methane.

MECHANISM FOR THE MONOCHLORINATION OF METHANE

$$:\!\overset{..}{\underset{..}{Cl}}\!-\!\overset{..}{\underset{..}{Cl}}\!: \;\xrightarrow[\substack{\text{or} \\ h\nu}]{\Delta}\; 2\,:\!\overset{..}{\underset{..}{Cl}}\!\cdot \quad \boxed{\text{initiation step}}$$

$$:\!\overset{..}{\underset{..}{Cl}}\!\cdot \;+\; H\!-\!CH_3 \;\longrightarrow\; H\overset{..}{\underset{..}{Cl}}: \;+\; \cdot CH_3$$
$$\text{a methyl radical}$$

$$\cdot CH_3 \;+\; :\!\overset{..}{\underset{..}{Cl}}\!-\!\overset{..}{\underset{..}{Cl}}\!: \;\longrightarrow\; CH_3Cl \;+\; :\!\overset{..}{\underset{..}{Cl}}\!\cdot$$

$$\left. \begin{array}{l} :\!\overset{..}{\underset{..}{Cl}}\!\cdot \;+\; :\!\overset{..}{\underset{..}{Cl}}\!\cdot \;\longrightarrow\; Cl_2 \\[4pt] \cdot CH_3 \;+\; \cdot CH_3 \;\longrightarrow\; CH_3CH_3 \\[4pt] :\!\overset{..}{\underset{..}{Cl}}\!\cdot \;+\; \cdot CH_3 \;\longrightarrow\; CH_3Cl \end{array} \right\} \boxed{\text{termination steps}}$$

- Heat or light supplies the energy required to break the Cl—Cl bond homolytically. This is the **initiation step** of the reaction because it creates radicals. A **radical** (often called a **free radical**) is a species containing an atom with an unpaired electron. A radical is highly reactive because acquiring an electron will complete its octet.

- The chlorine radical formed in the initiation step removes a hydrogen atom from the alkane (in this case methane), forming HCl and a methyl radical.

- The methyl radical removes a chlorine atom from Cl_2, forming chloromethane and another chlorine radical, which can remove a hydrogen atom from another molecule of methane. Steps 2 and 3 are **propagation steps** because the radical created in the first propagation step reacts in the second propagation step to produce the radical that participates in the first propagation step. A propagation step is one that propagates the chain. Thus, the two propagation steps are repeated over and over. The first propagation step is the rate-determining step of the overall reaction.

- Any two radicals in the reaction mixture can combine to form a molecule in which all the electrons are paired. The combination of two radicals is called a **termination step** because it helps bring the reaction to an end by decreasing the number of radicals available to propagate the reaction. Any two radicals present in the reaction mixture can combine in a termination step, so radical reactions produce a mixture of products.

> Radical reactions have initiation, propagation, and termination steps.

The radical chlorination of alkanes other than methane has the same mechanism. Because the reaction has radical intermediates and repeating propagation steps, it is called a **radical chain reaction**. This particular radical chain reaction—the reaction of an alkane with chlorine to form an alkyl halide—is called a **radical substitution reaction** because it substitutes a chlorine for one of the hydrogens of the alkane.

In order to maximize the amount of monohalogenated product obtained, a radical substitution reaction should be carried out in the presence of excess alkane. Excess alkane in the reaction mixture increases the probability that the halogen radical will collide with a molecule of alkane rather than with a molecule of alkyl halide—even toward the end of the reaction, by which time a considerable amount of alkyl halide will have been formed. If the halogen radical removes a hydrogen from a molecule of alkyl halide rather than from a molecule of alkane, a dihalogenated product will be obtained.

$$Cl\cdot + CH_3Cl \longrightarrow \cdot CH_2Cl + HCl$$
$$\cdot CH_2Cl + Cl_2 \longrightarrow CH_2Cl_2 + Cl\cdot$$

a dihalogenated compound

radical substitution/chain rxn—substitutes a chlorine for one of the hydrogens of the alkane

Bromination of alkanes has the same mechanism as chlorination.

MECHANISM FOR THE MONOBROMINATION OF ETHANE

$$Br - Br \xrightarrow[\text{or } h\nu]{\Delta} 2\,Br\cdot$$

initiation step   *(creation of a radical)*

$$Br\cdot + H - CH_2CH_3 \longrightarrow CH_3\dot{C}H_2 + HBr$$
$$CH_3\dot{C}H_2 + Br - Br \longrightarrow CH_3CH_2Br + Br\cdot$$

propagation steps

$$Br\cdot + Br\cdot \longrightarrow Br_2$$
$$CH_3\dot{C}H_2 + CH_3\dot{C}H_2 \longrightarrow CH_3CH_2CH_2CH_3$$
$$CH_3\dot{C}H_2 + Br\cdot \longrightarrow CH_3CH_2Br$$

termination steps

Why Radicals No Longer Have to Be Called Free Radicals

At one time an "R" group was called a radical. For example, the OH group in CH_3CH_2OH was said to be attached to an ethyl radical. To distinguish this kind of ethyl radical from one that was not attached to a group but instead had an unpaired electron, the latter was called a "free radical"—it was free from attachment to a group. Now that we no longer call "R" a *radical*, but instead call it a *group* or a *substituent*, we do not need to call a compound with an unpaired electron a "free radical"; the word "radical" is now unambiguous.

chem Tutorial:
place Radical chain reaction

> **PROBLEM 1**
>
> Show the initiation, propagation, and termination steps for the monochlorination of cyclohexane.
>
> **PROBLEM 2**
>
> Write the mechanism for the formation of tetrachloromethane, CCl_4, from the reaction of methane with $Cl_2 + h\nu$.

12.3 RADICAL STABILITY DEPENDS ON THE NUMBER OF ALKYL GROUPS ATTACHED TO THE CARBON WITH THE UNPAIRED ELECTRON

Like carbocations, radicals are stabilized by electron-donating alkyl groups. Therefore, the relative stabilities of **primary**, **secondary**, and **tertiary alkyl radicals** follow the same order as the relative stabilities of primary, secondary, and tertiary carbocations.

(like carbocations!)
(radicals are stabilized by R groups! (by hyperconjugation))

relative stabilities of alkyl radicals

Alkyl radical stability: 3° > 2° > 1°

tertiary radical   secondary radical   primary radical   methyl radical

The differences in the relative stabilities of the radicals are much smaller than the differences in the relative stabilities of the carbocations because alkyl groups do not stabilize radicals as well as they stabilize carbocations.

Alkyl groups stabilize both carbocations and radicals by hyperconjugation (Section 4.2). Stabilization of a carbocation results from overlap between a filled C—H or C—C σ bond and an empty p orbital: a two-electron system (Figure 12.1a). In contrast, stabilization of a radical results from overlap between a filled C—H or C—C σ bond and a p orbital that contains an electron: a three-electron system (Figure 12.1b). In the two-electron system, both electrons are in a bonding molecular orbital, but in the three-electron system, one of the electrons has to go into an antibonding molecular orbital.

Overall, the three-electron system is stabilizing because there are more electrons in the bonding MO than in the antibonding MO, but it is not as stabilizing as the two-electron system, which does not have an electron in the antibonding MO. Consequently, an alkyl group stabilizes a carbocation about 5–10 times better than it stabilizes a radical.

► **Figure 12.1**
Molecular orbital diagrams showing the stabilization achieved when the electrons of a C—H bond overlap with:
(a) an empty p orbital
(b) a p orbital that contains one electron.

PROBLEM 3 ◆

a. Which of the hydrogens in the following structure is the easiest for a chlorine radical to remove?

b. How many secondary hydrogens does the structure have?

12.4 THE DISTRIBUTION OF PRODUCTS DEPENDS ON PROBABILITY AND REACTIVITY

Two different alkyl halides are obtained from the monochlorination of butane. Substitution of a hydrogen bonded to one of the terminal carbons produces 1-chlorobutane, whereas substitution of a hydrogen bonded to one of the internal carbons forms 2-chlorobutane.

$$CH_3CH_2CH_2CH_3 + Cl_2 \xrightarrow{h\nu} CH_3CH_2CH_2CH_2Cl + CH_3CH_2CHCH_3 + HCl$$

butane   1-chlorobutane   2-chlorobutane
expected = 60%   expected = 40%
experimental = 29%   experimental = 71%

The expected (statistical) distribution of products is 60% 1-chlorobutane and 40% 2-chlorobutane because six of butane's 10 hydrogens can be substituted to form 1-chlorobutane, whereas only four can be substituted to form 2-chlorobutane. This assumes, however, that all of the C—H bonds in butane are equally easy to break. If that were the case, the relative amounts of the two products would depend only on the probability of a chlorine radical colliding with a primary hydrogen, compared with the probability of its colliding with a secondary hydrogen. When we carry out the reaction in the laboratory and analyze the product, however, we find 29% 1-chlorobutane and 71% 2-chlorobutane. Therefore, probability alone does not explain the product distribution.

When a chlorine radical reacts with butane, it can remove a hydrogen atom from an internal carbon, forming a secondary alkyl radical that leads to the formation of 2-chlorobutane, or it can remove a hydrogen atom from a terminal carbon, forming a primary alkyl radical that leads to the formation of 1-chlorobutane. Because more 2-chlorobutane is obtained than expected and *the rate-determining step of the overall reaction is the removal of the hydrogen atom,* we can conclude that it is easier to remove a hydrogen atom from a secondary carbon than from a primary carbon, causing 2-chlorobutane to be formed faster.

$$CH_3CH_2CH_2CH_3$$

$$\xrightarrow{Cl\cdot} CH_3CH_2\overset{\cdot}{C}HCH_3 \xrightarrow{Cl_2} CH_3CH_2CHCH_3 + Cl\cdot$$
a secondary alkyl radical + HCl   2-chlorobutane

$$\xrightarrow{Cl\cdot} CH_3CH_2CH_2\overset{\cdot}{C}H_2 \xrightarrow{Cl_2} CH_3CH_2CH_2CH_2Cl + Cl\cdot$$
a primary alkyl radical + HCl   1-chlorobutane

We should not be surprised that it is easier to remove a hydrogen atom from a secondary carbon than to remove it from a primary carbon, because a secondary radical is more stable than a primary radical. The more stable the radical, the more easily it is formed, because the stability of the radical is reflected in the stability of the transition state leading to its formation (Section 4.3).

After experimentally determining the amount of each chlorination product obtained from various hydrocarbons, chemists were able to conclude that *at room temperature* it is 5.0 times easier for a chlorine radical to remove a hydrogen atom from a tertiary carbon than from a primary carbon, and it is 3.8 times easier to remove a hydrogen atom from a secondary carbon than from a primary carbon. The precise ratios differ at different temperatures. (How relative rates can be determined experimentally is described in Problem 36.)

relative rates of alkyl radical formation by a chlorine radical at room temperature

tertiary > secondary > primary
5.0   3.8   1.0

increasing rate of formation

To determine the relative amounts of different products obtained from radical chlorination of an alkane, both *probability* (the number of hydrogens that can be removed that will lead to the formation of the particular product) and *reactivity* (the relative rate at which a particular hydrogen is removed) must be taken into account. When both factors are considered, the calculated amounts of 1-chlorobutane and 2-chlorobutane agree with the amounts obtained experimentally.

> **Both probability and reactivity must be taken into account when calculating the relative amounts of products.**

relative amount of 1-chlorobutane

number of hydrogens × relative reactivity
$6 \times 1.0 = 6.0$

relative amount of 2-chlorobutane

number of hydrogens × relative reactivity
$4 \times 3.8 = 15$

The percent yield of each alkyl chloride is calculated by dividing the relative amount of the particular product by the sum of the relative amounts of all the alkyl chloride products (6 + 15 = 21).

percent yield of 1-chlorobutane

$$\frac{6.0}{21} = 29 \%$$

percent yield of 2-chlorobutane

$$\frac{15}{21} = 71 \%$$

Because radical chlorination of an alkane can yield several different monosubstitution products as well as products that contain more than one chlorine atom, it is not the best method to use to synthesize an alkyl halide. Addition of a hydrogen halide to an alkene (Section 4.1) or conversion of an alcohol to an alkyl halide (Sections 10.1 and 10.2) is a much better way to make an alkyl halide. Radical halogenation of an alkane is nevertheless still a useful reaction because it is the only way to convert an inert alkane into a reactive compound; once the halogen is introduced into the alkane, it can be replaced by a variety of other substituents (Section 10.2).

PROBLEM 4♦

How many alkyl chlorides can be obtained from monochlorination of the following alkanes? Disregard stereoisomers.

a.

f.

b.

g.

c.

h.

d.

i.

e.

PROBLEM 5 **SOLVED**

If cyclopentane reacts with more than one equivalent of Cl$_2$ at a high temperature, how many dichlorocyclopentanes would you expect to obtain as products?

Solution Seven dichlorocyclopentanes would be obtained as products. Only one isomer is possible for the 1,1-dichloro compound. The 1,2- and 1,3-dichloro compounds have two asymmetric centers. Each has three stereoisomers because the cis isomer is a meso compound and the trans isomer is a pair of enantiomers.

meso compound   enantiomers

meso compound   enantiomers

12.5 THE REACTIVITY—SELECTIVITY PRINCIPLE

The relative rates of radical formation by a bromine radical are different from the relative rates of radical formation by a chlorine radical. For example, at 125 °C, a bromine radical removes a hydrogen atom from a tertiary carbon 1600 times faster than from a primary carbon and removes a hydrogen atom from a secondary carbon 82 times faster than from a primary carbon.

relative rates of alkyl radical formation by a bromine radical at 125 °C

tertiary > secondary > primary
1600   82   1

increasing rate of formation

When a bromine radical removes a hydrogen atom, the differences in reactivity are so great that the reactivity factor is vastly more important than the probability factor. For example, radical bromination of butane gives a 98% yield of 2-bromobutane, compared with the 71% yield of 2-chlorobutane obtained when butane is chlorinated (Section 12.4). In other words, bromination is more highly selective than chlorination.

more highly selective than Cl$_2$.

$$CH_3CH_2CH_2CH_3 + Br_2 \xrightarrow{h\nu} CH_3CH_2CH_2CH_2Br + CH_3CH_2\overset{\overset{\displaystyle Br}{|}}{C}HCH_3 + HBr$$

1-bromobutane
2%
reactivity factor

2-bromobutane
98%
react factor

PROBLEM 6 **SOLVED**

a. What is the major monochlorination product of the following reaction? Disregard stereoisomers.

b. What would be the percent yield of the major product?

$$CH_3\overset{\overset{\displaystyle CH_3}{|}}{C}HCH_2CH_3 \xrightarrow[h\nu]{Cl_2}$$

Solution

a. The relative amount of each product is determined by multiplying the number of hydrogens that can be removed that will lead to the formation of that product by the relative rate for removal of that hydrogen. Thus, the major product is 2-chloro-3-methylbutane.

$$\overset{\overset{\displaystyle CH_3}{|}}{C}H_2\overset{\overset{}{}}{C}HCH_2CH_3 \\ \overset{|}{Cl}$$

1-chloro-2-methylbutane

6 x 1.0 = 6

$$CH_3\overset{\overset{\displaystyle CH_3}{|}}{\underset{\underset{\displaystyle Cl}{|}}{C}}CH_2CH_3$$

2-chloro-2-methylbutane

1 x 5.0 = 5

$$CH_3\overset{\overset{\displaystyle CH_3}{|}}{C}H\underset{\underset{\displaystyle Cl}{|}}{C}HCH_3$$

2-chloro-3-methylbutane

2 x 3.8 = 7.6

$$CH_3\overset{\overset{\displaystyle CH_3}{|}}{C}HCH_2\underset{\underset{\displaystyle Cl}{|}}{C}H_2$$

1-chloro-3-methylbutane

3 x 1.0 = 3

b. The percent yield of the major product is obtained by dividing its relative amount by the relative amounts of all the products of the reaction. The major product would be obtained in 35 % yield.

$$6.0 + 5.0 + 7.6 + 3.0 = 21.6 \qquad \frac{7.6}{21.6} = 35 \%$$

PROBLEM 7 ◆

a. What would be the major product of the above reaction if it had reacted with Br_2 rather than Cl_2? Disregard stereoisomers.

b. What would be the percent yield of the major product?

Why are the relative rates of radical formation so different when a bromine radical rather than a chlorine radical is used as the hydrogen-removing reagent? To answer this question, we must compare the $\Delta H°$ values for forming primary, secondary, and tertiary radicals by a chlorine radical and by a bromine radical. These $\Delta H°$ values can be calculated using the bond dissociation energies in Table 3.2 on page 141. (Remember that $\Delta H°$ is equal to the energy of the bond being broken minus the energy of the bond being formed; Section 3.7.)

E of bond being broken – E of bond being formed

	$\Delta H°$ (kcal/mol)	$\Delta H°$ (kJ/mol)
Cl· + ⟋⟍ ⟶ ⟋⟍· + HCl	101 − 103 = −2	−8
Cl· + ⟋⟍ ⟶ ⟋⟍ + HCl	99 − 103 = −4	−17
Cl· + ⟋⟍ ⟶ ⟋⟍· + HCl	97 − 103 = −6	−25

	$\Delta H°$ (kcal/mol)	$\Delta H°$ (kJ/mol)
Br· + ⟋⟍ ⟶ ⟋⟍· + HBr	101 − 87 = 14	59
Br· + ⟋⟍ ⟶ ⟋⟍ + HBr	99 − 87 = 12	50
Br· + ⟋⟍ ⟶ ⟋⟍· + HBr	97 − 87 = 10	42

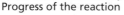

We must also be aware that bromination is a much slower reaction than chlorination. The activation energy for removing a hydrogen atom by a bromine radical has been found experimentally to be about 4.5 times greater than that for removing a hydrogen atom by a chlorine radical. Using the calculated $\Delta H°$ values and the experimental activation energies, we can draw reaction coordinate diagrams for the formation of primary, secondary, and tertiary radicals by a chlorine radical (Figure 12.2a) and by a bromine radical (Figure 12.2b).

> A bromine radical is less reactive and more selective than a chlorine radical.

▲ **Figure 12.2**
(a) Reaction coordinate diagrams for the formation of primary, secondary, and tertiary alkyl radicals as a result of removal of a hydrogen atom by a chlorine radical. The transition states have relatively little radical character because they resemble the reactants.
(b) Reaction coordinate diagrams for the formation of primary, secondary, and tertiary alkyl radicals as a result of removal of a hydrogen atom by a bromine radical. The transition states have a relatively high degree of radical character because they resemble the products.

Because the reaction of a chlorine radical with an alkane to form a primary, secondary, or tertiary radical is exothermic, the transition states resemble the reactants more than they resemble the products (see the Hammond postulate, Section 4.3). The reactants all have approximately the same energy, so there is only a small difference in the activation energies for removal of a hydrogen atom from a primary, secondary, or tertiary carbon. In contrast, the reaction of a bromine radical with an alkane is endothermic, so the transition states resemble the products more than they resemble the reactants. Because there are significant differences between the energies of the product radicals—depending on whether they are primary, secondary, or tertiary—there are significant differences between the activation energies. Therefore, a chlorine radical makes primary, secondary, and tertiary radicals with almost equal ease (Figure 12.2a), whereas a bromine radical has a clear preference for forming the easiest-to-form tertiary radical (Figure 12.2b). In other words, because a bromine radical is relatively unreactive, it is highly selective about which hydrogen atom it removes. In contrast, the much more reactive chlorine radical is considerably less selective. These observations illustrate the **reactivity–selectivity principle**, which states that *the greater the reactivity of a species, the less selective it will be.*

Because chlorination is relatively nonselective, it is a useful reaction only when there is only one kind of hydrogen in the alkane.

$$\text{(cyclohexane)} + Cl_2 \xrightarrow{h\nu} \text{(chlorocyclohexane)} + HCl$$

> **The more reactive a species is, the less selective it will be.**

> **chem place** Tutorial:
> Reactivity-selectivity

PROBLEM-SOLVING STRATEGY

Planning the Synthesis of an Alkyl Halide

Would chlorination or bromination of methylcyclohexane produce a greater yield of 1-halo-1-methylcyclohexane?

To solve this kind of problem, first draw the structures of the compounds being discussed.

$$\text{(methylcyclohexane)} \xrightarrow[h\nu]{X_2} \text{(1-halo-1-methylcyclohexane)}$$

1-Halo-1-methylcyclohexane is a tertiary alkyl halide, so the question becomes, "Will bromination or chlorination produce a greater yield of a tertiary alkyl halide?" Because bromination is more selective, it will produce a greater yield of the desired compound. Chlorination will form some of the tertiary alkyl halide, but it will also form significant amounts of primary and secondary alkyl halides.

Now continue on to Problem 8.

PROBLEM 8◆

a. Would chlorination or bromination produce a greater yield of 1-halo-2,3-dimethylbutane?
b. Would chlorination or bromination produce a greater yield of 2-halo-2,3-dimethylbutane?
c. Would chlorination or bromination be a better way to make 1-halo-2,2-dimethylpropane?

By comparing the $\Delta H°$ values for the sum of the two propagating steps in the monohalogenation of methane, we can understand why alkanes undergo chlorination and bromination but not iodination and why fluorination is too violent a reaction to be useful.

F_2

Cl_2

Br_2

I_2
Halogens

$$F\cdot + CH_4 \longrightarrow \cdot CH_3 + HF \qquad 105 - 136 = -31$$
$$\cdot CH_3 + F_2 \longrightarrow CH_3F + F\cdot \qquad \underline{38 - 115 = -77}$$
$$\Delta H° = -108 \text{ kcal/mol} \quad (\text{or} -452 \text{ kJ/mol})$$

$$Cl\cdot + CH_4 \longrightarrow \cdot CH_3 + HCl \qquad 105 - 103 = 2$$
$$\cdot CH_3 + Cl_2 \longrightarrow CH_3Cl + Cl\cdot \qquad \underline{58 - 84 = -26}$$
$$\Delta H° = -24 \text{ kcal/mol} \quad (\text{or} -100 \text{ kJ/mol})$$

$$Br\cdot + CH_4 \longrightarrow \cdot CH_3 + HBr \qquad 105 - 87 = 18$$
$$\cdot CH_3 + Br_2 \longrightarrow CH_3Br + Br\cdot \qquad \underline{46 - 72 = -26}$$
$$\Delta H° = -8 \text{ kcal/mol} \quad (\text{or} -23 \text{ kJ/mol})$$

$$I\cdot + CH_4 \longrightarrow \cdot CH_3 + HI \qquad 105 - 71 = 34$$
$$\cdot CH_3 + I_2 \longrightarrow CH_3I + I\cdot \qquad \underline{36 - 58 = -22}$$
$$\Delta H° = 12 \text{ kcal/mol} \quad (\text{or} 50 \text{ kJ/mol})$$

The fluorine radical is the most reactive of the halogen radicals, and it reacts violently with alkanes ($\Delta H° = -31$ kcal/mol). In contrast, the iodine radical is the least reactive of the halogen radicals. In fact, it is so unreactive ($\Delta H° = 34$ kcal/mol) that it is unable to remove a hydrogen atom from an alkane. Consequently, it reacts with another iodine radical and reforms I_2.

PROBLEM 9   **SOLVED**

How could butanone be prepared from butane?

butane   ?→   butanone

Solution   We know that the first reaction has to be a radical halogenation because that is the only reaction that an alkane undergoes. Bromination will lead to a greater yield of the desired 2-halo-substituted compound than will chlorination because a bromine radical is more selective than a chlorine radical. A nucleophilic substitution reaction forms the alcohol, which forms the target compound when it is oxidized.

12.6 FORMATION OF EXPLOSIVE PEROXIDES

Ethers are a laboratory hazard because they form explosive peroxides by reacting with O_2 when they are exposed to air. The mechanism for this reaction is shown below. This is the same mechanism that causes fats to become rancid (Section 27.3).

MECHANISM FOR PEROXIDE FORMATION

an α-carbon

R—O—CH—R + Y· ⟶ R—O—ĊH—R + HY
       |
       H

R—O—ĊH—R + ·Ö—Ö· ⟶ R—O—CH—R
                                    |
                                    O—O·

a peroxide radical

R—O—CH—R + R—O—CH—R ⟶ R—O—CH—R + R—O—ĊH—R
       | | |
       O—O·   H   O—OH

a peroxide

- A chain-initiating radical removes a hydrogen atom from an α-carbon of the ether.
- The radical formed in the initiation step reacts with oxygen in a propagation step, forming a peroxide radical.
- The peroxide radical reacts with another molecule of ether in the second propagation step to form a peroxide and regenerate the radical used in the first propagation step.

A **peroxide** is a compound with an O—O bond. Because an O—O bond is easily cleaved homolytically, a peroxide forms radicals that then can create new radicals; a peroxide is a **radical initiator**. Thus, the peroxide product of the above radical chain reaction can initiate another radical chain reaction—an explosive situation. To prevent the formation of explosive peroxides, ethers contain a stabilizer that traps the chain-initiating radical. Once an ether is purified, it has to be discarded within 24 hours.

PROBLEM 10♦

A	B	C	D

a. Which ether is most apt to form a peroxide?
b. Which ether is least apt to form a peroxide?

12.7 THE ADDITION OF RADICALS TO AN ALKENE

The addition of HBr to 1-butene forms 2-bromobutane, because the electrophile (H^+), following the rule that applies to all electrophilic addition reactions (Section 4.4), adds to the sp^2 carbon bonded to the greater number of hydrogens. If, however, you want to synthesize 1-bromobutane, you need to find a way to make bromine an electrophile so it, instead of H^+, will add to the sp^2 carbon bonded to the greater number of hydrogens.

$$CH_3CH_2CH{=}CH_2 \; + \; HBr \longrightarrow \underset{\textbf{2-bromobutane}}{CH_3CH_2\overset{\displaystyle Br}{\overset{|}{C}}HCH_3}$$

$$\underset{\textbf{1-butene}}{CH_3CH_2CH{=}CH_2} \; + \; HBr \xrightarrow{\textbf{peroxide}} \underset{\textbf{1-bromobutane}}{CH_3CH_2CH_2CH_2Br}$$

If a peroxide is added to the reaction mixture, the product of the addition reaction will be the desired 1-bromobutane. Thus, the peroxide changes the mechanism of the reaction in a way that causes the bromine radical to be the electrophile. The following mechanism for the addition of HBr to an alkene in the presence of a peroxide shows that it is a radical chain reaction with characteristic initiation, propagation, and termination steps:

MECHANISM FOR THE ADDITION OF HBr TO AN ALKENE IN THE PRESENCE OF A PEROXIDE

$$\underset{\textbf{a peroxide}}{R\ddot{O}{-}\ddot{O}R} \xrightarrow[\Delta]{\substack{\textbf{light} \\ \textbf{or}}} \underset{\textbf{alkoxy radicals}}{2\,R\ddot{O}\cdot}$$

$$R{-}\ddot{O}\cdot \; + \; H{-}\ddot{B}r{:} \longrightarrow R{-}\ddot{O}{-}H \; + \; \underset{\substack{\textbf{a bromine} \\ \textbf{radical}}}{\cdot\ddot{B}r{:}}$$

⟩ initiation steps

$${:}\ddot{B}r{\cdot} \; + \; CH_2{=}CHCH_2CH_3 \longrightarrow \underset{\underset{\textbf{an alkyl radical}}{:\ddot{B}r{:}}}{CH_2\dot{C}HCH_2CH_3}$$

$$\underset{\overset{|}{Br}}{CH_2\dot{C}HCH_2CH_3} \; + \; H{-}\ddot{B}r{:} \longrightarrow \underset{\overset{|}{Br}\quad\overset{|}{H}}{CH_2{-}CHCH_2CH_3} \; + \; {\cdot}\ddot{B}r{:}$$

⟩ propagation steps

$$\overset{\frown}{:\!\overset{..}{Br}\!\cdot} \ + \ \cdot\overset{..}{Br}\!: \ \longrightarrow \ :\!\overset{..}{Br}\!-\!\overset{..}{Br}\!:$$

$$BrCH_2\overset{\curvearrowright}{\overset{.}{C}HCH_2CH_3} \ + \ :\overset{..}{Br}\cdot \ \longrightarrow \ \underset{\underset{\displaystyle Br}{|}}{BrCH_2CHCH_2CH_3}$$

termination steps

$$2\ BrCH_2\overset{.}{C}HCH_2CH_3 \ \longrightarrow \ \underset{\underset{\displaystyle BrCH_2 \quad CH_2Br}{| \qquad\ \ |}}{CH_3CH_2CH-CHCH_2CH_3}$$

- The weak O—O bond of the peroxide readily breaks homolytically in the presence of light or heat to form alkoxy radicals. This is an initiation step because it creates radicals.
- The alkoxy radical completes its octet by removing a hydrogen atom from a molecule of HBr, forming a bromine radical. This too is an initiation step because it forms the chain-propagating radical (Br·).
- The bromine radical now seeks an electron to complete its octet. Because the double bond of an alkene is electron rich, the bromine radical completes its octet by combining with one of the electrons of the π bond of the alkene to form a C—Br bond. The second electron of the π bond is the unpaired electron in the resulting alkyl radical. If the bromine radical adds to the sp^2 carbon of 1-butene that is bonded to the greater number of hydrogens, a secondary alkyl radical is formed. If the bromine radical adds to the other sp^2 carbon, a primary alkyl radical is formed. The bromine radical, therefore, adds to the sp^2 carbon that is bonded to the greater number of hydrogens in order to form the more stable radical.
- The alkyl radical removes a hydrogen atom from another molecule of HBr to produce a molecule of the alkyl halide product and another bromine radical. This step and the preceding step are propagation steps; in the first propagation step, a radical (Br·) reacts to produce another radical; in the second propagation step, the radical produced in the first propagation step reacts to form the radical (Br·) that was the reactant in the first propagation step.
- The last three steps are termination steps.

Because the first species that adds to the alkene is a radical (Br·), the addition of HBr in the presence of a peroxide is called a **radical addition reaction**.

When HBr reacts with an alkene in the absence of a peroxide, the electrophile—the first species to add to the alkene—is H^+. In the presence of a peroxide, the electrophile is Br·. In both cases, the electrophile adds to the sp^2 carbon that is bonded to the greater number of hydrogens in order to form the more stable intermediate. Thus, both reactions follow the general rule for electrophilic addition reactions: *the electrophile adds to the sp^2 carbon that is bonded to the greater number of hydrogens.*

The electrophile adds to the sp^2 carbon that is bonded to the greater number of hydrogens.

Because the addition of HBr in the presence of a peroxide forms a radical intermediate rather than a carbocation intermediate, the intermediate does not rearrange. Radicals do not rearrange as readily as carbocations do.

carbon skeleton does not rearrange

$$\underset{\textbf{3-methyl-1-butene}}{\underset{\underset{\displaystyle CH_3}{|}}{CH_3CHCH}{=}CH_2} \ + \ HBr \ \xrightarrow{\textbf{peroxide}} \ \underset{\textbf{1-bromo-3-methylbutane}}{\underset{\underset{\displaystyle CH_3}{|}}{CH_3CHCH_2CH_2Br}}$$

PROBLEM 11

Write out the propagation steps for the addition of HBr to 1-methylcyclohexene in the presence of a peroxide.

Without peroxide (the radical initiator), the radical reaction we have just described would not occur. Any reaction that occurs in the presence of a radical initiator, but does not occur in its absence, must take place by a mechanism that involves radicals as intermediates. Any compound that can readily undergo homolysis (dissociate to form radicals) can act as a radical initiator. We will encounter radical initiators again when we discuss polymers in Chapter 29.

While radical initiators cause radical reactions to occur, *radical inhibitors* have the opposite effect; they trap radicals as they are formed, preventing reactions that depend on the presence of radicals. How radical inhibitors trap radicals is discussed in Section 12.11.

A peroxide has no effect on the addition of HCl or HI to an alkene; the addition that occurs when a peroxide is present is the same as the addition that occurs in the absence of a peroxide.

$$CH_3CH{=}CH_2 \ + \ HCl \ \xrightarrow{\text{peroxide}} \ CH_3CHCH_3 \\ \qquad\qquad\qquad\qquad\qquad\qquad\qquad\quad \overset{|}{Cl}$$

$$\overset{\displaystyle CH_3}{\underset{\displaystyle}{CH_3C}}{=}CH_2 \ + \ HI \ \xrightarrow{\text{peroxide}} \ CH_3\overset{\displaystyle CH_3}{\underset{\displaystyle I}{C}}CH_3$$

Why is the **peroxide effect** observed for the addition of HBr, but not for the addition of HCl or HI? This question can be answered by calculating the $\Delta H°$ for the two propagation steps in the radical chain reaction (using the bond dissociation energies in Table 3.2 on page 141).

Cl• + CH$_2$=CH$_2$ ⟶ ClCH$_2$ĊH$_2$ $\Delta H° = 63 - 85 = $ **–22 kcal/mol (or –91 kJ/mol)** ⟵ exothermic

ClCH$_2$ĊH$_2$ + HCl ⟶ ClCH$_2$CH$_3$ + Cl• $\Delta H° = 103 - 101 = $ **+2 kcal/mol (or +8 kJ/mol)** ⟵ endothermic

Br• + CH$_2$=CH$_2$ ⟶ BrCH$_2$ĊH$_2$ $\Delta H° = 63 - 72 = $ **–9 kcal/mol (or –38 kJ/mol)**

BrCH$_2$ĊH$_2$ + HBr ⟶ BrCH$_2$CH$_3$ + Br• $\Delta H° = 87 - 101 = $ **–14 kcal/mol (or –59 kJ/mol)** — exothermic

I• + CH$_2$=CH$_2$ ⟶ ICH$_2$ĊH$_2$ $\Delta H° = 63 - 57 = $ **+6 kcal/mol (or +25 kJ/mol)** ⟵ endothermic

ICH$_2$ĊH$_2$ + HI ⟶ ICH$_2$CH$_3$ + I• $\Delta H° = 71 - 101 = $ **–30 kcal/mol (or –126 kJ/mol)** ⟵ exothermic

For the radical addition of HCl, the first propagation step is exothermic and the second is endothermic. For the radical addition of HI, the first propagation step is endothermic and the second is exothermic. Only for the radical addition of HBr are both propagation steps exothermic. In a radical reaction, the steps that propagate the chain reaction compete with the steps that terminate it. Termination steps are always exothermic, because only bond making (and no bond breaking) occurs. Therefore, only when both propagation steps are exothermic can propagation compete successfully with termination. When HCl or HI adds to an alkene in the presence of a peroxide, any chain reaction that is initiated is then terminated rather than propagated because propagation cannot compete successfully with termination. Consequently, the radical chain reaction does not take place, and the only reaction that occurs is ionic addition (H$^+$ followed by Cl$^-$ or I$^-$).

PROBLEM 12 ♦

What will be the major product of the reaction of 2-methyl-2-butene with each of the following reagents?

a. HBr   **c.** HBr + peroxide

b. HCl   **d.** HCl + peroxide

12.8 THE STEREOCHEMISTRY OF RADICAL SUBSTITUTION AND RADICAL ADDITION REACTIONS

We have seen that when a reactant that does not have an asymmetric center undergoes a reaction that forms a product with one asymmetric center, the product will be a racemic mixture (Section 5.19). Thus, the following *radical substitution reaction* forms an equal amount of each enantiomer (that is, a racemic mixture).

an asymmetric center

$$CH_3CH_2CH_2CH_3 \ + \ Br_2 \ \xrightarrow{h\nu} \ CH_3CH_2\overset{|}{\underset{|}{C}}HCH_3 \ + \ HBr$$
$$\underset{Br}{}$$

configuration of the products

a pair of enantiomers

Similarly, the product of the following *radical addition reaction* is a racemic mixture:

> When a reactant that does not have an asymmetric center undergoes a reaction that forms a product with one asymmetric center, the product will be a racemic mixture.

an asymmetric center

$$\underset{CH_3CH_2C=CH_2}{\overset{CH_3}{|}} \ + \ HBr \ \xrightarrow{peroxide} \ \underset{CH_3CH_2CHCH_2Br}{\overset{CH_3}{|}}$$

2-methyl-1-butene   **1-bromo-2-methylbutane**

configuration of the products

a pair of enantiomers

Both the radical substitution and radical addition reactions form a racemic mixture because both reactions form a radical intermediate. The radical intermediate in the substitution reaction is formed when the bromine radical removes a hydrogen atom from the reactant; the radical intermediate in the addition reaction is formed when the bromine radical adds to one of the sp^2 carbons of the double bond.

radical intermediate
in the substitution reaction

radical intermediate
in the addition reaction

The carbon that bears the unpaired electron in the radical intermediate is sp^2 hybridized; therefore, the three atoms to which it is bonded lie in a plane (Section 1.10).

The incoming atom has equal access to both sides of the plane. Consequently, identical amounts of the *R* enantiomer and the *S* enantiomer are obtained in both the substitution and addition reactions.

Thus, the stereochemical outcome of a *radical substitution reaction* is identical to the stereochemical outcome of a *radical addition reaction* because both reactions form a radical intermediate, and it is the reaction of the intermediate that determines the configuration of the products.

Identical amounts of the *R* and *S* enantiomers are also obtained if a hydrogen bonded to an asymmetric center is substituted by a halogen. Breaking the bond to the asymmetric center destroys the configuration at the asymmetric center and forms a planar radical intermediate. The incoming halogen has equal access to both sides of the plane, so identical amounts of the two enantiomers are formed.

PROBLEM 13◆

a. What hydrocarbon with molecular formula C_4H_{10} forms only two monochlorinated products? Both products are achiral.
b. What hydrocarbon with the same molecular formula as in part **a** forms only three monochlorinated products? One is achiral and two are chiral.

PROBLEM 14

Draw the stereoisomers of the major monobromination products obtained from the following reaction.

12.9   RADICAL SUBSTITUTION OF BENZYLIC AND ALLYLIC HYDROGENS

An **allylic radical** has an unpaired electron on an allylic carbon and, like an allylic cation, has two resonance contributors.

Electron delocalization increases the stability of a molecule.

an allylic radical

See Special Topic VII in the *Study Guide and Solutions Manual* for additional information on drawing curved arrows in radical systems.

A **benzylic radical** has an unpaired electron on a benzylic carbon and, like a benzylic cation, has five resonance contributors.

a benzylic radical

Because electron delocalization stabilizes a molecule (Section 7.6), allyl and benzyl radicals are both more stable than other primary radicals. They are even more stable than tertiary radicals.

relative stabilities of radicals

We know that the more stable the radical, the faster it can be formed. This means that a hydrogen bonded to either a benzylic carbon or an allylic carbon will be preferentially substituted in a halogenation reaction. Because bromination is more highly regioselective than chlorination, the percent of substitution at the benzylic or allylic carbon is greater for bromination.

N-Bromosuccinimide (NBS) is frequently used to brominate allylic carbons because it allows a radical substitution reaction to be carried out in the presence of a low concentration of Br_2 and a low concentration of HBr. If a high concentration of Br_2 is present, electrophilic addition of Br_2 to the double bond will compete with allylic substitution. If a high concentration of HBr is present, radical addition of HBr to the double bond will compete with allylic substitution.

The reaction begins with homolytic cleavage of the N—Br bond of NBS. This generates the bromine radical needed to initiate the radical reaction. Light or heat and a radical initiator such as a peroxide are used to promote the reaction. In the first propagating step, the bromine radical removes an allylic hydrogen to form HBr and an allylic radical that is stabilized by electron delocalization. The allylic radical reacts with Br_2 in the second propagating step, forming the allyl bromide and a chain-propagating bromine radical.

The Br_2 used in the second step of the preceding reaction sequence is produced in low concentration from a fast ionic reaction between NBS and HBr.

When a radical removes a hydrogen atom from an allylic carbon, the unpaired electron of the allylic radical is shared by two carbons. In other words, the allylic radical has two resonance contributors. In both the reaction on page 485 and the following reaction, only one substitution product is formed, because the groups attached to the sp^2 carbons are the same in both resonance contributors:

3-bromopropene

However, if the groups attached to the two sp^2 carbons of the allylic radical are *not* the same in both resonance contributors, two substitution products are formed:

3-bromo-1-butene   1-bromo-2-butene

PROBLEM 15

Two products are formed when methylenecyclohexane reacts with NBS. Show how each is formed.

PROBLEM 16   SOLVED

How many allylic substituted bromoalkenes are formed from the reaction of 2-pentene with NBS? Disregard stereoisomers.

Solution   The bromine radical will more readily remove a secondary allylic hydrogen from C-4 of 2-pentene than a primary allylic hydrogen from C-1. The resonance contributors of the resulting radical intermediate have the same groups attached to the sp^2 carbons, so only one bromoalkene is formed. Because of the high selectivity of the bromine radical, an insignificant amount of radical will be formed by removal of a hydrogen from the less reactive primary allylic position.

PROBLEM 17♦

How many allylic substituted bromoalkenes are formed from the reaction in Problem 16 if stereoisomers are included?

PROBLEM 18

a. Give the major product(s) of the reaction of 1-methylcyclohexene with the following reagents, disregarding stereoisomers:
  1. NBS/Δ/peroxide   3. HBr
  2. Br₂/CH₂Cl₂   4. HBr/peroxide
b. Give the configuration of the products.

---

chem Tutorial:
place Allylic bromination

Why does the bromine radical from NBS remove an allylic hydrogen whereas the bromine radical from HBr + peroxide adds to the double bond? The bromine radical can in fact do both. However, when NBS is used, there is little HBr present to complete the addition reaction after the bromine radical has added to the double bond. Therefore, the reactant is reformed, since the addition of a bromine radical to a double bond is reversible, and allylic substitution becomes the major pathway.

$$CH_3CH = CH_2 \ + \ Br\cdot$$

Br· adds to the double bond
$$CH_3\overset{\cdot}{C}HCH_2Br$$

$$\overset{\cdot}{C}H_2CH=CH_2 \ + \ HBr$$
Br· removes an allylic hydrogen

 Cyclopropane

Although it is an alkane, cyclopropane undergoes electrophilic addition reactions as if it were an alkene. Cyclopropane is more reactive than propene toward addition of acids such as HBr and HCl, but is less reactive toward addition of Cl₂ and Br₂, so a Lewis acid (FeCl₃ or FeBr₃) is needed to catalyze halogen addition (Section 1.27).

△ + HBr ⟶ CH₃CH₂CH₂Br

△ + Cl₂ →[FeCl₃] ClCH₂CH₂CH₂Cl

△ + H₂ →[Ni][80 °C] CH₃CH₂CH₃

It is the strain in the small ring that makes it possible for cyclopropane to undergo electrophilic addition reactions. Because of the 60° bond angles in its three-membered ring, the compound's sp^3 orbitals cannot overlap head-on; this decreases the effectiveness of the orbital overlap (Section 2.11). Thus, the C—C bonds in cyclopropane are considerably weaker than normal C—C σ bonds (see Figure 2.6 on page 101). Consequently, the three-membered ring undergoes a ring-opening reaction with electrophilic reagents.

△ + XY ⟶ H₂C—CH₂—CH₂ with X and Y

12.10 DESIGNING A SYNTHESIS III: MORE PRACTICE WITH MULTISTEP SYNTHESIS

Now that the number of reactions that you are familiar with has increased, you can design the synthesis of a wide variety of compounds.

Example 1. Starting with the ether shown below, how could you prepare the carboxylic acid?

Heating the ether with one equivalent of HI forms a primary alcohol that, when oxidized, forms the desired carboxylic acid.

Example 2. Suggest a way to prepare 1,3-cyclohexadiene from cyclohexane.

Deciding what the first reaction should be is easy, because the only reaction that an alkane can undergo is a radical substitution reaction with Cl_2 or Br_2. Next, an E2 reaction, using a high concentration of a strong and bulky base and carried out at a relatively high temperature to encourage elimination over substitution, will form cyclohexene. Therefore, *tert*-butoxide ion should be used as the base and *tert*-butyl alcohol as the solvent. Radical bromination of cyclohexene forms an allylic bromide, which will form the desired target molecule by undergoing another E2 reaction.

Example 3. Starting with methylcyclohexane, how could the following vicinal *trans*-dihalide be prepared?

Again, since the starting material is an alkane, the first reaction must be a radical substitution: bromination leads to selective substitution of the tertiary hydrogen. Under E2 conditions, tertiary alkyl halides undergo only elimination, so there will be no competing substitution product formed in the next reaction. However, a relatively unhindered base should be used to favor removal of a proton from the secondary carbon over removal of a proton from the methyl group. The final step is addition of Br_2; only anti addition occurs in this reaction, so the target molecule (along with its enantiomer) is obtained.

Example 4. Design a synthesis for the target molecule from the indicated starting material.

It is not immediately obvious how to carry out this synthesis, so let's use retrosynthetic analysis to find a way. The only method you know for introducing a C≡N group into a molecule is nucleophilic substitution. The alkyl halide for that substitution reaction can be obtained from the addition of HBr to an alkene in the presence of a peroxide. The alkene for that addition reaction can be obtained from an elimination reaction using an alkyl halide obtained by benzylic substitution.

The reaction sequence can now be written in the forward direction. Notice that a bulky base is used to encourage elimination over substitution.

PROBLEM 19

Design a multistep synthesis to show how each of the following compounds could be prepared from the given starting material:

•

12.11 RADICAL REACTIONS OCCUR IN BIOLOGICAL SYSTEMS

Because of the large amount of energy—heat or light—required to initiate a radical reaction and the difficulty in controlling a radical chain reaction once it is initiated, scientists assumed for a long time that radical reactions were not important in biological systems. However, it is now widely recognized that many biological reactions involve radicals. Instead of being generated by heat or light, the radicals in these reactions are formed by the interaction of organic molecules with metal ions. The radical reactions take place at the active sites of enzymes (Section 24.9). Containing the reaction at a specific site allows the reaction to be controlled.

Water-soluble (polar) compounds are readily eliminated by the body. In contrast, water-insoluble (nonpolar) compounds are not readily eliminated but instead accumulate in the nonpolar components of cells. For cells to avoid becoming "toxic dumps," nonpolar compounds that are ingested (drugs, foods, environmental pollutants) must be converted into polar compounds that can be excreted.

A biological reaction carried out in the liver converts toxic nonpolar hydrocarbons into less toxic polar alcohols by substituting an H in the hydrocarbon with an OH. The reaction involves radicals and is catalyzed by an iron-containing enzyme called cytochrome P_{450}. An alkyl radical intermediate is created when $Fe^V = O$ removes a hydrogen atom from an alkane. Then $Fe^{IV}OH$ dissociates homolytically into Fe^{III} and $HO\cdot$, and the $HO\cdot$ immediately combines with the radical intermediate to form the alcohol.

This reaction can also have the opposite toxicological effect. That is, substituting an OH for an H in some compounds causes a nontoxic compound to become toxic. For example, studies done on animals showed that substituting an OH for an H caused dichloromethane (CH_2Cl_2) to become a carcinogen when inhaled. This shows that compounds that are nontoxic *in vitro* (in a test tube) are not necessarily nontoxic *in vivo* (in an organism).

Decaffeinated Coffee and the Cancer Scare

Animal studies revealing that dichloromethane becomes a carcinogen when inhaled caused some concern, because dichloromethane was the solvent used to extract caffeine from coffee beans in the manufacture of decaffeinated coffee. However, when dichloromethane was added to the drinking water given to laboratory rats and mice, researchers found no toxic effects, even in rats that had consumed an amount of dichloromethane equivalent to the amount that would be ingested by drinking 120,000 cups of decaffeinated coffee per day and in mice that had consumed an amount equivalent to drinking 4.4 million cups of decaffeinated coffee per day. In addition, no increased risk of cancer was found in a study of thousands of workers exposed daily to inhaled dichloromethane.

(This shows that the results of studies done on humans do not always agree with the results of those done on laboratory animals.)

Because of the initial concern, however, researchers sought alternative methods for extracting caffeine from coffee beans. Extraction by CO_2 at supercritical temperatures and pressures was found to be a better method because it extracts caffeine without simultaneously extracting some of the flavor compounds, as dichloromethane does. This was one of the first green (environmentally benign) commercial chemical processes to be developed; CO_2 is a relatively harmless waste product, whereas dichloromethane is not a substance we would want to release into the environment (Section 6.12).

Fats and oils react with radicals to form compounds that have strong odors. These compounds are responsible for the unpleasant taste and smell associated with sour milk and rancid butter. The molecules that form cell membranes can undergo this same radical reaction (Section 27.3). Furthermore, radical reactions in biological systems have been implicated in the aging process.

Clearly, unwanted radicals in biological systems must be destroyed before they do damage to cells. Unwanted radical reactions are prevented by **radical inhibitors**, compounds that destroy reactive radicals by converting them either into unreactive radicals or into compounds with only paired electrons. Hydroquinone is an example of a radical inhibitor. When hydroquinone traps a radical, it forms semiquinone, also a radical but it is stabilized by electron delocalization and is, therefore, less reactive than other radicals. Furthermore, semiquinone can trap another radical and form quinone, a compound whose electrons are all paired. Hydroquinones are found in the cells of all aerobic organisms.

$$\text{hydroquinone} + R\cdot \longrightarrow \text{semiquinone} + RH \longrightarrow \text{quinone} + RH$$

hydroquinone   reactive radical   semiquinone   quinone

PROBLEM 20◆

How many atoms share the unpaired electron in semiquinone?

Two other examples of radical inhibitors in biological systems are vitamins C and E. Like hydroquinone, they form relatively stable (unreactive) radicals. Vitamin C (also called ascorbic acid) is a water-soluble compound that traps radicals formed in the interior of cells and in blood plasma (both of which are aqueous environments). Vitamin E (also called α-tocopherol) is a water-insoluble (and therefore fat-soluble) compound that traps radicals formed in cell membranes, which are nonpolar. Vitamin E is the primary antioxidant for fat tissue in humans. It, therefore, is important in preventing the development of atherosclerosis (Sections 2.15 and 26.4). Why one vitamin functions in aqueous environments and the other in nonaqueous environments should be apparent from their structures and electrostatic potential maps, which show that vitamin C is a relatively polar compound and vitamin E is nonpolar.

vitamin C
ascorbic acid

vitamin E
α-tocopherol

Is Chocolate a Health Food?

We have long been told that our diets should include lots of fruits and vegetables because they are good sources of antioxidants. Antioxidants protect against cardiovascular disease, cancer, and cataracts, and they are thought to slow the effects of aging. Chocolate is made up of hundreds of organic compounds, including high levels of antioxidants called catechins. On a weight basis, the concentration of antioxidants in chocolate is higher than in red wine or green tea, and 20 times higher than in tomatoes. Another piece of good news for chocolate lovers is that stearic acid, the main fatty acid in chocolate, does not appear to raise blood cholesterol levels the way other saturated fatty acids do. Dark chocolate contains more than twice the level of antioxidants found in milk chocolate. Unfortunately, white chocolate contains no antioxidants.

catechins

PROBLEM 21

Explain using resonance structures why a catechin is an antioxidant.

Food Preservatives

Radical inhibitors that occur in or are added to foods are known as *preservatives* or *antioxidants*. They preserve food by preventing undesirable radical chain reactions. Vitamin E is a naturally occurring preservative found in vegetable oil. BHA and BHT are synthetic preservatives added to many packaged foods.

butylated hydroxyanisole
BHA

butylated hydroxytoluene
BHT

food preservatives

B I O G R A P H Y

In 1995, the Nobel Prize in Chemistry was awarded to **Sherwood Rowland**, **Mario Molina**, *and* **Paul Crutzen** *for their pioneering work in explaining the chemical processes responsible for the depletion of the ozone layer in the stratosphere. Their findings demonstrated that human activities could interfere with global processes that support life. This was the first time a Nobel Prize was presented for work in the environmental sciences.*

F. Sherwood Rowland *was born in Ohio in 1927. He received a Ph.D. from the University of Chicago and is a professor of chemistry at the University of California, Irvine.*

Mario Molina *was born in Mexico in 1943 and subsequently became a U.S. citizen. He received a Ph.D. from the University of California, Berkeley, and then worked as a postdoctoral fellow in Rowland's laboratory. He is currently a professor of earth, atmospheric, and planetary sciences at the Massachusetts Institute of Technology.*

Paul Crutzen *was born in Amsterdam in 1933. He was trained as a meteorologist and became interested in stratospheric chemistry and stratospheric ozone in particular. He is a professor at the Max Planck Institute for Chemistry in Mainz, Germany.*

12.13 RADICALS AND STRATOSPHERIC OZONE

Ozone (O_3), a major constituent of smog, is a health hazard at ground level. In the stratosphere, however, a layer of ozone shields the Earth from harmful solar radiation. The ozone layer is thinnest at the equator and densest toward the poles, with the greatest concentrations lying between 12 and 15 miles above the Earth's surface. Ozone is formed in the atmosphere from the interaction of molecular oxygen with very short wavelength ultraviolet light.

$$O_2 \xrightarrow{h\nu} O + O$$
$$O + O_2 \longrightarrow O_3$$
$$\text{ozone}$$

In the stratosphere, ozone acts as a filter for biologically harmful ultraviolet radiation that otherwise would reach the surface of the Earth. Among other effects, high-energy short-wavelength ultraviolet light can damage DNA in skin cells, causing mutations that trigger skin cancer (Section 30.6). We owe our very existence to this protective ozone layer. According to current theories of evolution, life could not have developed on land without it. Instead, most if not all living things would have had to remain in the ocean, where water screens out the harmful ultraviolet radiation.

Since about 1985, scientists have noted a precipitous drop in stratospheric ozone over Antarctica. This area of ozone depletion, dubbed the "ozone hole," is unprecedented in the history of ozone observations. Scientists subsequently noted a similar decrease in ozone over Arctic regions; then, in 1988, they detected a depletion of ozone over the United States for the first time. Three years later, scientists determined that the rate of ozone depletion was two to three times faster than originally anticipated.

The size of the ozone hole is dependent on weather conditions. In 2008, it extended over about 27 million square miles, compared to 25 million square miles in 2007 and 29 million square miles—about the size of the continent of North America—in 2006. Many in the scientific community blame recently observed increases in cataracts and skin cancer as well as diminished plant growth on the ultraviolet radiation that has penetrated the reduced ozone layer. Some predict that erosion of the protective ozone layer will cause an additional 200,000 deaths from skin cancer over the next 50 years.

Strong circumstantial evidence implicates synthetic chlorofluorocarbons (CFCs)—alkanes such as $CFCl_3$ and CF_2Cl_2, in which all the hydrogens have been replaced by fluorine and chlorine—as a major cause of ozone depletion. These gases, known commercially as Freon, have been used extensively as cooling fluids in refrigerators and air conditioners. They were also once widely used as propellants in aerosol spray cans (deodorant, hair spray, and so on) because of their odorless, nontoxic, and nonflammable properties and because, being chemically inert, they do not react with the contents of the can. Such use now, however, has been banned.

Chlorofluorocarbons remain very stable in the atmosphere until they reach the stratosphere. There they encounter wavelengths of ultraviolet light that cause the C—Cl bond to break homolytically, generating chlorine radicals.

$$
\begin{array}{ccc}
 & \text{Cl} & & & \text{Cl} \\
 & | & & & | \\
\text{F} - \text{C} - \text{Cl} & \xrightarrow{h\nu} & \text{F} - \text{C} \cdot & + & \text{Cl} \cdot \\
 & | & & & | \\
 & \text{F} & & & \text{F}
\end{array}
$$

These chlorine radicals are the ozone-removing agents. They react with ozone to form chlorine monoxide radicals and molecular oxygen. The chlorine monoxide radical then reacts with more ozone to form chlorine dioxide, which dissociates to regenerate a chlorine radical. These three steps—two of which each destroy an ozone molecule—are repeated over and over. It has been calculated that a single chlorine atom destroys 100,000 ozone molecules!

$$Cl\cdot \;+\; O_3 \;\longrightarrow\; ClO\cdot \;+\; O_2$$
$$ClO\cdot \;+\; O_3 \;\longrightarrow\; \cdot ClO_2 \;+\; O_2$$
$$\cdot ClO_2 \;\longrightarrow\; Cl\cdot \;+\; O_2$$

Polar stratospheric clouds increase the rate of ozone destruction. These clouds form over Antarctica during the cold winter months. Ozone depletion in the Arctic is less severe because the temperature generally does not get low enough for stratospheric clouds to form there.

1979   1985   1991

1997   2003   2008

*The ozone over a given area is compressed to 0 °C and 1 atm pressure, and the thickness of the slab is measured. 1 Dobson unit = 0.01 mm thickness

Dobson Units

100   200   300   400   500

Growth of the Antarctic ozone hole, located mostly over the continent of Antarctica, since 1979. The images were made from data supplied by total ozone-mapping spectrometers (TOMSs). The color scale depicts the total ozone values in Dobson units,* with the lowest ozone densities represented by dark blue.

Artificial Blood

Clinical trials are currently underway to test the use of perfluorocarbons—alkanes in which all the hydrogens have been replaced by fluorines—as compounds to replace blood volume and mimic hemoglobin's ability to carry oxygen to cells and transport carbon dioxide to the lungs.

These compounds are not a true blood substitute, for blood performs many functions that artificial blood cannot. For example, white blood cells fight against infection and platelets are involved in blood clotting. However, artificial blood has several advantages in trauma situations: it is safe from disease, it can be administered to any blood type, its availability is not dependent on blood donors, and it can be stored longer than whole blood, which is good for only about 40 days.

SUMMARY

Alkanes are called **saturated hydrocarbons** because they do not contain any double or triple bonds. Since they have only strong σ bonds and atoms with no partial charges, alkanes are very unreactive. Alkanes undergo **radical substitution reactions** with chlorine (Cl_2) or bromine (Br_2) at high temperatures or in the presence of light to form alkyl chlorides or alkyl bromides. The substitution reaction is a **radical chain reaction** with **initiation**, **propagation**, and **termination steps**.

In **heterolytic bond cleavage**, a bond breaks so that both electrons stay with one of the atoms; in **homolytic bond cleavage**, a bond breaks so that each of the atoms retains one of the bonding electrons.

The rate-determining step of the radical substitution is removal of a hydrogen atom to form an alkyl radical. Radicals are stabilized by electron-donating alkyl groups. Thus, a **tertiary alkyl radical** is more stable than a **secondary alkyl radical**, which is more stable than a **primary alkyl radical**. The relative rates of radical formation are benzylic ~ allyl > 3° > 2° > 1° > vinyl ~ methyl. Calculation of the relative amounts of products obtained from the radical halogenation of an alkane must take into account both probability and the relative rate at which a particular hydrogen is removed.

The **reactivity–selectivity principle** states that the more reactive a species is, the less selective it will be. A bromine radical is *less reactive* than a chlorine radical, so a bromine radical is *more selective* about which hydrogen atom it removes. *N*-Bromosuccinimide (NBS) is used to brominate allylic carbons. Unwanted radical reactions are prevented by **radical inhibitors**, compounds that destroy reactive radicals by creating radicals that are relatively stable or compounds that have only paired electrons.

Ethers form explosive peroxides when they are exposed to air. A **peroxide** is a **radical initiator** because it creates radicals. **Radical addition reactions** are also chain reactions with **initiation, propagation**, and **termination steps**. A peroxide reverses the order (and therefore the position)

of addition of H and Br to an alkene because it causes Br•, instead of H^+, to be the electrophile. The **peroxide effect** is observed only for the addition of HBr.

If a reactant that does not have an asymmetric center undergoes a radical substitution or a radical addition reaction that forms a product with an asymmetric center, a racemic mixture will be obtained. A racemic mixture is also obtained if a hydrogen bonded to an asymmetric center is substituted by a halogen.

Some biological reactions involve radicals formed by the interaction of organic molecules with metal ions. The reactions take place in the active site of an enzyme.

Strong circumstantial evidence implicates synthetic chlorofluorocarbons as being responsible for depletion of the ozone layer. The interaction of these compounds with UV light generates chlorine radicals, which are the ozone-removing agents.

SUMMARY OF REACTIONS

1. *Alkanes* undergo radical substitution reactions with Cl_2 or Br_2 in the presence of heat or light (Sections 12.2–12.5).

$$CH_3CH_3 + Cl_2 \xrightarrow{\Delta \text{ or } h\nu} CH_3CH_2Cl + HCl$$
excess

$$CH_3CH_3 + Br_2 \xrightarrow{\Delta \text{ or } h\nu} CH_3CH_2Br + HBr$$
excess
bromination is more selective than chlorination

2. A radical initiator removes a hydrogen atom from an α-carbon of an ether to form a peroxide (Section 12.6).

3. *Alkenes* undergo radical addition of hydrogen bromide in the presence of a peroxide (Br• is the electrophile; Section 12.7).

$$RCH{=}CH_2 + HBr \xrightarrow{\text{peroxide}} RCH_2CH_2Br$$

4. *Alkyl-substituted benzenes* undergo radical substitution at the benzylic position (Section 12.9).

5. *Alkenes* undergo radical substitution at allylic carbons. NBS is used for bromination at allylic carbons (Section 12.9).

KEY TERMS

alkane (p. 468)
alkoxy radical (p. 480)
allylic radical (p. 484)
benzylic radical (p. 484)
combustion (p. 470)
free radical (p. 470)
halogenation reaction (p. 470)
heterolysis (p. 470)
heterolytic bond cleavage (p. 470)

homolysis (p. 470)
homolytic bond cleavage (p. 470)
initiation step (p. 470)
peroxide (p. 479)
peroxide effect (p. 482)
primary alkyl radical (p. 472)
propagation step (p. 471)
radical (p. 470)
radical addition reaction (p. 481)

radical chain reaction (p. 471)
radical inhibitor (p. 490)
radical initiator (p. 480)
radical substitution reaction (p. 471)
reactivity–selectivity principle (p. 478)
saturated hydrocarbons (p. 468)
secondary alkyl radical (p. 472)
termination step (p. 471)
tertiary alkyl radical (p. 472)

PROBLEMS

22. Give the product(s) of each of the following reactions, disregarding stereoisomers:

a. $CH_2\!=\!CHCH_2CH_2CH_3$ + NBS $\xrightarrow[\text{peroxide}]{\Delta}$

d. ⬡ + Cl_2 $\xrightarrow{h\nu}$

b. $CH_3\overset{\overset{\displaystyle CH_3}{|}}{C}\!=\!CHCH_3$ + NBS $\xrightarrow[\text{peroxide}]{\Delta}$

e. ⬠ + Cl_2 $\xrightarrow{CH_2Cl_2}$

c. (structure) + Br_2 $\xrightarrow{h\nu}$

f. (cyclopentane with CH_3) + Cl_2 $\xrightarrow{h\nu}$

23. a. Identify an alkane with molecular formula C_5H_{12} that forms only one monochlorinated product when heated with Cl_2.
   b. Identify an alkane with molecular formula C_7H_{16} that forms seven monochlorinated products (disregarding stereoisomers) when heated with Cl_2.

24. For each of the following compounds, give the major product that would be obtained from treating an excess of the compound with Cl_2 in the presence of light at room temperature. Disregard stereoisomers.

a. (cyclohexane with two CH_3 groups)

b. (cyclohexane with two CH_3 groups)

c. H_3C (ring) CH_3 / CH_3

25. What would the answers be to Problem 24 if the same compounds were treated with Br_2 at 125 °C?

26. Give the major product of each of the following reactions, disregarding stereoisomers:

a. ⬠ + NBS $\xrightarrow[\text{peroxide}]{\Delta}$

d. (benzene with CH_2CH_3) + NBS $\xrightarrow[\text{peroxide}]{\Delta}$

b. (cyclopentadiene) + NBS $\xrightarrow[\text{peroxide}]{\Delta}$

e. (cyclopentene with two CH_3) + NBS $\xrightarrow[\text{peroxide}]{\Delta}$

c. (cyclohexene with CH_3) + NBS $\xrightarrow[\text{peroxide}]{\Delta}$

f. H_3C (structure) CH_3 + NBS $\xrightarrow[\text{peroxide}]{\Delta}$

27. When 2-methylpropane is monochlorinated in the presence of light at room temperature, 36% of the product is 2-chloro-2-methylpropane and 64% is 1-chloro-2-methylpropane. From these data, calculate how much easier it is to remove a hydrogen atom from a tertiary carbon than from a primary carbon under these conditions.

28. Iodine (I_2) does not react with ethane, even though I_2 is more easily cleaved homolytically than the other halogens. Explain.

29. Propose a mechanism to account for the products formed in the following reaction:

30. The deuterium kinetic isotope effect for halogenation of an alkane is defined in the following equation, where $X· = Cl·$ or $Br·$:

$$\frac{\textbf{deuterium kinetic}}{\textbf{isotope effect}} = \frac{\textbf{rate of homolytic cleavage of a C—H bond by Cl·}}{\textbf{rate of homolytic cleavage of a C—D bond by Cl·}}$$

Predict whether chlorination or bromination would have a greater deuterium kinetic isotope effect.

31. a. How many monobromination products would be obtained from the radical bromination of methylcyclohexane? Disregard stereoisomers.
b. Which product would be obtained in greatest yield? Explain.
c. How many monobromination products would be obtained if all stereoisomers are included?

32. Give the major product of each of the following reactions, disregarding stereoisomers:

33. a. Propose a mechanism for the following reaction:

b. Given that the $\Delta H°$ value for the reaction is −42 kcal/mol and the bond dissociation energies for the C—H, C—Cl, and O—H bonds are 101 kcal/mol, respectively, calculate the bond dissociation energy of the O—Cl bond.
c. Which set of propagation steps is more likely to occur?

34. What stereoisomers would be obtained from the following reaction?

$$CH_3CH_2 \quad \diagdown \quad CH_2CH_3$$
$$C=C$$
$$H_3C \diagup \quad \diagdown CH_3 \quad + \quad HBr \quad \xrightarrow{H_2O_2}$$

35. Using the given starting material and any necessary organic or inorganic reagents, indicate how the desired compounds could be synthesized:

a. HO⌒⌒⌒ ⟶ (tetrahydrofuran ring with O)

b. ⌒⌿ ⟶ ⌿⌿

c. (cyclohexane) ⟶ (cyclohexane with OH and OCH₃)

d. (cyclohexane) ⟶ (cyclohexane with OH and OCH₃)

36. A chemist wanted to determine experimentally the relative ease of removing a hydrogen atom from a tertiary, a secondary, and a primary carbon by a chlorine radical. He allowed 2-methylbutane to undergo chlorination at 300 °C and obtained as products 36% 1-chloro-2-methylbutane, 18% 2-chloro-2-methylbutane, 28% 2-chloro-3-methylbutane, and 18% 1-chloro-3-methylbutane. What values did he obtain for the relative ease of removing a hydrogen atom from tertiary, secondary, and primary hydrogen carbons by a chlorine radical under the conditions of his experiment?

37. At 600 °C, the ratio of the relative rates of formation of a tertiary, a secondary, and a primary radical by a chlorine radical is 2.6 : 2.1 : 1. Explain the change in the degree of regioselectivity compared to what was found in Problem 36.

38. a. What five-carbon alkene will form the same product whether it reacts with HBr in the *presence* of a peroxide or with HBr in the *absence* of a peroxide?
b. Give three 6-carbon alkenes that form the same product, whether they react with HBr in the *presence* of a peroxide or with HBr in the *absence* of a peroxide.

39. a. Calculate the $\Delta H°$ value for the following reaction:

$$CH_4 \quad + \quad Cl_2 \quad \xrightarrow{h\nu} \quad CH_3Cl \quad + \quad HCl$$

b. Calculate the sum of the $\Delta H°$ values for the following two propagation steps:

$$CH_3-H \quad + \quad \cdot Cl \quad \longrightarrow \quad \cdot CH_3 \quad + \quad H-Cl$$
$$\cdot CH_3 \quad + \quad Cl-Cl \quad \longrightarrow \quad CH_3-Cl \quad + \quad \cdot Cl$$

c. Why do both calculations give you the same value of $\Delta H°$?

40. A possible alternative mechanism to that shown in Problem 39 for the monochlorination of methane would involve the following propagation steps:

$$CH_3-H \quad + \quad \cdot Cl \quad \longrightarrow \quad CH_3-Cl \quad + \quad \cdot H$$
$$\cdot H \quad + \quad Cl-Cl \quad \longrightarrow \quad H-Cl \quad + \quad \cdot Cl$$

How do you know that the reaction does not take place by this mechanism?

41. Propose a mechanism for the following reaction:

42. Using the given starting material and any necessary organic or inorganic reagents, indicate how the desired compounds could be synthesized:

a.

b.

43. Explain why the rate of bromination of methane decreases if HBr is added to the reaction mixture.

Identification of Organic Compounds

By now you have worked through many problems that asked you to design the synthesis of an organic compound. But if you were actually to go into the laboratory to carry out a synthesis you designed, how would you know that the compound you obtained was the one you had set out to prepare?

When a scientist discovers a new compound with physiological activity, its structure must be ascertained. Only after its structure is known can the scientist design methods to synthesize the compound and carry out studies to provide insights into its biological behavior.

Clearly, chemists need to be able to determine the structures of compounds. **Part 4** discusses some of the techniques they use to do this.

CHAPTER 13
Mass Spectrometry, Infrared Spectroscopy, and Ultraviolet/Visible Spectroscopy

In Chapter 13 you will learn about three instrumental techniques that chemists use to analyze compounds. **Mass spectrometry** is used to find the molecular mass and the molecular formula of an organic compound; it is also used to identify certain structural features of the compound by identifying the fragments produced when the molecule is broken apart. **Infrared (IR) spectroscopy** allows us to identify the kinds of bonds and therefore the kinds of functional groups in an organic compound. **Ultraviolet/Visible (UV/Vis)** spectroscopy provides information about organic compounds with conjugated double bonds.

CHAPTER 14
NMR Spectroscopy

Chapter 14 discusses **nuclear magnetic resonance (NMR) spectroscopy**, which provides information about the carbon–hydrogen framework of an organic compound. The chapter also includes descriptions of **2-D NMR** and **X-ray crystallography**, techniques that can be used to determine the structures of large molecules.

13

Mass Spectrometry, Infrared Spectroscopy, and Ultraviolet/Visible Spectroscopy

DETERMINING THE STRUCTURES OF ORGANIC COMPOUNDS IS AN IMPORTANT PART OF organic chemistry. Whenever a chemist synthesizes a compound, its structure must be confirmed. For example, you were told that a ketone is formed when an alkyne undergoes the acid-catalyzed addition of water (Section 6.7). But how was it determined that the product of that reaction is actually a ketone?

Scientists search the world for new compounds with physiological activity. If a promising compound is found, its structure needs to be determined. Without knowing its structure, chemists cannot design ways to synthesize the compound, nor can they undertake studies to provide insights into its biological behavior.

Before the structure of a compound can be determined, the compound must be isolated. For example, if the product of a reaction carried out in the laboratory is to be identified, it must first be isolated from the solvent and from any unreacted starting materials, as well as from any side products that might have formed. A compound found in nature must be isolated from the organism that manufactures it.

Isolating products and figuring out their structures used to be daunting tasks. The only tools chemists had for isolating products were distillation (for liquids) and sublimation or fractional recrystallization (for solids). Today, a variety of chromatographic techniques allow compounds to be isolated with relative ease. You will learn about these techniques in your laboratory course.

At one time, determining the structure of an organic compound required finding out its molecular formula by elemental analysis, determining the compound's physical properties (its melting point, boiling point, and so on), and conducting simple chemical tests that indicate the presence (or absence) of certain functional groups. For example, when an aldehyde is added to a test tube containing a solution of silver oxide in aqueous ammonia, a silver mirror is formed on the inside of the test tube. Only aldehydes have this ability, so if a mirror forms, you can conclude that the unknown compound is an aldehyde; if a mirror does not form, the compound is not an aldehyde (Section 20.5). Another example of a simple test is the Lucas test, which distinguishes primary, secondary, and tertiary alcohols by how rapidly the test solution turns cloudy after the addition of Lucas reagent (Section 10.1). Unfortunately, these simple procedures were inadequate for characterizing molecules with complex structures, and because a relatively large sample of the compound was needed in order to perform all the tests, they were impractical for the analysis of compounds that were difficult to obtain.

Today, a number of different instrumental techniques are used to identify organic compounds. These techniques can be performed quickly on small amounts of a compound and can provide much more information about the compound's structure than simple chemical tests can give. In this chapter, we will look at three instrumental techniques:

- **Mass spectrometry** allows us to determine the *molecular mass* and the *molecular formula* of a compound, as well as some of its *structural features*.
- **Infrared spectroscopy** tells us the *kinds of functional groups* a compound has.
- **Ultraviolet/Visible (UV/Vis) spectroscopy** provides information about organic compounds with conjugated double bonds.

Of these instrumental techniques, mass spectrometry is the only one that does not employ electromagnetic radiation. Thus, it is called *spectrometry*, whereas the others are called *spectroscopy*.

We will be referring to different classes of organic compounds as we discuss various instrumental techniques; they are listed in Table 13.1. (They are also listed inside the back cover of the book for easy reference.)

Table 13.1	Classes of Organic Compounds		
Alkane	$-\overset{\shortmid}{\underset{\shortmid}{C}}-$ contains only C—C and C—H bonds	Aldehyde	$\underset{R}{\overset{O}{\|}}H$
Alkene	$\overset{\diagdown}{\diagup}C=C\overset{\diagup}{\diagdown}$	Ketone	$\underset{R}{\overset{O}{\|}}R$
Alkyne	—C≡C—	Carboxylic acid	$\underset{R}{\overset{O}{\|}}OH$
Nitrile	—C≡N	Ester	$\underset{R}{\overset{O}{\|}}OR$
Alkyl halide	R—X X = F, Cl, Br, or I	Amides	$\underset{R}{\overset{O}{\|}}NH_2$
Ether	R—O—R		$\underset{R}{\overset{O}{\|}}NHR$
Alcohol	R—OH		$\underset{R}{\overset{O}{\|}}NR_2$
Phenol	⬡—OH	Amine (primary)	R—NH$_2$
		Amine (secondary)	$R-\overset{R}{\underset{}{N}}H$
Aniline	⬡—NH$_2$	Amine (tertiary)	$R-\overset{R}{\underset{}{N}}-R$

13.1 MASS SPECTROMETRY

At one time, the molecular weight of a compound was determined by its vapor density or freezing-point depression, and molecular formulas were determined by elemental analysis, a technique for measuring the relative proportions of the elements in the compound.

These were long and tedious procedures that required a relatively large amount of a very pure sample of the compound. Today, molecular weights and molecular formulas can be rapidly determined from a very small sample by mass spectrometry.

In mass spectrometry, a small amount of a compound is introduced into an instrument called a mass spectrometer, where it is vaporized and then ionized (an electron is removed from each molecule). The sample can be ionized in several ways. Electron ionization (EI), the most common method used to convert the sample into ions, bombards the vaporized molecules with a beam of high-energy electrons. The energy of the beam can be varied but is typically about 70 electron volts (eV), or 68,000 kJ/mol. When the electron beam hits a molecule, it knocks out an electron, producing a **molecular ion**. A molecular ion is a **radical cation**, a species with an unpaired electron and a positive charge.

$$ M \xrightarrow{\text{electron beam}} M^{+\cdot} + e^- $$

$$ \underset{\text{molecule}}{} \qquad \underset{\substack{\text{molecular ion} \\ \text{a radical cation}}}{\phantom{M^{+\cdot}}} \qquad \underset{\text{electron}}{} $$

Electron bombardment injects so much kinetic energy into the molecular ions that most of them break apart (fragment) into smaller cations, radicals, neutral molecules, and other radical cations. Not surprisingly, the bonds most likely to break are the weakest ones and those that result in the formation of the most stable products. All the *positively charged fragments* of the molecule are drawn between two negatively charged plates, which accelerate the fragments into an analyzer tube (Figure 13.1). Neutral fragments are not attracted to the negatively charged plates and therefore are not accelerated. They are eventually pumped out of the spectrometer.

▶ **Figure 13.1**
Schematic diagram of an electron ionization mass spectrometer. A beam of high-energy electrons causes molecules to ionize and fragment. Positively charged fragments pass through the analyzer tube. Changing the magnetic field strength allows the separation of fragments of varying mass-to-charge ratios.

The analyzer tube is surrounded by a magnet whose magnetic field deflects the positively charged fragments in a curved path. At a given magnetic field strength, the degree to which the path is curved depends on the mass-to-charge ratio (*m/z*) of the fragment: the path of a fragment with a smaller *m/z* value will bend more than that of a heavier fragment. In this way, the particles with the same *m/z* values can be separated from all the others. If a fragment's path matches the curvature of the analyzer tube, the fragment will pass through the tube and out the ion exit slit. A collector records the relative number of fragments with a particular *m/z* passing through the slit. The more stable the fragment, the more likely it is to arrive at the collector without breaking down further. The strength of the magnetic field is gradually increased, so fragments with progressively larger *m/z* values are guided through the tube and out the exit slit.

The mass spectrometer records a **mass spectrum**—a graph of the relative abundance of each fragment plotted against its m/z value (Figure 13.2). Because the charge (z) on essentially all the fragments that reach the collector plate is $+1$, m/z is the molecular mass (m) of the fragment. *Remember that only positively charged species reach the collector.*

A mass spectrum records only positively charged fragments.

PROBLEM 1 ◆

Which of the following fragments produced in a mass spectrometer would be accelerated through the analyzer tube?

$$CH_3\overset{\cdot}{C}H_2 \qquad CH_3CH_2\overset{+}{C}H_2 \qquad [CH_3CH_2CH_3]\overset{\cdot\,+}{} \qquad \overset{\cdot}{C}H_2CH{=}CH_2 \qquad \overset{+}{C}H_2CH{=}CH_2$$

13.2 THE MASS SPECTRUM • FRAGMENTATION

The molecular ion and fragment ions produced in a mass spectrometer and recorded by it are unique for each compound. A mass spectrum, therefore, is like a fingerprint of the compound. A positive identification of an unknkown compound can be made by comparing its mass spectrum with those of known compounds.

The mass spectrum of pentane is shown in Figure 13.2. Each m/z value in the spectrum is the **nominal molecular mass**—the molecular mass to the nearest whole number—of one of the fragments. ^{12}C is defined as having a mass of 12.000 atomic mass units (amu), and the masses of other atoms are based on this standard. For example, a proton has a mass of 1.007825 amu. Pentane, therefore, has a *molecular mass* of 72.0939 and a *nominal molecular mass* of 72.

◀ **Figure 13.2**
The mass spectrum of pentane. The base peak represents the fragment that appears in greatest abundance. The m/z value of the molecular ion gives the molecular mass of the compound.

The peak with the highest m/z value in the spectrum—in this case, at $m/z = 72$—is the molecular ion (M), the fragment that results when an electron is knocked out of a molecule. (The extremely tiny peak at $m/z = 73$ will be explained later.) *The m/z value of the molecular ion gives the molecular mass of the compound.* Because it is not known what bond loses the electron, the molecular ion is written in brackets and the positive charge and unpaired electron are assigned to the entire structure.

$$CH_3CH_2CH_2CH_2CH_3 \xrightarrow[\text{beam}]{\text{electron}} [CH_3CH_2CH_2CH_2CH_3]\overset{\cdot\,+}{} + e^-$$
$$\text{molecular ion}$$
$$m/z = 72$$

The m/z value of the molecular ion gives the molecular mass of the compound.

Peaks with smaller m/z values—called **fragment ion peaks**—represent positively charged fragments of the molecular ion. The **base peak** is the tallest peak, due to its having the greatest relative abundance. The base peak is assigned a relative abundance of 100%, and the relative abundance of each of the other peaks is reported as a percentage of the base peak.

The way a molecular ion fragments depends on the strength of its bonds and the stability of the fragments.

A mass spectrum gives us structural information about the compound because the m/z values and relative abundances of the fragments depend on the strength of the molecular ion's bonds and the stability of the fragments. *Weak bonds break in preference to strong bonds, and bonds that break to form more stable fragments break in preference to those that form less stable fragments.*

For example, all the C—C bonds in the molecular ion formed from pentane have about the same strength. However, the C-2–C-3 bond is the one most likely to break because it leads to formation of a *primary* carbocation and a *primary* radical, which together are more stable than the *primary* carbocation and *methyl* radical (or *primary* radical and *methyl* cation) obtained from C-1–C-2 fragmentation. Ions formed by C-2–C-3 fragmentation have m/z values of 43 and 29, whereas ions formed by C-1–C-2 fragmentation have m/z values 57 and 15. The base peak of 43 in the mass spectrum of pentane indicates the greater likelihood of C-2–C-3 fragmentation. (See Sections 7.7 and 12.3 to review the relative stabilities of carbocations and radicals, respectively.)

$$[\overset{1}{C}H_3\overset{2}{C}H_2\overset{3}{C}H_2\overset{4}{C}H_2\overset{5}{C}H_3]^{\overset{+}{\cdot}}$$
molecular ion
$m/z = 72$

$$CH_3\dot{C}H_2 + \overset{+}{C}H_2CH_2CH_3 \quad m/z = 43$$
$$CH_3\overset{+}{C}H_2 + \dot{C}H_2CH_2CH_3 \quad m/z = 29$$
$$\dot{C}H_3 + \overset{+}{C}H_2CH_2CH_2CH_3 \quad m/z = 57$$
$$\overset{+}{C}H_3 + \dot{C}H_2CH_2CH_2CH_3 \quad m/z = 15$$

A method for identifying fragment ions makes use of the difference between the m/z value of a given fragment ion and that of the molecular ion. For example, the fragment ion with $m/z = 43$ in the mass spectrum of pentane is 29 units smaller than the molecular ion ($72 - 43 = 29$). An ethyl radical (CH_3CH_2) has a molecular mass of 29 (because the mass numbers of C and H are 12 and 1, respectively). Thus, the peak at 43 can be attributed to the molecular ion minus an ethyl radical. Similarly, the fragment ion with $m/z = 57$ can be attributed to the molecular ion minus a methyl radical ($72 - 57 = 15$). Peaks at $m/z = 15$ and $m/z = 29$ are readily recognizable as being due to methyl and ethyl cations, respectively. Appendix VI contains a table of common fragment ions and a table of common fragments lost.

Peaks are commonly observed at m/z values two units below the m/z values of the carbocations, because the carbocations can lose two hydrogen atoms.

$$CH_3CH_2\overset{+}{C}H_2 \longrightarrow \overset{+}{C}H_2CH=CH_2 + 2\,H\cdot$$
$$m/z = 43 \qquad\qquad m/z = 41$$

2-Methylbutane has the same molecular formula as pentane. Thus it, too, has a molecular ion with an m/z value of 72 (Figure 13.3). Its mass spectrum is similar to that of pentane, with one notable exception: the peak at $m/z = 57$, indicating loss of a methyl radical, is much more intense.

▶ **Figure 13.3**
The mass spectrum of 2-methylbutane.

2-Methylbutane is more likely than pentane to lose a methyl radical because, when it does, a *secondary* carbocation is formed. In contrast, when pentane loses a methyl radical, a less stable *primary* carbocation is formed.

$$[CH_3\overset{\mid}{\underset{}{C}}HCH_2CH_3]^{\overset{+}{\cdot}} \longrightarrow CH_3\overset{+}{C}HCH_2CH_3 + \overset{\cdot}{C}H_3$$

molecular ion
$m/z = 72$ $m/z = 57$

PROBLEM 2

What would distinguish the mass spectrum of 2,2-dimethylpropane from the mass spectra of pentane and 2-methylbutane?

PROBLEM 3 ♦

What is the likeliest m/z value for the base peak in the mass spectrum of 3-methylpentane?

PROBLEM-SOLVING STRATEGY

Using Mass Spectra to Determine Structures

The mass spectra of two very stable cycloalkanes both show a molecular ion peak at $m/z = 98$. One spectrum shows a base peak at $m/z = 69$, the other shows a base peak at $m/z = 83$. Identify the cycloalkanes.

Let's first see if we can determine the molecular formula of the compounds from the m/z values of their molecular ions. The molecular formula for a cycloalkane is C_nH_{2n}. Because the molecular mass of both cycloalkanes is 98, their molecular formulas must be C_7H_{14} ($7 \times 12 = 84$; $84 + 14 = 98$).

Now let's see what fragment is lost to give the base peak. A base peak of 69 means the loss of an ethyl radical ($98 - 69 = 29$), whereas a base peak of 83 means the loss of a methyl radical ($98 - 83 = 15$).

Because the two cycloalkanes are known to be very stable, we assume they do not have three- or four-membered rings. A seven-carbon cycloalkane with a base peak signifying the loss of an ethyl radical must be ethylcyclopentane. A seven-carbon cycloalkane with a base peak signifying the loss of a methyl radical must be methylcyclohexane.

ethyl-
cyclopentane $m/z = 69$ methylcyclohexane $m/z = 83$

Now continue on to Problem 4.

PROBLEM 4 ♦

Identify the hydrocarbon that has a molecular ion with an m/z value of 128, a base peak with an m/z value of 43, and significant peaks with m/z values of 57, 71, and 85.

PROBLEM 5

The "nitrogen rule" states that if a compound has an odd-mass molecular ion, the compound contains an odd number of nitrogen atoms.

a. Calculate the m/z value for the molecular ion of each of the following compounds:

1. /\/\NH$_2$ **2.** H$_2$N/\/\NH$_2$

b. Explain why the nitrogen rule holds.

c. State the rule in terms of an even-mass molecular ion.

13.3 ISOTOPES IN MASS SPECTROMETRY

Although the molecular ions of pentane and 2-methylbutane both have m/z values of 72, each spectrum shows a very small peak at $m/z = 73$ (Figures 13.2 and 13.3). This peak is called an M + 1 peak because the ion responsible for it is one unit heavier than the molecular ion. The M + 1 peak owes its presence to the fact that there are two naturally occurring isotopes of carbon: 98.89% of natural carbon is ^{12}C and 1.11% is ^{13}C (Section 1.1). Because mass spectrometry records individual molecules, any molecule containing a ^{13}C will appear at M + 1.

Peaks that are attributable to isotopes can help identify the compound responsible for a mass spectrum. For example, if a compound contains five carbon atoms, the relative abundance of the M + 1 ion is estimated to be 5(1.1%) = 5(.011), multiplied by the relative abundance of the molecular ion. This means that the number of carbon atoms in a compound can be calculated if the relative intensities of both the M and M + 1 peaks are known.

$$\text{number of carbon atoms} = \frac{\text{relative intensity of M + 1 peak}}{.011 \times (\text{relative intensity of M peak})}$$

The isotopic distributions of several elements commonly found in organic compounds are shown in Table 13.2. From the isotopic distributions, we see that the M + 1 peak can be used to determine the number of carbon atoms in compounds containing H, O, or halogens because the contributions to the M + 1 peak by isotopes of H, O, and the halogens are very small or nonexistent. This formula does not work as well in predicting the number of carbon atoms in a nitrogen-containing compound because the natural abundance of ^{15}N is relatively high.

Table 13.2	The Natural Abundance of Isotopes Commonly Found in Organic Compounds			
Element	**Natural abundance**			
Carbon	^{12}C	^{13}C		
	98.89%	1.11%		
Hydrogen	^{1}H	^{2}H		
	99.99%	0.01%		
Nitrogen	^{14}N	^{15}N		
	99.64%	0.36%		
Oxygen	^{16}O	^{17}O	^{18}O	
	99.76%	0.04%	0.20%	
Sulfur	^{32}S	^{33}S	^{34}S	^{36}S
	95.0%	0.76%	4.22%	0.02%
Fluorine	^{19}F			
	100%			
Chlorine	^{35}Cl		^{37}Cl	
	75.77%		24.23%	
Bromine	^{79}Br		^{81}Br	
	50.69%		49.31%	
Iodine	^{137}I			
	100%			

Mass spectra can show M + 2 peaks as a result of a contribution from ^{18}O or from having two heavy isotopes in the same molecule (say, ^{13}C and ^{2}H, or two ^{13}C's). Most of the time, the M + 2 peak is very small. The presence of a large M + 2 peak is evidence of a compound containing either chlorine or bromine, because each of these elements has a high percentage of a naturally occurring isotope that is two units heavier than the most abundant isotope. From the natural abundance of the isotopes of chlorine and bromine in Table 13.2, one can conclude that if the M + 2 peak is one-third the height of the molecular ion peak, then the compound contains one chlorine atom because the natural abundance of ^{37}Cl is one-third that of ^{35}Cl. If the M and M + 2 peaks are about the same height, then the compound contains one bromine atom because the natural abundances of ^{79}Br and ^{81}Br are about the same.

In calculating the molecular masses of molecular ions and fragments, the *atomic mass* of a single isotope of the atom must be used (Cl = 35 or 37, for example) because mass spectrometry records the *m/z* value of an *individual* fragment. The *atomic weights* in the periodic table (Cl = 35.453) cannot be used, because they are the *weighted averages* of all the naturally occurring isotopes for that element.

PROBLEM 6♦

The mass spectrum of an unknown compound has a molecular ion peak with a relative abundance of 43.27% and an M + 1 peak with a relative abundance of 3.81%. How many carbon atoms are in the compound?

PROBLEM 7♦

Predict the relative intensities of the molecular ion peak, the M + 2 peak, and the M + 4 peak for CH_2Br_2.

13.4 HIGH-RESOLUTION MASS SPECTROMETRY CAN REVEAL MOLECULAR FORMULAS

All the mass spectra shown in this text were produced with a low-resolution mass spectrometer. Such spectrometers give the **nominal molecular mass** of a fragment—the mass to the nearest whole number. High-resolution mass spectrometers can determine the *exact molecular mass* of a fragment to a precision of 0.0001 amu, making it possible to distinguish between compounds with the same nominal mass. For example, the following listing shows six compounds having a nominal molecular mass of 122 amu, but each of them has a different exact molecular mass.

Some Compounds with a Nominal Molecular Mass of 122 amu and Their Exact Molecular Masses and Molecular Formulas

Exact molecular mass (amu)	122.1096	122.0845	122.0732	122.0368	122.0579	122.0225
Molecular formula	C_9H_{14}	$C_7H_{10}N_2$	$C_8H_{10}O$	$C_7H_6O_2$	$C_4H_{10}O_4$	$C_4H_{10}S_2$

The exact masses of some common isotopes are listed in Table 13.3. There are computer programs that can determine the molecular formula of a compound from the compound's exact molecular mass.

Table 13.3   The Exact Masses of Some Common Isotopes

Isotope	Mass	Isotope	Mass
^1H	1.007825 amu	^{32}S	31.9721 amu
^{12}C	12.00000 amu	^{35}Cl	34.9689 amu
^{14}N	14.0031 amu	^{79}Br	78.9183 amu
^{16}O	15.9949 amu		

PROBLEM 8◆

Which molecular formula has an exact molecular mass of 86.1096 amu: C_6H_{14}, $C_4H_{10}N_2$, or $C_4H_6O_2$?

PROBLEM 9◆

a. Can a low-resolution mass spectrometer distinguish between $C_2H_5^+$ and CHO^+?
b. Can a high-resolution mass spectrometer distinguish them?

13.5 THE FRAGMENTATION PATTERNS OF FUNCTIONAL GROUPS

Each functional group has characteristic fragmentation patterns that can help identify a compound. The patterns began to be recognized after the mass spectra of many compounds containing a particular functional group had been studied. We will look at the fragmentation patterns of alkyl halides, ethers, alcohols, and ketones as examples.

Alkyl Halides

Let's look first at the mass spectrum of 1-bromopropane, shown in Figure 13.4. The relative heights of the M and M + 2 peaks are about equal, which we have seen is characteristic of a compound containing a bromine atom. Electron bombardment is most likely to dislodge a lone-pair electron if the molecule has any, because a molecule does not hold onto its lone-pair electrons as tightly as it holds onto its bonding electrons. Thus, the molecular ion is created when electron bombardment dislodges one of bromine's lone-pair electrons.

$$CH_3CH_2CH_2\overset{..}{\underset{..}{Br}}: \ + \ CH_3CH_2CH_2\overset{81}{\underset{..}{\overset{..}{Br}}}: \ \xrightarrow{-e^-} \ CH_3CH_2CH_2\overset{79}{\underset{..}{\overset{+}{Br}}}: \ + \ CH_3CH_2CH_2\overset{81}{\underset{..}{\overset{+}{Br}}}: \ \longrightarrow \ CH_3CH_2\overset{+}{C}H_2 \ + \ ^{79}\overset{..}{\underset{..}{Br}}: \ + \ ^{81}\overset{..}{\underset{..}{Br}}:$$

1-bromopropane   **m/z = 122**   **m/z = 124**   **m/z = 43**

▶ **Figure 13.4**
The mass spectrum of
1-bromopropane.

The weakest bond in the molecular ion is the C—Br bond (the C—Br bond dissociation energy is 69 kcal/mol; the C—C bond dissociation energy is 85 kcal/mol; see Table 3.2 on page 141). When the C—Br bond breaks, it breaks heterolytically, with both electrons going to the more electronegative of the atoms that were joined by the bond, forming a propyl cation and a bromine atom. As a result, the base peak in the mass spectrum of 1-bromopropane is at $m/z = 43$ [M − 79, or (M + 2) − 81].

The mass spectrum of 2-chloropropane is shown in Figure 13.5. We know that the compound contains a chlorine atom, because the M + 2 peak is one-third the height of the molecular ion peak (Section 13.3).

◀ **Figure 13.5**
The mass spectrum of
2-chloropropane.

The base peak at $m/z = 43$ results from *heterolytic cleavage* of the C—Cl bond. The peaks at $m/z = 63$ and $m/z = 65$ have a 3:1 ratio, indicating that these fragments contain a chlorine atom. They result from *homolytic cleavage* of a C—C bond at the α-carbon (the carbon bonded to the chlorine). This cleavage is known as **α-cleavage**.

The way a molecular ion fragments depends on the strength of its bonds and the stability of the fragments.

α-Cleavage occurs because it leads to a cation that is relatively stable since its positive charge is shared by two atoms:

α-Cleavage occurs in *alkyl chlorides* because the C—Cl (82 kcal/mol) and C—C (85 kcal/mol) bonds have similar strengths. α-Cleavage is much less likely to occur in *alkyl bromides* because the C—C bond is much stronger than the C—Br bond (69 kcal/mol).

α-Cleavage is less likely to occur in alkyl bromides because the C—C bond is much stronger than the C—Br bond.

Recall that an arrowhead with one barb represents the movement of one electron.

PROBLEM 10

Sketch the expected mass spectrum of 1-chloropropane.

chem Tutorial:
place Fragmentation of alkyl halides

Ethers

The mass spectrum of 2-isopropoxybutane is shown in Figure 13.6.

▶ **Figure 13.6**
The mass spectrum of
2-isopropoxybutane.

The fragmentation pattern of an ether is similar to that of an alkyl halide.

1. Electron bombardment dislodges one of the lone-pair electrons from oxygen.
2. Fragmentation of the resulting molecular ion occurs mainly in two ways:

    a. A C—O bond is cleaved *heterolytically*, with the electrons going to the more electronegative oxygen atom.

$$CH_3CH_2\underset{\underset{CH_3}{|}}{CH}-\ddot{\underset{..}{O}}-\underset{\underset{CH_3}{|}}{CHCH_3} \quad \xrightarrow{-e^-} \quad CH_3CH_2\underset{\underset{CH_3}{|}}{CH}-\overset{+}{\underset{..}{O}}-\underset{\underset{CH_3}{|}}{CHCH_3}$$

2-isopropoxybutane   *m/z* = **116**

$$\longrightarrow CH_3CH_2\overset{+}{\underset{\underset{CH_3}{|}}{CH}} \quad + \quad :\overset{..}{\underset{..}{O}}-\underset{\underset{CH_3}{|}}{CHCH_3}$$
m/z = **57**

$$\longrightarrow CH_3CH_2\underset{\underset{CH_3}{|}}{CH}-\ddot{\underset{..}{O}}: \quad + \quad \overset{+}{\underset{\underset{CH_3}{|}}{CHCH_3}}$$
m/z = **43**

    b. A C—C bond is cleaved *homolytically* at an α-carbon because such cleavage leads to a relatively stable cation in which the positive charge is shared by two atoms (a carbon and an oxygen). The alkyl group most easily cleaved is the one that forms the most stable radical. Thus, the peak at *m/z* = 87 is more abundant than the one at *m/z* = 101 because a primary radical is more stable than a methyl radical, even though the compound has three methyl groups bonded to α-carbons that can be cleaved to produce the peak at *m/z* = 101.

$$CH_3CH_2\overset{\frown}{-}\underset{\underset{CH_3}{|}}{CH}\overset{+}{-}\overset{+}{\underset{..}{O}}-\underset{\underset{CH_3}{|}}{CHCH_3} \xrightarrow{\textit{α-cleavage}} \underset{\underset{CH_3}{|}}{CH}=\overset{+}{\underset{..}{O}}-\underset{\underset{CH_3}{|}}{CHCH_3} + CH_3\dot{CH}_2$$
m/z = **87**

$$CH_3CH_2CH\overset{\frown}{-}\overset{+}{\underset{..}{O}}-\underset{\underset{CH_3}{|}}{CHCH_3} \xrightarrow{\textit{α-cleavage}} CH_3CH_2CH=\overset{+}{\underset{..}{O}}-\underset{\underset{CH_3}{|}}{CHCH_3} + \dot{C}H_3$$
m/z = **101**

$$CH_3CH_2\underset{\underset{CH_3}{|}}{CH}-\overset{+}{\underset{..}{O}}\overset{\frown}{-}\underset{\underset{CH_3}{|}}{CHCH_3} \xrightarrow{\textit{α-cleavage}} CH_3CH_2\underset{\underset{CH_3}{|}}{CH}-\overset{+}{\underset{..}{O}}=CHCH_3 + \dot{C}H_3$$

α-carbon   *m/z* = **101**

PROBLEM 11 ♦

The mass spectra of 1-methoxybutane, 2-methoxybutane, and 2-methoxy-2-methylpropane are shown in Figure 13.7. Match each compound with its spectrum.

chem Tutorial:
place Fragmentation of ethers

▲ **Figure 13.7**
The mass spectra referred to in Problem 11.

Alcohols

As with alkyl halides and ethers, the molecular ion of an alcohol is created by knocking out a lone-pair electron. The molecular ions obtained from alcohols fragment so readily that few of them survive to reach the collector. As a result, the mass spectrum of an alcohol shows a small molecular ion peak, if any. Notice the small molecular ion peak at $m/z = 102$ in the mass spectrum of 2-hexanol (Figure 13.8).

▶ **Figure 13.8**
The mass spectrum of 2-hexanol.

The molecular ion of an alcohol, like those of alkyl halides and ethers, undergoes α-cleavage. Consequently, the mass spectrum of 2-hexanol shows a base peak at $m/z = 45$ (α-cleavage leading to a more stable butyl radical) and a smaller peak at $m/z = 87$ (α-cleavage leading to a less stable methyl radical).

In all the fragmentations we have seen so far, only one bond is broken. With alcohols, however, an important fragmentation occurs in which two bonds are broken. Two bonds break because the fragmentation forms a stable water molecule. The water is composed of the OH group and γ-hydrogen. Loss of water results in a fragmentation peak at $m/z = M - 18$.

Notice that alkyl halides, ethers, and alcohols have the following fragmentation behaviors in common:

1. A bond between carbon and a *more electronegative* atom (a halogen or an oxygen) breaks heterolytically.

2. A bond between carbon and an atom of *similar electronegativity* (a carbon or a hydrogen) breaks homolytically.

3. The bonds most likely to break are the weakest bonds and those that lead to formation of the most stable products. (Look for a fragmentation that results in a cation with a positive charge shared by two atoms.)

PROBLEM 12♦

Primary alcohols have a strong peak at $m/z = 31$. What fragment is responsible for this peak?

chem Tutorial:
place Fragmentation of alcohols

Ketones

A ketone generally has an intense molecular ion peak that is formed by knocking out a lone-pair electron. The molecular ion fragments homolytically at the C—C bond adjacent to the C=O bond because this cleavage results in formation of a cation with a positive charge shared by two atoms. The alkyl group leading to the more stable radical is the one more easily cleaved.

$$CH_3CH_2CH_2\overset{\overset{\ddot{O}:}{\|}}{C}CH_3 \xrightarrow{-e^-} CH_3CH_2CH_2\overset{\overset{\overset{+}{\ddot{O}}:}{\|}}{C}CH_3$$

2-pentanone $m/z = 86$

$$\longrightarrow CH_3CH_2\dot{C}H_2 \ + \ CH_3C\overset{+}{\equiv}\ddot{O}:$$
$$m/z = 43$$

$$\longrightarrow CH_3CH_2CH_2C\overset{+}{\equiv}\ddot{O}: \ + \ \dot{C}H_3$$
$$m/z = 71$$

If one of the alkyl groups attached to a carbonyl carbon has a γ-hydrogen, a cleavage, which goes through a favorable six-membered-ring transition state, may occur. This cleavage is known as a **McLafferty rearrangement**. In this rearrangement, the bond between the α-carbon and the β-carbon breaks homolytically and a hydrogen atom from the γ-carbon migrates to the oxygen. Again, fragmentation has occurred in a way that produces a cation with a positive charge shared by two atoms.

$$\xrightarrow{\text{McLafferty rearrangement}} H_2C{=}CH_2 \ + \ \dot{C}H_2{-}\overset{\overset{\overset{+}{\ddot{O}}:}{\|}}{C}{-}CH_3$$

$m/z = 86$ $m/z = 58$

✦ Mass Spectrometry in Forensics

Forensic science is the application of science for the purpose of justice. Mass spectrometry is an important tool of the forensic scientist. It is used to analyze body fluids for the presence and levels of drugs and other toxic substances. It can also identify the presence of drugs in hair, which increases the window of detection from hours and days (after which body fluids are no longer useful) to months and even years. It was employed for the first time in 1955 to detect drugs in athletes at a cycling competition in France. (Twenty percent of those tests were positive.) Mass spectrometry is also used to identify residues of arson fires and explosives from post-explosion residues, and to analyze paints, adhesives, and fibers.

PROBLEM 13 ◆

Identify the ketones responsible for the mass spectra in Figure 13.9.

▲ **Figure 13.9**
The mass spectra referred to in Problem 13.

PROBLEM 14

How could their mass spectra be used to distinguish the following compounds?

$$CH_3CH_2-\overset{\overset{\displaystyle O}{\|}}{C}-CH_2CH_3 \quad CH_3-\overset{\overset{\displaystyle O}{\|}}{C}-CH_2CH_2CH_3 \quad CH_3-\overset{\overset{\displaystyle O}{\|}}{C}-\underset{\underset{\displaystyle CH_3}{|}}{CHCH_3}$$

PROBLEM 15

Using curved arrows, show the principal fragments that would be observed in the mass spectrum of each of the following compounds:

a. $CH_3CH_2CH_2CH_2CH_2OH$

b. $CH_3CH_2\underset{\underset{\displaystyle OH}{|}}{CH}CH_2CH_2CH_2CH_3$

c. $CH_3CH_2O\underset{\underset{\displaystyle CH_3}{|}}{\overset{\overset{\displaystyle CH_2CH_3}{|}}{C}}CH_2CH_2CH_3$

d. $CH_3\overset{\overset{\displaystyle O}{\|}}{C}CH_2CH_2CH_2CH_3$

e. $CH_3CH_2\underset{\underset{\displaystyle CH_3}{|}}{CH}Cl$

f. $CH_3-\underset{\underset{\displaystyle CH_3}{|}}{\overset{\overset{\displaystyle CH_3}{|}}{C}}-Br$

PROBLEM 16♦

The reaction of (*Z*)-2-pentene with water and a trace of H_2SO_4 forms two products. Identify the products from their mass spectra that are shown in Figure 13.10.

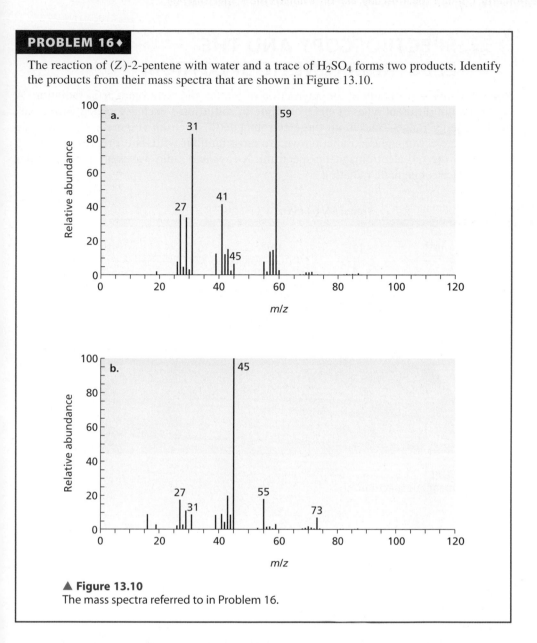

▲ **Figure 13.10**
The mass spectra referred to in Problem 16.

13.6 OTHER IONIZATION METHODS

Methods other than electron bombardment (EI-MS) can be used to obtain mass spectral data. In chemical ionization-mass spectrometry (CI-MS), the sample is sprayed with a pre-ionized gas such as methane or ammonia that causes the sample to ionize by electron transfer or proton transfer from the gas to the sample. Because the molecular ions produced by this technique are less apt to undergo fragmentation, the ability to obtain the molecular mass (and therefore the molecular formula) of the sample is enhanced.

Because EI-MS and CI-MS require the sample to be vaporized before it is ionized. Therefore, these methods can be used only for samples with relatively low molecular weights. Mass spectra of large molecules, even large biological molecules such as enzymes or oligonucleotides, can be obtained by desorption ionization (DI). In this technique, the sample is dissolved on a matrix compound, which is then ionized by one of several methods. The matrix compound transfers energy to the sample, causing some of the sample molecules to ionize and be ejected from the matrix. The ejected ions are accelerated in the mass spectrometer and recorded to give a mass spectrum as in EI-MS (Section 13.1). Ionization methods include bombarding the matrix compound with a high-energy beam of ions (called secondary ion MS [SIMS]), photons (called matrix-assisted laser desorption ionization [MALDI]), or neutral atoms (called fast-atom bombardment [FAB]).

13.7 SPECTROSCOPY AND THE ELECTROMAGNETIC SPECTRUM

Spectroscopy is the study of the interaction of matter and electromagnetic radiation. A continuum of different types of **electromagnetic radiation**—each associated with a particular energy range—makes up the electromagnetic spectrum (Figure 13.11). Visible light is the electromagnetic radiation we are most familiar with, but it represents only a fraction of the full electromagnetic spectrum. X-rays and radio waves are other familiar types of electromagnetic radiation.

▲ **Figure 13.11**
The electromagnetic spectrum.

The various kinds of electromagnetic radiation can be characterized briefly as follows:

- *Cosmic rays* are discharged by the sun; they have the highest energy, the highest frequencies, and the shortest wavelengths.
- *γ-Rays* (gamma rays) are emitted by the nuclei of certain radioactive elements. Because of their high energy, they can severely damage biological organisms.
- *X-Rays*, somewhat lower in energy than γ-rays, are less harmful, except in high doses. Low-dose X-rays are used to examine the internal structure of organisms. The denser the tissue, the more it blocks X-rays.
- *Ultraviolet (UV) light*, a component of sunlight, is responsible for sunburns, and repeated exposure to it can cause skin cancer by damaging DNA molecules in skin cells (Section 30.6).
- *Visible light* is the electromagnetic radiation we see.
- We feel *infrared radiation* as heat.
- We cook with *microwaves* and use them in radar.
- *Radio waves* have the lowest energy (lowest frequency) of the different kinds of electromagnetic radiation. We use them for radio and television communication, digital imaging, remote control devices, and wireless linkages for laptop computers. Radio waves are also used in NMR spectroscopy and in magnetic resonance imaging (MRI).

Each spectroscopic technique discussed in this book employs a different type of electromagnetic radiation. In this chapter, we will look at infrared (IR) spectroscopy and ultraviolet/visible (UV/Vis) spectroscopy, and in the next chapter we will see how compounds can be identified using nuclear magnetic resonance (NMR) spectroscopy.

Because electromagnetic radiation has wave-like properties, it can be characterized, as a wave can, by either its frequency (ν) or its wavelentlh (λ). **Frequency** is defined as the number of wave crests that pass by a given point in one second; frequency has units of hertz (Hz). **Wavelength** is the distance from any point on one wave to the corresponding point on the next wave; wavelength is generally measured in nanometers [one nanometer (nm) is 10^{-9} meter].

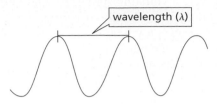

The relationship between the energy (E) and the frequency (ν) or wavelength (λ) of the electromagnetic radiation is described by the equation

$$E = h\nu = \frac{hc}{\lambda}$$

where h is the proportionality constant called *Planck's constant*, named after the German physicist who discovered the relationship (Section 3.7), and c is the speed of light ($c = 3.0 \times 10^{10}$ cm/s). The equation shows that short wavelengths have high frequencies and long wavelengths have low frequencies.

$$\nu = \frac{c}{\lambda}$$

Another way to describe the *frequency* of the electromagnetic radiation—and the one most often used in infrared spectroscopy—is **wavenumber** ($\bar{\nu}$), the number of waves in 1 cm. Therefore, it has units of reciprocal centimeters (cm^{-1}). The relationship between wavenumber (in cm^{-1}) and wavelength (in nm) is given by the equation

$$\bar{\nu}(cm^{-1}) = \frac{10^4}{\lambda(nm)} \quad \text{because 1 nm} = 10^{-4}cm$$

So *high frequencies, large wavenumbers*, and *short wavelengths* are associated with *high energy*.

High frequencies, large wavenumbers, and short wavelengths are associated with high energy.

PROBLEM 17◆

One of the following depicts the waves associated with infrared radiation, and one depicts the waves associated with ultraviolet light. Which is which?

PROBLEM 18◆

a. Which is higher in energy, electromagnetic radiation with wavenumber 100 cm^{-1} or with wavenumber 2000 cm^{-1}?

b. Which is higher in energy, electromagnetic radiation with wavelength 9 nm or with wavelength 8 nm?

c. Which is higher in energy, electromagnetic radiation with wavenumber 200 cm^{-1} or with wavelength 2 nm?

PROBLEM 19◆

a. What is the wavenumber of radiation that has a wavelength of 4 nm?

b. What is the wavelength of radiation that has a wavenumber of 200 cm^{-1}?

13.8 **INFRARED SPECTROSCOPY**

The length reported for a bond between two atoms is an average length, because in reality a bond behaves as if it were a vibrating spring. A bond vibrates with both stretching and bending motions. A *stretch* is a vibration occurring along the line of the bond that changes the bond length. A *bend* is a vibration that does *not* occur along the line of the bond; bending vibrations change the bond angles. A diatomic molecule such as H—Cl can undergo only a **stretching vibration** because it has no bond angles.

a stretching vibration

The vibrations of a molecule containing three or more atoms are more complex (Figure 13.12). Such molecules can experience symmetric and asymmetric stretches and bends, and their bending vibrations can be either in-plane or out-of-plane. **Bending vibrations** are often referred to by the descriptive terms *rock, scissor, wag,* and *twist*.

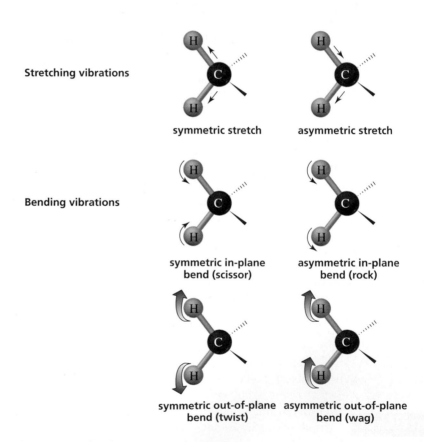

▶ **Figure 13.12**
Stretching and bending vibrations of bonds in organic molecules.

Each stretching and bending vibration of a given bond occurs with a characteristic frequency. **Infrared radiation** has just the right range of frequencies to correspond to the frequencies of the stretching and bending vibrations of the bonds in organic molecules. Infrared radiation ranges in wavenumbers from 4000 to 600 cm^{-1}. It is just below the "red region" of visible light. (*Infra* is Latin for "below.")

When a molecule is bombarded with radiation of a frequency that exactly matches the frequency of the vibration of one of its bonds, the molecule absorbs energy. This allows the bonds to stretch and bend a bit more. By experimentally determining the wavenumbers of the energy absorbed by a particular compound, we can ascertain what kinds of bonds it has. For example, the stretching vibration of a C=O bond absorbs energy with wavenumber $\sim 1700 \ cm^{-1}$, whereas the stretching vibration of an O—H bond absorbs energy with wavenumber $\sim 3450 \ cm^{-1}$ (Figure 13.13).

$$C{=}O \qquad\qquad O{-}H$$
$$\tilde{\nu} = \text{~1700 cm}^{-1} \qquad \tilde{\nu} = \text{~3400 cm}^{-1}$$

▲ Figure 13.13
The infrared spectrum of 4-hydroxy-4-methyl-2-pentanone. The spectrum shows the percent transmission of radiation versus the wavenumber or wavelength of the radiation.

chem Tutorial:
place IR stretching
and bending

Obtaining an Infrared Spectrum

An **infrared spectrum**, obtained by passing infrared radiation through a sample of a compound, is a plot of the percent transmission of radiation versus the wavenumber (or wavelength) of the radiation transmitted (Figure 13.13). The instrument used to obtain an infrared spectrum is called an IR spectrophotometer. At 100% transmission on an infrared spectrum, all the energy of the radiation (of a particular wavelength or wavenumber) passes through the molecule. Lower values of percent transmission mean that some of the energy is being absorbed by the compound. Each downward spike in an IR spectrum represents absorption of energy. The spikes are called **absorption bands**. Most chemists report the location of absorption bands using wavenumbers.

A newer type of IR spectrophotometer, called a Fourier transform IR (FT-IR) spectrophotometer, has several advantages over conventional spectrophotometers. Its sensitivity is better because, instead of scanning through the frequencies sequentially, it measures all frequencies simultaneously, allowing time for multiple measurements, which are averaged. The information is then digitized and Fourier transformed by a computer to produce an FT-IR spectrum. A conventional IR spectrophotometer can take 2 to 10 minutes to scan through all the frequencies. In contrast, FT-IR spectra can be taken in 1 to 2 seconds. The infrared spectra shown in this text are FT-IR spectra.

An IR spectrum can be taken of a gas, a solid, or a liquid. Gases are expanded into an evacuated cell (a small container). Solids can be compressed with anhydrous KBr into a disc that is placed in the path of the light beam. A solid can also be examined as a mull. A mull is prepared by grinding a few milligrams of the solid in a mortar, adding a drop or two of mineral oil, and then grinding further. Liquids can be examined neat (undiluted); a few drops are put between two optically polished plates of NaCl that are placed in the light beam. Alternatively, a cell with optically polished NaCl or AgCl windows is used to hold samples dissolved in solvents. The discs, plates, and cells used to hold samples are constructed of ionic substances because, not having covalent bonds, they do not absorb IR radiation, whereas glass, quartz, and plastics have covalent bonds that absorb IR radiation.

When compounds are analyzed in solutions, they must be in solvents that have few absorption bands in the region of interest. Commonly used solvents are CH_2Cl_2 and $CHCl_3$. In a double-beam spectrophotometer, the IR radiation is split into two beams—one that passes through the sample cell and another that passes through a cell containing only the solvent. Any absorptions of the solvent are canceled out, so the absorption spectrum is that of the solute alone.

The Functional Group and Fingerprint Regions

An infrared spectrum can be divided into two areas. The area on the left ($4000–1400$ cm^{-1}) is where most of the functional groups show absorption bands. This is called the **functional group region**. The area on the right ($1400–600$ cm^{-1}) is called the **fingerprint region** because it is characteristic of the compound as a whole, just as a fingerprint is characteristic of an individual. Even if two different molecules have the same functional groups, their IR spectra will not be identical because the functional groups are not in exactly the same environment in both compounds. This difference will be reflected in the pattern of absorption bands in the fingerprint region. For example, 2-pentanol and 3-pentanol have the same functional groups, so they show similar absorption bands in the functional group region. Their fingerprint regions are different, however, because the compounds are different (Figure 13.14). Thus, a compound can be positively identified by comparing its fingerprint region with the fingerprint region of the spectrum of a known sample of the compound.

a.

b.

▲ **Figure 13.14**
The IR spectra of (a) 2-pentanol and (b) 3-pentanol. The functional group regions are very similar because the two compounds have the same functional groups, but the fingerprint regions are unique for each compound.

13.9 CHARACTERISTIC INFRARED ABSORPTION BANDS

IR spectra can be quite complex because the stretching and bending vibrations of each bond in a molecule can produce an absorption band. Obviously, there is a lot more to infrared spectroscopy than we have room to cover here. However, organic chemists generally do not try to identify all the absorption bands in an IR spectrum. When identifying an unknown compound, they often use IR spectroscopy in conjunction with information obtained from other spectroscopic techniques. In this chapter, we will look at several characteristic absorption bands so you will be able to tell something about the structure of a compound that gives a particular IR spectrum. You can find an extensive table of characteristic functional group frequencies in Appendix VI. Some of the problems in this chapter and many of those in Chapter 14 provide practice in using information from two or more instrumental methods to identify compounds.

Because more energy is required to stretch a bond than to bend it, absorption bands for stretching vibrations are found in the functional group region ($4000–1400$ cm^{-1}), whereas absorption bands for bending vibrations are typically found in the fingerprint region ($1400–600$ cm^{-1}). Therefore, stretching vibrations are the ones most often used to determine what kinds of bonds a molecule has. The *frequencies of the stretching vibrations* associated with different types of bonds are shown in Table 13.4 and will be discussed in Sections 13.10 and 13.11.

It takes more energy to stretch a bond than to bend it.

Table 13.4	Frequencies of Important IR Stretching Vibrations	
Type of bond	**Wavenumber (cm^{-1})**	**Intensity**
C≡N	2260–2220	medium
C≡C	2260–2100	medium to weak
C=C	1680–1600	medium
C=N	1650–1550	medium
⬡	~1600 and ~1500–1430	strong to weak
C=O	1780–1650	strong
C—O	1250–1050	strong
C—N	1230–1020	medium
O—H (alcohol)	3650–3200	strong, broad
O—H (carboxylic acid)	3300–2500	strong, very broad
N—H	3500–3300	medium, broad
C—H	3300–2700	medium

13.10 THE INTENSITY OF ABSORPTION BANDS

When a bond stretches, the increasing distance between the atoms increases the dipole moment. (Recall from Section 1.3 that the dipole moment of a bond is equal to the magnitude of the charge on one of the bonded atoms multiplied by the distance between the two charges.) The intensity of the absorption band associated with the stretching vibration depends on the size of this change in dipole moment: the greater the change in dipole moment, the more intense the absorption. For example, absorption bands for the stretching vibrations of C=O and C=C bonds appear at similar frequencies, but they are easily distinguished because the one for C=O is much more intense because it is associated with a much greater change in dipole moment. (Compare the C=O absorption bands in Figures 13.15–13.18 with the C=C absorption band in Figure 13.22.)

The stretching vibration of an O—H bond is associated with a greater change in dipole moment than that of an N—H bond because the O—H bond is more polar. Consequently, an O—H bond will show more intense absorption than an N—H bond. Similarly, an N—H bond will show more intense absorption than a C—H bond because the N—H bond is more polar.

The greater the change in dipole moment, the more intense the absorption.

The more polar the bond, the more intense the absorption.

relative bond polarities
relative intensities of IR absorption

The intensity of an absorption band also depends on the number of bonds responsible for the absorption. For example, the absorption band for a C—H stretch will be more intense for a compound such as octyl iodide, which has 17 C—H bonds, than for methyl iodide, which has only three C—H bonds. The concentration of the sample used to obtain an IR spectrum also affects the intensity of the absorption bands. Concentrated samples have greater numbers of absorbing molecules and, therefore, more intense absorption bands. In the chemical literature, you will find intensities referred to as strong (s), medium (m), weak (w), broad, and sharp.

13.11 THE POSITION OF ABSORPTION BANDS

The frequency of a stretching vibration—the amount of energy required to stretch a bond—depends on the *strength* of the bond and the *masses* of the bonded atoms. The stronger the bond, the greater the energy required to stretch it. The frequency of the stretching vibration is also inversely related to the mass of the atoms joined by the bond; thus, heavier atoms vibrate at lower frequencies.

Hooke's Law

Lighter atoms show absorption bands at larger wavenumbers.

C—H
~3000 cm^{-1}
C—D
~2200 cm^{-1}
C—O
~1100 cm^{-1}
C—Cl
~700 cm^{-1}

The approximate wavenumber of an absorption band can be calculated from the following equation derived from **Hooke's law**, which describes the motion of a vibrating spring:

$$\bar{\nu} = \frac{1}{2\pi c}\left[\frac{f(m_1 + m_2)}{m_1 m_2}\right]^{1/2}$$

where $\bar{\nu}$ is wavenumber of an absorption band, c is the speed of light, f is the force constant of the bond (a measure of the strength of the bond), and m_1 and m_2 are the masses of the atoms (in grams) joined by the bond. This equation shows that *stronger bonds* and *lighter atoms* give rise to higher frequencies.

The Originator of Hooke's Law

Robert Hooke (1635–1703) was born on the Isle of Wight off the southern coast of England. A brilliant scientist, he contributed to almost every scientific field. He was the first to suggest that light had wave-like properties. He discovered that Gamma Arietis is a double star, and he discovered Jupiter's Great Red Spot. In a lecture published posthumously, he suggested that earthquakes are caused by the cooling and contracting of the Earth. He examined cork under a microscope and coined the term *cell* to describe what he saw. He wrote about evolutionary development based on his studies of microscopic fossils, and he produced some highly regarded studies of insects. Hooke also invented the balance spring for watches and the universal joint currently used in automobiles.

Robert Hooke's drawing of a "blue fly" appeared in *Micrographia*, the first book on microscopy, published by Hooke in 1665.

The Effect of Bond Order

Bond order affects bond strength. Therefore, bond order affects the position of absorption bands as predicted by Hooke's law. A C≡C bond is stronger than a C=C bond, so a C≡C bond stretches at a higher frequency (~2100 cm^{-1}) than does a C=C bond (~1650 cm^{-1}); C—C bonds show stretching vibrations in the region from 1300 to 800 cm^{-1}, but since they are weak and very common, these vibrations are of little value in identifying compounds. Similarly, a C=O bond stretches at a higher frequency (~1700 cm^{-1}) than does a C—O bond (~1100 cm^{-1}), and a C≡N bond stretches at a higher frequency ($\sim$2200 cm^{-1}) than does a C$=$N bond ($\sim$1600 cm^{-1}), which in turn stretches at a higher frequency than does a C$-$N bond ($\sim$1100 cm^{-1}) (Table 13.4).

Stronger bonds show absorption bands at larger wavenumbers.

C$\equiv$N	C$=$N	C$-$N
$\sim$2200 cm^{-1}	$\sim$1600 cm^{-1}	$\sim$1100 cm^{-1}

PROBLEM 20♦

a. Which will occur at a larger wavenumber
    1. a C$\equiv$C stretch or a C$=$C stretch?   **3.** a C$-$N stretch or a C$=$N stretch?
    2. a C$-$H stretch or a C$-$H bend?   **4.** a C$=$O stretch or a C$-$O stretch?
b. Assuming that the force constants are the same, which will occur at a larger wavenumber:
    1. a C$-$O stretch or a C$-$Cl stretch?   **2.** a C$-$O stretch or a C$-$C stretch?

13.12 THE POSITION OF AN ABSORPTION BAND IS AFFECTED BY ELECTRON DELOCALIZATION, ELECTRON DONATION AND WITHDRAWAL, AND HYDROGEN BONDING

Table 13.4 shows a range of wavenumbers for the frequency of the stretching vibration for each functional group because the exact position of a group's absorption band in the spectrum of a given compound depends on other structural features of the molecule, such as electron delocalization, the electronic effect of neighboring substituents, and hydrogen bonding. In fact, important details about the structure of a compound can be revealed by the exact positions of its absorption bands.

For example, the IR spectrum in Figure 13.15 shows that the carbonyl group (C$=$O) of 2-pentanone absorbs at 1720 cm^{-1}, whereas the IR spectrum in Figure 13.16 shows that the carbonyl group of 2-cyclohexenone absorbs at a lower frequency (1680 cm^{-1}). 2-Cyclohexenone's carbonyl group absorbs at a lower frequency because it has more single-bond character due to electron delocalization. A single bond is weaker than a double bond, so a carbonyl group with significant single-bond character will stretch at a lower frequency than will one with little or no single-bond character.

Figure 13.15

The IR spectrum of 2-pentanone. The intense absorption band at $\sim$1720 cm^{-1} indicates a C$=$O bond.

▶ **Figure 13.16**
The IR spectrum of 2-cyclohexenone. Electron delocalization gives its carbonyl group less double-bond character, so it absorbs at a lower frequency (~ 1680 cm^{-1}) than does a carbonyl group with localized electrons (~ 1720 cm^{-1}).

Putting an atom other than carbon next to the carbonyl group also causes the position of the carbonyl absorption band to shift. Whether it shifts to a lower or to a higher frequency depends on whether the predominant effect of the atom is to donate electrons by resonance or to withdraw electrons inductively.

The predominant effect of the nitrogen of an amide is electron donation by resonance (Section 7.9). In contrast, since oxygen is less able than nitrogen to accommodate a positive charge because of oxygen's greater electronegativity, the predominant effect of the oxygen of an ester is inductive electron withdrawal (Section 1.22). Therefore, the resonance contributor of the carbonyl group with the C—O single bond contributes less to the hybrid. (See also Section 17.2.) As a result, the carbonyl group of an ester has less single-bond character, so it requires more energy to stretch (1740 cm^{-1} in Figure 13.17) than the carbonyl group of an amide (1660 cm^{-1} in Figure 13.18).

▶ **Figure 13.17**
The IR spectrum of ethyl butanoate. The electron-withdrawing oxygen atom makes the carbonyl group of an ester harder to stretch (~ 1740 cm^{-1}) than the carbonyl group of a ketone (~ 1720 cm^{-1}).

▶ **Figure 13.18**
The IR spectrum of *N,N*-dimethylpropanamide. The carbonyl group of an amide has less double-bond character than does the carbonyl group of a ketone, so the former stretches more easily (~ 1660 cm^{-1}).

When we compare the frequency for the stretching vibration of the carbonyl group of an ester (1740 cm^{-1} in Figure 13.17) with that of the carbonyl group of a ketone (1720 cm^{-1} in Figure 13.15), we can see how important inductive electron withdrawal is to the position of the stretching vibration of the carbonyl group.

A C—O bond shows a stretching vibration between 1250 and 1050 cm^{-1}. If the C—O bond is in an alcohol (Figure 13.19) or an ether, the stretch will lie toward the lower end of the range. If, however, the C—O bond is in a carboxylic acid (Figure 13.20), the stretch will lie at the higher end of the range. The position of the C—O absorption varies because the C—O bond in an alcohol is a pure single bond, whereas the C—O bond in a carboxylic acid has partial double-bond character due to electron donation by resonance. Esters show C—O stretches at both ends of the range (Figure 13.18) because esters have two C—O single bonds: one that is a pure single bond and one that has partial double-bond character.

$$CH_3CH_2-OH$$
$$\sim 1050 \text{ cm}^{-1}$$

$$CH_3CH_2-O-CH_2CH_3$$
$$\sim 1050 \text{ cm}^{-1}$$

$$\sim 1250 \text{ cm}^{-1}$$

$$\sim 1250 \text{ cm}^{-1} \text{ and } \sim 1050 \text{ cm}^{-1}$$

◀ **Figure 13.19**
The IR spectrum of 1-hexanol.

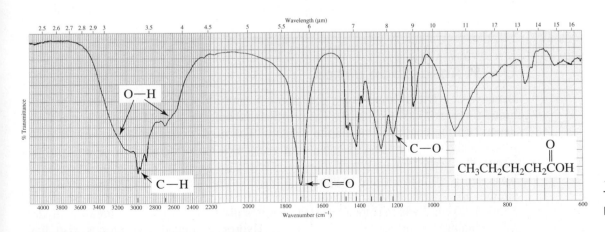

◀ **Figure 13.20**
The IR spectrum of pentanoic acid.

PROBLEM-SOLVING STRATEGY

Differences in IR Spectra

Which will occur at a larger wavenumber: the C—N stretch of an amine or the C—N stretch of an amide?

To answer this kind of question, we need to see if electron delocalization causes one of the bonds to be other than a pure single bond. When we do that we see that electron delocalization causes the C—N bond of the amide to have partial double-bond character, whereas the C—N bond of the amine is a pure single bond. The C—N stretch of an amide, therefore, will occur at a larger wavenumber.

no electron delocalization   **electron delocalization causes the C—N bond to have partial double-bond character**

Now continue on to Problem 21.

PROBLEM 21♦

Which will occur at a larger wavenumber

a. the C—O stretch of phenol or the C—O stretch of cyclohexanol?
b. the C=O stretch of a ketone or the C=O stretch of an amide?
c. the C—N stretch of cyclohexylamine or the C—N stretch of aniline?

PROBLEM 22♦

Which would show an absorption band at a larger wavenumber: a carbonyl group bonded to an sp^3 carbon or a carbonyl group bonded to an sp^2 carbon?

PROBLEM 23♦

Why is the C—O absorption band of 1-hexanol at a smaller wavenumber (1060 cm^{-1}) than the C—O absorption band of pentanoic acid (1220 cm^{-1})?

PROBLEM 24♦

List the following compounds in order of decreasing wavenumber of the C=O absorption band:

(*Hint:* Recall that hyperconjugation causes an alkyl group to be more electron donating than a hydrogen; see Section 4.2.)

O—H Absorption Bands

Because O—H bonds are polar, they show intense absorption bands that can be quite broad (Figures 13.19 and 13.20). The position and breadth of an O—H absorption band depend on the concentration of the solution. The more concentrated the solution, the more likely it is for the OH-containing molecules to form intermolecular hydrogen bonds. It is easier for an O—H bond to stretch if it is hydrogen bonded, because the hydrogen is attracted to the oxygen of a neighboring molecule. Therefore, the O—H stretch in a concentrated (hydrogen-bonded) solution of an alcohol occurs at $3550–3200 \text{ cm}^{-1}$ whereas the O—H stretch in a dilute solution (with little or no hydrogen bonding) occurs at $3650–3590 \text{ cm}^{-1}$. Hydrogen-bonded OH groups also have broader absorption bands because hydrogen bonds vary in strength.

concentrated solution
$3550–3200 \text{ cm}^{-1}$ **dilute solution**
$3650–3590 \text{ cm}^{-1}$

PROBLEM 25♦

Which will show an O—H stretch at a larger wavenumber: ethanol dissolved in carbon disulfide or an undiluted sample of ethanol?

C—H Absorption Bands

Important information about the identity of a compound is provided by the stretching and bending vibrations of the C—H bonds.

Stretching Vibrations The strength of a C—H bond depends on the hybridization of the carbon: the greater the *s* character of the carbon, the stronger is the bond that it forms (Section 1.14). Therefore, a C—H bond is stronger when the carbon is *sp* hybridized than when it is sp^2 hybridized, which in turn is stronger than when the carbon is sp^3 hybridized (see Table 1.7 on page 38). More energy is needed to stretch a stronger bond, and this is reflected in the absorption bands for a C—H stretch, which occur at ~3300 cm^{-1} for an *sp* carbon, at ~3100 cm^{-1} for an sp^2 carbon, and at ~2900 cm^{-1} for an sp^3 carbon (Table 13.5).

Table 13.5   IR Absorptions of Carbon–Hydrogen Bonds

Carbon–Hydrogen Stretching Vibrations	Wavenumber (cm^{-1})
C≡C—H	~3300
C=C—H	3100–3020
C—C—H	2960–2850
R—C(=O)—H	~2820 and ~2720

Carbon–Hydrogen Bending Vibrations		Wavenumber (cm^{-1})
CH₃— —CH₂— —CH—		1450–1420
CH₃—		1385–1365
C=C (H,R / R,H)	trans	980–960
C=C (R,R / H,H)	cis	730–675
C=C (R,R / R,H)	trisubstituted	840–800
C=C (R,R / H,H)	terminal alkene (disubstituted)	890
C=C (R,H / H,H)	terminal alkene (monosubstituted)	990 and 910

A useful step in the analysis of a spectrum is to look at the absorption bands in the vicinity of 3000 cm^{-1}. Figures 13.21, 13.22, and 13.23 show the IR spectra for methylcyclohexane, cyclohexene, and ethylbenzene, respectively. The only absorption band in the vicinity of 3000 cm^{-1} in Figure 13.21 is slightly to the right of that value.

This tells us that the compound has hydrogens bonded to sp^3 carbons, but none bonded to sp^2 or to sp carbons. Both Figures 13.22 and 13.23 show absorption bands slightly to the left and slightly to the right of 3000 cm^{-1}, indicating that the compounds that produced those spectra contain hydrogens bonded to sp^2 and sp^3 carbons.

▶ **Figure 13.21**
The IR spectrum of methylcyclohexane.

▶ **Figure 13.22**
The IR spectrum of cyclohexene.

▶ **Figure 13.23**
The IR spectrum of ethylbenzene.

Once we know that a compound has hydrogens bonded to sp^2 carbons, we need to find out whether those carbons are the sp^2 carbons of an alkene or of a benzene ring. A benzene ring is indicated by two sharp absorption bands, one at ~1600 cm^{-1} and one at 1500–1430 cm^{-1}, whereas an alkene is indicated by a band only at ~1600 cm^{-1} (Table 13.4). The compound whose spectrum is shown in Figure 13.22 is, therefore, an alkene, whereas the one whose spectrum is shown in Figure 13.23 has a benzene ring. Be aware that N—H bending vibrations also occur at 1600 cm^{-1}, so absorption at that wavelength does not always indicate a C=C bond. However, absorption bands resulting from N—H bends tend to be broader (due to hydrogen bonding) and more intense (due to being more polar) than those caused by C=C stretches (see Figure 13.25), and they will be accompanied by N—H stretches at 3500–3300 cm^{-1} (Table 13.4).

The stretch of the C—H bond of an aldehyde group shows two absorption bands— one at ~2820 cm^{-1} and the other at ~2720 cm^{-1} (Figure 13.24). This makes aldehydes relatively easy to identify because essentially no other absorption occurs at these wavenumbers.

◀ **Figure 13.24**
The IR spectrum of pentanal. The absorptions at ~2820 cm^{-1} and ~2720 cm^{-1} readily identify an aldehyde group. Note also the intense absorption band at ~1730 cm^{-1} indicating a C=O bond.

Bending Vibrations If a compound has sp^3 carbons, a look at 1400 cm^{-1} will tell you whether the compound has a methyl group. All hydrogens bonded to sp^3 carbons show a C—H bending vibration slightly to the *left* of 1400 cm^{-1}. Only methyl groups show a C—H bending vibration slightly to the *right* of 1400 cm^{-1}. So, if a compound has a methyl group, absorption bands will appear *both* to the left and to the right of 1400 cm^{-1}; otherwise, only the band to the left of 1400 cm^{-1} will be present. You can see evidence of a methyl group in Figure 13.21 (methylcyclohexane) and in Figure 13.23 (ethylbenzene), but not in Figure 13.22 (cyclohexene). Two methyl groups attached to the same carbon can sometimes be detected by a split in the methyl peak at ~1380 cm^{-1} (Figure 13.25).

◀ **Figure 13.25**
The IR spectrum of isopentylamine. The two-peak absorption band at ~1380 cm^{-1} indicates the presence of an isopropyl group.

The C—H bending vibrations for hydrogens bonded to sp^2 carbons give rise to absorption bands in the 1000–600 cm^{-1} region. As Table 13.5 shows, the frequency of the C—H bending vibration of an alkene depends on the number of alkyl groups attached to the sp^2 carbons and on the configuration of the alkene. It is important to realize that these absorption bands can be shifted out of the characteristic regions if strongly electron-withdrawing or electron-donating substituents are close to the double bond

(Section 13.10). Acyclic compounds with more than four adjacent methylene (CH_2) groups show a characteristic absorption band at 720 cm^{-1} that results from in-phase rocking of the methylene groups (Figure 13.19).

13.13 THE SHAPE OF ABSORPTION BANDS

The shape of an absorption band can be helpful in identifying the compound responsible for an IR spectrum. For example, both O—H and N—H bonds stretch at wavenumbers above 3100 cm^{-1}, but the shapes of their stretching absorption bands are distinctive. Notice the difference in the shape of these absorption bands in the IR spectra of 1-hexanol (Figure 13.19), pentanoic acid (Figure 13.20), and isopentylamine (Figure 13.25). An N—H absorption band ($\sim 3300 \text{ cm}^{-1}$) is narrower and less intense than an O—H absorption band ($\sim 3300 \text{ cm}^{-1}$), and the O—H absorption band of a carboxylic acid ($\sim 3300 – 2500 \text{ cm}^{-1}$) is broader than the O—H absorption band of an alcohol (Sections 13.9 and 13.10).

> The position, intensity, and shape of an absorption band are helpful in identifying functional groups.

13.14 THE ABSENCE OF ABSORPTION BANDS

The absence of an absorption band can be as useful as the presence of one in identifying a compound by IR spectroscopy. For example, the spectrum in Figure 13.26 shows a strong absorption at $\sim 1100 \text{ cm}^{-1}$, indicating the presence of a C—O bond. Clearly, the compound is not an alcohol because there is no absorption above 3100 cm^{-1}. Nor is it an ester or any other kind of carbonyl compound because there is no absorption at $\sim 1700 \text{ cm}^{-1}$. The compound has no C≡C, C=C, C≡N, C=N, or C—N bonds. We may deduce, then, that the compound is an ether. Its C—H absorption bands show that it has hydrogens only on sp^3 carbons and that it has a methyl group (2950 cm^{-1} and 1385 cm^{-1}). We also know that the compound has fewer than four adjacent methylene groups, because there is no absorption at $\sim 720 \text{ cm}^{-1}$. The compound is in fact diethyl ether.

▶ **Figure 13.26**
The IR spectrum of diethyl ether.

PROBLEM 26♦

How do we know that the absorption band at $\sim 1100 \text{ cm}^{-1}$ in Figure 13.26 is due to a C—O bond and not to a C—N bond?

PROBLEM 27♦

a. An oxygen-containing compound shows an absorption band at $\sim 1700 \text{ cm}^{-1}$ and no absorption bands at $\sim 3300 \text{ cm}^{-1}$, $\sim 2700 \text{ cm}^{-1}$, or $\sim 1100 \text{ cm}^{-1}$. What class of compound is it?

b. A nitrogen-containing compound shows no absorption band at $\sim 3400 \text{ cm}^{-1}$ and no absorption bands between $\sim 1700 \text{ cm}^{-1}$ and $\sim 1600 \text{ cm}^{-1}$. What class of compound is it?

PROBLEM 28

How could IR spectroscopy be used to distinguish between the following compounds?

a. a ketone and an aldehyde
b. a cyclic ketone and an open-chain ketone
c. benzene and cyclohexane

d. *cis*-2-hexene and *trans*-2-hexene
e. cyclohexene and cyclohexane
f. a primary amine and a tertiary amine

chem Tutorial:
place IR spectra

PROBLEM 29

For each of the following pairs of compounds, give one absorption band that could be used to distinguish between them:

a. $CH_3CH_2CH_2CH_3$ and $CH_3CH_2OCH_3$

d. $CH_3CH_2C{\equiv}CCH_3$ and $CH_3CH_2C{\equiv}CH$

b. [structure: CH_3–C(=O)–OCH_3] and [structure: CH_3–C(=O)–OH]

e. [structure: CH_3–C(=O)–OH] and [structure: –OH]

c. [cyclohexane] and [methylcyclohexane with CH_3]

f. [benzene ring] and [toluene ring with CH_3]

13.15 SOME VIBRATIONS ARE INFRARED INACTIVE

Not all bond vibrations give rise to absorption bands. In order for a bond's vibration to absorb IR radiation, the dipole moment of the bond must change when the bond vibrates. For example, the $C{=}C$ bond in 1-butene has a dipole moment because the molecule is not symmetrical about this bond. When the $C{=}C$ bond stretches, the increasing distance between the atoms increases the dipole moment (Section 1.3). Because the dipole moment changes when the bond stretches, an absorption band is observed for the $C{=}C$ stretching vibration.

asymmetrical about the $C{=}C$ bond; has a dipole moment

symmetrical about the $C{=}C$ bond; has no dipole moment

1-butene   2,3-dimethyl-2-butene   2,3-dimethyl-2-heptene

2,3-Dimethyl-2-butene, in contrast, is a symmetrical molecule, so its $C{=}C$ bond has no dipole moment. When the bond stretches, it still has no dipole moment. Since stretching is not accompanied by a change in dipole moment, no absorption band is observed for that bond. The vibration is said to be *infrared inactive*. 2,3-Dimethyl-2-heptene experiences a very small change in dipole moment when its $C{=}C$ bond stretches, so only an extremely weak absorption band (if any) will be detected for the stretching vibration of the bond.

PROBLEM 30◆

Which of the following compounds has a vibration that is infrared inactive: acetone, 1-butyne, 2-butyne, H_2, H_2O, Cl_2, ethene?

PROBLEM 31 ◆

The mass spectrum and infrared spectrum of compound A are shown in Figures 13.27 and 13.28, respectively. Identify compound A.

▶ **Figure 13.27**
The mass spectrum of compound A referred to in Problem 31.

▶ **Figure 13.28**
The IR spectrum of compound A referred to in Problem 31.

13.16 HOW TO INTERPRET AN INFRARED SPECTRUM

We will now look at some IR spectra and see what we can deduce about the structures of the compounds that give rise to the spectra. We might not be able to identify the compound precisely, but when we are told what it is, its structure should fit our observations.

Compound 1. The absorptions in the 3000 cm^{-1} region in Figure 13.29 indicate that hydrogens are attached both to sp^2 carbons (3075 cm^{-1}) and to sp^3 carbons (2950 cm^{-1}). Now we need to see if the sp^2 carbons belong to an alkene or to a benzene ring. The absorption at 1650 cm^{-1}, the absence of a band at 1500–1430 cm^{-1}, and the absorption at ~890 cm^{-1} (Table 13.5) suggest that the compound is a terminal alkene with two alkyl substituents at the 2-position. The absence of absorption at ~720 cm^{-1} indicates that the compound has fewer than four adjacent methylene groups. We are not surprised to find that the compound is 2-methyl-1-pentene.

Compound 2. The absorption in the 3000 cm^{-1} region in Figure 13.30 indicates that hydrogens are attached to sp^2 carbons (3050 cm^{-1}) but not to sp^3 carbons. The absorptions at 1600 cm^{-1} and 1460 cm^{-1} indicate that the compound has a benzene ring. The absorptions at 2810 cm^{-1} and 2730 cm^{-1} show that the compound is an aldehyde. The characteristically strong absorption band for the carbonyl group (C═O) is lower (~1700 cm^{-1}) than normal (1720 cm^{-1}), so the carbonyl group has partial single-bond character. Thus, it must be attached directly to the benzene ring. The compound is benzaldehyde.

◀ **Figure 13.30**
The IR spectrum of
Compound 2.

Compound 3. The absorptions in the 3000 cm^{-1} region in Figure 13.31 indicate that hydrogens are attached to sp^3 carbons (2950 cm^{-1}) but not to sp^2 carbons. The shape of the strong absorption band at 3300 cm^{-1} is characteristic of an O—H group of an alcohol. The absorption at 2100 cm^{-1} indicates that the compound has a triple bond. The sharp absorption band at 3300 cm^{-1} indicates that the compound has a hydrogen on an sp carbon, so we know it is a terminal alkyne. The compound is 2-propyn-1-ol.

◀ **Figure 13.31**
The IR spectrum of
Compound 3.

Compound 4. The absorption in the 3000 cm^{-1} region in Figure 13.32 indicates that hydrogens are attached to sp^3 carbons (2950 cm^{-1}). The relatively strong absorption band at 3300 cm^{-1} suggests that the compound has an N—H bond. The presence of the N—H bond is confirmed by the absorption band at 1560 cm^{-1}. The C=O absorption at 1660 cm^{-1} indicates that the compound is an amide. The compound is *N*-methylacetamide.

▶ **Figure 13.32**
The IR spectrum of Compound 4.

Compound 5. The absorptions in the 3000 cm^{-1} region in Figure 13.33 indicate that the compound has hydrogens attached to sp^2 carbons (>3000 cm^{-1}) and to sp^3 carbons (<3000 cm^{-1}). The absorptions at 1605 cm^{-1} and 1500 cm^{-1} indicate that the compound contains a benzene ring. The absorption at 1720 cm^{-1} for the carbonyl group indicates that the compound is a ketone and that the carbonyl group is not directly attached to the benzene ring. The absorption at ~1380 cm^{-1} indicates a methyl group. The compound is 1-phenyl-2-butanone.

▶ **Figure 13.33**
The IR spectrum of Compound 5.

PROBLEM 32♦

A compound with molecular formula C_4H_6O gives the infrared spectrum shown in Figure 13.34. Identify the compound.

▶ **Figure 13.34**
The IR spectrum referred to in Problem 32.

13.17 ULTRAVIOLET AND VISIBLE SPECTROSCOPY

Ultraviolet and visible (UV/Vis) spectroscopy provides information about compounds that have conjugated double bonds. Ultraviolet light and visible light have just the right energy to cause an electronic transition in a molecule, that is, to promote an electron from one molecular orbital to another of higher energy. Depending on the energy needed for the electronic transition, a molecule will absorb either ultraviolet or visible light. If it absorbs **ultraviolet light**, a UV spectrum is obtained; if it absorbs **visible light**, a visible spectrum is obtained. Ultraviolet light is electromagnetic radiation with wavelengths ranging from 180 to 400 nm (nanometers); visible light has wavelengths ranging from 400 to 780 nm. Recall from Section 13.6 that **wavelength** (λ) is inversely related to the energy of the radiation: the shorter the wavelength, the greater the energy. Ultraviolet light, therefore, has greater energy than visible light.

$$E = \frac{hc}{\lambda}$$

In the ground-state electronic configuration of a molecule, all the electrons are in the lowest-energy molecular orbitals. When a molecule absorbs light with sufficient energy to promote an electron to a higher-energy molecular orbital—when it undergoes an **electronic transition**—the molecule is then in an excited state. The relative energies of the bonding, nonbonding, and antibonding molecular orbitals are shown in Figure 13.35 (see Section 7.8).

The shorter the wavelength, the greater the energy of the radiation.

◀ **Figure 13.35**
Relative energies of the bonding, nonbonding, and antibonding orbitals.

Ultraviolet and visible light have only enough energy to cause the two electronic transitions shown in Figure 13.35. The electronic transition requiring the lower amount of energy is the promotion of a nonbonding (lone-pair) electron (n) into a π^* antibonding molecular orbital. This is called an $n \longrightarrow \pi^*$ (stated as "n to π star") transition. The higher-energy electronic transition is the promotion of an electron from a π bonding molecular orbital into a π^* antibonding molecular orbital, known as a $\pi \longrightarrow \pi^*$ (stated as "π to π star") transition. Because both transitions promote an electron into a π^* antibonding molecular orbital, *only organic compounds with π electrons can produce UV/Vis spectra.*

Only compounds with π electrons can produce ultraviolet and visible spectra.

The UV spectrum of acetone is shown in Figure 13.36. Acetone has both π electrons and lone-pair electrons. Thus, its UV spectrum has two **absorption bands**: one

◀ **Figure 13.36**
The UV spectrum of acetone.

— π^* antibonding MO

vibrational sublevels

— π^* bonding MO

▲ **Figure 13.37**
UV/Vis absorption bands are broad because each electronic state has vibrational sublevels.

for the $\pi \rightarrow \pi^*$ transition and one for the $n \rightarrow \pi^*$ transition. The λ_{max} (stated as "lambda max") is the wavelength at which the absorption band has its maximum absorbance. For the $\pi \rightarrow \pi^*$ transition, $\lambda_{max} = 195$ nm; for the $n \rightarrow \pi^*$ transition, $\lambda_{max} = 274$ nm. We know that the λ_{max} at the shorter wavelength in Figure 13.35 is the $\pi \rightarrow \pi^*$ transition because that transition requires more energy than the $n \rightarrow \pi^*$ transition. The absorption bands are broad because each electronic state has vibrational sublevels (Figure 13.37), and electronic transitions can occur from and to these different sublevels. Therefore, the electronic transitions span a range of wavelengths.

A **chromophore** is the part of a molecule that absorbs UV or visible light. The carbonyl group is the chromophore of acetone. The following four compounds all have the same chromophore, so they all have approximately the same λ_{max}.

PROBLEM 33◆

Explain why diethyl ether does not have a UV spectrum, even though it has lone-pair electrons.

Ultraviolet Light and Sunscreens

Exposure to ultraviolet (UV) light stimulates specialized cells in the skin to produce a black pigment known as melanin, which causes the skin to look tan. Melanin absorbs UV light, so it protects our bodies from the harmful effects of the sun. If more UV light reaches the skin than the melanin present can absorb, the light will "burn" the skin and cause photochemical reactions that can result in skin cancer (Section 30.6). UV-A is the lowest-energy UV light (315 to 400 nm) and does the least biological damage. Fortunately, most of the more dangerous, higher-energy UV light, UV-B (290 to 315 nm) and UV-C (180 to 290 nm), is filtered out by the ozone layer in the stratosphere. That is why we need to worry about the apparent thinning of the ozone layer (Section 12.12).

Applying a sunscreen can protect skin from UV light. The amount of protection from UV-B light provided by a particular sunscreen is indicated by its SPF (sun protection factor). The higher the SPF, the greater the protection. Some sunscreens contain an inorganic component, such as zinc oxide, that reflects the light as it reaches the skin. Others contain a compound that absorbs UV light. *para*-Aminobenzoic acid (PABA) was the first commercially available UV-absorbing sunscreen. PABA absorbs UV-B light, but is not very soluble in oily skin lotions. Less polar compounds, such as Padimate O, are now commonly used. Recent research has shown that sunscreens that absorb only UV-B light do not give adequate protection against skin cancer; both UV-A and UV-B protection are needed. Giv Tan F absorbs both UV-B and UV-A light, so it gives better protection.

para-aminobenzoic acid
PABA

2-ethylhexyl 4-(dimethylamino)benzoate
Padimate O

2-ethoxyethyl (*E*)-3-(4-methoxyphenyl)-2-propenoate
Giv Tan F

13.18 THE BEER—LAMBERT LAW

Wilhelm Beer and Johann Lambert independently proposed that the absorbance of a sample at a given wavelength depends on the amount of absorbing species that the light encounters as it passes through a solution of the sample. In other words, absorbance depends on both the concentration of the sample and the length of the light path through the sample. The relationship between absorbance, concentration, and length of the light path, known as the **Beer–Lambert law**, is given by

$$A = \varepsilon c l$$

where

A = absorbance of the sample = $\log \dfrac{I_0}{I}$

I_0 = intensity of the radiation entering the sample

I = intensity of the radiation emerging from the sample

c = concentration of the sample, in moles/liter

l = length of the light path through the sample, in centimeters

ε = molar absorptivity (liter $M^{-1}cm^{-1}$)

Wilhelm Beer (1797–1850), *born in Germany, was a banker whose hobby was astronomy. He was the first to make a map of the darker and lighter areas of Mars, and the first to make a map of the Moon.*

The **molar absorptivity** (ε) of a compound is a constant that is characteristic of the compound at a particular wavelength. (The abbreviation ε comes from the fact that molar absorptivity was formerly called the extinction coefficient.) It is the absorbance that would be observed for a 1.00 M solution in a cell with a 1.00-cm path length. The molar absorptivity of acetone dissolved in hexane, for example, is $9000\,M^{-1}\,cm^{-1}$ at 195 nm and $14\,M^{-1}cm^{-1}$ at 274 nm. The solvent in which the sample is dissolved is reported because molar absorptivity is not exactly the same in all solvents. Therefore, the UV spectrum of acetone in hexane would be reported as: λ_{max} = 195 nm (ε_{max} = 9000, hexane); λ_{max} = 274 nm (ε_{max} = 14, hexane). Because absorbance is proportional to concentration, the concentration of a solution can be determined if the absorbance and molar absorptivity of the solute at a particular wavelength are known.

The two absorption bands of acetone in Figure 13.36 are very different in size because of the difference in molar absorptivity at the two wavelengths. Small molar absorptivities are characteristic of $n \rightarrow \pi^*$ transitions, so these transitions can be difficult to detect. Consequently, $\pi \rightarrow \pi^*$ transitions are more useful for analyzing spectra.

The solution being used to produce a UV or visible spectrum is put into a cell. Most cells have 1-cm path lengths. Either glass or quartz cells can be used for visible spectra, but quartz cells (made of high-purity fused silica) must be used for UV spectra because glass absorbs UV light.

PROBLEM 34♦

A solution of 4-methyl-3-penten-2-one in ethanol shows an absorbance of 0.52 at 236 nm in a cell with a 1-cm light path. Its molar absorptivity in ethanol at that wavelength is $12,600\,M^{-1}cm^{-1}$. What is the concentration of the compound?

PROBLEM 35♦

A 4.0×10^{-5} M solution of nitrobenzene in hexane shows an absorbance of 0.40 at 252 nm in a cell with a 1-cm light path. What is the molar absorptivity of nitrobenzene in hexane at 252 nm?

Johann Heinrich Lambert (1728–1777), *a German-born mathematician, was the first to make accurate measurements of light intensities and to introduce hyperbolic functions into trigonometry. Although the equation that relates absorbance, concentration, and light path bears the names of Beer and Lambert, it is believed that* **Pierre Bouguer (1698–1758)**, *a French mathematician, first formulated the relationship in 1729.*

13.19 THE EFFECT OF CONJUGATION ON λ_{max}

The more conjugated double bonds that a compound has, the longer is the wavelength at which the $n \rightarrow \pi^*$ and $\pi \rightarrow \pi^*$ transitions occur. For example, the $n \rightarrow \pi^*$ transition for methyl vinyl ketone is at λ_{max} = 324 nm, and the $\pi \rightarrow \pi^*$ transition is at λ_{max} = 219 nm.

Both λ_{max} values are at longer wavelengths than the corresponding λ_{max} values of acetone because methyl vinyl ketone has two conjugated double bonds, whereas acetone has only one double bond.

	acetone	methyl vinyl ketone
$n \longrightarrow \pi^*$	$\lambda_{max} = 274$ nm ($\varepsilon_{max} = 14$)	$\lambda_{max} = 324$ nm ($\varepsilon_{max} = 25$)
$\pi \longrightarrow \pi^*$	$\lambda_{max} = 195$ nm ($\varepsilon_{max} = 9000$)	$\lambda_{max} = 219$ nm ($\varepsilon_{max} = 9600$)

The λ_{max} values of the $\pi \rightarrow \pi^*$ transition for several conjugated dienes are shown in Table 13.6. Notice that both the λ_{max} and the molar absorptivity increase as the number of conjugated double bonds increases. Thus, the λ_{max} of a compound can be used to estimate the number of conjugated double bonds in a compound.

The λ_{max} increases as the number of conjugated double bonds increases.

Table 13.6	Values of λ_{max} and ε for Ethylene and Conjugated Dienes	
Compound	λ_{max} (nm)	ε (M^{-1} cm^{-1})
$H_2C{=}CH_2$	165	15,000
	217	21,000
	256	50,000
	290	85,000
	334	125,000
	364	138,000

Conjugation raises the energy of the **HOMO (highest occupied molecular orbital)** and lowers the energy of the **LUMO (lowest unoccupied molecular orbital)**; (Figure 7.8 on page 300), so less energy is required for an electronic transition in a conjugated system than in a nonconjugated system (Figure 13.38). The more conjugated double bonds there are in a compound, the less energy is required for the electronic transition, and therefore the longer is the wavelength at which the electronic transition occurs.

▶ **Figure 13.38**
Conjugation raises the energy of the HOMO and lowers the energy of the LUMO.

If a compound has enough conjugated double bonds, it will absorb visible light (light with wavelengths >400 nm), and the compound will be colored. For example, β-carotene with a $\lambda_{max} = 455$ nm, a precursor of with a vitamin A, is an orange substance found in carrots, apricots, and sweet potatoes. Lycopene with a $\lambda_{max} = 474$ nm—found in tomatoes, watermelon, and pink grapefruit—is red.

β-carotene
$\lambda_{max} = 455$ nm

lycopene
$\lambda_{max} = 474$ nm

An **auxochrome** is a substituent that, when attached to a chromophore, alters both the λ_{max} and the intensity of the absorption, usually increasing both. For example, OH and NH_2 groups are auxochromes. The lone-pair electrons on oxygen and nitrogen in the compounds shown below are available to interact with the π electron cloud of the benzene ring; such an interaction increases λ_{max}. Because the anilinium ion does not have an auxochrome, its λ_{max} is similar to that of benzene.

| benzene | phenol | phenolate ion | aniline | anilinium ion |
| $\lambda_{max} =$ 255 nm | 270 nm | 287 nm | 280 nm | 254 nm |

Removing a proton from phenol and thereby forming a phenolate ion increases the λ_{max} because the resulting ion has an additional lone pair. Protonating aniline, thereby forming the anilinium ion, decreases the λ_{max} because the lone pair is no longer available to interact with the π cloud of the benzene ring.

PROBLEM 36♦

Rank each set of compounds in order of decreasing λ_{max}:

a.

b.

13.20 THE VISIBLE SPECTRUM AND COLOR

White light is a mixture of all visible wavelengths. If any of these wavelengths are removed from white light, the eye registers the remaining light as colored, the perceived color depending on the precise wavelengths reaching the eye. Therefore, any compound that absorbs visible light appears colored; the wavelengths that the compound does *not* absorb are reflected back to the viewer, producing the color the viewer sees.

The relationship between the wavelengths of the light that a substance absorbs and the substance's observed color is shown in Table 13.7. Notice that two absorption bands are necessary to produce green. Most colored compounds have fairly broad absorption bands, although vivid colors have narrow absorption bands. The human eye is able to distinguish more than a million different shades of color!

R = CH_3 in chlorophyll a

R = CH in chlorophyll b

Chlorophyll a and b are the pigments that make plants look green. These highly conjugated compounds absorb visible light. The light reflected from the surface tissues of plants is green.

Table 13.7   Dependence of the Color Observed on the Wavelength of Light Absorbed

Wavelengths absorbed (nm)	Color absorbed	Color observed
380–460	blue-violet	yellow
380–500	blue	orange
440–560	blue-green	red
480–610	green	purple
540–650	orange	blue
380–420 and 610–700	purple	green

Azobenzenes (benzene rings connected by an N=N bond) have an extended conjugated system that causes them to absorb light from the visible region of the spectrum. Some substituted azobenzenes, such as the two shown below, are used commercially as dyes. Variations in the extent of conjugation and the substituents attached to the conjugated system create a large number of different colors. Notice that the only difference between butter yellow and methyl orange is an $SO_3^- Na^+$ group. When margarine was first produced, it was colored with butter yellow to make it look more like butter. (White margarine would not be very appetizing.) This dye was abandoned after it was found to be carcinogenic. β-Carotene is now used to color margarine (page 539). Methyl orange is a commonly used acid–base indicator (see Problem 70a).

butter yellow
an azobenzene

methyl orange
an azobenzene

Anthocyanins: A Colorful Class of Compounds

A class of highly conjugated compounds called *anthocyanins* is responsible for the red, purple, and blue colors of many flowers (poppies, peonies, cornflowers), fruits (cranberries, rhubarb, strawberries, blueberries, red skin of apples, purple skin of grapes), and vegetables (beets, radishes, red cabbage).

In a neutral or basic solution, the monocyclic fragment (on the right-hand side of the anthocyanin) is not conjugated with the rest of the molecule, so the anthocyanin does not absorb visible light and is therefore a colorless compound. In an acidic environment, however, the OH group becomes protonated and

water is eliminated. (Recall that water, being a weak base, is a good leaving group; see Section 10.1.) Loss of water results in the third ring's becoming conjugated with the rest of the molecule. As a result of the extended conjugation, the anthocyanin absorbs visible light with wavelengths between 480 and 550 nm. The exact wavelength of light absorbed depends on the substituents (R and R′) on the anthocyanin. Thus, the flower, fruit, or vegetable appears red, purple, or blue, depending on what R and R′ are. You can see this color change if you alter the pH of cranberry juice so that it is no longer acidic.

(conjugation is disrupted)
colorless

(conjugation is disrupted)
colorless

anthocyanin
(three rings are conjugated)
red, blue, or purple

R = H, OH, or OCH_3
R′ = H, OH, or OCH_3

PROBLEM 37◆

a. At pH = 7, one of the ions shown below is purple and the other is blue. Which is which?

b. What would be the difference in the colors of the compounds at pH = 3?

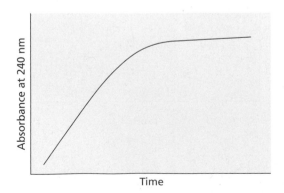

13.21 SOME USES OF UV/VIS SPECTROSCOPY

UV/Vis spectroscopy is not nearly as useful as other instrumental techniques for determining the structures of organic compounds. However, UV/Vis spectroscopy has many other important uses. For example, it is often used to measure reaction rates. The rate of any reaction can be measured, as long as one of the reactants or one of the products absorbs UV or visible light at a wavelength at which the other reactants and products have little or no absorbance. For example, the anion of nitroethane has a λ_{max} at 240 nm, but neither the other product (H_2O) nor the reactants show any significant absorbance at this wavelength. In order to measure the rate at which hydroxide ion removes a proton from nitroethane to form the nitroethane anion, the UV spectrophotometer is adjusted to measure absorbance at 240 nm as a function of time instead of absorbance as a function of wavelength. Nitroethane is added to a quartz cell containing a basic solution, and the rate of the reaction is determined by monitoring the increase in absorbance at 240 nm (Figure 13.39).

Lycopene, β-carotene, and anthocyanins are found in the leaves of trees, but their characteristic colors are usually obscured by the green color of chlorophyll. Chlorophyll is an unstable molecule, so plants must continually synthesize it. Its synthesis requires sunlight and warm temperatures. As the weather becomes colder in the fall, plants can no longer replace chlorophyll as it degrades, so the other colors become apparent.

$$CH_3CH_2NO_2 \ + \ HO^- \ \rightleftharpoons \ CH_3\bar{C}HNO_2 \ + \ H_2O$$

nitroethane   **nitroethane anion**
$$\lambda_{max} = \textbf{240 nm}$$

(graph: Absorbance at 240 nm vs. Time)

◀ **Figure 13.39**
The rate at which a proton is removed from nitroethane is determined by monitoring the increase in absorbance at 240 nm.

The enzyme lactate dehydrogenase catalyzes the reduction of pyruvate to lactate by NADH. NADH is the only species in the reaction mixture that absorbs light at 340 nm, so the rate of that reaction can be determined by monitoring the decrease in absorbance at 340 nm (Figure 13.40).

▶ **Figure 13.40**
The rate of reduction of pyruvate by NADH is measured by monitoring the decrease in absorbance at 340 nm.

PROBLEM 38◆

Describe a way to determine the rate of the alcohol dehydrogenase catalyzed oxidation of ethanol by NAD$^+$ (Section 25.1).

The pK_a of a compound can be determined by UV/Vis spectroscopy if either the acidic form or the basic form of the compound absorbs UV or visible light. For example, the phenolate ion has a λ_{max} at 287 nm. If the absorbance at 287 nm is monitored as a function of pH, the pK_a of phenol can be ascertained by determining the pH at which exactly one-half the increase in absorbance has occurred (Figure 13.41). At this pH, half of the phenol has been converted into phenolate ion. Recall that the Henderson–Hasselbalch equation (Section 1.25) states that the pK_a of a compound is the pH at which half the compound exists in its acidic form and half exists in its basic form ([HA] = [A$^-$]).

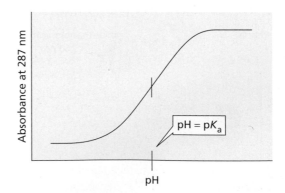

▶ **Figure 13.41**
The absorbance of an aqueous solution of phenol as a function of pH.

UV spectroscopy can also be used to estimate the nucleotide composition of DNA. The two strands of DNA are held together by hydrogen bonds between the bases in one strand and the bases in the other (see Figure 28.4 on page 1154): each guanine forms three hydrogen bonds with a cytosine (a G–C pair); each adenine forms two hydrogen bonds with a thymine (an A–T pair). When DNA is heated, the strands break apart and the absorbance increases because single-stranded DNA has a greater molar absorptivity at 260 nm than does double-stranded DNA. The melting temperature (T_m) of DNA is the midpoint of an absorbance-versus-temperature curve (Figure 13.42). For double-stranded

DNA, T_m increases with increasing numbers of G–C pairs, because they are held together by three hydrogen bonds, whereas A–T pairs are held together by only two hydrogen bonds. Therefore, T_m can be used to estimate the number of G–C pairs. These are just a few examples of the many uses of UV/Vis spectroscopy.

◄ **Figure 13.42**
The absorbance of a solution of DNA as a function of temperature.

PROBLEM 39 ◆

The absorbance of a solution of a weak acid was measured under the same conditions at a series of pH values. Its conjugate base is the only species in the solution that absorbs UV light at the wavelength used. Estimate the pK_a of the compound from the data obtained.

pH	1.0	2.0	3.0	4.0	5.0	6.0	7.0	8.0	9.0	10.0
Absorbance	0	0	0.10	0.50	0.80	1.10	1.50	1.60	1.60	1.60

SUMMARY

Mass spectrometry allows us to determine the *molecular mass* and the *molecular formula* of a compound and some of its structural features. In this analytical method, a small sample of the compound is vaporized and then ionized as a result of an electron's being removed from each molecule, producing a **molecular ion**—a radical cation. Many of the molecular ions break apart into cations, radicals, neutral molecules, and other radical cations. The bonds most likely to break are the weakest ones and those that result in the formation of the most stable products.

A **mass spectrum** is a graph of the relative abundance of each positively charged fragment plotted against its *m/z* value. The *m/z* value of the molecular ion (M) gives the molecular mass of the compound. Peaks with smaller *m/z* values—**fragment ion peaks**—represent positively charged fragments of the molecular ion. The **base peak** has the greatest intensity. High-resolution mass spectrometers determine the exact molecular mass, which allows a compound's molecular formula to be determined. The "nitrogen rule" states that if a compound has an odd-mass molecular ion, the compound contains an odd number of nitrogen atoms.

The M + 1 peak occurs because of the naturally occurring ^{13}C isotope of carbon. The number of carbon atoms in a compound can be calculated from the relative intensities of the M and M + 1 peaks. A large M + 2 peak is evidence of a compound containing either chlorine or bromine; if it is one-third the height of the M peak, the com-

pound contains one chlorine atom; if the M and M + 2 peaks are about the same height, the compound contains one bromine atom.

Characteristic fragmentation patterns are associated with specific functional groups. Electron bombardment is most likely to dislodge a lone-pair electron. A bond between carbon and a more electronegative atom breaks *heterolytically*, with the electrons going to the more electronegative atom, whereas a bond between carbon and an atom of similar electronegativity breaks *homolytically*. **α-Cleavage** occurs because the species it forms has a positive charge shared by two atoms.

Spectroscopy is the study of the interaction of matter and **electromagnetic radiation**. A continuum of different types of electromagnetic radiation constitutes the electromagnetic spectrum. High-energy radiation is associated with *high frequencies, large wavenumbers*, and *short wavelengths*.

Infrared spectroscopy identifies the kinds of functional groups in a compound. Bonds undergo stretching and bending vibrations with characteristic frequencies. It takes more energy to stretch a bond than to bend it. When a compound is bombarded with radiation of a frequency that matches the frequency of one of its vibrations, the molecule absorbs energy and exhibits an **absorption band** in its infrared spectrum. Most functional groups show absorption bands in the **functional group region** ($4000-1400$ cm^{-1}); absorption bands in the **fingerprint region** ($1400-600$ cm^{-1}) are characteristic of the compound as a whole.

The position, intensity, and shape of an absorption band identify functional groups. Stronger bonds show absorption bands at larger wavenumbers. Therefore, the frequency of the absorption band depends on bond order, hybridization, electron donation and withdrawal, and electron delocalization. Frequency is inversely related to the *mass* of the atoms, so heavier atoms vibrate at lower frequencies. The intensity of an absorption band depends on the size of the change in dipole moment associated with the vibration and on the number of bonds of that type in the compound. To absorb IR radiation, the dipole moment of the bond must change when the vibration occurs.

Ultraviolet and **visible (UV/Vis) spectroscopy** provide information about compounds with conjugated double bonds. UV light is higher in energy than visible light; the shorter the wavelength, the greater is the energy. UV and visible light cause $n \rightarrow \pi^*$ and $\pi \rightarrow \pi^*$ **electronic transitions**; $\pi \rightarrow \pi^*$ transitions have larger molar absorptivities. A **chromophore** is the part of a molecule that absorbs UV or visible light. The **Beer–Lambert law** is the relationship between absorbance, concentration, and length of the light path: $A = \varepsilon c l$. The more conjugated double bonds in a compound, the longer the λ_{max} at which absorption occurs. Reaction rates and pK_a values are commonly measured using UV/Vis spectroscopy.

KEY TERMS

absorption band (p. 519)
auxochrome (p. 539)
base peak (p. 503)
Beer–Lambert law (p. 537)
bending vibration (p. 518)
chromophore (p. 536)
α-cleavage (p. 509)
electromagnetic radiation (p. 516)
electronic transition (p. 535)
fingerprint region (p. 520)
fragment ion peak (p. 503)
frequency (p. 516)

functional group region (p. 520)
highest occupied molecular orbital
  (HOMO) (p. 538)
Hooke's law (p. 522)
infrared radiation (p. 518)
infrared spectroscopy (p. 501)
infrared spectrum (p. 519)
lowest unoccupied molecular orbital
  (LUMO) (p. 538)
mass spectrometry (p. 501)
mass spectrum (p. 503)
McLafferty rearrangement (p. 513)

molar absorptivity (p. 537)
molecular ion (p. 502)
nominal molecular mass (p. 507)
radical cation (p. 502)
spectroscopy (p. 516)
stretching vibration (p. 518)
ultraviolet light (p. 535)
UV/Vis spectroscopy (p. 501)
visible light (p. 535)
wavelength (p. 517)
wavenumber (p. 517)

PROBLEMS

40. In the mass spectrum of the following compounds, which would be more intense—the peak at $m/z = 57$ or the peak at $m/z = 71$?
  a. 3-methylpentane **b.** 2-methylpentane

41. List three factors that influence the intensity of an IR absorption band.

42. For each of the following pairs of compounds, identify one IR absorption band that could be used to distinguish between them:

a.

b.

c. $CH_3CH_2CH_2OH$ and $CH_3CH_2OCH_3$

d.

e.

f. *cis*-2-butene and *trans*-2-butene

g.

h.

i. $CH_3CH_2CH{=}CHCH_3$ and $CH_3CH_2C{\equiv}C\,CH_3$

j.

k.

l. $CH_3CH_2CH{=}CH_2$ and $CH_3CH_2CH{=}\overset{\overset{\displaystyle CH_3}{|}}{C}CH_3$

43. 4-Methyl-3-penten-2-one has two absorption bands in its UV spectrum, one at 236 nm and one at 314 nm.

4-methyl-3-penten-2-one

    a. Why are there two absorption bands?
    b. Which band shows the greater absorbance?

44. a. How could you use IR spectroscopy to determine whether the following reaction had occurred?

    b. After purifying the product, how could you determine whether all the NH_2NH_2 had been removed?

45. How could you use UV spectroscopy to distinguish between the compounds in each of the following pairs?

    a.   and

    c.   and

    b. CH_2=CHCH=CHCH=CH$_2$ and CH_2=CHCH=CHCCH$_3$

    d.   and

46. What identifying characteristics would be present in the mass spectrum of a compound containing two bromine atoms?

47. Assuming that the force constant is approximately the same for C—C, C—N, and C—O bonds, predict the relative positions of their stretching vibrations.

48. In the following boxes, list the types of bonds and the approximate wavenumber at which each type of bond is expected to show an IR absorption:

3600   3000   1800   1400   1000

Wavenumber (cm^{-1})

49. A mass spectrum shows significant peaks at $m/z = 87, 115, 140$, and 143. Which of the following compounds is responsible for that mass spectrum: 4,7-dimethyl-1-octanol, 2,6-dimethyl-4-octanol, or 2,2,4-trimethyl-4-heptanol?

50. How could IR spectroscopy distinguish between 1,5-hexadiene and 2,4-hexadiene?

51. A compound gives a mass spectrum with essentially only three peaks at $m/z = 77$ (40%), 112 (100%), 114 (33%). Identify the compound.

52. What hydrocarbons will have a molecular ion peak at $m/z = 112$?

53. Each of the IR spectra presented in Figures 13.43, 13.44, and 13.45 is accompanied by a set of four compounds. In each case, indicate which of the four compounds is responsible for the spectrum.

a. $CH_3CH_2CH_2C{\equiv}CCH_3$ $CH_3CH_2CH_2CH_2OH$ $CH_3CH_2CH_2CH_2C{\equiv}CH$ $CH_3CH_2CH_2\overset{O}{\underset{\|}{C}}OH$

► **Figure 13.43**
The IR spectrum for
Problem 53a.

b.

► **Figure 13.44**
The IR spectrum for
Problem 53b.

c.

► **Figure 13.45**
The IR spectrum for
Problem 53c.

54. List the following compounds in order of decreasing wavenumber of the C=O absorption band:

55. What peaks in their mass spectra could be used to distinguish between 4-methyl-2-pentanone and 2-methyl-3-pentanone?

56. A compound is known to be one of those shown here. What absorption bands in its IR spectrum would allow you to identify this compound?

A   B   C

57. How could IR spectroscopy distinguish between 1-hexyne, 2-hexyne, and 3-hexyne?

58. Five compounds are shown for each of the IR spectra in Figures 13.46, 13.47, and 13.48. Indicate which of the five compounds is responsible for each spectrum.

a.

◀ **Figure 13.46**
The IR spectrum for Problem 58a.

b.

◀ **Figure 13.47**
The IR spectrum for Problem 58b.

c.

►**Figure 13.48**
The IR spectrum for
Problem 58c.

59. A solution of ethanol has been contaminated with benzene—a technique employed to make ethanol unfit to drink. Benzene has a molar absorptivity of 230 M^{-1} cm^{-1} at 260 nm in ethanol, and ethanol shows no absorbance at 260 nm. How could the concentration of benzene in the solution be determined?

60. Each of the IR spectra shown in Figure 13.49 is the spectrum of one of the following compounds. Identify the compound that produced each spectrum.

► **Figure 13.49**
The IR spectra for
Problem 60.

▲ Figure 13.49
(Continued)

61. Predict the major characteristic IR absorption bands that would be given by each of the following:

a.

d.

b.

e.

c.

f.

62. Given that the force constants are similar for C—H and C—C bonds, explain why the stretching vibration of a C—H bond occurs at a larger wavenumber.

63. The IR spectrum of a compound with molecular formula C_5H_8O is shown in Figure 13.50. Identify the compound.

◀ Figure 13.50
The IR spectrum for
Problem 63.

64. Some credit-card sales slips have a top sheet of "carbonless paper" that transfers an imprint of your signature to a sheet lying underneath (the customer receipt). The paper contains tiny capsules filled with the following colorless compound:

When you press on the paper, the capsules burst, and the colorless compound comes into contact with the acid-treated bottom sheet, forming a highly colored compound. What is the structure of the colored compound?

65. Which one of the following compounds produced the IR spectrum shown in Figure 13.51?

▶ **Figure 13.51**
The IR spectrum for
Problem 65.

66. Which one of the following compounds produced the IR spectrum shown in Figure 13.52?

▶ **Figure 13.52**
The IR spectrum for
Problem 66.

67. What is the molecular formula of a saturated acyclic hydrocarbon that has an M peak at $m/z = 100$ with a relative abundance of 27.32% and an M + 1 peak with a relative abundance of 2.10%?

68. Calculate the approximate wavenumber at which a C=C stretch will occur, given that the force constant for the C=C bond is 10×10^5 g s^{-2}.

69. The IR and mass spectra for three different compounds are shown in Figures 13.53–13.55. Identify each compound.

a.

◀ **Figure 13.53**
The IR and mass
spectra for Problem
69a.

b.

◀ **Figure 13.54**
The IR and mass
spectra for Problem
69b.

▶ **Figure 13.55**
The IR and mass
spectra for
Problem 69c.

70. a. Methyl orange (whose structure is given in Section 13.19) is an acid–base indicator. In solutions of pH < 4, it is red; in solutions of pH > 4, it is yellow. Account for the change in color.

  b. Phenolphthalein, which is another indicator, exhibits a much more dramatic color change. In solutions of pH < 8.5, it is colorless; in solutions of pH > 8.5, it is deep red-purple. Account for the change in color.

phenolphthalein

14

NMR Spectroscopy

1-Nitropropane

CHAPTER 13 INTRODUCED THREE INSTRUMENTAL TECHNIQUES USED TO DETERMINE the structures of organic compounds: mass spectrometry, IR spectroscopy, and UV/Vis spectroscopy. Now we will look at a fourth technique, *nuclear magnetic resonance (NMR) spectroscopy*. **NMR spectroscopy** helps to identify the carbon–hydrogen framework of an organic compound.

The advantage of NMR spectroscopy over the other instrumental techniques we have studied is that it not only makes it possible to identify the functionality at a specific carbon, but it also enables us to connect neighboring carbons. In many cases, NMR spectroscopy can be used to determine a molecule's entire structure.

14.1 AN INTRODUCTION TO NMR SPECTROSCOPY

NMR spectroscopy was developed by physical chemists in the late 1940s to study the properties of atomic nuclei. In 1951, chemists realized that NMR spectroscopy could also be used to study the structures of organic compounds. Some nuclei have a property called spin that causes them to act as if they were spinning. Nuclei that possess spin have an odd number of protons or an odd number of neutrons (or both). Such nuclei (^{1}H, ^{13}C, ^{15}N, ^{19}F, and ^{31}P) can be studied by NMR. In contrast, ^{12}C and ^{16}O do not have spin and therefore cannot be studied by NMR. Because hydrogen nuclei (protons) were the first nuclei studied by nuclear magnetic resonance, the acronym "NMR" is generally assumed to mean ^{1}**H NMR (proton magnetic resonance)**.

As a result of its charge and spin, the nucleus has a magnetic moment and generates a magnetic field similar to the magnetic field generated by a small bar magnet. In the absence of an applied magnetic field, the magnetic moments of the nuclei of a sample are randomly oriented. However, when placed between the poles of a strong magnet (Figure 14.1), the magnetic moments align either *with* or *against* the applied magnetic field. Those that align with the field are in the lower-energy $\boldsymbol{\alpha}$**-spin state**; those that align against the field are in the higher-energy $\boldsymbol{\beta}$**-spin state**, because more energy is needed to align the magnetic moments against the field than with it. More nuclei are in the α-spin state than in the β-spin state. The difference in the populations is very small (about 20 out of 1 million protons), but it is sufficient to form the basis of NMR spectroscopy.

▶ **Figure 14.1**
In the absence of an applied magnetic field, the magnetic moments of the nuclei are randomly oriented. In the presence of an applied magnetic field, the magnetic moments of the nuclei line up with or against the field.

no applied magnetic field

magnetic field is applied

The energy difference (ΔE) between the α- and β-spin states depends on the strength of the **applied magnetic field** (B_0); the greater the strength of the magnetic field, the greater is ΔE (Figure 14.2).

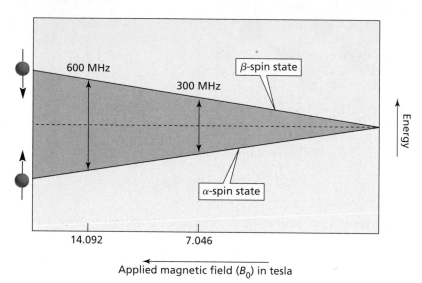

▶ **Figure 14.2**
The stronger the applied magnetic field, the greater is the difference in energy between the α- and β-spin states.

When a sample is subjected to a pulse of radiation whose energy corresponds to the difference in energy (ΔE) between the α- and β-spin states, nuclei in the α-spin state are promoted to the β-spin state. This transition is called "flipping" the spin. With currently available magnets, the energy difference between the α- and β-spin states is small, so only a small amount of energy is needed to flip the spin. The radiation used to supply this energy is in the radio frequency (rf) region of the electromagnetic spectrum and is called **rf radiation**. When the nuclei absorb rf radiation, they flip their spin, causing them to generate signals whose frequency depends on the difference in energy (ΔE) between the α- and β-spin states. The NMR spectrometer detects these signals and displays them as a plot of signal frequency versus intensity; this plot is the NMR spectrum. The nuclei are said to be *in resonance* with the rf radiation, hence the term **nuclear magnetic resonance**. In this context, "resonance" refers to the nuclei flipping back and forth between the α- and β-spin states in response to the rf radiation; it has nothing to do with the "resonance" associated with electron delocalization.

The equation displayed below shows that the energy difference between the spin states (ΔE) depends on the operating frequency of the spectrometer (ν), which in turn depends on the strength of the magnetic field (B_0), measured in tesla (T), and the *gyromagnetic ratio* (γ); h is Planck's constant (Section 13.7).

Until recently, the gauss (G) was the unit in which magnetic field strength was commonly measured (1 T = 10^4 G).

$$\Delta E = h\nu = h\frac{\gamma}{2\pi}B_0$$

The **gyromagnetic ratio**, also called the magnetogyric ratio, is a constant that depends on the magnetic moment of the particular kind of nucleus. In the case of a proton, the value of γ is $2.675 \times 10^8\ \text{T}^{-1}\text{s}^{-1}$; in the case of a ^{13}C nucleus, it is $6.688 \times 10^7\ \text{T}^{-1}\text{s}^{-1}$. Canceling Planck's constant on both sides of the equation gives

Earth's magnetic field is 5 × 10^{-5} T, measured at the equator. Its maximum surface magnetic field is 7 × 10^{-5} T, measured at the south magnetic pole.

$$\nu = \frac{\gamma}{2\pi}B_0$$

The following calculation shows that if an ^{1}H NMR spectrometer is equipped with a magnet that generates a magnetic field of 7.046 T, the spectrometer will require an operating frequency of 300 MHz (megahertz):

$$\nu = \frac{\gamma}{2\pi} B_0$$

$$= \frac{2.675 \times 10^8}{2(3.1416)} \text{T}^{-1}\text{s}^{-1} \times 7.046 \text{ T}$$

$$= 300 \times 10^6 \text{ Hz} = 300 \text{ MHz}$$

The magnetic field is proportional to the operating frequency.

The equation shows that the strength of the *magnetic field* (B_0) *is proportional to the operating frequency* (MHz). Therefore, if the spectrometer has a more powerful magnet, it must have a higher **operating frequency**. For example, a magnetic field of 14.092 T requires an operating frequency of 600 MHz.

Today's **NMR spectrometers** operate at frequencies between 60 and 950 MHz. The greater the operating frequency of the instrument—and the stronger the magnet—the better is the resolution of the NMR spectrum. (We will discuss resolution in Section 14.18.)

Because each kind of nucleus has its own gyromagnetic ratio, different energies are required to bring different kinds of nuclei into resonance. For example, an NMR spectrometer with a magnet requiring a frequency of 300 MHz to flip the spin of an ^{1}H nucleus requires a frequency of 75 MHz to flip the spin of a ^{13}C nucleus. NMR spectrometers are equipped with electromagnetic radiation sources that can be tuned to different frequencies so that they can be used to obtain NMR spectra of different kinds of nuclei (^{1}H, ^{13}C, ^{15}N, ^{19}F, ^{31}P).

 ## Nikola Tesla (1856–1943)

Nikola Tesla was born in Croatia, the son of a clergyman. He emigrated to the United States in 1884 and became a citizen in 1891. He was a proponent of the use of alternating current to distribute electricity and bitterly fought Thomas Edison, who promoted direct current. Tesla was granted a patent for developing the radio in 1900, but Guglielmo Marconi was also given a patent for its development in 1904. Not until 1943—a few months after his death—was Tesla's patent upheld by the U.S. Supreme Court.

Tesla held over 800 patents and is given credit for developing neon and fluorescent lighting, the electron microscope, the refrigerator motor, and the Tesla coil, a type of transformer for changing the voltage of alternating current. Perhaps his most important contribution was polyphase electric power, which became the prototype for all large power systems. He made most of his equipment himself, including insulators, a technology that was kept classified until recently because the same technology was being used for part of the Star Wars Program. Flamboyant high-voltage demonstrations occupied the later decades of Tesla's life and may have been responsible for his not receiving proper recognition for his work.

Nikola Tesla in his laboratory

14.2 FOURIER TRANSFORM NMR

To obtain an **NMR spectrum**, a small amount of a compound is dissolved in about 0.5 mL of solvent. This solution is put into a long, thin glass tube, which is then placed within a powerful magnetic field (Figure 14.3). (The solvents used in NMR are discussed in Section 14.17.) Spinning the sample tube about its long axis averages the position of the molecules in the magnetic field, thereby greatly increasing the resolution of the spectrum.

▶ **Figure 14.3**
Schematic diagram of an NMR spectrometer

B I O G R A P H Y

The 1991 Nobel Prize in Chemistry was awarded to **Richard R. Ernst** *for two important contributions: FT–NMR spectroscopy and an NMR tomography method that forms the basis of magnetic resonance imaging (MRI). Ernst was on a flight from Moscow to New York when the captain informed him that he had won the Nobel Prize. He was allowed to go to the cockpit to receive radioed congratulations from the president of Switzerland. Ernst was born in Switzerland in 1933, received a Ph.D. from the Swiss Federal Institute of Technology [Eidgenössische Technische Hochschule (ETH)] in Zurich, and became a research scientist at Varian Associates in Palo Alto, California. In 1968, he returned to his alma mater (ETH) as a professor of chemistry. Currently, he spends his time at the Scripps Research Institute in La Jolla, California, and at the Swiss Academy of Science.*

In modern instruments called *pulsed Fourier transform (FT) spectrometers*, the magnetic field is held constant and an rf pulse of short duration excites all the protons simultaneously. Because the short rf pulse covers a range of frequencies, the individual protons absorb the frequency each requires to come into resonance (flip their spin) and produce a complex signal—called a free induction decay (FID)—at a frequency corresponding to ΔE. The intensity of the signal decays as the nuclei lose the energy they gained from the rf pulse. A computer measures the change in intensity over time and converts it into intensity-versus-frequency data, in a mathematical operation known as a *Fourier transform*, to produce a spectrum called a **Fourier transform NMR (FT–NMR) spectrum**. An FT–NMR spectrum can be recorded in about 2 seconds—and large numbers of FIDs can be averaged in a few minutes—using less than 5 mg of compound. The NMR spectra in this book are FT–NMR spectra that were taken on a spectrometer with an operating frequency of 300 MHz. The discussions throughout the rest of this chapter pertain to FT–NMR, rather than to the older continuous wave (CW) NMR, because FT–NMR is both more modern and easier to understand.

14.3 SHIELDING CAUSES DIFFERENT HYDROGENS TO SHOW SIGNALS AT DIFFERENT FREQUENCIES

We have seen that the frequency of an NMR signal depends on the strength of the magnetic field (Figure 14.2) experienced by the nucleus. Therefore, if all the hydrogens in an organic compound were to experience the applied magnetic field to the same degree, they would all give signals of the same frequency. If this were the case, all NMR spectra would consist of one signal, which would tell us nothing about the structure of the compound, except that it contains hydrogens.

A nucleus, however, is embedded in a cloud of electrons that partly *shields* it from the applied magnetic field. Fortunately for chemists, the **shielding** varies for different hydrogens within a molecule. In other words, all the hydrogens do not experience the same magnetic field.

What causes shielding? In a magnetic field, the electrons circulate about the nuclei and induce a local magnetic field that acts in opposition to the applied magnetic field and subtracts from it. The **effective magnetic field**—the amount of magnetic field that the nuclei actually "sense" through the surrounding electronic environment—is therefore somewhat smaller than the applied magnetic field:

$$B_{\text{effective}} = B_{\text{applied}} - B_{\text{local}}$$

This means that the greater the electron density of the environment in which the proton* is located, the greater B_{local} is and the more the proton is shielded from the applied magnetic field. This type of shielding is called **diamagnetic shielding**. Thus, protons in electron-dense environments sense a *smaller effective magnetic field*. They therefore require a *lower frequency* to come into resonance—that is, flip their spin—because ΔE is smaller (Figure 14.2). Protons in electron-poor environments sense a *larger effective magnetic field* and, therefore, will require a *higher frequency* to come into resonance, because ΔE is larger.

> The larger the magnetic field sensed by the proton, the higher is the frequency of the signal.

An NMR spectrum exhibits a signal for each proton in a different environment. Protons in electron-rich environments are more shielded and appear at lower frequencies (on the right-hand side of the spectrum) (Figure 14.4). Protons in electron-poor environments are less shielded and appear at higher frequencies (on the left-hand side of the spectrum). For example, the signal for the methyl protons of CH_3F occurs at a higher frequency than the signal for the methyl protons of CH_3Br because fluorine is more electronegative and, therefore, withdraws electrons inductively more strongly than bromine does (Section 1.22); thus, the protons of CH_3F are in a less electron-rich environment. (Notice that high frequency in an NMR spectrum is on the left-hand side, just as it is in IR and UV/Vis spectra.)

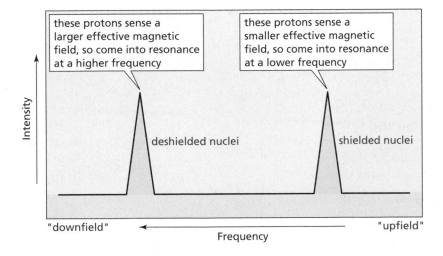

> deshielded = less shielded

> ◀ **Figure 14.4**
> Shielded nuclei come into resonance at lower frequencies than deshielded nuclei.

The terms *upfield* and *downfield*, which came into use when continuous-wave (CW) spectrometers were used (before the advent of Fourier transform spectrometers), are so entrenched in the vocabulary of NMR that you need to know what they mean. **Upfield** means farther to the right-hand side of the spectrum, and **downfield** means farther to the left-hand side of the spectrum. In contrast to FT–NMR techniques, which keep the magnetic field strength constant and vary the frequency, continuous-wave techniques keep the frequency constant and vary the magnetic field. The magnetic field increases from left to right across a spectrum because higher magnetic fields are required to bring shielded protons into resonance at a given frequency (Figure 14.4). Therefore, *upfield* is toward the right and *downfield* is toward the left.

---

*The terms *proton* and *hydrogen* are both used to describe a covalently bonded hydrogen in discussions of NMR spectroscopy.

14.4 THE NUMBER OF SIGNALS IN AN ^{1}H NMR SPECTRUM

Protons in the same environment are called **chemically equivalent protons**. For example, 1-bromopropane has three different sets of chemically equivalent protons: (1) the three methyl protons are chemically equivalent because of rotation about the C—C bond; (2) the two methylene (CH_2) protons on the middle carbon are chemically equivalent; and (3) the two methylene protons on the carbon bonded to the bromine atom make up the third set of chemically equivalent protons.

Each set of chemically equivalent protons in a compound gives rise to a signal in the ^{1}H NMR spectrum of that compound. (Sometimes the signals are not sufficiently separated and overlap each other. When this happens, one sees fewer signals than anticipated.) Because 1-bromopropane has three sets of chemically equivalent protons, it has three signals in its ^{1}H NMR spectrum.

2-Bromopropane has two sets of chemically equivalent protons, and, therefore, it has two signals in its ^{1}H NMR spectrum; the six methyl protons in 2-bromopropane are equivalent so they give rise to only one signal; the hydrogen bonded to the middle carbon gives the second signal. Ethyl methyl ether has three sets of chemically equivalent protons: the methyl protons on the carbon adjacent to the oxygen, the methylene protons on the carbon adjacent to the oxygen, and the methyl protons on the carbon that is one carbon removed from the oxygen. The chemically equivalent protons in the following compounds are designated by the same letter:

> chemically equivalent protons
>
> $CH_3CH_2CH_2Br$
>
> chemically equivalent protons   chemically equivalent protons

Each set of chemically equivalent protons gives rise to a signal.

You can tell how many sets of chemically equivalent protons a compound has from the number of signals in its ^{1}H NMR spectrum.

$$\overset{a}{CH_3}\overset{b}{CH_2}\overset{c}{CH_2}Br$$
three signals

$$\overset{a}{CH_3}\overset{b}{CH}\overset{a}{CH_3} \mid Br$$
two signals

$$\overset{a}{CH_3}\overset{c}{CH_2}O\overset{b}{CH_3}$$
three signals

$$\overset{a}{CH_3}O\overset{a}{CH_3}$$
one signal

$$\overset{a}{CH_3}\overset{a}{CH_3}\overset{}{COCH_3}\overset{b}{CH_3} \mid \overset{a}{CH_3}$$
two signals

$$\overset{a}{CH_3}O\overset{b}{CHCl_2}$$
two signals

$$\begin{array}{cc} \overset{a}{H_3C} & \overset{b}{H} \\ & C=C \\ H_3C & H \\ a & b \end{array}$$
two signals

$$\begin{array}{cc} Br & \overset{a}{H} \\ & C=C \\ H & Br \\ a & \end{array}$$
one signal

one signal (benzene ring, all a)

three signals (nitrobenzene ring, a, b, c)

If bonds are prevented from freely rotating, as in a compound with a double bond or in a cyclic compound, two protons on the same carbon may not be equivalent. For example, the H_a and H_b protons of bromoethene are not equivalent because they are not in the same environment: H_a is trans to Br and H_b is cis to Br. Thus, the ^{1}H NMR spectrum of bromoethene has three signals. The ^{1}H NMR spectrum of chlorocyclobutane has five signals. The H_a and H_b protons are not equivalent: H_a is trans to Cl and H_b is cis to Cl. Similarly, the H_c and H_d protons are not equivalent.

> its ^{1}H NMR spectrum has three signals

> its ^{1}H NMR spectrum has five signals

bromoethene
H_a and H_b are not equivalent

chlorocyclobutane
H_a and H_b are not equivalent
H_c and H_d are not equivalent

PROBLEM-SOLVING STRATEGY

Determining the Number of Signals in an ^{1}H NMR Spectrum

How many signals would you expect to see in the ^{1}H NMR spectrum of ethylbenzene?

$$CH_3CH_2-\text{(phenyl)}$$

To determine the number of signals you would expect to see in the spectrum, replace each hydrogen in turn by another atom (here we use Br) and name the resulting compound. The number of different names corresponds to the number of signals in the ^{1}H NMR spectrum. We get five different names for the bromosubstituted ethylbenzenes, so we expect to see five signals in the ^{1}H NMR spectrum of ethylbenzene.

1-bromo-2-phenylethane — BrCH$_2$CH$_2$—phenyl

1-bromo-1-phenylethane — CH$_3$CH(Br)—phenyl

1-bromo-2-ethylbenzene — CH$_3$CH$_2$—phenyl(Br)

1-bromo-3-ethylbenzene — CH$_2$CH$_2$—phenyl(Br)

1-bromo-4-ethylbenzene — CH$_3$CH$_2$—phenyl—Br

1-bromo-3-ethylbenzene — CH$_3$CH$_2$—phenyl(Br)

1-bromo-2-ethylbenzene — CH$_3$CH$_2$—phenyl(Br)

Now continue on to Problem 3.

PROBLEM 3 ◆

How many signals would you expect to see in the ^{1}H NMR spectrum of each of the following compounds?

a. $CH_3CH_2CH_2CH_3$

b. $BrCH_2CH_2Br$

c. $CH_2{=}CCl_2$

d. (cyclohexene ring)

e. $\underset{H}{\overset{Cl}{C}}{=}\underset{H}{\overset{Cl}{C}}$

f. $CH_3CH_2CH_2\overset{\displaystyle O}{\overset{\|}{C}}CH_3$

g. $CH_3CH_2\underset{Cl}{CH}CH_2CH_3$

h. $CH_3\underset{CH_3}{CH}CH_2\underset{CH_3}{CH}CH_3$

i. $CH_3\underset{Br}{CH}-\text{(phenyl)}$

j. $CH_3-\text{(phenyl)}-OCH_3$

k. $CH_3-\text{(phenyl)}-CH_3$

l. (benzene ring with two Br)

m. (phenyl)$-NO_2$

n. $CH_2{=}CH\overset{\displaystyle O}{\overset{\|}{C}}H$

o. $\underset{H}{\overset{Cl}{C}}{=}\underset{H}{\overset{CH_3}{C}}$

PROBLEM 4

How could you distinguish the ^{1}H NMR spectra of the following compounds?

$$CH_3OCH_2OCH_3 \qquad CH_3OCH_3 \qquad CH_3OCH_2\underset{\underset{\displaystyle CH_3}{|}}{\overset{\overset{\displaystyle CH_3}{|}}{C}}CH_2OCH_3$$

A · · · · · · · · · · · · · · · · B · · · · · · · · · · · · · · · · C

PROBLEM 5♦

There are three isomeric dichlorocyclopropanes. Their ¹H NMR spectra show one signal for isomer 1, two signals for isomer 2, and three signals for isomer 3. Draw the structures of isomers 1, 2, and 3.

14.5 THE CHEMICAL SHIFT TELLS HOW FAR THE SIGNAL IS FROM THE REFERENCE SIGNAL

$$CH_3-Si-CH_3$$

with CH₃ above and CH₃ below the Si

**tetramethylsilane
TMS**

A small amount of an inert **reference compound** is added to the sample tube containing the compound whose NMR spectrum is to be taken. The most commonly used reference compound is tetramethylsilane (TMS). Because TMS is a highly volatile compound (bp = 26.5 °C), it can easily be removed from the sample by evaporation after the NMR spectrum is taken.

The methyl protons of TMS are in a more electron-dense environment than are most protons in organic molecules because silicon is less electronegative than carbon (their electronegativities are 1.8 and 2.5, respectively). Consequently, the signal for the methyl protons of TMS is at a lower frequency than most other signals (that is, the TMS signal appears to the right of the other signals).

The position at which a signal occurs in an NMR spectrum is called the *chemical shift*. The **chemical shift** is a measure of how far the signal is from the signal for the reference compound. The most common scale for chemical shifts is the δ (delta) scale. The TMS signal defines the zero position on this scale. The chemical shift is determined by measuring the distance from the TMS peak in hertz and dividing by the operating frequency of the instrument in megahertz. Because the units are Hz/MHz, a chemical shift has units of parts per million (ppm) of the operating frequency:

Most proton chemical shifts are between 0 and 12 ppm.

$$\delta = \text{chemical shift (ppm)} = \frac{\text{distance downfield from TMS (Hz)}}{\text{operating frequency of the spectrometer (MHz)}}$$

The greater the value of the chemical shift (δ), the higher the frequency.

The ¹H NMR spectrum for 1-bromo-2,2-dimethylpropane in Figure 14.5 shows that the chemical shift (δ) of the methyl protons is at 1.05 ppm and the chemical shift of the methylene protons is at 3.28 ppm. *Notice that low-frequency (upfield, shielded) signals have small δ (ppm) values, whereas high-frequency (downfield, deshielded) signals have large δ values.*

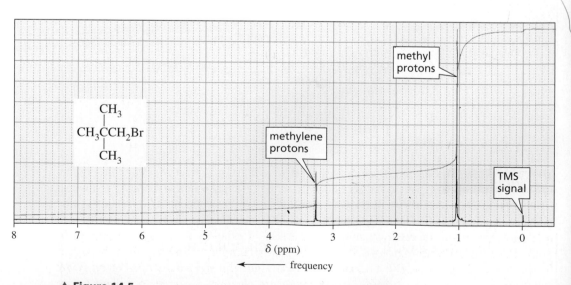

▲ **Figure 14.5**
The ¹H NMR spectrum of 1-bromo-2,2-dimethylpropane. The TMS signal is a reference signal from which chemical shifts are measured; it defines the zero position on the scale.

The advantage of the δ scale is that the chemical shift of a given nucleus is *independent of the operating frequency of the NMR spectrometer*. Thus, the chemical shift of the methyl protons of 1-bromo-2,2-dimethylpropane is at 1.05 ppm in both a 60-MHz and a 360-MHz instrument. If the chemical shift were instead reported in hertz, it would be at 63 Hz in a 60-MHz instrument and at 378 Hz in a 360-MHz instrument (1.05 = 63/60; 1.05 = 378/360). The following diagram will help you keep track of the terms associated with NMR spectroscopy:

protons in electron-poor environments	protons in electron-dense environments
deshielded protons	shielded protons
downfield	upfield
high frequency	low frequency
large δ values	small δ values

$\longleftarrow \quad \delta$ ppm

$\longleftarrow$ frequency

The chemical shift (δ) is independent of the operating frequency of the spectrometer.

PROBLEM 6 ◆

How many hertz downfield from the TMS signal would be the signal occurring at 1.0 ppm

a. in a 300-MHz spectrometer?
b. in a 500-MHz spectrometer?

PROBLEM 7 ◆

A signal is seen at 600 Hz downfield from the TMS signal in an NMR spectrometer with a 300-MHz operating frequency.

a. What is the chemical shift of the signal?
b. What would its chemical shift be in an instrument operating at 100 MHz?
c. How many hertz downfield from TMS would the signal be in a 100-MHz spectrometer?

PROBLEM 8 ◆

a. If two signals differ by 1.5 ppm in a 300-MHz spectrometer, by how much do they differ in a 100-MHz spectrometer?
b. If two signals differ by 90 Hz in a 300-MHz spectrometer, by how much do they differ in a 100-MHz spectrometer?

PROBLEM 9 ◆

Where would you expect to find the ^{1}H NMR signal of $(CH_3)_2Mg$ relative to the TMS signal? (*Hint:* Magnesium is less electronegative than silicon.)

14.6 THE RELATIVE POSITIONS OF ^{1}H NMR SIGNALS

The ^{1}H NMR spectrum of 1-bromo-2,2-dimethylpropane in Figure 14.5 has two signals because the compound has two different kinds of protons. The methylene protons are in a less electron-dense environment than are the methyl protons because the methylene protons are closer to the electron-withdrawing bromine. Because the methylene protons are in a less electron-dense environment, they are less shielded from the applied magnetic field. The signal for these protons therefore occurs at a higher frequency than the signal for the more shielded methyl protons. *Remember that the right-hand side of an NMR spectrum is the low-frequency side, where protons in electron-dense environments (more shielded) show a signal. The left-hand side is the high-frequency side, where protons in electron-poor environments (less shielded) show a signal* (Figure 14.4).

Protons in electron-poor environments show signals at high frequencies.

We expect the ^{1}H NMR spectrum of 1-nitropropane to have three signals because the compound has three different kinds of protons. The closer the protons are to the nitro group, which withdraws electrons inductively, the less they are shielded from the applied magnetic field, so the higher the frequency at which their signal will appear. Thus, the protons closest to the nitro group show a signal at the highest frequency (4.37 ppm), and the ones farthest from the nitro group show a signal at the lowest frequency (1.04 ppm).

Electron withdrawal causes NMR signals to appear at higher frequencies (at larger δ values).

1.04 ppm	2.07 ppm
	4.37 ppm

$$CH_3CH_2CH_2NO_2$$

Compare the chemical shifts of the methylene protons immediately adjacent to the halogen in each of the following alkyl halides. The position of the signal depends on the electronegativity of the halogen—the more electronegative the halogen, the less the protons are shielded, so the higher is the frequency of the signal. Thus, the signal for the methylene protons adjacent to fluorine (the most electronegative of the halogens) occurs at the highest frequency, whereas the signal for the methylene protons adjacent to iodine (the least electronegative of the halogens) occurs at the lowest frequency.

$CH_3CH_2CH_2CH_2CH_2F$ $CH_3CH_2CH_2CH_2CH_2Cl$ $CH_3CH_2CH_2CH_2CH_2Br$ $CH_3CH_2CH_2CH_2CH_2I$

4.50 ppm	3.50 ppm	3.40 ppm	3.20 ppm

PROBLEM 10♦

a. Which set of protons in each of the following compounds is the least shielded?

   1. $CH_3CH_2CH_2Cl$ **2.** $CH_3CH_2\overset{\displaystyle O}{\overset{\displaystyle \|}{C}}OCH_3$ **3.** $CH_3\underset{\underset{\displaystyle Br}{|}}{C}H\underset{\underset{\displaystyle Br}{|}}{C}HBr$

b. Which set of protons in each compound is the most shielded?

14.7 THE CHARACTERISTIC VALUES OF CHEMICAL SHIFTS

Approximate values of chemical shifts for different kinds of protons are shown in Table 14.1. (A more extensive compilation is given in Appendix VI.) An ^{1}H NMR spectrum can be divided into seven regions, one of which is empty. If you can remember the kinds of protons that appear in each region, you will be able to tell what kinds of protons a molecule has from a quick look at its NMR spectrum.

Carbon is more electronegative than hydrogen (Table 1.3 on page 10). Therefore, the chemical shift of a **methine proton** (a hydrogen attached to an sp^3 carbon that is attached to *three* carbons) is more deshielded and, therefore, shows a chemical shift at a higher

Table 14.1   Approximate Values of Chemical Shifts for ^{1}H NMR^a

Type of proton	Approximate chemical shift (ppm)	Type of proton	Approximate chemical shift (ppm)
—CH$_3$	0.85	I—C—H	2.5–4
—CH$_2$—	1.20	Br—C—H	2.5–4
—CH—	1.55	Cl—C—H	3–4
—C=C—CH$_3$	1.7	F—C—H	4–4.5
O‖ —C—CH$_3$	2.1	R—NH$_2$	Variable, 1.5–4
⟨benzene⟩—CH$_3$	2.3	R—OH	Variable, 2–5
—C≡C—H	2.4	⟨benzene⟩—OH	Variable, 4–7
R—O—CH$_3$	3.3	⟨benzene⟩—H	6.5–8
R—C=CH$_2$ R	4.7	O‖ —C—H	9.0–10
R—C=C—H R R	5.3	O‖ —C—OH	Variable, 10–12
		O‖ —C—NH$_2$	Variable, 5–8

^{a}The values are approximate because they are affected by neighboring substituents.

frequency than the chemical shift of **methylene protons** (hydrogens attached to an sp^3 carbon that is attached to *two* carbons) in a similar environment. Similarly, the chemical shift of methylene protons is at a higher frequency than is the chemical shift of **methyl protons** (hydrogens attached to an sp^3 carbon that is attached to *one* carbon) in a similar environment (Table 14.1).

—CH— methine

—CH$_2$— methylene

—CH$_3$ methyl

methine proton
1.55 ppm

methylene proton
1.20 ppm

methyl proton
0.85 ppm

In a similar environment, the signal for a methine proton occurs at a higher frequency than the signal for methylene protons, which in turn occurs at a higher frequency than the signal for methyl protons.

For example, the ^{1}H NMR spectrum of butanone shows three signals. The signal at the lowest frequency is the signal for the *a* protons of butanone; these protons are farthest from the electron-withdrawing carbonyl group. (In correlating an NMR spectrum with a structure, the set of protons responsible for the signal at the lowest frequency will be labeled *a*, the next set will be labeled *b*, the next set *c*, and so on.) The *b* and *c* protons are the same distance from the carbonyl group, but the signal for the *b* protons is at a lower frequency than the signal for the *c* protons because methyl protons appear at a lower frequency than do methylene protons in a similar environment.

$$CH_3CH_2 \overset{\overset{\displaystyle O}{\displaystyle \|}}{\underset{c}{C}} CH_3$$
$$\underset{a}{CH_3CH_2} \quad \underset{b}{CH_3}$$
butanone

$$\underset{b}{CH_3O}\underset{c}{CH}\underset{a}{CH_3}$$
$$\underset{a}{CH_3}$$
2-methoxypropane

The signal for the *a* protons of 2-methoxypropane is the signal at the lowest frequency in its ^{1}H NMR spectrum because these protons are farthest from the electron-withdrawing oxygen. The *b* and *c* protons are the same distance from the oxygen, but the signal for the *b* protons appears at a lower frequency because, in a similar environment, methyl protons appear at a lower frequency than does a methine proton.

PROBLEM 11♦

Which of the underlined protons (or sets of protons) has the greater chemical shift (that is, the higher frequency signal)?

a. CH$_3$CHCHBr
$$\quad\; | \;\; |$$
$$\quad\; Br\; Br$$

b. CH$_3$CHOCH$_3$
$$\quad\quad |$$
$$\quad\quad CH_3$$

c. CH$_3$CH$_2$CHCH$_3$
$$\quad\quad\quad\; |$$
$$\quad\quad\quad\; Cl$$

d.
$$CH_3CH \overset{\overset{\displaystyle O}{\displaystyle \|}}{C} CH_2CH_3$$
$$\quad\;\; |$$
$$\quad\; CH_3$$

e. CH$_3$CH$_2$CH=CH$_2$

f. CH$_3$OCH$_2$CH$_2$CH$_3$

PROBLEM 12♦

Which of the underlined protons (or sets of protons) has the greater chemical shift (that is, the higher frequency signal)?

a. CH$_3$CH$_2$CH$_2$Cl   or   CH$_3$CH$_2$CH$_2$Br

b. CH$_3$CH$_2$CH$_2$Cl   or   CH$_3$CH$_2$CHCH$_3$
$$\quad\quad\quad\quad\quad\quad\quad\quad\quad\quad\quad\; |$$
$$\quad\quad\quad\quad\quad\quad\quad\quad\quad\quad\quad\; Cl$$

c.
$$CH_3CH_2 \overset{\overset{\displaystyle O}{\displaystyle \|}}{C} H \quad or \quad CH_3CH_2 \overset{\overset{\displaystyle O}{\displaystyle \|}}{C} OCH_3$$

PROBLEM 13

For each compound, without referring to Table 14.1, label the proton or set of protons that gives the signal at the lowest frequency *a*, the next lowest *b*, and so on.

a.
$$CH_3CH_2 \overset{\overset{\displaystyle O}{\displaystyle \|}}{C} H$$

b. CH$_3$CH$_2$CHCH$_3$
$$\quad\quad\quad\; |$$
$$\quad\quad\quad OCH_3$$

c. ClCH$_2$CH$_2$CH$_2$Cl

d. CH$_3$CH$_2$CHCH$_2$CH$_3$
$$\quad\quad\quad\; |$$
$$\quad\quad\; OCH_3$$

e.
$$CH_3CH_2CH_2 \overset{\overset{\displaystyle O}{\displaystyle \|}}{C} OCH_3$$

f. CH$_3$CH$_2$CH$_2$OCHCH$_3$
$$\quad\quad\quad\quad\quad\quad\quad |$$
$$\quad\quad\quad\quad\quad\quad CH_3$$

g.
$$CH_3CH_2CH_2 \overset{\overset{\displaystyle O}{\displaystyle \|}}{C} CH_3$$

h. CH$_3$CHCH$_2$OCH$_3$
$$\quad\quad\; |$$
$$\quad\quad CH_3$$

i. CH$_3$CHCHCH$_3$
$$\quad\quad\; |\quad |$$
$$\quad\;\; CH_3\; Cl$$

14.8 DIAMAGNETIC ANISOTROPY

The chemical shifts of hydrogens bonded to sp^2 carbons are at higher frequencies than one would predict from the electronegativities of the sp^2 carbons. For example, a hydrogen bonded to a benzene ring appears at 6.5 to 8.0 ppm, a hydrogen bonded to a terminal sp^2 carbon of an alkene appears at 4.7 to 5.3 ppm, and a hydrogen bonded to a carbonyl carbon appears at 9.0 to 10.0 ppm (Table 14.1).

The unusual chemical shifts associated with hydrogens bonded to carbons that form π bonds are due to **diamagnetic anisotropy**. This term describes an environment in which different magnetic fields are found at different points in space. (*Anisotropic* is Greek for "different in different directions.") Because π electrons are less tightly held by nuclei than are σ electrons, π electrons are freer to move in response to a magnetic field. When a magnetic field is applied to a compound with π electrons, the π electrons move in a circular path that induces a small local magnetic field. How this induced magnetic field affects the chemical shift of a proton depends on the direction of the induced field in the region where the proton is located, relative to the direction of the applied magnetic field.

The magnetic field induced by the π electrons of a benzene ring in the region where benzene's protons are located is oriented in the same direction as the applied magnetic field (Figure 14.6). As a result, the protons sense a larger effective magnetic field—the sum of the strengths of the applied field and the induced field. Because frequency is proportional to the strength of the magnetic field experienced by the protons (Figure 14.2), the protons show signals at *higher frequencies* than they would if the π electrons did not induce a magnetic field.

▲ Figure 14.6
The magnetic field induced by the π electrons of a benzene ring in the vicinity of the protons attached to the sp^2 carbons has the same direction as the applied magnetic field. Since a larger effective magnetic field is sensed by the protons, they show signals at higher frequencies.

The magnetic field induced by the π electrons of an alkene or by the π electrons of an aldehyde (in the region where the protons bonded to the sp^2 carbons of the alkene or to the sp^2 carbon of the aldehyde are located) is also oriented in the *same direction* as the applied magnetic field (Figure 14.7). These protons, too, show signals at higher than expected frequencies.

▶ **Figure 14.7**
The magnetic fields induced by the π electrons of an alkene and by the π electrons of a carbonyl group in the vicinity of the vinylic and aldehydic protons have the same direction as the applied magnetic field. Because a larger effective magnetic field is sensed by the protons, they show signals at higher frequencies.

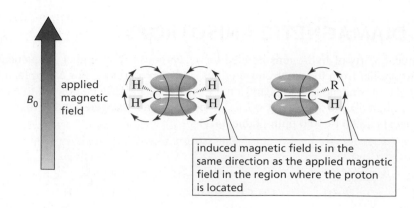

applied magnetic field

induced magnetic field is in the same direction as the applied magnetic field in the region where the proton is located

In contrast, the chemical shift of a hydrogen bonded to an *sp* carbon is at a lower frequency than one would predict from the electronegativity of the *sp* carbon. The direction of the magnetic field induced by the alkyne's cylinder of π electrons, in the region where the proton is located, is *opposite* to the direction of the applied magnetic field (Figure 14.8). Thus, the proton shows a signal at a *lower frequency* than it would if the π electrons did not induce a magnetic field.

▶ **Figure 14.8**
The magnetic field induced by the π electrons of an alkyne in the vicinity of the proton bonded to the *sp* carbon is in a direction opposite to that of the applied magnetic field. Because a smaller effective magnetic field is sensed by the proton, it shows a signal at a lower frequency.

induced magnetic field is in the direction opposite to that of the applied magnetic field in the region where the proton is located

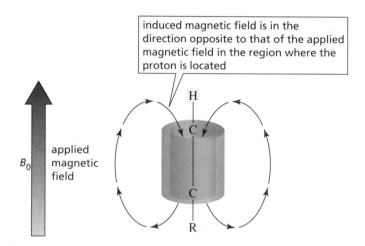

applied magnetic field

PROBLEM 14 ♦

[18]-Annulene shows two signals in its ^1H NMR spectrum: one at 9.25 ppm and the other very far upfield (to the right of the TMS signal) at −2.88 ppm. What hydrogens are responsible for each of the signals? (*Hint:* Look at the direction of the induced magnetic field outside and inside the benzene ring in Figure 14.6.)

14.9 THE INTEGRATION OF NMR SIGNALS REVEALS THE RELATIVE NUMBER OF PROTONS CAUSING EACH SIGNAL

The two signals in the ^{1}H NMR spectrum of 1-bromo-2,2-dimethylpropane in Figure 14.5 are not the same size, because *the area under each signal is proportional to the number of protons giving rise to the signal.* The spectrum is shown again in Figure 14.9. The area under the signal occurring at the lower frequency is larger because the signal is caused by *nine* methyl protons, whereas the smaller, higher-frequency signal results from *two* methylene protons.

▲ **Figure 14.9**
Analysis of the integration line in the ^{1}H NMR spectrum of 1-bromo-2, 2-dimethylpropane.

You probably remember from a calculus course that the area under a curve can be determined by an integral. An ^{1}H NMR spectrometer is equipped with a computer that calculates the integrals electronically and then displays them as an integral trace superimposed on the original spectrum (Figure 14.9). The height of each step in the integral trace is proportional to the area under the corresponding signal, which, in turn, is proportional to the number of protons giving rise to the signal. The heights of the integration steps in Figure 14.9, for example, tell us that the ratio of the integrals is approximately $1.6 : 7.0 = 1 : 4.4$. We multiply the ratio by a number that will cause all the numbers making up the ratio to be close to whole numbers—in this case, we multiply by 2. That means that the ratio of protons in the compound is $2 : 8.8$, which is rounded to $2 : 9$, as there can be only whole numbers of protons. In this way we find that the ratio of protons in the compound is $2 : 9$. (The measured integrals are approximate because of experimental error.) Modern spectrometers print the integrals as numbers on the spectrum; see Figure 14.11 on page 569.

The **integration** tells us the *relative* number of protons that give rise to each signal, not the *absolute* number. In other words, integration could not distinguish between 1,1-dichloroethane and 1,2-dichloro-2-methylpropane because both compounds would show an integral ratio of 1 : 3.

$$CH_3-CH-Cl$$
$$\mid$$
$$Cl$$

1,1-dichloroethane
ratio of protons = 1 : 3

$$CH_3$$
$$\mid$$
$$CH_3-C-CH_2Cl$$
$$\mid$$
$$Cl$$

1,2-dichloro-2-methylpropane
ratio of protons = 2 : 6 = 1 : 3

PROBLEM 15♦

How would integration distinguish the ^1H NMR spectra of the following compounds?

$$CH_3-\underset{\underset{CH_3}{|}}{\overset{\overset{CH_3}{|}}{C}}-CH_2Br \qquad CH_3-\underset{\underset{Br}{|}}{\overset{\overset{CH_3}{|}}{C}}-CH_2Br \qquad CH_3-\underset{\underset{CH_2Br}{|}}{\overset{\overset{CH_2Br}{|}}{C}}-CH_2Br$$

PROBLEM 16 **SOLVED**

a. Calculate the ratios of the different kinds of protons in a compound with an integral ratio of 6 : 4 : 18.4 (going from left to right across the spectrum).

b. Determine the structure of a compound with molecular formula $C_7H_{14}O_2$ that would give these relative integrals in the observed order.

Solution

a. Divide each number in the ratio by the smallest number:

$$\frac{6}{4} = 1.5 \qquad \frac{4}{4} = 1 \qquad \frac{18.4}{4} = 4.6$$

Multiply by a number that will cause all the resulting numbers to be close to whole numbers:

$$1.5 \times 2 = 3 \qquad 1 \times 2 = 2 \qquad 4.6 \times 2 = 9$$

The ratio 3 : 2 : 9 gives the relative numbers of the different kinds of protons. Because the total of the relative number of protons (14) is the same as the actual number of protons in the compound, we know that the actual ratio is the relative ratio and not some multiple of it.

b. The "3" suggests the presence of a methyl group, the "2" a methylene group, and the "9" a *tert*-butyl group. The methyl group is closest to the group in the molecule that causes deshielding, and the *tert*-butyl group is farthest away from the group that causes deshielding. The following compound meets these requirements:

$$CH_3CCH_2\underset{\underset{CH_3}{|}}{\overset{\overset{CH_3}{|}}{}}\overset{\overset{O}{\overset{||}{C}}}{}OCH_3$$

PROBLEM 17♦

Which of the following compounds is responsible for the ^1H NMR spectrum shown in Figure 14.10?

▲ **Figure 14.10**
The ^1H NMR spectrum for Problem 17.

14.10 THE SPLITTING OF THE SIGNALS IS DESCRIBED BY THE *N* + 1 RULE

Notice that the shapes of the signals in the ^{1}H NMR spectrum of 1,1-dichloroethane (Figure 14.11) are different from the shapes of the signals in the ^{1}H NMR spectrum of 1-bromo-2,2-dimethylpropane (Figure 14.5). Both signals in Figure 14.5 are **singlets**, meaning each is composed of a single peak. In contrast, the signal for the methyl protons of 1,1-dichloroethane (the lower-frequency signal) is split into two peaks (a **doublet**), and the signal for the methine proton is split into four peaks (a **quartet**). (Magnifications of the frequency axis for the doublet and quartet are shown as insets in Figure 14.11; integration numbers are given in green.)

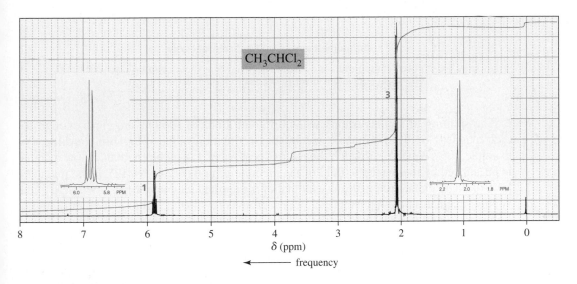

▲ **Figure 14.11**
The ^{1}H NMR spectrum of 1,1-dichloroethane. The higher-frequency signal is an example of a quartet; the lower-frequency signal is a doublet.

Splitting is caused by protons bonded to adjacent carbons. The splitting of a signal is described by the *N* + 1 **rule**, where *N* is the number of *equivalent* protons bonded to *adjacent* carbons. By "equivalent protons," we mean that the protons bonded to an adjacent carbon are equivalent to each other, but not equivalent to the proton giving rise to the signal. Both signals in Figure 14.5 are singlets; the three methyl groups of 1-bromo-2,2-dimethylpropane give an unsplit signal because they are attached to a carbon that is not bonded to a hydrogen; the methylene group also gives an unsplit signal because it too is attached to a carbon that is not bonded to a hydrogen ($N = 0$, so $N + 1 = 1$).

In contrast, the carbon adjacent to the methyl group in 1,1-dichloroethane (Figure 14.11) is bonded to one proton, so the signal for the methyl protons is split into a doublet ($N = 1$, so $N + 1 = 2$). The carbon adjacent to the carbon bonded to the methine proton is bonded to three equivalent protons, so the signal for the methine proton is split into a quartet ($N = 3$, so $N + 1 = 4$). The number of peaks in a signal is called the **multiplicity** of the signal. Splitting is always mutual: if the *a* protons split the *b* protons, then the *b* protons must split the *a* protons. The *a* and *b* protons, in this case, are *coupled protons*. **Coupled protons** split each other's signal. Note that coupled protons are bonded to adjacent carbons.

Keep in mind that it is not the number of protons giving rise to a signal that determines the multiplicity of the signal; rather, it is the number of protons bonded to the immediately adjacent carbons that determines the multiplicity. For example, the signal for the *a* protons in the following compound will be split into three peaks (a **triplet**) because the adjacent carbon is bonded to two protons. The signal for the *b* protons will appear as a

A ^{1}H NMR signal is split into *N* + 1 peaks, where *N* is the number of equivalent protons bonded to adjacent carbons.

Coupled protons split each other's signal.

Coupled protons are bonded to adjacent carbons.

quartet because the adjacent carbon is bonded to three protons, and the signal for the *c* protons will be a singlet.

$$
\underset{\substack{a \quad\quad b}}{CH_3CH_2}\underset{}{\overset{\displaystyle\overset{O}{\parallel}}{C}}\underset{c}{OCH_3}
$$

A signal for a proton is never split by *equivalent* protons. For example, the ¹H NMR spectrum of bromomethane shows one singlet. The three methyl protons are chemically equivalent, and chemically equivalent protons do not split each other's signal. The four protons in 1,2-dichloroethane are also chemically equivalent, so its ¹H NMR spectrum also shows one singlet.

<table>
<tr><td>CH_3Br</td><td>ClCH_2CH_2Cl</td></tr>
<tr><td>bromomethane</td><td>1,2-dichloroethane</td></tr>
</table>

each compound has an NMR spectrum that shows one singlet because equivalent protons do not split each other's signals

Equivalent protons do not split each other's signal.

The splitting of signals occurs when different kinds of protons are close enough for their magnetic fields to influence one another, a situation called **spin–spin coupling**. For example, the frequency at which the methyl protons of 1,1-dichloroethane show a signal is influenced by the magnetic field of the methine proton (Figure 14.12). If the magnetic field of the methine proton aligns *with* that of the applied magnetic field, it will add to the applied magnetic field, causing the methyl protons to show a signal at a slightly higher frequency. On the other hand, if the magnetic field of the methine proton aligns *against* the applied magnetic field, it will subtract from the applied magnetic field and the methyl protons will show a signal at a lower frequency. Therefore, the signal for the methyl protons is split into two peaks, one corresponding to the higher frequency and one corresponding to the lower frequency. Because the α- and β-spin states have almost the same population, about half the methine protons are lined up with the applied magnetic field and about half are lined up against it. Therefore, the two peaks of the *doublet* have approximately the same height and area.

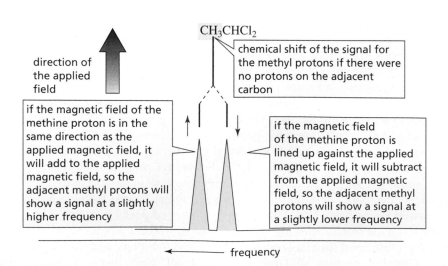

▶ **Figure 14.12**
The signal for the methyl protons of 1,1-dichloroethane is split into a doublet by the methine proton.

Similarly, the frequency at which the methine proton shows a signal is influenced by the magnetic fields of the three protons bonded to the adjacent carbon. The magnetic fields of all three methyl protons can align with the applied magnetic field, two can align with the field and one against it, one can align with it and two against it, or all three can align against it. Because the magnetic field that the methine proton senses is affected in four different ways, its signal is a *quartet* (Figure 14.13).

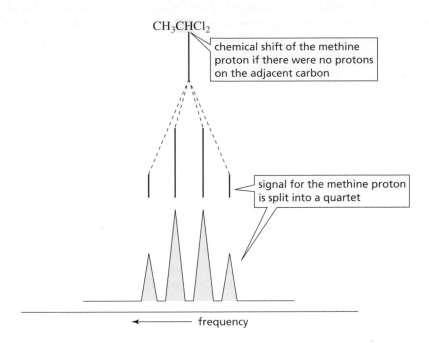

◀ **Figure 14.13**
The signal for the methine proton of 1,1-dichloroethane is split into a quartet by the methyl protons.

The relative intensities of the peaks in a signal reflect the number of ways the neighboring protons can be aligned relative to the applied magnetic field. There is only one way to align the magnetic fields of three protons so that they are all oriented with the applied magnetic field and only one way to align them so that they are all oriented against the applied field. However, there are three ways to align the magnetic fields of three protons so that two are lined up with the applied field and one is lined up against it (Figure 14.14), and there are three ways to align them so that one is lined up with the applied field and two are lined up against it. Therefore, a quartet has relative peak intensities of 1 : 3 : 3 : 1.

chem Tutorial:
place NMR signal splitting

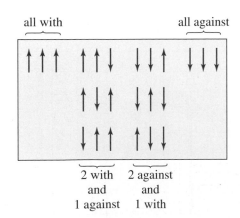

◀ **Figure 14.14**
The ways in which the magnetic fields of three protons can be aligned.

The relative peak intensities conform to the mathematical relationship known as *Pascal's triangle*. (You may remember this mnemonic device from one of your math classes.) In Pascal's scheme, each number at the bottom of the triangle in the rightmost column of Table 14.2 is the sum of the two numbers to its immediate left and right in the row above it.

Table 14.2   Multiplicity of the Signal and Relative Intensities of the Peaks in the Signal

Number of equivalent protons causing splitting	Multiplicity of the signal	Relative peak intensities
0	singlet	1
1	doublet	1 : 1
2	triplet	1 : 2 : 1
3	quartet	1 : 3 : 3 : 1
4	quintet	1 : 4 : 6 : 4 : 1
5	sextet	1 : 5 : 10 : 10 : 5 : 1
6	septet	1 : 6 : 15 : 20 : 15 : 6 : 1

Normally, *nonequivalent* protons split each other's signal only if they are on *adjacent* carbons. Splitting is a "through-bond" effect, not a "through-space" effect; it is rarely observed if the protons are separated by more than three σ bonds. However, if they are separated by more than three bonds and one of the bonds is a double or triple bond, a small splitting is sometimes observed. This phenomenon is called **long-range coupling**.

PROBLEM 18◆

One of the spectra in Figure 14.15 is produced by 1-chloropropane and the other by 1-iodopropane. Which is which?

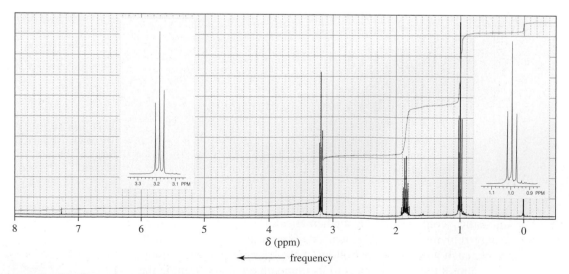

▲ **Figure 14.15**
The ^{1}H NMR spectrum for Problem 18.

▲ Figure 14.15 (*Continued*)

PROBLEM 19

Explain how the following compounds, each with the same molecular formula, could be distinguished by their ^1H NMR spectra.

$$ClCH_2—CH_2—CHCl_2 \qquad CH_3—CH—CHCl_2 \qquad CH_3—CH_2—CCl_3$$
$$\qquad\qquad\qquad\qquad\qquad\qquad | \qquad\qquad\qquad$$
$$\qquad\qquad\qquad\qquad\qquad\qquad Cl \qquad\qquad\qquad$$

$$\qquad\quad A \qquad\qquad\qquad\qquad B \qquad\qquad\qquad\qquad C$$

PROBLEM 20

Draw a diagram like the one in Figure 14.14 to predict
a. the relative intensities of the peaks in a triplet.
b. the relative intensities of the peaks in a quintet.

PROBLEM 21 ◆

The ^1H NMR spectra of two carboxylic acids with molecular formula $C_3H_5O_2Cl$ are shown in Figure 14.16. Identify the carboxylic acids. (The "offset" notation means that the farthest-left signal has been moved to the right by the indicated amount in order to fit on the spectrum; thus, the signal at 9.8 ppm offset by 2.4 ppm has an actual chemical shift of 12.2 ppm.)

a.

▲ Figure 14.16a
The ^1H NMR spectra for Problem 21.

▲ **Figure 14.16b**

14.11 MORE EXAMPLES OF ^{1}H NMR SPECTRA

We will now look at a few more spectra to give you additional practice in analyzing ^{1}H NMR spectra.

There are two signals in the ^{1}H NMR spectrum of 1,3-dibromopropane (Figure 14.17). The signal for the H_b protons is split into a triplet by the two protons on the adjacent carbon. The protons on the two carbons adjacent to the one bonded to the H_a protons are equivalent. Because the two sets of protons are equivalent, the $N + 1$ rule is applied to both sets at the same time. In other words, N is equal to the sum of the equivalent protons on both carbons. Thus, the signal for the H_a protons is split into a quintet (4 + 1 = 5). Integration confirms that two methylene groups contribute to the H_b signal because it shows that twice as many protons give rise to that signal as to the H_a signal.

▲ **Figure 14.17**
The ^{1}H NMR spectrum of 1,3-dibromopropane.

The ^{1}H NMR spectrum of isopropyl butanoate shows five signals (Figure 14.18). The signal for the H_a protons is split into a triplet by the H_c protons. The signal for the H_b protons is split into a doublet by the H_e proton. The signal for the H_d protons is split into a triplet by the H_c protons, and the signal for the H_e proton is split into a septet by the H_b protons. The signal for the H_c protons is split by both the H_a and H_d protons. Because the H_a and H_d protons are not equivalent, the $N + 1$ rule has to be applied separately to each set. Thus, the signal for the H_c protons will be split into a quartet by the

H_a protons, and each of these four peaks will be split into a triplet by the H_d protons: $(N_a + 1)(N_d + 1) = (4)(3) = 12$. As a result, the signal for the H_c protons is a **multiplet** (a signal that is more complex than a triplet, quartet, quintet, or such). The reason that 12 peaks are not apparent in the spectrum is that some of them overlap (Section 14.13).

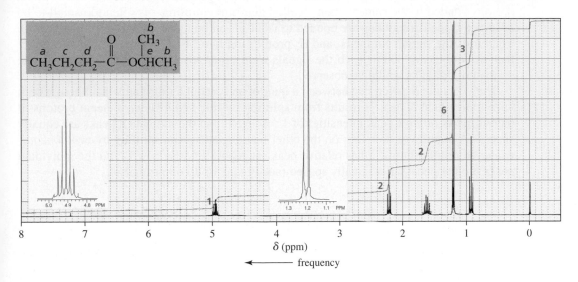

▲ **Figure 14.18**
The ^{1}H NMR spectrum of isopropyl butanoate.

PROBLEM 22

Indicate the number of signals and the multiplicity of each signal in the ^{1}H NMR spectrum of each of the following:

a. $ICH_2CH_2CH_2Br$ **b.** $ClCH_2CH_2CH_2Cl$ **c.** $ICH_2CH_2CHBr_2$

The ^{1}H NMR spectrum of 3-bromo-1-propene shows four signals (Figure 14.19). Although the H_b and H_c protons are bonded to the same carbon, they are not equivalent (one is cis to the bromomethyl group, and the other is trans to the bromomethyl group), so each produces a separate signal. The signal for the H_a protons is split into a doublet by the H_d proton. Notice that the signals for the three vinylic protons are at relatively high frequencies because of diamagnetic anisotropy (Section 14.7). The signal for the H_d proton is a multiplet because it is split separately by the H_a, H_b, and H_c protons.

▲ **Figure 14.19**
The ^{1}H NMR spectrum of 3-bromo-1-propene.

Because the H_b and H_c protons are not equivalent, they split one another's signal. This means that the signal for the H_b proton is split into a doublet by the H_d proton and that each of the peaks in the doublet is split into a doublet by the H_c proton. The signal for the H_b proton should therefore be what is called a **doublet of doublets**, and so should the signal for the H_c proton. However, the mutual splitting of the signals of two nonidentical protons bonded to the same carbon—called **geminal coupling**—is often too small to be observed if the carbon they are bonded to is an sp^2 carbon (see Table 14.3 on page 580). Therefore, the signals for the H_b and H_c protons in Figure 14.19 appear as doublets rather than as doublets of doublets. (If the signals were expanded along the frequency axis, the doublet of doublets would be observed.)

There is a clear difference between a quartet and a doublet of doublets, although both have four peaks. A quartet results from splitting by *three equivalent* adjacent protons; it therefore has relative peak intensities of 1 : 3 : 3 : 1, and the individual peaks are equally spaced. A doublet of doublets, on the other hand, results from splitting by *two nonequivalent* adjacent protons; it has relative peak intensities of 1 : 1 : 1 : 1, and the individual peaks are not necessarily equally spaced (see Figure 14.26 on page 583).

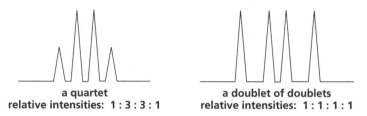

a quartet
relative intensities: 1 : 3 : 3 : 1

a doublet of doublets
relative intensities: 1 : 1 : 1 : 1

Ethylbenzene has five sets of chemically equivalent protons (Figure 14.20). We see the expected triplet for the H_a protons and the quartet for the H_b protons. (This is the characteristic pattern for an ethyl group.) We expect the signal for the H_c protons to be a doublet and the signal for the H_e proton to be a triplet. Because the H_c and H_e protons are not equivalent, they must be considered separately in determining the splitting of the signal for the H_d protons. Therefore, we expect the signal for the H_d protons to be split into a doublet by the H_c protons and each peak of the doublet to be split into another doublet by the H_e proton, forming a doublet of doublets. However, we do not see three distinct signals for the H_c, H_d, and H_e protons in Figure 14.20. Instead, we see overlapping signals. Apparently, the electronic effect (that is, the electron-donating or electron-withdrawing ability) of an ethyl substituent is not sufficiently different from that of a hydrogen to cause a difference in the environments of the H_c, H_d, and H_e protons that is large enough to allow them to appear as separate signals.

▶ **Figure 14.20**
The ^{1}H NMR spectrum of ethylbenzene. The signals for the H_c, H_d, and H_e protons overlap.

In contrast to the benzene protons of ethylbenzene (H_c, H_d, and H_e), the benzene protons of nitrobenzene (H_a, H_b, and H_c) show three distinct signals (Figure 14.21), and the multiplicity of each signal is what we would have predicted for the signals for the benzene ring protons in ethylbenzene (H_c is a doublet, H_b is a triplet, and H_a is a doublet of doublets). The nitro group is sufficiently electron withdrawing to cause the

H_a, H_b, and H_c protons to be in sufficiently different environments for their signals not to overlap.

◄ **Figure 14.21**
The ^{1}H NMR spectrum of nitrobenzene. The signals for the H_a, H_b, and H_c protons do not overlap.

Notice that the signals for the benzene ring protons in Figures 14.20 and 14.21 occur in the 7.0 to 8.5 ppm region. Other kinds of protons usually do not resonate in this region, so signals in this region of an ^{1}H NMR spectrum indicate that the compound probably contains an aromatic ring.

PROBLEM 23

Explain why the signal for the protons identified as H_a in Figure 14.21 appears at the lowest frequency and the signal for the protons identified as H_c appears at the highest frequency. (*Hint:* Draw the contributing resonance structures.)

PROBLEM 24

How could their ^{1}H NMR spectra distinguish among the following compounds?

A   **B**   **C**

PROBLEM 25

How would the ^{1}H NMR spectra for the four compounds with molecular formula $C_3H_6Br_2$ differ?

PROBLEM 26♦

Identify each compound from its molecular formula and its ^{1}H NMR spectrum:

a. C_9H_{12}

b. $C_5H_{10}O$

δ (ppm)

← frequency

c. $C_9H_{10}O_2$

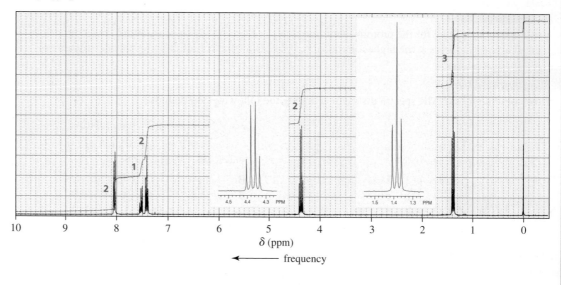

δ (ppm)

← frequency

chem Tutorial:
place NMR spectrum assignment

PROBLEM 27

Predict the splitting patterns for the signals given by compounds a–m in Problem 3.

PROBLEM 28

Identify the following compounds. (Relative integrals are given from left to right across the spectrum.)

a. The ^{1}H NMR spectrum of a compound with molecular formula $C_4H_{10}O_2$ has two singlets with an area ratio of 2 : 3.

b. The ^{1}H NMR spectrum of a compound with molecular formula $C_6H_{10}O_2$ has two singlets with an area ratio of 2 : 3.

c. The ^{1}H NMR spectrum of a compound with molecular formula $C_8H_6O_2$ has two singlets with an area ratio of 1 : 2.

PROBLEM 29

Describe the ^{1}H NMR spectrum you would expect for each of the following compounds, using relative chemical shifts rather than absolute chemical shifts:

a. $BrCH_2CH_2CH_2CH_2Br$

b. $CH_3OCH_2CH_2CH_2Br$

c. O=⟨⟩=O

d. $CH_3\overset{\underset{\displaystyle Br}{|}}{C}CH_2CH_3$

e. $CH_3\overset{\displaystyle O}{\overset{\|}{C}}CH_2\overset{\displaystyle O}{\overset{\|}{C}}OCH_3$

f. $\overset{H\quad\quad H}{\underset{H\quad\quad Cl}{C=C}}$

g. $CH_3CH_2OCH_2CH_3$

h. $CH_3CH_2OCH_2Cl$

i. $CH_3\overset{\underset{\displaystyle Cl}{|}}{CH}CHCl_2$

j. ⬜—O

k. $CH_3\overset{\underset{\displaystyle CH_3}{|}}{CH}\overset{\displaystyle O}{\overset{\|}{C}}H$

l. $CH_3OCH_2CH_2CH_2OCH_3$

m. $\overset{Cl\quad\quad Cl}{\underset{H\quad\quad Cl}{C=C}}$

n. $\overset{Cl\quad\quad H}{\underset{H\quad\quad Cl}{C=C}}$

o. ⬠

14.12 COUPLING CONSTANTS IDENTIFY COUPLED PROTONS

The distance, in hertz, between two adjacent peaks of a split NMR signal is called the **coupling constant** (denoted by J). The coupling constant for H_a being split by H_b is denoted by J_{ab}. The signals of coupled protons (protons that split each other's signal) have the same coupling constant; in other words, $J_{ab} = J_{ba}$ (Figure 14.22). Coupling constants are useful in analyzing complex NMR spectra because protons on adjacent carbons can be identified by their identical coupling constants.

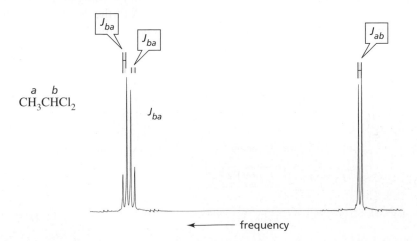

◀ **Figure 14.22**
The H_a and H_b protons of 1,1-dichloroethane are coupled protons, so their signals have the same coupling constant, $J_{ab} = J_{ba}$.

J is a constant; it has the same value regardless of the field strength or the operating frequency of the spectrometer. The magnitude of a coupling constant is a measure of how strongly the nuclear spins of the coupled protons influence each other. It, therefore, depends on the number and type of bonds that connect the coupled protons, as well as the geometric relationship of the protons. Characteristic coupling constants are shown in Table 14.3; they range from 0 to 15 Hz.

Table 14.3 Approximate Values of Coupling Constants			
Approximate value of J_{ab} (Hz)		**Approximate value of J_{ab} (Hz)**	
H_a / $-C-H_b$	12	H_a C=C H_b	15 (trans)
H_a H_b / $-C-C-$	7	H_a C=C H_b	10 (cis)
H_a H_b / $-C-C-C-$	0	H_a C=C—C H_b	1 (long-range coupling)
C=C H_a H_b	2		

BIOGRAPHY

The dependence of the coupling constant on the angle between the two C—H bonds is called the Karplus relationship after **Martin Karplus**, *who first recognized it. Karplus was born in 1930. He received a B.A. from Harvard University and a Ph.D. from the California Institute of Technology. He is currently a professor of chemistry at Harvard University.*

The coupling constant for two nonequivalent hydrogens on the *same sp³* carbon is large. (Two hydrogens on the *same sp³* carbon will be nonequivalent if the *sp³* carbon is attached to an asymmetric center; Section 14.14.) In contrast, the coupling constant for two nonequivalent hydrogens on the *same sp²* carbon is often too small to see (Figure 14.19), but it is large if the nonequivalent hydrogens are bonded to *adjacent sp²* carbons. Apparently, the interaction between the hydrogens is strongly affected by the intervening π electrons. We have seen that π electrons also allow long-range coupling, that is, coupling through four or more bonds (Section 14.10).

Coupling constants can be used to distinguish between the ¹H NMR spectra of cis and trans alkenes. The coupling constant of trans vinylic protons is significantly greater than the coupling constant of cis vinylic protons, because the coupling constant depends on the dihedral angle between the two C—H bonds in the H—C=C—H unit (Figure 14.23; also see Section 2.10). The coupling constant is greatest when the angle between the two C—H bonds is 180° (trans) and smallest when the angle is 0° (cis). Notice the difference between J_{bd} and J_{cd} in the spectrum of 3-bromo-1-propene (Figure 14.19 on page 575). The peaks in the doublets are not the same height because of **"leaning"**—an arrow drawn from the top of the outside peak of the doublet to the top of the inside peak will point at the signal of the proton responsible for the splitting.

The coupling constant for trans alkene protons is greater than the coupling constant for cis alkene protons.

▲ **Figure 14.23**
The doublets observed for the H$_a$ and H$_b$ protons in the ¹H NMR spectra of *trans*-3-chloropropenoic acid and *cis*-3-chloropropenoic acid. The coupling constant for trans protons (14 Hz) is greater than the coupling constant for cis protons (9 Hz).

PROBLEM 30

Why is there no coupling between H_a and H_c or between H_b and H_c in *cis*- or *trans*-3-chloro-propenoic acid?

Let's now summarize the kind of information that can be obtained from an ^{1}H NMR spectrum:

1. The number of signals indicates the number of different kinds of protons in the compound.
2. The position of a signal indicates the kind of proton(s) responsible for the signal (methyl, methylene, methine, allylic, vinylic, aromatic, and so on) and the kinds of neighboring substituents.
3. The integration of the signal tells the relative number of protons responsible for the signal.
4. The multiplicity of the signal ($N + 1$) tells the number of protons (N) bonded to adjacent carbons.
5. The coupling constants identify coupled protons.

PROBLEM-SOLVING STRATEGY

Using IR and ^{1}H NMR Spectra to Deduce a Chemical Structure

Identify the compound with molecular formula $C_9H_{10}O$ that gives the IR and ^{1}H NMR spectra in Figure 14.24.

▲ **Figure 14.24**
The IR and ^{1}H NMR spectra for this problem-solving strategy.

The best way to approach this kind of problem is to identify whatever structural features you can from the molecular formula and IR spectrum and then use the information from the ^{1}H NMR spectrum to expand on that knowledge. From the molecular formula and IR spectrum, we learn that the compound is a ketone: it has a carbonyl group at ~1680 cm^{-1}, only one oxygen, and no absorption bands at ~2820 and ~2720 cm^{-1} that would indicate an aldehyde. The carbonyl group absorption band is at a lower frequency than is typical, which suggests that it has partial single-bond character as a result of electron delocalization, indicating that it is attached to an sp^2 carbon. The compound contains a benzene ring (absorption bands > 3000 cm^{-1}, ~1600 cm^{-1}, and ~1440 cm^{-1}), and it has hydrogens bonded to sp^3 carbons (absorption in the region < 3000 cm^{-1}). In the NMR spectrum, the triplet at ~1.2 ppm and the quartet at ~3.0 ppm indicate the presence of an ethyl group that is attached to an electron-withdrawing group. The signals in the 7.4 to 8.0 ppm region confirm the presence of a benzene ring; the fact that the aromatic signals integrate to 5H indicates a monosubstituted benzene ring. From this information, we can conclude that the compound is the ketone shown below. The integration ratio (5 : 2 : 3) confirms this answer.

Now continue on to Problem 31.

PROBLEM 31 ♦

Identify the compound with molecular formula $C_8H_{10}O$ that gives the IR and ^{1}H NMR spectra shown in Figure 14.25.

▲ **Figure 14.25**
The IR and ^{1}H NMR spectra for Problem 31.

14.13 SPLITTING DIAGRAMS EXPLAIN THE MULTIPLICITY OF A SIGNAL

The splitting pattern obtained when a signal is split by more than one set of protons can best be understood by using a splitting diagram. In a **splitting diagram** (also called a **splitting tree**), the NMR peaks are shown as vertical lines, and the effect of each of the splittings is shown one at a time. The splitting diagram shown in Figure 14.26, for example, depicts the splitting of the signal for the H_c proton of 1,1,2-trichloro-3-methylbutane into a doublet of doublets by the H_b and H_d protons. Notice that we start with the largest (J_{cb}) of the two J values.

$$
\begin{array}{c}
\quad\quad\quad \overset{Cl\ Cl}{\underset{a}{}\ \ \ \overset{b}{|}\ \ \overset{}{|}} \\
CH_3CHCHCHCl \\
\quad\quad |\ \ \ \ c\ \ \ d \\
\ ^a CH_3
\end{array}
$$

1,1,2-trichloro-3-methylbutane

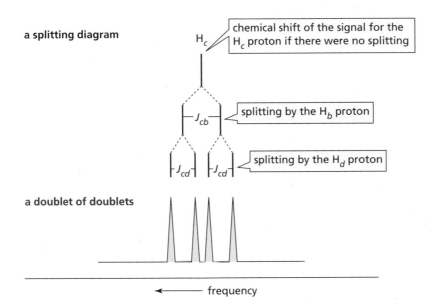

a splitting diagram

chemical shift of the signal for the H_c proton if there were no splitting

splitting by the H_b proton

splitting by the H_d proton

a doublet of doublets

◀──── frequency

▲ **Figure 14.26**
A splitting diagram for a doublet of doublets.

The signal for the H_b protons of 1-bromopropane is split into a quartet by the H_a protons (Figure 14.27), and each of the resulting four peaks is split into a triplet by the H_c protons. How many of the 12 peaks are actually seen in the spectrum depends on how many overlap one another, which in turn depends on the relative magnitudes of the two coupling constants, J_{ba} and J_{bc}. For example, Figure 14.27 shows that there are 12 peaks when J_{ba} is much greater than J_{bc}, 9 peaks when $J_{ba} = 2J_{bc}$, and only 6 peaks when $J_{ba} = J_{bc}$. When peaks overlap, their intensities add together.

We expect the signal for the H_a protons of 1-chloro-3-iodopropane to be a triplet of triplets (split into nine peaks) because the signal would be split into a triplet by the H_b protons and each of the resulting peaks would be split into a triplet by the H_c protons. The signal, however, in Figure 14.28 is actually a quintet.

▲ **Figure 14.27**
A splitting diagram for a quartet of triplets. The number of peaks actually observed when a signal is split by two sets of protons depends on the relative magnitudes of the two coupling constants.

▶ **Figure 14.28**
The ^{1}H NMR spectrum of 1-chloro-3-iodopropane.

Finding that the signal for the H_a protons of 1-chloro-3-iodopropane is a quintet indicates that J_{ab} and J_{ac} have about the same value. The splitting diagram shows that a quintet results if $J_{ab} = J_{ac}$.

We can conclude that *when two different sets of protons split a signal, the multiplicity of the signal can be determined by using the N + 1 rule separately for each set of protons, as long as the coupling constants for the two sets are different. When the coupling constants*

are similar, the multiplicity of a signal can be determined by treating both sets of adjacent protons as if they were equivalent. In other words, when the coupling constants are similar, the $N + 1$ rule can be applied to both sets of protons simultaneously.

PROBLEM 32

Draw a splitting diagram for H_b, where

a. $J_{ba} = 12\,Hz$ and $J_{bc} = 6\,Hz$ **b.** $J_{ba} = 12\,Hz$ and $J_{bc} = 12\,Hz$

$$-\overset{\displaystyle |}{\underset{\displaystyle H_a}{C}}-\overset{\displaystyle |}{\underset{\displaystyle H_b}{C}}-\overset{\displaystyle |}{\underset{\displaystyle H_c}{C}}-$$

14.14 DIASTEREOTOPIC HYDROGENS ARE NOT CHEMICALLY EQUIVALENT

If a carbon is bonded to two hydrogens and to two different groups, the two hydrogens are called **enantiotopic hydrogens**. For example, the two hydrogens (H_a and H_b) in the CH_2 group of ethanol are enantiotopic hydrogens because the other two groups bonded to the carbon (CH_3 and OH) are not identical. Replacing an enantiotopic hydrogen by a deuterium (or any other atom or group other than CH_3 or OH) forms a chiral molecule (Section 5.3).

The carbon to which the enantiotopic hydrogens are attached is called a **prochiral carbon** because it will become an asymmetric center (at one time called a chirality center) if one of the hydrogens is replaced by a deuterium (or any group other than CH_3 or OH). If the H_a hydrogen is replaced by a deuterium, the asymmetric center will have the R configuration. Thus, the H_a hydrogen is called the **pro-R-hydrogen**. The H_b hydrogen is called the **pro-S-hydrogen** because if it is replaced by a deuterium, the asymmetric center will have the S configuration. The pro-R- and pro-S-hydrogens are chemically equivalent, so they give only one NMR signal.

If a carbon is bonded to two hydrogens in a compound with an asymmetric center, the two hydrogens are called **diastereotopic hydrogens**, because replacing each of them in turn with deuterium (or another group) creates a pair of diastereomers.

Diastereotopic hydrogens are not chemically equivalent. Therefore, they do not have the same reactivity with achiral reagents. For example, in Section 9.5 we saw that because *trans*-2-butene is more stable than *cis*-2-butene, removal of H_b and Br to form *trans*-2-butene occurs more rapidly than removal of H_a and Br to form *cis*-2-butene.

Because diastereotopic hydrogens are not chemically equivalent, they have different chemical shifts. Typically, the chemical shifts are similar and, like other nonequivalent hydrogens, can even be the same by chance. The further the diastereotopic hydrogens are from the asymmetric center, the more similar their chemical shifts are expected to be. Because diastereotopic hydrogens are not equivalent, the $N + 1$ rule has to be applied to them separately.

chem Tutorial:
place Stereochemical nonequivalence

PROBLEM 33 ◆

a. Which of the following compounds have enantiotopic hydrogens?
b. Which have diastereotopic hydrogens?

PROBLEM 34   SOLVED

Applying the $N + 1$ rule separately to the two diastereotopic hydrogens of 2-bromobutane tells us that the signal for the adjacent methyl hydrogens should be a doublet of doublets. The signal, however, is a triplet. Use a splitting diagram to explain why it is a triplet rather than a doublet of doublets.

Solution   The observation of a triplet means that the $N + 1$ rule did not have to be applied to the diastereotopic hydrogens separately, in this case, but could have been applied to the two protons as a set ($N = 2$, so $N + 1 = 3$). This indicates that the coupling constant for splitting of the methyl signal by one of the diastereotopic hydrogens is similar to the coupling constant for splitting by the other diastereotopic hydrogen—that is, $J_{ab} \sim J_{ac}$.

14.15 THE TIME DEPENDENCE OF NMR SPECTROSCOPY

We have seen that the three methyl hydrogens of ethyl bromide give rise to just one signal in the ^{1}H NMR spectrum because they are chemically equivalent due to rotation about the C—C bond. At any given instant, however, the three hydrogens can be in quite different environments: one can be anti to the bromine, one can be gauche to the bromine, one can be eclipsed with the bromine.

anti   **gauche**   **eclipsed**

The average time to take an NMR spectrum is about one second; any process (in this case rotation about a C—C bond) that happens faster than once every second will cause the signals to average. Thus, we see one signal in the ^{1}H NMR spectrum for the three methyl hydrogens of ethyl bromide, which represents an average of their environments.

Similarly, the ^{1}H NMR spectrum of cyclohexane shows only one signal, even though cyclohexane has both axial and equatorial hydrogens. There is only one signal because the chair conformers of cyclohexane intervert too rapidly at room temperature for the NMR spectrometer to detect them individually. Because axial hydrogens in one chair conformer are equatorial hydrogens in the other chair conformer (Section 2.12), all the hydrogens in cyclohexane have the same average environment on the NMR time scale, so the NMR spectrum shows one signal.

axial

H

H

chair–chair interconversion

equatorial

equatorial

H

H

axial

The rate of chair–chair interconversion is temperature-dependent: the lower the temperature, the slower is the rate. Cyclohexane-d_{11} has 11 deuterium atoms, which means that it has only one hydrogen. Several ^{1}H NMR spectra of cyclohexane-d_{11} taken at various temperatures are shown in Figure 14.29. Cyclohexane with only one hydrogen was used for this experiment in order to prevent splitting of the signal, which would have complicated the spectrum. Deuterium signals are not detectable in ^{1}H NMR (Section 14.17).

At room temperature, the ^{1}H NMR spectrum of cyclohexane-d_{11} shows one sharp signal, which is an average for the axial hydrogen of one chair and the equatorial hydrogen of the other chair. As the temperature decreases, the signal becomes broader and eventually separates into two signals, which are equidistant from the original signal. At -89 °C, two sharp singlets are observed because at that temperature, the rate of chair–chair interconversion has decreased sufficiently to allow the two kinds of hydrogens (axial and equatorial) to be individually detected on the NMR time scale.

-49 °C

-57 °C

-60 °C

-63 °C

-68 °C

-89 °C

▲ **Figure 14.29**
A series of ^{1}H NMR spectra of cyclohexane-d_{11} obtained at various temperatures.

14.16 PROTONS BONDED TO OXYGEN AND NITROGEN

The chemical shift of a proton bonded to an oxygen or to a nitrogen depends on the degree of hydrogen bonding the proton experiences; the greater the extent of hydrogen bonding, the greater is the chemical shift, because the extent of hydrogen bonding affects the electron density around the proton. For example, the chemical shift of the OH proton of an alcohol ranges from 2 to 5 ppm; the chemical shift of the OH proton of a carboxylic acid, from 10 to 12 ppm; the chemical shift of the NH proton of an amine, from 1.5 to 4 ppm; and the chemical shift of the NH proton of an amide, from 5 to 8 ppm.

The ^{1}H NMR spectrum of pure dry ethanol is shown in Figure 14.30a, and the ^{1}H NMR spectrum of ethanol with a trace amount of acid is shown in Figure 14.30b. The spectrum shown in Figure 14.30a is what you would predict from what you have learned so far. The signal for the proton bonded to oxygen is farthest downfield and is split into a triplet by the neighboring methylene protons; the signal for the methylene protons is split into a multiplet by the combined effects of the methyl protons and the OH proton.

▲ **Figure 14.30**
(a) The ^{1}H NMR spectrum of pure ethanol.
(b) The ^{1}H NMR spectrum of ethanol containing a trace amount of acid.

The spectrum shown in Figure 14.30b is the type of spectrum most often obtained for alcohols. The signal for the proton bonded to oxygen is not split, and this proton does not split the signal of the adjacent protons. Therefore, the signal for the OH proton is a singlet, and the signal for the methylene protons is a quartet because it is split only by the methyl protons.

The two spectra differ because protons bonded to oxygen undergo **proton exchange**, which means that they are transferred from one molecule to another. Whether the OH proton and the methylene protons split each other's signals depends on how long a particular proton stays on the OH group.

In a sample of pure alcohol, the rate of proton exchange is very slow. This causes the spectrum to look no different from one that would be obtained if proton exchange did not occur. Acids and bases catalyze proton exchange, so if the alcohol is contaminated with just a trace of acid or base, proton exchange becomes rapid. When proton exchange is rapid, the spectrum records only an average of all possible environments. Therefore, a rapidly exchanging proton is recorded as a singlet. The effect of a rapidly exchanging proton on adjacent protons is also averaged. Thus, not only is its signal not split by adjacent protons, the rapidly exchanging proton does not cause splitting.

MECHANISM FOR ACID-CATALYZED PROTON EXCHANGE

$$R\ddot{O}-H + H\ddot{O}H \rightleftharpoons RO-H + H\ddot{O}H \rightleftharpoons R\ddot{O}: + H\ddot{O}H$$

Unless the sample is pure, the hydrogen of an OH group is not split by its neighbors and does not split its neighbors.

The signal for an OH proton is often easy to spot in an ^{1}H NMR spectrum because it is frequently somewhat broader than other signals (see the signal at δ 4.9 in Figure 14.32b on page 590). The broadening occurs because the rate of proton exchange is not slow enough to result in a cleanly split signal, as in Figure 14.28a, or fast enough for a cleanly averaged signal, as in Figure 14.30b. NH protons also show broad signals, not because of chemical exchange, which is generally quite slow for NH, but for reasons that are beyond the scope of this book.

PROBLEM 35

Explain why the chemical shift of the OH proton of a carboxylic acid is at a higher frequency than the chemical shift of an OH proton of an alcohol.

PROBLEM 36♦

Which would show a greater chemical shift for the OH proton, the ^{1}H NMR spectrum of pure ethanol or the ^{1}H NMR spectrum of ethanol dissolved in CH_2Cl_2?

PROBLEM 37

Propose a mechanism for base-catalyzed proton exchange.

PROBLEM 38♦

Identify the compound with molecular formula C_3H_7NO responsible for the ^{1}H NMR spectrum in Figure 14.31.

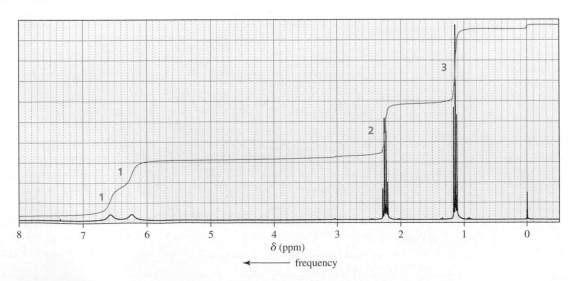

▲ **Figure 14.31**
The ^{1}H NMR spectrum for Problem 38.

14.17 THE USE OF DEUTERIUM IN ^{1}H NMR SPECTROSCOPY

Deuterium signals are not seen in an ^{1}H NMR spectrum. Therefore, substituting a deuterium for a hydrogen is a technique used to identify signals and to simplify ^{1}H NMR spectra (Section 14.15). For example, if the ^{1}H NMR spectrum of $CH_3CH_2OCH_3$ were compared with the ^{1}H NMR spectrum of $CH_3CD_2OCH_3$, the signal at the highest frequency in the first spectrum would be absent in the second spectrum, indicating that this signal corresponds to the methylene group.

To identify the OH signal in an alcohol's ^{1}H NMR spectrum, a spectrum of the alcohol is taken, and then another spectrum is taken after a few drops of D_2O are added to the sample. The OH signal will be the one that becomes less intense (or disappears) in the second spectrum because of the proton exchange process just discussed. This technique can be used with any proton that undergoes exchange.

$$R—O—\underbrace{H}_{\text{seen in }^1\text{H NMR}} + D—O—D \longrightarrow R—O—D + \underbrace{D—O—H}_{\text{not seen in }^1\text{H NMR}}$$

The sample used to obtain an ^{1}H NMR spectrum is made by dissolving the compound in an appropriate solvent. Solvents with protons cannot be used because the signals for solvent protons would be very intense, since there is more solvent than compound in a solution. Instead, deuterated solvents such as $CDCl_3$ (rather than $CHCl_3$) and D_2O (rather than H_2O) are commonly used in NMR spectroscopy.

14.18 THE RESOLUTION OF ^{1}H NMR SPECTRA

The ^{1}H NMR spectrum of 2-*sec*-butylphenol taken on a 60-MHz NMR spectrometer is shown in Figure 14.32a; the ^{1}H NMR spectrum of the same compound taken on a 300-MHz instrument is shown in Figure 14.32b. Why is the resolution of the second spectrum so much better?

To produce separate signals with "clean" splitting patterns, the difference in the chemical shifts (Δv in Hz) of two coupled protons must be at least 10 times the value of the coupling constant (J). The signals in Figure 14.33, produced by the H_a and H_b protons in an ethyl group, show that as $\Delta v/J$ decreases, the two signals appear closer to each other and the outer peaks of the signals become less intense while the inner peaks become more intense. The quartet and triplet of the ethyl group are clearly observed only when $\Delta v/J$ is greater than 10.

a.

▶ **Figure 14.32**
(a) A 60-MHz ^{1}H NMR spectrum of 2-*sec*-butylphenol.
(b) A 300-MHz ^{1}H NMR spectrum of 2-*sec*-butylphenol.

b.

δ (ppm)

← frequency

◀ **Figure 14.32**
(*Continued*)

$\overset{a}{CH_3}\overset{b}{CH_2}X$

$J_{ab} = 5.0$ Hz

Δν = 100 Hz   Δν/J = 20

Δν = 25 Hz   Δν/J = 5

Δν = 15 Hz   Δν/J = 3

Δν = 10 Hz   Δν/J = 2

Δν = 5 Hz   Δν/J = 1

◀ **Figure 14.33**
The splitting pattern of an ethyl group as a function of the Δν/J ratio.

The difference in the chemical shifts of the H_a and H_c protons of 2-*sec*-butylphenol is 0.8 ppm, which corresponds to 48 Hz in a 60-MHz spectrometer and 240 Hz in a 300-MHz spectrometer. (Recall that Δv values are dependent on the operating frequency of the spectrometer; see Section 14.5.) In contrast, *J* values are independent of the operating frequency, so J_{ac} is 7 Hz, whether the spectrum is taken on a 60-MHz or a 300-MHz instrument. Only in the case of the 300-MHz spectrometer is the difference in chemical shift more than 10 times the value of the coupling constant, so only in the 300-MHz spectrum do the signals show clean splitting patterns.

in a 300-MHz spectrometer   in a 60-MHz spectrometer

$$\frac{\Delta v}{J} = \frac{240}{7} = 34 \qquad\qquad \frac{\Delta v}{J} = \frac{48}{7} = 6.9$$

14.19 ^{13}C NMR SPECTROSCOPY

The number of signals in a ^{13}C **NMR** spectrum tells how many different kinds of carbons a compound has—just as the number of signals in an ^{1}H NMR spectrum tells how many different kinds of hydrogens a compound has. The principles behind ^{1}H NMR and ^{13}C NMR spectroscopy are essentially the same.

The use of ^{13}C NMR spectroscopy as a routine analytical procedure was not possible until computers were available that could carry out a Fourier transform. ^{13}C NMR requires Fourier transform techniques because the signals obtained from a single scan are too weak to be distinguished from background electronic noise. However, FT–^{13}C NMR scans can be repeated rapidly, so a large number of scans can be recorded and added together. When hundreds of scans are combined, ^{13}C signals stand out because electronic noise is random, so its sum is close to zero. Without Fourier transform, it could take days to record the number of scans required for a ^{13}C NMR spectrum using a continuous-wave (CW) spectrometer.

The individual ^{13}C signals are weak because the isotope of carbon (^{13}C) that gives rise to ^{13}C NMR signals constitutes only 1.11% of the carbon in nature (Section 13.3). (The most abundant isotope of carbon, ^{12}C, has no nuclear spin and therefore cannot produce an NMR signal.) The low abundance of ^{13}C would cause the intensities of the signals in ^{13}C NMR to be weaker than those in ^{1}H NMR by a factor of approximately 100. In addition, the gyromagnetic ratio (γ) of ^{13}C is about one-fourth that of ^{1}H, and the intensity of a signal is proportional to γ^3. Therefore, the overall intensity of a ^{13}C signal is about 6400 times ($100 \times 4 \times 4 \times 4$) weaker than the intensity of an ^{1}H signal.

One advantage to ^{13}C NMR spectroscopy is that the chemical shifts of carbon atoms range over about 220 ppm (Table 14.4), compared with about 12 ppm for protons (Table 14.1). This means that signals for carbons in different environments are more easily distinguished. For example, the data in Table 14.4 show that aldehyde (190 to 200 ppm) and ketone (205 to 220 ppm) carbonyl groups can be easily distinguished from other carbonyl groups. The reference compound used in ^{13}C NMR is TMS, the same reference compound used in ^{1}H NMR. You will find it helpful when analyzing ^{13}C NMR spectra to divide them into five regions and remember the kind of carbons that show signals in each.

A disadvantage of ^{13}C NMR spectroscopy is that, unless special techniques are used, the area under a ^{13}C NMR signal is *not* proportional to the number of carbons giving rise to the signal. Thus, the number of carbons giving rise to a ^{13}C NMR signal cannot routinely be determined by integration.

Table 14.4 Approximate Values of Chemical Shifts for ^{13}C NMR

Type of carbon	Approximate chemical shift (ppm)	Type of carbon	Approximate chemical shift (ppm)
$(CH_3)_4Si$	0	C—I	–20–10
R—CH$_3$	0–35	C—Br	10–40
R—CH$_2$—R	15–55	C—Cl C—N C—O	25–50 40–60 50–90
R—CH—R (R above)	25–55	RC=O, N	165–175
R—C—R (R above and below)	30–40	RC=O, RO	165–175
C≡C	70–90	RC=O, HO	175–185
C≡N	110–120		
C=C	80–145	RC=O, H	190–200
C=N	150–170		
⬡C (aromatic)	110–170	RC=O, R	205–220

The ^{13}C NMR spectrum of 2-butanol is shown in Figure 14.34. 2-Butanol has carbons in four different environments, so there are four signals in the spectrum. The relative positions of the signals depend on the same factors that determine the relative positions of the proton signals in an ^{1}H NMR spectrum: carbons in electron-dense environments produce low-frequency signals, and carbons close to electron-withdrawing groups produce high-frequency signals. This means that the signals for the carbons of 2-butanol are in the same relative order as the signals of the protons bonded to those carbons in its ^{1}H NMR spectrum. Thus, the carbon of the methyl group farthest away from the electron-withdrawing OH group gives the lowest-frequency signal. The other methyl carbon comes next in order of increasing frequency, followed by the methylene carbon; the carbon attached to the OH group gives the highest-frequency signal.

◀ **Figure 14.34**
A ^{13}C NMR spectrum of 2-butanol.

The signals in ^{13}C NMR are not normally split by neighboring carbons because there is little likelihood of an adjacent carbon being a ^{13}C; the probability of two ^{13}C carbons being next to each other is 1.11% × 1.11% (or about 1 in 10,000). ^{12}C, not having a magnetic moment, cannot split the signal of an adjacent ^{13}C. The signals in a ^{13}C NMR spectrum can be split by hydrogens, but such splitting is not usually observed because the spectra are recorded using spin-decoupling, which obliterates the carbon–proton interactions. Thus, in an ordinary ^{13}C NMR spectrum, all the signals are singlets (Figure 14.34).

If the spectrometer is run in a *proton-coupled* mode, however, each signal will be split by the *hydrogens* bonded to the carbon that produces the signal. The multiplicity of the signal is determined by the $N + 1$ rule. The coupling between ^{13}C and its attached hydrogens is called **heteronuclear coupling** because the coupling is between different types of nuclei. (The coupling between nuclei of the same type, such as the coupling between adjacent protons in ^{1}H NMR, is called **homonuclear coupling**.)

If the spectrometer is run in a proton-coupled mode, splitting by the directly attached protons is observed in a ^{13}C NMR spectrum.

The **proton-coupled ^{13}C NMR spectrum** of 2-butanol is shown in Figure 14.35. (The signal at 78 ppm is produced by the solvent, CDCl$_3$.) The signals for the methyl carbons are each split into a quartet because each methyl carbon is bonded to three hydrogens (3 + 1 = 4). The signal for the methylene carbon is split into a triplet (2 + 1 = 3), and the signal for the carbon bonded to the OH group is split into a doublet (1 + 1 = 2).

▶ **Figure 14.35**
A proton-coupled ^{13}C NMR spectrum of 2-butanol.

The ^{13}C NMR spectrum of 2,2-dimethylbutane is shown in Figure 14.36. The three methyl groups at one end of the molecule are equivalent, so they give one signal. Because the intensity of a signal is somewhat related to the number of carbons giving rise to it (and somewhat related to the number of protons on the carbon), the signal for these three methyl groups is the most intense signal in the spectrum. The tiny signal at ~31 ppm is for the quaternary carbon; carbons that are not attached to hydrogens give very small signals.

▶ **Figure 14.36**
A ^{13}C NMR spectrum of 2,2-dimethylbutane.

PROBLEM 39

Answer the following questions for each of the compounds:
a. How many signals are in its ¹³C NMR spectrum?
b. Which signal is at the lowest frequency?

1. $CH_3CH_2CH_2Br$

2. $(CH_3)_2C{=}CH_2$

3. CH_3CHCH_3
    |
    Br

4.

5.

6.   —Cl

7.

8.

9. $CH_2{=}CHBr$

chem Tutorial:
place ¹³C NMR interpretation

PROBLEM 40

Describe the proton-coupled ¹³C NMR spectra for compounds 1, 3, and 5 in Problem 39, showing relative values (not absolute values) of chemical shifts.

PROBLEM 41

How can 1,2-, 1,3-, and 1,4-dinitrobenzene be distinguished by
a. ¹H NMR spectroscopy?   b. ¹³C NMR spectroscopy?

PROBLEM-SOLVING STRATEGY

Deducing a Chemical Structure from a ¹³C NMR Spectrum

Identify the compound with molecular formula $C_9H_{10}O_2$ that gives the following ¹³C NMR spectrum:

First, pick out the signals that can be identified with certainty. For example, the two oxygen atoms in the molecular formula and the carbonyl carbon signal at 166 ppm indicate that the compound is an ester. The four signals at about 130 ppm suggest that the compound has a benzene ring with a single substituent. (One signal is for the carbon to which the substituent is attached, one signal is for the two adjacent carbons, and so on.) Subtracting those fragments (C_6H_5 and CO_2) from the molecular formula of the compound leaves C_2H_5, the molecular formula of an ethyl substituent. Therefore, we know that the compound is either ethyl benzoate or phenyl propanoate.

ethyl benzoate   phenyl propanoate

Since the signal for the methylene group is at about 60 ppm, we can conclude that it is adjacent to an oxygen. Thus, the compound must be ethyl benzoate.

Now continue on to Problem 42.

PROBLEM 42 ◆

Identify each compound in Figure 14.37 from its molecular formula and its ^{13}C NMR spectrum.

a. $C_{11}H_{22}O$

◀ **Figure 14.37**
The ^{13}C NMR spectra for Problem 42.

b. C_8H_9Br

c. $C_6H_{10}O$

d. C_6H_{12}

14.20 DEPT ^{13}C NMR SPECTRA

A technique called DEPT ^{13}C NMR (for Distortionless Enhancement by Polarization Transfer) has been developed to distinguish between CH_3, CH_2, and CH groups. It is now much more widely used than proton coupling to determine the number of hydrogens attached to each carbon in a compound.

A **DEPT ^{13}C NMR** recording shows four spectra produced by the same compound, as shown in Figure 14.38 for citronellal. The top spectrum is run under conditions that allow signals produced only by CH_3 carbons. The middle spectrum is run under conditions that allow signals produced only by CH_2 carbons, and the third spectrum shows signals produced only by CH carbons. The bottom spectrum shows signals for all carbons, thereby allowing carbons not bonded to hydrogens to be detected. Thus a DEPT ^{13}C NMR spectrum indicates whether a signal is produced by a CH_3, CH_2, CH, or C.

◄ **Figure 14.38**
The DEPT ^{13}C NMR spectrum of citronellal.

14.21 TWO-DIMENSIONAL NMR SPECTROSCOPY

Complex molecules such as proteins and nucleic acids are difficult to analyze by NMR because the signals in their spectra overlap. Such compounds are now being analyzed by two-dimensional NMR (2-D NMR), a technique that allows the structures of complex molecules in solution to be determined. This is particularly important for studying biological molecules whose properties depend on how they fold in water. More recently, 3-D and 4-D NMR spectroscopy have been developed and can be used to determine the structures of highly complex molecules. A thorough discussion of 2-D NMR is beyond the scope of this book, but the chapter would not be complete without a brief introduction to this increasingly important spectroscopic technique.

The ^{1}H NMR and ^{13}C NMR spectra discussed in the preceding sections have one frequency axis and one intensity axis; **2-D NMR** spectra have two frequency axes and one intensity axis. The most common 2-D spectra involve ^{1}H–^{1}H shift correlations, which identify protons that are coupled (that split each other's signal). This is called ^{1}H–^{1}H shift-COrrelated SpectroscopY, known by the acronym COSY.

A portion of the **COSY spectrum** of ethyl vinyl ether is shown in Figure 14.39a; it looks like a mountain range viewed from the air because intensity is the third axis. These "mountain-like" spectra, called *stack plots*, are not the spectra actually used to identify a compound. Instead, the compound is identified using a contour plot (Figure 14.37b) that represents each mountain in Figure 14.39a by a large dot (as if its top had been cut off). The two mountains shown in Figure 14.39a correspond to the dots labeled Y and Z in Figure 14.39b.

▲ **Figure 14.39**
(a) a portion of a COSY spectrum of ethyl vinyl ether (stack plot).
(b) a portion of a COSY spectrum of ethyl vinyl ether (contour plot). In a COSY spectrum, an ^{1}H NMR spectrum is plotted on both the *x*- and *y*-axes. Cross peaks Y and Z represent the mountains in (a).

In the contour plot (Figure 14.39b), the usual one-dimensional ^{1}H NMR spectrum is plotted on both the *x*- and *y*-axes. To analyze the spectrum, a diagonal line is drawn through the dots that bisect the spectrum. Dots that are *not* on the diagonal (X, Y, Z) are called *cross peaks*; they reveal pairs of protons that are coupled. For example, if we start at the cross peak labeled X and draw a straight line from X to the diagonal and parallel to the *y*-axis, we hit the dot on the diagonal at ~1.1 ppm produced by the H_a protons. If we then go back to X and draw a straight line from X to the diagonal and parallel to the *x*-axis, we hit the dot on the diagonal at ~3.8 ppm produced by the H_b protons. This means that the H_a and H_b protons are coupled. If we go next to the cross peak labeled Y and draw another two perpendicular lines back to the diagonal, we see that the H_c and H_e protons are coupled. Similarly, the cross peak labeled Z shows that the H_d and H_e protons are coupled.

Although we have been using cross peaks below the diagonal as examples, the cross peaks above the diagonal give the same information because a COSY spectrum is symmetrical with respect to the diagonal. The absence of a cross peak due to coupling of H_c and H_d is consistent with expectations—the two protons bonded to an sp^2 carbon are not coupled in the one-dimensional ^{1}H NMR spectrum shown in Figure 14.17. The power of a COSY experiment is that it reveals coupled protons without having to do coupling constant analysis.

The COSY spectrum of 1-nitropropane is shown in Figure 14.40. Cross peak X shows that the H_a and H_b protons are coupled, and cross peak Y shows that the H_b and H_c protons are coupled. Notice that the two triangles in the figure have a common vertex, since the H_b protons are coupled to both the H_a and H_c protons.

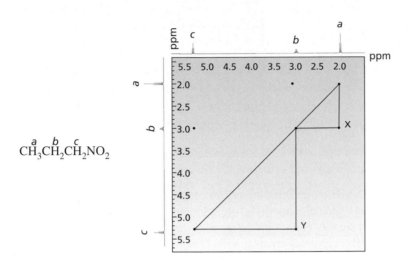

$$\overset{a}{C}H_3\overset{b}{C}H_2\overset{c}{C}H_2NO_2$$

◀ **Figure 14.40**
The COSY spectrum of 1-nitropropane.

PROBLEM 43

Identify pairs of coupled protons in 2-methyl-3-pentanone, using the COSY spectrum in Figure 14.41.

$$\underset{\underset{b}{CH_3}}{\overset{b}{CH_3}\overset{d}{CH}\overset{O}{\overset{\|}{C}}\overset{c}{CH_2}\overset{a}{CH_3}}$$

▲ **Figure 14.41**
The COSY spectrum for Problem 43.

HETCOR spectra (from HETeronuclear CORrelation) are 2-D NMR spectra that show ^{13}C–^{1}H shift correlations and thus reveal coupling between protons and the carbon to which they are attached.

In a HETCOR spectrum, a compound's ^{13}C NMR spectrum is shown on the x-axis, and its ^{1}H NMR spectrum is shown on the y-axis. The HETCOR spectrum of 2-methyl-3-pentanone is shown in Figure 14.42. The cross peaks identify which hydrogens are attached to which carbons. For example, in the HETCOR spectrum of 2-methyl-3-pentanone (Figure 14.42), cross peak X indicates that the hydrogens that produce a signal at ~0.9 ppm in the ^{1}H NMR spectrum are bonded to the carbon that produces a signal at ~6 ppm in the ^{13}C NMR spectrum. Cross peak Z shows that the hydrogens that produce a signal at ~2.5 ppm are bonded to the carbon that produces a signal at ~34 ppm.

▶ **Figure 14.42**
HETCOR spectrum of 2-methyl-3-pentanone. A HETCOR spectrum indicates coupling between protons and the carbons to which they are attached.

Clearly, 2-D NMR techniques are not necessary for interpreting the NMR spectra of simple compounds such as 2-methyl-3-pentanone. However, in the case of many complicated molecules, signals cannot be assigned without the aid of 2-D NMR. A number of different 2D NMR techniques are available. One involves the use of 2-D ^{13}C INADEQUATE* spectra, which show ^{13}C–^{13}C shift correlations and thus identify directly bonded carbons. Another method plots chemical shifts on one frequency axis and coupling constants on the other. Finally, there are techniques that use the nuclear Overhauser effect (NOESY for very large molecules, ROESY for midsize molecules)† to locate protons that are close together in space.

14.22 NMR USED IN MEDICINE IS CALLED MAGNETIC RESONANCE IMAGING

NMR has become an important tool in medical diagnosis because it allows physicians to examine internal organs and structures without resorting to surgery or the harmful ionizing radiation of X-rays. When NMR was first introduced into clinical practice in 1981, the selection of an appropriate name was a matter of some debate. Because many members of the general public associate the word "nuclear" with harmful radiation or radioactivity, the "N" was dropped from the medical application of NMR, which is known as **magnetic resonance imaging (MRI)**. The spectrometer is called an **MRI scanner**.

An MRI scanner consists of a magnet large enough to surround a person entirely, along with an apparatus for exciting the nuclei, modifying the magnetic field, and receiving signals. (By comparison, the NMR spectrometer used by chemists is only large enough to accommodate a 5-mm glass tube.) Different tissues yield different signals, which are separated into components by Fourier transform analysis (Section 14.2). Each component can be attributed to a specific location within the part of the body being scanned, so that a set of images through the scanned volume is generated. MRI can produce an image showing any cross section of the body, regardless of the person's position within the machine, allowing optimal visualization of the anatomical feature of interest.

---

*INADEQUATE is an acronym for Incredible Natural Abundance Double Quantum Transfer Experiment.
†NOESY and ROESY are the acronyms for Nuclear Overhauser Effect SpectroscopY and Rotation-frame Overhauser Effect SpectroscopY, respectively.

Most of the signals in an MRI scan originate from the hydrogens of water molecules because tissues contain far more of these hydrogens than they do hydrogens of organic compounds. The difference in the way water is bound in different tissues is what produces much of the variation in signal between different organs, as well as the variation between healthy and diseased tissue (Figure 14.43). MRI scans, therefore, can sometimes provide much more information than images obtained by other means. For example, MRI can provide detailed images of blood vessels. Flowing fluids, such as blood, respond differently to excitation in an MRI scanner than do stationary tissues, and proper processing will result in the display only of the moving fluids. The quality of these images has become high enough that it can often eliminate the need for more invasive diagnostic techniques.

The versatility of MRI has been enhanced by using gadolinium as a contrast agent. Gadolinium modifies the magnetic field in its immediate vicinity, altering the signal from nearby hydrogens. The distribution of gadolinium, which is infused into a patient's veins, may be affected by certain disease processes such as cancer and inflammation. Any abnormal patterns of distribution are revealed in the MRI images.

A brain tumor and a brain abscess may have very similar appearances in an MRI (Figure 14.43a). Suppressing the signal from water allows detection of signals from specific compounds such as choline and acetate. The tumor will produce an elevated choline signal, whereas an abscess is more likely to produce an elevated acetate signal (Figure 14.43b).

▲ **Figure 14.43**
(a) The white circle indicates a brain lesion that could be caused by either a tumor or an abscess.
(b) The major peak in the spectrum corresponds to acetate, supporting the diagnosis of a brain abscess. Signals from compounds, such as creatine, typically found in normal brain tissue are absent from this spectrum.

14.23 X-RAY CRYSTALLOGRAPHY

X-ray crystallography is a technique used to determine the arrangement of atoms within a crystal. With this technique, the structure of any material that can form a crystal can be determined. Dorothy Crowfoot Hodgkin was the pioneer of X-ray crystallography, using it to determine the structures of cholesterol (1937), penicillin (1945), vitamin B_{12} (1954), and insulin (1969). (The structures of these compounds can be found in Sections 5.11, 17.4, 25.6, and 23.8, respectively.) In 1953, Rosalind Franklin's X-ray images allowed James Watson and Francis Crick to accurately describe the structure of DNA (Section 28.1).

A crystal is a solid composed of atoms and molecules in a regular three-dimensional array, called a unit cell, that is repeated indefinitely throughout the crystal. Often the most difficult aspect of X-ray crystallography is obtaining the crystal, which should be at least 0.5 mm long in all three dimensions in order to provide good structural data.

A crystal of lysozyme from hen egg white (page 10). It appears blue because it was photographed under polarized light.

Dorothy Crowfoot Hodgkin (1910–1994) *was born in Egypt to English parents. She received an undergraduate degree from Somerville College at Oxford University and earned a Ph.D. from Cambridge University. She performed the first three-dimensional calculations in crystallography, and she was the first to use computers to determine the structures of compounds. For her work on vitamin B$_{12}$, she received the 1964 Nobel Prize in Chemistry. Hodgkin was a professor of chemistry at Somerville, where one of her graduate students was the future prime minister of England Margaret Thatcher. She was also a founding member of Pugwash, an organization whose purpose was to further communication between scientists on both sides of the Iron Curtain.*

Fortunately, crystallographers can get a head start by looking up over 14,000 crystallization conditions on the *Biological Macromolecule Crystallization Database* (xpdb.nist.gov:8060/BMCD4).

For something to be visible, it cannot be smaller than the wavelength of the light being used to observe it. The length of a C—C bond is 1.54 Å. Thus, in order to resolve atomic distances, the wavelength of the light used must be of about the same order of magnitude. Visible light, with wavelengths of 4000–8000 Å, obviously is of no use. The X-rays produced by bombarding a Cu-anode with electrons in a vacuum tube have a wavelength of 1.542 Å, which make them ideal for resolving most atomic distances. For high-resolution structures, crystallographers use more intense sources of X-rays. For example, synchrotron radiation coupled to high-speed particle accelerators produce X-rays with wavelengths less than 1 Å.

Once a suitable crystal has been obtained, it is bombarded with X-rays while being gradually rotated. X-rays, however, cannot be focused by conventional lenses to form an image of a molecule. This is where X-ray diffraction comes in. While most of the X-rays pass through the crystal, some are scattered by the electron clouds of the atoms (not by the nuclei of the atoms) and land on a detector, creating a diffraction pattern of regularly spaced dots (Figure 14.44).

▲ **Figure 14.44**
An X-ray diffraction.

▶ **Figure 14.45**
The structure of *E. coli* heat-labile enterotoxin determined by X-ray crystallography and downloaded from the Protein Data Bank (see page 603). The protein has seven subunits—that is seven protein chains (Section 23.16).
Five of them (blue, green purple, etc.) attach to a cell membrane. The toxin uses the red α-helical spike (Section 23.14) to deliver the catalytic subunit (gold) into the cell. The space filling model is glutamate, a base catalyst (Section 24.8). This toxin is responsible for what is known as traveler's diarrhea.

By means of complex mathematical methods, now facilitated by computers, a three-dimensional model of the electron density within the crystal is produced from the two-dimensional **X-ray diffraction** images taken at different angles of rotation. Electrons are found around atoms, so any two regions of electron density within bonding distance of each other can be assumed to represent atoms bonded to one another. The greater the density of the electron cloud around the atom, the more precisely the location of the atom can be assigned. Therefore, the position of electron-deficient hydrogen atoms cannot be assigned unambiguously. However, hydrogen atoms now can be located in the final structure by computational methods.

 ### Structural Databases

There are a variety of databases that provide structural information to chemists. Two important examples are the Chemical Abstracts Services Database (CAS) and the Research Collaboratory for Structural Bioinformatics Protein Data Bank (RCSB PDB).

CAS (http://www.cas.org/) is a subscription-based service with over 100 million organic, inorganic, protein, and nucleic acid structures. It can be accessed through SciFinder, which allows searches via a structural drawing program as well as searches by subject, author, or structure name.

The RCSB Protein Data Bank (www.pdb.org) is the repository of more than 57,000 three-dimensional structures that have been determined by X-ray crystallography (see Figure 14.45) or multidimensional NMR (Section 14.21). The structures are publicly available for download in a PDB format. The structures can be visualized and manipulated with free programs such as Visual Molecular Dynamics (http://www.ks.uiuc.edu/Research/vmd/) or Chimera (http://www.cgl.ucsf.edu/chimera).

SUMMARY

NMR spectroscopy is used to identify the carbon–hydrogen framework of an organic compound.

When a sample is placed in a magnetic field, protons whose magnetic moments align with the field are in the lower-energy α-spin state and those that align against the field are in the higher-energy β-spin state. The energy difference between the spin states depends on the strength of the **applied magnetic field**. When subjected to radiation with energy corresponding to the energy difference between the spin states, nuclei in the α-spin state are promoted to the β-spin state and emit signals whose frequency depends on the difference in energy between the spin states. An **NMR spectrometer** detects and displays these signals as a plot of their frequency versus their intensity—an **NMR spectrum**.

Each set of chemically equivalent protons gives rise to a signal, so the number of signals in an ^{1}H NMR spectrum indicates the number of different kinds of protons in a compound. The **chemical shift** (δ), which is independent of the operating frequency of the spectrometer, is a measure of how far the signal is from the reference TMS signal.

The larger the magnetic field sensed by the proton, the higher is the frequency of the signal. The electron density of the environment in which the proton is located **shields** the proton from the applied magnetic field. Therefore, a proton in an electron-dense environment shows a signal at a lower frequency than a proton near electron-withdrawing groups. Low-frequency (upfield) signals have small δ (ppm) values; high-frequency (downfield) signals have large δ values. Thus, the position of a signal indicates the kind of proton(s) responsible for the signal and the kinds of neighboring substituents. In a similar environment, the chemical shift of methyl protons is at a lower frequency than that of methylene protons, which is at a lower frequency than that of a methine proton. **Diamagnetic anisotropy** causes unusual chemical shifts for hydrogens bonded to carbons that form π bonds. **Integration** tells us the relative number of protons that give rise to each signal.

The **multiplicity** of a signal indicates the number of protons bonded to adjacent carbons. Multiplicity is described by the **N + 1 rule**, where N is the number of equivalent protons bonded to adjacent carbons. A **splitting diagram** describes the splitting pattern obtained when a signal is split by more than one set of protons. Deuterium substitution is a helpful technique for the analysis of complicated ^{1}H NMR spectra.

The **coupling constant (J)**, which is independent of the operating frequency of the spectrometer, is the distance between two adjacent peaks of a split NMR signal. Coupled protons have the same coupling constant. The coupling constant for trans alkene protons is greater than that for cis alkene protons. When two different sets of protons split a signal, the multiplicity of the signal is determined by using the N + 1 rule separately for each set of protons when the coupling constants for the two sets are different; when they are similar, the N + 1 rule is applied to both sets simultaneously.

The chemical shift of a proton bonded to an O or to an N depends on the degree to which the proton is hydrogen bonded. In the presence of trace amounts of acid or base, protons bonded to oxygen undergo **proton exchange**. In that case, the signal for a proton bonded to an O is not split and does not split the signal of adjacent protons.

The number of signals in a ^{13}C NMR spectrum tells how many kinds of carbons a compound has. Carbons in electron-dense environments produce low-frequency signals; carbons close to electron-withdrawing groups produce high-frequency signals. Chemical shifts for ^{13}C NMR range over about 220 ppm, compared with about 12 ppm for ^1H NMR.

^{13}C NMR signals are not split by attached protons unless the spectrometer is run in a proton-coupled mode.

NMR (known in medical applications as **MRI**) is an important tool in medical diagnosis because it allows internal structures to be examined without surgery or harmful X-rays. **2-D NMR** and **X-ray crystallography** are techniques that can be used to determine the structures of large molecules.

KEY TERMS

applied magnetic field (p. 554)
chemically equivalent protons (p. 558)
chemical shift (p. 560)
^{13}C NMR (p. 592)
COSY spectrum (p. 598)
coupled protons (p. 569)
coupling constant (J) (p. 579)
DEPT ^{13}C NMR spectrum (p. 597)
diamagnetic anisotropy (p. 565)
diamagnetic shielding (p. 557)
diastereotopic hydrogens (p. 585)
2-D NMR (p. 598)
doublet (p. 569)
doublet of doublets (p. 576)
downfield (p. 557)
effective magnetic field (p. 557)
enantiotopic hydrogens (p. 585)
Fourier transform NMR (FT–NMR)
    spectrum (p. 556)
geminal coupling (p. 576)

gyromagnetic ratio (p. 554)
HETCOR spectrum (p. 599)
heteronuclear coupling (p. 594)
^1H NMR (proton magnetic
    resonance) (p. 553)
homonuclear coupling (p. 594)
integration (p. 567)
leaning (p. 580)
long-range coupling (p. 572)
magnetic resonance imaging
    (MRI) (p. 600)
MRI scanner (p. 600)
multiplet (p. 575)
multiplicity (p. 569)
$N + 1$ rule (p. 569)
NMR spectrometer (p. 555)
NMR spectroscopy (p. 553)
NMR spectrum (p. 556)
nuclear magnetic resonance (p. 554)
operating frequency (p. 555)

prochiral carbon (p. 585)
pro-R-hydrogen (p. 585)
pro-S-hydrogen (p. 585)
proton-coupled ^{13}C NMR
    spectrum (p. 594)
proton exchange (p. 588)
quartet (p. 569)
reference compound (p. 560)
rf radiation (p. 554)
shielding (p. 556)
singlet (p. 569)
α-spin state (p. 553)
β-spin state (p. 553)
spin–spin coupling (p. 570)
splitting diagram (p. 583)
splitting tree (p. 583)
triplet (p. 569)
upfield (p. 557)
X-ray crystallography (p. 601)
X-ray diffraction (p. 603)

PROBLEMS

44. How many signals are produced by each of the following compounds in its
   a. ^1H NMR spectrum?
   b. ^{13}C NMR spectrum?

1. CH$_3$—⟨benzene ring⟩—OCHCH$_3$
          |
          CH$_3$

2. ⟨benzene ring⟩—C(=O)—OCH$_2$CH$_3$

3. ⟨ring with O and =O⟩

4. ⟨oxetane ring with O⟩

5. ⟨cyclopropane with Cl⟩

6. ⟨diene structure⟩

45. Draw a splitting diagram for the H$_b$ proton and give its multiplicity if
   a. $J_{ba} = J_{bc}$
   b. $J_{ba} = 2J_{bc}$

$$H_a—\overset{\displaystyle H_a}{\underset{\displaystyle H_a}{C}}—\overset{\displaystyle X}{\underset{\displaystyle H_b}{C}}—\overset{\displaystyle X}{\underset{\displaystyle H_c}{C}}—X$$

46. Label each set of chemically equivalent protons, using *a* for the set that will be at the lowest frequency (farthest upfield) in the ^{1}H NMR spectrum, *b* for the next lowest, and so on. Give the multiplicity of each signal.

a. CH$_3$CHNO$_2$
       |
      CH$_3$

b. CH$_3$CH$_2$CH$_2$OCH$_3$

c. CH$_3$CH—C(=O)—CH$_2$CH$_2$CH$_3$
       |
      CH$_3$

d. CH$_3$CH$_2$CH$_2$—C(=O)—CH$_2$Cl

e. ClCH$_2$CCHCl$_2$
with CH$_3$ above and CH$_3$ below the central C

f. ClCH$_2$CH$_2$CH$_2$CH$_2$CH$_2$Cl

47. Match each of the ^{1}H NMR spectra with one of the following compounds:

CH$_3$CH$_2$—C(=O)—CH$_3$ CH$_3$CNO$_2$ (with CH$_3$ above and CH$_3$ below)   CH$_3$CH$_2$—C(=O)—CH$_2$CH$_3$ CH$_3$CH$_2$CH$_2$NO$_2$ CH$_3$CH$_2$NO$_2$ CH$_3$CHBr (with CH$_3$ above)

a.

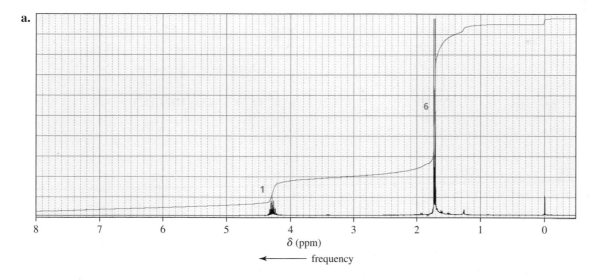

δ (ppm)

⟵ frequency

b.

δ (ppm)

⟵ frequency

c.

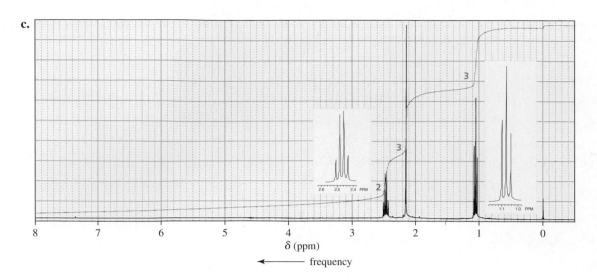

δ (ppm)

← frequency

48. Determine the ratios of the chemically nonequivalent protons in a compound if the steps of the integration curves measure 40.5, 27, 13, and 118 mm, from left to right across the spectrum. Give the structure of a compound whose ^{1}H NMR spectrum would show these integrals in the observed order.

49. How could ^{1}H NMR distinguish between the compounds in each of the following pairs?

a. $\sim\!\!\!\!\text{O}\!\!\sim$ and $\sim\!\!\text{O}\!\!\sim$

f. ⬡ and ⬡

b. Br$\sim\!\!\sim$Br and Br$\sim\!\!\sim$NO$_2$

g. CH$_3$CHCl and CH$_3$CDCl
          | |
         CH$_3$ CH$_3$

c. CH$_3$ CH$_3$
        | |
     CH$_3$CH—CHCH$_3$ and

        CH$_3$
        |
     CH$_3$CCH$_2$CH$_3$
        |
        CH$_3$

h. Cl   Cl
       | |
    H—┼—CH$_3$ and D—┼—CH$_3$
    D—┼—H   H—┼—H
       | |
       Cl   Cl

d. CH$_3$ O
        | ‖
     CH$_3$—C—C—OCH$_3$ and
        |
        CH$_3$

        OCH$_3$
        |
     CH$_3$—C—CH$_3$
        |
        OCH$_3$

i. H   H   H   Cl
       △   △
     Cl   Cl   and   Cl   H

e. CH$_3$O—⬡—CH$_2$CH$_3$ and CH$_3$—⬡—OCH$_2$CH$_3$

j. CH$_3$ CH$_3$
         | |
     CH$_3$—⬡—CCH$_3$ and ⬡—CH$_2$CCH$_3$
         | |
         CH$_3$ CH$_3$

50. Answer the following questions:
   a. What is the relationship between chemical shift in ppm and operating frequency?
   b. What is the relationship between chemical shift in hertz and operating frequency?
   c. What is the relationship between coupling constant and operating frequency?
   d. How does the operating frequency in NMR spectroscopy compare with the operating frequency in IR and UV/Vis spectroscopy?

51. The ^{1}H NMR spectra of three isomers with molecular formula C_4H_9Br are shown here. Which isomer produces which spectrum?

a.

b.

c.

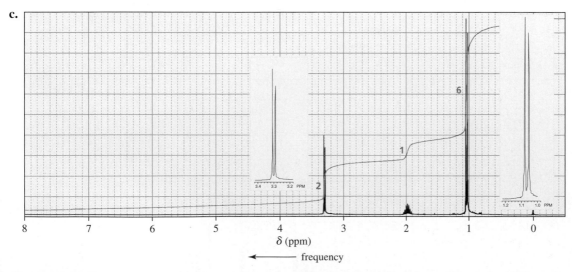

52. Identify each of the following compounds from the ^{1}H NMR data and molecular formula. The number of hydrogens responsible for each signal is shown in parentheses.

a. $C_4H_8Br_2$ 1.97 ppm (6) singlet
3.89 ppm (2) singlet

b. C_8H_9Br 2.01 ppm (3) doublet
5.14 ppm (1) quartet
7.35 ppm (5) broad singlet

c. $C_5H_{10}O_2$ 1.15 ppm (3) triplet
1.25 ppm (3) triplet
2.33 ppm (2) quartet
4.13 ppm (2) quartet

53. Identify the compound with molecular formula $C_7H_{14}O$ that gives the following proton-coupled ^{13}C NMR spectrum:

54. Compound A, with molecular formula C_4H_9Cl, shows two signals in its ^{13}C NMR spectrum. Compound B, an isomer of compound A, shows four signals, and in the proton-coupled mode, the signal farthest downfield is a doublet. Identify compounds A and B.

55. The ^1H NMR spectra of three isomers with molecular formula $C_7H_{14}O$ are shown here. Which isomer produces which spectrum?

a.

b.

c.

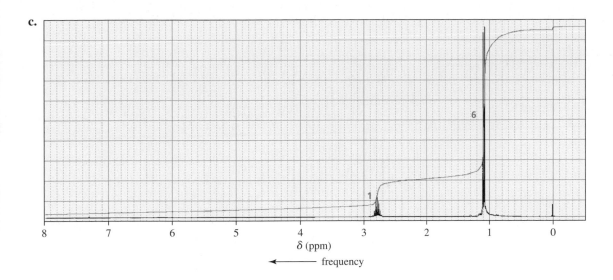

56. Would it be better to use ^{1}H NMR or ^{13}C NMR spectroscopy to distinguish between 1-butene, *cis*-2-butene, and 2-methylpropene? Explain your answer.

57. Determine the structure of each of the following unknown compounds based on its molecular formula and its IR and ^{1}H NMR spectra.

a. $C_5H_{12}O$

b. $C_6H_{12}O_2$

c. $C_4H_7ClO_2$

d. $C_4H_8O_2$

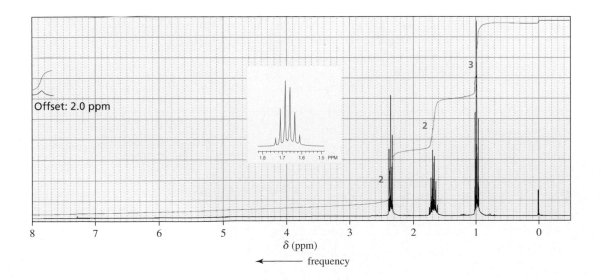

58. There are four esters with molecular formula $C_4H_8O_2$. How could they be distinguished by ^{1}H NMR?

59. An alkyl halide reacts with an alkoxide ion to form a compound whose ^1H NMR spectrum is shown here. Identify the alkyl halide and the alkoxide ion. (*Hint:* See Section 9.9.)

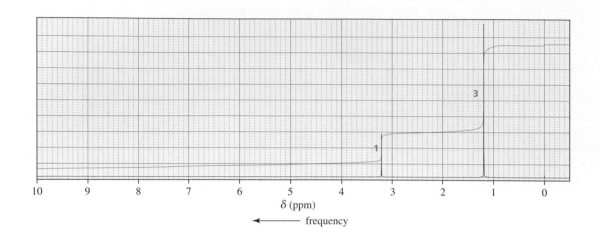

60. Determine the structure of each of the following compounds based on its molecular formula and its ^{13}C NMR spectrum:

a. $C_4H_{10}O$

b. $C_6H_{12}O$

61. The ^{1}H NMR spectrum of 2-propen-1-ol is shown here. Indicate the protons in the molecule that give rise to each of the signals in the spectrum.

62. How could the signals in the 6.5 to 8.1 ppm region of their ^{1}H NMR spectra distinguish the following compounds?

63. The ^{1}H NMR spectra of two compounds, each with molecular formula $C_{11}H_{16}$, are shown here. Identify the compounds.

a.

b.

64. Draw a splitting diagram for the H_b proton if $J_{bc} = 10$ and $J_{ba} = 5$.

$$\begin{array}{ccc}
Cl & & CH_2Cl \\
\diagdown & & \diagup \, a \\
& C{=}C & \\
\diagup & & \diagdown \\
H & & H \\
c & & b
\end{array}$$

65. Sketch the following spectra that would be obtained for 2-chloroethanol:
   a. The ^1H NMR spectrum for a dry sample of the alcohol.
   b. The ^1H NMR spectrum for a sample of the alcohol that contains a trace amount of acid.
   c. The ^{13}C NMR spectrum.
   d. The proton-coupled ^{13}C NMR spectrum.
   e. The four parts of a DEPT ^{13}C NMR spectrum.

66. How could ^1H NMR be used to prove that the addition of HBr to propene follows the rule that says that the electrophile adds to the sp^2 carbon bonded to the greater number of hydrogens?

67. Identify each of the following compounds from its molecular formula and its ^1H NMR spectrum.

   a. C_8H_8

   b. $C_6H_{12}O$

c. $C_9H_{18}O$

d. C_4H_8O

68. Dr. N. M. Arr was called in to help analyze the ^1H NMR spectrum of a mixture of compounds known to contain only C, H, and Br. The mixture showed two singlets—one at 1.8 ppm and the other at 2.7 ppm—with relative integrals of 1 : 6, respectively. Dr. Arr determined that the spectrum was that of a mixture of bromomethane and 2-bromo-2-methylpropane. What was the ratio of bromomethane to 2-bromo-2-methylpropane in the mixture?

69. Calculate the amount of energy (in calories) required to flip an ^1H nucleus in an NMR spectrometer that operates at 60 MHz.

70. The following ^1H NMR spectra are for four compounds each with molecular formula $C_6H_{12}O_2$. Identify the compounds.

a.

b.

c.

d.

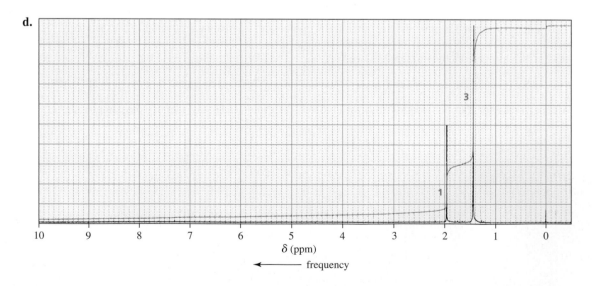

71. When compound A ($C_5H_{12}O$) is treated with HBr, it forms compound B ($C_5H_{11}Br$). The ^1H NMR spectrum of compound A has one singlet (1), two doublets (3, 6), and two multiplets (both 1). (The relative areas of the signals are indicated in parentheses.) The ^1H NMR spectrum of compound B has a singlet (6), a triplet (3), and a quartet (2). Identify compounds A and B.

72. Determine the structure of each of the following compounds, based on its molecular formula and its IR and ^{1}H NMR spectra.

a. $C_6H_{12}O$

b. $C_6H_{14}O$

c. $C_{10}H_{13}NO_3$

d. $C_{11}H_{14}O_2$

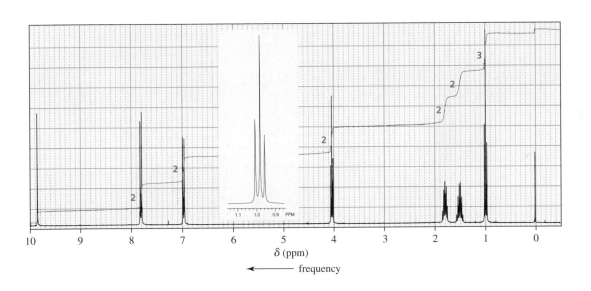

73. Determine the structure of each of the following compounds, based on the compound's mass spectrum, IR spectrum, and ^1H NMR spectrus.

a.

b.

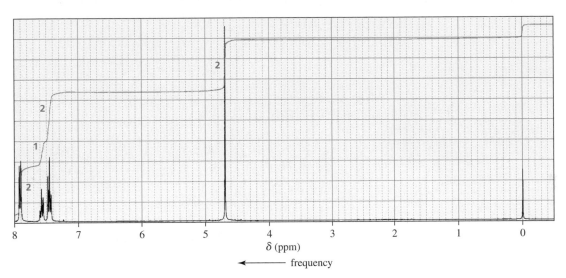

74. Identify the compound with molecular formula $C_6H_{10}O$ that is responsible for the following DEPT ^{13}C NMR spectrum:

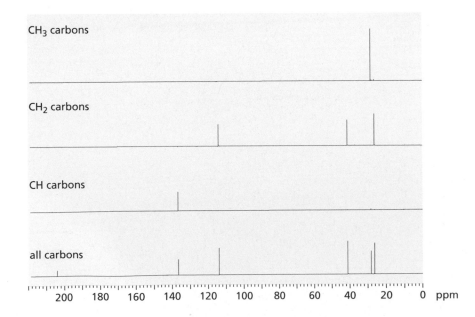

75. Identify the compound with molecular formula C_6H_{14} that is responsible for the following ^1H NMR spectrum:

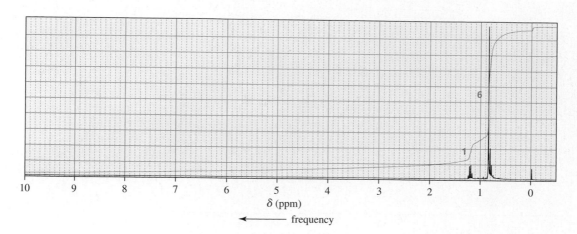

Aromatic Compounds

The two chapters in Part 5 deal with aromaticity and the reactions of aromatic compounds. Benzene is the most common aromatic compound. You learned about the structure of benzene in Chapter 7 and saw that it has a six-membered ring with three pairs of delocalized electrons. Now you will find out what the criteria are that a compound must meet to be classified as aromatic, and you will see the kinds of reactions that aromatic compounds undergo. Later, in Chapter 21, you will look at the reactions of aromatic compounds in which one of the ring atoms is an atom other than a carbon.

CHAPTER 15
Aromaticity • Reactions of Benzene

Chapter 15 starts with an examination of the structural features that cause a compound to be aromatic, as well as the features that cause a compound to be antiaromatic. It then explores the reactions that benzene undergoes. You will see that although benzene, alkenes, and dienes are all nucleophiles (because they have carbon–carbon π bonds), benzene's aromaticity causes it to react in a way that is quite different from the way alkenes and dienes react.

CHAPTER 16
Reactions of Substituted Benzenes

Chapter 16 focuses on the reactions of substituted benzenes. First you will see some reactions that change the substituent on a benzene ring. Then you will see how a substituent affects both the reactivity of a benzene ring and the placement of an incoming substituent. Chapter 16 also describes three types of reactions that can be used to synthesize substituted benzenes other than the reactions discussed in Chapter 15: reactions of arene diazonium salts, nucleophilic aromatic substitution reactions, and reactions that involve benzyne intermediates. You will also see that certain aromatic hydrocarbons are carcinogenic and how carcinogenicity is related to carbocation stability.

15

Aromaticity • Reactions of Benzene

Benzene

Pyrrole

Pyridine

THE COMPOUND WE KNOW AS BENZENE WAS FIRST ISOLATED IN 1825 BY MICHAEL Faraday. He extracted it from the liquid residue obtained after heating whale oil under pressure to produce the gas then being used to illuminate buildings in London.

In 1834, Eilhardt Mitscherlich correctly determined the molecular formula (C_6H_6) of Faraday's compound and named it benzin because of its relationship to benzoic acid, a known substituted form of the compound (Section 15.8). Later the name was changed to benzene.

Compounds like benzene that have relatively few hydrogens in relation to the number of carbons, are typically found in oils produced by trees and other plants. Early chemists called such compounds **aromatic compounds** because of their pleasing sweet fragrances. In this way, they were distinguished from **aliphatic compounds**, which have higher hydrogen-to-carbon ratios. Today, chemists use the word "aromatic" to signify certain kinds of chemical structures. We will look at the features that cause a compound to be classified as aromatic in Section 15.2.

15.1 AROMATIC COMPOUNDS ARE UNUSUALLY STABLE

In Chapter 7, we saw that benzene is a planar, cyclic compound with two cyclic clouds of delocalized π electrons. Because its π electrons are delocalized, all the C—C bonds in benzene have the same length, shorter than a typical single bond but longer than a typical double bond (Section 7.2).

benzene

electrostatic potential
map for benzene

BIOGRAPHY
Eilhardt Mitscherlich (1794–1863)
*was born in Germany. He studied
oriental languages at the University of Heidelberg and the Sorbonne,
where he concentrated on Farsi,
hoping to be included in a delegation Napoleon intended to send to
Persia. That ambition died with
Napoleon's defeat. After returning
to Germany to study science, and
simultaneously receiving a doctorate in Persian studies, Mitscherlich
became a professor of chemistry at
the University of Berlin. (See also
p. 227.)*

Benzene is a particularly stable compound because it has an unusually large delocalization energy. Most compounds with delocalized electrons have much smaller delocalization energies. Recall that delocalization energy (also called resonance energy) tells us how much more stable a compound with delocalized electrons is than it would be if all its electrons were localized (Section 7.6). Therefore, we can determine benzene's delocalization energy by comparing the stability of benzene—a compound with three pairs of delocalized π electrons—with the stability of "cyclohexatriene," an unknown, hypothetical compound with three localized π bonds.

The $\Delta H°$ for the hydrogenation of cyclohexene, a compound with one localized double bond, has been determined experimentally to be -28.6 kcal/mol. We would therefore expect the $\Delta H°$ for the hydrogenation of "cyclohexatriene," with three localized double bonds, to be three times that much, or $3 \times (-28.6) = -85.8$ kcal/mol (Section 4.12).

cyclohexene + H$_2$ $\xrightarrow{\text{Pd/C}}$ $\Delta H° = -28.6$ kcal/mol (–120 kJ/mol)
experimental

"cyclohexatriene"
hypothetical + 3 H$_2$ $\xrightarrow{\text{Pd/C}}$ $\Delta H° = -85.8$ kcal/mol (–359 kJ/mol)
calculated

When the $\Delta H°$ for the hydrogenation of benzene was determined experimentally, it was found to be -49.8 kcal/mol, much less than that calculated for hypothetical "cyclohexatriene."

benzene + 3 H$_2$ $\xrightarrow[\text{250 °C, 25 atm}]{\text{Pd/C}}$ $\Delta H° = -49.8$ kcal/mol (–208 kJ/mol)
experimental

Because the hydrogenation of "cyclohexatriene" and the hydrogenation of benzene both form cyclohexane, the difference in the $\Delta H°$ values can be accounted for by the difference in the energies of "cyclohexatriene" and benzene. Figure 15.1 shows that benzene must be 36 kcal/mol (or 151 kJ/mole) more stable than "cyclohexatriene" because the experimental $\Delta H°$ for the hydrogenation of benzene is 36 kcal/mol less than that calculated for "cyclohexatriene."

► Figure 15.1
The difference in energy between "cyclohexatriene" and benzene. Benzene is more stable, so it releases less heat when it is hydrogenated.

We can conclude from their different energies that benzene and "cyclohexatriene" are different compounds, although the only difference in their structures is that benzene has six delocalized π electrons and "cyclohexatriene" has six localized π electrons. The difference in their energies (36 kcal/mol) is the *delocalization energy* of benzene—the extra stability a compound has as a result of having delocalized electrons. This is an unusually large delocalization energy.

Aromatic compounds are particularly stable.

Compounds with unusually large resonance energies, like benzene, are called **aromatic compounds**. Now we can understand why nineteenth-century chemists, who did not know about delocalized electrons, were puzzled by benzene's unusual stability (Section 7.1).

15.2 THE TWO CRITERIA FOR AROMATICITY

How can we tell whether a compound is aromatic by looking at its structure? In other words, what structural features do aromatic compounds have in common? To be classified as aromatic, a compound must meet both of the following criteria:

For a compound to be aromatic, it must be cyclic and planar and have an uninterrupted cloud of π electrons. The π cloud must contain an odd number of pairs of π electrons.

1. *It must have an uninterrupted cyclic cloud of π electrons* (called a π cloud) *above and below the plane of the molecule.* Let's look a little more closely at what this means:
For the π cloud to be cyclic, *the molecule must be cyclic.*
For the π cloud to be uninterrupted, *every atom in the ring must have a p orbital.*
For the π cloud to form, each *p* orbital must overlap with the *p* orbitals on either side of it. Therefore, *the molecule must be planar.*

2. *The π cloud must contain an odd number of pairs of π electrons.*

Therefore, benzene is an aromatic compound because it is cyclic and planar, every carbon in the ring has a *p* orbital, and the π cloud contains *three* pairs of π electrons (Figure 15.2).

► Figure 15.2
(a) Each carbon of benzene has a *p* orbital.
(b) The overlap of the *p* orbitals forms a cloud of π electrons above and below the plane of the benzene ring.
(c) The electrostatic potential map for benzene.

a.

b.

c.

The German physicist Erich Hückel was the first to recognize that an aromatic compound must have an odd number of pairs of π electrons. In 1931, he described this requirement in what has come to be known as **Hückel's rule**, or the **4*n* + 2 rule**. The rule states that for a planar, cyclic compound to be aromatic, its uninterrupted π cloud must contain (4*n* + 2) π electrons, where *n* is any whole number. According to Hückel's rule, then, an aromatic compound must have 2 (*n* = 0), 6 (*n* = 1), 10 (*n* = 2), 14 (*n* = 3), 18 (*n* = 4), and so on π electrons. Because there are two electrons in a pair, Hückel's rule requires that an aromatic compound have 1, 3, 5, 7, 9 and so on pairs of π electrons. Thus, Hückel's rule is just a mathematical way of saying that an aromatic compound must have an *odd* number of pairs of π electrons.

PROBLEM 1 ◆

a. What is the value of *n* in Hückel's rule when a compound has nine pairs of π electrons?
b. Is such a compound aromatic?

15.3 APPLYING THE CRITERIA FOR AROMATICITY

Monocyclic hydrocarbons with alternating single and double bonds are called **annulenes**. A prefix in brackets denotes the number of carbons in the ring. Cyclobutadiene, benzene, and cyclooctatetraene are examples of annulenes.

cyclobutadiene
[4]-annulene

benzene
[6]-annulene

cyclooctatetraene
[8]-annulene

Cyclobutadiene has two pairs of π electrons, and cyclooctatetraene has four pairs of π electrons. Unlike benzene, these compounds are *not* aromatic because they have an *even* number of pairs of π electrons. There is an additional reason why cyclooctatetraene is not aromatic—it is not planar, it is tub-shaped. (See page 283). Earlier, we saw that, for an eight-membered ring to be planar, it must have bond angles of 135° (Chapter 2, Problem 37), and we know that sp^2 carbons have 120° bond angles. Therefore, if cyclooctatetraene were planar, it would have considerable angle strain. Because cyclobutadiene and cyclooctatetraene are not aromatic, they do not have the unusual stability of aromatic compounds.

Now let's look at some other compounds and determine whether they are aromatic. Cyclopentadiene is not aromatic because it does not have an uninterrupted ring of p orbital-bearing atoms. One of its ring atom is sp^3 hybridized, and only sp^2 and sp carbons have p orbitals. Therefore, cyclopentadiene does not fulfill the first criterion for aromaticity.

cyclopentadiene

cyclopentadienyl
cation

cyclopentadienyl
anion

The cyclopentadienyl cation also is not aromatic because, although it has an uninterrupted ring of p orbital-bearing atoms, its π cloud has *two* (an even number) pairs of π electrons. The cyclopentadienyl anion is aromatic: it has an uninterrupted ring of p orbital-bearing atoms, and the π cloud contains *three* (an odd number) pairs of delocalized π electrons.

Notice that the cyclopentadienyl anion's lone-pair electrons form a π bond in the resonance contributors. Thus, they are π electrons. The resonance hybrid shows that all the carbons in the cyclopentadienyl anion are equivalent. Each carbon has exactly one-fifth of the negative charge associated with the anion.

resonance contributors of the cyclopentadienyl anion

resonance hybrid

BIOGRAPHY

Erich Hückel (1896–1980) *was born in Berlin. After receiving a Ph.D. in experimental physics from the University of Göttingen, he went to the Federal Institute of Technology in Zurich to work with Peter Debye (page 12), where they developed the Debye-Hückel theory to describe the behavior of strong electrolytes in solution. Hückel received an appointment in chemical physics at the Technical Institute in Stuttgart. Later he became a professor of theoretical physics at the University of Marburg.*

The criteria that determine whether a monocyclic hydrocarbon is aromatic can also be used to determine whether a polycyclic hydrocarbon is aromatic. Naphthalene (five pairs of π electrons), phenanthrene (seven pairs of π electrons), and chrysene (nine pairs of π electrons) are aromatic.

naphthalene   **phenanthrene**   **chrysene**

Buckyballs and AIDS

Diamond and graphite are two familiar forms of pure carbon (Section 1.8). A third form was discovered unexpectedly in 1985, while scientists were conducting experiments designed to understand how long-chain molecules are formed in outer space. R. E. Smalley, R. F. Curl, Jr., and H. W. Kroto shared the 1996 Nobel Prize in Chemistry for discovering this new form of carbon. They named the substance buckminsterfullerene (often shortened to fullerene) because its structure reminded them of the geodesic domes popularized by R. Buckminster Fuller, an American architect and philosopher. Buckminsterfullerene's nickname is "buckyball."

Consisting of a hollow cluster of 60 carbons, fullerene is the most symmetrical large molecule known. Like graphite, fullerene has only sp^2 carbons, but instead of being arranged in layers, the carbons are arranged in rings that fit together like the seams of a soccer ball. Each molecule has 32 interlocking rings (20 hexagons and 12 pentagons). At first glance, fullerene would appear to be aromatic because of its benzene-like rings. However, the curvature of the ball prevents the molecule from fulfilling the first criterion for aromaticity—that it be planar. Therefore, fullerene is not aromatic.

Buckyballs have extraordinary chemical and physical properties. For example, they are exceedingly rugged, as shown by their ability to survive the extreme temperatures of outer space. Because they are essentially hollow cages, they can be manipulated to make materials never before known. For example, when a buckyball is "doped" by inserting potassium or cesium into its cavity, it becomes an excellent organic superconductor. These molecules are now being studied for use in many other applications, including the development of new polymers, catalysts, and drug delivery systems. The discovery of buckyballs is a strong reminder of the technological advances that can be achieved as a result of basic research.

Scientists have even turned to buckyballs in the quest for a cure for AIDS. An enzyme that the AIDS virus needs in order to reproduce has a nonpolar pocket in its three-dimensional structure. If this pocket is blocked, the production of the virus ceases. Because buckyballs are nonpolar and have approximately the same diameter as the pocket of the enzyme, they are being considered as possible blockers. The first step in exploring this possibility was to equip the buckyball with polar side chains to make it water soluble so that it could flow through the blood-

C₆₀
buckminsterfullerene
"buckyball"

a geodesic dome

stream. The next step was to modify the side chains so they would bind to the enzyme. This project is still a long way from providing a cure for AIDS, but it represents one example of the many and varied approaches that scientists are taking to find such a cure.

Richard E. Smalley (1943–2005) *was born in Akron, Ohio. He received a B.S. from the University of Michigan and a Ph.D. from Princeton University. He was a professor of chemistry and physics at Rice University.*

Robert F. Curl, Jr. *was born in Texas in 1933. He received a B.A. from Rice University and a Ph.D. from the University of California, Berkeley. He is a professor of chemistry at Rice University.*

Sir Harold W. Kroto *was born in 1939 in England, was a professor of chemistry at the University of Sussex, and now is a professor of chemistry at Florida State University.*

PROBLEM 2

a. Draw arrows to show the movement of electrons in going from one resonance contributor to the next in the cyclopentadienyl anion.
b. How many ring atoms share the negative charge?

PROBLEM 3 ♦

Which compound in each set is aromatic? Explain your choice.

a.

cyclopropene   cyclopropenyl   cyclopropenyl
                         cation   anion

b.

cycloheptatriene   cycloheptatrienyl   cycloheptatrienyl
                          cation   anion

PROBLEM 4 ♦

Which of the following are aromatic?

a.

b.

c.

d.

e.

f. $CH_2{=}CHCH{=}CHCH{=}CH_2$

PROBLEM 5 ♦   SOLVED

a. How many monobromonaphthalenes are there?
b. How many monobromophenanthrenes are there?

Solution to 5a   There are two monobromonaphthalenes. Substitution cannot occur at either of the carbons shared by both rings, because those carbons are not bonded to a hydrogen. Naphthalene is a flat molecule, so substitution for a hydrogen at any other carbon will result in one of the compounds shown.

PROBLEM 6

The [10]- and [12]-annulenes have been synthesized, and neither has been found to be aromatic. Explain.

chem Tutorial:
place Aromaticity

15.4 AROMATIC HETEROCYCLIC COMPOUNDS

A compound does not have to be a hydrocarbon to be aromatic. Many *heterocyclic compounds* are aromatic. A **heterocyclic compound** is a cyclic compound in which one or more of the ring atoms is an atom other than carbon. The atom that is not carbon is called a **heteroatom**. The name comes from the Greek word *heteros,* which means "different." The most common heteroatoms are N, O, and S.

benzene

pyridine

pyrrole

heterocyclic compounds

pyridine   pyrrole   furan   thiophene

Pyridine is an aromatic heterocyclic compound. Each of the six ring atoms of pyridine is sp^2 hybridized, which means that each has a p orbital, and the molecule contains three pairs of π electrons. (Do not be confused by the lone-pair electrons on the nitrogen; they are not π electrons.) Because nitrogen is sp^2 hybridized, it has three sp^2 orbitals and a p orbital. The p orbital is used to form the π bond. Two of nitrogen's sp^2 orbitals overlap the sp^2 orbitals of adjacent carbons, and its third sp^2 orbital contains the lone pair.

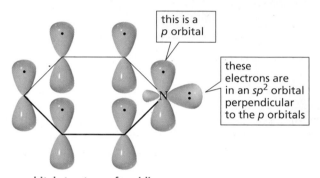

this is a p orbital

these electrons are in an sp^2 orbital perpendicular to the p orbitals

orbital structure of pyridine

PROBLEM 7♦

What orbital do the lone-pair electrons occupy in each of the following compounds?

a. $CH_3CH_3\ddot{N}H_2$ **b.** —CH≡$\ddot{N}CH_2CH_3$ **c.** $CH_3CH_2C≡N:$

It is not immediately apparent that the lone-pair electrons on the nitrogen atom of pyrrole are π electrons. The resonance contributors, however, show that lone-pair electrons form a π bond; thus, they are π electrons. The nitrogen atom is sp^2 hybridized. Thus, it has three sp^2 orbitals and a p orbital. It uses its three sp^2 orbitals to bond to two carbons and one hydrogen. The lone-pair electrons are in the p orbital that overlaps the p orbitals of adjacent carbons. Pyrrole, therefore, has three pairs of π electrons and is aromatic.

resonance contributors of pyrrole

these electrons are in a p orbital

these electrons are in a p orbital

these electrons are in an sp^2 orbital perpendicular to the p orbitals

orbital structure of pyrrole   **orbital structure of furan**

PROBLEM 8

a. Draw arrows to show the movement of electrons in going from one resonance contributor to the next in pyrrole.

b. How many ring atoms share the negative charge?

Similarly, furan and thiophene are stable aromatic compounds. Both the oxygen in furan and the sulfur in thiophene are sp^2 hybridized and have one lone pair in an sp^2 orbital. The orbital picture of furan on page 630 shows that the second lone pair is in a *p* orbital that overlaps the *p* orbitals of adjacent carbons, forming a π bond. Thus, they are π electrons.

resonance contributors of furan

Quinoline, indole, imidazole, purine, and pyrimidine are other examples of heterocyclic aromatic compounds. The heterocyclic compounds discussed in this section will be examined in greater detail in Chapter 21.

quinoline   **indole**   **imidazole**   **purine**   **pyrimidine**

PROBLEM 9 ♦

What orbitals contain the electrons represented as lone pairs in the structures of quinoline, indole, imidazole, purine, and pyrimidine?

PROBLEM 10 ♦

Which of the following compounds could be protonated without destroying its aromaticity?

A   **B**   **C**   **D**

PROBLEM 11

Refer to the electrostatic potential maps on page 630 to answer the following questions:

a. Why is the bottom part of the electrostatic potential map of pyrrole blue?

b. Why is the bottom part of the electrostatic potential map of pyridine red?

c. Why is the center of the electrostatic potential map of benzene more red than the center of the electrostatic potential map of pyridine?

15.5 SOME CHEMICAL CONSEQUENCES OF AROMATICITY

The pK_a of cyclopentadiene is 15, which is extraordinarily acidic for a hydrogen that is bonded to an sp^3 hybridized carbon. Ethane, for example, has a $pK_a > 60$.

cyclopentadiene
$pK_a = 15$

cyclopentadienyl anion

$$CH_3CH_3 \rightleftharpoons CH_3\overset{..}{C}H_2 + H^+$$
ethane $\qquad$ ethyl anion
$pK_a > 60$

chem Tutorial:
place Aromaticity and acidity

Why is the pK_a of cyclopentadiene so much lower than that of ethane? To answer this question, we must look at the stabilities of the anions that are formed when the compounds lose a proton. (Recall that the strength of an acid is determined by the stability of its conjugate base: the more stable its conjugate base, the stronger is the acid; see Section 1.21.) All the electrons in the ethyl anion are localized. In contrast, the anion formed when cyclopentadiene loses a proton is aromatic (Section 15.2). As a result of its aromaticity, the cyclopentadienyl anion is an unusually stable carbanion. Thus, its conjugate acid has an unusually low pK_a.

Another example of the influence of aromaticity on a chemical property is the unusual chemical behavior exhibited by cycloheptatrienyl bromide. Recall from Section 2.9 that alkyl halides tend to be relatively nonpolar covalent compounds—they are soluble in nonpolar solvents and *insoluble in water*. Cycloheptatrienyl bromide, however, is an alkyl halide that behaves like an ionic compound—it is insoluble in nonpolar solvents, but is readily *soluble in water*.

covalent
cycloheptatrienyl bromide

ionic
cycloheptatrienyl bromide
tropylium bromide

Cycloheptatrienyl bromide is an ionic compound because its cation is aromatic. The alkyl halide is *not* aromatic in the covalent form because it has an sp^3 hybridized carbon and therefore does *not* have an uninterrupted ring of p orbital-bearing atoms. However, the cycloheptatrienyl cation (also known as the tropylium cation) *is* aromatic: it is a planar cyclic ion, all the ring atoms are sp^2 hybridized (which means that each ring atom has a p orbital), and it has three pairs of delocalized π electrons. The stability associated with the aromatic cation causes the alkyl halide to exist in the ionic form.

PROBLEM 12 | **SOLVED**

a. Draw arrows to show the movement of electrons in going from one resonance contributor to the next in the cycloheptatrienyl cation.
b. How many ring atoms share the positive charge?

Solution to 12a

Solution to 12b All seven ring atoms share the positive charge.

PROBLEM-SOLVING STRATEGY

Analyzing Electron Distribution in Compounds
Which of the following compounds has the greater dipole moment?

We know that the dipole moment of these compounds results from the unequal sharing of electrons by carbon and oxygen. Therefore, the more unequal the sharing, the greater will be the dipole moment. So now the question becomes, which compound has a greater negative charge on its oxygen atom? To find out, we need to draw the structures with separated charges and determine their relative stabilities. The three-membered ring in the compound on the left becomes aromatic when the charges are separated, but the structure on the right does not. Because being aromatic makes a species more stable, the compound on the left has the greater charge separation and, therefore, the greater dipole moment.

Now continue on to Problem 13.

PROBLEM 13

a. In what direction is the dipole moment in fulvene? Explain.
b. In what direction is the dipole moment in calicene? Explain.

fulvene   **calicene**

15.6 ANTIAROMATICITY

An aromatic compound is *more stable* than an analogous cyclic compound with localized electrons. In contrast, an **antiaromatic compound** is *less stable* than an analogous cyclic compound with localized electrons. *Aromaticity is characterized by stability, whereas antiaromaticity is characterized by instability.*

Antiaromatic compounds are highly unstable.

relative stabilities

aromatic compound > cyclic compound with localized electrons > antiaromatic compound

increasing stability

A compound is classified as being antiaromatic if it fulfills the first criterion for aromaticity but does not fulfill the second. In other words, it must be a planar, cyclic compound with an uninterrupted ring of p orbital-bearing atoms, and the π cloud must contain an *even* number of pairs of π electrons. Hückel would state that the π cloud must contain $4n$ π electrons, where n is any whole number—a mathematical way of saying that the cloud must contain an *even* number of pairs of π electrons.

Cyclobutadiene is a planar, cyclic molecule with two pairs of π electrons. Hence, it is expected to be antiaromatic and highly unstable. In fact, it is too unstable to be isolated, although it has been trapped at very cold temperatures. The cyclopentadienyl cation also has two pairs of π electrons, so we can conclude that it, too, is antiaromatic and unstable.

cyclobutadiene   cyclopentadienyl
cation

PROBLEM 14 ◆

a. Predict the relative pK_a values of cyclopentadiene and cycloheptatriene.
b. Predict the relative pK_a values of cyclopropene and cyclopropane.

PROBLEM 15 ◆

Which is more soluble in water, 3-bromocyclopropene or bromocyclopropane?

PROBLEM 16 ◆

Which of the compounds in Problem 4 are antiaromatic?

15.7 A MOLECULAR ORBITAL DESCRIPTION OF AROMATICITY AND ANTIAROMATICITY

Why are planar molecules with uninterrupted cyclic π electron clouds highly stable (aromatic) if they have an odd number of pairs of π electrons and highly unstable (antiaromatic) if they have an even number of pairs of π electrons? To answer this question, we must turn to molecular orbital theory.

The relative energies of the π molecular orbitals of a planar molecule with an uninterrupted cyclic π electron cloud can be determined—without having to use any math—by first drawing the cyclic compound with one of its vertices pointed down. The relative energies of the π molecular orbitals can be thought of as corresponding to the relative levels of the vertices (Figure 15.3). Molecular orbitals below the midpoint of the cyclic structure are bonding molecular orbitals, those above the midpoint are antibonding molecular orbitals, and any at the midpoint are nonbonding molecular orbitals. This

▲ **Figure 15.3**
The distribution of electrons in the π molecular orbitals of (a) benzene, (b) the cyclopentadienyl anion, (c) the cyclopentadienyl cation, and (d) cyclobutadiene. The relative energies of the π molecular orbitals in a cyclic compound correspond to the relative levels of the vertices. Molecular orbitals below the midpoint of the cyclic structure are bonding, those above the midpoint are antibonding, and those at the midpoint are nonbonding.

simple scheme is sometimes called a Frost device (or a Frost circle) in honor of Arthur A. Frost, the scientist who devised it. Notice that the number of π molecular orbitals is the same as the number of atoms in the ring because each ring atom contributes a p orbital. (Recall that orbitals are conserved; see Section 1.6.)

The six π electrons of benzene occupy its three bonding π molecular orbitals, and the six π electrons of the cyclopentadienyl anion occupy its three bonding π molecular orbitals. Notice that there is always an odd number of bonding molecular orbitals because one corresponds to the lowest vertex and the others come in degenerate pairs. Consequently, aromatic compounds—such as benzene and the cyclopentadienyl anion, with their odd number of pairs of π electrons—have completely filled bonding orbitals and no electrons in either nonbonding or antibonding orbitals. This is what gives aromatic molecules their stability. (A more detailed description of the molecular orbitals in benzene was given in Section 7.8.)

Antiaromatic compounds have an even number of pairs of π electrons. Therefore, either they are unable to fill their bonding orbitals (cylopentadienyl cation) or they have a pair of π electrons left over after the bonding orbitals are filled (cyclobutadiene). Hund's rule requires that these two electrons go into two different degenerate orbitals (Section 1.2).

Aromatic compounds are stable because they have filled bonding π molecular orbitals.

PROBLEM 17◆

How many bonding, nonbonding, and antibonding π molecular orbitals does cyclobutadiene have? In which molecular orbitals are the π electrons?

PROBLEM 18◆

Can a radical be aromatic?

PROBLEM 19

Following the instructions for drawing the π molecular orbital energy levels of the compounds shown in Figure 15.3, draw the π molecular orbital energy levels for the cycloheptatrienyl cation, the cycloheptatrienyl anion, and the cyclopropenyl cation. For each compound, show the distribution of the π electrons. Which of the compounds are aromatic? Which are antiaromatic?

chem place Tutorial: Molecular orbital description of aromaticity

15.8 THE NOMENCLATURE OF MONOSUBSTITUTED BENZENES

Some monosubstituted benzenes are named simply by adding the name of the substituent to "benzene."

bromobenzene   chlorobenzene   nitrobenzene used as a solvent in shoe polish   ethylbenzene

Some monosubstituted benzenes have names that incorporate the substituent. Unfortunately, such names have to be memorized.

toluene   phenol   aniline   benzenesulfonic acid

anisole   styrene   benzaldehyde   benzoic acid   benzonitrile

When a benzene ring is a substituent, it is called a **phenyl group**. A benzene ring with a methylene group is called a **benzyl group**.

a phenyl group   a benzyl group

chloromethylbenzene
benzyl chloride   diphenyl ether   dibenzyl ether

With the exception of toluene, benzene rings with an alkyl substituent are named as alkyl-substituted benzenes (when the alkyl substituent has a name), or as phenyl-substituted alkanes (when the alkyl substituent does not have a name).

isopropylbenzene
cumene   *sec*-butylbenzene   *tert*-butylbenzene   2-phenylpentane   3-phenylpentane

Aryl group (Ar) is the general term for either a phenyl group or a substituted phenyl group, just as alkyl group (R) is the general term for a group derived from an alkane. In other words, ArOH could be used to designate any of the following phenols:

The Toxicity of Benzene

Benzene, which has been widely used in chemical synthesis and has been frequently used as a solvent, is a toxic substance. The major adverse effects of chronic exposure are seen in the central nervous system and bone marrow; it causes leukemia and aplastic anemia. A higher than average incidence of leukemia has been found in industrial workers with long-term exposure to as little as 1 ppm benzene in the atmosphere. Toluene has replaced benzene as a solvent because, although it too is a central nervous system depressant, it does not cause leukemia or aplastic anemia. "Glue sniffing," a highly dangerous activity, produces narcotic central nervous system effects because glue contains toluene.

PROBLEM 20♦

Draw the structure of each of the following:

a. 2-phenylhexane   **c.** 3-benzylpentane
b. benzyl alcohol   **d.** bromomethylbenzene

15.9 HOW BENZENE REACTS

Aromatic compounds such as benzene undergo **electrophilic aromatic substitution reactions**: an electrophile substitutes for one of the hydrogens attached to the benzene ring.

Now let's look at why this substitution reaction occurs. The cloud of π electrons above and below the plane of its ring causes benzene to be a nucleophile. It will, therefore, react with an electrophile (Y^+). When an electrophile attaches itself to a benzene ring, a carbocation intermediate is formed.

carbocation
intermediate

This description should remind you of the first step in an *electrophilic addition reaction* of an alkene: the nucleophilic alkene reacts with an electrophile and forms a carbocation intermediate (Section 3.6). In the second step of the reaction, the carbocation reacts with a nucleophile (Z^-) to form an addition product.

carbocation
intermediate

product of electrophilic
addition

If the carbocation intermediate that is formed from the reaction of benzene with an electrophile were to react similarly with a nucleophile (depicted as path *a* in Figure 15.4), the *addition product* would not be aromatic. But if the carbocation instead were to lose a proton from the site of electrophilic attack and form a *substitution product* (depicted as path *b* in Figure 15.4), the aromaticity of the benzene ring would be restored.

product of
electrophilic addition

a nonaromatic
compound

carbocation
intermediate

product of
electrophilic substitution

an aromatic
compound

◀ **Figure 15.4**
Reaction of benzene with an electrophile. Because of the greater stability of the aromatic product, the reaction is an electrophilic substitution reaction (b) rather than an electrophilic addition reaction (a).

Because the aromatic substitution product is much more stable than the nonaromatic addition product (Figure 15.5), benzene undergoes *electrophilic substitution reactions* that preserve aromaticity, rather than *electrophilic addition reactions*—the reactions characteristic of alkenes—that would destroy aromaticity. The substitution reaction is more accurately called an **electrophilic aromatic substitution reaction**, since the electrophile substitutes for a hydrogen of an aromatic compound.

► **Figure 15.5**
Reaction coordinate diagrams for reactions of benzene: electrophilic aromatic substitution *versus* electrophilic addition.

PROBLEM 21

If electrophilic addition to benzene is overall an endergonic reaction, how can electrophilic addition to an alkene be overall an exergonic reaction?

15.10 THE GENERAL MECHANISM FOR ELECTROPHILIC AROMATIC SUBSTITUTION REACTIONS

In an electrophilic aromatic substitution reaction, an electrophile becomes attached to a ring carbon and an H^+ comes off the same ring carbon.

an electrophilic aromatic substitution reaction

The following are the five most common electrophilic aromatic substitution reactions:

1. **Halogenation**: A bromine (Br), a chlorine (Cl), or an iodine (I) substitutes for a hydrogen.
2. **Nitration**: A nitro group (NO_2) substitutes for a hydrogen.
3. **Sulfonation**: A sulfonic acid group (SO_3H) substitutes for a hydrogen.
4. **Friedel–Crafts acylation**: An acyl group ($RC=O$) substitutes for a hydrogen.
5. **Friedel–Crafts alkylation**: An alkyl group (R) substitutes for a hydrogen.

All of these reactions take place by the same two-step mechanism.

GENERAL MECHANISM FOR ELECTROPHILIC AROMATIC SUBSTITUTION

the proton is removed from the carbon that has formed the bond with the electrophile

a base in the reaction mixture

- Benzene reacts with an electrophile (Y^+) forming a carbocation intermediate. The structure of the carbocation intermediate can be approximated by three resonance contributors.

- A base in the reaction mixture (:B) pulls off a proton from the carbocation intermediate, and the electrons that held the proton move into the ring to reestablish its aromaticity. Notice that *the proton is always removed from the carbon that has formed the bond with the electrophile.*

The first step is relatively slow and endergonic because an aromatic compound is being converted into a much less stable nonaromatic intermediate (Figure 15.5). The second step is fast and strongly exergonic because this step restores the stability-enhancing aromaticity.

We will look at each of these five electrophilic aromatic substitution reactions individually. As you study them, notice that they differ only in how the electrophile (Y^+) needed to start the reaction is generated. Once the electrophile is formed, all five reactions follow the same two-step mechanism for electrophilic aromatic substitution.

chem place Tutorial:
Electrophilic aromatic substitution

15.11 THE HALOGENATION OF BENZENE

The bromination or chlorination of benzene requires a Lewis acid catalyst such as ferric bromide or ferric chloride. Recall that a *Lewis acid* is a compound that accepts a share in an electron pair (Section 1.27).

bromination

bromobenzene

chlorination

chlorobenzene

Why does the reaction of benzene with Br_2 or Cl_2 require a catalyst when the reaction of an alkene with these reagents does not require a catalyst? Benzene's aromaticity makes it much more stable and therefore much less reactive than an alkene. Thus, benzene requires a better electrophile. Donating a lone pair to the Lewis acid weakens the Br—Br (or Cl—Cl) bond and thus makes Br_2 (or Cl_2) a better electrophile.

generation of the electrophile

| an electrophile | a better electrophile |

MECHANISM FOR BROMINATION

- The electrophile attaches to the benzene ring.
- A base (:B) in the reaction mixture (such as $^-FeBr_4$ or the solvent) removes the proton from the carbon that formed the bond with the electrophile.
- The catalyst is regenerated.

For the sake of clarity, only one of the three resonance contributors of the carbocation intermediate is shown in this and subsequent mechanisms for electrophilic aromatic substitution reactions. Bear in mind, however, that each carbocation intermediate actually has the three resonance contributors shown in Section 15.10.

Chlorination of benzene occurs by the same mechanism as bromination.

MECHANISM FOR CHLORINATION

The ferric bromide and ferric chloride catalysts react readily with moisture in the air during handling, which inactivates them. To avoid this problem, they are generated in situ (in the reaction mixture) by using iron filings and bromine (or chlorine). Therefore, the halogen component of the Lewis acid will be the same as the halogen reagent.

chem
place Tutorial:
The bromination of benzene 1

Tutorial:
The bromination of benzene 2

Tutorial:
The bromination of benzene 3

$$2\ Fe\ +\ 3\ Br_2\ \longrightarrow\ 2\ FeBr_3$$

$$2\ Fe\ +\ 3\ Cl_2\ \longrightarrow\ 2\ FeCl_3$$

PROBLEM 22

Why does hydration inactivate $FeBr_3$?

Iodobenzene can be prepared using I_2 and an oxidizing agent under acid conditions. Hydrogen peroxide is commonly used as the oxidizing agent.

iodination

iodobenzene

The oxidizing agent converts converts I_2 into the electrophilic iodonium ion (I^+).

generation of the electrophile

$$I_2\ \xrightarrow{\text{oxidizing agent}}\ 2\ I^+$$

Once the electrophile is formed, iodination of benzene occurs by the same mechanism as bromination and chlorination.

MECHANISM FOR IODINATION

- The electrophile attaches to the benzene ring.
- A base (:B) in the reaction mixture removes the proton from the carbon that formed the bond with the electrophile.

Thyroxine

Thyroxine, a hormone produced by the thyroid gland, increases the rate at which fats, carbohydrates, and proteins are metabolized. Humans obtain thyroxine from tyrosine (an amino acid) and iodine. The thyroid gland is the only part of the body that uses iodine, which we acquire primarily from seafood or iodized salt.

An enzyme called iodoperoxidase converts the I^- we ingest to I^+, the electrophile needed to place an iodo substituent on a benzene ring. A deficiency in iodine is the number one cause of preventable intellectual disability in children.

tyrosine

thyroxine

Chronically low levels of thyroxine cause enlargement of the thyroid gland as it tries in vain to make more thyroxine, a condition known as goiter. Low thyroxine levels can be corrected by

taking thyroxine orally. Synthroid, the most popular brand of thyroxine, is the fifth most-prescribed drug in the United States (see Table 31.1 on page 1240).

15.12 THE NITRATION OF BENZENE

The nitration of benzene with nitric acid requires sulfuric acid as a catalyst.

nitration

$$\text{benzene} + HNO_3 \xrightarrow{H_2SO_4} \text{nitrobenzene} (NO_2) + H_2O$$

nitrobenzene

nitric acid

To generate the necessary electrophile, sulfuric acid protonates nitric acid. Protonated nitric acid loses water to form a nitronium ion, the electrophile required for nitration.

generation of the electrophile

$$HO-NO_2 + H-OSO_3H \rightleftharpoons HO^+_2-NO_2 \rightleftharpoons {}^+NO_2 + H_2O$$

nitric acid   nitronium ion

$$+ HSO_4^-$$

$O=\overset{+}{N}=O$

nitronium ion

The mechanism for the electrophilic aromatic substitution reaction is the same as the mechanisms for the electrophilic aromatic substitution reactions we looked at in Section 15.11.

MECHANISM FOR NITRATION

$$\text{benzene} + {}^+NO_2 \rightleftharpoons \text{(intermediate)} \rightarrow \text{(nitrobenzene)} NO_2 + HB^+$$

- The electrophile attaches to the ring.
- A base (:B) in the reaction mixture (for example, H_2O, HSO_4^-, or solvent) removes the proton from the carbon that formed the bond with the electrophile.

PROBLEM 23   **SOLVED**

Propose a mechanism for the following reaction:

Solution   The only electrophile available is D^+. Therefore, D^+ attaches to a ring carbon and H^+ comes off the same ring carbon. This reaction can be repeated at each of the other five ring carbons.

15.13 THE SULFONATION OF BENZENE

Fuming sulfuric acid (a solution of SO_3 in sulfuric acid) or concentrated sulfuric acid is used to sulfonate aromatic rings.

sulfonation

benzenesulfonic acid

    Take a minute to note the similarities in the mechanisms for forming the $^+SO_3H$ electrophile for sulfonation and the $^+NO_2$ electrophile for nitration. A substantial amount of electrophilic sulfur trioxide (SO_3) is generated when concentrated sulfuric acid is heated, as a result of the $^+SO_3H$ electrophile losing a proton.

generation of the electrophile

MECHANISM FOR SULFONATION

- The electrophile attaches to the ring.
- A base (:B) in the reaction mixture (for example, H_2O, HSO_4^-, solvent) removes the proton from the carbon that formed the bond with the electrophile.

A sulfonic acid is a strong acid because of the three electron-withdrawing oxygens as well as the stability of its conjugate base—the electrons left behind when a proton is lost are shared by three oxygens (Section 7.6).

benzenesulfonic acid   benzenesulfonate ion

Sulfonation is reversible. If benzenesulfonic acid is heated in dilute acid, an H^+ adds to the ring and the sulfonic acid group comes off the ring.

MECHANISM FOR DESULFONATION

The **principle of microscopic reversibility** applies to all reactions. It states that the mechanism of a reaction in the reverse direction must retrace each step of the mechanism in the forward direction in microscopic detail. This means that the forward and reverse reactions must have the same intermediates, and that the "hill" with the highest point on the reaction coordinate represents the rate-determining step in both the forward and reverse directions. For example, sulfonation is described by the reaction coordinate diagram in Figure 15.6, going from left to right. Therefore, desulfonation is described by the same reaction coordinate diagram going from right to left. In sulfonation, the rate-determining step is nucleophilic attack of benzene on the $^+SO_3H$ ion. In desulfonation, the rate-limiting step is loss of the $^+SO_3H$ ion from the carbocation intermediate. You will see how desulfonation can be useful in synthesizing compounds when you do Problem 23 in Chapter 16.

transition state for the rate-determining step in the forward direction and for the rate-determining step in the reverse direction

► **Figure 15.6**
Reaction coordinate diagram for the sulfonation of benzene (left to right) and the desulfonation of benzenesulfonic acid (right to left).

PROBLEM 24

The reaction coordinate diagram in Figure 15.6 shows that the rate-determining step for sulfonation is the slower of the two steps in the mechanism, whereas the rate-determining step for desulfonation is the faster of the two steps. Explain how the faster step can be the rate-determining step.

Charles Friedel (1832–1899), *born in Strasbourg, France, was a professor of chemistry and director of research at the Sorbonne. At one point, his interest in mineralogy led him to attempt to make synthetic diamonds. He met James Crafts when they both were doing research at L'Ecole de Médicine in Paris. They collaborated scientifically for most of their lives, discovering the Friedel–Crafts reactions in Friedel's laboratory in 1877.*

15.14 THE FRIEDEL–CRAFTS ACYLATION OF BENZENE

Two electrophilic substitution reactions bear the names of chemists Charles Friedel and James Crafts. *Friedel–Crafts acylation* places an acyl group on a benzene ring, and *Friedel–Crafts alkylation* places an alkyl group on a benzene ring. These reactions are useful to synthetic chemists because they increase the number of carbons in the starting material (Section 6.11).

an acyl group   an alkyl group

Either an acyl chloride or an acid anhydride can be used for Friedel–Crafts acylation. An acyl chloride has a chlorine in place of the OH group of a carboxylic acid.

Friedel–Crafts acylation

The electrophile (an acylium ion) required for a Friedel–Crafts acylation reaction is formed by the reaction of an acyl chloride or an acid anhydride with $AlCl_3$, a Lewis acid. Oxygen and carbon share the positive charge in the acylium ion, which stabilizes it.

generation of the electrophile

an acyl chloride   an acylium ion

MECHANISM FOR FRIEDEL—CRAFTS ACYLATION

James Mason Crafts (1839–1917) *was born in Boston, the son of a woolen-goods manufacturer. He graduated from Harvard in 1858 and was a professor of chemistry at Cornell University and at the Massachusetts Institute of Technology. He was president of MIT from 1897 to 1900, when he was forced to retire because of poor health.*

- The electrophile attaches to the ring.
- A base (:B) in the reaction mixture removes the proton from the carbon that formed the bond with the electrophile.

Because the product of a Friedel–Crafts acylation reaction contains a carbonyl group that can complex with $AlCl_3$, Friedel–Crafts acylation reactions must be carried out with more than one equivalent of $AlCl_3$. When the reaction is over, water is added to the reaction mixture to liberate the product from the complex.

PROBLEM 25

Show the mechanism for the generation of the acylium ion if an acid anhydride is used instead of an acyl chloride in a Friedel–Crafts acylation reaction.

PROBLEM 26

Propose a mechanism for the following reaction:

The synthesis of benzaldehyde from benzene poses a problem because formyl chloride, the acyl halide required for the reaction, is unstable and must be generated in situ. The **Gatterman–Koch reaction** uses a high-pressure mixture of carbon monoxide and HCl to generate formyl chloride; it uses an aluminum chloride–cuprous chloride catalyst for the acylation reaction itself.

15.15 THE FRIEDEL–CRAFTS ALKYLATION OF BENZENE

Friedel–Crafts alkylation substitutes an alkyl group for a hydrogen.

The electrophile required for the reaction, a carbocation, is formed from the reaction of an alkyl halide with $AlCl_3$. Alkyl chlorides, alkyl bromides, and alkyl iodides can all be used. Vinyl halides and aryl halides cannot be used because their carbocations are too unstable to be formed (Section 8.7).

generation of the electrophile

MECHANISM FOR FRIEDEL—CRAFTS ALKYLATION

- The electrophile attaches to the ring.
- A base (:B) in the reaction mixture removes the proton from the carbon that formed the bond with the electrophile.

In Section 16.3, we will see that an alkyl-substituted benzene is more reactive than benzene. Therefore, to prevent the alkyl-substituted benzene from being alkylated, a large excess of benzene is used in Friedel–Crafts alkylation reactions. When benzene is in excess, the electrophile is more likely to encounter a molecule of benzene than a molecule of the more reactive alkyl-substituted benzene.

Recall that a carbocation will rearrange if rearrangement leads to a more stable carbocation (Section 4.7). When the carbocation employed in a Friedel–Crafts alkylation reaction rearranges, the major product will be the product with the rearranged alkyl group on the benzene ring. For example, when benzene reacts with 1-chlorobutane, 60%–80% of the product (the actual percentage depends on the reaction conditions) has the rearranged alkyl substituent. (See "Incipient Carbocations" on page 645.)

rearrangement of the carbocation

When benzene reacts with 1-chloro-2,2-dimethylpropane, 100% of the product (under all reaction conditions) has the rearranged alkyl substituent.

rearrangement of the carbocation

Incipient Primary Carbocations

For simplicity, the two reactions on page 646 that involve carbocation rearrangements were written showing the formation of a primary carbocation. However, we know that primary carbocations are too unstable to be formed (Section 8.5). Not surprisingly, a true primary carbocation is never formed in a Friedel–Crafts alkylation reaction. Instead, the carbocation remains complexed with the Lewis acid; it is called an "incipient" carbocation. A carbocation rearrangement occurs because the incipient carbocation has sufficient carbocation character to permit the rearrangement.

$$CH_3CH_2CH_2Cl \ + \ AlCl_3 \ \longrightarrow \ CH_3\overset{H}{\underset{\delta+}{C}}HCH_2\text{---}\overset{\delta-}{Cl}\text{---}AlCl_3 \ \xrightarrow{\substack{\textbf{1,2-hydride}\\ \textbf{shift}}} \ CH_3\overset{\delta+}{C}HCH_3$$

incipient primary carbocation

A Biological Friedel–Crafts Alkylation Reaction

A Friedel–Crafts alkylation reaction is one of the steps in the biosynthesis of Vitamin KH_2, the coenzyme required to form blood clots (Section 25.8). The pyrophosphate group, an excellent leaving group (Section 26.2), departs in an S_N1 reaction, forming an allyl cation. A Friedel–Crafts alkylation reaction places the long-chain alkyl group on the benzene ring. Conversion of the carboxyl group to a methyl group, which requires several steps, forms vitamin KH_2.

pyrophosphate

several steps

vitamin KH_2

PROBLEM 27◆

What would be the major product of a Friedel–Crafts alkylation reaction using the following alkyl chlorides?

a. CH_3CH_2Cl

b. $CH_3CH_2CH_2Cl$

c. $CH_3CH_2CH(Cl)CH_3$

d. $(CH_3)_3CCl$

e. $(CH_3)_2CHCH_2Cl$

f. $CH_2 = CHCH_2Cl$

15.16 THE ALKYLATION OF BENZENE BY ACYLATION—REDUCTION

A Friedel–Crafts alkylation reaction cannot produce a good yield of an alkylbenzene containing a straight-chain alkyl group because the incipient primary carbocation will rearrange to a more stable carbocation.

major product   **minor product**

Acylium ions, however, do not rearrange. Consequently, a straight-chain alkyl group can be placed on a benzene ring by means of a Friedel–Crafts acylation reaction, followed by reduction of the carbonyl group to a methylene group. It is called a reduction reaction because the two C—O bonds are replaced by two C—H bonds (Section 4.11). Only a ketone carbonyl group that is adjacent to a benzene ring can be reduced to a methylene group by catalytic hydrogenation (H_2, Pd/C).

acyl-substituted benzene   **alkyl-substituted benzene**

B I O G R A P H Y

E. C. Clemmensen (1876–1941) *was born in Denmark and received a Ph.D. from the University of Copenhagen. He was the president of Clemmensen Chemical Corp. in Newark, New York.* **Ludwig Wolff (1857–1919)** *was born in Germany. He received a Ph.D. from the University of Strasbourg. He was a professor at the University of Jena in Germany.* **N. M. Kishner (1867–1935)** *was born in Moscow. He received a Ph.D. from the University of Moscow under the direction of Vladimir Markovnikov (page 162). He was a professor at the University of Tomsk and later at the University of Moscow.*

Besides avoiding carbocation rearrangements, another advantage to preparing alkyl-substituted benzenes by acylation–reduction rather than by direct alkylation is that a large excess of benzene does not have to be used (Section 15.15). Unlike alkyl-substituted benzenes, which are more reactive than benzene (Section 15.2), acyl-substituted benzenes are less reactive than benzene, so they will not undergo additional Friedel–Crafts reactions.

Several other methods are available for reducing a ketone carbonyl group to a methylene group. These methods reduce all ketone carbonyl groups, not just those adjacent to benzene rings. Two of the most effective are the Clemmensen reduction and the Wolff–Kishner reduction. The **Clemmensen reduction** uses an acidic solution of zinc dissolved in mercury as the reducing reagent. The **Wolff–Kishner reduction** employs hydrazine (H_2NNH_2) under basic conditions. The mechanism of the Wolff–Kishner reduction is shown in Section 18.8.

15.17 USING COUPLING REACTIONS TO ALKYLATE BENZENE

Alkylbenzenes with straight-chain alkyl groups can also be prepared from bromobenzene or chlorobenzene, using one of the coupling reactions described in Sections 11.4 and 11.5.

reaction with a Gilman reagent

the Suzuki reaction

PROBLEM 28

Describe how the following compounds could be prepared from benzene:

a. $-CHCH_2CH_2CH_3$
$\qquad\qquad$ CH_3

b. $-CH_2CH_2CH_2CH_2CH_3$

15.18 IT IS IMPORTANT TO HAVE MORE THAN ONE WAY TO CARRY OUT A REACTION

At this point, you may wonder why it is necessary to have more than one way to carry out the same reaction. Alternative methods are useful when there is another functional group in the molecule that could react with the reagents you are using to carry out the desired reaction. For example, heating the following compound with HCl (as required by the Clemmensen reduction) would cause the alcohol to undergo substitution (Section 10.1). Under the basic conditions of the Wolff–Kishner reduction, however, the alcohol group would remain unchanged.

15.19 POLYCYCLIC BENZENOID HYDROCARBONS

Polycyclic benzenoid hydrocarbons are compounds that contain two or more fused benzene rings. **Fused rings** share two adjacent carbons. Naphthalene has two fused rings, anthracene and phenanthrene have three fused rings, and tetracene, triphenylene, pyrene, and chrysene have four fused rings. There are many polycyclic benzenoid hydrocarbons with more than four fused rings.

naphthalene   anthracene   phenanthrene   tetracene

triphenylene   pyrene   chrysene

Like benzene, all the larger polycyclic benzenoid hydrocarbons undergo electrophilic aromatic substitution reactions. Some of these fused-ring compounds are well-known carcinogens. We will now see why these compounds cause cancer and how you can predict which of them are most apt to be carcinogenic.

15.20 ARENE OXIDES

benzene

benzene oxide

After an aromatic hydrocarbon (also called an **arene**) such as benzene is ingested or inhaled, it is converted into an *arene oxide* by an enzyme. An **arene oxide** is a compound in which one of the "double bonds" of the aromatic ring has been converted into an epoxide. Formation of an arene oxide is the first step in changing an aromatic compound that enters the body as a foreign substance (for example, a drug, cigarette smoke, automobile exhaust) into a more water-soluble compound that can eventually be eliminated. The enzyme that converts arenes into arene oxides is called cytochrome P_{450}.

benzene $\xrightarrow[\text{O}_2]{\text{cytochrome P}_{450}}$ benzene oxide
an arene oxide

An arene oxide can react in two ways. It can react as a typical epoxide, undergoing attack by a nucleophile (Y^-) to form addition products (Section 10.7). Alternatively, it can rearrange to form a phenol, which other epoxides cannot do.

addition products

rearranged product

SUMMARY

To be classified as **aromatic**, a compound must have an uninterrupted cyclic cloud of π electrons that contains an *odd number of pairs* of π electrons. An **antiaromatic compound** has an uninterrupted cyclic cloud of π electrons with an *even number of pairs* of π electrons. Molecular orbital theory shows that aromatic compounds are stable because their bonding orbitals are completely filled, with no electrons in either nonbonding or antibonding orbitals. In contrast, antiaromatic compounds are unstable because they either are unable to fill their bonding orbitals or they have a pair of π electrons left over after the bonding orbitals are filled. As a result of their aromaticity, the cyclopentadienyl anion and the cycloheptatrienyl cation are unusually stable.

An **annulene** is a monocyclic hydrocarbon with alternating single and double bonds. A **heterocyclic compound** is a cyclic compound in which one or more of the ring atoms is a **heteroatom**, an atom other than carbon. Pyridine, pyrrole, furan, and thiophene are aromatic heterocyclic compounds.

Benzene's aromaticity causes it to undergo **electrophilic aromatic substitution reactions**. Electrophilic addition reactions that are characteristic of alkenes and dienes would lead to much less stable nonaromatic products. The most common electrophilic aromatic substitution reactions are halogenation, nitration, sulfonation, and Friedel–Crafts acylation and alkylation. Once the electrophile is generated, all electrophilic aromatic substitution reactions take place by the same two-step mechanism: (1) the electrophile forms a bond with benzene, forming a carbocation intermediate; and (2) a base pulls off a proton from the carbon that formed the bond with the electrophile. The first step is relatively slow and endergonic because an aromatic compound is being converted into a much less stable nonaromatic intermediate; the second step is fast and strongly exergonic because the stability-enhancing aromaticity is being restored.

Some monosubstituted benzenes are named as substituted benzenes (for example, bromobenzene, nitrobenzene); others have names that incorporate the substituent (for example, toluene, phenol, aniline, anisole). Bromination or chlorination requires a Lewis acid catalyst; iodination requires an oxidizing agent. **Nitration** with nitric acid requires sulfuric acid as a catalyst; **sulfonation** requires heating benzene with concentrated sulfuric acid. **Sulfonation** is a reversible reaction; heating benzenesulfonic acid in dilute acid removes the sulfonic acid group. The **principle of microscopic reversibility** states that the mechanism of a reaction in the reverse direction must retrace each step of the mechanism in the forward direction in microscopic detail.

Either an acyl halide or an acid anhydride can be used for **Friedel–Crafts acylation**, a reaction that places an acyl group on a benzene ring. If the carbocation formed from the alkyl halide used in a **Friedel–Crafts alkylation** reaction can rearrange, the major product will be the product with the rearranged alkyl group. A straight-chain alkyl group can be placed on a benzene ring via a Friedel–Crafts acylation reaction, followed by reduction of the carbonyl group by catalytic hydrogenation, a **Clemmensen reduction**, or a **Wolff–Kishner reduction**. Alkylbenzenes with straight-chain alkyl groups can also be prepared by coupling reactions.

Polycyclic benzenoid hydrocarbons contain two or more fused benzene rings; **fused rings** share two adjacent carbons. Like benzene, polycyclic benzenoid hydrocarbons undergo electrophilic aromatic substitution reactions.

Aromatic hydrocarbons **(arenes)** are oxidized to **arene oxides** that undergo rearrangement to form phenols, or nucleophilic attack to form addition products. An arene oxide's cancer-causing potential depends on the stability of the carbocation formed during rearrangement.

SUMMARY OF REACTIONS

1. Electrophilic aromatic substitution reactions
    a. Halogenation (Section 15.11)

b. Nitration, sulfonation, and desulfonation (Sections 15.12 and 15.13)

c. Friedel–Crafts acylation and alkylation (Sections 15.14 and 15.15)

d. Formation of benzaldehyde by a Gatterman–Koch reaction (Section 15.15)

2. Clemmensen reduction and Wolff–Kishner reduction (Section 15.16)

3. Alkyation via coupling reactions (Section 15.17)
   a. Alkylation with a Gilman reagent

   b. Alkylation by a Suzuki reaction

4. Reactions of *arene oxides*: ring opening and rearrangement (Section 15.20)

KEY TERMS

aliphatic compound (p. 624)
annulene (p. 627)
antiaromatic compound (p. 633)
arene (p. 650)
arene oxide (p. 650)
aromatic compound (p. 626)
benzyl group (p. 636)
Clemmensen reduction (p. 648)
electrophilic aromatic substitution
   reaction (p. 636)

Friedel–Crafts acylation (p. 638)
Friedel–Crafts alkylation (p. 638)
fused rings (p. 649)
Gatterman–Koch reaction (p. 645)
halogenation (p. 638)
heteroatom (p. 629)
heterocyclic compound (p. 629)
Hückel's rule, or the $4n+2$
   rule (p. 626)

nitration (p. 638)
phenyl group (p. 636)
principle of microscopic reversibility
   (p. 643)
sulfonation (p. 638)
Suzuki reaction (p. 649)
Wolff–Kishner reduction (p. 648)

PROBLEMS

35. Draw the structure of the following:
   a. phenol
   b. benzyl phenyl ether
   c. benzonitrile

   d. benzaldehyde
   e. anisole
   f. styrene

   g. toluene
   h. *tert*-butylbenzene
   i. benzyl chloride

36. Classify the following species as aromatic, nonaromatic, antiaromatic:

37. Give the product of the reaction of excess benzene with the following reagents:
   a. isobutyl chloride + $AlCl_3$
   b. 1-chloro-2,2-dimethylpropane + $AlCl_3$
   c. dichloromethane + $AlCl_3$

38. Which ion in each of the following pairs is more stable and why?

39. Which can lose a proton more readily, a methyl group bonded to cyclohexane or a methyl group bonded to benzene?

40. How could you prepare the following compounds with benzene as one of the starting materials?

   a.

   b.

41. Benzene underwent a Friedel–Crafts acylation reaction followed by a Clemmensen reduction. The product gave the following ^1H NMR spectrum. What acyl chloride was used in the Friedel–Crafts acylation reaction?

42. Which compound is a stronger base? Why?

or

43. Which compound undergoes an S_N1 reaction more rapidly?

or

44. Purine is a heterocyclic compound with four nitrogen atoms.
  a. Which nitrogen is most apt to be protonated?
  b. Which nitrogen is least apt to be protonated?

purine

45. A chemist isolated an aromatic compound with molecular formula $C_6H_4Br_2$. He treated this compound with nitric acid and sulfuric acid (conditions that replace an H with an NO_2 group) and isolated three different isomers with molecular formula $C_6H_3Br_2NO_2$. What was the structure of the original compound?

46. Friedel–Crafts alkylation reactions can be carried out with carbocations formed from sources other than the reaction of an alkyl halide with $AlCl_3$. Propose a mechanism for the following reaction:

47. Propose a mechanism for each of the following reactions:

  a. $\xrightarrow{\text{HCl}}$

  b. $CH=CH_2$ $\xrightarrow{\text{HCl}}$ CH_3

48. An aromatic hydrocarbon with a molecular formula of $C_{13}H_{20}$ has an ^1H NMR spectrum with a signal at ~7 ppm that integrates to 5H. It also has two singlets; one of the singlets has 1.5 times the area of the second. What is the structure of the aromatic hydrocarbon?

49. When deuterated phenanthrene oxide undergoes a rearrangement in water to form a phenol, 81% of the deuterium is retained in the product.

   a. What percentage of the deuterium will be retained if an NIH shift occurs?
   b. What percentage of the deuterium will be retained if an NIH shift does not occur?

50. Which of the following compounds is the strongest acid?

51 a. Propose a mechanism for the following reaction:

   b. Give the product of the following reaction:

52. Give the structure of an arene with a molecular formula of $C_{13}H_{20}$ that gives an NMR spectrum with a signal at ~7 ppm (5H) and two singlets, one of which has 1.5 times the area of the other.

53. In a reaction called the Birch reduction, benzene can be partially reduced to 1,4-cyclohexadiene by an alkali metal (Na, Li, or K) in liquid ammonia and a low-molecular-weight alcohol. Propose a mechanism for this reaction. (*Hint:* See Section 6.9.)

1,4-cyclohexadiene

54. Draw the resonance contributors of the cyclooctatrienyl dianion.
   a. Which of the resonance contributors is the least stable?
   b. Which of the resonance contributors makes the smallest contribution to the hybrid?

55. Investigation has shown that cyclobutadiene is actually a rectangular molecule rather than a square molecule. In addition, it has been established that there are two different 1,2-dideuterio-1,3-cyclobutadienes. Explain the reason for these unexpected observations.

cyclobutadiene

56. The principle of least motion, which states that the reaction that involves the least change in atomic positions or electronic configuration (all else being equal) is favored, has been suggested to explain why the Birch reduction forms only 1,4-hexadiene. How does this account for the observation that no 1,3-cyclohexadiene is obtained from a Birch reduction?

16
Reactions of Substituted Benzenes

Chlorobenzene

***meta*-Bromobenzoic acid**

***ortho*-Chloronitrobenzene**

***para*-Iodobenzenesulfonic acid**

MANY SUBSTITUTED BENZENES ARE FOUND IN NATURE. A FEW THAT HAVE PHYSIOLOGICAL activity are shown here.

adrenaline
epinephrine
a hormone released
by the body in
response to stress

ephedrine
a bronchodilator

chloramphenicol
an antibiotic that is particularly
effective against typhoid fever

mescaline
active agent of
the peyote cactus

Many other physiologically active substituted benzenes are not found in nature, but exist because chemists have synthesized them. Acetyl salicylic acid (aspirin) became commercially available in 1899 (page 94). Hexachlorophene is a common disinfectant. The now-banned diet drug "fen-phen" is a mixture of two synthetic substituted benzenes: fenfluramine and phentermine. Two other synthetic substituted benzenes, BHA and BHT, are preservatives (Section 12.11) found in a wide variety of packaged foods.

hexachlorophene
a disinfectant

acetylsalicylic acid
aspirin

fenfluramine

phentermine

When naturally occurring compounds are found to have desirable physiological activities, chemists will attempt to synthesize structurally similar compounds with the hope of developing them into useful products. For example, chemists have synthesized compounds with structures similar to that of adrenaline, producing amphetamine, a central nervous system stimulant, and the closely related methamphetamine (methylated amphetamine); both are used clinically as appetite suppressants. Methamphetamine, known as "speed" because of its rapid and intense psychological effects, is also made and sold illegally. These compounds represent just a few of the many substituted benzenes that have been synthesized for commercial use by the chemical and pharmaceutical industries. The physical properties of several substituted benzenes are given in Appendix I.

amphetamine
an appetite
suppressant

methamphetamine
"speed"

saccharin
an artificial
sweetener

***p*-dichlorobenzene**
in mothballs and
air fresheners

Measuring Toxicity

Agent Orange, a defoliant widely used in the Vietnam War, is a mixture of two synthetic substituted benzenes: 2,4-D and 2,4,5-T. Dioxin (TCDD), a contaminant formed during the manufacture of Agent Orange, has been implicated as the causative agent of the various symptoms suffered by those exposed to the defoliant during the war.

2,4-dichlorophenoxyacetic acid
2,4-D

2,4,5-trichlorophenoxyacetic acid
2,4,5-T

2,3,7,8-tetrachlorodibenzo[*b*,*e*][1,4]dioxin
TCDD

The toxicity of a compound is indicated by its LD_{50} value—the dosage found to kill 50% of the test animals exposed to it. Dioxin, with an LD_{50} value of 0.0006 mg/kg for guinea pigs, is an extremely toxic compound. Compare this with the LD_{50} values of some well-known but far less toxic poisons: 0.96 mg/kg for strychnine and 15 mg/kg for both arsenic trioxide and sodium cyanide. One of the most toxic agents known is the toxin that causes botulism; it has an LD_{50} value of about 1×10^{-8} mg/kg.

16.1   HOW SOME SUBSTITUENTS ON A BENZENE RING CAN BE CHEMICALLY CHANGED

Benzene rings with substituents other than the ones listed in Section 15.10 can be prepared by first synthesizing one of those substituted benzenes and then chemically changing the substituent. Several of these reactions will be familiar.

Reactions of Alkyl Substituents

We have seen that a bromine will selectively substitute for a benzylic hydrogen in a radical substitution reaction (Section 12.9).

CH$_2$CH$_2$CH$_3$ +   Br$_2$ $\xrightarrow{h\nu}$ CHCH$_2$CH$_3$ (Br)   +   HBr

propylbenzene   **1-bromo-1-phenylpropane**

Once a halogen has been placed in the benzylic position, it can be replaced by a nucleophile by means of an S_N2 or S_N1 reaction (Sections 8.1 and 8.4). A wide variety of substituted benzenes can be prepared this way.

Remember that halo-substituted alkyl groups can also undergo E2 and E1 reactions (Sections 9.1 and 9.3). Notice that a bulky base (*tert*-BuO⁻) is used to encourage elimination over substitution.

Substituents with double and triple bonds can undergo catalytic hydrogenation (Sections 4.12 and 6.9). The catalyst used for hydrogenation of a C≡N to an amine is Raney nickel (Section 20.2). Recall that addition of hydrogen to a double or triple bond is an example of a reduction reaction, a reaction that increases the number of C—H bonds or decreases the number of C—O, C—N, or C—X bonds in a compound (X denotes a halogen).

Because benzene is an unusually stable compound (Section 15.1), it can be reduced only at high temperature and pressure.

An alkyl group bonded to a benzene ring can be oxidized to a carboxyl group. Recall that when an organic compound is *oxidized,* either the number of C—O, C—N, or C—X (X denotes a halogen) bonds increases or the number of C—H bonds decreases (Section 4.9). Commonly used oxidizing agents are potassium permanganate ($KMnO_4$) and acidic solutions of sodium dichromate (H^+, $Na_2Cr_2O_7$). Because the benzene ring is so stable, it will not be oxidized—only the alkyl group is oxidized.

toluene   benzoic acid

Regardless of the length of the alkyl substituent, it will be oxidized to a COOH group, provided that a hydrogen is bonded to the benzylic carbon.

m-butylisopropylbenzene   *m*-benzenedicarboxylic acid

If the alkyl group lacks a benzylic hydrogen, the oxidation reaction will not occur because the first step in the oxidation reaction is removal of a hydrogen from the benzylic carbon.

tert-butylbenzene

The same reagents that oxidize alkyl substituents will oxidize benzylic alcohols to benzoic acid.

1-phenylethanol   benzoic acid

If, however, a mild oxidizing agent such as MnO_2 is used, benzylic alcohols are oxidized to aldehydes or ketones, depending on the substituent attached to the benzylic carbon.

1-phenylethanol   acetophenone   phenylmethanol   benzaldehyde
                       a ketone   benzyl alcohol   an aldehyde

Reducing a Nitro Substituent

A nitro substituent can be reduced to an amino substituent. Catalytic hydrogenation is commonly used to carry out this reaction.

PROBLEM 1 ♦

Give the product of each of the following reactions:

a.

b.

c.

d.

PROBLEM 2   SOLVED

Show how the following compounds could be prepared from benzene:

a. benzaldehyde
b. styrene
c. 1-bromo-2-phenylethane
d. 2-phenyl-1-ethanol
e. aniline
f. benzoic acid

Solution to 2a   Benzaldehyde cannot be prepared by a Friedel–Crafts acylation because formyl chloride, the required acyl halide, is unstable (Section 15.14). Benzaldehyde can be prepared by the Gatterman–Koch reaction (page 645) or by the following sequence of reactions:

16.2 THE NOMENCLATURE OF DISUBSTITUTED AND POLYSUBSTITUTED BENZENES

Section 15.8 described how monosubstituted benzenes are named. Now we will look at how benzene rings that have more than one substituent are named.

Naming Disubstituted Benzenes

The relative positions of two substituents on a benzene ring can be indicated either by numbers or by the prefixes *ortho, meta,* and *para.* Adjacent substituents are called *ortho,* substituents separated by one carbon are called *meta,* and substituents located opposite one another are designated *para.* Often, the abbreviations for these prefixes (*o, m, p*) are used in compounds' names.

1,2-dibromobenzene
ortho-dibromobenzene
o-dibromobenzene

1,3-dibromobenzene
meta-dibromobenzene
m-dibromobenzene

1,4-dibromobenzene
para-dibromobenzene
p-dibromobenzene

If the two substituents are different, they are listed in alphabetical order. The first mentioned substituent is given the 1-position, and the ring is numbered in the direction that gives the second substituent the lowest possible number.

1-chloro-3-iodobenzene
meta-**chloroiodobenzene**
not
1-iodo-3-chlorobenzene or
meta-**iodochlorobenzene**

1-bromo-3-nitrobenzene
meta-**bromonitrobenzene**

1-chloro-4-ethylbenzene
para-**chloroethylbenzene**

If one of the substituents can be incorporated into a name (Section 14.8), that name is used and the incorporated substituent is given the 1-position.

2-chlorotoluene
ortho-**chlorotoluene**
not
ortho-**chloromethylbenzene**

4-nitroaniline
para-**nitroaniline**
not
para-**aminonitrobenzene**

2-ethylphenol
ortho-**ethylphenol**
not
ortho-**ethylhydroxybenzene**

A few disubstituted benzenes have names that incorporate both substituents.

ortho-**toluidine**

meta-**xylene**

para-**cresol**
used as a wood preservative
until prohibited for
environmental reasons

PROBLEM 3◆

Name the following:

a.   **b.** Cl—⟨ ⟩—Br   **c.** Br—⟨ ⟩—C(=O)H   **d.**

PROBLEM 4◆

Draw structures of the following:

a. *para*-toluidine
b. *meta*-cresol

c. *para*-xylene
d. *ortho*-chlorobenzenesulfonic acid

Naming Polysubstituted Benzenes

If the benzene ring has more than two substituents, the substituents are numbered in the direction that results in the lowest possible numbers. The substituents are listed in alphabetical order, each preceded by its assigned number.

2-bromo-4-chloro-1-nitrobenzene   **4-bromo-1-chloro-2-nitrobenzene**   **1-bromo-4-chloro-2-nitrobenzene**

As with disubstituted benzenes, if one of the substituents can be incorporated into a name, that name is used and the incorporated substituent is given the 1-position. The ring is then numbered in the direction that results in the lowest possible numbers.

5-bromo-2-nitrotoluene   **3-bromo-4-chlorophenol**   **2-ethyl-4-iodoaniline**

PROBLEM 5

Draw the structure of each of the following:

a. *m*-chlorotoluene

b. *p*-bromophenol

c. *o*-nitroaniline

d. *m*-chlorobenzonitrile

e. 2-bromo-4-iodophenol

f. *m*-dichlorobenzene

g. 2,5-dinitrobenzaldehyde

h. 4-bromo-3-chloroaniline

PROBLEM 6 ◆

Correct the following incorrect names:

a. 2,4,6-tribromobenzene

b. 3-hydroxynitrobenzene

c. *para*-methylbromobenzene

d. 1,6-dichlorobenzene

16.3 THE EFFECT OF SUBSTITUENTS ON REACTIVITY

Like benzene, substituted benzenes undergo the five electrophilic aromatic substitution reactions discussed in Chapter 15:

halogenation   + Br_2 $\xrightarrow{\text{FeBr}_3}$ + HBr

nitration   + HNO_3 $\xrightarrow{\text{H}_2\text{SO}_4}$ + H_2O

sulfonation   + H_2SO_4 $\xrightleftharpoons{\Delta}$ + H_2O

acylation

alkylation

Now we need to find out whether a substituted benzene is more reactive or less reactive than benzene itself. The answer depends on the substituent. Some substituents make the ring more reactive toward electrophilic aromatic substitution than benzene, and some make it less reactive than benzene.

The slow step of an electrophilic aromatic substitution reaction is the addition of an electrophile to the nucleophilic aromatic ring to form a carbocation intermediate (see Figure 15.5 on page 638). The transition state for the slow step resembles the positively charged carbocation intermediate (in accordance with the Hammond postulate, Section 4.3). Thus, the transition state has a partial positive charge.

Substituents that donate electrons to the benzene ring will stabilize the partially positively charged transition state, thereby increasing the rate of electrophilic aromatic substitution; these are called **activating substituents**. In contrast, substituents that withdraw electrons from the benzene ring will destabilize the transition state, thereby decreasing the rate of electrophilic aromatic substitution; these are called **deactivating substituents**. We will now review the ways a substituent can donate or withdraw electrons.

relative rates of electrophilic aromatic substitution

Inductive Electron Withdrawal

If a substituent that is bonded to a benzene ring is *more electron withdrawing than a hydrogen*, it will draw the σ electrons away from the benzene ring more strongly than a hydrogen will. Withdrawal of electrons through a σ bond is called **inductive electron withdrawal** (Section 1.22). The $^+NH_3$ group is an example of a substituent that withdraws electrons inductively because it is more electronegative than a hydrogen.

Electron Donation by Hyperconjugation

We have seen that alkyl substituents (such as CH_3) are more electron donating than a hydrogen because of hyperconjugation (Section 4.2). Notice that we compare the electron-donating ability of an alkyl group—not just a carbon—with the electron-donating ability of a hydrogen. Carbon is actually a little more electron withdrawing than hydrogen (because C is more electronegative than H; see Table 1.3 on page 10, but hyperconjugation more than makes up for this inductive effect.

Resonance Electron Donation and Withdrawal

If a substituent has a lone pair on the atom directly attached to the benzene ring, the lone pair can be delocalized into the ring; these substituents are said to **donate electrons by resonance** (Section 7.9). Substituents such as NH_2, OH, OR, and Cl donate electrons by resonance. These substituents also withdraw electrons inductively because the atom attached to the benzene ring is more electronegative than a hydrogen.

donation of electrons by resonance into a benzene ring

anisole

If a substituent is attached to the benzene ring by an atom that is doubly or triply bonded to a more electronegative atom, the electrons of the ring can be delocalized onto the substituent; these substituents are said to **withdraw electrons by resonance**. Substituents such as C=O, C≡N, SO_3H, and NO_2 withdraw electrons by resonance. These substituents also withdraw electrons inductively because the atom attached to the benzene ring has a full or partial positive charge and therefore is more electronegative than a hydrogen.

withdrawal of electrons by resonance from a benzene ring

nitrobenzene

PROBLEM 7 ◆

For each of the following substituents, indicate whether it withdraws electrons inductively, donates electrons by hyperconjugation, withdraws electrons by resonance, or donates electrons by resonance. (Effects should be compared with that of a hydrogen; remember that many substituents can be characterized in more than one way.)

a. Br

b. CH_2CH_3

c. $\overset{\overset{\text{O}}{\parallel}}{C}CH_3$

d. $NHCH_3$

e. OCH_3

f. $\overset{+}{N}(CH_3)_3$

Relative Reactivity of Substituted Benzenes

The substituents shown in Table 16.1 are listed according to how they affect the reactivity of the benzene ring toward electrophilic aromatic substitution compared with benzene—in which the substituent is a hydrogen. *The activating substituents make the benzene ring more reactive toward electrophilic aromatic substitution; the deactivating substituents make the benzene ring less reactive.* Remember that activating substituents donate electrons to the ring and deactivating substituents withdraw electrons from the ring.

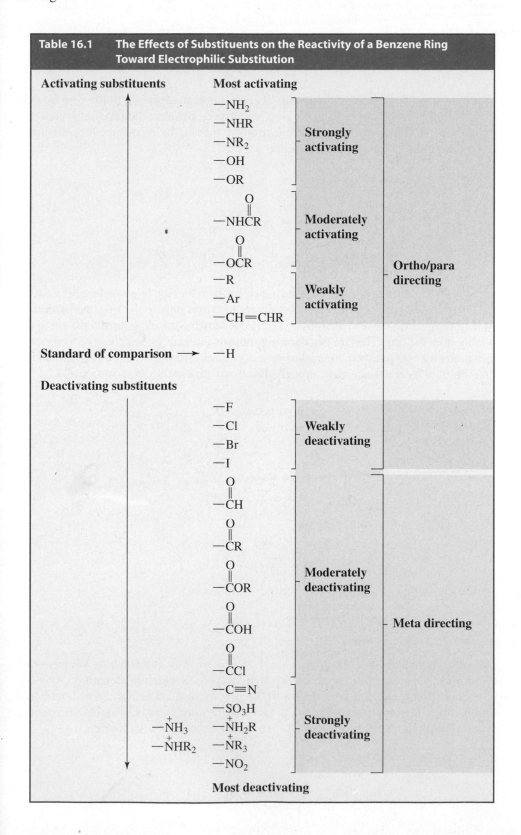

Table 16.1   The Effects of Substituents on the Reactivity of a Benzene Ring Toward Electrophilic Substitution

Electron-donating substituents increase the reactivity of the benzene ring toward electrophilic aromatic substitution.

Electron-withdrawing substituents decrease the reactivity of the benzene ring toward electrophilic aromatic substitution.

All the *strongly activating substituents* donate electrons to the ring by resonance *and* withdraw electrons from the ring inductively. The fact that these substituents have been found experimentally to make the benzene ring more reactive indicates that their electron donation to the ring by resonance is more significant than their inductive electron withdrawal from the ring.

strongly activating substituents

The *moderately activating substituents* also both donate electrons to the ring by resonance and withdraw electrons from the ring inductively. Because they are only moderately activating, we know that they donate electrons to the ring by resonance less effectively than do the strongly activating substituents.

moderately activating substituents

These substituents are less effective at donating electrons to the ring by resonance because, unlike the strongly activating substituents that donate electrons only to the ring, the moderately activating substituents donate electrons by resonance in two competing directions: to the ring and away from the ring. The fact that these substituents increase the reactivity of the benzene ring indicates that, despite their diminished resonance electron donation to the ring, overall they donate electrons by resonance more strongly than they withdraw electrons inductively.

substituent donates electrons by resonance to the benzene ring

substituent donates electrons by resonance away from the benzene ring

Alkyl, aryl, and CH=CHR groups are *weakly activating substituents*. We have seen that an alkyl substituent, compared with a hydrogen, is electron donating. Aryl and CH=CHR groups can donate electrons to the ring by resonance and can also withdraw electrons from the ring by resonance. The fact that they are weak activators indicates that they are slightly more electron donating than they are electron withdrawing.

weakly activating substituents

The halogens are weakly deactivating substituents. Like the strongly and moderately activating substituents, the halogens donate electrons to the ring by resonance and withdraw electrons from the ring inductively. Because the halogens have been found experimentally to make the benzene ring less reactive, we can conclude that they withdraw electrons inductively more strongly than they donate electrons by resonance.

weakly deactivating substituents

Let's look at why the halogens are deactivating, whereas OH and OCH₃ are strongly activating. The electronegativities of chlorine and oxygen are similar, so they have similar inductive electron-withdrawing abilities. However, chlorine does not donate electrons by resonance as well as oxygen does because chlorine uses a 3p orbital to overlap with the 2p orbital of carbon. A 3p–2p orbital overlap is much less effective than the 2p–2p orbital overlap that occurs between oxygen and carbon. Fluorine, which uses a 2p orbital, donates electrons by resonance better than chlorine, but this is outweighed by fluorine's greater electronegativity, which causes it to strongly withdraw electrons inductively. Bromine and iodine are less effective than chlorine at withdrawing electrons inductively, but they are also less effective at donating electrons by resonance because they use 4p and 5p orbitals, respectively. Thus, all the halogens withdraw electrons inductively more strongly than they donate electrons by resonance.

The moderately deactivating substituents all have a carbonyl group directly attached to the benzene ring. A carbonyl group withdraws electrons from a benzene ring both inductively and by resonance.

moderately deactivating substituents

The strongly deactivating substituents are powerful electron withdrawers. Except for the ammonium ions (⁺NH₃, ⁺NH₂R, ⁺NHR₂, and ⁺NR₃), these substituents withdraw electrons both inductively and by resonance. The ammonium ions have no resonance effect, but the positive charge on the nitrogen atom causes them to withdraw electrons strongly through the bond (inductively).

strongly deactivating substituents

Take a minute to compare the electrostatic potential maps for anisole, benzene, and nitrobenzene. Notice that an electron-donating substituent (OCH₃) makes the ring more red (more negative), whereas an electron-withdrawing substituent (NO₂) makes the ring less red (less negative).

anisole   benzene   nitrobenzene

PROBLEM 8♦

List the compounds in each set in order of decreasing reactivity toward electrophilic aromatic substitution:

a. benzene, phenol, toluene, nitrobenzene, bromobenzene
b. dichloromethylbenzene, difluoromethylbenzene, toluene, chloromethylbenzene

PROBLEM 9 **SOLVED**

Explain why the halo-substituted benzenes have the relative reactivities shown in Table 16.1.

Solution Table 16.1 shows that fluorine is the least deactivating of the halogen substituents and iodine is the most deactivating. We know that fluorine is the most electronegative of the halogens, which means that it is best at withdrawing electrons inductively. Fluorine is also best at donating electrons by resonance because its $2p$ orbital—compared with the $3p$ orbital of chlorine, the $4p$ orbital of bromine, or the $5p$ orbital of iodine—can better overlap with the $2p$ orbital of carbon. So the fluorine substituent is best both at donating electrons by resonance and at withdrawing electrons inductively. Because Table 16.1 shows that fluorine is the weakest deactivator of the halogens, we can conclude that electron donation by resonance is the more important factor in determining the relative reactivities of halo-substituted benzenes.

16.4 THE EFFECT OF SUBSTITUENTS ON ORIENTATION

When a substituted benzene undergoes an electrophilic substitution reaction, where does the new substituent attach itself? Is the product of the reaction the ortho isomer, the meta isomer, or the para isomer?

ortho isomer   meta isomer   para isomer

The substituent already attached to the benzene ring determines the location of the new substituent. The attached substituent will have one of two effects: it will direct an incoming substituent either to the ortho *and* para positions, or it will direct an incoming substituent to the meta position. All activating substituents and the weakly deactivating halogens are **ortho–para directors**, and all substituents that are more deactivating than the halogens are **meta directors**. Thus, the substituents can be divided into three groups:

1. All *activating substituents* direct an incoming electrophile to the ortho and para positions.

All activating substituents are ortho–para directors.

toluene   *o*-bromotoluene   *p*-bromotoluene

2. The *weakly deactivating* halogens also direct an incoming electrophile to the ortho and para positions.

The weakly deactivating halogens are ortho–para directors.

bromobenzene   *o*-bromochlorobenzene   *p*-bromochlorobenzene

3. All *moderately and strongly deactivating* substituents direct an incoming electrophile to the meta position.

acetophenone + HNO$_3$ $\xrightarrow{\text{H}_2\text{SO}_4}$ *m*-nitroacetophenone

nitrobenzene + Br$_2$ $\xrightarrow{\text{FeBr}_3}$ *m*-bromonitrobenzene

To understand why a substituent directs an incoming electrophile to a particular position, we must look at the stability of the carbocation intermediate. We have seen that the transition state of the rate-limiting step resembles the carbocation intermediate (Section 16.3). Thus, anything that stabilizes the carbocation intermediate will stabilize the transition state for its formation.

When a substituted benzene undergoes an electrophilic substitution reaction, three different carbocation intermediates can be formed: an *ortho*-substituted carbocation, a *meta*-substituted carbocation, and a *para*-substituted carbocation (Figure 16.1). The relative stabilities of the three carbocations enable us to determine the preferred pathway of the reaction because the more stable the carbocation, the more stable the transition state for its formation will be, and therefore the more rapidly it will be formed (Section 4.3).

When the substituent is one that can donate electrons by *resonance,* the carbocations formed by putting the incoming electrophile on the ortho and para positions have a fourth resonance contributor (Figure 16.1). This is an especially stable resonance contributor because it is the only one whose atoms (except for hydrogen) all have complete octets; it is obtained only by directing an incoming substituent to the ortho and para positions. Therefore, *all substituents that donate electrons by resonance are ortho–para directors.*

All deactivating substituents (except the halogens) are meta directors.

▲ **Figure 16.1**
The structures of the carbocation intermediates formed from the reaction of an electrophile with anisole at the ortho, meta, and para positions.

When the substituent is an alkyl group, the resonance contributors that are highlighted in Figure 16.2 are the most stable. In those contributors, the alkyl group is attached directly to the positively charged carbon and can stabilize it by hyperconjugation.

A relatively stable resonance contributor is obtained only when the incoming group is directed to an ortho or para position. Therefore, *alkyl substituents are ortho–para directors because they donate electrons by hyperconjugation.*

▶ **Figure 16.2**
The structures of the carbocation intermediates formed from the reaction of an electrophile with toluene at the ortho, meta, and para positions.

Substituents with a positive charge or a partial positive charge on the atom attached to the benzene ring will withdraw electrons inductively from the benzene ring, and most will withdraw electrons by resonance as well. For all such substituents, the resonance contributors highlighted in Figure 16.3 are the least stable because they have a positive charge on each of two adjacent atoms, so the most stable carbocation is formed when the incoming electrophile is directed to the meta position. Thus, *all substituents that withdraw electrons (except for the halogens, which are ortho–para directors because they donate electrons by resonance) are meta directors.*

▶ **Figure 16.3**
The structures of the carbocation intermediates formed from the reaction of an electrophile with protonated aniline at the ortho, meta, and para positions.

Notice that the three possible carbocation intermediates in Figures 16.2 and 16.3 are the same, except for the substituent. The nature of that substituent determines whether the resonance contributors with the substituent directly attached to the positively charged carbon are the most stable (as with electron-donating substituents) or the least stable (as with electron-withdrawing substituents).

In summary, as shown in Table 16.1: *all the activating substituents and the weakly deactivating halogens are ortho–para directors. All substituents more deactivating than the halogens are meta directors.* In other words, all substituents that donate electrons either by resonance or by hyperconjugation are ortho–para directors; all substituents that cannot donate electrons are meta directors.

You do not need to resort to memorization to be able to identify a substituent as an ortho–para director or a meta director. It is easy to tell them apart: all ortho–para directors, except for alkyl, aryl, and CH=CHR groups, have at least one lone pair on the atom directly attached to the ring; all meta directors have a positive charge or a partial positive charge on the atom attached to the ring. Take a few minutes to examine the substituents listed in Table 16.1 to see that this is true.

> **All substituents that donate electrons either by resonance or by hyperconjugation are ortho–para directors.**
>
> **All substituents that cannot donate electrons are meta directors.**

PROBLEM 10

a. Draw the resonance contributors for nitrobenzene.
b. Draw the resonance contributors for chlorobenzene.

PROBLEM 11♦

What product(s) would result from nitration of each of the following?
a. propylbenzene   **c.** benzaldehyde   **e.** benzenesulfonic acid
b. bromobenzene   **d.** benzonitrile   **f.** cyclohexylbenzene

PROBLEM 12♦

Are the following substituents ortho–para directors or meta directors?
a. CH=CHC≡N   **b.** NO$_2$ **c.** CH$_2$OH   **d.** COOH   **e.** CF$_3$ **f.** N=O

PROBLEM 13   SOLVED

Give the product(s) obtained from the reaction of each of the following with one equivalent of Br$_2$ and employing the catalyst, FeBr$_3$:

Solution to 13a   The left-hand ring is attached to a substituent that activates that ring by donating electrons to it by resonance. In contrast, the right-hand ring is attached to a substituent that deactivates that ring by withdrawing electrons from it by resonance.

Thus, the left-hand ring is more reactive toward electrophilic aromatic substitution. The activating substituent will direct the bromine to the positions that are ortho and para to it.

> **chem place**   Tutorial: Intermediates in electrophilic aromatic substitution
>
> Tutorial: Nitration of anisole I
>
> Tutorial: Nitration of anisole II

16.5 THE EFFECT OF SUBSTITUENTS ON pK_a

When a substituent either withdraws electrons from a benzene ring or donates electrons to a benzene ring, the pK_a values of substituted phenols, benzoic acids, and protonated anilines will reflect this withdrawal or donation.

Electron-withdrawing groups stabilize a base and, therefore, increase the strength of its conjugate acid. Electron-donating groups destabilize a base, and this decreases the strength of its conjugate acid (Section 1.22). Remember: the stronger the acid, the more stable (weaker) its conjugate base.

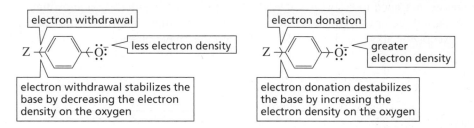

For example, the pK_a of phenol in H_2O at 25 °C is 9.95. The pK_a of *para*-nitrophenol is lower (7.14) because the nitro substituent withdraws electrons from the ring, whereas the pK_a of *para*-methyl phenol is higher (10.19) because the methyl substituent donates electrons to the ring.

OH	OH	OH	OH	OH	OH
OCH$_3$	CH$_3$		Cl	HC=O	NO$_2$
pK_a = 10.20	pK_a = 10.19	pK_a = 9.95	pK_a = 9.38	pK_a = 7.66	pK_a = 7.14
		phenol			

Take a minute to compare the effect a substituent has on the reactivity of a benzene ring toward electrophilic aromatic substitution with the effect the same substituent has on the pK_a of phenol. Notice that the more strongly deactivating the substituent, the lower the pK_a of the phenol; and the more strongly activating the substituent, the higher the pK_a of the phenol. In other words, *electron withdrawal decreases reactivity toward electrophilic aromatic substitution and increases acidity, whereas electron donation increases reactivity toward electrophilic aromatic substitution and decreases acidity.*

A similar substituent effect on pK_a is observed for substituted benzoic acids and substituted protonated anilines: electron-withdrawing substituents increase acidity; electron-donating substituents decrease acidity.

COOH	COOH	COOH	COOH	COOH	COOH
OCH$_3$	CH$_3$		Br	CH$_3$C=O	NO$_2$
pK_a = 4.47	pK_a = 4.34	pK_a = 4.20	pK_a = 4.00	pK_a = 3.70	pK_a = 3.44

The more deactivating (electron withdrawing) the substituent, the more it increases the acidity of a COOH, an OH, or an $^+$NH$_3$ group attached to a benzene ring.

The more activating (electron donating) the substituent, the more it decreases the acidity of a COOH, an OH, or an $^+$NH$_3$ group attached to a benzene ring.

$^+$NH$_3$	$^+$NH$_3$	$^+$NH$_3$	$^+$NH$_3$	$^+$NH$_3$	$^+$NH$_3$
OCH$_3$	CH$_3$		Br	HC=O	NO$_2$
pK_a = 5.29	pK_a = 5.07	pK_a = 4.58	pK_a = 3.91	pK_a = 1.76	pK_a = 0.98

PROBLEM 14 ♦

Which of the compounds in each of the following pairs is more acidic?

a. CH_3COOH or $ClCH_2COOH$

b. O_2NCH_2COOH or $O_2NCH_2CH_2COOH$

c. CH_3CH_2COOH or $\overset{+}{H_3N}CH_2COOH$

d.
or

e. $HOOCCH_2COOH$ or $^-OOCCH_2COOH$

f. $HCOOH$ or CH_3COOH

g. FCH_2COOH or $ClCH_2COOH$

h.
or

chem place Tutorial: Effect of substituents on pK_a

PROBLEM-SOLVING STRATEGY

Explaining the Effect of Substituents on pK_a

The *para*-nitroanilinium ion is 3.60 pK_a units more acidic than the anilinium ion (pK_a = 0.98 versus 4.58), but *para*-nitrobenzoic acid is only 0.76 pK_a unit more acidic than benzoic acid (pK_a = 3.44 versus 4.20). Explain why the nitro substituent causes a large change in pK_a in one case and a small change in pK_a in the other.

Do not expect to be able to solve this kind of problem simply by reading it. First, you need to remember that the acidity of a compound depends on the stability of its conjugate base (Sections 1.18 and 7.9). Next, draw structures of the conjugate bases in question in order to compare their stabilities.

When a proton is lost from the *para*-nitroanilinium ion, the electrons it leaves behind are shared by five atoms. (Draw resonance contributors if you want to see which atoms share the electrons.) In contrast, when a proton is lost from *para*-nitrobenzoic acid, the electrons it leaves behind are shared by two atoms. In other words, loss of a proton leads to greater electron delocalization in one base than in the other. Electron delocalization stabilizes a compound, so the difference in electron delocalization explains why the addition of a nitro substituent has a greater effect on the acidity of an anilinium ion than on benzoic acid.

Now continue on to Problem 15.

PROBLEM 15

Explain why *p*-nitrophenol has a pK_a of 7.14, whereas the pK_a of *m*-nitrophenol is 8.39.

PROBLEM 16 ♦

a. Which is the strongest acid, benzoic acid, *o*-fluorobenzoic acid, or *o*-chlorobenzoic acid? (*Hint*: see Problem 9.)

b. Which of these compounds is the weakest acid?

16.6 THE ORTHO–PARA RATIO

When a benzene ring with an ortho–para-directing substituent undergoes an electrophilic aromatic substitution reaction, what percentage of the product is the ortho isomer and what percentage is the para isomer? Solely on the basis of probability, one would expect more of the ortho product because two ortho positions are available to the incoming electrophile and only one para position. The ortho position, however, is sterically hindered, whereas the para position is not. Consequently, the para isomer will be formed preferentially if either the substituent on the ring or the incoming electrophile is large.

The following nitration reactions illustrate the decrease in the ortho–para ratio as the size of the alkyl substituent increases:

toluene + HNO$_3$ $\xrightarrow{\text{H}_2\text{SO}_4}$ **61%** *o*-nitrotoluene + **39%** *p*-nitrotoluene

ethylbenzene + HNO$_3$ $\xrightarrow{\text{H}_2\text{SO}_4}$ **50%** *o*-ethylnitrobenzene + **50%** *p*-ethylnitrobenzene

tert-butylbenzene + HNO$_3$ $\xrightarrow{\text{H}_2\text{SO}_4}$ **18%** *o-tert*-butylnitrobenzene + **82%** *p-tert*-butylnitrobenzene

Fortunately, the difference in the physical properties of the ortho- and para-substituted isomers is large enough to allow them to be easily separated. Consequently, electrophilic aromatic substitution reactions that lead to both ortho and para isomers are useful in syntheses because the desired product can be easily separated from the reaction mixture.

16.7 ADDITIONAL CONSIDERATIONS REGARDING SUBSTITUENT EFFECTS

It is important to know whether a substituent is activating or deactivating in order to determine the conditions needed to carry out a reaction. For example, methoxy and hydroxy substituents are so strongly activating that halogenation is carried out without the Lewis acid (FeBr$_3$ or FeCl$_3$) catalyst.

anisole + Br$_2$ $\longrightarrow$ *p*-bromoanisole + *o*-bromoanisole

If the Lewis acid catalyst and excess bromine are used, the tribromide is obtained.

anisole + 3 Br$_2$ $\xrightarrow{\text{FeBr}_3}$ **2,4,6-tribromoanisole**

Friedel–Crafts reactions are the slowest of the electrophilic aromatic substitution reactions. Therefore, if a benzene ring has been moderately or strongly deactivated—and remember that all meta directors are moderate or strong deactivators—it will be too unreactive to undergo either Friedel–Crafts acylation or Friedel–Crafts alkylation. In fact, nitrobenzene is so unreactive that it is often used as a solvent for Friedel–Crafts reactions.

A benzene ring with a meta director cannot undergo a Friedel–Crafts reaction.

benzenesulfonic acid

nitrobenzene

Aniline and *N*-substituted anilines also do not undergo Friedel–Crafts reactions. The lone pair on the amino group will complex with the Lewis acid catalyst ($AlCl_3$) needed to carry out the reaction, converting the NH_2 substituent into a deactivating meta director. As we have just seen, Friedel–Crafts reactions do not occur with deactivated benzene rings.

aniline

Phenol and anisole can undergo Friedel–Crafts reactions—at the ortho and para positions—because oxygen, being a weaker base than nitrogen, does not complex with the Lewis acid.

Aniline also cannot be nitrated, because nitric acid is an oxidizing agent and an NH_2 group is easily oxidized. (Nitric acid and aniline can be an explosive combination.)

PROBLEM 17

Show how the following compounds could be synthesized from benzene:

a.   **b.**   **c.**

PROBLEM 18◆

Give the products, if any, of each of the following reactions:
a. benzonitrile + methyl chloride + $AlCl_3$ **c.** benzoic acid + CH_3CH_2Cl + $AlCl_3$
b. aniline + 3 Br_2 **d.** benzene + 2 CH_3Cl + $AlCl_3$

16.8 DESIGNING A SYNTHESIS IV: SYNTHESIS OF MONOSUBSTITUTED AND DISUBSTITUTED BENZENES

As the number of reactions with which we are familiar increases, the more possibilities we are able to choose from when we design a synthesis. For example, we can now design two very different routes for the synthesis of 2-phenylethanol from benzene.

Which route we choose depends on such factors as convenience, expense, and expected yield of the target molecule (the desired product). For example, the first route shown for the synthesis of 2-phenylethanol is the better procedure. The second route has more steps, requires excess benzene to prevent polyalkylation, and uses a radical reaction that can produce unwanted side products. Moreover, the yield of the elimination reaction is not high (because some substitution product is formed as well).

Designing the synthesis of a disubstituted benzene requires careful consideration of the order in which the substituents are to be placed on the ring. For example, if you want to synthesize *m*-bromobenzenesulfonic acid, the sulfonic acid group has to be placed on the ring first, because that group will direct the bromo substituent to the desired meta position.

However, if the desired product is *p*-bromobenzenesulfonic acid, the order of the two reactions must be reversed because only the bromo substituent is an ortho–para director.

Both substituents of *m*-nitroacetophenone are meta directors. However, the Friedel–Crafts acylation reaction must be carried out first because the benzene ring of nitrobenzene is too deactivated to undergo a Friedel–Crafts reaction (Section 16.7).

Another question to consider is, at what point in a reaction sequence should a substituent be chemically modified? In the synthesis of *p*-chlorobenzoic acid from toluene, the methyl group is oxidized *after* it directs the chloro substituent to the para position. (*o*-Chlorobenzoic acid is also formed in this reaction.)

p-chlorobenzoic acid

In the synthesis of *m*-chlorobenzoic acid, the methyl group is oxidized *before* chlorination because a meta director is needed to obtain the desired product.

m-chlorobenzoic acid

Although chemists often have several ways to carry out a reaction, there may be factors that require the use of one particular method. For example, we have seen that there is more than one way to get a straight-chain alkyl group onto a benzene ring (Section 15.18). A Friedel–Crafts alkylation/reduction cannot be used to do so when synthesizing *m*-dipropylbenzene, because a meta-directing acyl group is required to get the second alkyl substituent onto the ring and a Friedel–Crafts reaction cannot be done on a ring with a meta director. Instead, the target molecule can be prepared using a coupling reaction.

m-dipropylbenzene

PROBLEM 19♦

a. Does a coupling reaction have to be used to synthesize *p*-dipropylbenzene?
b. Can a coupling reaction be used to synthesize *p*-dipropylbenzene?

In the following synthesis of *p*-propylbenzenesulfonic acid, the type of reaction employed, the order in which the substituents are put on the benzene ring, and the point at which a substituent is chemically modified must all be considered. The straight-chain propyl substituent must be put on the ring by a Friedel–Crafts acylation rather than alkylation reaction, to avoid the carbocation rearrangement that would occur with the alkylation reaction. The Friedel–Crafts acylation must be carried out before sulfonation because acylation could not be carried out on a ring with a meta-directing sulfonic acid substituent. Finally, the sulfonic acid group must be put on the ring after the carbonyl group is reduced to a methylene group, so that the sulfonic acid group will be directed primarily to the para position by the alkyl group.

p-propylbenzenesulfonic acid

Alternatively, propylbenzene could be prepared using bromobenzene and a coupling reaction (Section 15.17).

p-propylbenzenesulfonic acid

PROBLEM 20

Show how each of the following compounds can be synthesized from benzene:

a. *p*-chloroaniline
b. *m*-chloroaniline
c. *m*-xylene
d. 2-phenylpropene
e. *m*-nitrobenzoic acid

f. *p*-nitrobenzoic acid
g. *m*-bromopropylbenzene
h. *o*-bromopropylbenzene
i. 1-phenyl-2-propanol

16.9 THE SYNTHESIS OF TRISUBSTITUTED BENZENES

When a disubstituted benzene undergoes an electrophilic aromatic substitution reaction, the directing effects of both substituents have to be considered. If both substituents direct the incoming substituent to the same position, the product of the reaction is easily predicted.

both the methyl and nitro substituents direct the incoming substituent to these positions

p-nitrotoluene

2,4-dinitrotoluene

Notice that three positions are activated in the following reaction, but the new substituent ends up on only two of the three. Steric hindrance makes the position between the substituents less accessible.

both the methyl and chloro substituents direct the incoming substituent to these indicated positions

m-chlorotoluene

5-chloro-2-nitrotoluene

3-chloro-4-nitrotoluene

If the two substituents direct the new substituent to different positions, a strongly activating substituent will win out over a weakly activating substituent or a deactivating substituent.

p-methylphenol   2-bromo-
                                4-methylphenol
                                major product

If the two substituents have similar activating properties, neither will dominate and a mixture of products will be obtained.

p-ethyltoluene   4-ethyl-   4-ethyl-
                             2-nitrotoluene   3-nitrotoluene

PROBLEM 21 ◆

Give the major product(s) of each of the following reactions:

a. bromination of *p*-methylbenzoic acid
b. chlorination of *o*-benzenedicarboxylic acid
c. bromination of *p*-chlorobenzoic acid
d. nitration of *p*-fluoroanisole
e. nitration of *p*-methoxybenzaldehyde
f. nitration of *p*-*tert*-butyltoluene

chem Tutorial:
place Synthesis of benzene derivatives

PROBLEM 22 ◆

How many products are obtained from the chlorination of:

a. *o*-xylene?   **b.** *p*-xylene?   **c.** *m*-xylene?

PROBLEM 23   SOLVED

When phenol is treated with Br_2, a mixture of monobromo-, dibromo-, and tribromophenols is obtained. Design a synthesis that would convert phenol primarily to *ortho*-bromophenol.

Solution   In the following synthesis, the bulky sulfonic acid group will add preferentially to the para position. Both the OH and SO_3H groups will direct bromine to the position ortho to the OH group. Heating in dilute acid removes the sulfonic acid group (Section 15.13).

Use of a sulfonic acid group to block the para position is a common strategy for synthesizing high yields of ortho-substituted compounds.

16.10 THE SYNTHESIS OF SUBSTITUTED BENZENES USING ARENEDIAZONIUM SALTS

So far, we have learned how to place a limited number of different substituents on a benzene ring—the substituents listed in Section 16.3 and those that can be obtained from these substituents by chemical conversion (Section 16.1). However, the list of substituents that can be placed on a benzene ring can be greatly expanded using **arenediazonium salts**.

an arenediazonium salt

Displacing the leaving group of a diazonium ion by any of a wide variety of nucleophiles occurs readily because it results in the formation of a molecule of stable nitrogen gas. The mechanism by which the nucleophile displaces the diazonium group depends on the particular nucleophile: some displacements involve phenyl cations, whereas others involve radicals.

benzenediazonium
chloride

Aniline can be converted into an arenediazonium salt by treatment with nitrous acid (HNO_2). Because nitrous acid is unstable, it must be formed in situ, using an aqueous solution of sodium nitrite and HCl or HBr; indeed, N_2 is such a good leaving group that the diazonium salt is synthesized at 0 °C and used immediately without isolation. [The mechanism for conversion of a primary amino group (NH_2) to a diazonium group ($^+N{\equiv}N$) is shown in Section 16.12.]

$$\xrightarrow[\text{0 °C}]{\text{NaNO}_2, \text{HCl}}$$

The nucleophiles $C{\equiv}N$, Cl^-, and Br^- will replace the diazonium group if the appropriate copper(I) salt is added to the solution containing the arenediazonium salt. The reaction of an arenediazonium salt with a copper(I) salt is known as a **Sandmeyer reaction**.

Sandmeyer reactions

benzenediazonium
bromide   bromobenzene

p-toluenediazonium
chloride   p-chlorotoluene

m-bromobenzenediazonium
chloride   m-bromobenzonitrile

chem place Tutorial:
Sandmeyer reaction

KCl and KBr cannot be used in place of CuCl and CuBr in Sandmeyer reactions; the cuprous salts are required. This indicates that the copper(I) ion has a role in the reaction. Although the precise mechanism is not known, it is thought that the copper(I) ion donates an electron to the diazonium salt, forming an aryl radical and nitrogen gas.

Although chloro and bromo substituents can be placed directly on a benzene ring by halogenation, the Sandmeyer reaction can be a useful alternative. For example, if you wanted to make *para*-chloroethylbenzene, the chlorination of ethylbenzene leads to a mixture of ortho and para isomers.

ethylbenzene + Cl_2 $\xrightarrow{FeCl_3}$ o-chloroethylbenzene + p-chloroethylbenzene

If, however, you started with *para*-ethylaniline and used a Sandmeyer reaction for chlorination, only the desired para product would be formed.

p-ethylaniline $\xrightarrow[0\ °C]{NaNO_2,\ HCl}$ (diazonium salt) $\xrightarrow{CuCl}$ p-chloroethylbenzene

PROBLEM 24

Explain why a diazonium group on a benzene ring cannot be used to direct an incoming substituent to the meta position.

PROBLEM 25

Explain why HBr should be used to generate the benzenediazonium salt if bromobenzene is the desired product of the Sandmeyer reaction, whereas HCl should be used if chlorobenzene is the desired product.

An iodo substituent will replace the diazonium group if potassium iodide is added to the solution containing the diazonium ion.

p-toluenediazonium chloride + KI $\longrightarrow$ p-iodotoluene + $N_2\uparrow$ + KCl

Fluoro substitution occurs if the arenediazonium salt is heated with fluoroboric acid (HBF_4). This is known as the **Schiemann reaction**.

Schiemann reaction

$\xrightarrow{HBF_4}$ ... + HCl $\xrightarrow{\Delta}$ fluorobenzene + BF_3 + $N_2\uparrow$

If the acidic aqueous solution in which the diazonium salt has been synthesized is allowed to warm up, an OH group will replace the diazonium group. (H_2O is the nucleophile.)

$\xrightarrow[\Delta]{H_3O^+}$ phenol + $N_2\uparrow$ + HCl

A better yield of phenol is obtained if aqueous copper(I) oxide and copper(II) nitrate are added to the cold solution.

$\xrightarrow[Cu(NO_3)_2,\ H_2O]{Cu_2O}$ p-cresol + $N_2\uparrow$

A hydrogen will replace a diazonium group if the arenediazonium salt is treated with hypophosphorous acid (H_3PO_2). This is a useful reaction if an amino group or a nitro group is needed for directing purposes and subsequently must be removed. It is difficult to envision how 1,3,5-tribromobenzene could be synthesized without such a reaction.

1,3,5-tribromobenzene

PROBLEM 26 ◆

Why is $FeBr_3$ not used as a catalyst in the above reaction?

PROBLEM 27

Write the sequence of steps required for the conversion of benzene into benzenediazonium chloride.

PROBLEM 28   SOLVED

Show how the following compounds could be synthesized from benzene:
a. *m*-dibromobenzene
b. *m*-bromophenol
c. *o*-chlorophenol
d. *m*-nitrotoluene
e. *p*-methylbenzonitrile
f. *m*-chlorobenzaldehyde

Solution to 28a   A bromo substituent is an ortho–para director, so halogenation cannot be used to put both bromo substituents on the ring. Knowing that a bromo substituent can be put on a benzene ring with a Sandmeyer reaction and that the bromo substituent in a Sandmeyer reaction replaces what originally was a meta-directing nitro substituent, we have a route to the synthesis of the target compound.

16.11   THE ARENEDIAZONIUM ION AS AN ELECTROPHILE

In addition to being used to synthesize substituted benzenes, arenediazonium ions can be used as electrophiles in electrophilic aromatic substitution reactions. Because an arenediazonium ion is unstable at room temperature, it can be used as an electrophile only in reactions that can be carried out well below room temperature. In other words, only highly activated benzene rings (phenols, anilines, and *N*-alkylanilines) can undergo electrophilic aromatic substitution reactions with arenediazonium ion electrophiles. The product of the reaction is an *azo compound*. The N=N linkage is called an **azo linkage**. Because the electrophile is so large, substitution takes place preferentially at the less sterically hindered para position. However, if the para position is blocked, substitution will occur at an ortho position.

phenol

m-bromobenzenediazonium chloride

an azo linkage

3-bromo-4'-hydroxyazobenzene
an azo compound

PROBLEM 29

What product is formed from the reaction of *p*-methyphenol with benzenediazonium choride?

The mechanism for electrophilic aromatic substitution with an arenediazonium ion electrophile is the same as the mechanism for electrophilic aromatic substitution with any other electrophile.

MECHANISM FOR ELECTROPHILIC AROMATIC SUBSTITUTION USING AN ARENEDIAZONIUM ION ELECTROPHILE

p-**N,N**-dimethylaminoazobenzene

- The nucleophilic benzene ring reacts with the electrophile.
- A base in the solution removes a proton from the carbon that formed a bond with the electrophile.

Azo compounds, like alkenes, can exist in cis and trans forms. The trans isomer is considerably more stable because the cis isomer has steric strain (Section 4.13).

trans-**azobenzene**   *cis*-**azobenzene**

Azobenzenes are colored compounds because of their extended conjugation (Section 13.19). They are used commercially as dyes.

PROBLEM 30

In the mechanism for electrophilic aromatic substitution with a diazonium ion as the electrophile, why does nucleophilic attack occur on the terminal nitrogen of the diazonium ion rather than on the nitrogen that has the formal positive charge?

PROBLEM 31

Give the structure of the activated benzene ring and the diazonium ion used in the synthesis of each of the following compounds, whose structures can be found on page 539.

a. butter yellow   **b.** methyl orange

16.12 THE MECHANISM FOR THE REACTION OF AMINES WITH NITROUS ACID

We have seen that an NH_2 group attached to a benzene ring forms a diazonium salt by reacting with nitrous acid. An NH_2 group attached to an alkyl group undergoes the same reaction.

an arenediazonium salt

an alkenediazonium salt

Conversion of an NH_2 group to a diazonium group requires a nitrosonium ion. A nitrosonium ion is formed when water is eliminated from protonated nitrous acid, similar to the way the nitronium ion is generated from nitric acid (Section 15.12) and the sulfonium ion is generated from sulfuric acid (Section 15.13).

sodium nitrite

nitrous acid

nitrosonium ion

The mechanism for formation of a diazonium ion is shown below.

MECHANISM FOR FORMATION OF A DIAZONIUM ION FROM ANILINE

aniline
a primary amine

nitrosonium ion

a nitrosamine

a diazonium ion

an *N*-hydroxyazo compound

- In the first step, aniline shares an electron pair with the nitrosonium ion.
- Removal of a proton from nitrogen forms a **nitrosamine** (also called an ***N*-nitroso compound** because a nitroso substituent is bonded to a nitrogen).
- Delocalization of nitrogen's lone pair and protonation on oxygen form a protonated *N*-hydroxyazo compound.
- The protonated *N*-hydroxyazo compound is in equilibrium with its nonprotonated form.
- The *N*-hydroxyazo compound can be reprotonated on nitrogen (reverse reaction) or protonated on oxygen (forward reaction).
- Delocalization of nitrogen's lone pair and elimination of water forms the diazonium ion.

Remember that reactions involving arenediazonium ions must be carried out at 0 °C because they are unstable at higher temperatures. Alkanediazonium ions are even less stable. They lose molecular N_2—even at 0 °C—as they are formed, reacting with whatever nucleophiles are present in the reaction mixture by both $S_N1/E1$ and $S_N2/E2$ mechanisms. Because of the mixture of products obtained, alkanediazonium ions are of limited synthetic use.

A New Cancer-Fighting Drug

Temozolomide, the drug used to treat Senator Ted Kennedy's brain tumor, is a relatively new member in the arsenal of cancer-fighting drugs. The drug can be taken orally, and, while in the circulatory system, it is converted to its active form by reacting with water and losing CO_2. Once inside the cell, the drug eliminates a methyldiazonium ion, a very reactive methylating agent. As we saw in Section 10.11, methylating DNA triggers the death of cancer cells.

(reaction scheme showing)

temozolomide → activated form

methyldiazonium

DNA—Nu—CH₃ + N₂ ← (S_N2 reaction) CH₃—N≡N + ...

PROBLEM 32 ◆

What products would be formed from the reaction of isopropylamine with sodium nitrite and aqueous HCl?

PROBLEM 33

Diazomethane can be used to convert a carboxylic acid into a methyl ester. Propose a mechanism for this reaction.

$$\underset{\substack{\text{a carboxylic}\\\text{acid}}}{\overset{O}{\underset{R}{\parallel}}\!\!C\!\!-\!OH} + \overset{-}{:}CH_2\!\!-\!\overset{+}{N}\!\!\equiv\!\!N \longrightarrow \underset{\substack{\text{a methyl}\\\text{ester}}}{\overset{O}{\underset{R}{\parallel}}\!\!C\!\!-\!OCH_3} + N_2\uparrow$$

a carboxylic acid   diazomethane   a methyl ester

Secondary aryl and alkyl amines react with a nitrosonium ion to form nitrosamines rather than diazonium ions. The mechanism of the reaction is similar to that for the reaction of a primary amine with a nitrosonium ion, except that the reaction stops at the nitrosamine stage. The reaction stops because a secondary amine, unlike a primary amine, does not have the second proton that must be lost in order to generate the diazonium ion.

(reaction scheme)

N-methylaniline
a secondary amine

+ ⁺N=O ⟶ ... ⇌ ...

HB

N-methyl-*N*-nitrosoaniline
a nitrosamine

The product formed when the nitrogen of a *tertiary* amine shares its lone pair with a nitrosonium ion cannot be stabilized by loss of a proton. A tertiary aryl amine, therefore, can undergo an electrophilic aromatic substitution reaction with a nitrosonium ion. The product of the reaction is primarily the para isomer because the bulky dialkylamino group blocks approach of the nitrosonium ion to the ortho position.

N,N-dimethylaniline
a tertiary amine

p-nitroso-N,N-dimethylaniline
85%

Nitrosamines and Cancer

A 1962 outbreak of food poisoning in sheep in Norway was traced to their ingestion of nitrite-treated fish meal. This incident immediately raised concerns about human consumption of nitrite-treated foods, because sodium nitrite, a commonly used food preservative, can react with naturally occurring secondary amines present in food, to produce nitrosamines, which are known to be carcinogenic. Smoked fish, cured meats, and beer all contain nitrosamines. Nitrosamines are also found in cheese because some cheeses are preserved with nitrite and cheese is rich in secondary amines. When consumer groups in the United States asked the Food and Drug Administration to ban the use of sodium nitrite as a preservative, the request was vigorously opposed by the meat-packing industry.

Despite extensive investigations, it has not yet been determined whether the small amounts of nitrosamines present in our food pose a hazard to our health. Until this question is answered, it will be hard to avoid sodium nitrite in our diet. Meanwhile, it is worrisome to note that Japan has both one of the highest gastric cancer rates and the highest average ingestion of sodium nitrite. Some good news, however, is that the concentration of nitrosamines present in bacon has been considerably reduced in recent years by the addition of ascorbic acid—a nitrosamine inhibitor—to the curing mixture. Also, improvements in the malting process have reduced the level of nitrosamines in beer. Dietary sodium nitrite does have a redeeming feature: there is some evidence that it protects against botulism, a type of severe food poisoning.

16.13 NUCLEOPHILIC AROMATIC SUBSTITUTION: AN ADDITION–ELIMINATION MECHANISM

We have seen that aryl halides do not react with nucleophiles under standard reaction conditions because the π electron cloud repels the approach of a nucleophile (Section 8.7).

If, however, the aryl halide has one or more substituents that strongly withdraw electrons from the ring by resonance, a **nucleophilic aromatic substitution** reaction can take place. The electron-withdrawing groups must be positioned ortho or para to the halogen. The greater the number of electron-withdrawing substituents, the more easily the nucleophilic aromatic substitution reaction occurs. Notice the different conditions under which the following reactions occur:

Recall that the strongly electron-withdrawing nitro substituent that *activates* the benzene ring toward *nucleophilic aromatic substitution* reaction *deactivates* the ring toward *electrophilic aromatic substitution* (Section 16.16). In other words, making the ring less electron rich makes it more reactive toward a nucleophile but less reactive toward an electrophile.

Nucleophilic aromatic substitution takes place by a two-step mechanism. The reaction is called an **S_NAr reaction** (substitution nucleophilic aromatic).

An electron-withdrawing substituent increases the reactivity of the benzene ring toward nucleophilic substitution and decreases the reactivity of the benzene ring toward electrophilic substitution.

GENERAL MECHANISM FOR NUCLEOPHILIC AROMATIC SUBSTITUTION

- The nucleophile attacks the carbon bearing the leaving group from a trajectory that is nearly perpendicular to the aromatic ring. (Recall from Section 8.9 that groups cannot be displaced from sp^2 carbon atoms by back-side attack.) Nucleophilic attack forms a resonance-stabilized carbanion intermediate called a *Meisenheimer complex*.

- The leaving group is eliminated, reestablishing the aromaticity of the ring.

In a nucleophilic aromatic substitution reaction, the incoming nucleophile must be a stronger base than the substituent that is being replaced, because the weaker of the two bases will be the one eliminated from the intermediate.

The electron-withdrawing substituent must be ortho or para to the site of nucleophilic attack because the electrons of the attacking nucleophile can be delocalized onto the substituent only if the substituent is in one of those positions.

electrons are delocalized onto the NO$_2$ group

BIOGRAPHY

Jakob Meisenheimer (1876–1934) *was born in Germany. He received a Ph.D. from the University of Munich. He was a professor of chemistry at the Universities of Munich, Greitswald, and Tubingen.*

A variety of substituents can be placed on a benzene ring by means of a nucleophilic aromatic substitution reaction. The only requirement is that the incoming group be a stronger base than the group that is being replaced.

p-fluoronitrobenzene + CH$_3$O$^-$ $\xrightarrow{\Delta}$ p-nitroanisole + F$^-$

1-bromo-2,4-dinitrobenzene + CH$_3$CH$_2$NH$_2$ $\xrightarrow{\Delta}$ [intermediate] $\xrightarrow{HO^-}$ N-ethyl-2,4-dinitro-aniline + H$_2$O

PROBLEM 34

Draw resonance contributors for the carbanion that would be formed if *meta*-chloronitrobenzene were to react with hydroxide ion. Why does it not react?

PROBLEM 35 ♦

a. List the following compounds in order of decreasing tendency to undergo nucleophilic aromatic substitution:

   chlorobenzene   1-chloro-2,4-dinitrobenzene   *p*-chloronitrobenzene

b. List the same compounds in order of decreasing tendency to undergo electrophilic aromatic substitution.

PROBLEM 36

Show how each of the following compounds could be synthesized from benzene:

a. *o*-nitrophenol   **c.** *p*-bromoanisole
b. *p*-nitroaniline   **d.** anisole

BIOGRAPHY

Martin D. Kamen (1913–2002), *born in Toronto, was the first person to isolate* ^{14}C*, which immediately became the most useful of all the isotopes in chemical and biochemical research. Kamen received a B.S. and a Ph.D. from the University of Chicago and became a U.S. citizen in 1938. He was a professor at the University of California, Berkeley; at Washington University, St. Louis; and at Brandeis University. He was also one of the founding professors of the University of California, San Diego. In later years, he became a member of the faculty at the University of Southern California. He received the Fermi medal in 1996.*

16.14 NUCLEOPHILIC AROMATIC SUBSTITUTION: AN ELIMINATION–ADDITION MECHANISM THAT FORMS A BENZYNE INTERMEDIATE

An aryl halide such as chlorobenzene can undergo a nucleophilic substitution reaction in the presence of a very strong base such as $^-$NH$_2$. This reaction has two surprising aspects: the aryl halide does not have to contain an electron-withdrawing group, and the incoming substituent does not always end up on the carbon vacated by the leaving group. For example, when chlorobenzene—with the carbon to which the chlorine is attached isotopically labeled with ^{14}C—is treated with amide ion in liquid ammonia, aniline is obtained as the product. Half of the product has the amino group attached to the isotopically labeled carbon (denoted by the asterisk) as expected, but the other half has the amino group attached to the carbon adjacent to the labeled carbon. These are the only products formed. Anilines with the amino group two or three carbons removed from the labeled carbon are not formed.

chlorobenzene   + $^-NH_2$ $\xrightarrow{\text{NH}_3 \text{ (liq)}}$

approximately equal amounts of the two products are obtained

The fact that the two products are formed in approximately equal amounts indicates that the reaction takes place by a mechanism that forms an intermediate in which the two carbons to which the amino group is attached in the product are equivalent. The mechanism that accounts for the experimental observations involves the formation of a **benzyne intermediate**. Benzyne has a triple bond between two adjacent carbons of benzene.

MECHANISM FOR FORMATION OF A BENZYNE INTERMEDIATE

benzyne

- The strongly basic $^-NH_2$ removes a proton from the position ortho to the halogen.
- The halide ion is eliminated, thereby forming benzyne.

MECHANISM FOR REACTION OF A BENZYNE INTERMEDIATE

benzyne

- The incoming nucleophile can attack either of the carbons of the "triple bond" of benzyne.
- Protonation of the resulting anion forms the substitution product.

The overall reaction is an elimination–addition reaction: benzyne is formed in an elimination reaction and immediately undergoes an addition reaction.

Substitution at the carbon that was attached to the leaving group is called **direct substitution**. Substitution at the adjacent carbon is called **cine substitution** (cine comes from *kinesis,* which is Greek for "movement"). In the following reaction, *o*-toluidine is the direct-substitution product; *m*-toluidine is the cine-substitution product.

o-bromotoluene   +   NaNH$_2$ $\xrightarrow{\text{NH}_3 \text{ (liq)}}$ *o*-toluidine
direct-substitution product   +   *m*-toluidine
cine-substitution product

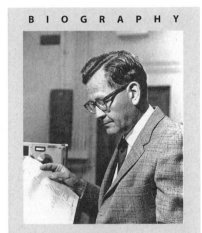

BIOGRAPHY

*The labeling experiment that proved the formation of a benzyne intermediate was done by **John D. Roberts**, who was born in Los Angeles in 1918. He received both his B.A. and Ph.D. degrees from UCLA. Roberts arrived at the California Institute of Technology in 1952 as a Guggenheim fellow and has been a professor there since 1953.*

Benzyne is an extremely reactive species. In Section 6.4, we saw that in a molecule with a triple bond, the two *sp* carbons and the atoms attached to these carbons (C—C ≡C—C) are linear because the bond angles are 180°. Four linear atoms cannot be incorporated into a six-membered ring, so the C—C≡C—C system in benzyne is distorted: the original π bond is unchanged, but the *p* orbitals that form the new π bond are not parallel to one another (Figure 16.4). Therefore, they cannot overlap as well as the *p* orbitals that form a normal π bond, resulting in a much weaker and much more reactive bond.

▶ **Figure 16.4**
Orbital pictures of the bond formed: (a) by overlapping *p* orbitals in a normal triple bond and (b) by overlapping *p* orbitals in the distorted "triple bond" in benzyne.

good overlap

poor overlap

a.

b.

R—C═════C—R

Although benzyne is too unstable to be isolated, evidence that it is formed can be obtained by a trapping experiment. When furan is added to a reaction that forms a benzyne intermediate, furan traps the benzyne intermediate by reacting with it in a Diels–Alder reaction (Section 7.12). The product of the Diels–Alder reaction can be isolated.

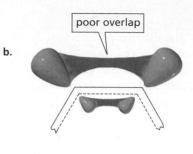

benzyne
a dienophile

furan
a diene

the product of the Diels–Alder reaction

A synthesis employing a benzyne intermediate is a good way to prepare *meta*-amino-substituted aryl ethers (see Problem 78). The amide ion preferentially attacks the meta position because there is less steric hindrance at this position and the resulting negative charge can be stabilized by the adjacent electron-withdrawing oxygen.

chem Tutorial:
place Terms for the reactions of substituted benzenes

PROBLEM 37

Propose a mechanism to account for the fact that when a basic solution of *p*-chlorotoluene is heated with sodium amide in liquid ammonia, both *p*-cresol and *m*-cresol are formed.

PROBLEM 38

Give the products that would be obtained from the reaction of the following compounds with sodium amide in liquid ammonia:

a.

CH₃

Cl

b.

CH₂CH₃

Br

c.

CH₃

Br

CH₃

d.

CH₃

Br

SUMMARY

Benzene rings with substituents other than halo, nitro, sulfonic acid, alkyl, and acyl can be prepared by synthesizing one of these substituted benzenes and then chemically changing the substituent. The relative positions of two substituents on a benzene ring are indicated in the compound's name either by numbers or by the prefixes *ortho, meta,* and *para.*

The nature of the substituent affects the reactivity of the benzene ring: the rate of electrophilic aromatic substitution is increased by electron-donating substituents and decreased by electron-withdrawing substituents. Substituents can withdraw electrons **inductively**, donate electrons by hyperconjugation, and withdraw and donate electrons by resonance.

The ability of a substituent to withdraw electrons from or donate electrons to a benzene ring is reflected in the pK_a values of substituted phenols, benzoic acids, and protonated anilines: electron withdrawal increases acidity, electron donation decreases acidity.

The nature of the substituent affects the placement of an incoming substituent The stability of the carbocation intermediate determines the position to which a substituent directs an incoming electrophile. All activating substituents and the weakly deactivating halogens are **ortho–para directors**; all substituents more deactivating than the halogens are **meta directors**. Ortho–para directors, with the exception of alkyl, aryl, and CH=CHR, have a lone pair on the atom attached to the ring; meta directors have a positive or partial positive charge on the atom attached to the ring. Ortho–para-directing substituents form the para isomer preferentially if either the substituent or the incoming electrophile is large.

In planning the synthesis of disubstituted benzenes, the order in which the substituents are placed on the ring and the point in a reaction sequence at which a substituent is chemically modified are important considerations. When a disubstituted benzene undergoes an electrophilic aromatic substitution reaction, the directing effect of both substituents has to be considered.

RO- and HO-substituted benzenes are halogenated without a Lewis acid. Benzene rings with meta-directing substituents cannot undergo Friedel–Crafts reactions. Aniline and *N*-alkyl substituted anilines also cannot undergo Friedel–Crafts reactions.

The kinds of substituents that can be placed on benzene rings are greatly expanded by reactions of arene diazonium salts, nucleophilic aromatic substitution reactions, and reactions involving a benzyne intermediate. Aniline and substituted anilines react with nitrous acid to form **arenediazonium salts**; a diazonium group can be displaced by a nucleophile. Arenediazonium ions can be used as electrophiles with highly activated benzene rings to form **azo compounds** that can exist in cis and trans forms. Secondary amines react with nitrous acid to form **nitrosamines**.

An aryl halide with one or more substituents ortho or para to the leaving group that strongly withdraws electrons by resonance can undergo a **nucleophilic aromatic substitution** (S_NAr) reaction: the nucleophile forms a resonance-stabilized carbanion intermediate, and then the leaving group departs, reestablishing the aromaticity of the ring. The incoming nucleophile must be a stronger base than the substituent being replaced. A substituent that deactivates a benzene ring toward electrophilic substitution activates it toward nucleophilic substitution.

In the presence of a strong base, an aryl halide undergoes a nucleophilic substitution reaction via a **benzyne intermediate**. After a hydrogen halide is eliminated, the nucleophile can attack either of the carbons of the distorted triple bond in benzyne. **Direct substitution** is substitution at the carbon that was attached to the leaving group; **cine substitution** is substitution at the adjacent carbon.

SUMMARY OF REACTIONS

1. Reactions of a substituent on a benzene ring (Section 16.1)

2. Reactions of amines with nitrous acid (Section 16.12)

primary amine

$C_6H_5-NH_2$ $\xrightarrow[\text{0 °C}]{\text{NaNO}_2\text{, HCl}}$ $C_6H_5-\overset{+}{N}\equiv N$ Cl^-

secondary amine

$C_6H_5-NHCH_3$ $\xrightarrow[\text{0 °C}]{\text{NaNO}_2\text{, HCl}}$ $C_6H_5-\underset{|}{\overset{CH_3}{N}}-N=O$

tertiary amine

$C_6H_5-N(CH_3)_2$ $\xrightarrow[\text{0 °C}]{\text{NaNO}_2\text{, HCl}}$ $O=N-C_6H_4-N(CH_3)_2$

3. Replacement of a diazonium group (Section 16.10)

$C_6H_5-\overset{+}{N}\equiv N$ Br^- $\xrightarrow{\text{CuBr}}$ C_6H_5-Br + $N_2\uparrow$

$C_6H_5-\overset{+}{N}\equiv N$ Cl^- $\xrightarrow[\Delta]{\text{HBF}_4}$ C_6H_5-F + BF_3 + $N_2\uparrow$

$C_6H_5-\overset{+}{N}\equiv N$ Cl^- $\xrightarrow{\text{CuCl}}$ C_6H_5-Cl + $N_2\uparrow$

$C_6H_5-\overset{+}{N}\equiv N$ Cl^- $\xrightarrow{\text{H}_3\text{PO}_2}$ C_6H_5-H + $N_2\uparrow$

$C_6H_5-\overset{+}{N}\equiv N$ Cl^- $\xrightarrow{\text{CuC}\equiv\text{N}}$ $C_6H_5-C\equiv N$ + $N_2\uparrow$

$C_6H_5-\overset{+}{N}\equiv N$ Cl^- $\xrightarrow[\Delta]{\text{H}_3\text{O}^+}$ C_6H_5-OH + HCl + $N_2\uparrow$

$C_6H_5-\overset{+}{N}\equiv N$ Cl^- $\xrightarrow[\text{Cu(NO}_3)_2\text{, H}_2\text{O}]{\text{Cu}_2\text{O}}$ C_6H_5-OH + $N_2\uparrow$

$C_6H_5-\overset{+}{N}\equiv N$ Cl^- $\xrightarrow{\text{KI}}$ C_6H_5-I + $N_2\uparrow$

4. Formation of an azo compound (Section 16.11)

C_6H_5-OH + $C_6H_5-\overset{+}{N}\equiv N$ Cl^- $\longrightarrow$ $HO-C_6H_4-N=N-C_6H_5$

5. Nucleophilic aromatic substitution reactions (Section 16.13)

6. Nucleophilic substitution via a benzyne intermediate (Section 16.14)

direct-substitution   cine-substitution
product   product

KEY TERMS

activating substituent (p. 667)
arenediazonium salt (p. 683)
azo linkage (p. 686)
benzyne intermediate (p. 693)
cine substitution (p. 693)
deactivating substituent (p. 667)

direct substitution (p. 693)
donate electrons by resonance (p. 668)
inductive electron withdrawal (p. 667)
meta director (p. 672)
nitrosamine (p. 688)
N-nitroso compound (p. 688)

nucleophilic aromatic substitution (p. 690)
ortho–para director (p. 672)
Sandmeyer reaction (p. 684)
Schiemann reaction (p. 685)
S$_N$Ar reaction (p. 691)
withdraw electrons by resonance (p. 681)

PROBLEMS

39. Draw the structure of each of the following:
   a. *m*-ethylphenol
   b. *p*-nitrobenzenesulfonic acid
   c. (*E*)-2-phenyl-2-pentene

   d. *o*-bromoaniline
   e. 2-chloroanthracene
   f. *m*-chlorostyrene

   g. *o*-nitroanisole
   h. 2,4-dichlorotoluene

40. Name the following:

41. Provide the necessary reagents next to the arrows.

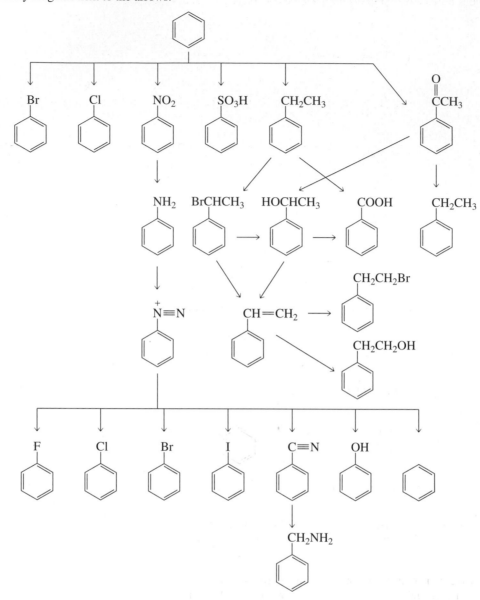

42. Answer the following questions, referring to the four structures shown below:

| COOH pKₐ = 4.2 | COOH (F, ortho) pKₐ = 3.3 | COOH (Cl, ortho) pKₐ = 2.9 | COOH (Br, ortho) pKₐ = 2.8 |

a. Why are the *ortho*-halo-substituted benzoic acids stronger acids than benzoic acid?
b. Why is *o*-fluorobenzoic acid the weakest of the *ortho*-halo-substituted benzoic acids?
c. Why do *o*-chlorobenzoic acid and *o*-bromobenzoic have similar pK_a values?

43. Give the product(s) of each of the following reactions:
a. benzoic acid + HNO_3/H_2SO_4
b. isopropylbenzene + Cl_2 + $FeCl_3$
c. *p*-xylene + acetyl chloride + $AlCl_3$ followed by H_2O
d. *o*-methylaniline + benzenediazonium chloride

e. cyclohexyl phenyl ether + Br_2
f. phenol + H_2SO_4 + Δ
g. ethylbenzene + $Br_2/FeBr_3$
h. *m*-xylene + $Na_2Cr_2O_7$ + HCl + Δ

44. Rank the following substituted anilines in order of decreasing basicity:

CH_3—⟨⟩—NH_2 CH_3O—⟨⟩—NH_2 $CH_3\overset{O}{\overset{\|}{C}}$—⟨⟩—$NH_2$ Br—⟨⟩—NH_2

45. Explain why anisole is nitrated more rapidly than thioanisole under the same conditions.

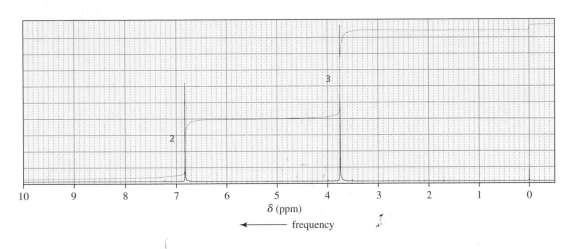

anisole   thioanisole

46. The compound with the following ^{1}H NMR spectrum is known to be highly reactive toward electrophilic aromatic substitution. Identify the compound.

47. Give the product of each of the following reactions:

a. $\xrightarrow[\text{2. H}_2\text{O}]{\text{1. AlCl}_3}$

b. $\xrightarrow[\text{2. H}_2\text{O}]{\text{1. AlCl}_3}$

48. Give the product of each of the following reactions:

a. $\xrightarrow{\text{AlCl}_3}$

b.   + $\xrightarrow{\text{AlCl}_3}$

49. Show how the following compounds could be synthesized from benzene:
   a. *m*-chlorobenzenesulfonic acid
   b. *m*-chloroethylbenzene
   c. benzyl alcohol
   d. *m*-bromobenzonitrile
   e. 1-phenylpentane
   f. *m*-hydroxybenzoic acid
   g. *m*-bromobenzoic acid
   h. *p*-cresol

50. For each horizontal row of substituted benzenes shown below indicate
   a. the one that would be the most reactive in an electrophilic aromatic substitution reaction.
   b. the one that would be the least reactive in an electrophilic aromatic substitution reaction.
   c. the one that would yield the highest percentage of meta product in an electrophilic aromatic substitution reaction.

CH_3 CHF_2 CF_3

$\overset{+}{N}(CH_3)_3$ $CH_2\overset{+}{N}(CH_3)_3$ $CH_2CH_2\overset{+}{N}(CH_3)_3$

OCH_2CH_3 CH_2OCH_3 $\overset{O}{\overset{\|}{C}}OCH_3$

51. Arrange the following groups of compounds in order of decreasing reactivity toward electrophilic aromatic substitution:
a. benzene, ethylbenzene, chlorobenzene, nitrobenzene, anisole
b. 1-chloro-2,4-dinitrobenzene, 2,4-dinitrophenol, 2,4-dinitrotoluene
c. toluene, *p*-cresol, benzene, *p*-xylene
d. benzene, benzoic acid, phenol, propylbenzene
e. *p*-nitrotoluene, 2-chloro-4-nitrotoluene, 2,4-dinitrotoluene, *p*-chlorotoluene
f. bromobenzene, chlorobenzene, fluorobenzene, iodobenzene

52. Give the products of the following reactions:

53. For each of the statements in Column I, choose a substituent from Column II that fits the description for the following compound:

Column I	Column II
a. Z donates electrons by hyperconjugation and does not donate or withdraw electrons by resonance.	OH
b. Z withdraws electrons inductively and withdraws electrons by resonance.	Br
c. Z deactivates the ring and directs ortho–para.	$^{+}NH_3$
d. Z withdraws electrons inductively, donates electrons by resonance, and activates the ring.	CH_2CH_3
e. Z withdraws electrons inductively and does not donate or withdraw electrons by resonance.	NO_2

54. Describe two ways to prepare anisole from benzene.

55. For each of the following compounds, indicate the ring carbon that would be nitrated if the compound is treated with HNO_3/H_2SO_4:

56. Show two ways that the following compound could be synthesized:

57. Show how the following compounds could be synthesized from benzene:

a. *N,N,N*-trimethylanilinium iodide
b. benzyl methyl ether
c. *p*-benzylchlorobenzene
d. 2-methyl-4-nitrophenol
e. *p*-nitroaniline

f. *m*-bromoiodobenzene
g. *p*-dideuteriobenzene
h. *p*-nitro-*N*-methylaniline
i. 1-bromo-3-nitrobenzene

58. A mixture of 0.10 mol benzene and 0.10 mol *p*-xylene was allowed to react with 0.10 mol nitronium ion until all the nitronium ion was gone. Two products were obtained: 0.002 mol of one and 0.098 mol of the other.

a. What was the major product?
b. Why was more of one product obtained than of the other?

59. Which of the following compounds will react with HBr more rapidly?

$$CH_3 - \bigcirc - CH=CH_2 \quad \text{or} \quad CH_3O - \bigcirc - CH=CH_2$$

60. Would *m*-xylene or *p*-xylene react more rapidly with $Cl_2 + FeCl_3$? Explain your answer.

61. What products would be obtained from the reaction of the following compounds with $Na_2Cr_2O_7 + HCl + \Delta$?

a. [structure: benzene ring with CH₂CH₃ and CH₃ substituents]

b. [structure: benzene ring with CH₂CH₂CH₂CH₃ and CHCH₃/CH₃ substituents]

c. [structure: benzene ring with CH₃ and C(CH₃)₃ substituents]

62. Which set of underlined hydrogens will have its ^1H NMR signal at a higher frequency?

a. $CH_3CH_2C\underline{H}_3$ or $CH_3OCH_2C\underline{H}_3$

b. $CH_3CH=C\underline{H}_2$ or $CH_3OCH=C\underline{H}_2$

63. A student had prepared three ethyl-substituted benzaldehydes, but had neglected to label them. The premed student at the next bench said they could be identified by brominating a sample of each and determining how many bromo-substituted products were formed. Is the premed student's advice sound?

64. Describe how naphthalene could be prepared from the given starting material.

[structure: benzene ring with CH₂CH₂CH₂Cl] $\xrightarrow{?}$ [naphthalene structure]

65. Identify A–L:

[reaction scheme: benzene with 1. CH₃CCl / AlCl₃, 2. H₂O → A; A with HNO₃/H₂SO₄ → B; down H₂NNH₂, HO⁻, Δ; D ← Na₂Cr₂O₇, HCl — C — Br₂/hν → E — CH₃O⁻ → F — HI/Δ → G; down (CH₃)₃CO⁻; K + L ← CH₃Cl/AlCl₃ — H — HBr/peroxide → I — ⁻C≡N → J]

66. Using resonance contributors for the intermediate carbocation, explain why a phenyl group is an ortho–para director.

$$+ \ Cl_2 \ \xrightarrow{FeCl_3} \quad + $$

biphenyl

67. The pK_a values of a few ortho-, meta-, and para-substituted benzoic acids are shown here:

pK_a = 2.94   pK_a = 3.83   pK_a = 3.99   pK_a = 2.17   pK_a = 3.49   pK_a = 3.44

pK_a = 4.95   pK_a = 4.73   pK_a = 4.89

The relative pK_a values depend on the substituent. For chloro-substituted benzoic acids, the ortho isomer is the most acidic and the para isomer is the least acidic; for nitro-substituted benzoic acids, the ortho isomer is the most acidic and the meta isomer is the least acidic; and for amino-substituted benzoic acids, the meta isomer is the most acidic and the ortho isomer is the least acidic. Explain these relative acidities.

$$Cl: ortho > meta > para \qquad NO_2: ortho > para > meta \qquad NH_2: meta > para > ortho$$

68. When heated with an acidic solution of sodium dichromate, compound A forms benzoic acid. Identify compound A from its ^{1}H NMR spectrum.

69. Describe two synthetic routes for the preparation of *p*-methoxyaniline with benzene as the starting material.

70. Which is a more stable intermediate in each pair?

a.   or

b.   or

71. If phenol is allowed to sit in D_2O that contains a small amount of D_2SO_4, what products will be formed?

72. Show how the following compounds could be prepared from benzene:

a.

b.

c.

d.

73. An unknown compound reacts with ethyl chloride and aluminum trichloride to form a compound that has the following ^1H NMR spectrum. Give the structure of the compound.

δ (ppm)

⟵ frequency

74. How could you distinguish among the following compounds, using
    a. their infrared spectra?   **b.** their ^1H NMR spectra?

A   B   C   D   E   F   G

75. The following tertiary alkyl bromides undergo an S_N1 reaction in aqueous acetone to form the corresponding tertiary alcohols. List the alkyl bromides in order of decreasing reactivity.

A   B   C   D   E

76. *p*-Fluoronitrobenzene is more reactive than *p*-chloronitrobenzene toward hydroxide ion. What does this tell you about the rate-determining step for nucleophilic aromatic substitution?

77. Propose a mechanism for the following reaction:

78. Starting with benzene, show how *meta*-aminoanisole could be prepared by a synthesis that
  a. involves a benzyne intermediate.
  b. does not involve a benzyne intermediate.

79. a. Explain why the following reaction leads to the products shown:

  b. What product would be obtained from the following reaction?

80. Describe how mescaline could be synthesized from benzene. The structure of mescaline is given on page 660.

81. Propose a mechanism for the following reaction that explains why the configuration of the asymmetric center in the reactant is retained in the product:

82. Explain why hydroxide ion catalyzes the reaction of piperidine with 2,4-dinitroanisole but has no effect on the reaction of piperidine with 1-chloro-2,4-dinitrobenzene.

piperidine

83. Propose a reasonable mechanism for the following reactions.

Carbonyl Compounds

The three chapters in Part 6 focus on the reactions of compounds that contain a carbonyl group. Carbonyl compounds can be placed in one of two classes: those that contain a group that can be replaced by another group (Class I) and those that contain a group that cannot be replaced by another group (Class II).

CHAPTER 17
Carbonyl Compounds I:
Reactions of Carboxylic Acids and Carboxylic Acid Derivatives

Class I carbonyl compounds undergo *nucleophilic addition–elimination reactions* that are essentially *nucleophilic acyl substitution reactions*. These reactions are discussed in **Chapter 17**, where you will see that all Class I carbonyl compounds react with nucleophiles in the same way: the nucleophile adds to the carbonyl carbon, forming an unstable tetrahedral intermediate that collapses by eliminating the weakest base. As a result, all you need to know to determine the product of one of these reactions—or even whether a reaction will occur—is the relative basicity of the groups in the tetrahedral intermediate.

CHAPTER 18
Carbonyl Compounds II:
Reactions of Aldehydes and Ketones •
More Reactions of Carboxylic Acid Derivatives •
Reactions of α, β-Unsaturated Carbonyl Compounds

Chapter 18 compares Class I and Class II carbonyl compounds by discussing their reactions with good nucleophiles—carbon nucleophiles and hydride ion. It then looks at the reactions of

Class II carbonyl compounds with poor nucleophiles—nitrogen and oxygen nucleophiles. You will have seen in Chapter 17 that Class I carbonyl compounds undergo *nucleophilic addition–elimination* reactions with poor nucleophiles; now you will see that they also undergo addition–elimination reaction with good nucleophiles (and the species eliminated is always the group attached to the acyl group in the reactant). Class II carbonyl compounds, by contrast, undergo *nucleophilic addition* reactions with good nucleophiles and *nucleophilic addition–elimination* reactions with poor nucleophiles (and the species eliminated is always water). What you learn in Chapter 17 about the partitioning of tetrahedral intermediates formed by Class I carbonyl compounds is revisited in this chapter with Class II carbonyl compounds. The reactions of α, β-unsaturated Class I and Class II carbonyl compounds are also discussed.

CHAPTER 19
Carbonyl Compounds III:
Reactions at the α-Carbon

Many carbonyl compounds have two sites of reactivity: the carbonyl group *and* the α-carbon. Chapter 17 and Chapter 18 discuss the reactions of carbonyl compounds that take place at the carbonyl group. **Chapter 19** examines the reactions of carbonyl compounds that take place at the α-carbon.

17

Carbonyl Compounds I: Reactions of Carboxylic Acids and Carboxylic Acid Derivatives

Penicillin G

THE **CARBONYL GROUP**—A CARBON DOUBLE BONDED TO AN OXYGEN—IS PROBABLY THE most important functional group. Compounds containing carbonyl groups—called **carbonyl** ("car-bo-neel") **compounds**—are abundant in nature, and many play important roles in biological processes. Hormones, vitamins, amino acids, proteins, drugs, and flavorings are just a few of the carbonyl compounds that affect us daily.

An **acyl group** consists of a carbonyl group attached to an alkyl group (R) or to an aryl group (Ar).

a carbonyl group   acyl groups

The group (or atom) attached to the acyl group strongly affects the reactivity of the carbonyl compound. In fact, carbonyl compounds can be divided into two classes determined by that group. Class I carbonyl compounds are those in which the acyl group is attached to a group (or atom) that *can* be replaced by another group. Carboxylic acids, acyl halides, acid anhydrides, esters, and amides belong to this class. All of these compounds contain a group (OH, Cl, OR, NH$_2$, NHR, NR$_2$) that can be replaced by a nucleophile.

Acyl halides, acid anhydrides, esters, and amides are all called **carboxylic acid derivatives** because they differ from a carboxylic acid only in the nature of the group or atom that has replaced the OH group of the carboxylic acid.

Class II carbonyl compounds are those in which the acyl group is attached to a group that *cannot* be readily replaced by another group. Aldehydes and ketones belong to this class. The H bonded to the acyl group of an aldehyde and the R group bonded to the acyl group of a ketone cannot be readily replaced by a nucleophile.

carbonyl compounds with groups that cannot be replaced by a nucleophile

R—$\overset{\overset{\displaystyle O}{\|}}{C}$—$H$	R'—$\overset{\overset{\displaystyle O}{\|}}{C}$—$R$
an aldehyde	a ketone

We have seen that weak bases are good leaving groups and strong bases are poor leaving groups because weak bases do not share their electrons as well as strong bases do (Section 8.2). The pK_a values of the conjugate acids of the leaving groups of various carbonyl compounds are listed in Table 17.1. Notice that the acyl groups of Class I carbonyl compounds are attached to weaker bases (except for $^-NH_2$, which we will see can be converted to NH_3 with a conjugate acid p$K_a = 9.4$) than are the acyl groups of Class II carbonyl compounds. (Remember that the lower the pK_a, the stronger the acid and the weaker its conjugate base.) The hydrogen of an aldehyde and the alkyl group of a ketone are too basic to be replaced by another group.

a carboxylic acid

an acyl chloride

an ester

an amide

Table 17.1	The pK_a Values of the Conjugate Acids of the Leaving Groups of Carbonyl Compounds		
Carbonyl compound	**Leaving group**	**Conjugate acid of the leaving group**	**pK_a**
Class I			
R—$\overset{\overset{O}{\|}}{C}$—$Br$	Br^-	HBr	−9
R—$\overset{\overset{O}{\|}}{C}$—$Cl$	Cl^-	HCl	−7
R—$\overset{\overset{O}{\|}}{C}$—$O$—$\overset{\overset{O}{\|}}{C}$—$R$	^-O—$\overset{\overset{O}{\|}}{C}$—$R$	R—$\overset{\overset{O}{\|}}{C}$—$OH$	~3–5
R—$\overset{\overset{O}{\|}}{C}$—$OR'$	$^-OR'$	$R'OH$	~15–16
R—$\overset{\overset{O}{\|}}{C}$—$OH$	^-OH	H_2O	15.7
R—$\overset{\overset{O}{\|}}{C}$—$NH_2$	$^-NH_2$	NH_3	36
Class II			
R—$\overset{\overset{O}{\|}}{C}$—$H$	H^-	H_2	35
R—$\overset{\overset{O}{\|}}{C}$—$R$	R^-	RH	> 60

This chapter discusses the reactions of Class I carbonyl compounds. We will see that these compounds undergo substitution reactions, because they have an acyl group attached to a group that can be replaced by a nucleophile. The reactions of Class II carbonyl compounds—aldehydes and ketones—will be considered in Chapter 18, where we will see that these compounds *do not* undergo substitution reactions because their acyl group is attached to a group that *cannot* be replaced by a nucleophile.

17.1 THE NOMENCLATURE OF CARBOXYLIC ACIDS AND CARBOXYLIC ACID DERIVATIVES

We will look at the names of carboxylic acids first because their names form the basis of the names of the other carbonyl compounds.

Naming Carboxylic Acids

The functional group of a carboxylic acid is called a **carboxyl group**.

In systematic (IUPAC) nomenclature, a **carboxylic acid** is named by replacing the terminal "e" of the alkane name with "oic acid." For example, the one-carbon alkane is methan*e*, so the one-carbon carboxylic acid is methan*oic acid*.

Carboxylic acids containing six or fewer carbons are frequently called by their common names. These names were chosen by early chemists to describe some feature of the compound, usually its origin. For example, formic acid is found in ants, bees, and other stinging insects; its name comes from *formica*, which is Latin for "ant." Acetic acid—contained in vinegar—got its name from *acetum*; the Latin word for "vinegar." Propionic acid is the smallest acid that shows some of the characteristics of the larger fatty acids (Section 27.1); its name comes from the Greek words *pro* ("the first") and *pion* ("fat"). Butyric acid is found in rancid butter; the Latin word for "butter" is *butyrum*. Caproic acid is found in goat's milk; if you have the occasion to smell both a goat and caproic acid, you will find they have similar odors. *Caper* is the Latin word for "goat."

In systematic nomenclature, the position of a substituent is designated by a number. The carbonyl carbon is always the C-1 carbon. In common nomenclature, the position of a substituent is designated by a lowercase Greek letter, and the carbonyl carbon is not given a designation. The carbon adjacent to the carbonyl carbon is the α-carbon, the carbon adjacent to the α-carbon is the β-carbon, and so on.

α = alpha
β = beta
γ = gamma
δ = delta
ε = epsilon

Take a careful look at the following examples to make sure that you understand the difference between systematic (IUPAC) and common nomenclature:

systematic name:	2-methoxybutanoic acid	3-bromopentanoic acid	4-chlorohexanoic acid
common name:	α-methoxybutyric acid	β-bromovaleric acid	γ-chlorocaproic acid

Carboxylic acids in which a carboxyl group is attached to a ring are named by adding "carboxylic acid" to the name of the cyclic compound.

cyclohexanecarboxylic acid

trans-3-methylcyclopentanecarboxylic acid

1,2-benzenedicarboxylic acid

Naming Acyl Halides

Acyl halides have a Cl or Br in place of the OH group of a carboxylic acid. The most common acyl halides are acyl chlorides. Acyl halides are named by replacing "ic acid" of the acid name with "yl chloride" (or "yl bromide"). For acids ending with "carboxylic acid," "carboxylic acid" is replaced with "carbonyl chloride" (or "carbonyl bromide").

systematic name:	ethanoyl chloride	3-methylpentanoyl bromide	cyclopentanecarbonyl chloride
common name:	acetyl chloride	β-methylvaleryl bromide	

Acid Anhydrides

Loss of water from two molecules of a carboxylic acid results in an **acid anhydride**. "Anhydride" means "without water."

an acid anhydride

If the two carboxylic acid molecules forming the acid anhydride are the same, the anhydride is a **symmetrical anhydride**. If they are different, the anhydride is a **mixed anhydride**. Symmetrical anhydrides are named by replacing "acid" of the acid name with "anhydride." Mixed anhydrides are named by stating the names of both acids in alphabetical order, followed by "anhydride."

systematic name:	ethanoic anhydride
common name:	acetic anhydride
	a symmetrical anhydride

ethanoic methanoic anhydride
acetic formic anhydride
a mixed anhydride

Naming Esters

An **ester** has an OR group in place of the OH group of a carboxylic acid. In naming an ester, the name of the group (R′) attached to the **carboxyl oxygen** is stated first, followed by the name of the acid, with "ic acid" replaced by "ate." (R′ indicates that the alkyl group it designates does not have to be the same as the alkyl group designated by R.)

carbonyl oxygen

carboxyl oxygen

systematic name:	ethyl ethanoate	phenyl propanoate	methyl 3-bromobutanoate	ethyl cyclohexanecarboxylate
common name:	ethyl acetate	phenyl propionate	methyl β-bromobutyrate	

Salts of carboxylic acids are named in the same way. The cation is named first, followed by the name of the acid, again with "ic acid" replaced by "ate."

systematic name:	sodium methanoate	potassium ethanoate	sodium benzenecarboxylate
common name:	sodium formate	potassium acetate	sodium benzoate

Cyclic esters are called **lactones**. In systematic nomenclature, they are named as "2-oxacycloalkanones." Their common names are derived from the common name of the carboxylic acid, which designates the length of the carbon chain, and a Greek letter to indicate the carbon to which the carboxyl oxygen is attached. Thus, four-membered ring lactones are β-lactones (the carboxyl oxygen is on the β-carbon), five-membered ring lactones are γ-lactones, and six-membered ring lactones are δ-lactones.

2-oxacyclopentanone	2-oxacyclohexanone	3-methyl-2-oxacyclohexanone	3-ethyl-2-oxacyclopentanone
γ-butyrolactone	δ-valerolactone	δ-caprolactone	γ-caprolactone

---

PROBLEM 1

The word "lactone" has its origin in lactic acid, a three-carbon carboxylic acid with an OH group on the α-carbon. Ironically, lactic acid cannot form a lactone. Why not?

Naming Amides

An **amide** has an NH_2, NHR, or NR_2 group in place of the OH group of a carboxylic acid. Amides are named by replacing "oic acid," "ic acid," or "ylic acid" of the acid name with "amide."

systematic name:	ethanamide	4-chlorobutanamide	benzenecarboxamide
common name:	acetamide	γ-chlorobutyramide	benzamide

cis-2-ethylcyclohexanecarboxamide

If a substituent is bonded to the nitrogen, the name of the substituent is stated first (if there is more than one substituent bonded to the nitrogen, they are stated alphabetically), followed by the name of the amide. The name of each substituent is preceded by a capital *N* to indicate that the substituent is bonded to a nitrogen.

N-cyclohexylpropanamide   *N*-ethyl-*N*-methylpentanamide   *N,N*-diethylbutanamide

Cyclic amides are called **lactams**. Their nomenclature is similar to that of lactones. In systematic nomenclature, they are named as "2-azacycloalkanones" ("aza" is used to designate the nitrogen atom). For their common names, the length of the carbon chain is indicated by the common name of the carboxylic acid, and a Greek letter specifies the carbon to which the nitrogen is attached.

2-azacyclohexanone   2-azacyclopentanone   2-azacyclobutanone
δ-valerolactam γ-butyrolactam β-propiolactam

Naming Nitriles

Nitriles are compounds that contain a $C \equiv N$ functional group, called a cyano group. They are considered carboxylic acid derivatives because, like all class I carbonyl compounds, they react with water to form carboxylic acids (Section 17.19). In systematic nomenclature, nitriles are named by adding "nitrile" to the parent alkane name. Notice that the triple-bonded carbon of the nitrile group is counted in the number of carbons in the longest continuous chain. In common nomenclature, nitriles are named by replacing "ic acid" of the carboxylic acid name with "onitrile." They can also be named as alkyl cyanides—using the name of the alkyl group that is attached to the triply bonded carbon.

$CH_3C \equiv N$ ⬡—$C \equiv N$ $CH_3CHCH_2CH_2CH_2C \equiv N$ (with CH_3 on the CH) $CH_2 = CHC \equiv N$

systematic name: ethanenitrile   benzenecarbonitrile   5-methylhexanenitrile   propenenitrile
common name: acetonitrile   benzonitrile   δ-methylcapronitrile   acrylonitrile
           methyl cyanide   phenyl cyanide   isohexyl cyanide

---

PROBLEM 2◆

Name the following:

a. $CH_3CH_2CH_2C \equiv N$

b. (CH₃CH₂—C(=O)—O—C(=O)—CH₃ anhydride structure)

c. (CH₃CH₂CH₂—C(=O)—O⁻ K⁺)

d. (pentanoyl chloride, —C(=O)Cl)

e. (ester, —C(=O)—O—isobutyl)

f. (amide, —C(=O)—N(CH₃)₂)

g. (2-pyrrolidinone, ring with NH and C=O)

h. (cyclopentane with COOH)

i. (δ-lactone ring with CH₃ substituent)

PROBLEM 3

Write the structure of each of the following:

a. phenyl acetate
b. γ-caprolactam
c. butanenitrile
d. N-benzylethanamide
e. γ-methylcaproic acid

f. ethyl 2-chloropentanoate
g. β-bromobutyramide
h. propanoic anhydride
i. cyclohexanecarbonyl chloride
j. butanoic ethanoic anhydride

---

chem place   Tutorial:
Nomenclature of carboxylic acids and their derivatives

Tutorial:
Common terms pertaining to carboxylic acids and their derivatives

---

17.2 THE STRUCTURES OF CARBOXYLIC ACIDS AND CARBOXYLIC ACID DERIVATIVES

The **carbonyl carbon** in carboxylic acids and carboxylic acid derivatives is sp^2 hybridized. It uses its three sp^2 orbitals to form σ bonds to the carbonyl oxygen, the α-carbon, and a substituent (Y). The three atoms attached to the carbonyl carbon are in the same plane, and the bond angles are each approximately 120°.

(structure showing C=O with ~120° angles to substituent Y)

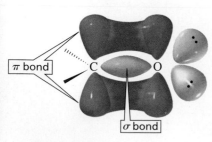

▲ **Figure 17.1**
Bonding in a carbonyl group. The π bond is formed by side-to-side overlap of a p orbital of carbon with a p orbital of oxygen.

The **carbonyl oxygen** is also sp^2 hybridized. One of its sp^2 orbitals forms a σ bond with the carbonyl carbon, and each of the other two sp^2 orbitals contains a lone pair. The remaining p orbital of the carbonyl oxygen overlaps the remaining p orbital of the carbonyl carbon to form a π bond (Figure 17.1).

Esters, carboxylic acids, and amides each have two major resonance contributors. The resonance contributor on the right is much less important for acyl chlorides and acid anhydrides, so those contributors are not shown here.

The resonance contributor on the right makes a greater contribution to the hybrid in the amide than in the ester or the carboxylic acid, because the less electronegative nitrogen atom can better accommodate a positive charge.

PROBLEM 4◆

Which is a correct statement?

A The resonance energy of an ester is about 18 kcal/mol, and the resonance energy of an amide is about 10 kcal/mol.

B The resonance energy of an ester is about 10 kcal/mol, and the resonance energy of an amide is about 18 kcal/mol.

PROBLEM 5

Which is longer, the carbon–oxygen single bond in a carboxylic acid or the carbon–oxygen bond in an alcohol? Why?

PROBLEM 6◆

There are three carbon–oxygen bonds in methyl acetate.

a. What are their relative lengths?

b. What are the relative infrared (IR) stretching frequencies of these bonds?

PROBLEM 7◆

Match the compound to the appropriate carbonyl IR absorption band:

acyl chloride	1800 and 1750 cm^{-1}
acid anhydride	1640 cm^{-1}
ester	1730 cm^{-1}
amide	1800 cm^{-1}

17.3 THE PHYSICAL PROPERTIES OF CARBONYL COMPOUNDS

The acid properties of carboxylic acids were discussed in Sections 1.22 and 7.9. Recall that carboxylic acids have pK_a values of approximately 3–5 (Appendix II; see also "Special Topics I" in the *Study Guide and Solutions Manual*).

Carbonyl compounds have the following relative boiling points:

relative boiling points

amide > carboxylic acid > nitrile ≫ ester ~ acyl chloride ~ aldehyde ~ ketone

The boiling points of an ester, acyl chloride, ketone, and aldehyde of comparable molecular weight are similar and are lower than the boiling point of an alcohol of similar molecular weight because only the alcohol molecules can form hydrogen bonds with each other. The boiling points of these four carbonyl compounds are higher than the boiling point of the same-size ether because of the polar carbonyl group.

CH₃CH₂CH₂OH
bp = 97.4 °C

H—C(=O)—OCH₃
bp = 32 °C

CH₃—C(=O)—Cl
bp = 51 °C

CH₃—C(=O)—CH₃
bp = 56 °C

CH₃CH₂—C(=O)—H
bp = 49 °C

CH₃CH₂OCH₃
bp = 10.8 °C

CH₃—C(=O)—OH
bp = 118 °C

CH₃—C(=O)—NH₂
bp = 221 °C

CH₃CH₂C≡N
bp = 97 °C

Carboxylic acids have relatively high boiling points because they form intermolecular hydrogen bonds, giving them larger effective molecular weights.

intermolecular hydrogen bonds

Amides have the highest boiling points because they have strong dipole–dipole interactions, since the resonance contributor with separated charges contributes significantly to the overall structure of the compound (Section 17.2). In addition, if the nitrogen of an amide is bonded to a hydrogen, hydrogen bonds will form between the molecules. The strong dipole–dipole interactions of a nitrile give it a boiling point similar to that of an alcohol (Section 2.9). Tables of boiling points and other physical properties can be found in Appendix I.

dipole–dipole interactions

intermolecular hydrogen bond

dipole–dipole interactions

Carboxylic acid derivatives are soluble in solvents such as ethers, chloroalkanes, and aromatic hydrocarbons. Like alcohols and ethers, carbonyl compounds with fewer than four carbons are soluble in water.

Esters, *N*,*N*-disubstituted amides, and nitriles are often used as solvents because they are polar but do not have reactive OH or NH₂ groups. We have seen that dimethylformamide (DMF) is a common aprotic polar solvent (Section 8.2).

17.4 NATURALLY OCCURRING CARBOXYLIC ACIDS AND CARBOXYLIC ACID DERIVATIVES

Acyl halides and acid anhydrides are much more reactive than carboxylic acids and esters, which, in turn, are more reactive than amides. We will see the reason for these differences in reactivity in Section 17.6.

Because of their high reactivity, acyl halides and acid anhydrides are not found in nature. Carboxylic acids, on the other hand, being less reactive *are* found widely in nature. For example, glucose is metabolized to pyruvic acid (Section 26.7). (*S*)-Lactic acid is the compound responsible for the burning sensation felt in muscles during anaerobic exercise, and it is also found in sour milk. Spinach and other leafy green vegetables are rich in oxalic acid. Succinic acid and citric acid are important intermediates in the citric acid cycle, a series of reactions in biological systems that oxidize the compounds formed from the metabolism of fatty acids, carbohydrates, and amino acids to CO_2 (Section 26.10). Citrus fruits are rich in citric acid; the concentration is greatest in lemons, less in grapefruit, and still less in oranges.

B I O G R A P H Y

Sir Alexander Fleming (1881–1955) *was born in Scotland, the seventh of eight children of a farmer. In 1902, he received a legacy from an uncle that, together with a scholarship, allowed him to study medicine at the University of London. He subsequently became a professor there in 1928. He was knighted in 1944.*

| pyruvic acid | (*S*)-(+)-lactic acid | oxalic acid | succinic acid | citric acid |

(*S*)-(−)-Malic acid is responsible for the sharp taste of unripe apples and pears. As these fruits ripen, the amount of malic acid decreases and the amount of sugar increases. The inverse relationship between the levels of malic acid and sugar is important for the propagation of the plant: malic acid prevents animals from eating the fruit until it becomes ripe, at which time its seeds are mature enough to germinate when they are scattered about. Prostaglandins are locally acting hormones that have several different physiological functions (Sections 17.10 and 27.5), such as stimulating inflammation, raising blood pressure, and producing pain and swelling.

| (*S*)-(−)-malic acid | prostaglandin A$_2$ | prostaglandin F$_{2\alpha}$ |

B I O G R A P H Y

Sir Howard W. Florey (1898–1968) *was born in Australia and received a medical degree from the University of Adelaide. He went to England as a Rhodes Scholar and studied at both Oxford and Cambridge Universities. He became a professor of pathology at the University of Sheffield in 1931 and then at Oxford in 1935. Knighted in 1944, he was given a peerage in 1965 that made him Baron Florey of Adelaide.*

Esters are also commonly found in nature. The aromas of many flowers and fruits are due to esters. (See Problems 30 and 54.)

| benzyl acetate jasmine | isopentyl acetate banana | methyl butyrate apple |

Carboxylic acids with an amino group on the α-carbon are commonly called **amino acids**. Amino acids are linked together by amide bonds to form peptides and proteins (Section 23.8).

B I O G R A P H Y

Ernest B. Chain (1906–1979) *was born in Germany and received a Ph.D. from Friedrich-Wilhelm University in Berlin. In 1933, he left Germany for England because Hitler had come to power. Chain studied at Cambridge, and in 1935 Florey invited him to Oxford. In 1948, he became the director of an institute in Rome, but he returned to England in 1961 to become a professor at the University of London.*

| an amino acid | general structure for a peptide or a protein |

Caffeine, another naturally occurring amide, is found in cocoa and in coffee beans, and piperine is the major component of black pepper. Penicillin G is an antibacterial compound with two amide bonds (one of which is in a β-lactam ring).

caffeine   **piperine**   **penicillin G**

The Discovery of Penicillin

Sir Alexander Fleming was a professor of bacteriology at the University of London. The story is told that one day Fleming was about to throw away a culture of staphylococcal bacteria that had been contaminated by a rare strain of the mold *Penicillium notatum*. He noticed that the bacteria had disappeared wherever there was a particle of mold. This suggested to him that the mold must have produced an antibacterial substance. Ten years later, in 1938, Howard Florey and Ernest Chain isolated the active substance—penicillin G (Section 17.17)—but the delay allowed the sulfa drugs to be the first antibiotics (Section 31.4). After penicillin G was found to cure bacterial infections in mice, it was used successfully in 1941 on nine cases of human bacterial infections. By 1943, it was being produced for the military and was first used for war casualties in Sicily and Tunisia. The drug became available to the civilian population in 1944. The pressure of the war made the determination of penicillin G's structure a priority because once its structure was determined, large quantities of the drug could conceivably be synthesized.

Fleming, Florey, and Chain shared the 1945 Nobel Prize in Physiology or Medicine. Chain also discovered penicillinase, the enzyme that destroys penicillin (Section 17.17). Although Fleming is generally given credit for the discovery of penicillin, there is clear evidence that the germicidal activity of the mold was recognized in the nineteenth century by Lord Joseph Lister (1827–1912), the English physician renowned for the introduction of aseptic surgery in 1865. Unfortunately, it took several years for the surgical profession to follow his example.

Nature's Sleeping Pill

Melatonin, a naturally occurring amide, is a hormone synthesized by the pineal gland from the amino acid tryptophan. Melatonin regulates the dark–light clock in our brains that governs such things as the sleep–wake cycle, body temperature, and hormone production.

Melatonin levels increase from evening to night and then decrease as morning approaches. People with high levels of melatonin sleep longer and more soundly than those with low levels. The concentration of the hormone in our bodies varies with age—6-year-olds have more than five times the concentration that 80-year-olds have—which is one of the reasons young people have less trouble sleeping than older people. Melatonin supplements are used to treat insomnia, jet lag, and seasonal affective disorder.

tryptophan
an amino acid   **melatonin**

17.5 HOW CLASS I CARBONYL COMPOUNDS REACT

The reactivity of carbonyl compounds is due to the polarity of the carbonyl group that results from oxygen being more electronegative than carbon. The carbonyl carbon is therefore electron deficient (an electrophile), so we can safely predict that it will be attacked by nucleophiles.

When a nucleophile adds to the carbonyl carbon of a carboxylic acid derivative, the weakest bond in the molecule—the carbon–oxygen π bond—breaks, and an intermediate is formed. The intermediate is called a **tetrahedral intermediate** because the sp^2 carbon in the reactant has become an sp^3 carbon in the intermediate. Generally, *a compound that has an* sp^3 *carbon bonded to an oxygen atom will be unstable if the* sp^3 *carbon is bonded to another electronegative atom.* The tetrahedral intermediate, therefore, is unstable because Y and Z are both electronegative atoms. A lone pair on the oxygen re-forms the π bond, and either $Y^-(k_2)$ or $Z^-(k_{-1})$ is eliminated along with its bonding electrons.

a tetrahedral intermediate

A compound that has an sp^3 carbon bonded to an oxygen atom generally will be unstable if the sp^3 carbon is bonded to another electronegative atom.

Whether Y^- or Z^- is eliminated from the tetrahedral intermediate depends on their relative basicities. The weaker base is eliminated preferentially, making this another example of the principle we first saw in Section 8.2: *the weaker the base, the better it is as a leaving group.* Because a weak base does not share its electrons as well as a strong base does, a weaker base forms a weaker bond—one that is easier to break. If Z^- is a much weaker base than Y^-, Z^- will be eliminated. In such a case, $k_{-1} > k_2$, and the reaction above can be re-written as follows:

In this case, no new product is formed. The nucleophile adds to the carbonyl carbon, but the tetrahedral intermediate eliminates the nucleophile and re-forms the reactants.

On the other hand, if Y^- is a much weaker base than Z^-, Y^- will be eliminated and a new product will be formed. In this case, $k_2 > k_{-1}$, and the reaction can be re-written as follows:

The weaker the base, the better it is as a leaving group.

This reaction is a **nucleophilic acyl substitution reaction** because a nucleophile (Z^-) has replaced the substituent (Y^-) attached to the acyl group in the reactant. It is also called an **acyl transfer reaction** because an acyl group has been transferred from one group to another. Most chemists, however, prefer to call it a **nucleophilic addition–elimination reaction** to emphasize the two-step nature of the reaction: a nucleophile adds to the carbonyl carbon in the first step, and a group is eliminated in the second step.

If the basicities of Y^- and Z^- are similar, the values of k_{-1} and k_2 will be similar. Therefore, some molecules of the tetrahedral intermediate will eliminate Y^- and others will eliminate Z^-. When the reaction is over, both reactant and product will be present. The relative amounts of each depend on the relative basicities of Y^- and Z^- (that is, the relative values of k_2 and k_{-1} as well as the relative nucleophilicities of Y^- and Z^- (that is, the relative values of k_1 and k_{-2}).

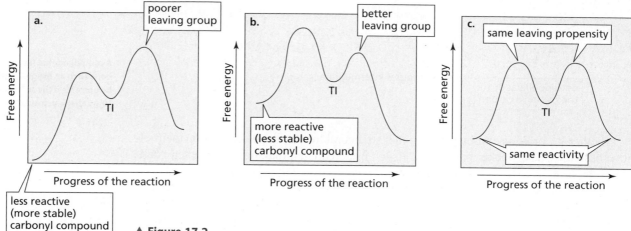

These three cases are illustrated by the reaction coordinate diagrams shown in Figure 17.2.

▲ **Figure 17.2**
Reaction coordinate diagrams for nucleophilic addition–elimination reactions with nucleophiles of varying basicity. (TI is the tetrahedral intermediate):
(a) The nucleophile is a weaker base than the group attached to the acyl group in the reactant.
(b) The nucleophile is a stronger base than the group attached to the acyl group in the reactant.
(c) The nucleophile and the group attached to the acyl group in the reactant have similar basicities.

1. If the new group in the tetrahedral intermediate is a weaker base than the group attached to the acyl group in the reactant, the easier pathway—the lower energy hill— is for the tetrahedral intermediate (TI) to eliminate the newly added group and re-form the reactants, so no reaction takes place (Figure 17.2a).

2. If the new group in the tetrahedral intermediate is a stronger base than the group attached to the acyl group in the reactant, the easier pathway is for the tetrahedral intermediate to eliminate the group attached to the acyl group in the reactant and form a substitution product (Figure 17.2b).

3. If both groups in the tetrahedral intermediate have similar basicities, the tetrahedral intermediate can eliminate either group with similar ease. A mixture of reactant and substitution product will result (Figure 17.2c).

A carboxylic acid derivatives will undergo a nucleophilic addition–elimination reaction if the newly added group in the tetrahedral intermediate is not a weaker base than the group attached to the acyl group in the reactant.

We can therefore make the following general statement about the reactions of carboxylic acid derivatives: *a carboxylic acid derivative will undergo a nucleophilic addition–elimination reaction, provided that the newly added group in the tetrahedral intermediate is not a weaker base than the group attached to the acyl group in the reactant.*

Let's compare this two-step addition–elimination reaction with a one-step S_N2 reaction. When a nucleophile attacks a carbon, the weakest bond in the molecule breaks. The weakest bond in an S_N2 reaction is the bond to the leaving group, so this is the bond that breaks in the first and only step of the reaction (Section 8.1). In contrast, the weakest bond in an addition–elimination reaction is the π bond, so this bond breaks first and the leaving group is eliminated in a subsequent step.

$$CH_3CH_2-Y + Z:^- \longrightarrow CH_3CH_2-Z + Y:^-$$

an S_N2 reaction

PROBLEM 8◆

Is the following statement true or false?

If the newly added group in the tetrahedral intermediate is a stronger base than the group attached to the acyl group in the reactant, formation of the tetrahedral intermediate is the rate-limiting step of a nucleophilic addition–elimination reaction.

Let's now look at a molecular orbital description of how carbonyl compounds react. In Section 1.6, which first introduced you to molecular orbital theory, you saw that because oxygen is more electronegative than carbon, the $2p$ orbital of oxygen contributes more to the π bonding molecular orbital (it is closer to it in energy) and the $2p$ orbital of carbon contributes more to the π^* antibonding molecular orbital (see Figure 1.8). Therefore, the π^* antibonding orbital is largest at the carbon atom, so that is where the nucleophile's nonbonding orbital, in which the lone pair resides, overlaps. This allows the greatest amount of orbital overlap, and greater overlap means greater stability. When two orbitals overlap, the result is a molecular orbital—in this case, a σ molecular orbital—that is more stable than either of the overlapping orbitals (Figure 17.3).

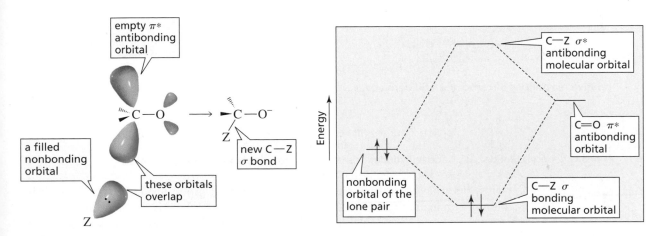

▲ Figure 17.3
The filled nonbonding orbital containing the nucleophile's lone pair overlaps the empty $\pi*$ antibonding orbital of the carbonyl group, forming the new σ bond in the tetrahedral intermediate.

PROBLEM-SOLVING STRATEGY

Using Basicity to Predict the Outcome of a Nucleophilic Addition-Elimination Reaction

The pK_a of HCl is -7; the pK_a of CH_3OH is 15.5. What is the product of the reaction of acetyl chloride with CH_3O^-?

In order to determine what the product of the reaction will be, we need to compare the basicities of the two groups in the tetrahedral intermediate so that we can see which one will be eliminated. Because HCl is a stronger acid than CH_3OH, Cl^- is a weaker base than CH_3O^-. Therefore, Cl^- will be eliminated from the tetrahedral intermediate, so the product of the reaction will be methyl acetate.

chem Tutorial:
place Free-energy diagrams for nucleophilic acyl substitution reactions

Now continue on to Problem 9.

PROBLEM 9 ◆

a. The pK_a of HCl is -7; the pK_a of H_2O is 15.7. What is the product of the reaction of acetyl chloride with HO^-?

b. The pK_a of NH_3 is 36; the pK_a of H_2O is 15.7. What is the product of the reaction of acetamide with HO^-?

17.6 RELATIVE REACTIVITIES OF CARBOXYLIC ACIDS AND CARBOXYLIC ACID DERIVATIVES

We have just seen that there are two steps in a nucleophilic addition–elimination reaction: *formation* of a tetrahedral intermediate and *collapse* of the tetrahedral intermediate. The weaker the base attached to the acyl group, the easier it is for *both steps* of the reaction to take place. Therefore, the reactivity of a carboxylic acid derivative depends on the basicity of the substituent attached to the acyl group: the less basic the substituent, the more reactive the carboxylic acid derivative.

relative basicities of the leaving groups

relative reactivities of carboxylic acid derivatives

How does having a weak base attached to the acyl group make the *first* step of the addition–elimination reaction easier? First of all, a weaker base is a more electronegative base; that is, it is better able to accommodate a negative charge (Section 1.21). Thus, weaker bases are better at withdrawing electrons inductively from the carbonyl carbon (Section 1.22); electron withdrawal increases the size of the partial positive charge on the carbonyl carbon and therefore its susceptibility to nucleophilic addition.

relative reactivity: acyl chloride > anhydride > ester ~ carboxylic acid > amide

Second, weak (electronegative) bases are less able to accommodate a positive charge. Therefore, the weaker the basicity of Y, the smaller is the contribution from the resonance contributor with a positive charge on Y (Section 17.2), and the less the carboxylic acid derivative is stabilized by electron delocalization, the more reactive it will be.

resonance contributors of a carboxylic acid or carboxylic acid derivative

---

PROBLEM 10 ◆

a. Which compound will have the stretching vibration for its carbonyl group at the highest frequency: acetyl chloride, methyl acetate, or acetamide?

b. Which one will have the stretching vibration for its carbonyl group at the lowest frequency?

A weak base attached to the acyl group also makes the *second* step of the addition–elimination reaction easier, because weak bases—which form weak bonds—are easier to eliminate when the tetrahedral intermediate collapses.

$$R-\overset{\overset{\displaystyle :\!\ddot{O}\!:^-}{|}}{\underset{\underset{\displaystyle Z}{|}}{C}}-Y \quad \boxed{\text{the weaker the base, the easier it is to eliminate}}$$

In Section 17.4 we saw that in a nucleophilic addition–elimination reaction, the nucleophile that adds to the carbonyl carbon must be a stronger base than the base that is already there. This means that *a carboxylic acid derivative can be converted into a less reactive carboxylic acid derivative in a nucleophilic addition-elimination reaction, but not into one that is more reactive*. For example, an acyl chloride can be converted into an ester because an alkoxide ion, such as methoxide ion, is a stronger base than a chloride ion.

$$\underset{R}{\overset{O}{\underset{\parallel}{C}}}\diagdown_{Cl} \; + \; CH_3O^- \; \longrightarrow \; \underset{R}{\overset{O}{\underset{\parallel}{C}}}\diagdown_{OCH_3} \; + \; Cl^-$$

An ester, however, cannot be converted into an acyl chloride because a chloride ion is a weaker base than an alkoxide ion.

$$\underset{R}{\overset{O}{\underset{\parallel}{C}}}\diagdown_{OCH_3} \; + \; Cl^- \; \longrightarrow \; \text{no reaction}$$

PROBLEM 11 ◆

Using the pK_a values in Table 17.1, predict the products of the following reactions:

a. $\underset{CH_3}{\overset{O}{\underset{\parallel}{C}}}\diagdown_{OCH_3} \; + \; NaCl \longrightarrow$

b. $\underset{CH_3}{\overset{O}{\underset{\parallel}{C}}}\diagdown_{Cl} \; + \; NaOH \longrightarrow$

c. $\underset{CH_3}{\overset{O}{\underset{\parallel}{C}}}\diagdown_{Cl} \; + \; \underset{CH_3}{\overset{O}{\underset{\parallel}{C}}}\diagdown_{O^- Na^+} \longrightarrow$

d. $\underset{CH_3}{\overset{O}{\underset{\parallel}{C}}}\diagdown_{O}\diagup_{\overset{\parallel}{\underset{C}{O}}}\diagdown_{CH_3} \; + \; NaCl \longrightarrow$

17.7 THE GENERAL MECHANISM FOR NUCLEOPHILIC ADDITION–ELIMINATION REACTIONS

All carboxylic acid derivatives undergo nucleophilic addition–elimination reactions by the same mechanism. If the nucleophile is negatively charged, the mechanism shown below and described on page 717 is followed:

All carboxylic acid derivatives react by the same mechanism.

MECHANISM FOR A NUCLEOPHILIC ADDITION–ELIMINATION REACTION WITH A NEGATIVELY CHARGED NUCLEOPHILE

$$\underset{R}{\overset{\overset{\displaystyle \ddot{O}}{\parallel}}{C}}\diagdown_{Y} \; + \; CH_3\ddot{O}:^- \; \rightleftharpoons \; R-\overset{\overset{\displaystyle :\ddot{O}:^-}{|}}{\underset{\underset{\displaystyle :\ddot{O}CH_3}{|}}{C}}-Y \; \rightleftharpoons \; \underset{R}{\overset{\overset{\displaystyle \ddot{O}}{\parallel}}{C}}\diagdown_{\ddot{O}CH_3} \; + \; Y:^-$$

$\boxed{\text{negatively charged nucleophile adds to the carbonyl carbon}}$ $\boxed{\text{elimination of the weaker base from the tetrahedral intermediate}}$

- The nucleophile adds to the carbonyl carbon, forming a tetrahedral intermediate.
- The tetrahedral intermediate collapses, eliminating the weaker base.

If the nucleophile is neutral, the mechanism has an additional step.

MECHANISM FOR A NUCLEOPHILIC ADDITION–ELIMINATION REACTION WITH A NEUTRAL NUCLEOPHILE

neutral nucleophile adds to the carbonyl carbon

removal of a proton from the tetrahedral intermediate

elimination of the weaker base from the tetrahedral intermediate

where :B represents any species in the solution that is capable of removing a proton; and HB^+ represents any species in the solution that is capable of donating a proton.

- The nucleophile adds to the carbonyl carbon, forming a tetrahedral intermediate.
- A proton is lost from the tetrahedral intermediate, resulting in a tetrahedral intermediate equivalent to the one formed by a negatively charged nucleophile.
- This π bond re-forms and the weaker of the two bases is eliminated—either the newly added group after it has lost a proton or the group that was attached to the acyl group in the reactant.

The weakest base is eliminated from the tetrahedral intermediate.

The remaining sections of this chapter show specific examples of these general principles. Keep in mind that *all the reactions follow the same mechanism.* Therefore, you can always determine the outcome of the reactions of carboxylic acids and carboxylic acid derivatives presented in this chapter by examining the tetrahedral intermediate and remembering that the weaker base is preferentially eliminated (Section 17.5).

chem Tutorial:
place A nucleophilic-addition elimination reaction

PROBLEM 12♦

What will be the product of a nucleophilic addition–elimination reaction—a new carboxylic acid derivative, a mixture of two carboxylic acid derivatives, or no reaction—if the new group in the tetrahedral intermediate is the following?

a. a stronger base than the group that was already there
b. a weaker base than the group that was already there
c. similar in basicity to the group that was already there

17.8 **THE REACTIONS OF ACYL HALIDES**

Acyl halides react with carboxylate ions to form anhydrides, with alcohols to form esters, with water to form carboxylic acids, and with amines to form amides because in each case the incoming nucleophile is a stronger base than the departing halide ion (Table 17.1).

acetyl chloride

$$\underset{R}{\overset{O}{\underset{\|}{C}}}\!\!-\!Cl \;+\; H_2O \;\longrightarrow\; \underset{R}{\overset{O}{\underset{\|}{C}}}\!\!-\!OH \;+\; HCl$$

$$\underset{R}{\overset{O}{\underset{\|}{C}}}\!\!-\!Cl \;+\; 2\,CH_3NH_2 \;\longrightarrow\; \underset{R}{\overset{O}{\underset{\|}{C}}}\!\!-\!NHCH_3 \;+\; CH_3\overset{+}{N}H_3\,Cl^-$$

All the reactions follow the general mechanisms described on pages 721 and 722.

MECHANISM FOR THE CONVERSION OF AN ACYL CHLORIDE INTO AN ACID ANHYDRIDE

the weaker base is eliminated

formation of a tetrahedral intermediate

- The nucleophilic carboxylate ion adds to the carbonyl carbon of the acyl chloride, forming a tetrahedral intermediate.
- The π bond re-forms and the chloride ion is eliminated because it is a weaker base than the carboxylate ion. The final product is an anhydride.

The following mechanism has one more step than the one above because, since the nucleophile is neutral rather than negatively charged, a proton must be removed from the tetrahedral intermediate before the intermediate eliminates the leaving group.

MECHANISM FOR THE CONVERSION OF AN ACYL CHLORIDE INTO AN ESTER

the weaker base is eliminated

formation of a tetrahedral intermediate

a proton is removed

- The nucleophilic alcohol adds to the carbonyl carbon of the acyl chloride, forming a tetrahedral intermediate.
- Because the protonated ether group is a strong acid (Section 1.18), the tetrahedral intermediate loses a proton.
- Chloride ion is eliminated from the deprotonated tetrahedral intermediate because chloride ion is a weaker base than the alkoxide ion.

Notice that the reaction of an acyl chloride with an amine (on the top of this page) or with ammonia (on page 724) to form an amide is carried out with twice as much amine or ammonia as acyl chloride because the HCl formed as a product of the reaction will protonate any amine or ammonia that has yet to react. Once protonated, it is no longer a nucleophile, so it cannot react with the acyl chloride. Using twice as much amine or ammonia as acyl chloride guarantees that there will be enough unprotonated compound to react with all the acyl halide.

$$
\underset{R}{\overset{O}{\underset{\displaystyle Cl}{||}}}C + NH_3 \longrightarrow \underset{R}{\overset{O}{\underset{\displaystyle NH_2}{||}}}C + HCl \xrightarrow{NH_3} \overset{+}{N}H_4\ Cl^-
$$

An equivalent of a tertiary amine such as triethylamine can be used instead of excess amine (see Problem 14b).

$$
\underset{R}{\overset{O}{\underset{\displaystyle Cl}{||}}}C + CH_3NH_2 \xrightarrow{(CH_3CH_2)_3N} \underset{R}{\overset{O}{\underset{\displaystyle NHCH_3}{||}}}C + CH_3\overset{+}{N}H_3\ Cl^-
$$

PROBLEM 13 ◆

If you were starting with acetyl chloride, what nucleophile would you use to make each of the following compounds?

a. $\underset{CH_3}{\overset{O}{\underset{\displaystyle OCH_2CH_2CH_3}{||}}}C$

d. $\underset{CH_3}{\overset{O}{\underset{\displaystyle OH}{||}}}C$

b. $\underset{CH_3}{\overset{O}{\underset{\displaystyle NH_2}{||}}}C$

e. $\underset{CH_3}{\overset{O}{\underset{\displaystyle O}{||}}}C\underset{}{\overset{O}{\underset{\displaystyle CH_3}{||}}}C$

c. $\underset{CH_3}{\overset{O}{\underset{\displaystyle N(CH_3)_2}{||}}}C$

f. $\underset{CH_3}{\overset{O}{\underset{\displaystyle O}{||}}}C$—◯—$NO_2$

PROBLEM 14   SOLVED

a. Two amides are obtained from the reaction of acetyl chloride with a mixture of ethylamine and propylamine. Identify the amides.
b. Why is only one amide obtained from the reaction of acetyl chloride with a mixture of ethylamine and triethylamine?

Solution to 14a   Either of the amines can react with acetyl chloride, so both *N*-ethylacetamide and *N*-propylacetamide are formed.

$$
\underset{CH_3}{\overset{O}{\underset{\displaystyle Cl}{||}}}C + \overset{}{\diagup}NH_2 + \overset{}{\diagup\diagdown}NH_2 \longrightarrow \underset{CH_3}{\overset{O}{\underset{\displaystyle \underset{H}{N}}{||}}}C\diagup + \underset{CH_3}{\overset{O}{\underset{\displaystyle \underset{H}{N}}{||}}}C\diagup\diagdown
$$

N-ethylacetamide   **N-propylacetamide**

$$
+ \quad \diagup\overset{+}{N}H_3\ Cl^- \quad + \quad \diagup\diagdown\overset{+}{N}H_3\ Cl^-
$$

Solution to 14b   Initially, two amides are formed. However, the amide formed by triethylamine is very reactive because it has a positively charged nitrogen, which makes it an excellent leaving group. Therefore, it will react immediately with unreacted ethylamine, causing *N*-ethylacetamide to be the only amide formed in the reaction.

$$
\underset{CH_3}{\overset{O}{\underset{\displaystyle Cl}{||}}}C + \diagup NH_2 + \diagup\overset{N}{\diagdown} \longrightarrow \underset{CH_3}{\overset{O}{\underset{\displaystyle \underset{H}{N}}{||}}}C\diagup + \underset{CH_3}{\overset{O}{\underset{\displaystyle \overset{+}{N}}{||}}}C
$$

N-ethylacetamide

$$
\bigg\downarrow \diagup NH_2
$$

$$
\underset{CH_3}{\overset{O}{\underset{\displaystyle \underset{H}{N}}{||}}}C\diagup
$$

N-ethylacetamide

PROBLEM 15

We have seen that it is necessary to use excess amine in the reaction of an acyl chloride with an amine. Explain why it is not necessary to use excess alcohol in the reaction of an acyl chloride with an alcohol.

PROBLEM 16

Write the mechanism for each of the following reactions:
a. the reaction of acetyl chloride with water to form acetic acid.
b. the reaction of acetyl bromide with excess methylamine to form *N*-methylacetamide.

17.9 THE REACTIONS OF ACID ANHYDRIDES

Acid anhydrides do not react with sodium chloride (or with sodium bromide) because the incoming halide ion is a weaker base than the departing carboxylate ion (Table 17.1).

acetic anhydride

Because the incoming halide ion is the weaker base, it will be the substituent eliminated from the tetrahedral intermediate. (Recall that a carboxylic acid derivative cannot be converted into a more reactive carboxylic acid derivative, only to one that is less reactive; Section 17.6.)

An acid anhydride reacts with an alcohol to form an ester and a carboxylic acid, with water to form two equivalents of a carboxylic acid, and with an amine to form an amide and a carboxylate ion. In each case, the incoming nucleophile—after it loses a proton—is a stronger base than the departing carboxylate ion. In the reaction of an amine with an anhydride, two equivalents of the amine or one equivalent of the amine plus one equivalent of a tertiary amine must be used so that sufficient amine will be present to react with both the carbonyl compound and the proton produced in the reaction.

All these reactions follow the general mechanism described in Section 17.7. For example, compare the following mechanism for conversion of an acid anhydride into an ester with the mechanism for conversion of an acyl chloride into an ester presented on page 723.

MECHANISM FOR THE CONVERSION OF AN ACID ANHYDRIDE INTO AN ESTER (AND A CARBOXYLIC ACID)

PROBLEM 17

a. Propose a mechanism for the reaction of acetic anhydride with water.
b. How does this mechanism differ from the mechanism for the reaction of acetic anhydride with an alcohol?

PROBLEM 18

We have seen that acid anhydrides react with alcohols, water, and amines. In which of these reactions does the tetrahedral intermediate not have to lose a proton before it eliminates the carboxylate ion? Explain.

17.10 THE REACTIONS OF ESTERS

methyl acetate

Esters do not react with halide ions or with carboxylate ions because these nucleophiles are much weaker bases than the RO^- leaving group of the ester and therefore would be expelled from the tetrahedral intermediate (Table 17.1).

An ester reacts with water to form a carboxylic acid and an alcohol. This is an example of a hydrolysis reaction. A **hydrolysis reaction** is a reaction with water that converts one compound into two compounds (*lysis* is Greek for "breaking down").

a hydrolysis reaction

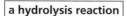

An ester reacts with an alcohol to form a new ester and a new alcohol. This is an example of an **alcoholysis reaction**—a reaction with an alcohol that converts one compound into two compounds. This particular alcoholysis reaction is also called a **transesterification reaction** because one ester is converted to another ester.

a transesterification reaction

Both the hydrolysis and the alcoholysis of an ester are very slow reactions because water and alcohols are poor nucleophiles and esters have poor (basic) leaving groups. These reactions are therefore always catalyzed when carried out in the laboratory. Both hydrolysis and alcoholysis of an ester can be catalyzed by acids (Section 17.11). The rate of hydrolysis can also be increased by hydroxide ion (Section 17.12), and the rate of alcoholysis can be increased by the conjugate base (RO^-) of the reactant alcohol.

Aspirin, NSAIDs, and COX-2 Inhibitors

Salicylic acid, found in willow bark and myrtle leaves, is perhaps the oldest known drug. As early as the fifth century BC, Hippocrates wrote about the curative powers of willow bark. In 1897, Felix Hoffmann, a scientist working at Bayer and Co. in Germany, found that acetylating salicylic acid produced a more potent drug to control fever and pain. They called it aspirin; "a" for acetyl, "spir" for the spiraea flower that also contains salicylic acid, and "in" was a common ending for drugs at that time. It soon became the world's best-selling drug. However, its mode of action was not discovered until 1971, when it was found that the anti-inflammatory and fever-reducing activity of aspirin was due to a transesterification reaction that blocks prostaglandin synthesis.

Prostaglandins have several different biological functions, one being to stimulate inflammation and another to induce fever. The enzyme prostaglandin synthase catalyzes the conversion of arachidonic acid into PGH_2, a precursor of all prostaglandins and the related thromboxanes (Section 27.5).

$$\text{arachidonic acid} \xrightarrow{\text{prostaglandin synthase}} PGH_2 \diagdown \begin{array}{l} \text{prostaglandins} \\ \text{thromboxanes} \end{array}$$

Prostaglandin synthase is composed of two enzymes. One of them—cyclooxygenase—has a CH_2OH group (called a serine hydroxyl group because it is part of the amino acid called serine; see Table 23.1 on page 979). The serine hydroxyl group is necessary for enzymatic activity. When the serine hydroxyl group reacts with aspirin in a transesterification reaction, the enzyme is inactivated. Therefore, prostaglandins cannot be synthesized, so inflammation is suppressed and fever is reduced. Because aspirin inhibits the formation of PGH_2, it inhibits the synthesis of thromboxanes, compounds involved in blood clotting. Presumably, this is why low levels of aspirin have been reported to reduce the incidence of strokes and heart attacks that result from formation of blood clots. Because of aspirin's activity as an anticoagulant, doctors caution patients not to take aspirin for several days before surgery.

acetylsalicylic acid
aspirin

enzyme
active
cyclooxygenase

serine hydroxyl group

active enzyme

$\xrightarrow{\text{transesterification}}$

acetyl group

acetylated enzyme
inactive
cyclooxygenase

inactive enzyme

salicylic acid

Compounds called NSAIDs (nonsteroidal anti-inflammatory agents), such as ibuprofen (the active ingredient in Advil, Motrin, and Nuprin) and naproxen (the active ingredient in Aleve), also inhibit the synthesis of prostaglandins (Section 27.5).

aspirin

ibuprofen

naproxen

There are two forms of prostaglandin synthase: one carries out the normal physiological production of prostaglandin, and the other synthesizes additional prostaglandin in response to inflammation. Aspirin and NSAIDs inhibit the synthesis of all prostaglandins. However, one prostaglandin regulates the production of acid in the stomach, so when prostaglandin synthesis stops, the acidity of the stomach can rise above normal levels. Celebrex, a relatively new drug, inhibits only the enzyme that produces prostaglandin in response to inflammation. Thus, inflammatory conditions now can be treated without some of the harmful side effects.

Celebrex®

Esters react with amines to form amides. A reaction with an amine that converts one compound into two compounds is called **aminolysis**. Notice that the aminolysis of an ester requires only one equivalent of amine, unlike the aminolysis of an acyl halide or an acid anhydride, which requires two equivalents (Sections 17.8 and 17.9). This is because the leaving group of an ester (RO^-) is more basic than the amine, so the alkoxide ion—rather than unreacted amine—picks up the proton generated in the reaction.

an aminolysis reaction

ethyl propionate

N-methylpropionamide

The reaction of an ester with an amine is not as slow as the reaction of an ester with water or an alcohol because an amine is a better nucleophile. This is fortunate because the reaction of an ester with an amine cannot be catalyzed by an acid. The acid would protonate the amine, and a protonated amine is not a nucleophile. The rate of the reaction, however, can be increased by heat.

In Section 7.9, we saw that phenol is a stronger acid than alcohol. Therefore, a phenolate ion (ArO^-) is a weaker base than an alkoxide ion (RO^-), which means that a phenyl ester is more reactive than an alkyl ester.

phenyl acetate   is more reactive than   methyl acetate

$pK_a = 10.0$ $pK_a = 15.5$

PROBLEM 19

Write a mechanism for the following reactions:

a. the noncatalyzed hydrolysis of methyl propionate.
b. the aminolysis of phenyl formate, using methylamine.

PROBLEM 20 ◆

a. State three factors that help make the noncatalyzed hydrolysis of an ester a slow reaction.
b. Which is faster, hydrolysis of an ester or aminolysis of the same ester?

PROBLEM 21   SOLVED

List the following esters in order of decreasing reactivity toward hydrolysis:

Solution   Both *formation of the tetrahedral intermediate* and *collapse of the tetrahedral intermediate* will be fastest for the ester with the electron-withdrawing nitro substituent and slowest for the ester with the electron-donating methoxy substituent.

Formation of the tetrahedral intermediate: An ester's susceptibility to nucleophilic addition is increased by an electron-withdrawing substituent and decreased by an electron-donating substituent.

Collapse of the tetrahedral intermediate: Electron withdrawal increases acidity, and electron donation decreases acidity. Therefore, *para*-nitrophenol with its strong electron-withdrawing group is a stronger acid than phenol; and phenol is a stronger acid than *para*-methoxyphenol, which has a strong electron-donating group. Therefore, the *para*-nitrophenolate ion is the weakest base and the best leaving group of the three, whereas the *para*-methoxyphenolate ion is the strongest base and the worst leaving group. Thus,

17.11 ACID-CATALYZED ESTER HYDROLYSIS AND TRANSESTERIFICATION

We have seen that esters hydrolyze slowly because water is a poor nucleophile and esters have very basic leaving groups. However, the rate of hydrolysis can be increased by either acid or hydroxide ion. When you examine the mechanisms for these reactions, notice the two following features that hold for all organic reactions:

1. All organic intermediates and products in acidic solutions are positively charged or neutral; *negatively charged organic intermediates and products are not formed in acidic solutions.*

2. All organic intermediates and products in basic solutions are negatively charged or neutral; *positively charged organic intermediates and products are not formed in basic solutions.*

Hydrolysis of Esters with Primary or Secondary Alkyl Groups

We have seen that when an acid is added to a reaction, the first thing that happens is the acid protonates the atom in the reactant that has the greatest electron density. Therefore, the acid protonates the carbonyl oxygen.

The resonance contributors of the ester show why the carbonyl oxygen is the atom with the greatest electron density.

The mechanism for the acid-catalyzed hydrolysis of an ester is shown on page 730. (HB$^+$ represents any species in the solution that is capable of donating a proton and :B represents any species in the solution that is capable of removing a proton.)

MECHANISM FOR ACID-CATALYZED ESTER HYDROLYSIS

- The acid protonates the carbonyl oxygen.

- The nucleophile (H_2O) adds to the carbonyl carbon of the protonated carbonyl group, forming a protonated tetrahedral intermediate.

- The protonated tetrahedral intermediate (tetrahedral intermediate I) is in equilibrium with its nonprotonated form (tetrahedral intermediate II).

- Once the nonprotonated tetrahedral intermediate has been formed, either an OH group or the OR group of this intermediate (in this case, OR is OCH_3) can be protonated, in the one case re-forming tetrahedral intermediate I (OH is protonated) and in the other case forming tetrahedral intermediate III (OR is protonated). (From Section 1.25, we know that the relative amounts of the three tetrahedral intermediates depend on the pH of the solution and the pK_a values of the protonated intermediates.)

- When tetrahedral intermediate I collapses, it eliminates H_2O in preference to CH_3O^- (because H_2O is a weaker base), and re-forms the ester. When tetrahedral intermediate III collapses, it eliminates CH_3OH rather than HO^- (because CH_3OH is a weaker base) and forms the carboxylic acid. Because H_2O and CH_3OH have approximately the same basicity, it will be as likely for tetrahedral intermediate I to collapse to re-form the ester as it will for tetrahedral intermediate III to collapse to form the carboxylic acid. (Tetrahedral intermediate II is much less likely to collapse because both HO^- and CH_3O^- are strong bases.)

- Removal of a proton from the protonated carboxylic acid or protonated ester forms the neutral carbonyl compounds.

Because tetrahedral intermediates I and III are equally likely to collapse, both ester and carboxylic acid will be present in approximately equal amounts when the reaction has reached equilibrium. Excess water can be used to force the equilibrium to the right (Le Châtelier's principle; Section 3.7). Or, if the boiling point of the product alcohol is significantly lower than the boiling points of the other components of the reaction, the reaction can be driven to the right by distilling off the product alcohol as it is formed.

The mechanism for the acid-catalyzed reaction of a carboxylic acid and an alcohol to form an ester and water is the exact reverse of the mechanism for the acid-catalyzed hydrolysis of an ester to form a carboxylic acid and an alcohol. If the ester is the desired product, the reaction should be carried out under conditions that will drive the equilibrium to the left (for example, using excess alcohol or removing water as it is formed (Section 17.15).

PROBLEM 22◆

What products would be formed from the acid-catalyzed hydrolysis of the following esters?

PROBLEM 23

Referring to the mechanism for the acid-catalyzed hydrolysis of an ester, write the mechanism—showing all the curved arrows—for the acid-catalyzed reaction of acetic acid and methanol to form methyl acetate. Use HB^+ and $:B$ to represent proton-donating and proton-removing species, respectively.

Now let's see how the acid increases the rate of ester hydrolysis. The acid is a catalyst. Recall that a **catalyst** is a substance that increases the rate of a reaction without being consumed or changed in the overall reaction (Section 3.7). For a catalyst to increase the rate of a reaction, it must increase the rate of the slow step of the reaction because changing the rate of a fast step will not affect the rate of the overall reaction. Four of the six steps in the mechanism for acid-catalyzed ester hydrolysis are proton transfer steps. Proton transfer to or from an electronegative atom such as oxygen or nitrogen is always a fast step. The other two steps in the mechanism—formation of the tetrahedral intermediate and collapse of the tetrahedral intermediate—are relatively slow. The acid increases the rates of both these steps.

The acid increases *the rate of formation of the tetrahedral intermediate* by protonating the carbonyl oxygen. Protonated carbonyl groups are more susceptible than nonprotonated carbonyl groups to nucleophilic addition, because a positively charged oxygen is more electron withdrawing than a neutral oxygen. Increased electron withdrawal by the oxygen makes the carbonyl carbon more electron deficient, which increases its attractiveness to nucleophiles.

protonation of the carbonyl oxygen increases the susceptibility of the carbonyl carbon to nucleophilic addition

An acid catalyst increases the reactivity of a carbonyl group.

The acid increases *the rate of collapse of the tetrahedral intermediate* by decreasing the basicity of the leaving group, so the group is more easily eliminated. In the acid-catalyzed hydrolysis of an ester, the leaving group is ROH (in this case CH_3OH), a weaker base than the leaving group (RO^-; in this case CH_3O^-) in the uncatalyzed reaction.

An acid catalyst increases the leaving propensity of a group.

leaving group in acid-catalyzed ester hydrolysis

leaving group in uncatalyzed ester hydrolysis

PROBLEM 24 ♦

In the mechanism for the acid-catalyzed hydrolysis of an ester:

a. what species could be represented by HB^+?
b. what species could be represented by $:B$?
c. what species is HB^+ most likely to be in the hydrolysis reaction?
d. what species is HB^+ most likely to be in the reverse reaction?

PROBLEM 25   SOLVED

How could butanone be prepared from butane?

butane $\xrightarrow{?}$ butanone

Solution   We know that the first reaction has to be a radical halogenation because that is the only reaction that an alkane undergoes. Bromination will lead to a greater yield of the desired 2-halo-substituted compound than will chlorination because a bromine radical is more selective than a chlorine radical. To maximize the yield of the desired substitution product over the elimination product (Section 9.8), the alkyl bromide is treated with acetate ion (a weak base). The ester is hydrolyzed to an alcohol that forms the target molecule when it is oxidized.

$\xrightarrow[h\nu]{Br_2}$ $\xrightarrow{CH_3COO^-}$ $\xrightarrow{HCl, H_2O}$ $\xrightarrow[H_2SO_4]{Na_2Cr_2O_7}$

Hydrolysis of Esters with Tertiary Alkyl Groups

The hydrolysis of an ester with a *tertiary alkyl group* forms the same products as the hydrolysis of an ester with a *primary* or *secondary alkyl group*—a carboxylic acid and an alcohol—but does so by a completely different mechanism. The hydrolysis of an ester with a tertiary alkyl group is an S_N1 reaction because when the carboxylic acid leaves, it leaves behind a relatively stable tertiary carbocation.

MECHANISM FOR HYDROLYSIS OF AN ESTER WITH A TERTIARY ALKYL GROUP

departure of the leaving group to form a tertiary carbocation

reaction of the carbocation with a nucleophile

- An acid protonates the carbonyl oxygen.
- The leaving group departs, forming a tertiary carbocation.
- A nucleophile reacts with the carbocation.
- A base removes a proton from the strongly acidic protonated alcohol.

Transesterification

Transesterification—the reaction of an ester with an alcohol—is also catalyzed by acid. The mechanism for acid-catalyzed transesterification is identical to the mechanism for acid-catalyzed ester hydrolysis (for esters with primary or secondary alkyl groups), except that the nucleophile is ROH rather than H_2O. As in the hydrolysis of an ester, the leaving groups in the tetrahedral intermediate formed in transesterification have approximately the same basicity. Consequently, an excess of the reactant alcohol must be used to produce more of the desired product.

PROBLEM 26◆

What products would be obtained from the following reactions?
a. ethyl benzoate, excess isopropanol, HCl
b. phenyl acetate, excess ethanol, HCl

PROBLEM 27

Write the mechanism for the acid-catalyzed transesterification reaction of ethyl acetate with methanol.

PROBLEM 28

Write the mechanism for the acid-catalyzed transesterification reaction of *tert*-butyl acetate with methanol.

chem Tutorial:
place Manipulating the equilibrium

17.12 HYDROXIDE-ION-PROMOTED ESTER HYDROLYSIS

The rate of hydrolysis of an ester can be increased by carrying out the reaction in a basic solution. Like an acid catalyst, hydroxide ion increases the rates of the two slow steps of the reaction—formation of the tetrahedral intermediate and collapse of the tetrahedral intermediate.

MECHANISM FOR HYDROXIDE-ION-PROMOTED HYDROLYSIS OF AN ESTER

the more basic the solution, the lower its concentration

Hydroxide ion increases the rate of formation of the tetrahedral intermediate because HO^- is a better nucleophile than H_2O. Hydroxide ion increases the rate of collapse of the tetrahedral intermediate because a smaller fraction of the negatively charged tetrahedral intermediate becomes protonated in a basic solution; a negatively charged oxygen can more readily expel the very basic leaving group (RO^-) because the oxygen does not develop a partial positive charge in the transition state. (The relative amounts of the neutral and negatively charged tetrahedral intermediates depend on the pH of the solution and the pK_a value of the neutral tetrahedral intermediate; see Section 1.25.)

Notice that when CH_3O^- is eliminated, the final products are not the carboxylic acid and methoxide ion because if only one species is protonated, it will be the more basic one. The final products are the carboxylate ion and methanol because CH_3O^- is more basic than CH_3COO^-.

Because carboxylate ions are negatively charged, they do not react with nucleophiles. Therefore, the hydroxide-ion-promoted hydrolysis of an ester, unlike the acid-catalyzed hydrolysis of an ester, is *not* a reversible reaction.

Hydroxide ion is a better nucleophile than water.

The hydrolysis of an ester in the presence of hydroxide ion is called a *hydroxide-ion-promoted reaction* rather than a base-catalyzed reaction because hydroxide ion increases the rate of the first step of the reaction by being a better nucleophile than water—not by being a stronger base than water—and because hydroxide ion is consumed in the overall reaction. To be a catalyst, a species must not be changed by or consumed in the reaction (Section 17.11). Therefore, hydroxide ion is actually a reagent rather than a catalyst, so it is more accurate to call the reaction a hydroxide-ion-*promoted* reaction than a hydroxide-ion-*catalyzed* reaction.

Hydroxide ion promotes only hydrolysis reactions; it does not promote transesterification reactions or aminolysis reactions. Hydroxide ion cannot promote reactions of carboxylic acid derivatives with alcohols or with amines because one function of hydroxide ion is to provide a strong nucleophile for the first step of the reaction. When the nucleophile is supposed to be an alcohol or an amine, nucleophilic addition by hydroxide ion would form a different product from the one that would be formed by the alcohol or amine. Hydroxide can be used to promote a hydrolysis reaction because the same product is formed, whether the nucleophile that adds to the carbonyl carbon is H_2O or HO^-.

Reactions in which the nucleophile is an alcohol can be promoted by the conjugate base of the alcohol. The function of the alkoxide ion is to provide a strong nucleophile for the reaction, so only reactions in which the nucleophile is an alcohol can be promoted by the conjugate base of the alcohol.

PROBLEM 29

a. What species other than an acid can be used to increase the rate of a transesterification reaction that converts methyl acetate to propyl acetate?

b. Explain why the rate of aminolysis of an ester cannot be increased by H^+, HO^-, or RO^-.

17.13 HOW THE MECHANISM FOR NUCLEOPHILIC ADDITION–ELIMINATION WAS CONFIRMED

We have seen that nucleophilic addition–elimination reactions take place by a mechanism in which a tetrahedral intermediate is formed and subsequently collapses. The tetrahedral intermediate, however, is too unstable to be isolated. How, then, do we know that it is formed? How do we know that the reaction doesn't take place by a one-step direct-displacement mechanism (similar to the mechanism of an S_N2 reaction) in which the incoming nucleophile attacks the carbonyl carbon and displaces the leaving group—a mechanism that does not break the π bond and so does not form a tetrahedral intermediate?

B I O G R A P H Y

Myron L. Bender (1924–1988) *was born in St. Louis. He was a professor of chemistry at the Illinois Institute of Technology and at Northwestern University.*

transition state for a hypothetical one-step direct-displacement mechanism

To answer this question, Myron Bender investigated the hydroxide-ion-promoted hydrolysis of ethyl benzoate after first labeling the carbonyl oxygen of ethyl benzoate with ^{18}O. When he isolated ethyl benzoate from the reaction mixture, he found that some of the ester was no longer labeled. If the reaction had taken place by a one-step direct-displacement mechanism, all the isolated ester would have remained labeled because the carbonyl group would not have participated in the reaction. On the other hand, if the mechanism involved a tetrahedral intermediate, some of the isolated ester would no longer be labeled because some of the label would have been transferred to the hydroxide ion. By this experiment, Bender provided evidence for the reversible formation of a tetrahedral intermediate.

unlabeled ester

PROBLEM 30♦

If butanoic acid and ^{18}O labeled methanol are allowed to react under acidic conditions, what compounds will be labeled when the reaction has reached equilibrium?

PROBLEM 31♦

D. N. Kursanov, a Russian chemist, proved that the bond that is broken in the hydroxide-ion-promoted hydrolysis of an ester is the acyl C—O bond, rather than the alkyl C—O bond, by studying the reaction of the following ester with HO^-/H_2O:

$$CH_3CH_2-\overset{\overset{\textstyle O}{\|}}{C}\overset{\textbf{18}}{\underset{}{O}}-CH_2CH_3$$

alkyl C—O bond

acyl C—O bond

a. Which of the products contained the ^{18}O label?
b. What product would have contained the ^{18}O label if the alkyl C—O bond had broken?

PROBLEM 32 **SOLVED**

Early chemists could envision several possible mechanisms for hydroxide-ion-promoted ester hydrolysis:

1. A nucleophilic addition–elimination reaction

$$R-\overset{\overset{\textstyle \cdot\overset{\cdot\cdot}{O}\cdot}{\|}}{C}-O-R' + H\overset{\cdot\cdot}{\underset{\cdot\cdot}{O}}{}^- \longrightarrow R-\overset{\overset{\textstyle :\overset{\cdot\cdot}{O}:^-}{|}}{\underset{\underset{\textstyle OH}{|}}{C}}-O-R' \longrightarrow R-\overset{\overset{\textstyle \cdot\overset{\cdot\cdot}{O}\cdot}{\|}}{C}-O^- + R'OH$$

2. An S_N2 reaction

$$R-\overset{\overset{\textstyle \cdot\overset{\cdot\cdot}{O}\cdot}{\|}}{C}-O-R' + H\overset{\cdot\cdot}{\underset{\cdot\cdot}{O}}{}^- \longrightarrow R-\overset{\overset{\textstyle \cdot\overset{\cdot\cdot}{O}\cdot}{\|}}{C}-O^- + R'OH$$

3. An S_N1 reaction

$$R-\overset{\overset{\textstyle \cdot\overset{\cdot\cdot}{O}\cdot}{\|}}{C}-O-R' \longrightarrow R-\overset{\overset{\textstyle \cdot\overset{\cdot\cdot}{O}\cdot}{\|}}{C}-O^- + R'^+ \overset{H\overset{\cdot\cdot}{\underset{\cdot\cdot}{O}}{}^-}{\longrightarrow} R'OH$$

Devise an experiment that would show which was the actual mechanism.

Solution Start with a single stereoisomer of an alcohol whose OH group is bonded to an asymmetric center, and determine the specific rotation of the alcohol. Then convert the alcohol into an ester, using a method that does not break any bonds to the asymmetric center. Next, hydrolyze the ester, isolate the alcohol obtained from hydrolysis, and determine its specific rotation.

$$\underset{\textbf{\textit{(S)}-2-butanol}}{CH_3\overset{\overset{\textstyle CH_2CH_3}{|}}{\underset{\underset{\textstyle OH}{|}}{C}}\cdots\text{\tiny'''}H} \xrightarrow{\overset{\overset{\textstyle O}{\|}}{CH_3CCl}} \underset{\textbf{\textit{(S)}-2-butyl acetate}}{CH_3\overset{\overset{\textstyle CH_2CH_3}{|}}{\underset{\underset{\textstyle OCCH_3}{|}}{\underset{\underset{\textstyle O}{\|}}{C}}\cdots\text{\tiny'''}H}} \xrightarrow[\textstyle H_2O]{HO^-} \underset{\textbf{2-butanol}}{CH_3\overset{}{\underset{\underset{\textstyle OH}{|}}{C}HCH_2CH_3}} + CH_3\overset{\overset{\textstyle O}{\|}}{C}O^-$$

If the reaction is a nucleophilic addition–elimination reaction, the product alcohol will have the same specific rotation as the reactant alcohol because no bonds to the asymmetric center are broken (Section 5.14).

If the reaction is an S_N2 reaction, the product alcohol and the reactant alcohol will have opposite specific rotations because the mechanism requires back-side attack on the asymmetric center (Section 8.1).

If the reaction is an S_N1 reaction, the product alcohol will have a small (or zero) specific rotation because the mechanism requires carbocation formation, which leads to racemization of the alcohol (Section 8.4).

17.14 SOAPS, DETERGENTS, AND MICELLES

Fats and **oils** are triesters of glycerol. Glycerol contains three alcohol groups and therefore can form three ester groups. When the ester groups of a fat or an oil are hydrolyzed in a basic solution, glycerol and carboxylate ions are formed. The carboxylic acids that are bonded to glycerol in fats and oils have long, unbranched R groups. Because they are obtained from fats, long-chain unbranched carboxylic acids are called **fatty acids**. In Section 27.1, we will see that the difference between a fat and an oil resides in the structure of the fatty acids.

$$
\begin{array}{ccc}
\text{CH}_2\text{O}\!-\!\overset{\displaystyle \text{O}}{\overset{\|}{\text{C}}}\!-\!\text{R}^1 & & \text{CH}_2\text{OH} \qquad \text{R}^1\!-\!\overset{\displaystyle \text{O}}{\overset{\|}{\text{C}}}\!-\!\text{O}^-\,\text{Na}^+ \\[2pt]
\text{CHO}\!-\!\overset{\displaystyle \text{O}}{\overset{\|}{\text{C}}}\!-\!\text{R}^2 \;+\; \text{H}_2\text{O} \;\xrightarrow{\text{NaOH}}\; & & \text{CHOH} \;+\; \text{R}^2\!-\!\overset{\displaystyle \text{O}}{\overset{\|}{\text{C}}}\!-\!\text{O}^-\,\text{Na}^+ \\[2pt]
\text{CH}_2\text{O}\!-\!\overset{\displaystyle \text{O}}{\overset{\|}{\text{C}}}\!-\!\text{R}^3 & & \text{CH}_2\text{OH} \qquad \text{R}^3\!-\!\overset{\displaystyle \text{O}}{\overset{\|}{\text{C}}}\!-\!\text{O}^-\,\text{Na}^+
\end{array}
$$

a fat or an oil   **glycerol**   **sodium salts of fatty acids**
                                        soap

Soaps are sodium or potassium salts of fatty acids. Thus, soaps are obtained when fats or oils are hydrolyzed under basic conditions. The hydrolysis of an ester in a basic solution is called **saponification**—the Latin word for "soap" is *sapo*. Three of the most common soaps are:

$$\text{CH}_3(\text{CH}_2)_{16}\overset{\displaystyle \text{O}}{\overset{\|}{\text{C}}}\text{O}^-\,\text{Na}^+ \qquad \text{CH}_3(\text{CH}_2)_7\text{CH}\!=\!\text{CH}(\text{CH}_2)_7\overset{\displaystyle \text{O}}{\overset{\|}{\text{C}}}\text{O}^-\,\text{Na}^+$$

        sodium stearate   **sodium oleate**

$$\text{CH}_3(\text{CH}_2)_4\text{CH}\!=\!\text{CHCH}_2\text{CH}\!=\!\text{CH}(\text{CH}_2)_7\overset{\displaystyle \text{O}}{\overset{\|}{\text{C}}}\text{O}^-\,\text{Na}^+$$

                        sodium linoleate

PROBLEM 33   **SOLVED**

An oil obtained from coconuts is unusual in that all three fatty acid components are identical. The molecular formula of the oil is $C_{45}H_{86}O_6$. What is the molecular formula of the carboxylate ion obtained when the oil is saponified?

Solution When the oil is saponified, it forms glycerol and three equivalents of carboxylate ion. In losing glycerol, the fat loses three carbons and five hydrogens. Thus, the three equivalents of carboxylate ion have a combined molecular formula of $C_{42}H_{81}O_6$. Dividing by three gives a molecular formula of $C_{14}H_{27}O_2$ for the carboxylate ion.

Long-chain carboxylate ions do not exist as individual ions in aqueous solution. Instead, they arrange themselves in spherical clusters called **micelles** as shown in Figure 17.4. Each micelle contains 50 to 100 long-chain carboxylate ions and resembles a large ball. The polar heads of the carboxylate ions, each accompanied by a counterion, are on the outside of the ball because of their attraction for water, whereas the nonpolar tails are buried in the interior of the ball to minimize their contact with water. The attractive forces between hydrocarbon chains in water (such as those experienced by the tails of the carboxylate ions in micelles) are called **hydrophobic interactions** (Section 23.15).

Water by itself is not a very effective cleaner because dirt is carried by nonpolar oil molecules. Soap has cleansing ability because the nonpolar oil molecules dissolve in the nonpolar interior of the micelles and are washed away with the micelle during rinsing.

Because the surface of the micelle is charged, the individual micelles repel each other instead of clustering together to form larger aggregates. However, in "hard' water—water containing high concentrations of calcium and magnesium ions—micelles do form aggregates. In hard water, therefore, soap forms a precipitate that we know as "bathtub ring" or "soap scum."

stearate ion

▲ **Figure 17.4**
In aqueous solution, soap forms micelles. The polar heads (carboxylate groups) of the soap molecules form the micelle's outer surface; the nonpolar tails (fatty acid R groups) extend into the micelle's interior.

Making Soap

For thousands of years, soap was prepared by heating animal fat with wood ashes. Because the ashes contain potassium carbonate, the solution that results is basic. In the modern commercial method of making soap, fats or oils are boiled in aqueous sodium hydroxide. Sodium chloride is then added to precipitate the soap, which is dried and pressed into bars. Perfume can be added for scented soaps, dyes can be added for colored soaps, sand can be added for scouring soaps, and air can be blown into the soap to make it float in water.

Making soap

The formation of soap scum in hard water led to a search for synthetic materials that would have the cleansing properties of soap but would not form scum when they encountered calcium and magnesium ions. The synthetic "soaps" that were developed, known as **detergents** (from the Latin *detergere*, which means "to wipe off"), are salts of benzene sulfonic acids. Calcium and magnesium sulfonate salts do not form aggregates. After the initial introduction of detergents into the marketplace, it was discovered that straight-chain alkyl groups are biodegradable, whereas branched-chain alkyl groups are not. Thus, to prevent detergents from polluting rivers and lakes, they should be made only with straight-chain alkyl groups.

R—⟨benzene⟩—S(=O)(=O)—OH   CH₃(CH₂)₁₁—⟨benzene⟩—S(=O)(=O)—O⁻ Na⁺

a benzenesulfonic acid   **a detergent**

17.15 REACTIONS OF CARBOXYLIC ACIDS

Carboxylic acids can undergo nucleophilic acyl substitution reactions only when they are in their acidic forms. The basic form of a carboxylic acid cannot undergo nucleophilic acyl substitution reactions because the negatively charged carboxylate ion is resistant to nucleophilic addition. Therefore, carboxylate ions are even less reactive in nucleophilic acyl substitution reactions than are amides.

acetic acid

relative reactivities toward nucleophilic acyl substitution

$$\boxed{\text{most reactive}} \quad \underset{R}{\overset{O}{\underset{}{\parallel}}}\underset{OH}{C} > \underset{R}{\overset{O}{\underset{}{\parallel}}}\underset{NH_2}{C} > \underset{R}{\overset{O}{\underset{}{\parallel}}}\underset{O^-}{C} \quad \boxed{\text{least reactive}}$$

   Carboxylic acids have approximately the same reactivity as esters, because the HO⁻ leaving group of a carboxylic acid has about the same basicity as the RO⁻ leaving group of an ester. Therefore, like esters, carboxylic acids do not react with halide ions or with carboxylate ions.

   Carboxylic acids react with alcohols to form esters. The reaction must be carried out in an acidic solution, not only to catalyze the reaction but also to keep the carboxylic acid in its acidic form so that the nucleophile will react with it. Because the tetrahedral intermediate formed in this reaction has two potential leaving groups of approximately the same basicity, the reaction must be carried out with excess alcohol to drive it toward products. Emil Fischer (Section 22.10) was the first to discover that an ester could be prepared by treating a carboxylic acid with excess alcohol in the presence of an acid catalyst, so the reaction is called a **Fischer esterification**. Its mechanism is the exact reverse of the mechanism for the acid-catalyzed hydrolysis of an ester shown on page 730. See also Problem 23.

$$\underset{R}{\overset{O}{\underset{}{\parallel}}}\underset{OH}{C} + CH_3OH \underset{}{\overset{HCl}{\rightleftharpoons}} \underset{R}{\overset{O}{\underset{}{\parallel}}}\underset{OCH_3}{C} + H_2O$$

excess

chem Tutorial:
place Fischer esterification

   Carboxylic acids do not undergo nucleophilic acyl substitution reactions with amines. Because a carboxylic acid is an acid and an amine is a base, the carboxylic acid immediately donates a proton to the amine when the two compounds are mixed. The resulting ammonium carboxylate salt is the final product of the reaction; the carboxylate ion is unreactive, and the protonated amine is not a nucleophile.

$$\underset{R}{\overset{O}{\underset{}{\parallel}}}\underset{OH}{C} + CH_3CH_2NH_2 \longrightarrow \underset{R}{\overset{O}{\underset{}{\parallel}}}\underset{O^- \overset{+}{H_3}NCH_2CH_3}{C}$$

**an ammonium
carboxylate salt**

$$\underset{R}{\overset{O}{\underset{}{\parallel}}}\underset{OH}{C} + NH_3 \longrightarrow \underset{R}{\overset{O}{\underset{}{\parallel}}}\underset{O^- \overset{+}{N}H_4}{C}$$

An ammonium carboxylate salt can lose water to form an amide if it is heated.

$$\underset{R}{\overset{O}{\underset{}{\parallel}}}\underset{O^- \overset{+}{H_3}NCH_2CH_3}{C} \overset{225\ ^\circ C}{\longrightarrow} \underset{R}{\overset{O}{\underset{}{\parallel}}}\underset{NHCH_2CH_3}{C} + H_2O$$

PROBLEM 34♦

Show how each of the following esters could be prepared using a carboxylic acid as one of the starting materials:

a. methyl butyrate (odor of apples)   **b.** octyl acetate (odor of oranges)

PROBLEM-SOLVING STRATEGY

Proposing a Mechanism

Propose a mechanism for the following reaction:

When you are asked to propose a mechanism, look carefully at the reagents to determine the first step of the mechanism. One of the reagents has two functional groups: a carboxyl group and a carbon–carbon double bond. The other reagent, Br_2, does not react with carboxylic acids, but does react with alkenes (Section 4.8). Approach to one side of the double bond is sterically hindered by the carboxyl group. Therefore, Br_2 will add to the other side of the double bond, forming a cyclic bromonium ion. We know that in the second step of this addition reaction, a nucleophile attacks the bromonium ion. Of the two nucleophiles present, the carbonyl oxygen is the one best positioned to attack the back side of the bromonium ion, resulting in a compound with the observed configuration. Loss of a proton gives the final product of the reaction.

Now continue on to Problem 35.

PROBLEM 35

Propose a mechanism for the following reaction. (*Hint:* Number the carbons to help you see where they end up in the product.)

$$CH_2=CHCH_2CH_2CH=CCH_3 \quad + \quad$$

17.16 REACTIONS OF AMIDES

acetamide

Amides are very unreactive compounds, which is comforting, since proteins that impart strength to biological structures and catalyze reactions that take place in biological systems are composed of amino acids linked together by amide bonds (Sections 17.4 and 23.8). Amides do not react with halide ions, carboxylate ions, alcohols, or water because, in each case, the incoming nucleophile is a weaker base than the leaving group of the amide (Table 17.1).

$$R-C(=O)-NHCH_2CH_2CH_3 \quad + \quad Cl^- \longrightarrow \text{no reaction}$$

$$R-C(=O)-N(CH_3)_2 \quad + \quad CH_3-C(=O)-O^- \longrightarrow \text{no reaction}$$

$$\underset{R}{\overset{O}{\underset{NHCH_3}{\parallel}}}C \quad + \quad CH_3OH \quad \longrightarrow \quad \text{no reaction}$$

$$\underset{R}{\overset{O}{\underset{NHCH_2CH_3}{\parallel}}}C \quad + \quad H_2O \quad \longrightarrow \quad \text{no reaction}$$

Amides do, however, react with water and alcohols if the reaction mixture is heated in the presence of an acid. The reason for this will be explained in Section 17.17.

$$\underset{R}{\overset{O}{\underset{NHCH_2CH_3}{\parallel}}}C \quad + \quad H_2O \quad \xrightarrow[\Delta]{HCl} \quad \underset{R}{\overset{O}{\underset{OH}{\parallel}}}C \quad + \quad CH_3CH_2\overset{+}{N}H_3$$

$$\underset{R}{\overset{O}{\underset{NHCH_3}{\parallel}}}C \quad + \quad CH_3CH_2OH \quad \xrightarrow[\Delta]{HCl} \quad \underset{R}{\overset{O}{\underset{OCH_2CH_3}{\parallel}}}C \quad + \quad CH_3\overset{+}{N}H_3$$

Molecular orbital theory can explain why amides are unreactive. In Section 17.2, we saw that amides have an important resonance contributor in which nitrogen shares its lone pair with the carbonyl carbon; the orbital that contains the lone pair overlaps the empty π^* antibonding orbital of the carbonyl carbon (Figure 17.3). This overlap lowers the energy of the lone pair—so that it is neither basic nor nucleophilic—and raises the energy of the π^* antibonding orbital of the carbonyl group, making it less reactive to nucleophiles (Figure 17.5).

▲ **Figure 17.5**
The filled nonbonding orbital containing nitrogen's lone pair overlaps the empty π^* antibonding orbital of the carbonyl carbon. This stabilizes the lone pair, making it less reactive, and raises the energy of the π^* orbital of the carbonyl carbon, making it less able to react with nucleophiles.

An amide with an NH_2 group can be dehydrated to a nitrile. The dehydrating reagent most commonly employed for this purpose is P_2O_5.

$$\underset{R}{\overset{O}{\underset{NH_2}{\parallel}}}C \quad \xrightarrow[80\,°C]{P_2O_5} \quad R_2C\equiv N$$

Dalmatians: Do Not Fool with Mother Nature

When amino acids are metabolized, the excess nitrogen is concentrated into uric acid, a compound with five amide bonds. A series of enzyme-catalyzed amide hydrolysis reactions degrades uric acid all the way to ammonium ion. The extent to which uric acid is degraded depends on the species. Birds, reptiles, and insects excrete excess nitrogen as uric acid. Mammals excrete excess nitrogen as allantoin. Excess nitrogen in aquatic animals is excreted as allantoic acid, urea, or as ammonium salts.

uric acid
excreted by:
birds, reptiles, insects

→ urate oxidase →

allantoin
mammals

→ allantoinase →

allantoic acid
marine vertebrates

→ allantoicase →

urea
cartilaginous fish, amphibia

↓ urease

$^+NH_4 X^-$
ammonium salt
marine invertebrates

Dalmatians, unlike other mammals, excrete high levels of uric acid. This is because breeders of Dalmatians have selected dogs that have no white hairs in their black spots, and the gene that causes the white hairs is linked to the gene that causes uric acid to be converted to allantoin. Dalmatians are, therefore, susceptible to gout, a painful buildup of uric acid in joints.

PROBLEM 36 ◆

What acyl chloride and what amine would be required to synthesize the following amides?

a. *N*-ethylbutanamide   **b.** *N,N*-dimethylbenzamide

PROBLEM 37 ◆

a. Which of the following reactions would lead to the formation of an amide?

1. R–C(=O)–OH + CH_3NH_2 ⟶

2. R–C(=O)–OCH_3 + CH_3NH_2 ⟶

3. R–C(=O)–OCH_3 + CH_3NH_2 $\xrightarrow{CH_3O^-}$

4. R–C(=O)–O^- + CH_3NH_2 ⟶

5. R–C(=O)–Cl + $2\ CH_3NH_2$ ⟶

6. R–C(=O)–OCH_3 + CH_3NH_2 $\xrightarrow{HO^-}$

b. For those reactions that do form amides, what could be done to improve either the rate of amide formation or the yield of the amide product?

17.17 THE HYDROLYSIS OF AMIDES IS CATALYZED BY ACIDS

The mechanism for the acid-catalyzed hydrolysis of an amide is similar to the mechanism for the acid-catalyzed hydrolysis of an ester shown on page 730.

MECHANISM FOR ACID-CATALYZED HYDROLYSIS OF AN AMIDE

tetrahedral intermediate I

tetrahedral intermediate II

tetrahedral intermediate III

- The acid protonates the carbonyl oxygen, which increases the susceptibility of the carbonyl carbon to nucleophilic addition.

- Addition of the nucleophile (H_2O) to the carbonyl carbon leads to tetrahedral intermediate I, which is in equilibrium with its nonprotonated form, tetrahedral intermediate II.

- Reprotonation can occur either on oxygen to re-form tetrahedral intermediate I or on nitrogen to form tetrahedral intermediate III. Protonation on nitrogen is favored because the NH_2 group is a stronger base than the OH group.

- Of the two possible leaving groups in tetrahedral intermediate III (HO^- and NH_3), NH_3 is the weaker base, so it is the one eliminated.

- Because the reaction is carried out in an acidic solution, NH_3 will be protonated after it is eliminated from the tetrahedral intermediate. This prevents the reverse reaction from occurring, because $^+NH_4$ is not a nucleophile.

Let's take a minute to see why an amide cannot be hydrolyzed without a catalyst. In an uncatalyzed reaction, the amide would not be protonated. Therefore, water, a very poor nucleophile, would have to add to a neutral amide that is much less susceptible to nucleophilic addition than a protonated amide would be. More importantly, the NH_2 group of the tetrahedral intermediate would not be protonated in the uncatalyzed reaction. Therefore, HO^- is the group that would be eliminated from the tetrahedral intermediate, because HO^- is a weaker base than $^-NH_2$. This would re-form the amide.

chem Tutorial:
place Conversions between carboxylic acid derivatives

the leaving group in acid-catalyzed amide hydrolysis

the leaving group in uncatalyzed amide hydrolysis

An amide reacts with an alcohol in the presence of acid for the same reason that it reacts with water in the presence of acid.

Penicillin and Drug Resistance

Penicillin is a substituted β-lactam. It is thought that the antibiotic activity of penicillin results from its ability to acylate (put an acyl group on) a CH_2OH group of an enzyme that has a role in the synthesis of bacterial cell walls. (The CH_2OH group adds to the carbonyl carbon of the β-lactam, forming a tetrahedral intermediate; when the π bond re-forms, the strain in the four-membered ring increases the leaving propensity of the amino group.) Acylation inactivates the enzyme, and actively growing bacteria die because they are unable to synthesize functional cell walls. Penicillin has no effect on mammalian cells because mammalian cells are not enclosed by cell walls. Penicillins are stored at cold temperatures to minimize hydrolysis of the β-lactam.

Bacteria that are resistant to penicillin secrete penicillinase, an enzyme that catalyzes hydrolysis of the β-lactam. The ring-opened product has no antibacterial activity.

Penicillins in Clinical Use

More than 10 different penicillins are currently in clinical use. They differ only in the group (R) attached to the carbonyl group. Some of these penicillins are shown here. In addition to their structural differences, the penicillins differ in the organisms against which they are most effective. They also differ in their susceptibility to penicillinase. For example, methicillin, a synthetic penicillin, is effective against bacteria that are resistant to penicillin G, a naturally occurring penicillin. Almost 19% of humans are allergic to penicillin G.

Penicillin V is a semisynthetic penicillin in clinical use. It is not a naturally occurring penicillin, but it is also not a true synthetic penicillin because chemists do not synthesize it. The *Penicillium* mold synthesizes it after being fed 2-phenoxyethanol, the compound needed for the side chain.

2-phenoxyethanol $\xrightarrow{\textit{Penicillium mold}}$ **penicillin V**

PROBLEM 38

Suggest reasons to explain why methicillin is effective in treating patients infected with bacteria resistant to penicillin G.

PROBLEM 39◆

List the following amides in order of decreasing reactivity toward acid-catalyzed hydrolysis:

A   B   C   D

17.18 THE HYDROLYSIS OF AN IMIDE: A WAY TO SYNTHESIZE PRIMARY AMINES

Athough primary amines can be prepared by S_N2 reactions, the yields are poor because it is difficult to stop the reaction after one alkyl group has been placed on the nitrogen (see Problem 13 on page 346). A much better way to prepare a primary amine is by means of a **Gabriel synthesis**, which synthesizes it from an alkyl halide. The Gabriel synthesis involves the hydrolysis of an imide. An **imide** is a compound with two acyl groups bonded to a nitrogen.

$$RCH_2Br \xrightarrow{\text{Gabriel synthesis}} RCH_2NH_2$$

alkyl halide   **primary amine**

The steps involved in the synthesis are shown below.

phthalimide   **an N-substituted imide**   **phthalic acid**   **primary alkyl ammonium ion**

primary amine

- A base removes a proton from the nitrogen of phthalimide.
- The resulting nucleophile reacts with an alkyl halide. Because this is an S_N2 reaction, it works best with primary alkyl halides (Section 8.1).
- Hydrolysis of the *N*-substituted imide is catalyzed by acid. Because the solution is acidic, the final products are a primary alkyl ammonium ion and phthalic acid.
- Neutralization of the ammonium ion with base forms the primary amine.

Notice that the alkyl group of the primary amine is identical to the alkyl group of the alkyl halide.
Only one alkyl group can be placed on the nitrogen because there is only one hydrogen bonded to the nitrogen of phthalimide. This means that the Gabriel synthesis can be used only for the preparation of primary amines.

PROBLEM 40♦

What alkyl bromide would you use in a Gabriel synthesis to prepare each of the following amines?

a. pentylamine

c. benzylamine

b. isohexylamine

d. cyclohexylamine

PROBLEM 41

Primary amines can also be prepared by the reaction of an alkyl halide with azide ion, followed by catalytic hydrogenation. What advantage do this method and the Gabriel synthesis have over the synthesis of a primary amine using an alkyl halide and ammonia?

$$CH_3CH_2CH_2Br \xrightarrow{\ ^-N_3\ } CH_3CH_2CH_2N \overset{+}{=} N \overset{..}{=} \overset{..}{N} \xrightarrow[Pd/C]{H_2} CH_3CH_2CH_2NH_2 + N_2$$

---

acetonitrile

17.19 THE HYDROLYSIS OF NITRILES

Nitriles are even harder to hydrolyze than amides, but they can be slowly hydrolyzed to carboxylic acids when heated with water and an acid.

$$R_2C \equiv N \xrightarrow[\Delta]{HCl, H_2O} \underset{R}{\overset{O}{\underset{\|}{C}}} OH$$

The mechanism for the acid-catalyzed hydrolysis of a nitrile is shown below:

MECHANISM FOR ACID-CATALYZED HYDROLYSIS OF A NITRILE

- The acid protonates the nitrogen of the cyano group ($C \equiv N$), making it easier for water to add to the carbon of the cyano group in the next step.
- Addition of the nucleophile (H_2O) to the protonated cyano group is analogous to addition of water to a protonated carbonyl group.

- Because nitrogen is a stronger base than oxygen, oxygen loses a proton and nitrogen gains a proton, resulting in a protonated amide (whose two resonance contributors are shown).

- The amide is immediately hydrolyzed to a carboxylic acid—because an amide is easier to hydrolyze than a nitrile—by means of the acid-catalyzed mechanism shown in on page 743.

Nitriles can be prepared from an S_N2 reaction of alkyl halide with cyanide ion. Because a nitrile can be hydrolyzed to a carboxylic acid, you now know how to convert an alkyl halide into a carboxylic acid. Notice that the carboxylic acid has one more carbon than the alkyl halide.

Another way to make a primary amine is to reduce a nitrile by catalytic hydrogenation (Section 16.1).

$$RC{\equiv}N \xrightarrow[\text{Raney Nickel}]{H_2} RCH_2NH_2$$

PROBLEM 42♦

Which alkyl halides form the carboxylic acids listed below after reaction with sodium cyanide followed by heating the product in an acidic aqueous solution?

a. butyric acid   **b.** isovaleric acid   **c.** cyclohexanecarboxylic acid

---

17.20 DESIGNING A SYNTHESIS V: THE SYNTHESIS OF CYCLIC COMPOUNDS

Most of the reactions we have been studying are intermolecular reactions: the two reacting groups are in different molecules. *Cyclic compounds are formed from intramolecular reactions*: the two reacting groups are in the same molecule. We have seen that intramolecular reactions are particularly favored if the reaction forms a compound with a five- or a six-membered ring (Section 8.10).

In designing the synthesis of a cyclic compound, we must determine the kinds of reactive groups that are necessary for a successful synthesis. For example, we know that an ester is formed from the reaction of a carboxylic acid with an alcohol. Therefore, a lactone (cyclic ester) can be prepared from a reactant that has a carboxylic acid group and an alcohol group in the same molecule. The size of the ring will be determined by the number of carbons between the two reacting groups.

four intervening carbon atoms

three intervening carbon atoms

A compound with a ketone group attached to a benzene ring can be prepared using a Friedel–Crafts acylation reaction (Section 15.14). Therefore, a cyclic ketone will result if a Lewis acid ($AlCl_3$) is added to a compound that contains both a benzene ring and an acyl chloride separated by the appropriate number of carbon atoms.

A cyclic ether can be prepared by an intramolecular Williamson ether synthesis (Section 9.9).

A cyclic ether can also be prepared by an intramolecular electrophilic addition reaction.

The product obtained from an intramolecular reaction can undergo further reactions allowing for the synthesis of many different compounds. For example, the cyclic alkyl bromide formed in the following reaction could undergo an elimination reaction, or could undergo substitution with a wide variety of nucleophiles, or could be converted into a Grignard reagent that could react with many different electrophiles (Section 11.2).

PROBLEM 43

Design a synthesis for each of the following, using an intramolecular reaction:

a.

b.

c.

d.

COOH

e.

O   CH₂CH=CH₂

f.

O   CH₂CH₂CH₂OH

17.21 HOW CHEMISTS ACTIVATE CARBOXYLIC ACIDS

Of the various classes of carbonyl compounds discussed in this chapter—acyl halides, acid anhydrides, esters, carboxylic acids, and amides—carboxylic acids are the most commonly available both in the laboratory and in biological systems. Therefore, carboxylic acids are the reagents most likely to be available when a chemist or a cell needs to synthesize a carboxylic acid derivative. However, we have seen that carboxylic acids are relatively unreactive toward nucleophilic addition-elimination reactions because the OH group of a carboxylic acid is a strong base and therefore a poor leaving group. In neutral solutions (physiological pH = 7.3), a carboxylic acid is even more resistant to nucleophilic addition-elimination reactions because it exists predominantly in its unreactive, negatively charged basic form (Sections 1.25 and 17.15). Therefore, both organic chemists and cells need a way to activate carboxylic acids so that they can readily undergo nucleophilic addition-elimination reactions. First we will look at how chemists activate carboxylic acids, and then in Section 17.22 we will see how cells do it.

Because acyl halides are the most reactive of the carboxylic acid derivatives, the easiest way to synthesize any other carboxylic acid derivative is to add the appropriate nucleophile to an acyl halide. Consequently, one way organic chemists activate carboxylic acids is by converting them into acyl halides.

A carboxylic acid can be converted into an acyl chloride by being heated either with thionyl chloride ($SOCl_2$) or with phosphorus trichloride (PCl_3). Acyl bromides can be synthesized by using phosphorus tribromide (PBr_3).

$$R-C(=O)-OH \ + \ SOCl_2 \ \xrightarrow{\Delta} \ R-C(=O)-Cl \ + \ SO_2 \ + \ HCl$$

thionyl chloride

$$3 \ R-C(=O)-OH \ + \ PCl_3 \ \xrightarrow{\Delta} \ 3 \ R-C(=O)-Cl \ + \ H_3PO_3$$

phosphorus trichloride

$$3 \ R-C(=O)-OH \ + \ PBr_3 \ \xrightarrow{\Delta} \ 3 \ R-C(=O)-Br \ + \ H_3PO_3$$

phosphorus tribromide

These three reagents convert the OH group of a carboxylic acid into a better leaving group than the halide ion (Section 10.2).

$$R-C(=O)-O-S(=O)-Cl \qquad R-C(=O)-O-PCl_2 \qquad R-C(=O)-O-PBr_2$$

good leaving groups

As a result, when the halide ion subsequently adds to the carbonyl carbon and forms a tetrahedral intermediate, the halide ion is *not* the group that is eliminated.

a better leaving group than a chloride ion

Notice that the reagents that cause the OH group of a carboxylic acid to be replaced by a halogen are the same reagents that cause the OH group of an alcohol to be replaced by a halogen (Section 10.2).

Once the acyl halide has been prepared, a wide variety of carboxylic acid derivatives can be synthesized by adding the appropriate nucleophile (Section 17.8).

an anhydride

an ester

an amide

Carboxylic acids can also be activated for nucleophilic addition-elimination reactions by being converted into anhydrides. Treating a carboxylic acid with a strong dehydrating agent such as P_2O_5 yields an anhydride.

Carboxylic acids and carboxylic acid derivatives can also be prepared by methods other than nucleophilic addition-elimination reactions. A summary of the methods used to synthesize these compounds is provided in Appendix IV.

PROBLEM 44◆

How would you synthesize the following compounds starting with a carboxylic acid?

a. CH_3CH_2—

b.

17.22 HOW CELLS ACTIVATE CARBOXYLIC ACIDS

The synthesis of compounds by biological organisms is called **biosynthesis**. Acyl halides and acid anhydrides are too reactive to be used as reagents in biological organisms. Cells live in a predominantly aqueous environment, and acyl halides and acid anhydrides are rapidly hydrolyzed in water. So biological organisms must activate carboxylic acids in a different way.

One way biological organisms activate carboxylic acids is to convert them into acyl phosphates, acyl pyrophosphates, or acyl adenylates.

an acyl phosphate   an acyl pyrophosphate   an acyl adenylate

An **acyl phosphate** is a mixed anhydride of a carboxylic acid and phosphoric acid. An **acyl pyrophosphate** is a mixed anhydride of a carboxylic acid and pyrophosphoric acid.

phosphoric acid   pyrophosphoric acid

An **acyl adenylate** is a mixed anhydride of a carboxylic acid and adenosine monophosphate (AMP). The structure of adenosine triphosphate (ATP) is shown below, both in its entirety and with "Ad" in place of the adenosyl group. AMP has two fewer phosphate groups than ATP.

adenosine triphosphate
ATP

Acyl phosphates are formed by nucleophilic attack of a carboxylate ion on the γ-phosphorus (the terminal phosphorus) of ATP. Attack of a nucleophile on the P=O group breaks a **phosphoanhydride bond** (rather than the π bond), so an intermediate is not formed. Essentially, it is an S_N2 reaction with an adenosine pyrophosphate leaving group. This reaction and the ones that follow will be discussed in greater detail in Sections 26.2 and 26.3.

adenosine triphosphate   an acyl phosphate   adenosine diphosphate
ATP   ADP

Acyl pyrophosphates are formed by nucleophilic attack of a carboxylate ion on the β-phosphorus of ATP.

adenosine triphosphate   an acyl pyrophosphate   adenosine monophosphate
ATP   AMP

Acyl adenylates are formed by nucleophilic attack of a carboxylate ion on the α-phosphorus of ATP.

Which phosphorus atom the nucleophile attacks depends on the enzyme that catalyzes the reaction.

Because these mixed anhydrides are negatively charged, they are not readily approached by nucleophiles. Thus, they are used only in enzyme-catalyzed reactions. One of the functions of enzymes that catalyze biological nucleophilic addition-elimination reactions is to neutralize the negative charges of the mixed anhydride (see Figure 26.1 on page 1100). Another function of the enzyme is to exclude water from the site where the reaction takes place. Otherwise hydrolysis of the mixed anhydride would compete with the desired nucleophilic addition-elimination reaction.

Carboxylic acids can also be activated by being converted to thioesters. A **thioester** is an ester with a sulfur in place of the alkoxy oxygen.

O
‖
C
R   SR′

a thioester

Thioesters are the most common forms of activated carboxylic acids in a cell. Although thioesters hydrolyze at about the same rate as oxygen esters, they are much more reactive than oxygen esters toward addition of nitrogen and carbon nucleophiles. This allows a thioester to survive in the aqueous environment of the cell—without being hydrolyzed—while waiting to be used as a substrate in a nucleophilic addition-elimination reaction.

The carbonyl carbon of a thioester is more susceptible to nucleophilic addition than is the carbonyl carbon of an oxygen ester because electron delocalization onto the carbonyl oxygen is weaker when Y is S than when Y is O. The electron delocalization is weaker because less overlap occurs between the 3p orbital of sulfur and the 2p orbital of carbon than between the 2p orbital of oxygen and the 2p orbital of carbon (Section 17.2). In addition, the tetrahedral intermediate formed from a thioester undergoes elimination more rapidly because a thiolate ion is a weaker base and therefore a better leaving group than an alkoxide ion.

:O: :Ö:⁻
‖ |
C   ⟷   C
R   ̈YR   R   ̈Y⁺R

CH₃CH₂SH   CH₃CH₂OH
pK_a = 10.5   pK_a = 15.9

The thiol used in biological systems for the formation of thioesters is coenzyme A. The compound is written "CoASH" to emphasize that the thiol group is the reactive part of the molecule.

When an organism converts a carboxylic acid into a thioester, it first converts the carboxylic acid into an acyl adenylate. The acyl adenylate then reacts with CoASH to form the thioester. The most common thioester in cells is acetyl-CoA.

Acetylcholine is one example of a carboxylic acid derivative that cells synthesize using acetyl-CoA. Acetylcholine is a *neurotransmitter*—a compound that transmits nerve impulses across the synapses (spaces) between nerve cells.

One way a gene is activated is by formation of an amide linkage between acetyl-CoA and an amino group of a lysine residue of a DNA-bound protein.

Nerve Impulses, Paralysis, and Insecticides

After an impulse is transmitted between two nerve cells, acetylcholine must be hydrolyzed immediately to enable the recipient cell to receive another impulse. Acetylcholinesterase, the enzyme that catalyzes this hydrolysis, has a CH_2OH group that is necessary for its catalytic activity. The enzyme participates in a transesterification reaction and then hydrolysis occurs.

Diisopropyl fluorophosphate (DFP), a military nerve gas used during World War II, inactivates acetylcholinesterase by reacting with the CH_2OH group. When the enzyme is inactivated, the nerve impulses cannot be transmitted properly, and paralysis occurs. DFP is extremely toxic. Its LD_{50} (the lethal dose for 50% of the test animals) is only 0.5 mg/kg of body weight (page 661).

Malathion and parathion, widely used as insecticides, are compounds related to DFP. The LD_{50} of malathion is 2800 mg/kg. Parathion is much more toxic, with an LD_{50} of 2 mg/kg.

17.23 DICARBOXYLIC ACIDS AND THEIR DERIVATIVES

The structures of some common dicarboxylic acids and their pK_a values are shown in Table 17.2.

Table 17.2	Structures, Names, and pK_a Values of Some Simple Dicarboxylic Acids		
Dicarboxylic acid	**Common name**	**pK_{a1}**	**pK_{a2}**
	Carbonic acid	6.37	10.25
	Oxalic acid	1.27	4.27
	Malonic acid	2.86	5.70
	Succinic acid	4.21	5.64
	Glutaric acid	4.34	5.27
	Adipic acid	4.41	5.28
	Phthalic acid	2.95	5.41

Although the two carboxyl groups of a dicarboxylic acid are identical, the two pK_a values are different because the protons are lost one at a time and therefore leave from different species. The first proton is lost from a neutral molecule, whereas the second proton is lost from a negatively charged ion.

A COOH group withdraws electrons (more strongly than does an H) and therefore increases the stability of the conjugate base formed when the first COOH group loses a proton, thereby increasing its acidity. The pK_a values of the dicarboxylic acids show that the acid-strengthening effect of the COOH group decreases as the separation between the two carboxyl groups increases.

Dicarboxylic acids readily lose water when heated if they can form a cyclic anhydride with a five- or a six-membered ring.

glutaric acid

glutaric anhydride

phthalic acid

phthalic anhydride

Cyclic anhydrides are more easily prepared if the dicarboxylic acid is heated in the presence of acetyl chloride or acetic anhydride or if it is treated with a strong dehydrating agent such as P_2O_5.

succinic acid

acetic anhydride

succinic anhydride

glutaric acid

glutaric anhydride

PROBLEM 45

a. Propose a mechanism for the formation of succinic anhydride in the presence of acetic anhydride.

b. How does acetic anhydride help in the formation of succinic anhydride?

Carbonic acid—a compound with two OH groups bonded to the carbonyl carbon—is unstable, readily breaking down to CO_2 and H_2O. The reaction is reversible, so carbonic acid is formed when CO_2 is bubbled into water (Section 1.17).

carbonic acid

$\rightleftharpoons CO_2 + H_2O$

We have seen that the OH group of a carboxylic acid can be substituted to give a variety of carboxylic acid derivatives. Similarly, the OH groups of carbonic acid can be substituted by other groups.

phosgene   dimethyl carbonate   urea   carbamic acid   methyl carbamate

Synthetic Polymers

Synthetic polymers play important roles in our daily lives. Polymers are compounds that are made by linking together many small molecules called monomers. In many synthetic polymers, the monomers are held together by ester and amide bonds. For example, Dacron is a polyester and nylon is a polyamide.

Dacron®

nylon 6

Synthetic polymers have taken the place of metals, fabrics, glass, wood, and paper, allowing us to have a greater variety and larger quantities of materials than nature could have provided. New polymers are continually being designed to fit human needs. For example, Kevlar has a tensile strength greater than steel. It is used for high-performance skis and bulletproof vests. Lexan is a strong and transparent polymer used for such things as traffic light lenses and compact disks.

Kevlar®

Lexan®

These and other synthetic polymers are discussed in detail in Chapter 29.

Dissolving Sutures

Dissolving sutures, such as dexon and poly(dioxanone) (PDS), are synthetic polymers that are now routinely used in surgery. The many ester groups they contain are slowly hydrolyzed to small molecules that are then metabolized to compounds easily excreted by the body. Patients no longer have to undergo the second medical procedure that was required to remove the sutures when traditional suture materials were used.

Depending on their structures, these synthetic sutures lose 50% of their strength after two to three weeks and are completely absorbed within 3 to 6 months.

Dexon   **PDS**

PROBLEM 46 ♦

One of the two polymers for dissolving sutures shown in the box on page 756 loses 50% of its strength in two weeks, and the other loses that much strength in three weeks. Which suture material lasts longer?

PROBLEM 47

What products would you expect to obtain from the following reactions?

a. phosgene + excess diethylamine

b. malonic acid + 2 acetyl chloride

c. methyl carbamate + methylamine

d. urea + water

e. urea + water + HCl

f. β-ethylglutaric acid + acetyl chloride + Δ

SUMMARY

A **carbonyl group** is a carbon double bonded to an oxygen; an **acyl group** is a carbonyl group attached to an alkyl or aryl group. **Acyl halides**, **acid anhydrides**, **esters**, and **amides** are called **carboxylic acid derivatives** because they differ from a carboxylic acid only in the nature of the group that has replaced the OH group of the carboxylic acid. Cyclic esters are called **lactones**; cyclic amides are **lactams**. There are **symmetrical anhydrides** and **mixed anhydrides**.

Carbonyl compounds can be placed in one of two classes. Class I carbonyl compounds contain a group that can be replaced by another group; carboxylic acids and carboxylic acid derivatives belong to this class. Class II carbonyl compounds do not contain a group that can be replaced by another group; aldehydes and ketones belong to this class.

The reactivity of carbonyl compounds resides in the polarity of the carbonyl group; the carbonyl carbon has a partial positive charge that is attractive to nucleophiles. Class I carbonyl compounds undergo **nucleophilic addition–elimination reactions**, in which a nucleophile replaces the substituent attached to the acyl group in reactant. All class I carbonyl compounds react with nucleophiles in the same way: the nucleophile adds to the carbonyl carbon, forming an unstable **tetrahedral intermediate**, which re-forms the carbonyl compound by eliminating the weakest base. (Generally, a compound with an sp^3 carbon bonded to an oxygen is unstable if the sp^3 carbon is bonded to another electronegative atom.)

A carboxylic acid derivative will undergo a nucleophilic addition–elimination reaction provided that the newly added group in the tetrahedral intermediate is not a much weaker base than the group attached to the acyl group in the reactant. The weaker the base attached to the acyl group, the more easily both steps of the nucleophilic addition–elimination reaction can take place. The relative reactivities toward nucleophilic addition-elimination are: acyl halides > acid anhydrides > esters and carboxylic acids > amides > carboxylate ions.

Hydrolysis, **alcoholysis**, and **aminolysis** are reactions in which water, alcohols, and amines, respectively, convert one compound into two compounds. A **transesterification reaction** converts one ester to another ester. Treating a carboxylic acid with excess alcohol and an acid catalyst is called a **Fischer esterification**. An ester with a tertiary alkyl group hydrolyzes by an S_N1 reaction.

The rate of hydrolysis can be increased by either acid or HO^-; the rate of alcoholysis can be increased by either acid or RO^-. An acid increases the rate of formation of the tetrahedral intermediate by protonating the carbonyl oxygen, which increases the electrophilicity of the carbonyl carbon, and by decreasing the basicity of the leaving group, which makes it easier to eliminate. Hydroxide (or alkoxide) ion increases the rate of formation of the tetrahedral intermediate—it is a better nucleophile than water (or an alcohol)—and increases the rate of collapse of the tetrahedral intermediate. Hydroxide ion promotes only hydrolysis reactions; alkoxide ion promotes only alcoholysis reactions. In an acid-catalyzed reaction, all organic reactants, intermediates, and products are positively charged or neutral; in hydroxide-ion- or alkoxide-ion-promoted reactions, all organic reactants, intermediates, and products are negatively charged or neutral.

Fats and **oils** are triesters of glycerol. Hydrolyzing the ester groups in a basic solution forms glycerol and fatty acid salts (soaps). In water, long-chain carboxylate ions arrange themselves in spherical clusters called **micelles**. The attractive forces of hydrocarbon chains for each other in water are called **hydrophobic interactions**.

Amides are unreactive compounds but do react with water and alcohols if the reaction mixture is heated in an acidic solution. Nitriles are harder to hydrolyze than amides. The **Gabriel synthesis**, which converts an alkyl halide into a primary amine, involves the hydrolysis of an **imide**.

Organic chemists activate carboxylic acids by converting them into acyl halides or acid anhydrides. Cells activate carboxylic acids by converting them into **acyl phosphates**, **acyl pyrophosphates**, **acyl adenylates**, and **thioesters**.

SUMMARY OF REACTIONS

1. Reactions of acyl halides (Section 17.8)

$$
R-\overset{O}{\underset{}{C}}-Cl + CH_3-\overset{O}{\underset{}{C}}-O^- \longrightarrow R-\overset{O}{\underset{}{C}}-O-\overset{O}{\underset{}{C}}-CH_3 + Cl^-
$$

$$
R-\overset{O}{\underset{}{C}}-Cl + CH_3OH \longrightarrow R-\overset{O}{\underset{}{C}}-OCH_3 + HCl
$$

$$
R-\overset{O}{\underset{}{C}}-Cl + H_2O \longrightarrow R-\overset{O}{\underset{}{C}}-OH + HCl
$$

$$
R-\overset{O}{\underset{}{C}}-Cl + 2\ CH_3NH_2 \longrightarrow R-\overset{O}{\underset{}{C}}-NHCH_3 + CH_3\overset{+}{N}H_3\ Cl^-
$$

2. Reactions of acid anhydrides (Section 17.9)

$$
R-\overset{O}{\underset{}{C}}-O-\overset{O}{\underset{}{C}}-R + CH_3OH \longrightarrow R-\overset{O}{\underset{}{C}}-OCH_3 + R-\overset{O}{\underset{}{C}}-OH
$$

$$
R-\overset{O}{\underset{}{C}}-O-\overset{O}{\underset{}{C}}-R + H_2O \longrightarrow 2\ R-\overset{O}{\underset{}{C}}-OH
$$

$$
R-\overset{O}{\underset{}{C}}-O-\overset{O}{\underset{}{C}}-R + 2\ CH_3NH_2 \longrightarrow R-\overset{O}{\underset{}{C}}-NHCH_3 + R-\overset{O}{\underset{}{C}}-O^-\ H_3\overset{+}{N}CH_3
$$

3. Reactions of esters (Sections 17.10–17.13)

$$
R-\overset{O}{\underset{}{C}}-OR + CH_3OH \underset{}{\overset{HCl}{\rightleftharpoons}} R-\overset{O}{\underset{}{C}}-OCH_3 + ROH
$$

$$
R-\overset{O}{\underset{}{C}}-OR + CH_3OH \xrightarrow{CH_3O^-} R-\overset{O}{\underset{}{C}}-OCH_3 + ROH
$$

$$
R-\overset{O}{\underset{}{C}}-OR + H_2O \underset{}{\overset{HCl}{\rightleftharpoons}} R-\overset{O}{\underset{}{C}}-OH + ROH
$$

$$
R-\overset{O}{\underset{}{C}}-OR + H_2O \xrightarrow{HO^-} R-\overset{O}{\underset{}{C}}-O^- + ROH
$$

$$
R-\overset{O}{\underset{}{C}}-OR + CH_3NH_2 \longrightarrow R-\overset{O}{\underset{}{C}}-NHCH_3 + ROH
$$

4. Reactions of carboxylic acids (Section 17.15)

$$\underset{R}{\overset{O}{\underset{\|}{C}}}\text{—OH} \ + \ CH_3OH \ \overset{\textbf{HCl}}{\rightleftharpoons} \ \underset{R}{\overset{O}{\underset{\|}{C}}}\text{—OCH}_3 \ + \ H_2O$$

$$\underset{R}{\overset{O}{\underset{\|}{C}}}\text{—OH} \ + \ CH_3NH_2 \ \longrightarrow \ \underset{R}{\overset{O}{\underset{\|}{C}}}\text{—O}^-\ \overset{+}{H_3NCH_3} \ \overset{\textbf{225 °C}}{\longrightarrow} \ \underset{R}{\overset{O}{\underset{\|}{C}}}\text{—NH}_2 \ + \ H_2O$$

5. Reactions of amides (Sections 17.16 and 17.17)

$$\underset{R}{\overset{O}{\underset{\|}{C}}}\text{—NH}_2 \ + \ H_2O \ \overset{\textbf{HCl}}{\underset{\Delta}{\longrightarrow}} \ \underset{R}{\overset{O}{\underset{\|}{C}}}\text{—OH} \ + \ \overset{+}{NH_4}Cl^-$$

$$\underset{R}{\overset{O}{\underset{\|}{C}}}\text{—NH}_2 \ + \ CH_3OH \ \overset{\textbf{HCl}}{\underset{\Delta}{\longrightarrow}} \ \underset{R}{\overset{O}{\underset{\|}{C}}}\text{—OCH}_3 \ + \ \overset{+}{NH_4}Cl^-$$

$$\underset{R}{\overset{O}{\underset{\|}{C}}}\text{—NH}_2 \ \overset{\textbf{P}_2\textbf{O}_5}{\underset{\Delta}{\longrightarrow}} \ RC\equiv N$$

6. Gabriel synthesis of primary amines (Section 17.18)

$$\text{phthalimide} \ \overset{\begin{array}{l}\textbf{1. HO}^-\\ \textbf{2. RCH}_2\textbf{Br}\\ \textbf{3. HCl, H}_2\textbf{O, } \Delta\\ \textbf{4. HO}^-\end{array}}{\longrightarrow} \ RCH_2NH_2$$

7. Hydrolysis of nitriles (Section 17.19)

$$RC\equiv N \ + \ H_2O \ \overset{\textbf{HCl}}{\underset{\Delta}{\longrightarrow}} \ \underset{R}{\overset{O}{\underset{\|}{C}}}\text{—OH} \ + \ \overset{+}{NH_4}Cl^-$$

8. Activation of carboxylic acids by chemists (Section 17.21)

$$\underset{R}{\overset{O}{\underset{\|}{C}}}\text{—OH} \ + \ SOCl_2 \ \overset{\Delta}{\longrightarrow} \ \underset{R}{\overset{O}{\underset{\|}{C}}}\text{—Cl} \ + \ SO_2 \ + \ HCl$$

$$3 \ \underset{R}{\overset{O}{\underset{\|}{C}}}\text{—OH} \ + \ PCl_3 \ \overset{\Delta}{\longrightarrow} \ 3 \ \underset{R}{\overset{O}{\underset{\|}{C}}}\text{—Cl} \ + \ H_3PO_3$$

$$2 \ \underset{R}{\overset{O}{\underset{\|}{C}}}\text{—OH} \ \overset{\textbf{P}_2\textbf{O}_5}{\longrightarrow} \ \underset{R}{\overset{O}{\underset{\|}{C}}}\text{—O—}\underset{R}{\overset{O}{\underset{\|}{C}}} \ + \ H_2O$$

9. Activation of carboxylic acids by cells (Section 17.22)

10. Dehydration of dicarboxylic acids (Section 17.23)

KEY TERMS

acid anhydride (p. 709)
acyl adenylate (p. 751)
acyl group (p. 706)
acyl halide (p. 709)
acyl phosphate (p. 751)
acyl pyrophosphate (p. 751)
acyl transfer reaction (p. 717)
alcoholysis (p. 726)
amide (p. 711)
amino acid (p. 715)
aminolysis (p. 728)
biosynthesis (p. 750)
carbonyl carbon (p. 712)
carbonyl compound (p. 706)
carbonyl group (p. 706)
carbonyl oxygen (p. 710)

carboxyl group (p. 708)
carboxylic acid (p. 708)
carboxylic acid derivative (p. 707)
carboxyl oxygen (p. 710)
catalyst (p. 731)
detergent (p. 738)
ester (p. 710)
fat (p. 737)
fatty acid (p. 737)
Fischer esterification (p. 739)
Gabriel synthesis (p. 745)
hydrolysis reaction (p. 726)
hydrophobic interactions (p. 737)
imide (p. 745)
lactam (p. 711)
lactone (p. 710)

micelle (p. 737)
mixed anhydride (p. 710)
nitrile (p. 711)
nucleophilic acyl substitution
 reaction (p. 717)
nucleophilic addition–elimination
 reaction (p. 717)
oil (p. 737)
phosphoanhydride bond (p. 751)
saponification (p. 737)
soap (p. 737)
symmetrical anhydride (p. 710)
tetrahedral intermediate (p. 717)
thioester (p. 752)
transesterification reaction (p. 726)

PROBLEMS

48. Write a structure for each of the following:
a. *N,N*-dimethylhexanamide
b. 3,3-dimethylhexanamide
c. cyclohexanecarbonyl chloride
d. propanenitrile
e. propionyl bromide
f. sodium acetate
g. benzoic anhydride
h. β-valerolactone
i. 3-methylbutanenitrile
j. cycloheptanecarboxylic acid

49. Name the following:

a.

b.

c.

d.

e.

f.

g.

h.

i.

50. What products would be formed from the reaction of benzoyl chloride with the following reagents?
a. sodium acetate
b. water
c. excess dimethylamine
d. aqueous HCl
e. aqueous NaOH
f. cyclohexanol
g. excess benzylamine
h. 4-chlorophenol
i. isopropyl alcohol
j. excess aniline

51. What products would be obtained from the following hydrolysis reactions?

a.

b.

c.

d.

52. a. List the following esters in order of decreasing reactivity in the first slow step of a nucleophilic acyl substitution reaction (formation of the tetrahedral intermediate):

A   B   C   D

b. List the same esters in order of decreasing reactivity in the second slow step of a nucleophilic addition-elimination reaction (collapse of the tetrahedral intermediate).

53. Because bromocyclohexane is a secondary alkyl halide, both cyclohexanol and cyclohexene are formed when the alkyl halide reacts with hydroxide ion. Suggest a method to synthesize cyclohexanol from bromocyclohexane that would form little or no cyclohexene.

54. a. Which compound would you expect to have a higher dipole moment, methyl acetate or butanone?

b. Which would you expect to have a higher boiling point?

55. How could you use ^{1}H NMR spectroscopy to distinguish among the following esters?

A   B   C   D

56. If propionyl chloride is added to one equivalent of methylamine, only a 50% yield of *N*-methylpropanamide is obtained. If, however, the acyl chloride is added to two equivalents of methylamine, the yield of *N*-methylpropanamide is almost 100%. Explain these observations.

57. a. When a carboxylic acid is dissolved in isotopically labeled water ($H_2^{18}O$), and an acid catalyst is added, the label is incorporated into both oxygens of the acid. Propose a mechanism to account for this.

b. If a carboxylic acid is dissolved in isotopically labeled methanol ($CH_3^{18}OH$) and an acid catalyst is added, where will the label reside in the product?
c. If an ester is dissolved in isotopically labeled water ($H_2^{18}O$) and an acid catalyst is added, where will the label reside in the product?

58. Using an alcohol for one method and an alkyl halide for the other, show two ways to make each of the following esters:

a. propyl acetate (odor of pears)
b. isopentyl acetate (odor of bananas)

c. ethyl butyrate (odor of pineapple)
d. methyl phenylethanoate (odor of honey)

59. What reagents would you use to convert methyl propanoate into the following compounds?
a. isopropyl propanoate
b. sodium propanoate

c. *N*-ethylpropanamide
d. propanoic acid

60. A compound with molecular formula $C_5H_{10}O_2$ gives the following IR spectrum:

When it undergoes acid-catalyzed hydrolysis, the compound with the following ^{1}H NMR spectrum is formed. Identify the compounds.

Offset: 2.0 ppm

δ (ppm)

← frequency

61. Aspartame, the sweetener used in the commercial products NutraSweet and Equal, is 160 times sweeter than sucrose. What products would be obtained if aspartame were hydrolyzed completely in an aqueous solution of HCl?

aspartame

62. a. Which of the following reactions will not give the carbonyl product shown?

1.

6.

2.

7.

3.

8.

4.

9.

5.

10.

b. Which of the reactions that do not occur can be made to occur if an acid catalyst is added to the reaction mixture?

63. 1,4-Diazabicyclo[2.2.2]octane (abbreviated DABCO) is a tertiary amine that catalyzes transesterification reactions. Propose a mechanism to show how it does this.

1,4-diazabicyclo[2.2.2]octane
DABCO

64. Two products, A and B, are obtained from the reaction of 1-bromobutane with NH_3. Compound A reacts with acetyl chloride to form C, and B reacts with acetyl chloride to form D. The IR spectra of C and D are shown. Identify A, B, C, and D.

65. Phosgene ($COCl_2$) was used as a poison gas in World War I. Give the product that would be formed from the reaction of phosgene with each of the following reagents:

1. one equivalent of methanol
2. excess methanol
3. excess propylamine
4. one equivalent of ethanol followed by one equivalent of methylamine

66. What reagent should be used to carry out the following reaction?

![Reaction structure: HOCH2-benzene-COOCH3 converts to benzene-CO-O-CH2-benzene-COOCH3]

67. When a student treated butanedioic acid with thionyl chloride, she was surprised to find that the product she obtained was an anhydride rather than an acyl chloride. Propose a mechanism to explain why she obtained an anhydride.

68. Give the products of the following reactions:

a. CH₃-C(=O)-Cl + KF ⟶

b. [2-pyrrolidinone] + H₂O $\xrightarrow{\text{HCl} \atop \Delta}$

c. [benzoic acid] C(=O)OH $\xrightarrow{\text{1. SOCl}_2 \atop \text{2. 2 CH}_3\text{NH}_2}$

d. [succinic anhydride] + H₂O ⟶

e. Cl-C(=O)-Cl + [catechol, benzene with two OH] ⟶

f. [γ-butyrolactone] + H₂O (excess) $\xrightarrow{\text{HCl}}$

g.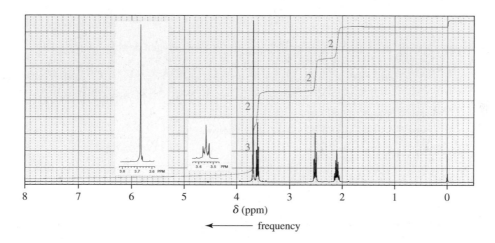

h.

i.

j.

69. When treated with an equivalent of methanol, compound A, with molecular formula $C_4H_6Cl_2O$, forms the compound whose ^1H NMR spectrum is shown below. Identify compound A.

δ (ppm)

← frequency

70. a. Identify the two products obtained from the following reaction:

b. A student carried out the preceding reaction, but stopped it before it was half over, whereupon he isolated the major product. He was surprised to find that the product he isolated was neither of the products obtained when the reaction was allowed to go to completion. What product did he isolate?

71. An aqueous solution of a primary or secondary amine reacts with an acyl chloride to form an amide as the major product. However, if the amine is tertiary, an amide is not formed. What product *is* formed? Explain.

72. Identify the major and minor products of the following reaction:

73. a. A student did not obtain any ester when he added 2,4,6-trimethylbenzoic acid to an acidic solution of methanol. Why? (*Hint:* Build models.)

b. Would he have encountered the same problem if he had tried to synthesize the methyl ester of *p*-methylbenzoic acid in the same way?

c. How could he prepare the methyl ester of 2,4,6-trimethylbenzoic acid? (*Hint:* See Problem 33 on page 689.)

74. When a compound with molecular formula $C_{11}H_{14}O_2$ undergoes acid-catalyzed hydrolysis, one of the products that is isolated gives the following ^1H NMR spectrum. Identify the compound.

δ (ppm)

← frequency

75. List the following compounds in order of decreasing frequency of the carbon–oxygen double-bond stretch:

76. Cardura, a drug used to treat hypertension, is synthesized as shown below.

a. Identify the intermediate (A) and show the mechanism for its formation.
b. Show the mechanism for conversion of A to B. Which would be formed more rapidly, A or B?

77. a. If the equilibrium constant for the reaction of acetic acid and ethanol to form ethyl acetate is 4.02, what will be the concentration of ethyl acetate at equilibrium if the reaction is carried out with equal amounts of acetic acid and ethanol?
   b. What will be the concentration of ethyl acetate at equilibrium if the reaction is carried out with 10 times more ethanol than acetic acid? *Hint:* Recall the quadratic equation: for $ax^2 + bx + c = 0$,

$$x = \frac{-b \pm (b^2 - 4ac)^{1/2}}{2a}$$

   c. What will be the concentration of ethyl acetate at equilibrium if the reaction is carried out with 100 times more ethanol than acetic acid?

78. The ^1H NMR spectra for two esters with molecular formula $C_8H_8O_2$ are shown below. If each of the esters is added to an aqueous solution with a pH of 10, which of the esters will be hydrolyzed more completely when the hydrolysis reactions have reached equilibrium?

δ (ppm)

← frequency

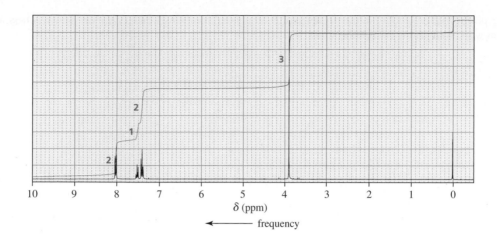

79. Propose a mechanism for the reaction of an amide with thionyl chloride to form a nitrile. (*Hint:* In the first step of the reaction, the amide is the nucleophile and thionyl chloride is the electrophile.)

80. Show how the following compounds could be prepared from the given starting materials. You can use any necessary organic or inorganic reagents.

a.

b.

c.   a detergent

d.

e.

f.

81. Is the acid-catalyzed hydrolysis of acetamide a reversible or an irreversible reaction? Explain.

82. What product would you expect to obtain from each of the following reactions?

a. $\xrightarrow{\text{HCl}}$

b. $\xrightarrow{\text{HCl}}$

c. $\xrightarrow[\substack{\text{1. SOCl}_2 \\ \text{2. AlCl}_3 \\ \text{3. H}_2\text{O}}]{}$

83. Sulfonamides, the first antibiotics, were introduced clinically in 1934 (Sections 25.7 and 31.4). Show how a sulfonamide can be prepared from benzene.

a sulfonamide

84. The reaction of a nitrile with an alcohol in the presence of a strong acid forms a secondary amide. This reaction, known as the *Ritter reaction*, does not work with primary alcohols.

$$RC{\equiv}N \; + \; R'OH \quad \xrightarrow{\;HCl\;} \quad$$

the Ritter reaction

  a. Propose a mechanism for the Ritter reaction.
  b. Why does the Ritter reaction not work with primary alcohols?
  c. How does the Ritter reaction differ from the acid-catalyzed hydrolysis of a nitrile to form a primary amide?

85. The intermediate shown here is formed during the hydroxide-ion-promoted hydrolysis of the ester group. Propose a mechanism for the reaction.

86. a. How could aspirin be synthesized, starting with benzene?
  b. Ibuprofen is the active ingredient in pain relievers such as Advil, Motrin, and Nuprin. How could ibuprofen be synthesized, starting with benzene?
  c. Acetaminophen is the active ingredient in Tylenol. How could acetominophen be synthesized, starting with benzene?

aspirin   **ibuprofen**   **acetaminophen**

87. The following compound has been found to be an inhibitor of penicillinase. The enzyme can be reactivated by hydroxylamine (NH_2OH). Propose a mechanism to account for the inhibition and for the reactivation.

88. For each of the following reactions, propose a mechanism that will account for the formation of the product:

  a.

  b.

89. Show how Novocain, a painkiller used frequently by dentists (Section 31.3), can be prepared from benzene and compounds containing no more than four carbons.

Novocain®

90. Catalytic antibodies catalyze a reaction by forcing the conformation of the substrate in the direction of the transition state. The synthesis of the antibody is carried out in the presence of a transition state analog—a stable molecule that structurally resembles the transition state. This causes an antibody to be generated that will recognize and bind to the transition state, thereby stabilizing it. For example, the following transition state analog has been used to generate a catalytic antibody that catalyzes the hydrolysis of the structurally similar ester:

transition state analog

a. Draw the transition state for the hydrolysis reaction.
b. The following transition state analog is used to generate a catalytic antibody for the catalysis of ester hydrolysis. Give the structure of an ester whose rate of hydrolysis would be increased by this catalytic antibody.

c. Design a transition state analog that would catalyze amide hydrolysis at the amide group indicated.

hydrolyze here

91. Show how lidocaine, one of the most widely used injectable anesthetics (Section 31.3), can be prepared from benzene and compounds containing no more than four carbons.

lidocaine

92. Saccharin, an artificial sweetener, is about 300 times sweeter than sucrose. Describe how saccharin could be prepared, using benzene as the starting material.

saccharin

93. Information about the mechanism of a reaction undergone by a series of substituted benzenes can be obtained by plotting the logarithm of the observed rate constant determined at a particular pH against the Hammett substituent constant (σ) for the particular substituent. The σ value for hydrogen is 0. Electron-donating substituents have negative σ values; electron-withdrawing substituents have positive σ values. The more strongly electron donating the substituent, the more negative its σ value will be; the more strongly electron withdrawing the substituent, the more positive its σ value will be. The slope of a plot of the logarithm of the rate constant versus σ is called the ρ (rho) value. The ρ value for the hydroxide-ion-promoted hydrolysis of a series of meta- and para-substituted ethyl benzoates is $+2.46$; the ρ value for amide formation for the reaction of a series of meta- and para-substituted anilines with benzoyl chloride is -2.78.

a. Why does one set of experiments give a positive ρ value, whereas the other set of experiments gives a negative ρ value?

b. Why were ortho-substituted compounds not included in the experiment?

c. What would you predict the sign of the ρ value to be for the ionization of a series of meta- and para-substituted benzoic acids?

18
Carbonyl Compounds II

Reactions of Aldehydes and Ketones •
More Reactions of Carboxylic Acid Derivatives •
Reactions of α,β-Unsaturated Carbonyl Compounds

acetaldehyde

formaldehyde

acetone

THE CARBONYL CARBON OF THE SIMPLEST ALDEHYDE, FORMALDEHYDE, IS BONDED TO TWO hydrogens. The carbonyl carbon in all other **aldehydes** is bonded to a hydrogen and to an alkyl (or an aryl) group. The carbonyl carbon of a **ketone** is bonded to two alkyl (or aryl) groups.

formaldehyde **an aldehyde** **a ketone**

The physical properties of aldehydes and ketones are discussed in Section 17.3 (see also Appendix I), and the methods used to prepare aldehydes and ketones are summarized in Appendix IV.

Many compounds found in nature have aldehyde or ketone functional groups. Aldehydes have pungent odors, whereas ketones tend to smell sweet. Vanillin and cinnamaldehyde are examples of naturally occurring aldehydes. A whiff of vanilla extract will allow you to appreciate the pungent odor of vanillin. The ketones carvone and camphor are responsible for the characteristic sweet odors of spearmint leaves, caraway seeds, and the leaves of the camphor tree.

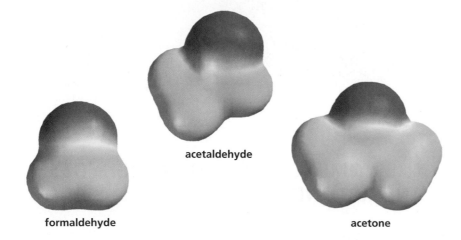

vanillin
vanilla flavoring

cinnamaldehyde
cinnamon flavoring

camphor

(R)-(–)-carvone
spearmint oil

(S)-(+)-carvone
caraway seed oil

In ketosis, a pathological condition that can occur in people with diabetes, the body produces more acetoacetate than can be metabolized. The excess acetoacetate breaks down to acetone (a ketone) and CO_2. Ketosis can be recognized by the smell of acetone on a person's breath.

Two biologically important ketones illustrate how a small difference in structure can be responsible for a large difference in biological activity: progesterone is a sex hormone synthesized primarily in the ovaries, whereas testosterone is a sex hormone synthesized primarily in the testes.

progesterone   **testosterone**

18.1 THE NOMENCLATURE OF ALDEHYDES AND KETONES

Naming Aldehydes

formaldehyde

acetaldehyde

acetone

The systematic (IUPAC) name of an aldehyde is obtained by replacing the final "e" on the name of the parent hydrocarbon with "al." For example, a one-carbon aldehyde is called methan*al*; a two-carbon aldehyde is called ethan*al*. The position of the carbonyl carbon does not have to be designated because it is always at the end of the parent hydrocarbon and therefore always has the 1-position.

The common name of an aldehyde is the same as the common name of the corresponding carboxylic acid (Section 17.1), except that "aldehyde" is substituted for "ic acid" (or "oic acid"). When common names are used, the position of a substituent is designated by a lowercase Greek letter. The carbonyl carbon is not given a letter; the carbon adjacent to the carbonyl carbon is the α-carbon.

systematic name:	methanal	ethanal
common name:	formaldehyde	acetaldehyde

2-bromopropanal
α-bromopropionaldehyde

systematic name:	3-chlorobutanal	3-methylbutanal	hexanedial
common name:	β-chlorobutyraldehyde	isovaleraldehyde	

Notice that the terminal "e" is not removed in hexanedial; the "e" is removed only to avoid two successive vowels.

If the aldehyde group is attached to a ring, the aldehyde is named by adding "carbaldehyde" to the name of the cyclic compound.

systematic name:	*trans*-**2-methylcyclohexanecarbaldehyde**
common name:	

benzenecarbaldehyde
benzaldehyde

In Section 6.2, we saw that a carbonyl group has a higher nomenclature priority than an alcohol group or an amino group. However, all carbonyl compounds do not have the same priority. Nomenclature priorities of the various functional groups, including the carbonyl groups, are shown in Table 18.1.

Table 18.1	Summary of Functional Group Nomenclature		
	Class	**Suffix name**	**Prefix name**
	Carboxylic acid	-oic acid	Carboxy
	Ester	-oate	Alkoxycarbonyl
	Amide	-amide	Amido
	Nitrile	-nitrile	Cyano
	Aldehyde	-al	Oxo $(=O)$
	Aldehyde	-al	Formyl $(CH=O)$
	Ketone	-one	Oxo $(=O)$
	Alcohol	-ol	Hydroxy
	Amine	-amine	Amino
	Alkene	-ene	Alkenyl
	Alkyne	-yne	Alkynyl
increasing priority	Alkane	-ane	Alkyl
	Ether	—	Alkoxy
	Alkyl halide	—	Halo

If a compound has two functional groups, the one with the lower priority is indicated by a prefix and the one with the higher priority by a suffix (unless one of the functional groups is an alkene).

3-hydroxybutanal	**methyl 5-oxopentanoate**	**ethyl 4-formylhexanoate**

If one of the functional groups is an alkene, suffix endings are used for both groups and the alkene functional group is stated first. Again, the "e" ending is omitted to avoid two successive vowels (Section 6.2).

$$CH_3CH=CHCH_2 \quad C \quad H$$

3-pentenal

Naming Ketones

The systematic name of a ketone is obtained by replacing the final "e" on the end of the name of the parent hydrocarbon with "one." The chain is numbered in the direction that gives the carbonyl carbon the smaller number. Cyclic ketones do not need a number because the carbonyl carbon is assumed to be at the 1-position. Derived names are often used for ketones: in a derived name, the substituents attached to the carbonyl group are cited in alphabetical order, followed by "ketone."

Aldehydes and ketones are named using a functional group suffix.

systematic name:	propanone	3-hexanone	6-methyl-2-heptanone
common name:	acetone		
derived name:	dimethyl ketone	ethyl propyl ketone	isohexyl methyl ketone

systematic name:	cyclohexanone	butanedione	2,4-pentanedione
common name:			acetylacetone

4-hexen-2-one

Only a few ketones have common names. The smallest ketone, propanone, is usually referred to by its common name, acetone. Acetone is a widely used laboratory solvent. Common names are also used for some phenyl-substituted ketones; the number of carbons (other than those of the phenyl group) is indicated by the common name of the corresponding carboxylic acid, substituting "ophenone" for "ic acid."

common name:	acetophenone	butyrophenone	benzophenone
derived name:	methyl phenyl ketone	phenyl propyl ketone	diphenyl ketone

If the ketone has a second functional group of higher naming priority, the ketone oxygen is indicated by the prefix "oxo."

systematic name:	4-oxopentanal	methyl 3-oxobutanoate	2-(3-oxopentyl)-cyclohexanone

---

Butanedione: An Unpleasant Compound

Fresh perspiration is odorless. The smells we associate with perspiration result from a chain of events initiated by bacteria that are always present on our skin. These bacteria produce lactic acid, which creates an acidic environment that allows other bacteria to break down the components of perspiration, producing compounds with the unappealing odors we associate with armpits and sweaty feet. One such compound is butanedione.

butanedione

PROBLEM 1♦

Why are numbers not used to designate the position of the functional group in propanone and butanedione?

PROBLEM 2♦

Give two names for each of the following:

a.

d.

b.

e.

c.

f.

PROBLEM 3♦

Name the following:

a.

b.

c.

chem place Tutorial: Nomenclature of aldehydes and ketones

18.2 THE RELATIVE REACTIVITIES OF CARBONYL COMPOUNDS

We have seen that the carbonyl group is polar because oxygen, being more electronegative than carbon, has a greater share of the double bond's electrons (Section 17.5). Thus, the carbonyl carbon is electron deficient. It is therefore an electrophile, and reacts with nucleophiles. The electron deficiency of the carbonyl carbon is indicated by the blue region in the electrostatic potential maps.

An aldehyde has a greater partial positive charge on its carbonyl carbon than does a ketone because a hydrogen is more electron withdrawing than an alkyl group (Section 4.2). An aldehyde therefore is more reactive than a ketone toward nucleophilic addition. We have now seen that alkyl groups stabilize carbonyl groups, alkenes, alkynes, carbocations, and radicals.

relative reactivities

acetone

acetaldehyde

formaldehyde

Steric factors also contribute to the greater reactivity of an aldehyde. The carbonyl carbon of an aldehyde is more accessible to a nucleophile because the hydrogen attached to the carbonyl carbon of an aldehyde is smaller than the second alkyl group attached to the carbonyl carbon of a ketone.

Steric factors are also important in the tetrahedral transition state because the bond angles are 109.5°, causing the alkyl groups to be closer to one another than they are in the carbonyl compound, where the bond angles are 120°. Because ketones have greater steric crowding in their transition states, they have less stable transition states than aldehydes have. In summary, alkyl groups stabilize the reactant and destabilize the transition state; both factors cause ketones to be less reactive than aldehydes.

Aldehydes are more reactive than ketones.

Steric crowding also causes ketones with large alkyl groups bonded to the carbonyl carbon to be less reactive than those with small alkyl groups.

relative reactivities

PROBLEM 4♦

Which ketone in each pair is more reactive?

a. 2-heptanone or 4-heptanone   **b.** *p*-nitroacetophenone or *p*-methoxyacetophenone

---

How does the reactivity of an aldehyde or a ketone toward nucleophiles compare with the reactivity of the carbonyl compounds whose reactions we looked at in Chapter 17? Aldehydes and ketones are right in the middle; they are less reactive than acyl halides and acid anhydrides, but are more reactive than esters, carboxylic acids, and amides.

relative reactivities of carbonyl compounds

acyl halide > acid anhydride > aldehyde > ketone > ester ~ carboxylic acid > amide > carboxylate ion

most reactive   least reactive

Why are aldehydes and ketones in the middle? Carbonyl compounds other than aldehydes and ketones have a lone pair on an atom (:Y) attached to the carbonyl group that can be shared with the carbonyl carbon by resonance electron donation. This makes the carbonyl carbon less electron deficient and therefore less reactive.

Aldehydes and ketones are less reactive than acyl chlorides and acid anhydrides but more reactive than esters, carboxylic acids, and amides.

We have seen that weak bases are less able to share their lone pair with the carbonyl carbon; they are also better at withdrawing electrons inductively from the carbonyl carbon, which increases its electron deficiency (Section 17.6). Consequently, aldehydes and ketones are not as reactive as carbonyl compounds in which (:Y) is a very weak base (acyl halides and acid anhydrides), but are more reactive than carbonyl compounds in which (:Y) is a relatively strong base (carboxylic acids, esters, and amides). (For a molecular orbital explanation of why resonance electron donation decreases the reactivity of the carbonyl group, see Section 17.16.)

18.3 HOW ALDEHYDES AND KETONES REACT

In Section 17.5, we saw that the carbonyl group of a carboxylic acid or a carboxylic acid derivative is attached to a group that can be replaced by another group. Therefore, these compounds undergo **nucleophilic addition–elimination** reactions—the nucleophile adds to the carbonyl carbon, and a group is eliminated from the tetrahedral intermediate. Overall, it is a substitution reaction: Z^- substitutes for Y^-.

a group that can be replaced by another group

product of nucleophilic addition-elimination

Carboxylic acid derivatives undergo nucleophilic addition–elimination reactions with nucleophiles.

In contrast, the carbonyl group of an aldehyde or a ketone is attached to a group that is too strong a base (H^- or R^-) to be eliminated under normal conditions, so it cannot be replaced by another group. Consequently, aldehydes and ketones react with nucleophiles to form *addition products*, not *substitution products*.

The addition of a nucleophile to the carbonyl carbon of an aldehyde or a ketone forms a tetrahedral compound. If the nucleophile is a strong base, the tetrahedral compound does not have a group that can be eliminated. Thus, the reaction is an *irreversible* **nucleophilic addition reaction**.

a nucleophile that is a strong base

the reaction is irreversible because Z^- is too basic to be eliminated

product of nucleophilic addition

Aldehydes and ketones undergo irreversible nucleophilic addition reactions with nucleophiles that are strong bases.

If the nucleophile is a relatively weak base, the product of the reaction will again be the tetrahedral compound. However, the reaction will be a *reversible* **nucleophilic addition reaction** because the tetrahedral compound can eliminate the weak base and revert to the starting materials.

a nucleophile that is a relatively weak base

the reaction is reversible because Z^- can be eliminated

product of nucleophilic addition

Aldehydes and ketones undergo reversible nucleophilic addition reactions with nucleophiles that are weak bases.

If the attacking atom of the nucleophile has a lone pair and there is enough acid in the solution to protonate the OH group of the tetrahedral compound, water can be eliminated from the addition product. The reaction is reversible because there are two groups attached to the tetrahedral intermediate, either one of which can be protonated and

chem place Tutorial: Formation of a tetrahedral intermediate.

therefore eliminated. We will see that the fate of the dehydrated product depends on the identity of Z.

Aldehydes and ketones undergo nucleophilic addition–elimination reactions with nucleophiles that have a lone pair on the attacking atom.

This is also called a **nucleophilic addition–elimination reaction**. However, unlike carboxylic acid derivatives that undergo nucleophilc addition–eliminations that eliminate a group attached to the acyl group, aldehydes and ketones undergo nucleophilic addition–elimination reactions that eliminate water.

18.4 THE REACTIONS OF CARBONYL COMPOUNDS WITH GRIGNARD REAGENTS

Addition of a Grignard reagent to a carbonyl compound is a versatile reaction that forms a new C—C bond. This reaction can produce compounds with a variety of structures because both the structure of the carbonyl compound and the structure of the Grignard reagent can be varied.

We have seen that a Grignard reagent is prepared by adding an alkyl halide to magnesium shavings in diethyl ether under anhydrous conditions (Section 11.1). We also saw that a Grignard reagent reacts as if it were a carbanion; therefore, it is a strongly basic nucleophile. Consequently, aldehydes and ketones undergo nucleophilic addition reactions with Grignard reagents (Section 18.3).

$$CH_3CH_2Br \xrightarrow[\text{Et}_2\text{O}]{\textbf{Mg}} CH_3CH_2MgBr$$

$$CH_3CH_2MgBr \quad \textbf{reacts as if it were} \quad CH_3\overset{..}{C}H_2 \quad \overset{+}{M}gBr$$

The Reactions of Aldehydes and Ketones with Grignard Reagents

The mechanism for the reaction of a Grignard reagent with an aldehyde or a ketone is shown below.

MECHANISM FOR THE REACTION OF AN ALDEHYDE OR A KETONE WITH A GRIGNARD REAGENT

• Nucleophilic addition of a Grignard reagent to the carbonyl carbon forms an alkoxide ion that is complexed with magnesium ion.

• Addition of dilute acid breaks up the complex.

The reaction is a nucleophilic addition reaction: the nucleophile has added to the carbonyl carbon. The tetrahedral alkoxide ion is stable because it does not have a group that can be eliminated. (We saw in Section 17.5 that a tetrahedral compound is unstable only if the sp^3 carbon is attached to an oxygen *and* to another electronegative atom.)

When a Grignard reagent reacts with formaldehyde, the product of the addition reaction is a *primary alcohol*.

| formaldehyde | ethylmagnesium bromide | an alkoxide ion | 1-propanol a primary alcohol |

When a Grignard reagent reacts with an aldehyde other than formaldehyde, the product of the addition reaction is a *secondary alcohol*.

| propanal | methylmagnesium bromide | | 2-butanol a secondary alcohol |

When a Grignard reagent reacts with a ketone, the product of the addition reaction is a *tertiary alcohol*.

| 2-pentanone | ethylmagnesium bromide | | 3-methyl-3-hexanol a tertiary alcohol |

In the following reactions, the reagents are numbered in order of use, indicating that the acid is not added until after the Grignard reagent has reacted with the carbonyl compound.

3-pentanone → 3-methyl-3-pentanol

butanal → 1-phenyl-1-butanol

A Grignard reagent can also react with carbon dioxide. The product of the reaction is a carboxylic acid that has one more carbon than the Grignard reagent.

| carbon dioxide | propylmagnesium bromide | | butanoic acid |

PROBLEM 5 ◆

What products are formed when the following compounds react with CH_3MgBr, followed by the addition of dilute acid? Disregard stereoisomers.

PROBLEM 6 ♦

We saw that 3-methyl-3-hexanol can be synthesized from the reaction of 2-pentanone with ethylmagnesium bromide. What other combinations of ketone and Grignard reagent could be used to prepare the same tertiary alcohol?

PROBLEM 7 ♦

a. How many stereoisomers are obtained from the reaction of 2-pentanone with ethylmagnesium bromide followed by treatment with dilute acid?

b. How many stereoisomers are obtained from the reaction of 2-pentanone with methylmagnesium bromide followed by treatment with dilute acid?

The Reactions of Esters and Acyl Chlorides with Grignard Reagents

In addition to reacting with aldehydes and ketones (Class II carbonyl compounds), Grignard reagents react with esters and acyl chlorides (Class I carbonyl compounds). These compounds undergo two successive reactions with the Grignard reagent. The first reaction is a *nucleophilic addition–elimination reaction* because an ester or an acyl chloride, unlike an aldehyde or a ketone, has a group that can be replaced by the Grignard reagent. The second reaction is a *nucleophilic addition reaction*.

The product of the reaction of an ester with a Grignard reagent is a tertiary alcohol. Because the tertiary alcohol is formed as a result of two successive reactions with the Grignard reagent, the alcohol has two identical alkyl groups bonded to the tertiary carbon.

MECHANISM FOR THE REACTION OF AN ESTER WITH A GRIGNARD REAGENT

- Nucleophilic addition of the Grignard reagent to the carbonyl carbon forms a tetrahedral intermediate that is unstable because it has a group that can be eliminated.

- The tetrahedral intermediate eliminates methoxide ion, forming a ketone.

- Reaction of the ketone with a second molecule of the Grignard reagent, followed by protonation of the alkoxide ion, forms a tertiary alcohol.

Tertiary alcohols are also formed from the reaction of two equivalents of a Grignard reagent with an acyl chloride. The mechanism for the reaction of a Grignard reagent with an acyl chloride is the same as the mechanism for the reaction a Grignard reagent with an ester.

butyryl chloride → 3-ethyl-3-hexanol

PROBLEM 8   SOLVED

a. Which of the following tertiary alcohols cannot be prepared from the reaction of an ester with excess Grignard reagent?

$$\text{OH}$$
1. $CH_3\overset{|}{\underset{|}{C}}CH_3$
$\quad\quad CH_3$

$$\text{OH}$$
3. $CH_3CH_2\overset{|}{\underset{|}{C}}CH_2CH_2CH_3$
$\quad\quad\quad\quad CH_3$

$$\text{OH}$$
5. $CH_3\overset{|}{\underset{|}{C}}CH_2CH_2CH_2CH_3$
$\quad\quad CH_2CH_3$

$$\text{OH}$$
2. $CH_3\overset{|}{\underset{|}{C}}CH_2CH_3$
$\quad\quad CH_3$

$$\text{OH}$$
4. $CH_3CH_2\overset{|}{\underset{|}{C}}CH_2CH_3$
$\quad\quad\quad\quad CH_3$

6.

b. For those alcohols that can be prepared by the reaction of an ester with excess Grignard reagent, what ester and what Grignard reagent should be used?

Solution to 8a   A tertiary alcohol prepared by the reaction of an ester with two equivalents of a Grignard reagent must have two identical substituents bonded to the carbon to which the OH is bonded because two substituents come from the Grignard reagent. Alcohols 3 and 5 do not have two identical substituents, so they cannot be prepared in this way.

Solution to 8b (2)   An ester of propanoic acid and excess methylmagnesium bromide.

PROBLEM 9 ◆

Which of the following secondary alcohols can be prepared from the reaction of methyl formate with excess Grignard reagent?

$CH_3CH_2\overset{|}{\underset{\underset{OH}{|}}{C}}HCH_3$

$CH_3\overset{|}{\underset{\underset{OH}{|}}{C}}HCH_3$

$CH_3\overset{|}{\underset{\underset{OH}{|}}{C}}HCH_2CH_2CH_3$

$CH_3CH_2\overset{|}{\underset{\underset{OH}{|}}{C}}HCH_2CH_3$

A   B   C   D

PROBLEM-SOLVING STRATEGY

Predicting Reactions with Grignard Reagents

Why does a Grignard reagent not add to the carbonyl carbon of a carboxylic acid?

We know that Grignard reagents add to carbonyl carbons, so if we find that a Grignard reagent does not add to the carbonyl carbon, we can conclude that it must react more rapidly with another part of the molecule. A carboxylic acid has an acidic proton that reacts rapidly with the Grignard reagent, converting it to an alkane.

Now continue on to Problem 10.

chem
place Tutorial:
Addition of a Grignard reagent
to a ketone

Tutorial:
Addition of the first equivalent
of a Grignard reagent to an ester

Tutorial:
Addition of one equivalent of a
Grignard reagent to an acyl
chloride

Tutorial:
Grignard reagents in synthesis

PROBLEM 10◆

Which of the following compounds will not undergo a nucleophilic addition reaction with a Grignard reagent?

$$CH_3CH_2-\overset{\overset{\displaystyle O}{\|}}{C}-NHCH_3 \qquad CH_3CH_2-\overset{\overset{\displaystyle O}{\|}}{C}-OCH_3 \qquad HOCH_2CH_2-\overset{\overset{\displaystyle O}{\|}}{C}-OCH_3$$

A   B   C

18.5 THE REACTIONS OF CARBONYL COMPOUNDS WITH ACETYLIDE IONS

We have seen that a terminal alkyne can be converted into an acetylide ion by a strong base (Section 6.10).

$$CH_3C{\equiv}CH \xrightarrow{\text{NaNH}_2} CH_3C{\equiv}C{:}^-$$

An acetylide ion is another example of a strongly basic nucleophile that reacts with a carbonyl compound to form a nucleophilic addition product. Because it is a reaction that forms a new C—C bond, it is an important reaction to synthetic chemists. When the reaction is over, a weak acid (one that will not react with the triple bond, such as pyridinium ion shown here), is added to the reaction mixture to protonate the alkoxide ion.

$$CH_3CH_2-\overset{\overset{\displaystyle \cdot\overset{\cdot\cdot}{O}\cdot}{\|}}{C}-H \;+\; CH_3C{\equiv}C{:}^- \longrightarrow CH_3CH_2CHC{\equiv}CCH_3 \xrightarrow{\text{pyridinium}} CH_3CH_2CHC{\equiv}CCH_3$$

Tutorial:
Nucleophilic addition to carbonyls 1

Tutorial:
Nucleophilic addition to carbonyls 2

PROBLEM 11

Show how the following compounds could be prepared, using ethyne as one of the starting materials. Explain why ethyne should be alkylated before, rather than after, nucleophilic addition.

a. 1-pentyn-3-ol   **b.** 1-phenyl-2-butyn-1-ol   **c.** 2-methyl-3-hexyn-2-ol

PROBLEM 12◆

What is the product of the reaction of an ester with excess acetylide ion followed by the addition of pyridinium ion?

18.6 THE REACTIONS OF CARBONYL COMPOUNDS WITH HYDRIDE ION

The Reactions of Aldehydes and Ketones with Hydride Ion

A hydride ion is another strongly basic nucleophile (Table 17.1 on page 707) that reacts with aldehydes and ketones to form nucleophilic addition products.

MECHANISM FOR THE REACTION OF AN ALDEHYDE OR A KETONE WITH HYDRIDE ION

- Addition of a hydride ion to the carbonyl carbon of an aldehyde or a ketone forms an alkoxide ion.
- Protonation by a dilute acid produces an alcohol. The overall reaction adds H_2 to the carbonyl group.

Recall that the addition of hydrogen to a compound is a **reduction reaction** (Section 4.12). Aldehydes and ketones are generally reduced using sodium borohydride ($NaBH_4$) as the source of hydride ion. Aldehydes are reduced to primary alcohols, and ketones are reduced to secondary alcohols. Notice that the acid is not added to the reaction mixture until after the hydride ion has reacted with the carbonyl compound.

PROBLEM 13♦

What alcohols are obtained from the reduction of the following compounds with sodium borohydride?

a. 2-methylpropanal
b. cyclohexanone

c. benzaldehyde
d. acetophenone

The Reactions of Acyl Chlorides, Esters, Carboxylic Acids, and Amides with Hydride Ion

Because Class I carbonyl compounds have a group that can be replaced by another group, they undergo two successive reactions with hydride ion, just as they undergo two successive reactions with a Grignard reagent (Section 18.4). Therefore, the reaction of an acyl chloride with sodium borohydride forms an alcohol.

The mechanism for the reaction is shown below.

MECHANISM FOR THE REACTION OF AN ACYL CHLORIDE WITH HYDRIDE ION

- The acyl chloride undergoes a nucleophilic addition–elimination reaction because it has a group (Cl^-) that can be replaced by hydride ion. The product of this reaction is an aldehyde.
- The aldehyde undergoes a nucleophilic addition reaction with a second equivalent of hydride ion, forming an alkoxide ion.
- Protonation of the alkoxide ion gives a primary alcohol.

Sodium borohydride ($NaBH_4$) is not a sufficiently strong hydride donor to react with carbonyl compounds that are less reactive than aldehydes and ketones. Therefore, esters, carboxylic acids, and amides must be reduced with lithium aluminum hydride ($LiAlH_4$), a more reactive hydride donor. Lithium aluminum hydride is not as safe or as easy to use as sodium borohydride. It reacts violently with protic solvents, so it must be used in a dry, aprotic solvent, and it is never used if $NaBH_4$ can be used instead.

The reaction of an ester with $LiAlH_4$ produces two alcohols, one corresponding to the acyl portion of the ester and one corresponding to the alkyl portion.

The mechanism for the reaction is shown below.

MECHANISM FOR THE REACTION OF AN ESTER WITH HYDRIDE ION

Esters and acyl chlorides undergo two successive reactions with hydride ion and with Grignard reagents.

- The ester undergoes a nucleophilic addition–elimination reaction because an ester has a group (CH_3O^-) that can be replaced by hydride ion. The product of this reaction is an aldehyde.
- The aldehyde undergoes a nucleophilic addition reaction with a second equivalent of hydride ion, forming an alkoxide ion.
- Protonation of the alkoxide ion gives a primary alcohol.

The reaction of an ester with hydride ion cannot be stopped at the aldehyde because an aldehyde is more reactive than an ester toward nucleophilic addition (Section 18.2). However, chemists have found that if diisobutylaluminum hydride (DIBALH) is used as the hydride donor at a low temperature, the reaction can be stopped at the aldehyde. This reagent therefore makes it possible to convert esters into aldehydes.

$$CH_3CHCH_2-Al-CH_2CHCH_3$$

| | |
| CH_3 | H | CH_3 |

diisobutylaluminum hydride
DIBALH

methyl butanoate → 1. [(CH₃)₂CHCH₂]₂AlH, −78 °C / 2. H₂O → butanal + CH₃OH (methanol)

The reaction is carried out at −78 °C (the temperature of a dry ice/acetone bath). At this cold temperature, the initially formed tetrahedral intermediate is stable, so it does not eliminate the alkoxide ion. If all of the unreacted hydride donor is removed before the solution warms up, there will be no hydride ion available to react with the aldehyde that is formed when the tetrahedral intermediate eliminates the alkoxide ion.

The reaction of a carboxylic acid with hydride ion forms a primary alcohol.

propanoic acid → 1. LiAlH₄ / 2. H₃O⁺ → CH₃CH₂CH₂OH (1-propanol)

The reaction of a carboxylic acid with LiAlH₄ forms a single primary alcohol.

The mechanism for the reaction is shown below.

MECHANISM FOR THE REACTION OF A CARBOXYLIC ACID WITH HYDRIDE ION

- A hydride ion reacts with the acidic hydrogen of the carboxylic acid, forming H_2 and a carboxylate ion.

- We have seen that nucleophiles do not add to a carboxylate ion because of its negative charge. However, in this case, an electrophile (AlH_3) is present that accepts a pair of electrons from the carboxylate ion and forms a new hydride donor.

- Then, as in the reduction of an ester by $LiAlH_4$, two successive additions of hydride ion take place, with an aldehyde being formed as an intermediate on the way to the primary alcohol.

PROBLEM 14♦

What products would be obtained from the reaction of the following compounds with LiAlH₄ followed by treatment with dilute acid?

a. ethyl butanoate
b. benzoic acid

c. methyl benzoate
d. pentanoic acid

Amides also undergo two successive additions of hydride ion when they react with $LiAlH_4$. Overall, the reaction converts a carbonyl group into a methylene (CH_2) group. The product of the reaction is an amine. Primary, secondary, or tertiary amines can be formed, depending on the number of substituents bonded to the nitrogen of the amide. (Notice that H_2O rather than H_3O^+ is used in the second step of the reaction. If H_3O^+ were used, the product would be an ammonium ion rather than an amine.)

benzamide → **benzylamine** **a primary amine**

N-methylacetamide → **ethylmethylamine** **a secondary amine**

N-methyl-γ-butyrolactam → **N-methylpyrrolidine** **a tertiary amine**

The mechanism for the reaction shows why the product of the reaction is an amine. Take a minute to note the similarities between this mechanism for the reaction of hydride ion with an N-substituted amide and the mechanism for the reaction of hydride ion with a carboxylic acid.

MECHANISM FOR THE REACTION OF AN N-SUBSTITUTED AMIDE WITH HYDRIDE ION

The mechanisms for the reaction of $LiAlH_4$ with unsubstituted and N,N-disubstituted amides are somewhat different, but have the same result: the conversion of a carbonyl group into a methylene group.

Biological reactions also need reagents that can deliver hydride ions to carbonyl groups. Biological systems use NADH and NADPH as hydride donors. (Sodium borohydride and lithium aluminum hydride are too reactive to be used in living organisms.) These hydride donors are discussed in Section 25.1.

PROBLEM 15 ◆

What amides would you treat with $LiAlH_4$ in order to prepare the following amines?

a. benzylmethylamine

b. ethylamine

c. diethylamine

d. triethylamine

PROBLEM 16

Starting with *N*-benzylbenzamide, how would you make the following compounds?

a. dibenzylamine   **b.** benzoic acid   **c.** benzyl alcohol

18.7 THE REACTIONS OF ALDEHYDES AND KETONES WITH HYDROGEN CYANIDE

Hydrogen cyanide adds to an aldehyde or a ketone to form a **cyanohydrin**. Because hydrogen cyanide is a toxic gas, it is generated in situ by adding HCl to a mixture of the aldehyde or ketone and excess sodium cyanide. Excess sodium cyanide is used in order to ensure that some cyanide ion is available to act as a nucleophile.

a cyanohydrin

The mechanism for the reaction is shown below.

MECHANISM FOR THE REACTION OF AN ALDEHYDE OR KETONE WITH HYDROGEN CYANIDE

acetone cyanohydrin

- Cyanide ion adds to the carbonyl carbon.
- The alkoxide ion is protonated by an undissociated molecule of hydrogen cyanide.

Compared with Grignard reagents, acetylide ionds, and hydride ion, cyanide ion is a relatively weak base. (The pK_a of CH_3CH_3 is > 60, the pK_a of $RC\equiv CH$ is 25, the pK_a of H_2 is 35, but the pK_a of $HC\equiv N$ is 9.14; recall that the stronger the acid, the weaker the conjugate base.) Therefore, the cyano group has a much better chance than R^-, $RC\equiv C^-$, or 35 of being eliminated from the addition product. Cyanohydrins, however, are stable: the OH group will not eliminate the cyano group because the transition state for that elimination reaction would be relatively unstable since the oxygen atom would have a partial positive charge. If the OH group loses its proton, however, the cyano group will be eliminated because the oxygen atom would then have a partial negative charge in the transition state. Therefore, in basic solutions, a cyanohydrin is converted back to the carbonyl compound.

cyclohexanone cyanohydrin

Cyanide ion does not react with esters because the cyanide ion is a weaker base than an alkoxide ion, so the cyanide ion would be eliminated from the tetrahedral intermediate.

The addition of hydrogen cyanide to aldehydes and ketones is a synthetically useful reaction because of the subsequent reactions that can be carried out on the cyanohydrin. For example, the acid-catalyzed hydrolysis of a cyanohydrin forms an α-hydroxycarboxylic acid (Section 17.19).

$$
\underset{\textbf{a cyanohydrin}}{R\!-\!\overset{\displaystyle OH}{\underset{\displaystyle R}{C}}\!-\!C\!\equiv\!N} \quad \xrightarrow[\Delta]{HCl,\ H_2O} \quad \underset{\textbf{an } \alpha\textbf{-hydroxy carboxylic acid}}{R\!-\!\overset{\displaystyle OH}{\underset{\displaystyle R}{C}}\!-\!\overset{\displaystyle O}{\overset{\displaystyle \|}{C}}OH}
$$

The catalytic addition of hydrogen to the triple bond of a cyanohydrin produces a primary amine with an OH group on the α-carbon.

$$
R\!-\!\overset{\displaystyle OH}{CH}\!-\!C\!\equiv\!N \quad \xrightarrow[\textbf{Raney Nickel}]{H_2} \quad R\!-\!\overset{\displaystyle OH}{CH}\!-\!CH_2NH_2
$$

PROBLEM 17 ♦

Can a cyanohydrin be prepared by treating a ketone with sodium cyanide?

PROBLEM 18 ♦

Explain why aldehydes and ketones react with a weak acid such as hydrogen cyanide but do not react with strong acids such as HCl or H_2SO_4.

PROBLEM 19   SOLVED

How can the following compounds be prepared, starting with a carbonyl compound that has one less carbon than the desired product?

a. $HOCH_2CH_2NH_2$

b. $CH_3\overset{\displaystyle }{\underset{\displaystyle OH}{CH}}\overset{\displaystyle O}{\overset{\displaystyle \|}{C}}CH$

Solution to 19a   The starting material for the synthesis of this two-carbon compound must be formaldehyde. Addition of hydrogen cyanide followed by addition of H_2 to the triple bond of the cyanohydrin forms the target molecule.

$$
\underset{H \quad H}{\overset{\displaystyle O}{\overset{\displaystyle \|}{C}}} \quad \xrightarrow[HCl]{NaC\equiv N} \quad HOCH_2C\equiv N \quad \xrightarrow[\textbf{Raney Nickel}]{H_2} \quad HOCH_2CH_2NH_2
$$

Solution to 19b   The addition of cyanide ion adds one carbon to the reactant, so the starting material for the synthesis of this three-carbon α-hydroxycarboxylic acid must be ethanal. Addition of hydrogen cyanide, followed by hydrolysis of the cyanohydrin, forms the target molecule.

$$
CH_3\overset{\displaystyle O}{\overset{\displaystyle \|}{C}}H \quad \xrightarrow[HCl]{NaC\equiv N} \quad CH_3\overset{\displaystyle }{\underset{\displaystyle OH}{CH}}C\equiv N \quad \xrightarrow[\Delta]{HCl,\ H_2O} \quad CH_3\overset{\displaystyle }{\underset{\displaystyle OH}{CH}}\overset{\displaystyle O}{\overset{\displaystyle \|}{C}}OH
$$

18.8 THE REACTIONS OF ALDEHYDES AND KETONES WITH AMINES AND AMINE DERIVATIVES

Aldehydes and Ketones Form Imines with Primary Amines

An aldehyde or a ketone reacts with a *primary* amine to form an imine. The reaction requires a trace amount of acid. An **imine** is a compound with a carbon–nitrogen double bond. The imine obtained from the reaction of a carbonyl compound and a primary amine is sometimes called a **Schiff base**.

$$C=O \quad + \quad R-NH_2 \quad \underset{\longleftarrow}{\overset{\text{trace acid}}{\rightleftharpoons}} \quad C=N-R \quad + \quad H_2O$$

an aldehyde or   a primary amine   an imine
a ketone   a Schiff base

A C=N group (Figure 18.1) is similar to a C=O group (Figure 17.1 on page 707). The imine nitrogen is sp^2 hybridized. One of its sp^2 orbitals forms a bond with the imine carbon, one forms a bond with a substituent, and the third contains a lone pair. The p orbital of nitrogen and the p orbital of carbon overlap to form a π bond.

Notice that imine formation replaces a C=O with a C=NR.

▲ **Figure 18.1**

$$\begin{array}{c} R \\ \backslash \\ C=O \\ / \\ H \end{array} \quad + \quad CH_3CH_2NH_2 \quad \underset{\longleftarrow}{\overset{\text{trace acid}}{\rightleftharpoons}} \quad \begin{array}{c} R \\ \backslash \\ C=NCH_2CH_3 \\ / \\ H \end{array} \quad + \quad H_2O$$

an aldehyde   a primary amine   an imine

Aldehydes and ketones react with primary amines to form imines.

$$\begin{array}{c} R \\ \backslash \\ C=O \\ / \\ R \end{array} + \quad \text{⬡}-CH_2NH_2 \quad \underset{\longleftarrow}{\overset{\text{trace acid}}{\rightleftharpoons}} \quad \begin{array}{c} R \\ \backslash \\ C=NCH_2-\text{⬡} \\ / \\ R \end{array} \quad + \quad H_2O$$

a ketone   a primary amine   an imine

The mechanism for imine formation is shown below. We will see that the pH of the reaction mixture must be carefully controlled. (Recall that HB$^+$ represents any species in the solution that is capable of donating a proton, and :B represents any species in the solution that is capable of removing a proton.)

MECHANISM FOR IMINE FORMATION

nucleophile adds to the carbonyl carbon

N–protonated carbinolamine

neutral tetrahedral intermediate
a carbinolamine

O–protonated carbinolamine

elimination of water

an imine   a protonated imine

removal of a proton

- The amine adds to the carbonyl carbon.
- Protonation of the alkoxide ion and deprotonation of the ammonium ion form a neutral tetrahedral intermediate.
- The neutral tetrahedral intermediate, called a *carbinolamine*, is in equilibrium with two protonated forms because either its oxygen or its nitrogen can be protonated.
- Because the nucleophile has a lone pair, water is eliminated from the oxygen-protonated intermediate, thereby forming a protonated imine (Section 18.3).
- The protonated imine loses a proton from the nitrogen to give the imine.

Unlike the stable tetrahedral compounds that are formed when a Grignard reagent or a hydride ion adds to an aldehyde or a ketone, the tetrahedral compound formed when an amine adds to an aldehyde or a ketone is unstable because the sp^3 carbon is bonded to an oxygen and to another electronegative atom.

$$\underset{\text{stable tetrahedral compounds}}{R-\overset{\overset{\displaystyle OH}{|}}{\underset{\underset{\displaystyle H}{|}}{C}}-R \qquad R-\overset{\overset{\displaystyle OH}{|}}{\underset{\underset{\displaystyle CH_3}{|}}{C}}-R} \qquad \underset{\text{unstable tetrahedral compounds}}{R-\overset{\overset{\displaystyle OH}{|}}{\underset{\underset{\displaystyle NHCH_3}{|}}{C}}-R \qquad R-\overset{\overset{\displaystyle OH}{|}}{\underset{\underset{\displaystyle OCH_3}{|}}{C}}-R}$$

Imine formation is reversible because there are two protonated tetrahedral intermediates that can eliminate a group. The equilibrium favors the nitrogen-protonated tetrahedral intermediate because nitrogen is more basic than oxygen. However, the equilibrium can be forced toward the oxygen-protonated tetrahedral intermediate and therefore toward the imine by removing water as it is formed or by precipitation of the imine.

Overall, the addition of an amine to an aldehyde or a ketone is a *nucleophilic addition–elimination reaction*: nucleophilic addition of an amine to form a tetrahedral intermediate, followed by elimination of water. The tetrahedral intermediate is unstable because it contains a group that can be protonated and thereby become a weak enough base to be eliminated.

The pH at which imine formation is carried out must be carefully controlled. There must be sufficient acid present to protonate the tetrahedral intermediate so that H_2O rather than the much more basic HO^- is the leaving group. However, if too much acid is present, it will protonate all of the reactant amine. Protonated amines are not nucleophiles, so they cannot react with carbonyl groups. Therefore, unlike the acid-catalyzed reactions we have seen previously (Sections 17.11 and 17.17), there is not sufficient acid present to protonate the carbonyl group in the first step of the reaction (see Problem 22).

A plot of the observed rate constant for the reaction of acetone with hydroxylamine as a function of the pH of the reaction mixture is shown in Figure 18.2. This type of plot is called a **pH–rate profile**. Here it is a bell-shaped curve, with the maximum rate occurring at about pH 4.5, which is 1.5 pH units below the pK_a of protonated hydroxylamine (pK_a 6.0). As the acidity increases below pH 4.5, the rate of the reaction decreases because more and more of the amine becomes protonated. As a result, less and less of the amine is present in the nucleophilic nonprotonated form. As the acidity decreases above pH 4.5, the rate decreases because less and less of the tetrahedral intermediate is present in the reactive protonated form.

Imine formation is reversible: in an acidic aqueous solution, an imine is hydrolyzed back to the carbonyl compound and amine.

▲ **Figure 18.2**
A pH-rate profile for the reaction of acetone with hydroxylamine. It shows the dependence of the reaction rate on the pH of the reaction mixture.

An imine undergoes acid-catalyzed hydrolysis to form a carbonyl compound and a primary amine.

$$\underset{R}{\overset{R}{\diagdown}}C=NCH_2CH_3 \;+\; H_2O \;\xrightarrow{\;HCl\;}\; \underset{R}{\overset{R}{\diagdown}}C=O \;+\; CH_3CH_2\overset{+}{N}H_3$$

In an acidic solution, the amine is protonated and, therefore, is unable to react with the carbonyl compound to re-form the imine.

Imine formation and hydrolysis are important reactions in biological systems. For example, we will see that all the reactions that require vitamin B_6 involve imine formation (Section 25.5), and imine hydrolysis is the reason that DNA contains T nucleotides instead of U nucleotides (Section 28.10).

PROBLEM 20♦

Why is the pK_a value of protonated hydroxylamine (6.0) so much lower than the pK_a value of a protonated primary amine such as protonated methylamine?

PROBLEM 21♦

At what pH should imine formation be carried out if the amine's protonated form has a pK_a value of 10.0?

PROBLEM 22♦

The pK_a of protonated acetone is about -7.5, and the pK_a of protonated hydroxylamine is 6.0.

a. In a reaction with hydroxylamine at pH 4.5 (Figure 18.2), what fraction of acetone will be present in its acidic, protonated form? (*Hint*: See Section 1.25.)
b. In a reaction with hydroxylamine at pH 1.5, what fraction of acetone will be present in its acidic, protonated form?
c. In a reaction with acetone at pH 1.5 (Figure 18.2), what fraction of hydroxylamine will be present in its reactive basic form?

PROBLEM 23

A ketone can be prepared from the reaction of a nitrile with a Grignard reagent. Describe the intermediate formed in this reaction, and show how it can be converted to a ketone.

Formation of Imine Derivatives

Compounds such as hydroxylamine, phenylhydrazine, 2,4-dinitrophenylhydrazine, and semicarbazide (shown below) are similar to primary amines in that they all have an NH_2 group. Thus, like primary amines, they react with aldehydes and ketones to form imines—often called *imine derivatives* because the substituent attached to the imine nitrogen is not an R group. The imine obtained from the reaction with hydroxylamine is called an **oxime**, the imine obtained from the reaction with hydrazine is called a **hydrazone**, and the imine obtained from the reaction with semicarbazide is called a **semicarbazone**.

Identifying Aldehydes and Ketones Without Using Spectroscopy

Before spectrophotometric techniques were available for analyzing compounds, unknown aldehydes and ketones were identified by preparing imine derivatives. For example, suppose you have an unknown ketone whose boiling point you have determined to be 140 °C. This information allows you to narrow the possibilities to the five ketones (A to E) listed in the following table. (Ketones boiling at 139 °C and 141 °C cannot be excluded, unless your thermometer is calibrated perfectly and your laboratory technique is sensational.)

| | | 2,4-Dinitrophenylhydrazone | Oxime | Semicarbazone |
Ketone	bp (°C)	mp (°C)	mp (°C)	mp (°C)
A	140	94	57	98
B	140	102	68	123
C	139	121	79	121
D	140	101	69	112
E	141	90	61	101

Adding 2,4-dinitrophenylhydrazine to a sample of the unknown ketone produces crystals of a 2,4-dinitrophenylhydrazone that melt at 102 °C. You can now narrow the choice to two ketones: B and D. Preparing the oxime of the unknown ketone will not distinguish between B and D because the oximes of B and D have similar melting points, but preparing the semicarbazone will allow you to identify the ketone. Finding that the semicarbazone of the unknown ketone has a melting point of 112 °C establishes that the unknown ketone is D.

chem **Tutorial:**
place Imines and oximes

PROBLEM 24

Imines can exist as stereoisomers. The isomers are named by the *E,Z* system of nomenclature. (The lone pair has the lowest priority.)

$$R \quad X \qquad R$$

Draw the structure of each of the following compounds:

a. (*E*)-benzaldehyde semicarbazone
b. (*Z*)-propiophenone oxime
c. cyclohexanone 2,4-dinitrophenylhydrazone

PROBLEM 25 ◆

Semicarbazide has two NH_2 groups. Explain why only one of them forms an imine.

The Wolff–Kishner Reduction

In Section 15.16, we saw that when a ketone or an aldehyde is heated in a basic solution of hydrazine, the carbonyl group is converted into a methylene group. This process is called **deoxygenation** because an oxygen is removed from the reactant. The reaction is known as the *Wolff–Kishner reduction*.

$$R-\overset{\overset{\displaystyle O}{\|}}{C}-R \xrightarrow[\text{HO}^-,\, \Delta]{NH_2NH_2} R-CH_2-R$$

Hydroxide ion and heat differentiate the Wolff–Kishner reduction from ordinary hydrazone formation.

MECHANISM FOR THE WOLFF–KISHNER REDUCTION

- Initially, the ketone reacts with hydrazine to form a hydrazone following the mechanism for imine formation on page 789, as expected.
- Hydroxide ion removes a proton from the NH_2 group. The reaction requires heat because this proton is not easily removed.
- The negative charge can be delocalized onto carbon, which removes a proton from water.
- The last two steps are repeated to form the deoxygenated product and nitrogen gas.

chem place Tutorial: Wolff-Kishner reduction in synthesis

Aldehydes and Ketones Form Enamines with Secondary Amines

An aldehyde or a ketone reacts with a *secondary amine* to form an enamine (pronounced "ENE-amine"). An **enamine** is an α,β-unsaturated tertiary amine—a tertiary amine with a double bond in the α,β-position relative to the nitrogen. Notice that the double bond is in the part of the molecule that comes from the aldehyde or ketone, not from the part that is provided by the secondary amine. The name comes from "ene" "amine," with the "e" omitted in order to avoid two successive vowels. Like imine formation, the reaction requires a trace amount of an acid catalyst.

The mechanism for enamine formation is exactly the same as that for imine formation, except for the last step.

MECHANISM FOR ENAMINE FORMATION

nucleophile adds to
the carbonyl compound

N–protonated
carbinolamine

neutral tetrahedral
intermediate
a carbinolamine

O–protonated
carbinolamine

elimination
of water

an enamine

HB⁺

this intermediate cannot lose
a proton from N, so it loses
a proton from an α-carbon

- The amine adds to the carbonyl carbon.
- Protonation of the alkoxide ion and deprotonation of the ammonium ion form a neutral tetrahedral intermediate.
- The neutral tetrahedral intermediate is in equilibrium with two protonated forms because either its oxygen or its nitrogen can be protonated.
- Because the nucleophile has a lone pair, water is eliminated from the oxygen-protonated intermediate, thereby forming a compound with a positively charged nitrogen.
- When a primary amine reacts with an aldehyde or a ketone, the positively charged nitrogen loses a proton in the last step of the mechanism, forming a neutral imine. However, when the amine is secondary, the positively charged nitrogen is not bonded to a hydrogen. In this case, a stable neutral molecule is obtained by loss of a proton from the α-carbon of the compound derived from the carbonyl compound. An enamine is the result.

Aldehydes and ketones react with secondary amines to form enamines.

In an aqueous acidic solution, an enamine is hydrolyzed back to the carbonyl compound and secondary amine, a reaction similar to the acid-catalyzed hydrolysis of an imine back to the carbonyl compound and primary amine.

An enamine undergoes acid-catalyzed hydrolysis to form a carbonyl compound and a secondary amine.

PROBLEM 26

a. Write the mechanism for the following reactions:

1. The acid-catalyzed hydrolysis of an imine to a carbonyl compound and a primary amine
2. The acid-catalyzed hydrolysis of an enamine to a carbonyl compound and a secondary amine

b. How do these mechanisms differ?

PROBLEM 27

Give the products of the following reactions. (A trace amount of acid is present in each case.)

a. cyclopentanone + ethylamine

b. cyclopentanone + diethylamine

c. acetophenone + hexylamine

d. acetophenone + cyclohexylamine

Reductive Amination

The imine formed from the reaction of an aldehyde or a ketone with ammonia is relatively unstable because it does not have a substituent other than a hydrogen bonded to the nitrogen. Nevertheless, such an imine is a useful intermediate. For example, if the reaction with ammonia is carried out in the presence of H_2 and an appropriate metal catalyst, H_2 will add to the $C=N$ bond as it is formed, forming a primary amine. The reaction of an aldehyde or a ketone with excess ammonia in the presence of a reducing agent is called **reductive amination**.

A primary amine can also be formed by reducing the oxime formed from the reaction of an aldehyde or a ketone with hydroxylamine.

Secondary and tertiary amines can be prepared from imines and enamines by reducing the imine or enamine. Sodium cyanoborohydride ($NaBH_3CN$) is a commonly used reducing agent for these reactions because it is easily handled and is stable even in acidic solutions. Reductive animation using $NaBH_3CN$ as the reducing agent is called the Borch reaction.

PROBLEM 28♦

Excess ammonia must be used when a primary amine is synthesized by reductive amination. What product will be obtained if the reaction is carried out with excess carbonyl compound?

PROBLEM 29

The compounds commonly known as "amino acids" are actually α-aminocarboxylic acids (Section 23.0). What carbonyl compounds should be used to synthesize the following amino acids?

a. CH_3CH—$\overset{\overset{O}{\|}}{C}$—$O^-$
     $\underset{NH_2}{\,}$

b. $(CH_3)_2CHCH$—$\overset{\overset{O}{\|}}{C}$—$O^-$
     $\underset{NH_2}{\,}$

18.9 THE REACTIONS OF ALDEHYDES AND KETONES WITH WATER

The addition of water to an aldehyde or a ketone forms a *hydrate*. A **hydrate** is a molecule with two OH groups bonded to the same carbon. Hydrates are also called **gem-diols** (*gem* comes from *geminus*, Latin for "twin"). Hydrates of aldehydes or ketones are generally too unstable to be isolated because the sp^3 carbon is attached to two oxygens.

Most hydrates are too unstable to be isolated.

$$\underset{\substack{\textbf{an aldehyde or} \\ \textbf{a ketone}}}{R-\overset{\overset{O}{\|}}{C}-R\,(H)} \;+\; H_2O \;\overset{HCl}{\rightleftharpoons}\; \underset{\substack{\textbf{a } \textit{gem}\text{-diol} \\ \textbf{a hydrate}}}{R-\overset{\overset{OH}{|}}{\underset{OH}{C}}-R\,(H)}$$

Water is a poor nucleophile and therefore adds relatively slowly to a carbonyl group. The rate of the reaction can be increased by an acid catalyst (Figure 18.3). Keep in mind that a catalyst affects the *rate* at which an aldehyde or a ketone is converted to a hydrate; it has no effect on the *amount* of aldehyde or ketone converted to hydrate (Section 3.7). The mechanism for the reaction is shown below.

MECHANISM FOR ACID-CATALYZED HYDRATE FORMATION

▲ Figure 18.3
The electrostatic potential maps show that the carbonyl carbon of the protonated aldehyde is more electrophilic (the blue is more intense) than the carbonyl carbon of the unprotonated aldehyde.

- The acid protonates the carbonyl oxygen, which makes the carbonyl carbon more susceptible to nucleophilic attack (Figure 18.3).
- Water adds to the carbonyl carbon.
- Loss of a proton from the protonated tetrahedral intermediate gives the hydrate.

PROBLEM 30

Hydration of an aldehyde can also be catalyzed by hydroxide ion. Propose a mechanism for hydroxide-ion-catalyzed hydration.

The extent to which an aldehyde or a ketone is hydrated in an aqueous solution depends on the substituents attached to the carbonyl group. For example, only 0.2% of acetone is hydrated at equilibrium, but 99.9% of formaldehyde is hydrated.

			K_{eq}
acetone 99.8%	$+$ H$_2$O $\rightleftharpoons$	0.2%	2×10^{-3}
acetaldehyde 42%	$+$ H$_2$O $\rightleftharpoons$	58%	1.4
formaldehyde 0.1%	$+$ H$_2$O $\rightleftharpoons$	99.9%	2.3×10^3

Why is there such a difference in the extent of hydration? The equilibrium constant for a reaction depends on the relative stabilities of the reactants and products (Section 3.7). The equilibrium constant for hydrate formation, which is a measure of the extent of hydration, therefore, depends on the relative stabilities of the carbonyl compound and the hydrate. We have seen that electron-donating alkyl groups make a carbonyl compound *more stable* (less reactive) (Section 18.2).

In contrast, alkyl groups make the hydrate *less stable* because of steric interactions between the alkyl groups when the bond angle changes from 120° to 109.5° (Section 18.2).

Alkyl groups, therefore, shift the equilibrium to the left (toward reactants) because they stabilize the carbonyl compound and destabilize the hydrate. As a result, less acetone than formaldehyde is hydrated at equilibrium.

In summary, the percentage of hydrate present in solution at equilibrium depends on both electronic and steric effects. Electron-donating substituents and bulky substituents (such as the methyl groups of acetone) *decrease* the percentage of hydrate present at equilibrium, whereas electron-withdrawing substituents and small substituents (the hydrogens of formaldehyde) *increase* the percent of hydration present at equilibrium.

Preserving Biological Specimens

A 37% solution of formaldehyde in water, known as *formalin*, was commonly used to preserve biological specimens. Formaldehyde is an eye and skin irritant, however, so formalin has been replaced in most biology laboratories by other preservatives. One frequently used preparation is a solution of 2%–5% phenol in ethanol with added antimicrobial agents.

If the amount of hydrate formed from the reaction of water with a ketone is too small to detect, how do we know that the reaction has even occurred? We can prove that it occurs by adding the ketone to ^{18}O-labeled water and isolating the ketone after equilibrium has been established. Finding that the label has been incorporated into the ketone indicates that hydration has occurred.

PROBLEM 31

When trichloroacetaldehyde is dissolved in water, almost all of it is converted to the hydrate. Chloral hydrate, the product of the reaction, is a sedative that can be lethal. A cocktail laced with it is known—in detective novels, at least—as a "Mickey Finn." Explain why an aqueous solution of trichloroacetaldehyde is almost all hydrate.

trichloroacetaldehyde   chloral hydrate

PROBLEM 32 ◆

Which of the following ketones forms the most hydrate in an aqueous solution?

18.10 THE REACTIONS OF ALDEHYDES AND KETONES WITH ALCOHOLS

The product formed when one equivalent of an alcohol adds to an *aldehyde* is called a **hemiacetal**. The product formed when a second equivalent of alcohol is added is called an **acetal** (ass-ett-AL). Like water, an alcohol is a poor nucleophile, so an acid catalyst is required for the reaction to take place at a reasonable rate.

an aldehyde   a hemiacetal   an acetal

When the carbonyl compound is a *ketone* instead of an aldehyde, the addition products are called a **hemiketal** and a **ketal**, respectively.

Hemi is the Greek word for "half." When one equivalent of alcohol has added to an aldehyde or a ketone, the compound is halfway to the final acetal or ketal, which contains groups from two equivalents of alcohol. The mechanism for ketal (or acetal) formation is shown below.

MECHANISM FOR ACID-CATALYZED ACETAL OR KETAL FORMATION

- The acid protonates the carbonyl oxygen, making the carbonyl carbon more susceptible to nucleophilic attack (Figure 18.3).
- The alcohol adds to the carbonyl carbon.
- Loss of a proton from the protonated tetrahedral intermediate gives the hemiketal (or hemiacetal).
- Because the reaction is carried out in an acidic solution, the hemiacetal (or hemiketal) is in equilibrium with its protonated form. The two oxygen atoms of the hemiketal (or hemiacetal) are equally basic, so either one can be protonated.
- Because the nucleophile has a lone pair, water is eliminated from the protonated intermediate, thereby forming an intermediate that is very reactive because of its positively charged oxygen.
- Nucleophilic attack on this intermediate by a second molecule of alcohol, followed by loss of a proton, forms the acetal (or ketal).

Although the sp^3 carbon of an acetal (or ketal) is bonded to two oxygens, leading us to predict that it is not stable, the acetal (or ketal) can be isolated if the water that is eliminated is removed from the reaction mixture. If water is not available, the only compound the acetal or ketal can form is the *O*-alkylated intermediate, which is even less stable than the acetal or ketal.

The acetal or ketal can be hydrolyzed back to the aldehyde or ketone in an acidic aqueous solution.

Notice that the mechanisms for imine, enamine, hydrate, and acetal (or ketal) formation are similar. All these reactions employ a nucleophile with a lone pair on the attacking atom. After the nucleophile has added to the carbonyl carbon, water is eliminated from a protonated tetrahedral intermediate, forming a positively charged species. In imine and hydrate formation, a neutral product is achieved by loss of a proton from a nitrogen and an oxygen, respectively. In enamine formation, a neutral product is achieved by loss of a proton from an α-carbon. In acetal formation, a neutral compound is achieved by addition of a second equivalent of alcohol. (Because the nucleophile in hydrate formation is water, elimination of water gives back the original aldehyde or ketone.)

Carbohydrates

When we look at carbohydrates in Chapter 22, we will see that the individual sugar units in a carbohydrate are held together by acetal or ketal groups. For example, the reaction of an alcohol group and an aldehyde group of D-glucose forms a cyclic D-glucose molecule that is a hemiacetal. Molecules of cylic D-glucose are then hooked up as a result of the reaction of the OH group of one molecule with the hemiacetal group of another, resulting in the formation of an acetal.

PROBLEM 33 ♦

Which of the following are

a. hemiacetals?   **b.** acetals?   **c.** hemiketals?   **d.** ketals?   **e.** hydrates?

1.
$$CH_3-\underset{\underset{OCH_3}{|}}{\overset{\overset{OH}{|}}{C}}-CH_3$$

3.
$$CH_3-\underset{\underset{OCH_3}{|}}{\overset{\overset{OCH_3}{|}}{C}}-H$$

5.
$$CH_3-\underset{\underset{OCH_3}{|}}{\overset{\overset{OCH_3}{|}}{C}}-CH_3$$

7.
$$CH_3-\underset{\underset{OCH_3}{|}}{\overset{\overset{OH}{|}}{C}}-H$$

2.
$$CH_3-\underset{\underset{OCH_2CH_3}{|}}{\overset{\overset{OCH_2CH_3}{|}}{C}}-H$$

4.
$$CH_3-\underset{\underset{OH}{|}}{\overset{\overset{OH}{|}}{C}}-CH_3$$

6.
$$CH_3-\underset{\underset{OH}{|}}{\overset{\overset{OH}{|}}{C}}-H$$

8.
$$CH_3-\underset{\underset{OCH_3}{|}}{\overset{\overset{OH}{|}}{C}}-CH_2CH_3$$

PROBLEM-SOLVING STRATEGY

Analyzing the Behavior of Acetals and Ketals

Explain why acetals and ketals are hydrolyzed back to the aldehyde or ketone in acidic aqueous solutions, but are stable in basic aqueous solutions.

The best way to approach this kind of question is to write out the structures and the mechanism that describe the situation to which the question is referring. When the mechanism is written, the answer may become apparent. In an acidic solution, the acid protonates an oxygen of the acetal. This creates a weak base (CH_3OH) that can be eliminated. When the group is eliminated, water can attack the reactive intermediate, and you are on your way back to the ketone (or aldehyde).

In a basic solution, the CH_3O group cannot be protonated. Therefore, a very basic CH_3O^- group has to be eliminated to re-form the ketone (or aldehyde), and a CH_3O^- group is too basic to be eliminated.

Now continue on to Problem 34.

PROBLEM 34

a. Would you expect hemiacetals to be stable in basic solutions? Explain your answer.
b. Acetal formation must be catalyzed by an acid. Explain why it cannot be catalyzed by CH_3O^-.
c. Can the rate of hydrate formation be increased by hydroxide ion as well as by acid? Explain.

PROBLEM 35

Explain why an acetal or ketal can be isolated but most hydrates cannot be isolated.

18.11 PROTECTING GROUPS

Ketones (or aldehydes) react with 1,2-diols to form five-membered ring ketals (or acetals) and with 1,3-diols to form six-membered ring ketals (or acetals). Recall that five- and six-membered rings are formed relatively easily (Section 8.10). The mechanism is the same as that shown in Section 18.10 for acetal formation, except that instead of reacting with two separate molecules of alcohol, the carbonyl compound reacts with the two alcohol groups of a single molecule of the diol.

If a compound has two functional groups that will react with a given reagent and you want only one of them to react, it is necessary to protect the other functional group from the reagent. A group that protects a functional group from a synthetic operation that it would not otherwise survive is called a **protecting group**.

If you have ever painted a room with a spray gun, you may have taped over the things you did not want to paint, such as baseboards and window frames. In a similar way, 1,2-diols and 1,3-diols are used to protect ("tape over") the carbonyl group of aldehydes and ketones. For example, suppose you wanted to convert the keto ester shown below into a hydroxyketone. Both functional groups of the keto ester will be reduced by $LiAlH_4$, and the one that you don't want to react—the keto group—is the more reactive of the two.

However, if the keto group is first converted to a ketal, only the ester group will react with $LiAlH_4$. The protecting group can be removed by acid-catalyzed hydrolysis after the ester has been reduced. It is critical that the conditions used to remove a protecting group do not affect other groups in the molecule. Acetals and ketals are good protecting groups because they are ethers, and ethers do not react with bases, reducing agents, or oxidizing agents.

PROBLEM 36◆

a. What would have been the product of the preceding reaction with $LiAlH_4$ if the keto group had not been protected?

b. What reagent could you use to reduce only the keto group?

PROBLEM 37

Explain why acetals do not react with nucleophiles.

In the following reaction, the aldehyde reacts with the diol because aldehydes are more reactive than ketones. The Grignard reagent will then react only with the ketone. The protecting group can be removed by acid-catalyzed hydrolysis.

One of the best ways to protect an OH group of an alcohol is to convert it to a triethylsilyl (TES) ether by treating the alcohol with chlorotriethylsilane and a tertiary amine. The ether is formed by an S_N2 reaction. Although a tertiary alkyl halide does not undergo an

S_N2 reaction, the tertiary silyl compound does because Si—C bonds are longer than C—C bonds, which reduces steric hindrance at the site of nucleophilic attack. The amine prevents the solution from becoming acidic by reacting with the HCl generated in the reaction. The TES ether, which is stable in neutral and basic solutions, can have its protecting group removed with aqueous acid under mild conditions.

chlorotrimethylsilane   a trimethylsilyl ether
                                a TMS ether

The OH group of a carboxylic acid group can be protected by converting the carboxylic acid into an ester.

PROBLEM 38

What products would be formed from the preceding reaction if the alcohol group were not protected?

An amino group can be protected by being converted into an amide (Section 17.8). The acetyl group can subsequently be removed by acid-catalyzed hydrolysis (Section 17.17).

aniline   acetanilide   p-nitroacetanilide   p-nitroaniline

Protecting groups should be used only when absolutely necessary because attaching and then removing them adds two steps to the synthesis, which decreases the overall yield of the target molecule (the desired product).

PROBLEM 39 ◆

a. In a six-step synthesis, what is the yield of the target compound if each of the reactions employed gives an 80% yield? (An 80% yield is a relatively high laboratory yield.)
b. What would the yield be if two more steps (each of 80% yield) were added to the synthesis?

PROBLEM 40

Show how each of the following compounds can be prepared from the given starting material. In each case, you will need to use a protecting group.

a. HO⌒⌒Br ⟶ HO⌒⌒⌒OH (OH)

b. [structure: 3-bromobenzaldehyde] ⟶ [structure: 3-carboxybenzaldehyde]

18.12 THE ADDITION OF SULFUR NUCLEOPHILES

Aldehydes and ketones react with thiols to form thioacetals and thioketals. The mechanism for addition of a thiol is the same as the mechanism for addition of an alcohol. Recall that thiols are sulfur analogs of alcohols (Section 10.11).

$$R-\overset{O}{\underset{\|}{C}}-R + 2\,CH_3SH \underset{}{\overset{HCl}{\rightleftharpoons}} R-\overset{SCH_3}{\underset{SCH_3}{\overset{|}{\underset{|}{C}}}}-R + H_2O$$

methanethiol   a thioketal

[structure: cyclohexanone] + HS⌒⌒SH $\overset{HCl}{\rightleftharpoons}$ [structure: 1,5-dithiaspiro compound] + H₂O

1,3-propanedithiol   a thioketal

Thioacetal (or thioketal) formation is useful in organic synthesis because a thioacetal (or thioketal) is desulfurized when it reacts with H₂ and Raney nickel. Desulfurization replaces the C—S bonds with C—H bonds.

[structure: dithiane] $\overset{H_2}{\underset{Raney\ Ni}{\longrightarrow}}$ [structure: cyclohexane]

PROBLEM 41

a. Describe four ways the following reaction could be carried out.

[structure: acetophenone] ⟶ [structure: ethylbenzene]

b. Describe three ways the following reaction could be carried out.

18.13 THE WITTIG REACTION FORMS AN ALKENE

An aldehyde or a ketone reacts with a phosphonium ylide ("ILL-id") to form an alkene. This is called a **Wittig reaction**. Overall, it amounts to interchanging the double-bonded oxygen of the carbonyl compound and the double-bonded carbon group of the phosphonium ylide.

$$
\begin{array}{c}
\text{R} \\ \diagdown \\ \text{C=O} \\ \diagup \\ \text{R}
\end{array}
\; + \;
(C_6H_5)_3P{=}C \begin{array}{c} CH_3 \\ \diagup \\ \diagdown \\ H \end{array}
\longrightarrow
\begin{array}{c} \text{R} \\ \diagdown \\ \text{C=C} \\ \diagup \\ \text{R} \end{array} \begin{array}{c} CH_3 \\ \diagup \\ \diagdown \\ H \end{array}
\; + \;
(C_6H_5)_3P{=}O
$$

a phosphonium ylide   triphenylphosphine oxide

An **ylide** is a compound with opposite charges on adjacent covalently bonded atoms that have complete octets. The ylide can be written in the double-bonded form because phosphorus can have more than eight valence electrons.

$$(C_6H_5)_3\overset{+}{P}{-}\overset{..}{\overset{-}{C}}H_2 \quad \longleftrightarrow \quad (C_6H_5)_3P{=}CH_2$$

a phosphonium ylide

Evidence has accumulated that the Wittig reaction is a concerted [2 + 2] cycloaddition reaction. (Cycloaddition reactions were introduced in Section 7.12.) It is called a [2 + 2] cycloaddition reaction because, of the four electrons involved in the cyclic transition state, two come from the carbonyl group and two come from the ylide.

MECHANISM FOR THE WITTIG REACTION

$$
\begin{array}{c}
\text{O} \\ \| \\ \text{C} \\ \diagup \;\; \diagdown \\ \text{R} \quad\;\; \text{R}
\end{array}
\begin{array}{c} \overset{+}{P}(C_6H_5)_3 \\ + \\ :CH_2 \end{array}
\longrightarrow
\begin{array}{c}
\text{O}{-}\text{P}(C_6H_5)_3 \\ | \qquad\;\; | \\ R{-}\underset{\underset{R}{|}}{C}{-}CH_2
\end{array}
\longrightarrow
\begin{array}{c}
\text{O=P}(C_6H_5)_3 \\ + \\ \begin{array}{c} R \\ \diagdown \\ \text{C=CH}_2 \\ \diagup \\ R \end{array}
\end{array}
$$

a [2 + 2] cycloaddition reaction

- The nucleophilic carbon of the ylide adds to the carbonyl carbon while the carbonyl oxygen adds to the electrophilic phosphorus.
- Elimination of triphenylphosphine oxide forms the alkene product.

The phosphonium ylide needed for a particular synthesis is obtained by an S_N2 reaction between triphenylphosphine and an alkyl halide with the appropriate number of carbons. A proton on the carbon adjacent to the positively charged phosphorus atom is sufficiently acidic ($pK_a = 35$) to be removed by a strong base such as butyllithium (Section 11.1).

$$
(C_6H_5)_3P: \quad + \quad CH_3CH_2{-}Br \xrightarrow{S_N2} (C_6H_5)_3\overset{+}{P}{-}CH_2CH_3 \xrightarrow{CH_3CH_2CH_2\overset{-}{C}H_2 \; \overset{+}{Li}} (C_6H_5)_3\overset{+}{P}{-}\overset{..}{\overset{-}{C}}HCH_3
$$

triphenylphosphine   Br$^-$ a phosphonium ylide

If two sets of reagents are available for the synthesis of an alkene, the better choice is one that requires the less sterically hindered alkyl halide for synthesis of the ylide. (Recall that the more sterically hindered the alkyl halide, the less reactive it is in an S_N2 reaction; see Section 8.1.) For example, it is better to use the three-carbon alkyl halide and the five-carbon carbonyl compound than the five-carbon alkyl halide and the three-carbon carbonyl compound for the synthesis of 3-ethyl-3-hexene because it would be easier to form an ylide from a primary alkyl halide (1-bromopropane) than from a secondary alkyl halide (3-bromopentane).

The Wittig reaction is a very powerful way to make an alkene because the reaction is completely regioselective—the double bond will be in only one place.

The Wittig reaction also is the best way to make a terminal alkene, such as the one shown above, because other methods would form a terminal alkene only as a minor product.

The stereoselectivity of the Wittig reaction depends on the structure of the ylide. Ylides can be divided into two types: *stabilized ylides* have a group, such as a carbonyl group, that can share carbon's negative charge; *unstabilized ylides* do not have such a group.

Stabilized ylides form primarily *E* isomers, and unstabilized ylides form primarily *Z* isomers.

chem Tutorial:
place Wittig reaction-synthesis

β-Carotene

β-Carotene is found in orange and yellow-orange fruits and vegetables such as apricots, mangoes, carrots, and sweet potatoes. The synthesis of β-carotene from vitamin A for use in foods is an important example of the use of the Wittig reaction in industry. Notice that the ylide is one that can be stabilized, so the product has the E configuration at the reaction site.

vitamin A aldehyde

β-carotene

β-Carotene is used in the food industry to color margarine. Many people take β-carotene as a dietary supplement because there is some evidence associating high levels of β-carotene with a low incidence of cancer. More recent evidence, however, suggests that β-carotene taken in pill form does not have the cancer-preventing effects of β-carotene obtained from vegetables.

PROBLEM 42 | SOLVED

a. What carbonyl compound and what phosphonium ylide are required for the synthesis of each of the following alkenes?

1. $CH_3CH_2CH_2CH{=}CCH_3$
        $|$
        CH_3

3. $(C_6H_5)_2C{=}CHCH_3$

2. ⬡$=CHCH_2CH_3$

4. ⬡$-CH{=}CH_2$

b. What alkyl halide is required to prepare each of the phosphonium ylides in part **a**?

Solution to 42a (1)   The atoms on either side of the double bond can come from the carbonyl compound, so two pairs of compounds could be used.

$$CH_3\overset{\displaystyle O}{\overset{\|}{C}}CH_3 \ + \ (C_6H_5)_3P{=}CHCH_2CH_2CH_3 \quad \textbf{or} \quad CH_3CH_2CH_2\overset{\displaystyle O}{\overset{\|}{C}}{}^{}_{\,}H \ + \ (C_6H_5)_3P{=}C\overset{\displaystyle CH_3}{\underset{CH_3}{\big\langle}}$$

Solution to 42b (1)   The alkyl halide required to make the phosphonium ylide would be 1-bromobutane for the first pair of reagents or 2-bromopropane for the second pair.

$$CH_3CH_2CH_2CH_2Br \quad \textbf{or} \quad CH_3CHCH_3$$
$$\phantom{CH_3CH_2CH_2CH_2Br \quad \textbf{or} \quad CH_3CH}|$$
$$\phantom{CH_3CH_2CH_2CH_2Br \quad \textbf{or} \quad CH_3CH}Br$$

The primary alkyl halide would be more reactive in the S_N2 reaction required to make the ylide, so the best method would be to use the first pair of reagents (acetone and the ylide obtained from 1-bromobutane).

18.14 THE STEREOCHEMISTRY OF NUCLEOPHILIC ADDITION REACTIONS: *RE* AND *SI* FACES

A carbonyl carbon bonded to two different substituents is a **prochiral carbonyl carbon** because it will become an asymmetric center if it acquires an additional group unlike either of the groups already bonded to it.

the *Si* face

the *Re* face

The carbonyl carbon and the three atoms attached to it define a plane. In a nucleophilic addition reaction, the nucleophile can approach either side of the plane with equal ease. Consequently, an addition reaction forms equal amounts of a pair of enantiomers.

One side of the carbonyl compound is called the *Re* (pronounced "ree") face, and the other side is called the *Si* (pronounced "sigh") face; *Re* is for *rectus* and *Si* is for *sinister*—similar to *R* and *S*. To distinguish between the *Re* and *Si* faces, the three groups attached to the carbonyl carbon are assigned priorities using the Cahn–Ingold–Prelog system from *E,Z* and *R,S* nomenclature (Sections 3.5 and 5.7, respectively). The *Re* face is the face closest to the observer when priorities decrease (1 > 2 > 3) in a clockwise direction, and the *Si* face is the opposite face, the one closest to the observer when the priorities decrease in a counterclockwise direction.

Attack by a nucleophile on the *Re* face forms one enantiomer, whereas attack on the *Si* face forms the other enantiomer. For example, attack by hydride ion on the *Re* face of butanone forms (*S*)-2-butanol, and attack on the *Si* face forms (*R*)-2-butanol.

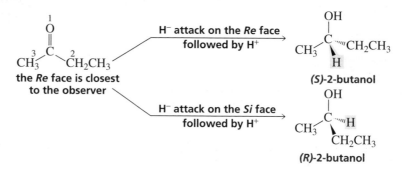

Whether attack on the *Re* face forms the *R* or *S* enantiomer depends on the priority of the attacking nucleophile relative to the priorities of the groups attached to the carbonyl carbon. For example, although attack by hydride ion on the *Re* face of butanone forms (*S*)-2-butanol (above), attack by a methyl Grignard reagent on the *Re* face of propanal forms (*R*)-2-butanol (below).

Enzyme-Catalyzed Carbonyl Additions

In an enzyme-catalyzed addition to a carbonyl compound, only one of the enantiomers is formed. The enzyme can block one face of the carbonyl compound so that it cannot be attacked, or it can position the nucleophile so it is able to attack the carbonyl group from only one side.

PROBLEM 43 ♦

Which enantiomer is formed when a methyl Grignard reagent attacks the *Re* face of each of the following carbonyl compounds?

a. propiophenone

b. benzaldehyde

c. 2-pentanone

d. 3-hexanone

18.15 DESIGNING A SYNTHESIS VI: DISCONNECTIONS, SYNTHONS, AND SYNTHETIC EQUIVALENTS

The route to the synthesis of a complicated molecule from simple starting materials is not always obvious. We have seen that it is often easier to work backward from the desired product—a process called *retrosynthetic analysis* (Section 6.12). In a retrosynthetic analysis, the chemist dissects a molecule into smaller and smaller pieces to arrive at readily available starting materials.

retrosynthetic analysis

target molecule $\Longrightarrow$ Y $\Longrightarrow$ X $\Longrightarrow$ W $\Longrightarrow$ starting materials

A useful step in a retrosynthetic analysis is a **disconnection**—breaking a bond to produce two fragments. Typically, one fragment is positively charged and one is negatively charged. The fragments of a disconnection are called **synthons**. Synthons are often not real compounds. For example, if we consider the retrosynthetic analysis of cyclohexanol, a disconnection gives two synthons—an α-hydroxycarbocation and a hydride ion.

retrosynthetic analysis

HO H [cyclohexanol structure] $\xrightarrow{\alpha \text{ disconnection}}$ OH [cyclohexyl cation structure] synthons + H⁻

open arrow represents a retrosynthetic operation

A **synthetic equivalent** is the reagent that is actually used as the source of a synthon. In the synthesis of cyclohexanol, cyclohexanone is the synthetic equivalent for the α-hydroxycarbocation and sodium borohydride is the synthetic equivalent for hydride ion. Thus, cyclohexanol, the target molecule, can be prepared by treating cyclohexanone with sodium borohydride.

synthesis

When carrying out a disconnection, we must decide, after breaking the bond, which fragment gets the positive charge and which gets the negative charge. In the retrosynthetic analysis of cyclohexanol, we could have given the positive charge to the hydrogen, and many acids (HCl, HBr, and so on) could have been used for the synthetic equivalent for H$^+$. However, we would have been at a loss to find a synthetic equivalent for an α-hydroxycarbanion. Therefore, when we carried out the disconnection, we assigned the positive charge to the carbon and the negative charge to the hydrogen.

Cyclohexanol can also be disconnected by breaking the C—O bond instead of the C—H bond, forming a carbocation and hydroxide ion.

retrosynthetic analysis

The problem then becomes choosing a synthetic equivalent for the carbocation. A synthetic equivalent for a positively charged synthon needs an electron-withdrawing group at just the right place. Cyclohexyl bromide, with an electron-withdrawing bromine, is a synthetic equivalent for the cyclohexyl carbocation. Cyclohexanol, therefore, can be prepared by treating cyclohexyl bromide with hydroxide ion. This method, however, is not as satisfactory as the first synthesis we proposed—reduction of cyclohexanone—because some of the alkyl halide is converted to an alkene, so the overall yield of the target molecule is lower.

synthesis

Retrosynthetic analysis shows that 1-methylcyclohexanol can be formed from the reaction of cyclohexanone, the synthetic equivalent for the α-hydroxycarbocation and methylmagnesium bromide, the synthetic equivalent for the methyl anion.

retrosynthetic analysis

synthesis

Other disconnections of 1-methylcyclohexanol are possible because any bond to carbon can serve as a disconnection site. For example, one of the ring C—C bonds could be broken. However, these are not useful disconnections because the synthetic equivalents of the synthons they produce are not easily prepared. A retrosynthetic step must lead to readily obtainable starting materials.

PROBLEM 44

Using bromocyclohexane as a starting material, how could you synthesize the following compounds?

a.

c.

e.

b.

d.

f.

Synthesizing Organic Compounds

Organic chemists synthesize compounds for many reasons: to study their properties, to answer a variety of chemical questions, or because they have useful properties. One reason chemists synthesize natural products is to provide us with larger supplies of those compounds than nature can produce. For example, Taxol—a compound that has been successful in treating ovarian cancer, breast cancer, and certain forms of lung cancer by inhibiting mitosis—is extracted from the bark of *Taxus*, the yew tree found in the Pacific Northwest. The supply of natural Taxol is limited because yew trees are uncommon, grow very slowly, and stripping the bark kills the tree. Moreover, the bark of a 40-foot tree, which may have taken 200 years to grow, provides only 0.5 g of the drug. In addition, *Taxus* forests serve as habitats for the spotted owl, an endangered species, so harvesting the trees would accelerate the owl's demise. Once chemists were successful in determining the structure of Taxol, efforts were undertaken to synthesize it in order to make it more widely available as an anticancer drug. Several syntheses have been successful.

Once a compound has been synthesized, chemists can study its properties to learn how it works; then they may be able to design and synthesize safer or more potent analogs.

Taxol®

Semisynthetic Drugs

Taxol is difficult to synthesize because of its many functional groups and 11 asymmetric centers. Chemists have made the synthesis a lot easier by allowing the common English yew shrub to carry out the first part of the synthesis. A precursor of the drug is extracted from the shrub's needles, and the precursor is converted

to Taxol in a four-step procedure in the laboratory. Thus, the precursor is isolated from a renewable resource, whereas the drug itself could be obtained only by killing a slow-growing tree. This is an example of how chemists have learned to synthesize compounds jointly with nature.

18.16 NUCLEOPHILIC ADDITION TO α,β-UNSATURATED ALDEHYDES AND KETONES

The resonance contributors for an α,β-unsaturated carbonyl compound show that the molecule has two electrophilic sites: the carbonyl carbon and the β-carbon.

This means that a nucleophile can add either to the carbonyl carbon or to the β-carbon. Nucleophilic addition to the carbonyl carbon is called **direct addition** or 1,2- addition.

Nucleophilic addition to the β-carbon is called **conjugate addition** or 1,4-addition, because it occurs at the 1- and 4-positions. The product of 1,4-addition—an enol—tautomerizes to a ketone or to an aldehyde (Section 6.7). Thus, the overall reaction amounts to addition to the carbon–carbon double bond, with the nucleophile adding to the β-carbon and a proton from the reaction mixture adding to the α-carbon.

Whether the product obtained from nucleophilic addition to an α,β-unsaturated aldehyde or ketone is the direct addition product or the conjugate addition product depends on the nature of the nucleophile, the structure of the carbonyl compound, and the conditions under which the reaction is carried out.

We have seen that if both competing reactions are irreversible, the reaction will be under kinetic control. If one or both of the two reactions is reversible, the reaction will be under thermodynamic control (Section 7.11). Addition to the β-carbon (conjugate addition) is generally irreversible. Direct addition can be irreversible or reversible.

If the nucleophile is a *strong base*, such as Grignard reagent or hydride ion, direct addition is irreversible. Because both competing reactions are irreversible, the reaction will be under *kinetic control*.

If the nucleophile is a *weak base*, such as a halide ion, cyanide ion, thiol, alcohol, or amine, direct addition is reversible. Therefore, the reaction will be under *thermodynamic control*.

The reaction that prevails when the reaction is under thermodynamic control is the one that forms the more stable product (Section 7.11). The conjugate addition product is always the more stable product because it retains the very stable carbonyl group. Therefore, weak bases form conjugate addition products.

Nucleophiles that are weak bases form conjugate addition products.

The reaction that prevails when the reaction is under kinetic control is the one that is faster. Therefore, the product depends on the reactivity of the carbonyl group. Compounds with reactive carbonyl groups form primarily direct addition products because for *those* compounds, direct addition is faster, whereas compounds with less reactive carbonyl groups can form conjugate addition products because for *those* compounds, conjugate addition is faster. For example, aldehydes have more reactive carbonyl groups than do ketones, so sodium borohydride forms primarily direct addition products with aldehydes. Compared with aldehydes, ketones form less of the direct addition product and more of the conjugate addition product. Ethanol (EtOH) is used to protonate the alkoxide ion.

Nucleophiles that are strong bases form direct addition products with reactive carbonyl groups and conjugate addition products with less reactive carbonyl groups.

Notice that an alcohol is the final product of conjugate addition in the preceding reaction because the carbonyl group of the ketone will react with a second equivalent of hydride ion.

Like hydride ions, Grignard reagents are strong bases and therefore add irreversibly to carbonyl groups. Thus, Grignard reagents react with α,β-unsaturated aldehydes and α,β-unsaturated ketones to form direct addition products.

If, however, the rate of direct addition is slowed down by steric hindrance, a Grignard reagent will form a conjugate addition product because conjugate addition then becomes the faster reaction.

Only conjugate addition occurs when Gilman reagents (lithium dialkylcuprates, Section 11.4) react with α,β-unsaturated aldehydes and ketones. Therefore, Grignard reagents should be used when you want to add an alkyl group to the carbonyl carbon, whereas Gilman reagents should be used when you want to add an alkyl group to the β-carbon.

Electrophiles and nucleophiles can be classified as either *hard* or *soft*. Hard electrophiles and nucleophiles are more polarized than soft ones. Hard nucleophiles prefer to react with hard electrophiles, and soft nucleophiles prefer to react with soft electrophiles. Therefore, a Grignard reagent with a highly polarized C—Mg bond prefers to react with the harder C=O bond, whereas a Gilman reagent with a much less polarized C—Cu bond prefers to react with the softer C=C bond.

Cancer Chemotherapy

Two compounds—vernolepin and helenalin—owe their effectiveness as anticancer drugs to conjugate addition reactions.

vernolepin

helenalin

Cancer cells are cells that have lost the ability to control their growth; therefore, they proliferate rapidly. DNA polymerase is an enzyme that a cell needs in order to make a copy of its DNA for a new cell. DNA polymerase has an SH group at its active site (Section 23.8), and each of these drugs has two α,β-unsaturated carbonyl groups. When an SH group of DNA polymerase reacts with one of the α,β-unsaturated carbonyl groups of vernolepin or helenalin, the enzyme is inactivated.

active enzyme $\xrightarrow{\text{conjugate addition}}$ inactive enzyme

---

PROBLEM 45

Give the major product of each of the following reactions:

a. $\xrightarrow[\text{HCl}]{\text{NaC}\equiv\text{N}}$

b. $\xrightarrow[\text{2. EtOH}]{\text{1. NaBH}_4}$

c. $\text{CH}_3\text{C}=\text{CH}\overset{\displaystyle O}{\underset{}{\text{C}}}\text{CH}_3$ with CH_3 substituent $\xrightarrow[\text{2. EtOH}]{\text{1. CH}_3\text{MgBr}}$

d. $\text{CH}_3\text{CH}=\text{CH}\overset{\displaystyle O}{\underset{}{\text{C}}}\text{H}$ $\xrightarrow[\text{2. EtOH}]{\text{1. NaBH}_4}$

PROBLEM 46 ◆

Which would give a higher yield of an unsaturated alcohol when treated with sodium borohydride, a sterically hindered α,β-unsaturated ketone or a nonsterically hindered α,β-unsaturated ketone?

chem place   Tutorial:
1,2-Addition vs. 1,4-Addition to α,β-unsaturated carbonyl compounds

18.17 NUCLEOPHILIC ADDITION TO α,β-UNSATURATED CARBOXYLIC ACID DERIVATIVES

α,β-Unsaturated carboxylic acid derivatives (Class I carbonyl compounds), like α,β-unsaturated aldehydes and ketones (Class II carbonyl compounds), have two electrophilic sites for nucleophilic attack: they can undergo *conjugate addition* or *nucleophilic addition-elimination*. Notice that α,β-unsaturated carboxylic acid derivatives undergo *nucleophilic addition-elimination* rather than *direct nucleophilic addition* because they have a group that can be replaced by a nucleophile. In other words, direct nucleophilic addition becomes nucleophilic addition–elimination if the carbonyl group is attached to a group that can be replaced by a nucleophile (Section 18.3).

Nucleophiles react with α,β-unsaturated carboxylic acid derivatives with reactive carbonyl groups, such as acyl chlorides, to form nucleophilic addition–elimination products. Conjugate addition products are formed from the reaction of nucleophiles with less reactive carbonyl groups, such as esters and amides.

PROBLEM 47

Give the major product of each of the following reactions:

18.18 ENZYME-CATALYZED ADDITIONS TO α,β-UNSATURATED CARBONYL COMPOUNDS

The following are examples of reactions in biological systems that involve addition to α,β-unsaturated carbonyl compounds. Because the carbonylate groups are unreactive toward the nucleophile, conjugate addition occurs in each case.

Enzyme-Catalyzed Cis–Trans Interconversion

Enzymes that catalyze the interconversion of cis and trans isomers are called cis–trans isomerases. These isomerases are all known to contain thiol (SH) groups. Thiols are weak bases and therefore add to the β-carbon of an α,β-unsaturated carbonyl compound (conjugate addition), forming a carbon–carbon single bond that rotates before the enol is able to tautomerize to the ketone. When tautomerization occurs, the thiol is eliminated, leaving the compound as it was originally except for the configuration about the double bond.

SUMMARY

Aldehydes and **ketones** have an acyl group attached to a group (H, R, or Ar) that cannot be readily replaced by another group. Aldehydes and ketones undergo **nucleophilic addition reactions** with strongly basic nucleophiles and **nucleophilic addition–elimination reactions** with less basic nucleophiles that have a lone pair on the attacking atom.

With the exception of amides, a carboxylic acid derivative (a Class I carbonyl compound) undergoes a **nucleophilic addition–elimination** reaction with strongly basic nucleophiles to form a Class II carbonyl compound, which then undergoes a **nucleophilic addition** reaction with a second equivalent of the nucleophile.

Electronic and steric factors cause an aldehyde to be more reactive than a ketone toward nucleophilic addition. Aldehydes and ketones are less reactive than acyl halides and acid anhydrides and are more reactive than esters, carboxylic acids, and amides.

Grignard reagents react with aldehydes to form secondary alcohols, with ketones, esters, and acyl halides to form tertiary alcohols, and with carbon dioxide to form carboxylic acids. Aldehydes, acyl chlorides, and carboxylic acids are reduced by hydride ion to primary alcohols, ketones to secondary alcohols, and amides to amines.

Aldehydes and ketones react with primary amines to form **imines** and with secondary amines to form **enamines**. The mechanisms are the same, except for the site from which a proton is lost in the last step of the reaction. Imines and enamines are hydrolyzed under acidic conditions back to the carbonyl compound and amine. A **pH–rate profile** is a plot of the observed rate constant as a function of the pH of the reaction mixture. Hydroxide ion and heat differentiate the Wolff–Kishner reduction from ordinary **hydrazone** formation.

Aldehydes and ketones undergo acid-catalyzed addition of water to form hydrates. Electron donating and bulky substituents decrease the percentage of hydrate present at equilibrium. Most hydrates are too unstable to be isolated. Acid-catalyzed addition of an alcohol to an aldehyde forms **hemiacetals** and **acetals**, and to a ketone forms **hemiketals** and **ketals**. Acetal and ketal formation are reversible. Cyclic acetals and ketals serve as **protecting groups** for aldehyde and ketone functional groups. Aldehydes and ketones react with thiols to form thioacetals and thioketals; desulfurization replaces the C—S bonds with C—H bonds.

An aldehyde or a ketone reacts with a phosphonium ylide in a **Wittig reaction** to form an alkene. A Wittig reaction is a concerted [2 + 2] cycloaddition reaction; it is completely regioselective. Stabilized ylides form primarily E isomers; unstabilized ylides form primarily Z isomers.

A **prochiral carbonyl carbon** is a carbonyl carbon that is bonded to two different substituents. The Re face is the one closest to the observer when priorities decrease in a clockwise direction; the Si face is the opposite face. Addition of a nucleophile to both the Re face and the Si face forms a racemic mixture.

A useful step in a retrosynthetic analysis is a **disconnection**—breaking a bond to produce two fragments. **Synthons** are fragments produced by a disconnection. A **synthetic equivalent** is the reagent used as the source of a synthon.

Nucleophilic addition to the carbonyl carbon of an α,β-unsaturated Class II carbonyl compound is called **direct addition**; addition to the β-carbon is called **conjugate addition**. Whether direct or conjugate addition occurs depends on the nature of the nucleophile, the structure of the carbonyl compound, and the reaction conditions. Nucleophiles that form unstable direct addition products—halide ions, cyanide ion, thiols, alcohols, and amines—form conjugate addition products. Nucleophiles that form stable addition products—hydride ion and carbanions—form direct addition products with reactive carbonyl groups and conjugate addition products with less reactive carbonyl groups. A Grignard reagent with a highly polarized C—Mg bond reacts with the harder C=O bond; a Gilman reagent with a less polarized C—Cu bond reacts with the softer C=C bond.

Nucleophiles form nucleophilic addition–elimination products with α,β-unsaturated Class I carbonyl compounds that have reactive carbonyl groups and conjugate addition products with compounds with less reactive carbonyl groups.

SUMMARY OF REACTIONS

1. Reactions of *carbonyl compounds* with Grignard reagents (Section 18.4)
   a. Reaction of *formaldehyde* with a Grignard reagent forms a primary alcohol.

   b. Reaction of an *aldehyde* (other than formaldehyde) with a Grignard reagent forms a secondary alcohol.

   c. Reaction of a *ketone* with a Grignard reagent forms a tertiary alcohol.

d. Reaction of CO_2 with excess Grignard reagent forms a carboxylic acid.

$$O{=}C{=}O \xrightarrow[\text{2. H}_3\text{O}^+]{\text{1. CH}_3\text{MgBr}} CH_3\overset{\displaystyle O}{\underset{}{\overset{\|}{C}}}OH$$

e. Reaction of an *ester* with excess Grignard reagent forms a tertiary alcohol with two identical subunits.

$$\underset{R}{\overset{O}{\underset{}{\parallel}}}\underset{OR'}{C} \xrightarrow[\text{2. H}_3\text{O}^+]{\text{1. 2 CH}_3\text{MgBr}} R{-}\underset{\underset{CH_3}{|}}{\overset{\overset{OH}{|}}{C}}{-}CH_3$$

f. Reaction of an *acyl chloride* with a Grignard reagent forms a tertiary alcohol with two identical substituents.

$$\underset{R}{\overset{O}{\underset{}{\parallel}}}\underset{Cl}{C} \xrightarrow[\text{2. H}_3\text{O}^+]{\text{1. 2 CH}_3\text{MgBr}} R{-}\underset{\underset{CH_3}{|}}{\overset{\overset{OH}{|}}{C}}{-}CH_3$$

2. Reaction of *carbonyl compounds* with acetylide ions (Section 18.5)

$$\underset{R}{\overset{O}{\underset{}{\parallel}}}\underset{R}{C} \xrightarrow[\text{2. H}_3\text{O}^+]{\text{1. RC}{\equiv}\text{C}^-} R{-}\underset{\underset{R}{|}}{\overset{\overset{OH}{|}}{C}}{-}C{\equiv}CR$$

3. Reactions of *carbonyl compounds* with hydride ion donors (Section 18.6)
   a. Reaction of an *aldehyde* with sodium borohydride forms a primary alcohol.

$$\underset{R}{\overset{O}{\underset{}{\parallel}}}\underset{H}{C} \xrightarrow[\text{2. H}_3\text{O}^+]{\text{1. NaBH}_4} RCH_2OH$$

   b. Reaction of a *ketone* with sodium borohydride forms a secondary alcohol.

$$\underset{R}{\overset{O}{\underset{}{\parallel}}}\underset{R}{C} \xrightarrow[\text{2. H}_3\text{O}^+]{\text{1. NaBH}_4} R{-}\overset{\overset{OH}{|}}{CH}{-}R$$

   c. Reaction of an *acyl chloride* with sodium borohydride forms a primary alcohol.

$$\underset{R}{\overset{O}{\underset{}{\parallel}}}\underset{Cl}{C} \xrightarrow[\text{2. H}_3\text{O}^+]{\text{1. NaBH}_4} R{-}CH_2{-}OH$$

   d. Reaction of an *ester* with lithium aluminum hydride forms two alcohols.

$$\underset{R}{\overset{O}{\underset{}{\parallel}}}\underset{OR'}{C} \xrightarrow[\text{2. H}_3\text{O}^+]{\text{1. LiAlH}_4} RCH_2OH \ + \ R'OH$$

   e. Reaction of an *ester* with diisobutylaluminum hydride forms an aldehyde.

$$\underset{R}{\overset{O}{\underset{}{\parallel}}}\underset{OR'}{C} \xrightarrow[\text{2. H}_2\text{O}]{\text{1. [(CH}_3)_2\text{CHCH}_2]_2\text{AlH, }-78\text{ °C}} \underset{R}{\overset{O}{\underset{}{\parallel}}}\underset{H}{C}$$

   f. Reaction of a *carboxylic acid* with lithium aluminum hydride forms a primary alcohol.

$$\underset{R}{\overset{O}{\underset{}{\parallel}}}\underset{OH}{C} \xrightarrow[\text{2. H}_3\text{O}^+]{\text{1. LiAlH}_4} R{-}CH_2{-}OH$$

g. Reaction of an *amide* with lithium aluminum hydride forms an amine.

$$
\underset{\substack{R}}{\overset{\substack{O \\ \parallel}}{C}}\!\!-\!\!NH_2 \quad \xrightarrow[\text{2. H}_2\text{O}]{\text{1. LiAlH}_4} \quad R-CH_2-NH_2
$$

$$
\underset{\substack{R}}{\overset{\substack{O \\ \parallel}}{C}}\!\!-\!\!NHR' \quad \xrightarrow[\text{2. H}_2\text{O}]{\text{1. LiAlH}_4} \quad R-CH_2-NHR'
$$

$$
\underset{\substack{R}}{\overset{\substack{O \\ \parallel}}{C}}\!\!-\!\!\underset{\substack{| \\ R''}}{N}R' \quad \xrightarrow[\text{2. H}_2\text{O}]{\text{1. LiAlH}_4} \quad R-CH_2-\underset{\substack{| \\ R''}}{N}-R'
$$

4. Reaction of an *aldehyde* or a *ketone* with hydrogen cyanide forms a cyanohydrin (Section 18.7).

$$
\underset{\substack{R \quad R}}{\overset{\substack{O \\ \parallel}}{C}} \quad \xrightarrow[\text{HCl}]{^-C\equiv N} \quad R-\underset{\substack{| \\ R}}{\overset{\substack{OH \\ |}}{C}}-C\equiv N
$$

5. Reactions of *aldehydes* and *ketones* with amines and amine derivatives (Section 18.8)
  a. Reaction with a *primary amine* forms an imine.

$$
\underset{\substack{R}}{\overset{\substack{R'}}{C}}\!\!=\!\!O \;+\; H_2NZ \quad \underset{\text{acid}}{\overset{\text{trace}}{\rightleftharpoons}} \quad \underset{\substack{R}}{\overset{\substack{R'}}{C}}\!\!=\!\!NZ \;+\; H_2O
$$

When Z is an alkyl substituent, the product is an imine; Z can also be OH, NH_2, NHC_6H_5, $NHC_6H_3(NO_2)_2$, or $NHCONH_2$.

  b. The Wolff–Kishner reduction converts a carbonyl group to a methylene group.

$$
\underset{\substack{R \quad R'}}{\overset{\substack{O \\ \parallel}}{C}} \quad \xrightarrow[\text{HO}^-, \Delta]{\text{NH}_2\text{NH}_2} \quad R-CH_2-R'
$$

  c. Reaction with a *secondary amine* forms an enamine.

$$
\underset{\substack{-CH}}{\overset{\substack{R}}{C}}\!\!=\!\!O \;+\; R'NHR'' \quad \underset{\text{acid}}{\overset{\text{trace}}{\rightleftharpoons}} \quad \underset{\substack{-C}}{\overset{\substack{R}}{C}}\!\!=\!\!\underset{\substack{R''}}{\overset{\substack{R'}}{N}} \;+\; H_2O
$$

6. Reaction of an *aldehyde* or a *ketone* with water forms a hydrate (Section 18.9).

$$
\underset{\substack{R \quad R'}}{\overset{\substack{O \\ \parallel}}{C}} \;+\; H_2O \quad \rightleftharpoons[\text{HCl}] \quad R-\underset{\substack{| \\ OH}}{\overset{\substack{OH \\ |}}{C}}-R'
$$

7. Reaction of an *aldehyde* or a *ketone* with excess alcohol forms an acetal or a ketal (Section 18.10).

$$
\underset{\substack{R \quad R'}}{\overset{\substack{O \\ \parallel}}{C}} \;+\; 2\,R''OH \quad \overset{\text{HCl}}{\rightleftharpoons} \quad R-\underset{\substack{| \\ OR''}}{\overset{\substack{OH \\ |}}{C}}-R' \quad \rightleftharpoons \quad R-\underset{\substack{| \\ OR''}}{\overset{\substack{OR'' \\ |}}{C}}-R' \;+\; H_2O
$$

8. Protecting groups (Section 18.11)

a. *Aldehydes* and *ketones* can be protected by being converted to acetals.

$$\underset{R}{\overset{O}{\underset{}{\parallel}}}\overset{}{C}\underset{R}{} \ + \ HO\diagup\diagdown OH \ \overset{HCl}{\rightleftharpoons} \ \underset{R}{\overset{O\diagdown\diagup O}{C}}\underset{R}{} \ + \ H_2O$$

b. The OH group of an *alcohol* can be protected by being converted to a TMS ether.

$$R-OH \ + \ (CH_3)_3SiCl \ \xrightarrow{(CH_3CH_2)_3N} \ R-OSi(CH_3)_3$$

c. The OH group of a *carboxylic acid* can be protected by being converted to an ester.

$$\underset{R}{\overset{O}{\underset{}{\parallel}}}\overset{}{C}\underset{OH}{} \ + \ \underset{excess}{CH_3OH} \ \overset{HCl}{\rightleftharpoons} \ \underset{R}{\overset{O}{\underset{}{\parallel}}}\overset{}{C}\underset{OCH_3}{} \ + \ H_2O$$

d. An *amino group* can be protected by being converted to an amide.

$$2 \ R'NH_2 \ + \ \underset{R}{\overset{O}{\underset{}{\parallel}}}\overset{}{C}\underset{Cl}{} \ \longrightarrow \ \underset{R}{\overset{O}{\underset{}{\parallel}}}\overset{}{C}\underset{NHR'}{} \ + \ R\overset{+}{N}H_3 \ Cl^-$$

9. Reaction of an *aldehyde* or a *ketone* with a thiol forms a thioacetal or a thioketal (Section 18.12).

$$\underset{R}{\overset{O}{\underset{}{\parallel}}}\overset{}{C}\underset{R'}{} \ + \ 2 \ R''SH \ \overset{HCl}{\rightleftharpoons} \ R-\overset{SR''}{\underset{SR''}{\overset{|}{\underset{|}{C}}}}-R' \ + \ H_2O$$

10. Desulfurization of a *thioacetal* or a *thioketal* forms an alkane (Section 18.12).

$$R-\overset{SR''}{\underset{SR''}{\overset{|}{\underset{|}{C}}}}-R' \ \xrightarrow[Raney \ Ni]{H_2} \ R-CH_2-R'$$

11. Reaction of an *aldehyde* or a *ketone* with a phosphonium ylide (a Wittig reaction) forms an alkene (Section 18.13).

$$\underset{R'}{\overset{R}{\diagdown}}C{=}O \ + \ (C_6H_5)_3P{=}C\underset{R}{\overset{R}{\diagup}} \ \longrightarrow \ \underset{R'}{\overset{R}{\diagdown}}C{=}C\underset{R}{\overset{R}{\diagup}} \ + \ (C_6H_5)_3P{=}O$$

12. Reaction of an *α,β-unsaturated aldehyde* or a *ketone* with a nucleophile (Section 18.16)

$$RCH{=}CH\overset{O}{\overset{\parallel}{C}}R' \ + \ NuH \ \longrightarrow \ RCH{=}CH-\overset{OH}{\underset{Nu}{\overset{|}{\underset{|}{C}}}}-R \ + \ RCHCH_2\overset{O}{\overset{\parallel}{C}}R'$$

$$\underset{\text{direct addition}}{} \qquad \underset{\text{conjugate addition}}{\underset{Nu}{}}$$

Nucleophiles that are weak bases ($^-$C≡N, RSH, RNH$_2$, Br$^-$) form conjugate addition products. Nucleophiles that are strong bases (RLi, RMgBr, H$^-$) form direct addition products with reactive carbonyl groups and conjugate addition products with less reactive carbonyl groups. Gilman (R$_2$CuLi) reagents form conjugate addition products.

13. Reaction of an *α,β-unsaturated carboxylic acid derivative* with a nucleophile (Section 18.17)

$$RCH{=}CH-\overset{\overset{\displaystyle O}{\|}}{C}-Cl + NuH \longrightarrow RCH{=}CH-\overset{\overset{\displaystyle O}{\|}}{C}-Nu + HCl$$

**nucleophilic
addition-elimination**

$$RCH{=}CH-\overset{\overset{\displaystyle O}{\|}}{C}-NHR + NuH \longrightarrow R\underset{\underset{\displaystyle Nu}{|}}{CH}CH_2-\overset{\overset{\displaystyle O}{\|}}{C}-NHR$$

conjugate addition

Nucleophiles form nucleophilic addition–elimination products with reactive carbonyl groups and conjugate addition products with less reactive carbonyl groups.

KEY TERMS

acetal (p. 798)
aldehyde (p. 771)
Borch reaction (p. 795)
conjugate addition (p. 812)
cyanohydrin (p. 787)
deoxygenation (p. 792)
direct addition (p. 812)
disconnection (p. 809)
enamine (p. 793)
gem-diol (p. 796)
hemiacetal (p. 798)

hemiketal (p. 799)
hydrate (p. 796)
hydrazone (p. 791)
imine (p. 789)
ketal (p. 799)
ketone (p. 771)
nucleophilic addition reaction (p. 777)
nucleophilic addition–elimination
   reaction (p. 777)
oxime (p. 791)
pH–rate profile (p. 790)

prochiral carbonyl carbon (p. 808)
protecting group (p. 802)
Re and *Si* faces (p. 808)
reduction reaction (p. 783)
reductive amination (p. 795)
Schiff base (p. 789)
semicarbazone (p. 791)
synthetic equivalent (p. 809)
synthon (p. 809)
Wittig reaction (p. 805)
ylide (p. 805)

PROBLEMS

48. Draw the structure for each of the following:
  a. isobutyraldehyde
  b. 4-hexenal
  c. diisopentyl ketone
  d. 3-methylcyclohexanone
  e. 2,4-pentanedione
  f. 4-bromo-3-heptanone
  g. γ-bromocaproaldehyde
  h. 2-ethylcyclopentanecarbaldehyde
  i. 4-methyl-5-oxohexanal
  j. benzene-1,3-dicarbaldehyde

49. Give the products of the following reactions:

a.
$$CH_3CH_2-\overset{\overset{\displaystyle O}{\|}}{C}-H + CH_3CH_2OH \xrightarrow{\text{HCl}}$$
excess

b.
$$\text{(phenyl)}-\overset{\overset{\displaystyle O}{\|}}{C}-CH_2CH_3 + NH_2NH_2 \xrightarrow{\substack{\text{trace} \\ \text{acid}}}$$

c.
$$\text{(phenyl)}-\overset{\overset{\displaystyle O}{\|}}{C}-CH_2CH_3 + NH_2NH_2 \xrightarrow[\Delta]{HO^-}$$

d.
$$CH_3CH_2-\overset{\overset{\displaystyle O}{\|}}{C}-CH_3 \xrightarrow{\substack{\text{1. NaBH}_4 \\ \text{2. H}_3O^+}}$$

e.
$$CH_3CH_2-\overset{\overset{\displaystyle O}{\|}}{C}-CH_2CH_3 + NaC{\equiv}N \xrightarrow{\text{HCl}}$$
excess

f.
$$CH_3CH_2CH_2-\overset{\overset{\displaystyle O}{\|}}{C}-OCH_2CH_3 \xrightarrow{\substack{\text{1. LiAlH}_4 \\ \text{2. H}_3O^+}}$$

g.
$$CH_3CH_2CH_2-\overset{\overset{\displaystyle O}{\|}}{C}-CH_3 + HOCH_2CH_2OH \xrightarrow{\text{HCl}}$$

h.
$$\text{(cyclohexenone with CH}_3\text{)} + NaC{\equiv}N \xrightarrow{\text{HCl}}$$
excess

50. List the following compounds in order of decreasing reactivity toward nucleophilic attack:

51. a. Show the reagents required to form the primary alcohol.

b. Which of the reactions cannot be used for the synthesis of isobutyl alcohol?
c. Which of the reactions changes the carbon skeleton of the starting material?

52. Using cyclohexanone as the starting material, describe how each of the following compounds could be synthesized:

a. OH   **d.** NH₂   **g.** CH=CH₂

b.   **e.** CH₂NH₂   **h.** (show two methods)

c. Br   **f.** N(CH₃)₂   **i.** CH₂CH₃ (show two methods)

53. Propose a mechanism for the following reaction:

54. List the following compounds in order of decreasing K_{eq} for hydrate formation:

55. Fill in the boxes:

a. $CH_3OH \longrightarrow CH_3Br \longrightarrow \square \xrightarrow[2.]{1.} CH_3CH_2OH$

b. $CH_4 \longrightarrow CH_3Br \longrightarrow \square \xrightarrow[2.]{1.} CH_3CH_2CH_2OH$

56. Give the products of the following reactions:

a. 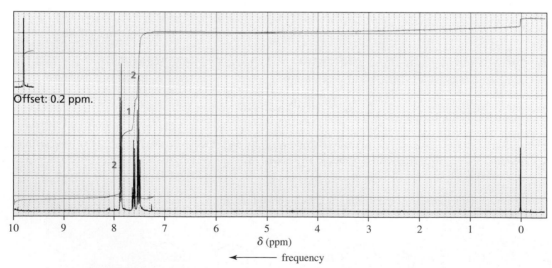C=NCH₂CH₃ + H₂O →(HCl) with CH₂CH₃ substituent

f. (pyrrolidinone) →(1. LiAlH₄ / 2. H₂O)

b. CH₃CH₂—C(=O)—CH₃ →(1. CH₃CH₂MgBr / 2. H₃O⁺)

g. (cyclohexanone) + CH₃CH₂NH₂ →(trace acid)

c. (cyclopentanone) + (C₆H₅)₃P=CHCH₃ →

h. (cyclohexanone) + (CH₃CH₂)₂NH →(trace acid)

d. CH₃CH₂—C(=O)—OCH₃ →(1. CH₃CH₂MgBr excess / 2. H₃O⁺)

i. CH₂=CH—C(=O)—OCH₃ + CH₃NH₂ →

e. (phenyl vinyl ketone) + CH₃OH →(HCl)

j. 2 CH₂=CH—C(=O)—OCH₃ + CH₃NH₂ →

57. Thiols can be prepared from the reaction of thiourea with an alkyl halide, followed by hydroxide-ion-promoted hydrolysis.

H₂N—C(=S)—NH₂ →(1. CH₃CH₂Br / 2. HO⁻, H₂O) H₂N—C(=O)—NH₂ + CH₃CH₂SH
thiourea   urea   ethanethiol

a. Propose a mechanism for the reaction.   **b.** What thiol would be formed if the alkyl halide employed were pentyl bromide?

58. The only organic compound obtained when compound Z undergoes the following sequence of reactions gives the ¹H NMR spectrum shown. Identify compound Z.

Compound Z →(1. phenylmagnesium bromide / 2. H₃O⁺) →(MnO₂ / Δ)

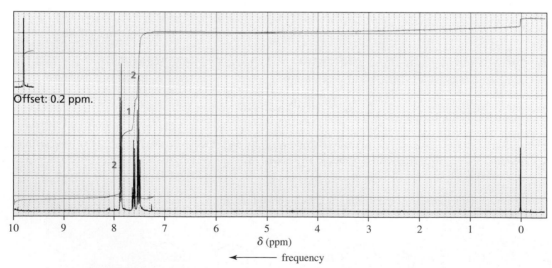

δ (ppm)

← frequency

59. Propose a mechanism for each of the following reactions:

a. (bicyclic enamine) →(HCl / H₂O) cyclohexanone with CH₂CH₂CH₂N⁺H₃ substituent

c. (dihydropyran) + CH₃CH₂OH →(HCl) (tetrahydropyran-OCH₂CH₃)

(methoxy cyclohexene, OCH₃) →(HCl / H₂O) (cyclohexanone, =O)

60. How many signals would the product of the following reaction show in the following spectra?
   a. its ^{1}H NMR spectrum
   b. its ^{13}C NMR spectrum

1. excess CH₃MgBr
2. H₃O⁺

61. Fill in the boxes:

62. How could you convert N-methylbenzamide into the following compounds?
   a. N-methylbenzylamine
   b. benzoic acid
   c. methyl benzoate
   d. benzyl alcohol

63. Give the products of the following rections. Show all stereoisomers that are formed.

   a. 1. (CH₃)₂CuLi 2. EtOH

   b. 1. CH₃MgBr 2. H₃O⁺

   c. + trace acid

   d. 1. NaBH₄ 2. H₃O⁺

64. List three different sets of reagents (each set consisting of a carbonyl compound and a Grignard reagent) that could be used to prepare each of the following tertiary alcohols:

   a. CH₃CH₂CCH₂CH₂CH₃ (OH)

   b. CH₃CH₂CCH₂CH₂CH₃ (OH, CH₂CH₃)

65. Give the product of the reaction of 3-methyl-2-cyclohexenone with each of the following reagents:

   a. CH₃MgBr followed by H₃O⁺
   b. excess NaCN, HCl
   c. H₂, Pd/C
   d. HBr
   e. (CH₃CH₂)₂CuLi followed by H₃O⁺
   f. CH₃CH₂SH

66. Norlutin and Enovid are ketones that suppress ovulation. Consequently, they have been used clinically as contraceptives. For which of these compounds would you expect the infrared carbonyl absorption (C=O stretch) to be at a higher frequency? Explain.

Norlutin®   Enovid®

67. Give the product of each of the following reactions:

   a. , HCl

   b. HO   OH , HCl

68. Give the product of each of the following reactions:

69. Propose a reasonable mechanism for each of the following reactions:

70. A compound gives the following IR spectrum. Upon reaction with sodium borohydride followed by acidification, it forms the product with the following ^{1}H NMR spectrum. Identify the compounds.

71. a. Propose a mechanism for the following reaction:

$$CH_2=CHCHC\equiv N \xrightarrow[H_2O]{HO^-} N\equiv CCH_2CH_2CH$$

with OH on the middle carbon of the reactant and O (double bond) on the product carbonyl.

b. What is the product of the following reaction?

$$CH_3CCH=CH_2 \xrightarrow[H_2O]{HO^-}$$

with OH and C≡N substituents.

72. Unlike a phosphonium ylide, which reacts with an aldehyde or a ketone to form an alkene, a sulfonium ylide reacts with an aldehyde or a ketone to form an epoxide. Explain why one ylide forms an alkene, whereas the other forms an epoxide.

$$CH_3CH_2\overset{\overset{\displaystyle O}{\|}}{C}H + (CH_3)_2S{=}CH_2 \longrightarrow CH_3CH_2\overset{\overset{\displaystyle O}{\diagup\backslash}}{CH}{-}CH_2 + CH_3SCH_3$$

73. Indicate how the following compounds could be prepared from the given starting materials:

a.

b.

c.

d.

e.

74. Propose a reasonable mechanism for each of the following reactions:

a.

b.

75. a. In aqueous solution, D-glucose exists in equilibrium with two six-membered ring compounds. Draw the structures of these compounds.

$$\begin{array}{c}HC{=}O\\ H{-}\!\!-OH\\ HO{-}\!\!-H\\ H{-}\!\!-OH\\ H{-}\!\!-OH\\ CH_2OH\end{array}$$

D-glucose

b. Which of the six-membered ring compounds will be present in greater amount?

76. The ^{1}H NMR spectrum of the alkyl bromide used to make the ylide to form a compound with molecular formula $C_{11}H_{14}$ is shown below. What product is obtained from the Wittig reaction?

δ (ppm)

⟵ frequency

77. In the presence of an acid catalyst, acetaldehyde forms a trimer known as paraldehyde. Because it induces sleep when it is administered to animals in large doses, paraldehyde is used as a sedative or hypnotic. Propose a mechanism for the formation of paraldehyde.

paraldehyde

78. The addition of hydrogen cyanide to benzaldehyde forms a compound called mandelonitrile. (*R*)-Mandelonitrile also is formed from the hydrolysis of amygdalin, a compound found in the pits of peaches and apricots. Amygdalin is the principal constituent of laetrile, a compound that was once highly touted as a treatment for cancer but subsequently found to be ineffective. Is (*R*)-mandelonitrile formed by attack of cyanide ion on the *Re* face or the *Si* face of benzaldehyde?

79. What carbonyl compound and what phosphonium ylide are needed to synthesize the following compounds?

a. ⟨benzene⟩—CH=CHCH₂CH₂CH₃

b. ⟨cyclopentane with ⟩=CHCH₂CH₃

c. ⟨benzene⟩—CH=CH—⟨benzene⟩

d. ⟨cyclohexane⟩=CH₂

80. Identify compounds A and B:

$$A \xrightarrow[\text{2. H}_3\text{O}^+]{\text{1. (CH}_2\text{=CH)}_2\text{CuLi}} B \xrightarrow[\text{2. H}_3\text{O}^+]{\text{1. CH}_3\text{Li}} CH_2=CHCCH_2CHCH_3$$

with substituents CH₃ OH on the product and CH₃ below.

81. Propose a reasonable mechanism for each of the following reactions:

a. ⟨reaction scheme with HCl, Δ⟩

b. ⟨reaction scheme with trace acid⟩

82. A compound reacts with methylmagnesium bromide followed by acidification to form the product with the following ¹H NMR spectrum. Identify the compound.

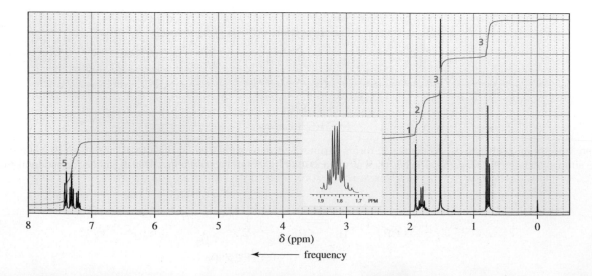

83. Show how each of the following compounds can be prepared from the given starting material. In each case, you will need to use a protecting group.

a. CH$_3$CHCH$_2$COCH$_3$ $\longrightarrow$ CH$_3$CHCH$_2$CCH$_3$
       | | |
       OH   OH OH

b.

c.

84. When a cyclic ketone reacts with diazomethane, the next larger cyclic ketone is formed. This is called a ring expansion reaction. Provide a mechanism for this reaction.

cyclohexanone   diazomethane   cycloheptanone

85. Describe how 1-ethylcyclohexanol can be prepared from cyclohexane. You can use any inorganic reagents, solvents, and any organic reagents provided they contain no more than two carbons.

86. The pK_a values of oxaloacetic acid are 2.22 and 3.98.

oxaloacetic acid

a. Which carboxyl group is more acidic?
b. The amount of hydrate present in an aqueous solution of oxaloacetic acid depends on the pH of the solution: 95% at pH 0, 81% at pH 1.3, 35% at pH 3.1, 13% at pH 4.7, 6% at pH 6.7, and 6% at pH 12.7. Explain this pH dependence.

87. The *Horner-Wardsworth-Emmons reaction* is a variation of a Wittig reaction in which a phosphonate-stabilized carbanion is used instead of a phosphonium ylide.

Et = CH$_3$CH$_2$

The phosphonate-stabilized carbanion is prepared from an appropriate alkyl halide. This is called the *Arbuzov reaction*.

(EtO)$_3$P: + CH$_3$CHCH$_3$ $\longrightarrow$ CH$_3$CH—P(OEt)$_2$ $\xrightarrow[\text{base}]{\text{strong}}$ CH$_3$C̈—P(OEt)$_2$
               | | |
              Br   CH$_3$ CH$_3$
                        + CH$_3$CH$_2$Br

Because the Arbuzov reaction can be carried out with an α-bromo ketone or an α-bromo ester (in which case it is called a *Perkow reaction*), it provides a way to synthesize α,β-unsaturated ketones and esters.

(EtO)$_3$P: + Br—CH$_2$CR $\longrightarrow$ (EtO)$_2$P—CH$_2$CR $\xrightarrow[\text{base}]{\text{strong}}$ (EtO)$_2$P—C̈HCR
                        + CH$_3$CH$_2$Br

a. Propose a mechanism for the Arbuzov reaction.
b. Propose a mechanism for the Horner-Wardsworth-Emmons reaction.
c. Show how the following compounds can be prepared from the given starting material:

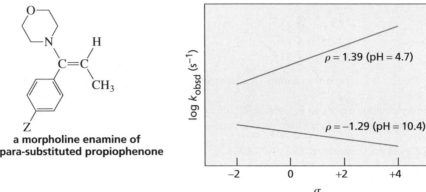

88. In order to solve this problem, you must read the description of the Hammett σ, ρ treatment given in Chapter 17, Problem 93. When the rate constants for the hydrolysis of several morpholine enamines of para-substituted propiophenones are determined at pH 4.7, the ρ value is positive; however, when the rates of hydrolysis are determined at pH 10.4, the ρ value is negative.
a. What is the rate-determining step of the hydrolysis reaction when it is carried out in a basic solution?
b. What is the rate-determining step of the hydrolysis reaction when it is carried out in an acidic solution?

**a morpholine enamine of
a para-substituted propiophenone**

$\rho = 1.39$ (pH = 4.7)

$\rho = -1.29$ (pH = 10.4)

log k_{obsd} (s^{-1})

σ

89. Describe how 3-methyl-1-phenyl-3-pentanol can be prepared from benzene. You can use any inorganic reagents and solvents, and any organic reagents provided they contain no more than two carbons.

90. Propose a mechanism for each of the following reactions:

a.

$\xrightarrow[\text{H}_2\text{O}]{\text{HCl}}$

b.

$\xrightarrow[\text{H}_2\text{O}]{\text{HCl}}$ (HOCH$_2$CH$_2$CH$_2$)$_2$CH

c. + CH$_3$CH$_2$SH $\longrightarrow$

91. Tyramine is an alkaloid found in mistletoe, ripe cheese, and putrefied animal tissue. Dopamine is a neurotransmitter involved in the regulation of the central nervous system.

HO—⟨ ⟩—CH$_2$CH$_2$NH$_2$

tyramine

HO—⟨ ⟩—CH$_2$CH$_2$NH$_2$

dopamine

a. How can tyramine be prepared from β-phenylethylamine?
b. How can dopamine be prepared from tyramine?
c. Give two ways to prepare β-phenylethylamine from β-phenylethyl chloride.
d. How can β-phenylethylamine be prepared from benzyl chloride?
e. How can β-phenylethylamine be prepared from benzaldehyde?

19

Carbonyl Compounds III

Reactions at the α-Carbon

acetyl-CoA

WHEN WE LOOKED AT THE REACTIVITY OF CARBONYL COMPOUNDS IN CHAPTERS 17 and 18, we saw that their site of reactivity is the partially positively charged carbonyl carbon, which is attacked by nucleophiles.

Aldehydes, ketones, esters, and *N,N*-disubstituted amides have a second site of reactivity. A hydrogen bonded to *a carbon adjacent to a carbonyl carbon* is sufficiently acidic to be removed by a strong base. The carbon adjacent to a carbonyl carbon is called an **α-carbon**. A hydrogen bonded to an α-carbon is therefore called an **α-hydrogen**.

In Section 19.1, you will find out why a hydrogen bonded to a carbon adjacent to a carbonyl carbon is more acidic than hydrogens attached to other sp^3 carbons, and you will look at some reactions that result from this acidity. Later in the chapter, you will see that a proton is not the only substituent that can be removed from an α-carbon: a carboxyl group bonded to an α-carbon can be removed as CO_2. At the end of the chapter, you will be introduced to some synthetic schemes that rely on the ability to remove protons and carboxyl groups from α-carbons.

19.1 THE ACIDITY OF AN α-HYDROGEN

Hydrogen and carbon have similar electronegativities, which means that the two atoms share the electrons bonding them together almost equally. Consequently, a hydrogen bonded to a carbon is usually not acidic. This is particularly true for hydrogens bonded to sp^3 carbons because these carbons are the most similar to hydrogen in electronegativity (Section 6.10). For example, the pK_a value of ethane is greater than 60.

$$CH_3CH_3$$

$pK_a > 60$

A hydrogen bonded to an sp^3 carbon adjacent to a carbonyl carbon, however, is much more acidic than hydrogens bonded to other sp^3 carbons. For example, the pK_a value for dissociation of a proton from the α-carbon of an aldehyde or a ketone ranges from 16 to 20, and the pK_a value for dissociation of a proton from the α-carbon of an ester is about 25 (Table 19.1). Notice that, although an α-hydrogen is more acidic than most other carbon-bound hydrogens, it is less acidic than a hydrogen of water (pK_a 15.7). A compound that contains a relatively acidic hydrogen bonded to an sp^3 carbon is called a **carbon acid**.

Table 19.1	The pK_a Values of Some Carbon Acids		
	pK_a		pK_a

Table 19.1 — structures with pK_a values:

- $CH_2(H)C(=O)N(CH_3)_2$ — 30
- $CH_2(H)C(=O)OCH_2CH_3$ — 25
- $CH_2(H)C\equiv N$ — 25
- $CH_2(H)C(=O)CH_3$ — 20
- $CH_2(H)C(=O)H$ — 17
- $CH_3CH_2O C(=O) CH(H) C(=O) OCH_2CH_3$ — 13.3

- $N\equiv C CH(H) C\equiv N$ — 11.8
- $CH_3 C(=O) CH(H) C(=O) OCH_2CH_3$ — 10.7
- (phenyl) $C(=O) CH(H) C(=O) CH_3$ — 9.4
- $CH_3 C(=O) CH(H) C(=O) CH_3$ — 8.9
- $CH_3CH(H)NO_2$ — 8.6
- $CH_3 C(=O) CH(H) C(=O) H$ — 5.9
- $O_2N CH(H) NO_2$ — 3.6

The α-hydrogen of a ketone or an aldehyde is more acidic than the α-hydrogen of an ester.

Why is a hydrogen bonded to an sp^3 carbon adjacent to a carbonyl carbon so much more acidic than hydrogens bonded to other sp^3 carbons? An α-hydrogen is more acidic because the base formed when a proton is removed from an α-carbon is relatively stable. As we have seen, the more stable the base, the stronger is its conjugate acid (Section 1.18).

Why is the base formed by removing a proton from an α-carbon more stable than bases formed by removing a proton from other sp^3 carbons? When a proton is removed from ethane, the electrons left behind reside solely on a carbon. Because carbon is not very electronegative, a carbanion is unstable. As a result, the pK_a of its conjugate acid is very high.

In contrast, when a proton is removed from a carbon adjacent to a carbonyl carbon, two factors combine to increase the stability of the base that is formed. First, the electrons left behind when the proton is removed are delocalized, and electron delocalization increases stability (Section 7.6). More importantly, the electrons are delocalized onto an oxygen, an atom that is better able to accommodate them because it is more electronegative than carbon.

PROBLEM 1♦

Explain why the pK_a of a hydrogen bonded to the sp^3 carbon of propene is greater ($pK_a = 42$) than that of any of the carbon acids listed in Table 19.1 but is less than the pK_a of an alkane.

Now we can understand why aldehydes and ketones ($pK_a = 16 - 20$) are more acidic than esters ($pK_a = 25$). The electrons left behind when a proton is removed from the α-carbon of an ester are not as readily delocalized onto the carbonyl oxygen as they would be in an aldehyde or a ketone. This is because the oxygen of the OR group of the ester also has a lone pair that can be delocalized onto the carbonyl oxygen. Thus, the two pairs of electrons compete for delocalization onto the same oxygen.

Nitroalkanes, nitriles, and *N,N*-disubstituted amides also have a relatively acidic α-hydrogen (Table 19.1) because in each case the electrons left behind when the proton is removed can be delocalized onto an atom that is more electronegative than carbon.

$$CH_3CH_2NO_2 \qquad CH_3CH_2C{\equiv}N$$

nitroethane
pK_a = 8.6

propanenitrile
pK_a = 26

N,N-**dimethylacetamide**
pK_a = 30

If the α-carbon is *between* two carbonyl groups, the acidity of an α-hydrogen is even greater (Table 19.1). For example, the pK_a value for dissociation of a proton from the α-carbon of 2,4-pentanedione, a compound with an α-carbon between two ketone carbonyl groups, is 8.9; the pK_a value for dissociation of a proton from the α-carbon of ethyl 3-oxobutyrate, a compound with an α-carbon between a ketone carbonyl group and an ester carbonyl group, is 10.7. Ethyl 3-oxobutyrate is classified as a **β-keto ester** because the ester has a carbonyl group at the β-position; 2,4-pentanedione is a **β-diketone**.

pK_a = 8.9

pK_a = 10.7

2,4-pentanedione
acetylacetone
a β-diketone

ethyl 3-oxobutyrate
ethyl acetoacetate
a β-keto ester

The acidity of α-hydrogens bonded to carbons flanked by two carbonyl groups increases because the electrons left behind when the proton is removed can be delocalized onto *two* oxygen atoms. β-Diketones have lower pK_a values than β-keto esters because, as we have seen, electrons are more readily delocalized onto the carbonyl oxygen of a ketone than they are onto the carbonyl oxygen of an ester.

resonance contributors for the 2,4-pentanedione anion

2,4-pentanedione

PROBLEM 2◆

Give an example of each of the following:

a. a β-keto nitrile   **b.** a β-diester   **c.** a β-keto aldehyde

---

PROBLEM-SOLVING STRATEGY

The Acid–Base Behavior of a Carbonyl Compound

Explain why HO⁻ cannot remove a proton from the α-carbon of a carboxylic acid.

Finding that HO⁻ cannot remove a proton from the α-carbon of a carboxylic acid suggests that HO⁻ reacts with another portion of the molecule more rapidly. Because the proton on the carboxyl group is more acidic (pK_a ~ 5) than the proton on the α-carbon, we can conclude that HO⁻ removes a proton from the carboxyl group rather than from the α-carbon.

Now continue on to Problem 3.

PROBLEM 3♦

Explain why a proton can be removed from the α-carbon of *N,N*-dimethylethanamide but not from the α-carbon of either *N*-methylethanamide or ethanamide.

N,N-dimethylethanamide   *N*-methylethanamide   ethanamide

PROBLEM 4♦

Explain why an *N,N*-disubstituted amide is less acidic than an ester.

PROBLEM 5♦

List the compounds in each of the following groups in order of decreasing acidity:

a. $CH_2{=}CH_2$ CH_3CH_3 $HC{\equiv}CH$

b.

c.

19.2 KETO–ENOL TAUTOMERS

A ketone exists in equilibrium with its enol tautomer. Recall that **tautomers** are isomers that are in rapid equilibrium (Section 6.7). Keto–enol tautomers differ in the location of a double bond and a hydrogen.

For most ketones, the **enol tautomer** is much less stable than the **keto tautomer**. For example, an aqueous solution of acetone exists as an equilibrium mixture of more than 99.9% keto tautomer and less than 0.1% enol tautomer.

The fraction of the enol tautomer in an aqueous solution is considerably greater for a β-diketone because the enol tautomer is stabilized both by intramolecular hydrogen bonding and by conjugation of the carbon–carbon double bond with the second carbonyl group.

Phenol is unusual in that its enol tautomer is *more* stable than its keto tautomer because the enol tautomer is aromatic, but the keto tautomer is not.

PROBLEM 6

Explain why 92% of 2,4-pentanedione exists as the enol tautomer in hexane but only 15% of this compound exists as the enol tautomer in water.

19.3 KETO–ENOL INTERCONVERSION

Now that we know that a hydrogen bonded to a carbon adjacent to a carbonyl carbon is somewhat acidic, we can understand why keto and enol tautomers interconvert as we first saw in Chapter 6. The interconversion of the keto and enol tautomers is called **keto–enol interconversion**, **keto–enol tautomerization**, or **enolization**. The interconversion can be catalyzed by either a base or an acid. The mechanism for base-catalyzed keto–enol interconversion is shown below.

MECHANISM FOR BASE-CATALYZED KETO–ENOL INTERCONVERSION

- Hydroxide ion removes a proton from the α-carbon of the keto tautomer, forming an anion called an **enolate ion**. The enolate ion has two resonance contributors.
- Protonation on oxygen forms the enol tautomer, whereas protonation on the α-carbon re-forms the keto tautomer.

The mechanism for acid-catalyzed keto–enol interconversion is shown below.

MECHANISM FOR ACID-CATALYZED KETO–ENOL INTERCONVERSION

keto tautomer

enol tautomer

removal of a proton
from the α-carbon

- The acid protonates the carbonyl oxygen of the keto tautomer.
- Water removes a proton from the α-carbon, forming the enol tautomer.

Notice that the steps are reversed in the base- and acid-catalyzed reactions. In the base-catalyzed reaction, the base removes a proton from an α-carbon in the first step and the oxygen is protonated in the second step. In the acid-catalyzed reaction, the oxygen is protonated in the first step and the proton is removed from the α-carbon in the second step. Notice also that the catalyst is regenerated in both the acid- and base-catalyzed reactions.

PROBLEM 7♦

Give the relative concentrations of enol and enolate ion in a solution of pH = 8, if the enol has a pK_a value of

a. 20   **b.** 16   **c.** 10

PROBLEM 8♦

Draw the enol tautomers for each of the following compounds. For compounds that have more than one enol tautomer, indicate which one is more stable.

19.4 HOW ENOLATE IONS AND ENOLS REACT

The resonance contributors of the enolate ion show that it has two electron-rich sites: the α-carbon and the oxygen. The resonance contributor with the negatively charged oxygen makes the greater contribution to the hybrid (Section 7.5). The enolate ion is an example of an *ambident nucleophile* (*ambi* is Latin for "both"; *dent* is Latin for "teeth"). An **ambident nucleophile** is a nucleophile with two nucleophilic sites ("two teeth").

electron-rich oxygen

electron-rich α-carbon

resonance contributors of an enolate ion

Which nucleophilic site (C or O) reacts with an electrophile depends on the electrophile and on the reaction conditions. Protonation occurs preferentially on oxygen (the kinetic product), because of the greater concentration of negative charge on the more electronegative oxygen atom. The protonation reaction is reversible, so the ketone (the thermodynamic product) predominates at equilibrium (Section 18.16).

When the electrophile is something other than a proton, carbon is more likely to be the nucleophile because carbon is a better nucleophile than oxygen. The mechanism for the formation of an enolate ion and its subsequent reaction with an electrophile is shown below.

MECHANISM FOR BASE-CATALYZED α-SUBSTITUTION

- A base removes a proton from the α-carbon, forming an enolate ion.
- The enolate ion reacts with an electrophile.

The overall reaction is an **α-substitution reaction**; one electrophile (E⁺) is substituted for another (H⁺) at the α-carbon.

The resonance contributors of the enol show that it too has two electron-rich sites: the α-carbon and the oxygen.

resonance contributors of an enol

The mechanism for the formation of an enol and its subsequent reaction with an electrophile is shown below.

MECHANISM FOR ACID-CATALYZED α-SUBSTITUTION

- The acid protonates the oxygen, the most electron-dense atom in the molecule.
- Water removes a proton from the α-carbon.
- The enol reacts with an electrophile.

In summary, a carbonyl compound with an α-hydrogen can undergo a substitution reaction at the α-carbon. The substitution reaction can be catalyzed by a base (forming an enolate ion) or by an acid (forming an enol). As various α-substitution reactions are discussed in this chapter, notice that they all follow one of the two mechanisms shown above. The reactions differ only in the nature of the electrophile.

Notice the similarity between keto–enol interconversion and α-substitution. Actually, keto–enol interconversion is an α-substitution reaction in which hydrogen serves as both the electrophile that is removed from the α-carbon and the electrophile that is added to the α-carbon when the enol or enolate ion reverts back to the keto tautomer.

PROBLEM 9

When a dilute solution of acetaldehyde is shaken in NaOD in D_2O, explain why the methyl hydrogens are exchanged with deuterium but the aldehyde hydrogen (the one attached to the carbonyl carbon) is not.

19.5 HALOGENATION OF THE α-CARBON OF ALDEHYDES AND KETONES

When Br_2, Cl_2, or I_2 is added to a solution of an aldehyde or a ketone, a halogen replaces *one or more* of the α-hydrogens of the carbonyl compound.

Acid-Catalyzed Halogenation

In the acid-catalyzed reaction, the halogen replaces *one* of the α-hydrogens:

Under acidic conditions, one α-hydrogen is substituted for a halogen.

The mechanism for the reaction is shown below.

MECHANISM FOR ACID-CATALYZED HALOGENATION

- The carbonyl oxygen is protonated.
- Water removes a proton from the α-carbon, forming an enol.
- The enol reacts with an electrophilic halogen.
- The very acidic protonated carbonyl group loses a proton.

Base-Promoted Halogenation

When excess Br_2, Cl_2, or I_2 is added to a *basic* solution of an aldehyde or a ketone, the halogen replaces *all* the α-hydrogens.

Under basic conditions, all the α-hydrogens are substituted for halogens.

The mechanism for the reaction is shown below.

MECHANISM FOR BASE-PROMOTED HALOGENATION

- Hydroxide ion removes a proton from the α-carbon, forming an enolate ion.
- The enolate ion reacts with the electrophilic halogen.

These two steps are repeated until all the α-hydrogens are replaced by the halogen. Each successive halogenation is *more rapid* than the previous one because the electron-withdrawing halogen—in this case, bromine—increases the acidity of the remaining α-hydrogens. This is why *all* the α-hydrogens are replaced by bromines.

Under acidic conditions, on the other hand, each successive halogenation is *slower* than the previous one because the electron-withdrawing bromine decreases the basicity of the carbonyl oxygen, thereby making protonation of the carbonyl oxygen less favorable.

The Haloform Reaction

In the presence of excess base and excess halogen, a methyl ketone is converted into a carboxylate ion.

The mechanism for the haloform reaction is shown below.

MECHANISM FOR THE HALOFORM REACTION

- All the hydrogens of the methyl group are replaced by halogens, following the mechanism for base-promoted halogenation. The product is a trihalo-substituted ketone.

- Hydroxide ion attacks the carbonyl carbon of the trihalo-substituted ketone.

- Because the trihalomethyl ion is a weaker base than hydroxide ion (the pK_a of CHI_3 is 14; the pK_a of H_2O is 15.7), the trihalomethyl ion is the group more easily eliminated from the tetrahedral intermediate, forming a carboxylic acid.

- Transfer of a proton forms a carboxylate ion and iodoform.

The conversion of a methyl ketone to a carboxylate ion is called a **haloform reaction** because one of the products is haloform—either $CHCl_3$ (chloroform), $CHBr_3$ (bromoform), or CHI_3 (iodoform). Before spectroscopy became a routine analytical tool, the haloform reaction served as a test for methyl ketones: the formation of iodoform, a bright yellow compound, signaled that a methyl ketone was present.

PROBLEM 10♦

Why do only methyl ketones undergo the haloform reaction?

PROBLEM 11♦

Is the haloform reaction a base-catalyzed reaction, a hydroxide-ion catalyzed reaction, a hydroxide-ion promoted, or a base promoted reaction?

PROBLEM 12♦

A ketone undergoes acid-catalyzed bromination, acid-catalyzed chlorination, and acid-catalyzed deuterium exchange at the α-carbon, all at about the same rate. What does this tell you about the mechanism of these reactions?

19.6 HALOGENATION OF THE α-CARBON OF CARBOXYLIC ACIDS: THE HELL–VOLHARD–ZELINSKI REACTION

Carboxylic acids cannot undergo substitution reactions at the α-carbon, because a base will remove a proton from the OH group instead of from the α-carbon, since the OH group is more acidic. If, however, a carboxylic acid is treated with PBr_3 and Br_2, the α-carbon can be brominated. (Red phosphorus can be used in place of PBr_3 since P and excess Br_2 react to form PBr_3.) This halogenation reaction is called the **Hell–Volhard–Zelinski reaction** or, more simply, the **HVZ reaction**.

the HVZ reaction

You will see, when you examine its mechanism, that α-substitution occurs because an acyl bromide, rather than a carboxylic acid, is the compound that undergoes α-substitution.

Steps in the Hell–Volhard–Zelinski Reaction

- PBr$_3$ converts the carboxylic acid into an acyl bromide by the mechanism shown in Section 17.21.
- The acyl bromide is in equilibrium with its enol.
- Bromination of the enol forms the α-brominated acyl bromide, which is hydrolyzed to the α-brominated carboxylic acid.

19.7 α-HALOGENATED CARBONYL COMPOUNDS ARE USEFUL IN SYNTHESIS

You have seen that when a base removes a proton from an α-carbon of an aldehyde or a ketone, the α-carbon becomes *nucleophilic*—it reacts with electrophiles (Section 19.4).

Removing a proton from an α-carbon makes the α-carbon a nucleophile.

However, when the α-position is halogenated, the α-carbon becomes *electrophilic*—it reacts with nucleophiles. Now we know how to place both electrophiles and nucleophiles on an α-carbon.

Substituting a bromine for a hydrogen bonded to an α-carbon makes the α-carbon an electrophile.

α-Brominated carbonyl compounds are also useful to synthetic chemists because once a bromine has been introduced into the α-position of a carbonyl compound, an α,β-unsaturated carbonyl compound can be prepared by means of an (E2) elimination reaction.

an α,β-unsaturated
carbonyl compound

PROBLEM 13

How could you prepare the following compounds from the given starting materials?

a. CH_3CH_2—C(=O)—H → CH_3CH(—N(CH_3)_2)—C(=O)—H

b. CH_3CH_2—C(=O)—H → CH_3CH(—OH)—C(=O)—H

c. (cyclohexanone) → (2-methoxycyclohexanone, OCH_3)

d. (cyclohexanone) → (2-ethylcyclohexanone, CH_2CH_3)

chem Tutorial:
place α-Halogenated carbonyl
compounds in synthesis

why can't just have OH

PROBLEM 14

How could the following compounds be prepared from a carbonyl compound with no carbon–carbon double bonds?

a. (structure)

b. (structure)

PROBLEM 15

How could the following compounds be prepared from cyclohexanone?

a. (structure with C≡N)

b. (structure with C≡N)

c. (structure with SCH_3)

d. (structure with CH_3)

19.8 USING LDA TO FORM AN ENOLATE ION

The amount of carbonyl compound converted to an enolate ion depends on the pK_a of the carbonyl compound and the particular base used to remove the α-hydrogen. For example, when hydroxide ion or an alkoxide ion (the pK_a of their conjugate acids is ~15) is used to remove an α-hydrogen from cyclohexanone ($pK_a = 17$), only a small amount of the carbonyl compound is converted into the enolate ion because hydroxide ion is a weaker base than the base being formed. (Recall that the equilibrium of an acid–base reaction favors reaction of the strong acid and formation of the weak acid; see Section 1.20.)

$$ \text{(cyclohexanone)} + HO^- \rightleftharpoons \text{(enolate)} \longleftrightarrow \text{(enolate)} + H_2O $$

$pK_a = 17$ < 0.1% $pK_a = 15.7$

In contrast, when LDA (lithium diisopropylamide) (the pK_a of LDA's conjugate acid is ~35) is used to remove the α-hydrogen, essentially all the carbonyl compound is converted to the enolate ion because LDA is a much stronger base than the base being formed. Therefore, LDA is the base of choice for those reactions that require the carbonyl compound to be completely converted to an enolate ion before it reacts with an electrophile (Section 19.9).

$$ \text{(cyclohexanone)} + LDA \longrightarrow \text{(enolate)} \longleftrightarrow \text{(enolate)} + DIA $$

$pK_a = 17$ ~100% $pK_a = 35$

Using a nitrogen base to form an enolate ion can be a problem because a nitrogen base can also react as a nucleophile and attack the carbonyl carbon (Section 18.8). However, the two bulky alkyl substituents bonded to the nitrogen of LDA make it difficult for the nitrogen to get close enough to the carbonyl carbon to react with it. Consequently, LDA is a strong base but a poor nucleophile: it removes an α-hydrogen much faster than it attacks a carbonyl carbon. LDA is easily prepared by adding butyllithium to diisopropylamine (DIA) in THF at −78 °C. (Recall that −78 °C is the temperature of an acetone/dry ice bath.)

diisopropylamine
pK_a = 35

butyllithium

THF
−78 °C

lithium diisopropylamide
LDA

butane
pK_a > 60

19.9 ALKYLATING THE α-CARBON OF CARBONYL COMPOUNDS

Putting an alkyl group on the α-carbon of a carbonyl compound is an important reaction because it gives us another way to form a carbon–carbon bond. Alkylation is carried out by first removing a proton from the α-carbon with a strong base such as LDA and then adding the appropriate alkyl halide. Because the alkylation is an S_N2 reaction, it works best with methyl halides and primary alkyl halides (Section 8.2).

an S_N2 reaction

LDA/THF

CH_3CH_2—Br

CH_2CH_3

+ Br$^-$

It is important that a strong base such as LDA be used to form the enolate ion. If a weaker base such as hydroxide ion or an alkoxide ion is used, very little of the desired monoalkylated product will be obtained. We have seen that these weaker bases form only a small amount of enolate ion at equilibrium (Section 19.8). Therefore, after monoalkylation has occurred, there is still a lot of base present in solution, which can form an enolate ion from the monoalkyated ketone as well as from the unalkylated ketone. As a result, di-, tri-, and even tetra-alkylated products may be produced.

Enolate ions can be alkylated on the α-carbon.

1. HO$^-$
2. CH_3Br

CH_3

H_3C CH_3

CH_3
CH_3

H_3C CH_3
CH_3

H_3C CH_3
H_3C CH_3

Esters and nitriles can also be alkylated at the α-carbon. Aldehydes, however, give relatively poor yields of α-alkylated products (Section 19.12).

OCH_3

1. LDA/THF
2. CH_3I

CH_3

OCH_3

$CH_3CH_2CH_2C≡N$

1. LDA/THF
2. CH_3CH_2I

$CH_3CH_2CHC≡N$
CH_2CH_3

If the ketone is not symmetrical and has hydrogens on both α-carbons, two monoalky-lated products can be obtained because either α-carbon can be alkylated. For example, methylation of 2-methylcyclohexanone with one equivalent of methyl iodide forms both 2,6-dimethylcyclohexanone and 2,2-dimethylcyclohexanone. The relative amounts of the two products depend on the reaction conditions.

2,6-dimethylcyclohexanone   **2,2-dimethylcyclohexanone**

The enolate ion leading to 2,6-dimethylcyclohexanone is the *kinetic* enolate ion because the α-hydrogen that is removed to make this enolate ion is more accessible to the base (particularly if a hindered base like LDA is used) and is slightly more acidic. There-fore, 2,6-dimethylcyclohexanone is formed faster and is the major product if the reaction is carried out under conditions (−78 °C) that cause the reaction to be irreversible (Section 7.11).

The enolate ion leading to 2,2-dimethylcyclohexanone is the *thermodynamic* enolate ion because it is the more stable enolate ion since it has the more substituted double bond. (Alkyl substitution increases enolate ion stability for the same reason it increases alkene stability; Section 4.13.) Therefore, 2,2-dimethylcyclohexanone is the major product if the reaction is carried out under conditions that cause enolate ion formation to be reversible, and if a less hindered base (KH) is used to cause steric differences in enolate ion forma-tion to be less important.

The less substituted α-carbon can be alkylated—without having to control the condi-tions to make certain that the reaction does not become reversible—by first making the *N,N*-dimethylhydrazone of the ketone.

an *N,N*-dimethyl-hydrazone

The dimethylamino group of the *N,N*-dimethylhydrazone points away from the more substituted α-carbon. The nitrogen of the dimethylamino group directs butyllithium (Bu⁻Li⁺), the base employed in this reaction, to the less substituted carbon by coor-dinating with the lithium ion. Hydrolysis of the hydrazone re-forms the ketone (Section 18.8).

The Synthesis of Aspirin

The first step in the industrial synthesis of aspirin is known as the **Kolbe–Schmitt carboxylation reaction**. In this step, the phenolate ion reacts with carbon dioxide under pressure to form

o-hydroxybenzoic acid, also known as salicylic acid. Acetylation of salicylic acid with acetic anhydride forms acetylsalicylic acid (aspirin).

salicylic acid
o-hydroxybenzoic acid

acetylsalicylic acid
aspirin

During World War I, the Bayer Company bought as much phenol as it could on the international market, knowing that eventually all of it could be used to manufacture aspirin. This left little phenol available for other countries to purchase for the synthesis of 2,4,6-trinitrophenol (picric acid), a common explosive at that time.

BIOGRAPHY

Hermann Kolbe (1819–1884) *and* **Rudolph Schmitt (1830–1898)** *were born in Germany. Kolbe was a professor at the University of Marburg and the University of Leipzig. Schmitt received a Ph.D. from the University of Marburg and was a professor at the University of Dresden. Kolbe devised a way to prepare aspirin in 1859. Schmitt modified the synthesis in 1885, making aspirin available in large quantities at a low price.*

PROBLEM 16♦

What compound is formed when a dilute solution of cyclohexanone is shaken with NaOD in D_2O for several hours?

PROBLEM 17

Explain why alkylation of an α-carbon works best if the alkyl halide used in the reaction is a primary alkyl halide, and why alkylation does not work at all if a tertiary alkyl halide is used.

PROBLEM-SOLVING STRATEGY

Alkylating a Carbonyl Compound

How could you prepare 4-methyl-3-hexanone from a ketone containing no more than six carbons?

4-methyl-3-hexanone

Either of two sets of ketone and alkyl halide could be used for the synthesis: one set is 3-hexanone and a methyl halide; the other is 3-pentanone and an ethyl halide.

3-hexanone + CH_3Br or **3-pentanone** + CH_3CH_2Br

3-Pentanone and an ethyl halide are the preferred starting materials. Because 3-pentanone is symmetrical, only one α-substituted ketone will be formed. In contrast, 3-hexanone can form two different enolate ions, so two α-substituted ketones can be formed.

3-pentanone → LDA → → CH_3CH_2Br → **4-methyl-3-hexanone**

3-hexanone   →LDA   (intermediate enolate ions)   +   (intermediate enolate ion)

CH₃Br   CH₃Br

4-methyl-3-hexanone   +   **2-methyl-3-hexanone**

Now continue on to Problem 18.

PROBLEM 18

How could each of the following compounds be prepared from a ketone and an alkyl halide?

a.   b.

19.10 ALKYLATION AND ACYLATION OF THE α-CARBON USING AN ENAMINE INTERMEDIATE

We have seen that an enamine is formed when an aldehyde or a ketone reacts with a secondary amine (Section 18.8).

pyrrolidine
secondary amine   **enamine**   + H_2O

Enamines react with electrophiles in the same way that enolate ions do.

an enamine reacts with   **an enolate ion reacts with**
an electrophile   **an electrophile**

This means that aldehydes and ketones can be alkylated at the α-carbon via an enamine intermediate:

- The carbonyl compound is converted to an enamine (by treating it with a secondary amine).
- The electrophile is added.

• The imine is hydrolyzed back to the ketone.

Because the alkylation step is an S_N2 reaction, only primary alkyl halides or methyl halides should be used (Section 8.2). One advantage to using an enamine intermediate to alkylate an aldehyde or a ketone is that only the monoalkylated product is formed.

In addition to using enamine intermediates to *alkylate* aldehydes and ketones, they can also be used to *acylate* these compounds.

PROBLEM 19

Describe how the following compounds could be prepared using an enamine intermediate:

a.

b.

19.11 ALKYLATION OF THE β-CARBON: THE MICHAEL REACTION

In Section 18.16, we saw that nucleophiles react with α,β-unsaturated aldehydes and ketones, forming either nucleophilic (direct) addition products or conjugate addition products; in Section 18.17, we saw that nucleophiles react with α,β-unsaturated carboxylic acid derivatives, forming either nucleophilic addition-elimination products or conjugate addition products.

BIOGRAPHY

Arthur Michael (1853–1942) *was born in Buffalo, New York. He studied at the University of Heidelberg, the University of Berlin, and L'École de Médicine in Paris. He was a professor of chemistry at Tufts and Harvard Universities, retiring from Harvard when he was 83.*

direct addition   conjugate addition

When the nucleophile in these reactions is an enolate ion, the addition reaction has a special name: it is called a **Michael reaction**. The enolate ions that work best in Michael reactions are those formed from carbon acids that are flanked by two electron-withdrawing groups: enolate ions of β-diketones, β-diesters, β-keto esters, and β-keto nitriles. Because these enolate ions are relatively weak bases, conjugate addition occurs—that is, addition at the β-carbon of α,β-unsaturated aldehydes and ketones. These enolate ions also add to the β-carbon of α,β-unsaturated esters and amides because of the low reactivity of the carbonyl group. Notice that *Michael reactions form 1,5-dicarbonyl compounds*; that is, if a carbonyl carbon of the enolate ion is given the 1-position, the carbonyl carbon of the other reactant is at the 5-position.

All these reactions take place by the same mechanism:

MECHANISM FOR THE MICHAEL REACTION

- A base removes a proton from the α-carbon of the carbon acid.
- The enolate ion adds to the β-carbon of an α,β-unsaturated carbonyl compound.
- The α-carbon is protonated.

Notice that if either of the reactants in a Michael reaction has an ester group, the base used to remove the α-proton must be the same as the leaving group of the ester. This is necessary because the base, in addition to being able to remove an α-proton, can react as a nucleophile and add to the carbonyl group of the ester. If the nucleophile is identical to the OR group of the ester, nucleophilic addition to the carbonyl group will not change the reactant.

Enamines can be used in place of enolate ions in Michael reactions. When an enamine is used as a nucleophile in a Michael reaction, the reaction is called a **Stork enamine reaction**.

MECHANISM FOR THE STORK ENAMINE REACTION

PROBLEM 20

Give the products of the following reactions:

a.

$$CH_3CH=CH-\overset{\displaystyle O}{\overset{\|}{C}}-NH_2 \quad + \quad CH_3CH_2-\overset{\displaystyle O}{\overset{\|}{C}}-CH_2-\overset{\displaystyle O}{\overset{\|}{C}}-OCH_3 \quad \xrightarrow{\ CH_3O^-\ }$$

b.

$$CH_3CH_2CH=CH-\overset{\displaystyle O}{\overset{\|}{C}}-OCH_3 \quad + \quad CH_3-\overset{\displaystyle O}{\overset{\|}{C}}-CH_2C\equiv N \quad \xrightarrow{\ CH_3O^-\ }$$

PROBLEM 21 ♦

What reagents would you use to prepare the following compounds?

a.

b.

19.12 AN ALDOL ADDITION FORMS β-HYDROXYALDEHYDES OR β-HYDROXYKETONES

We saw in Chapter 18 that the carbonyl carbon of an aldehyde or a ketone is an electrophile. We have just seen that a proton can be removed from the α-carbon of an aldehyde or a ketone, converting the α-carbon into a nucleophile. An **aldol addition** is a reaction in which *both* of these activities are observed: one molecule of a carbonyl compound—after a proton is removed from an α-carbon—reacts as a *nucleophile* and adds to the *electrophilic* carbonyl carbon of a second molecule of the carbonyl compound.

Thus, an aldol addition is a reaction between two molecules of an *aldehyde* or two molecules of a *ketone*. When the reactant is an aldehyde, the product is a β-hydroxyaldehyde, which is why the reaction is called an aldol addition ("ald" for aldehyde, "ol" for alcohol). When the reactant is a ketone, the product is a β-hydroxyketone. Notice that the reaction forms a new C—C bond between the α-carbon of one molecule and the carbon that was originally the carbonyl carbon of the other molecule.

aldol additions

Because the addition reaction is reversible, good yields of the addition product are obtained only if it is removed from the solution as it is formed. The mechanism for the reaction is shown below.

MECHANISM FOR THE ALDOL ADDITION

- A base removes a proton from the α-carbon, creating an enolate ion.
- The enolate ion adds to the carbonyl carbon of a second molecule of the carbonyl compound.
- The negatively charged oxygen is protonated.

Because an aldol addition reaction occurs between two molecules of the same carbonyl compound, the product has twice as many carbons as the reacting aldehyde or ketone.

Ketones are less susceptible than aldehydes to attack by nucleophiles (Section 18.2), so aldol additions occur more slowly with ketones.

a β-hydroxyketone

The relatively high reactivity of aldehydes in competing aldol addition reactions is what causes them to give low yields of α-alkylation products (Section 19.9).

PROBLEM 22

Show the aldol addition product that would be formed from each of the following compounds:

a. $CH_3CH_2CH_2CH_2$—$\overset{\overset{\displaystyle O}{\|}}{C}$—$H$

b. CH_3CH_2—$\overset{\overset{\displaystyle O}{\|}}{C}$—$CH_2CH_3$

c. (cyclohexanone)

PROBLEM 23 ◆

For each of the following compounds, indicate the aldehyde or ketone from which it would be formed by an aldol addition:

a. 2-ethyl-3-hydroxyhexanal
b. 4-hydroxy-4-methyl-2-pentanone

c. 2,4-dicyclohexyl-3-hydroxybutanal
d. 5-ethyl-5-hydroxy-4-methyl-3-heptanone

PROBLEM 24

An aldol addition can be catalyzed by acids as well as by bases. Propose a mechanism for the acid-catalyzed aldol addition of propanal.

19.13 DEHYDRATION OF ALDOL ADDITION PRODUCTS FORMS α,β-UNSATURATED ALDEHYDES AND KETONES

We have seen that alcohols undergo dehydration when they are heated with acid (Section 10.4). The β-hydroxyaldehyde and β-hydroxyketone products of aldol addition reactions are easier to dehydrate than many other alcohols because the double bond formed as the result of dehydration is conjugated with a carbonyl group. Conjugation increases the stability of the product (Section 7.7) and therefore makes it easier to form.

If the product of an aldol addition undergoes dehydration, the overall reaction is called an **aldol condensation**. A **condensation reaction** is a reaction that combines two molecules by forming a new C—C bond while removing a small molecule (usually water or an alcohol). Notice that an aldol condensation forms an α,β-unsaturated aldehyde or an α,β-unsaturated ketone.

a β-hydroxyaldehyde   an α,β-unsaturated aldehyde

An aldol addition product loses water to form an aldol condensation product.

β-Hydroxyaldehydes and β-hydroxyketones can also undergo dehydration under basic conditions. Thus, heating the aldol addition product in either acid or base leads to dehydration. The product of dehydration is called an enone—"ene" for the double bond and "one" for the carbonyl group.

a β-hydroxyketone   an α,β-unsaturated ketone
                              an enone

In Chapter 9 we looked at E1 reactions (two-step elimination reactions that form a carbocation intermediate) and E2 reactions (concerted elimination reactions). The above base-catalyzed dehydration reaction represents the third kind of elimination reaction—it is an **E1cB** (elimination unimolecular conjugate base) **reaction**, a two-step elimination reaction that forms a carbanion intermediate. E1cB reactions occur only if the carbanion can be stabilized by electron delocalization. The mechanism for the reaction is shown below.

MECHANISM FOR THE E1cB REACTION

- a base removes a proton from the α-carbon, forming an enolate ion
- the enolate ion eliminates the OH group, which picks up a proton as it leaves to make it a better leaving group

Dehydration often occurs under the conditions in which the aldol addition is carried out, without requiring additional heat. In such cases, the β-hydroxycarbonyl compound is an intermediate and the enone is the final product of the reaction. In the following reaction, the β-hydroxyketone formed from the aldol addition of acetophenone loses water as soon as it is formed because the new double bond is conjugated not only with the carbonyl group but also with the benzene ring.

PROBLEM 25◆

What product is obtained from the aldol condensation of cyclohexanone?

PROBLEM 26 SOLVED

How could you prepare the following compounds using a starting material containing no more than three carbons?

a. CH₃CH₂CHCH—C(=O)H with Br and CH₃ substituents

b. CH₃CH₂CH₂—C(=O)—CH₃

c. CH₃CH₂CH₂—C(=O)—OH

Solution to 26a A compound with the correct six-carbon skeleton can be obtained if a three-carbon aldehyde undergoes an aldol addition. Dehydration of the addition product forms an α,β-unsaturated aldehyde. Conjugate addition of HBr (Section 18.16) forms the target molecule.

CH₃CH₂—C(=O)—H $\xrightarrow{\text{HO}^-,\ \text{H}_2\text{O}}$ CH₃CH₂CHCH—C(=O)H (with OH and CH₃) $\xrightarrow[\text{HO}^-]{\Delta}$ CH₃CH₂CH=C—C(=O)H (with CH₃) $\xrightarrow{\text{HBr}}$ CH₃CH₂CHCH—C(=O)H (with Br and CH₃)

PROBLEM 27

The reaction of cyclopentadiene with benzophenone in the presence of base involves the following steps in the given order: deprotonation, an addition reaction, protonation, an E1cB reaction. What is the product of the reaction?

19.14 THE CROSSED ALDOL ADDITION

If two different carbonyl compounds are used in an aldol addition, four products can be formed because each enolate ion can react with either of the two carbonyl compounds. In the following example, both carbonyl compound A and carbonyl compound B can lose a proton from an α-carbon to form enolate ions A⁻ and B⁻; A⁻ can react with either A or B, and B⁻ can react with either A or B:

The preceding reaction is called a **crossed aldol addition** or a **mixed aldol addition**. The four products have similar physical properties, making them difficult to separate. Consequently, a crossed aldol addition that forms four products is not a synthetically useful reaction.

PROBLEM 28

Give the products obtained from crossed aldol additions of the following compounds:

PROBLEM 29   SOLVED

The following crossed aldol condensation is sufficiently important to have been given its own name: it is a Claisen–Schmidt condensation. Explain why it forms essentially only one product.

First of all, benzaldehyde does not have any α-hydrogens, so it cannot form an enolate. That cuts the possible products from four to two. Second, the enolate formed from the ketone is more likely to add to the aldehyde because aldehydes are more reactive than ketones toward nucleophilic addition and this particular ketone has more than the usual amount of steric hindrance (Section 18.2).

Primarily one aldol product can be obtained if LDA is used to remove the α-hydrogen that creates the enolate ion. Because LDA is a strong base (Section 19.8), all the carbonyl compound will be converted into an enolate ion, so none of that carbonyl compound will be left for the enolate ion to react with in an aldol addition. An aldol addition will not be able to occur until the second carbonyl compound is added to the reaction mixture. If the second carbonyl compound is added slowly, the chance that it will form an enolate ion and then react with another molecule of its parent carbonyl compound will be minimized.

PROBLEM 30

Describe how the following compounds could be prepared using an aldol addition in the first step of the synthesis:

PROBLEM 31

Propose a mechanism for the following reaction:

Ludwig Claisen (1851–1930) *was born in Germany and received a Ph.D. from the University of Bonn, studying under Kekulé (Section 7.1). He was a professor of chemistry at the University of Bonn, Owens College (Manchester, England), the University of Munich, the University of Aachen, the University of Kiel, and the University of Berlin.*

19.15 A CLAISEN CONDENSATION FORMS A β-KETO ESTER

Claisen Condensation

When two molecules of an *ester* undergo a condensation reaction, the reaction is called a **Claisen condensation**. The product of a Claisen condensation is a β-keto ester. In a Claisen condensation, as in an aldol addition, one molecule of carbonyl compound is the nucleophile and a second molecule is the electrophile. The new C—C bond connects the α-carbon of one molecule and the carbon that was formerly the carbonyl carbon of the other molecule.

the new bond is formed between the α-carbon and the carbonyl carbon

$$2 \quad CH_3CH_2-\overset{\overset{\displaystyle O}{\|}}{C}-OCH_2CH_3 \quad \xrightarrow[\text{2. HCl}]{\text{1. } CH_3CH_2O^-} \quad CH_3CH_2-\overset{\overset{\displaystyle O}{\|}}{C}-\underset{\underset{\displaystyle CH_3}{|}}{CH}-\overset{\overset{\displaystyle O}{\|}}{C}-OCH_2CH_3 \quad + \quad CH_3CH_2OH$$

a β-keto ester

The mechanism for the Claisen condensation is shown below.

MECHANISM FOR THE CLAISEN CONDENSATION

$$RCH\overset{\overset{\displaystyle O}{\|}}{C}-OCH_3 \xrightarrow{CH_3\ddot{O}\colon^-} RCH\overset{\overset{\displaystyle O}{\|}}{C}-OCH_3 \xrightarrow{RCH_2COCH_3} RCH_2\overset{:\ddot{O}:^-}{\underset{CH_3O\ \ R}{\overset{|}{C}-CH}}-\overset{\overset{\displaystyle O}{\|}}{C}-OCH_3$$

$$+ \quad CH_3OH$$

$$RCH_2\overset{\overset{\displaystyle O}{\|}}{C}-\underset{\underset{\displaystyle R}{|}}{CH}-\overset{\overset{\displaystyle O}{\|}}{C}-OCH_3 \quad + \quad CH_3O^-$$

- A base removes a proton from the α-carbon, creating an enolate ion. The base employed corresponds to the leaving group of the ester so that the reactant would not change if the base were to act as a nucleophile and add to the carbonyl group (Section 19.11).

- The enolate ion adds to the carbonyl carbon of a second molecule of the carbonyl compound.

- The π bond re-forms, eliminating an alkoxide ion.

After nucleophilic addition, the Claisen condensation and the aldol addition differ. In the Claisen condensation, the negatively charged oxygen re-forms the carbon–oxygen π bond and eliminates the ⁻OR group. In the aldol addition, the negatively charged oxygen obtains a proton from the solvent.

Claisen condensation   **aldol addition**

formation of a π bond
by elimination of RO⁻

protonation of O⁻

The difference between the last step of the Claisen condensation and the last step of the aldol addition arises from the difference between esters and aldehydes or ketones. With esters (class I carbonyl compounds), the carbon bonded to the negatively charged oxygen is also bonded to a group that can be eliminated. With aldehydes or ketones (class II carbonyl compounds), the carbon bonded to the negatively charged oxygen is not bonded to a group that can be eliminated. Thus, the Claisen condensation is a nucleophilic addition–elimination reaction, whereas the aldol addition is a nucleophilic addition reaction.

Elimination of the alkoxide ion is reversible because the alkoxide ion can re-form the tetrahedral intermediate by reacting with the β-keto ester. The condensation reaction can be driven to completion, however, if a proton is removed from the β-keto ester. Removing a proton prevents the reverse reaction from occurring because the negatively charged alkoxide ion will not approach the negatively charged anion of the β-keto ester. A proton is easily removed from the β-keto ester because the central α-carbon is flanked by two carbonyl groups, making its α-hydrogen much more acidic than the α-hydrogens of the ester starting material.

β-keto ester   **β-keto ester anion**

Consequently, a successful Claisen condensation requires an ester with two α-hydrogens and an equivalent amount of base rather than a catalytic amount of base. When the reaction is over, addition of acid to the reaction mixture reprotonates the β-keto ester anion. Any remaining alkoxide ion that could cause the reaction to reverse is also protonated.

PROBLEM 32◆

Give the products of the following reactions:

a. CH₃CH₂CH₂—C(=O)—OCH₃ →(1. CH₃O⁻ 2. HCl)

b. CH₃CHCH₂—C(=O)—OCH₂CH₃ (with CH₃ branch) →(1. CH₃CH₂O⁻ 2. HCl)

PROBLEM 33◆

Which of the following esters cannot undergo a Claisen condensation?

A: CH₃CH=CH—C(=O)—OCH₃   B: H—C(=O)—OCH₃   C: CH₃—C(=O)—OCH₃   D: C₆H₅—C(=O)—OCH₃

A Crossed Claisen Condensation

A **crossed Claisen condensation** is a condensation reaction between two different esters. Like a crossed aldol addition, a crossed Claisen condensation is a useful reaction only if it is carried out under conditions that foster the formation of primarily one product. Otherwise, the reaction will form a mixture of products that are difficult to separate.

Primarily one product will be formed from a crossed Claisen condensation if one of the esters has no α-hydrogens (and therefore cannot form an enolate ion) and the ester with α-hydrogens is added slowly to a solution of the ester without α-hydrogens and the alkoxide ion.

CH₃CH₂CH₂—C(=O)—OCH₂CH₃ (**add slowly**) + C₆H₅—C(=O)—OCH₂CH₃ →(1. CH₃CH₂O⁻ 2. HCl) C₆H₅—C(=O)—CH(CH₂CH₃)—C(=O)—OCH₂CH₃ + CH₃CH₂OH

PROBLEM 34

Give the product of each of the following reactions:

a. CH₃CH₂—C(=O)—OCH₂CH₃ (**add slowly**) + CH₃CH₂O—C(=O)—OCH₂CH₃ →(1. CH₃CH₂O⁻ 2. HCl)

b. CH₃CH₂CH₂—C(=O)—OCH₃ (**add slowly**) + H—C(=O)—OCH₃ →(1. CH₃O⁻ 2. HCl)

chem place Tutorial: Claisen condensations—synthesis

19.16 OTHER CROSSED CONDENSATIONS

In addition to crossed aldol and crossed Claisen condensations, a crossed condensation between a ketone and an ester is possible. Because the α-hydrogens of a ketone are more acidic than those of an ester, primarily one product is formed if the ketone and the base are both added slowly to the ester. Notice that all these condensations form 1,3-dicarbonyl compounds.

A *β-diketone* is formed when a ketone condenses with an *ester*.

A *β-keto aldehyde* is formed when a ketone condenses with a *formate ester*.

A *β-keto ester* is formed when a ketone condenses with *diethyl carbonate*.

PROBLEM 35

Give the product of the following reaction:

PROBLEM 36   SOLVED

Show how the following compounds could be prepared from cyclohexanone:

a.   b.   c.

Solution to 36a   Because the desired compound is a 1,3-dicarbonyl compound, it can be prepared by a crossed condensation reaction in which one of the reactants is an ester.

Solution to 36b   Because the desired compound is a 1,5-dicarbonyl compound, it can be prepared by adding an α,β-unsaturated carbonyl compound to an enolate ion (a Michael reaction).

19.17 INTRAMOLECULAR CONDENSATION AND ADDITION REACTIONS

We have seen that if a compound has two functional groups that can react with each other, an intramolecular reaction readily occurs if the reaction leads to the formation of five- or six-membered rings (Section 8.10). Consequently, if base is added to a compound that contains two carbonyl groups, an intramolecular reaction occurs if a product with a five- or six-membered ring can be formed. Thus, a compound with two ester groups would undergo an intramolecular Claisen condensation, and a compound with two aldehyde or ketone groups would undergo an intramolecular aldol addition.

Intramolecular Claisen Condensations

The addition of base to a 1,6-diester causes the diester to undergo an intramolecular Claisen condensation, thereby forming a five-membered ring β-keto ester. An intramolecular Claisen condensation is called a **Dieckmann condensation**.

A six-membered ring β-keto ester is formed from a Dieckmann condensation of a 1,7-diester.

B I O G R A P H Y

Walter Dieckmann (1869–1925) *was born in Germany. He received a Ph.D. from the University of Munich and became a professor of chemistry there.*

The mechanism of the Dieckmann condensation is the same as the mechanism of the Claisen condensation. The only difference between the two reactions is that the enolate ion and the carbonyl group undergoing nucleophilic addition are in different molecules in the Claisen condensation but are in the same molecule in the Dieckmann condensation.

MECHANISM FOR THE DIECKMANN CONDENSATION

- A base removes a proton from the α-carbon, creating an enolate ion.
- The enolate ion adds to a carbonyl carbon.
- The π bond re-forms, eliminating an alkoxide ion.

The Dieckmann condensation, like the Claisen condensation, can be driven to completion by carrying out the reaction with enough base to remove a proton from the α-carbon of the β-keto ester product. When the reaction is over, acid is added to reprotonate the condensation product.

Write the mechanism for the base-catalyzed formation of a cyclic β-keto ester from a 1,7-diester.

Intramolecular Aldol Additions

Because a 1,4-diketone has two different sets of α-hydrogens, two different intramolecular addition products can potentially form, one with a five-membered ring, the other with a three-membered ring. The greater stability of five- and six-membered rings causes them to be formed preferentially (Section 2.11). In fact, the five-membered ring product is the only product formed from the intramolecular aldol addition of a 1,4-diketone.

The intramolecular aldol addition of a 1,6-diketone can potentially lead to either a seven- or a five-membered ring product. Again, the more stable product—the one with the five-membered ring—is the only product of the reaction.

1,5-Diketones and 1,7-diketones undergo intramolecular aldol additions to form six-membered ring products.

a 1,5-diketone

a 1,7-diketone

If the preference for formation of a six-membered ring were not so great, what other cyclic product would be formed from the intramolecular aldol addition of

a. 2,6-heptanedione?   **b.** 2,8-nonanedione?

Can 2,4-pentanedione undergo an intramolecular aldol addition? If so, why? If not, why not?

PROBLEM 40   SOLVED

What products can be obtained if the following keto aldehyde is treated with a base? Which would you expect to be the major product?

Solution   Three products are possible because there are three different sets of α-hydrogens. More B and C are formed than A because a five-membered ring is formed in preference to a seven-membered ring. The major product depends on the reaction conditions. B is the thermodynamic product because it is formed from the more stable enolate. C is the kinetic product because the α-hydrogen of the aldehyde is more acidic than the α-hydrogen of the ketone (Table 19.1).

PROBLEM 41 ♦

Give the product of the reaction of each of the following compounds with a base:

19.18 THE ROBINSON ANNULATION

Reactions that form carbon–carbon bonds are important to synthetic chemists. Without such reactions, large organic molecules could not be prepared from smaller ones. We have seen that Michael reactions and aldol additions form carbon–carbon bonds. The **Robinson annulation** is a reaction that puts these two carbon–carbon bond-forming reactions together, providing a route to the synthesis of many complicated organic molecules. "Annulation" comes from *annulus,* Latin for "ring." Thus, an **annulation reaction** is a ring-forming reaction.

the Robinson annulation

* The first stage of a Robinson annulation is a Michael reaction that forms a 1,5-diketone.
* The second stage is an intramolecular aldol addition.
* Heating the basic solution dehydrates the alcohol.

Notice that a Robinson annulation results in a product that has a 2-cyclohexenone ring.

PROBLEM-SOLVING STRATEGY

Analyzing a Robinson Annulation

Propose a synthesis for each of the following compounds, using a Robinson annulation:

a.

b.

Careful examination of a Robinson annulation tells us which part of the molecule comes from which reactant. This knowledge, then, allows us to choose the appropriate reactants. Analysis shows that the keto group of the cyclohexenone comes from the α,β-unsaturated carbonyl compound and the double bond results from addition of the enolate ion of the α,β-unsaturated carbonyl compound to the carbonyl group of the other reactant.

α,β**-unsaturated**
carbonyl compound

Therefore, the required reactants for part **a** are

We can arrive at the appropriate reactants for any other Robinson annulation by cutting through the double bond of the target molecule and cutting between the β- and γ-carbons on the other side of the carbonyl group.

By cutting through the compound in part **b**, we can determine the required reactants for its synthesis:

The required reactants for part **b** are

Now continue on to Problem 42.

PROBLEM 42

Propose a synthesis for each of the following compounds, using a Robinson annulation:

chem Tutorial:
place Robinson annulation—synthesis

•

19.19 CARBOXYLIC ACIDS WITH A CARBONYL GROUP AT THE 3-POSITION CAN BE DECARBOXYLATED

Carboxylate ions do not lose CO_2, for the same reason that alkanes such as ethane do not lose a proton—the leaving group would be a carbanion. Carbanions are very strong bases and therefore are very poor leaving groups.

If, however, the CO_2 group is bonded to a carbon adjacent to a carbonyl carbon, the CO_2 group can be removed, because the electrons left behind can be delocalized onto the carbonyl oxygen. Consequently, carboxylate ions with a carbonyl group at the 3-position (3-oxocarboxylate ions) lose CO_2 with gentle heating (~50 °C). Loss of CO_2 from a molecule is called **decarboxylation**.

3-Oxocarboxylic acids decarboxylate when heated.

removing CO₂ from an α-carbon

Notice the similarity between removal of CO_2 from a 3-oxocarboxylate ion and removal of a proton from an α-carbon. In both reactions, a substituent—CO_2 in one case, H^+ in the other—is removed from an α-carbon, and its bonding electrons are delocalized onto an oxygen.

removing a proton from an α-carbon

Decarboxylation is even easier (~30 °C) under acidic conditions because the reaction is catalyzed by an intramolecular transfer of a proton from the carboxyl group to the carbonyl oxygen. The enol that is formed immediately tautomerizes to a ketone.

We saw in Section 19.1 that it is harder to remove a proton from an α-carbon if the electrons are delocalized onto the carbonyl group of an ester rather than onto the carbonyl group of a ketone. For the same reason, a higher temperature (~135 °C) is required to decarboxylate a β-dicarboxylic acid such as malonic acid than to decarboxylate a β-keto acid.

malonic acid

In summary, carboxylic acids with a carbonyl group at the 3-position lose CO_2 when they are heated.

3-oxohexanoic acid   **2-pentanone**

2-oxocyclohexanecarboxylic acid   **cyclohexanone**

PROBLEM 43 ◆

Which of the following compounds would be expected to decarboxylate when heated?

a.   b.   c.   d.

A   B   C   D

19.20 THE MALONIC ESTER SYNTHESIS: A WAY TO SYNTHESIZE A CARBOXYLIC ACID

A combination of two of the reactions discussed in this chapter—alkylation of an α-carbon and decarboxylation of a β-dicarboxylic acid—can be used to prepare carboxylic acids of any desired chain length. The procedure is called the **malonic ester synthesis** because the starting material for the synthesis is the diester of malonic acid.

The first two carbons of the carboxylic acid being synthesized come from malonic ester, and the rest of the carboxylic acid comes from the alkyl halide used in the second step of the synthesis. A malonic ester synthesis forms a carboxylic acid with two more carbons than the alkyl halide.

malonic ester synthesis

The steps in the malonic ester synthesis are shown below.

steps in the malonic ester synthesis

- A proton is easily removed from the α-carbon because it is flanked by two ester groups ($pK_a = 13$).
- The resulting α-carbanion reacts with an alkyl halide, forming an α-substituted malonic ester. Because alkylation is an S_N2 reaction, it works best with primary alkyl halides and methyl halides (Section 8.2).
- Heating the α-substituted malonic ester in an acidic aqueous solution hydrolyzes both ester groups to carboxylic acid groups, forming an α-substituted malonic acid.
- Further heating decarboxylates the 3-oxocarboxylic acid.

Carboxylic acids with two substituents bonded to the α-carbon can be prepared by carrying out two successive α-carbon alkylations.

Next, we need to determine which of the atoms that form the bond should be the nucleophile and which should be the electrophile. In this case, it is easy to choose between the two possibilities because we know that a carbonyl carbon is an electrophile.

Now we need to determine what compound would give the desired electrophilic and nucleophilic sites. If we know what the starting material is, we can use it as a clue to arrive at the desired compound. For example, an ester carbonyl group would be a good electrophile for this synthesis because it has a group that would be eliminated. Moreover, the α-hydrogens of the ketone are more acidic than the α-hydrogens of the ester, so the desired nucleophile would be easy to obtain. The ester can be prepared from the carboxylic acid starting material (Section 17.21).

In the next synthesis, two new carbon–carbon bonds must be formed.

After we have identified the electrophilic and nucleophilic sites, we can see that two successive alkylations of a diester of malonic acid, using 1,5-dibromopentane for the alkyl halide, will produce the desired compound.

In planning the following synthesis, the diester given as the starting material suggests that a Dieckmann condensation should be used to obtain the cyclic compound:

Alkylation of the α-carbon of the cyclopentanone ring formed by the Dieckmann condensation, followed by hydrolysis of the β-keto ester and decarboxylation, forms the desired product.

$$+ \ CO_2 \ + \ C_2H_5OH$$

PROBLEM 48

Design a synthesis for each of the following compounds using the given starting material:

a.

b.

c.

d.

---

chem place Tutorial: Retrosynthesis

Tutorial: Hints in retrosynthetic analysis

19.23 REACTIONS AT THE α-CARBON IN BIOLOGICAL SYSTEMS

Many reactions that occur in biological systems involve reactions at the α-carbon—the kinds of reactions you have studied in this chapter. We will now look at a few examples.

A Biological Aldol Addition

Glucose, the most abundant sugar found in nature, is synthesized in biological systems from two molecules of pyruvate. The series of reactions that convert two molecules of pyruvate into glucose is called **gluconeogenesis**. The reverse process—the breakdown of glucose into two molecules of pyruvate—is called **glycolysis** (Section 26.7).

Because glucose has twice as many carbons as pyruvate, you should not be surprised to learn that one of the steps in the biosynthesis of glucose is an aldol addition. An enzyme called aldolase catalyzes an aldol addition between dihydroxyacetone phosphate and glyceraldehyde-3-phosphate. The product is fructose-1,6-diphosphate, which is subsequently converted to glucose. The mechanism for this reaction will be discussed in Section 24.9.

PROBLEM 49

Propose a mechanism for the formation of fructose-1,6-diphosphate from dihydroxyacetone phosphate and glyceraldehyde-3-phosphate, using HO^- as the catalyst.

A Biological Aldol Condensation

Collagen is the most abundant protein in mammals, amounting to about one-fourth of the total protein. It is the major fibrous component of bone, teeth, skin, cartilage, and tendons. Individual collagen molecules—called tropocollagen—can be isolated only from tissues of young animals. As animals age, the individual molecules become cross-linked, which is why meat from older animals is tougher than meat from younger ones. Collagen cross-linking is an example of an aldol condensation.

Before collagen molecules can cross-link, the primary amino groups of the lysine residues of collagen must be converted to aldehyde groups. The enzyme that catalyzes this reaction is called lysyl oxidase. An aldol condensation between two aldehyde residues results in a cross-linked protein.

A Biological Claisen Condensation

Fatty acids are long-chain, unbranched carboxylic acids (Sections 17.14 and 27.1). Most naturally occurring fatty acids contain an even number of carbons because they are synthesized from acetate, which has two carbons.

In Section 17.22, you saw that carboxylic acids can be activated in biological systems by being converted to thioesters of coenzyme A.

One of the necessary reactants for fatty acid synthesis is malonyl-CoA, which is obtained by carboxylation of acetyl-CoA. The mechanism for this reaction will be discussed in Section 25.4.

Before fatty acid synthesis can occur, the acyl groups of acetyl-CoA and malonyl-CoA are transferred to other thiols by means of a transesterification reaction.

A molecule of acetyl thioester and a molecule of malonyl thioester are the reactants for the first round in the biosynthesis of a fatty acid.

- The first step is a Claisen condensation. We have seen that the nucleophile needed for a Claisen condensation is obtained by using a strong base to remove an α-hydrogen. Strong bases are not available in living cells, however, because biological reactions take place at neutral pH. Thus, the required nucleophile is generated by removing CO_2—rather than a proton—from the α-carbon of malonyl thioester. (Recall that 3-oxocarboxylic acids are easily decarboxylated; Section 19.19.) Loss of CO_2 also drives the condensation reaction to completion.

- The product of the condensation reaction undergoes a reduction, a dehydration, and a second reduction to give a four-carbon thioester.

The four-carbon thioester and a molecule of malonyl thioester are the reactants for the second round.

• Again, the product of the Claisen condensation reaction undergoes a reduction, a dehydration, and a second reduction, this time to form a six-carbon thioester.

• The sequence of reactions is repeated, and each time two more carbons are added to the chain.

This sequence of reactions explains why naturally occurring fatty acids are unbranched and generally contain an even number of carbons. Once a thioester with the appropriate number of carbon is obtained, it undergoes a transesterification reaction with glycerol in order to form fats, oils, and phospholipids (Sections 27.3 and 27.4).

PROBLEM 50♦

Palmitic acid is a straight-chain saturated 16-carbon fatty acid. How many moles of malonyl-CoA are required for the synthesis of one mole of palmitic acid?

PROBLEM 51♦

a. If the biosynthesis of palmitic acid were carried out with CD_3COSR and nondeuterated malonyl thioester, how many deuterium atoms would be incorporated into palmitic acid?

b. If the biosynthesis of palmitic acid were carried out with $^-OOCCD_2COSR$ and nondeuterated acetyl thioester, how many deuterium atoms would be incorporated into palmitic acid?

A Biological Decarboxylation

An example of a decarboxylation that occurs in biological systems is the decarboxylation of acetoacetate.

- Acetoacetate decarboxylase, the enzyme that catalyzes the reaction, forms an imine with acetoacetate.
- Under physiological conditions, the imine is protonated and therefore readily accepts the pair of electrons left behind when the substrate loses CO_2.
- Decarboxylation forms an enamine.
- Hydrolysis of the enamine produces the decarboxylated product (acetone) and regenerates the enzyme (Section 18.8).

PROBLEM 52

When the enzymatic decarboxylation of acetoacetate is carried out in $H_2^{18}O$, the acetone that is formed contains ^{18}O. What does this tell you about the mechanism of the reaction?

SUMMARY

A hydrogen bonded to an α-carbon of an aldehyde, ketone, ester, or N,N-disubstituted amide is sufficiently acidic to be removed by a strong base because the base formed when the proton is removed is stabilized by delocalization of its negative change onto an oxygen. A **carbon acid** is a compound with a relatively acidic hydrogen bonded to an sp^3 hybridized carbon. Aldehydes and ketones ($pK_a \sim 16$ to 20) are more acidic than esters ($pK_a \sim 25$). **β-Diketones** ($pK_a \sim 9$) and β-keto esters ($pK_a = 11$) are even more acidic.

Keto–enol interconversion can be catalyzed by acids or by bases. Generally, the **keto tautomer** is more stable. When an **α-substitution reaction** takes place under acidic conditions, an enol reacts with an electrophile; when the reaction takes place under basic conditions, an enolate ion reacts with an electrophile. Whether C or O reacts with the electrophile depends on the electrophile and the reaction conditions.

Aldehydes and ketones react with Br_2, Cl_2, or I_2: under acidic conditions, a halogen replaces one of the α-hydrogens of the carbonyl compound; under basic conditions, halogens replace all the α-hydrogens. The **HVZ** reaction brominates the α-carbon of a carboxylic acid. When the α-position is halogenated, the α-carbon can react with nucleophiles.

LDA is used to form an enolate ion in reactions that require the carbonyl compound to be completely converted to the enolate ion before it reacts with an electrophile. If the electrophile is an alkyl halide, the enolate ion is alkylated. The less substituted α-carbon is alkylated when the reaction is under kinetic control; the more substituted α-carbon is alkylated when the reaction is under thermodynamic control. Aldehydes and ketones can be alkylated or acylated via an enamine intermediate. Enolate

ions of β-diketones, β-diesters, β-keto esters, and β-keto nitriles undergo **Michael reactions** with α,β-unsaturated carbonyl compounds. Michael reactions form 1,5-dicarbonyl compounds.

In an **aldol addition**, the enolate ion of an aldehyde or a ketone reacts with the carbonyl carbon of a second molecule of aldehyde or ketone, forming a β-hydroxyaldehyde or a β-hydroxyketone. The new C—C bond forms between the α-carbon of one molecule and the carbon that formerly was the carbonyl carbon of the other molecule. The product of an aldol addition can be dehydrated to give an **aldol condensation** product. Base-catalyzed dehydration is an **E1cB reaction**. In a **Claisen condensation**, the enolate ion of an ester reacts with a second molecule of ester, eliminating an ^-OR group to form a β-keto ester. A **Dieckmann condensation** is an intramolecular Claisen condensation. A **Robinson annulation** is a ring-forming reaction in which a Michael reaction and an intramolecular aldol addition occur sequentially.

Carboxylic acids with a carbonyl group at the 3-position **decarboxylate** when they are heated. Carboxylic acids can be prepared by a **malonic ester synthesis**; the resulting carboxylic acid has two more carbons than the alkyl halide. Similarly, methyl ketones can be prepared by an **acetoacetic ester synthesis**; the carbonyl group and the carbon on either side of it come from acetoacetic ester, and the rest of the methyl ketone comes from the alkyl halide.

When planning the synthesis of a compound that requires the formation of a new carbon–carbon bond, first locate the new bond that must be made, and then determine which of the carbons that form the bond should be the nucleophile and which should be the electrophile.

SUMMARY OF REACTIONS

1. Keto–enol interconversion (Section 19.3)

2. Halogenation of the α-carbon of aldehydes and ketones (Section 19.5)

$$X_2 = Cl_2, Br_2, \text{ or } I_2$$

3. Halogenation of the α-carbon of carboxylic acids: the Hell–Volhard–Zelinski reaction (Section 19.6)

4. When an α-hydrogen is removed, the α-carbon is a nucleophile and reacts with an electrophile (Section 19.7).

5. When the α-carbon is halogenated, the α-carbon is an electrophile and reacts with a nucleophile (Section 19.7).

6. Compounds with halogenated α-carbons can form α,β-unsaturated carbonyl compounds (Section 19.7).

7. Alkylation of the α-carbon of carbonyl compounds (Section 19.9)

8. Alkylation and acylation of the α-carbon of aldehydes and ketones by means of an enamine intermediate (Sections 19.10)

9. Michael reaction: addition of an enolate ion to an α,β-unsaturated carbonyl compound (Sections 19.12 and 19.14)

10. Aldol addition of two aldehydes, two ketones, or an aldehyde and a ketone (Section 19.12)

11. Aldol condensation: dehydration of the product of an aldol addition (Section 19.13)

12. Claisen condensation of two esters (Section 19.15)

13. Condensation of a ketone and an ester (Section 19.16)

add slowly

add slowly

add slowly

14. Robinson annulation (Section 19.18)

15. Decarboxylation of 3-oxocarboxylic acids (Section 19.19)

16. Malonic ester synthesis: preparation of carboxylic acids (Section 19.20)

17. Acetoacetic ester synthesis: preparation of methyl ketones (Section 19.21)

KEY TERMS

acetoacetic ester synthesis (p. 867)
aldol addition (p. 850)
aldol condensation (p. 852)
ambident nucleophile (p. 837)
annulation reaction (p. 862)
α-carbon (p. 831)
carbon acid (p. 831)
Claisen condensation (p. 856)
condensation reaction (p. 852)
crossed aldol addition (p. 855)
crossed Claisen condensation (p. 858)
decarboxylation (p. 864)

Dieckmann condensation (p. 860)
β-diketone (p. 834)
E1cB reaction (p. 853)
enolization (p. 836)
enol tautomer (p. 835)
gluconeogenesis (p. 870)
glycolysis (p. 870)
haloform reaction (p. 841)
Hell–Volhard–Zelinski (HVZ)
   reaction (p. 841)
α-hydrogen (p. 831)
keto–enol interconversion (p. 836)

keto–enol tautomerization (p. 836)
β-keto ester (p. 834)
keto tautomer (p. 835)
Kolbe–Schmitt carboxylation
   reaction (p. 836)
malonic ester synthesis (p. 866)
Michael reaction (p. 849)
mixed condensation (p. 855)
Robinson annulation (p. 862)
Stork enamine reaction (p. 850)
α-substitution reaction (p. 838)
tautomers (p. 835)

PROBLEMS

53. Write a structure for each of the following:
   a. ethyl acetoacetate
   b. α-methylmalonic acid
   c. a β-keto ester
   d. the enol tautomer of cyclopentanone
   e. the carboxylic acid obtained from the malonic ester synthesis when the alkyl halide is propyl bromide

54. Give the products of the following reactions:
   a. diethyl heptanedioate: (1) sodium ethoxide; (2) HCl
   b. pentanoic acid + PBr_3 + Br_2, followed by hydrolysis
   c. acetone + ethyl acetate: (1) sodium ethoxide; (2) HCl
   d. diethyl 2-ethylhexanedioate: (1) sodium ethoxide; (2) HCl
   e. diethyl malonate: (1) sodium ethoxide; (2) isobutyl bromide; (3) HCl, H_2O + Δ
   f. acetophenone + diethyl carbonate: (1) sodium ethoxide; (2) HCl

55. Label the following compounds in order of increasing pK_a value. (Label the most acidic compound 1.)

56. The chemical shifts of nitromethane, dinitromethane, and trinitromethane are at δ 6.10, δ 4.33, and δ 7.52. Match each chemical shift with the compound. Explain how chemical shift correlates with pK_a.

57. Which compound decarboxylates at the lowest temperature?

   A   B   C

58. Give the products of the following reactions:
   a. 1,3-cyclohexanedione + LDA/THF, followed by allyl bromide
   b. dibenzyl ketone + methyl vinyl ketone + excess sodium hydroxide
   c. cyclopentanone: (1) pyrrolidine + trace acid; (2) ethyl bromide; (3) HCl, H_2O
   d. γ-butyrolactone + LDA in THF, followed by methyl iodide
   e. 2,7-octanedione + sodium hydroxide
   f. diethyl 1,2-benzenedicarboxylate + ethyl acetate: (1) excess sodium ethoxide; (2) HCl

59. a. Explain why a racemic mixture of 2-methyl-1-phenyl-1-butanone is formed when (R)-2-methyl-1-phenyl-1-butanone is dissolved in an acidic or basic aqueous solution.
   b. Give an example of another ketone that would undergo acid- or base-catalyzed racemization.

60. What is the product of the following reaction?

$$2 \quad \text{PhCHO} \quad + \quad \text{CH}_3\text{CH}_2\text{COCH}_2\text{CH}_3 \quad \xrightarrow[\Delta]{\text{HO}^-, \text{H}_2\text{O}}$$

add slowly

61. Identify A–L. (*Hint:* A shows three singlets in its ^{1}H NMR spectrum with integral ratios $3 : 2 : 3$ and gives a positive iodoform test; see Section 19.4)

A
$C_5H_8O_3$
$\xrightarrow[\Delta]{\text{HCl, H}_2\text{O}}$ B $\xrightarrow{\text{HO}^-}$ C $\xrightarrow[\Delta]{\text{HCl}}$ D

$\downarrow$ 1. CH$_3$O$^-$
2. CH$_3$Br

E $\xrightarrow[\Delta]{\text{HCl, H}_2\text{O}}$ H $\xrightarrow[\substack{\text{I}_2 \\ \text{excess}}]{\text{HO}^- \\ \text{excess}}$ I $\xrightarrow{\text{SOCl}_2}$ J $\xrightarrow{\text{CH}_3\text{OH}}$ K $\xrightarrow[\text{2. HCl}]{\text{1. CH}_3\text{O}^-}$ L

$\downarrow$ 1. CH$_3$O$^-$
2. CH$_3$Br

F $\xrightarrow[\Delta]{\text{HCl, H}_2\text{O}}$ G

62. Using cyclopentanone as the reactant, show the product of:
   a. acid-catalyzed keto–enol interconversion   **b.** an aldol addition   **c.** an aldol condensation

63. Show how the following compounds could be prepared from cyclohexanone:

64. A β,γ-unsaturated carbonyl compound rearranges to a more stable conjugated α,β-unsaturated compound in the presence of either acid or base.
   a. Propose a mechanism for the base-catalyzed rearrangement.
   b. Propose a mechanism for the acid-catalyzed rearrangement.

a β,γ-unsaturated
carbonyl compound

an α,β-unsaturated
carbonyl compound

$\xrightarrow{\text{H}_3\text{O}^+ \text{ or HO}^-}$

65. There are other condensation reactions similar to the aldol and Claisen condensations:

a. The *Perkin condensation* is the condensation of an aromatic aldehyde and acetic anhydride. Give the product obtained from the following Perkin condensation:

b. What compound would result if water were added to the product of a Perkin condensation?

c. The *Knoevenagel condensation* is the condensation of an aldehyde or a ketone that has no α-hydrogens and a compound such as diethyl malonate that has an α-carbon flanked by two electron-withdrawing groups. Give the product obtained from the following Knoevenagel condensation:

d. What product would be obtained if the product of a Knoevenagel condensation were heated in an aqueous acidic solution?

66. The *Reformatsky reaction* is an addition reaction in which an organozinc reagent is used instead of a Grignard reagent to attack the carbonyl group of an aldehyde or a ketone. Because the organozinc reagent is less reactive than a Grignard reagent, a nucleophilic addition to the ester group does not occur. The organozinc reagent is prepared by treating an α-bromo ester with zinc.

Describe how each of the following compounds could be prepared, using a Reformatsky reaction:

67. The ketone whose ^1H NMR spectrum is shown here was obtained as the product of an acetoacetic ester synthesis. What alkyl halide was used in the synthesis?

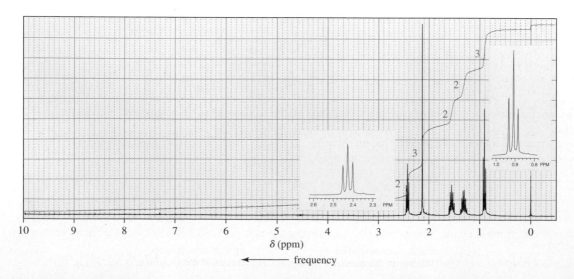

68. Indicate how the following compounds could be synthesized from cyclohexanone and any other necessary reagents:

a.

b.
(two ways)

c.

d.

e.

f.

69. Compound A with molecular formula C_6H_{10} has two peaks in its ^1H NMR spectrum, both of which are singlets (with ratio 9 : 1). Compound A reacts with an acidic aqueous solution containing mercuric sulfate to form compound B, which gives a positive iodoform test (Section 19.4) and has an ^1H NMR spectrum that shows two singlets (with ratio 3 : 1). Identify A and B.

70. Indicate how each of the following compounds could be synthesized from the given starting material and any other necessary reagents:

a.

d.

b.

e.

c.

f.

71. What reagents would be required to carry out the following transformations?

72. Give the products of the following reactions:

a.
1. $CH_3CH_2O^-$
2. H_3O^+

b.
HO^-

c.
HO^-

d.

73. Show how the following compound can be prepared from starting materials that have no more than five carbons.

74. a. Show how the amino acid alanine can be synthesized from propanoic acid. (The structures of the amino acids can be found on page 979.)

b. Show how the amino acid glycine can be synthesized from phthalimide and diethyl 2-bromomalonate.

75. A student tried to prepare the following compounds using aldol condensations. Which of these compounds was she successful in synthesizing? Explain why the other syntheses were not successful.

CH₂=CH—C(=O)—CH₃

A

CH₃CH=C(CH₃)—C(=O)—H

B

CH₂=C(CH₃)—C(=O)—CH₂CH₂CH₃

C

CH₃C(CH₃)=CH—C(=O)—H

D

2-ethylcyclohexenone

E

cyclohexene carbaldehyde

F

2-methylcyclohexene carbaldehyde

G

(CH₃)₂CHC(CH₃)=C(CH₃)—C(=O)—H

H

(CH₃)₂CHCH₂CH=C(CH₃)—C(=O)—H

I

76. Show how the following compounds could be synthesized. The only carbon-containing compounds available to you for each synthesis are shown.

a. CH₃CH₂CH₂OH —?→ CH₃CH₂CH₂CH(CH₃)CH₂OH

b. (CH₃)₂CHOH —?→ (CH₃)₂CHCH₂CH₂CH₃

c. CH₃CH₂OH + (CH₃)₂CHOH —?→ 1,3-dioxane derivative

77. Explain why the following bromoketone forms different bicyclic compounds under different reaction conditions:

25 °C CH₃O⁻ CH₃OH

−78 °C LDA THF

78. A *Mannich reaction* puts a ⟩NCH₂— group on the α-carbon of a carbon acid. Propose a mechanism for the reaction.

HCH(=O) + HN(CH₃)CH₃ + cyclohexanone —trace acid→ 2-(dimethylaminomethyl)cyclohexanone

79. What carbonyl compounds are required to prepare a compound with molecular formula C₁₀H₁₀O whose ¹H NMR spectrum is shown?

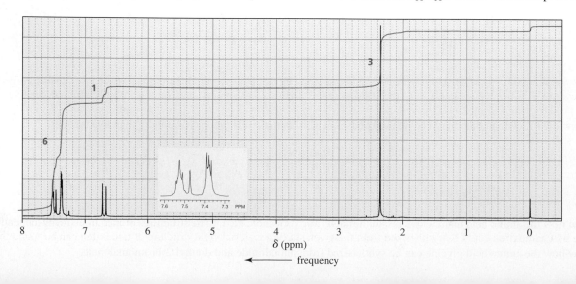

80. Ninhydrin reacts with an amino acid to form a purple-colored compound. Propose a mechanism to account for the formation of the colored compound.

ninhydrin   an amino acid   purple-colored compound

81. A carboxylic acid is formed when an α-haloketone reacts with hydroxide ion. This reaction is called a *Favorskii reaction*. Propose a mechanism for the following Favorskii reaction. (*Hint:* In the first step, HO⁻ removes a proton from the α-carbon that is not bonded to Br; a three-membered ring is formed in the second step; and HO⁻ is a nucleophile in the third step.)

82. An α,β-unsaturated carbonyl compound can be prepared by a reaction known as a selenenylation–oxidation reaction. A selenoxide is formed as an intermediate. Propose a mechanism for the reaction.

a selenoxide

83. a. What carboxylic acid would be formed if the malonic ester synthesis were carried out with one equivalent of malonic ester, one equivalent of 1,5-dibromopentane, and two equivalents of base?
   b. What carboxylic acid would be formed if the malonic ester synthesis were carried out with two equivalents of malonic ester, one equivalent of 1,5-dibromopentane, and two equivalents of base?

84. A *Cannizzaro reaction* is the reaction of an aldehyde that has no α-hydrogens with concentrated aqueous sodium hydroxide. In this reaction, half the aldehyde is converted to a carboxylic acid and the other half is converted to an alcohol. Propose a reasonable mechanism for the following Cannizzaro reaction:

85. Propose a reasonable mechanism for each of the following reactions:

86. The following reaction is known as the *benzoin condensation*. The reaction will not take place if sodium hydroxide is used instead of sodium cyanide. Propose a mechanism for the reaction and explain why the reaction will not occur if hydroxide ion is the base.

benzoin

87. Tamoxifen is a drug that interferes with estrogen binding and therefore helps prevent the occurrence of estrogen-dependent tumors. Describe how tamoxifen could be synthesized from the given starting material. The structure of tamoxifen can be found in Chapter 3, Problem 43.

88. Orsellinic acid, a common constituent of lichens, is synthesized from the condensation of acetyl thioester and malonyl thioester. If a lichen were grown on a medium containing acetate that was radioactively labeled with ^{14}C at the carbonyl carbon, which carbons would be labeled in orsellinic acid?

orsellinic acid

89. Propose a mechanism for the following reaction. (*Hint:* The intermediate has a cumulated double bond.)

90. A compound known as *Hagemann's ester* can be prepared by treating a mixture of formaldehyde and ethyl acetoacetate first with base and then with acid and heat. Write the structure for the product of each of the steps.
  a. The first step is an aldol-like condensation.
  b. The second step is a Michael addition.
  c. The third step is an intramolecular aldol addtion.
  d. The final transformation includes a dehydration and a hydrolysis followed by a decarboxylation.

Hagemann's ester

91. Amobarbital is a sedative marketed under the trade name Amytal. Propose a synthesis of amobarbital, using diethyl malonate and urea (page 2) as two of the starting materials.

Amytal®

92. Propose a reasonable mechanism for each of the following reactions:

  a.

93. a. Ketoprofen, like ibuprofen, is an anti-inflammatory analgesic. How could ketoprofen be synthesized from the given starting material?

ketoprofen

  b. Ketoprofen and ibuprofen both have a propanoic acid substituent (see Problem 86 in Chapter 17). Explain why the identical subunits are synthesized in different ways.

More About Oxidation–Reduction Reactions and Amines

The two chapters in Part 7 discuss in greater detail two topics that were first presented in preceding chapters: oxidation–reduction reactions and amines.

CHAPTER 20
More About Oxidation–Reduction Reactions

The first oxidation reaction of an organic compound we encountered was in Chapter 4. There we saw that oxidation reactions *decrease* the number of C—H bonds or *increase* the number of C—O, C—N, or C—X bonds (where X denotes a halogen). We also encountered the first reduction reaction of an organic compound in Chapter 4, where we saw that reduction reactions *increase* the number of C—H bonds or *decrease* the number of C—O, C—N, or C—X bonds. **Chapter 20** reviews some of the oxidation and reduction reactions you have seen previously and introduces you to many more.

CHAPTER 21
More About Amines • Heterocyclic Compounds

Chapter 21 extends the coverage of amines and discusses the chemistry of heterocyclic compounds. We have seen that amines do not undergo addition, substitution, or elimination reactions. Their importance lies in their reactions with other organic compounds as bases and nucleophiles. We first met amines in Chapter 1, and we have continued to encounter them in almost every chapter since.

20

More About Oxidation–Reduction Reactions

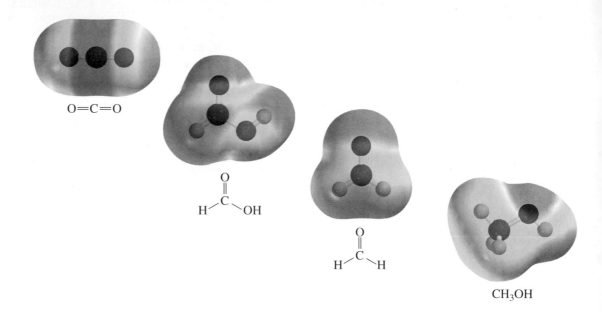

O=C=O

$$H-C(=O)-OH$$

$$H-C(=O)-H$$

CH_3OH

AN IMPORTANT GROUP OF ORGANIC REACTIONS CONSISTS OF THOSE THAT INVOLVE the transfer of electrons from one molecule to another. Organic chemists use these reactions—called **oxidation–reduction reactions** or **redox reactions**—to synthesize a large variety of compounds. Redox reactions are also important in biological systems because many of these reactions release energy. These will be discussed in Chapters 25 and 26. You have already seen a number of oxidation and reduction reactions in other chapters, but discussing them as a group will give you the opportunity to compare them.

In an oxidation–reduction reaction, one species loses electrons and one gains electrons. The species that loses electrons is oxidized, and the one that gains electrons is reduced. One way to remember the difference between oxidation and reduction is with the phrase "LEO the lion says GER": *Loss of Electrons is Oxidation; Gain of Electrons is Reduction.*

The following is an example of an oxidation–reduction reaction involving inorganic reagents:

$$Cu^+ + Fe^{3+} \longrightarrow Cu^{2+} + Fe^{2+}$$

In this reaction, Cu^+ loses an electron. Thus, Cu^+ is oxidized. Fe^{3+} gains an electron, and it is therefore reduced. This reaction demonstrates two important features of oxidation–reduction reactions. First, *oxidation is always coupled with reduction.* In other words, a species cannot gain electrons (be reduced) unless another species in the reaction simultaneously loses electrons (is oxidized). Second, the species that is oxidized (Cu^+) is called the **reducing agent**: it loses the electrons that the species being reduced (Fe^{3+}) gains. Similarly, the species that is reduced (Fe^{3+}) is called the **oxidizing agent**: it gains the electrons the species being oxidized (Cu^+) loses.

20.1 OXIDATION–REDUCTION REACTIONS OF ORGANIC COMPOUNDS: AN OVERVIEW

It is easy to tell whether an organic compound has been oxidized or reduced simply by looking at the change in the compound's structure. We will be looking primarily at reactions where **oxidation** or **reduction** has taken place on carbon: if the reaction increases the number of $C—H$ bonds or decreases the number of $C—O$, $C—N$, or $C—X$ bonds (where X denotes a halogen), the compound has been reduced. If the reaction decreases the number of $C—H$ bonds or increases the number of $C—O$, $C—N$, or $C—X$ bonds, the compound has been oxidized.

Let's now look at some examples of oxidation–reduction reactions that take place on carbon. Notice that in each of the following reactions, the product has more $C—H$ bonds than the reactant has: the alkene, ketone, and aldehyde, therefore, have been reduced. Hydrogen, hydrazine, and sodium borohydride are the reducing agents. You have seen these reactions in previous chapters (Sections 4.12, 15.16, and 18.8).

> **Reduction at carbon increases the number of C—H bonds or decreases the number of C—O, C—N, or C—X bonds.**
>
> **Oxidation at carbon decreases the number of C—H bonds or increases the number of C—O, C—N, or C—X bonds.**

$$RCH{=}CHR \xrightarrow[\text{Pd/C}]{H_2} RCH_2CH_2R$$

an alkene

$$\underset{\text{a ketone}}{\overset{\displaystyle\overset{O}{\|}}{R{-}C{-}R}} \xrightarrow[HO^-,\ \Delta]{H_2NNH_2} RCH_2R$$

$$\underset{\text{an aldehyde}}{\overset{\displaystyle\overset{O}{\|}}{R{-}C{-}H}} \xrightarrow[\text{2. } H_3O^+]{\text{1. NaBH}_4} RCH_2OH$$

In the first reaction of the next group, the number of $C—Br$ bonds increases. In the second and third reactions, the number of $C—H$ bonds decreases, and the number of $C—O$ bonds increases. Thus, the alkene, aldehyde, and alcohol have been oxidized. Bromine and chromic acid (H_2CrO_4) are the oxidizing agents. You have also seen these reactions in previous chapters (Sections 4.8 and 10.5).

$$RCH{=}CHR \xrightarrow{Br_2} \underset{}{\overset{\overset{\text{Br Br}}{\displaystyle|\ \ |}}{RCHCHR}}$$

an alkene

$$\underset{\text{an aldehyde}}{\overset{\displaystyle\overset{O}{\|}}{R{-}C{-}H}} \xrightarrow{H_2CrO_4} \underset{}{\overset{\displaystyle\overset{O}{\|}}{R{-}C{-}OH}}$$

$$\underset{\text{an alcohol}}{\overset{\overset{\text{OH}}{\displaystyle|}}{RCHR}} \xrightarrow{H_2CrO_4} \underset{}{\overset{\displaystyle\overset{O}{\|}}{R{-}C{-}R}}$$

When water is added to an alkene, the product has one more $C—H$ bond than the reactant, but it also has one more $C—O$ bond. In this reaction, one carbon is reduced and another is oxidized. The two processes cancel each other as far as the overall molecule is concerned, so the overall reaction is neither an oxidation nor a reduction.

$$RCH{=}CHR \xrightarrow[H_2O]{H_2SO_4} \underset{\underset{\text{OH}}{\displaystyle|}}{RCH_2CHR}$$

Oxidation–reduction reactions that take place on nitrogen or sulfur produce similar structural changes. The number of N—H or S—H bonds increases in reduction reactions, and the number of N—O or S—O bonds increases in oxidation reactions. In the following reactions, nitrobenzene and the disulfide are reduced (Sections 16.1 and 23.8), and the thiol is oxidized to a sulfonic acid:

Many oxidizing and reducing reagents are available to organic chemists. This chapter highlights only a small fraction of the available reagents. The ones selected are some of the more common ones that illustrate particular types of transformations caused by oxidation or reduction.

chem Tutorial:
place Oxidation-reduction reactions

PROBLEM 1♦

Identify each of the following reactions as an oxidation reaction, a reduction reaction, or neither:

a.

b. $RCH{=}CHR \xrightarrow{HBr} RCH_2CHR$ (Br)

c.

d. $CH_3CH_2OH \xrightarrow{H_2CrO_4}$

e. $CH_3C{\equiv}N \xrightarrow[\text{Raney Nickel}]{H_2} CH_3CH_2NH_2$

f. $CH_3CH_2CH_2Br \xrightarrow{HO^-} CH_3CH_2CH_2OH$

20.2 REDUCTION REACTIONS

An organic compound is reduced when hydrogen (H_2) is added to it. A molecule of H_2 can be thought of as being composed of (1) two hydrogen atoms, (2) two electrons and two protons, or (3) a hydride ion and a proton. In the sections that follow, you will see that these three ways to describe H_2 correspond to the three mechanisms by which H_2 is added to an organic compound.

components of H:H

Reduction by Addition of Two Hydrogen Atoms

We have seen that hydrogen can be added to carbon–carbon double and triple bonds in the presence of a metal catalyst (Sections 4.11 and 6.9). These reactions, called **catalytic hydrogenations**, are reduction reactions because there are more C—H bonds in the products than in the reactants. Alkenes and alkynes are both reduced to alkanes.

$$CH_3CH_2CH{=}CH_2 \; + \; H_2 \quad \xrightarrow{\text{Pd/C or PtO}_2} \quad CH_3CH_2CH_2CH_3$$
1-butene — **butane**

$$CH_3CH_2CH_2C{\equiv}CH \; + \; 2\,H_2 \quad \xrightarrow{\text{Pd/C or PtO}_2} \quad CH_3CH_2CH_2CH_2CH_3$$
1-pentyne — **pentane**

We have seen that the catalytic hydrogenation of an alkyne can be stopped at a cis alkene if a partially deactivated catalyst is used (Section 6.9).

$$CH_3C{\equiv}CCH_3 \; + \; H_2 \quad \xrightarrow[\text{catalyst}]{\text{Lindlar}} \quad$$

cis-**2-butene**

2-butyne

In a catalytic hydrogenation, the H—H bond breaks homolytically (Section 4.11). This means that reduction occurs through the addition of two hydrogen atoms to the organic molecule.

Catalytic hydrogenation can also be used to reduce carbon–nitrogen double and triple bonds. The reaction products are amines (Sections 17.19 and 18.8).

$$CH_3CH_2CH{=}NCH_3 \; + \; H_2 \quad \xrightarrow{\text{Pd/C}} \quad CH_3CH_2CH_2NHCH_3$$
methylpropylamine

$$CH_3CH_2CH_2C{\equiv}N \; + \; 2\,H_2 \quad \xrightarrow{\text{Raney Nickel}} \quad CH_3CH_2CH_2CH_2NH_2$$
butylamine

The carbonyl group of ketones and aldehydes can be reduced by catalytic hydrogenation. A palladium catalyst is not very effective at reducing these carbonyl groups. However, they are reduced easily over a nickel catalyst. (Raney nickel is finely dispersed nickel with adsorbed hydrogen, so an external source of H_2 is not needed.) Aldehydes are reduced to primary alcohols, and ketones are reduced to secondary alcohols.

an aldehyde — RCH$_2$OH — **a primary alcohol**

a ketone — RCHR (OH) — **a secondary alcohol**

The reduction of an acyl chloride can be stopped at an aldehyde if a partially deactivated catalyst is used. This reaction is known as the **Rosenmund reduction**. The catalyst for the Rosenmund reduction is similar to the partially deactivated palladium catalyst used to stop the reduction of an alkyne at a cis alkene (Section 6.9).

an acyl chloride — **an aldehyde**

B I O G R A P H Y

Murray Raney (1885–1966) *was born in Kentucky. He received a B.A. from the University of Kentucky in 1909, and in 1951 the university awarded him an honorary Doctor of Science. He worked at the Gilman Paint and Varnish Co. in Chattanooga, Tennessee, where he patented several chemical and metallurgical processes. In 1963, the company was sold and renamed W. R. Grace & Co., Raney Catalyst Division.*

B I O G R A P H Y

Karl W. Rosenmund (1884–1965) *was born in Berlin. He received a Ph.D. from the University of Bern, studying under Otto Diels (Section 7.12), and was a professor of chemistry at the University of Kiel.*

The carbonyl groups of carboxylic acids, esters, and amides are less reactive than the carbonyl groups of aldehydes and ketones and therefore are harder to reduce (Section 18.6). They cannot be reduced by catalytic hydrogenation (except under extreme conditions). They can, however, be reduced by a method we will discuss later in this section.

PROBLEM 2♦

Give the products of the following reactions:

a. [benzaldehyde] $\xrightarrow[\text{Raney Ni}]{H_2}$

b. $CH_3CH_2CH_2C{\equiv}N \xrightarrow[\text{Raney Ni}]{H_2}$

c. $CH_3CH_2CH_2C{\equiv}CCH_3 \xrightarrow[\substack{\text{Lindlar}\\\text{catalyst}}]{H_2}$

d. [cyclohexanone] $\xrightarrow[\text{Raney Ni}]{H_2}$

e. $CH_3\text{–C(=O)–}OCH_3 \xrightarrow[\text{Raney Ni}]{H_2}$

f. $CH_3\text{–C(=O)–}Cl \xrightarrow[\text{Raney Ni}]{H_2}$

g. $CH_3\text{–C(=O)–}Cl \xrightarrow[\substack{\text{partially}\\\text{deactivated}\\\text{Pd}}]{H_2}$

h. [cyclohexylidene]$=NCH_3 \xrightarrow[\text{Pd/C}]{H_2}$

Reduction by Addition of an Electron, a Proton, an Electron, and a Proton

When a compound is reduced using sodium in liquid ammonia, sodium donates an electron to the compound and ammonia donates a proton. This sequence is repeated, so the overall reaction adds two electrons and two protons to the compound. Such a reaction is known as a **dissolving-metal reduction**.

In Section 6.9, you saw the mechanism for the dissolving-metal reduction that converts an alkyne to a trans alkene.

$$CH_3C{\equiv}CCH_3 \xrightarrow[\text{NH}_3\text{ (liq)}]{\text{Na or Li}}$$
2-butyne

[structure of *trans*-2-butene with H₃C and H on one side, H and CH₃ on other]

***trans*-2-butene**

Sodium (or lithium) in liquid ammonia cannot reduce a carbon–carbon double bond. This reagent is therefore useful for reducing a triple bond in a compound that also contains a double bond.

$$CH_3\overset{\displaystyle CH_3}{C}{=}CHCH_2C{\equiv}CCH_3 \xrightarrow[\text{NH}_3\text{ (liq)}]{\text{Na or Li}} CH_3\overset{\displaystyle CH_3}{C}{=}CHCH_2\text{–}[C{=}C]$$

Reduction by Addition of a Hydride Ion and a Proton

Carbonyl groups are easily reduced by metal hydrides such as sodium borohydride ($NaBH_4$) or lithium aluminum hydride ($LiAlH_4$). The actual reducing agent in **metal-hydride reductions** is hydride ion ($H{:}^-$). Hydride ion adds to the carbonyl carbon, forming an alkoxide ion that is subsequently protonated. In other words, the carbonyl group is reduced by the addition of an H⁻ followed by the addition of an H⁺. The mechanisms for reduction by these reagents were discussed in Section 18.6.

Aldehydes, ketones, and acyl halides can be reduced to alcohols by sodium borohydride.

$$\underset{\text{an aldehyde}}{\overset{\displaystyle O}{\underset{R}{\parallel}}\underset{}{C}\diagup H} \xrightarrow[\text{2. H}_3\text{O}^+]{\text{1. NaBH}_4} \underset{\text{a primary alcohol}}{RCH_2OH}$$

$$\underset{\text{a ketone}}{\overset{\displaystyle O}{\underset{R}{\parallel}}\underset{}{C}\diagup R} \xrightarrow[\text{2. H}_3\text{O}^+]{\text{1. NaBH}_4} \underset{\text{a secondary alcohol}}{\overset{\displaystyle OH}{\underset{}{RCHR}}}$$

$$\underset{\text{an acyl chloride}}{\overset{\displaystyle O}{\underset{R}{\parallel}}\underset{}{C}\diagup Cl} \xrightarrow[\text{2. H}_3\text{O}^+]{\text{1. NaBH}_4} \underset{\text{a primary alcohol}}{RCH_2OH}$$

The metal–hydrogen bonds in lithium aluminum hydride are more polar (that is, the difference in electronegativity between aluminum and hydrogen is larger) than those in sodium borohydride, so $LiAlH_4$ is a stronger reducing agent. Consequently, both $LiAlH_4$ and $NaBH_4$ reduce aldehydes, ketones, and acyl halides, but $LiAlH_4$ is not generally used for this purpose since $NaBH_4$ is safer and easier to use. $LiAlH_4$ is generally used to reduce only compounds—such as carboxylic acids, esters, and amides—that cannot be reduced by the milder reagent.

> The numbers in front of the reagents above or below a reaction arrow indicate that the second reagent is not added until reaction with the first reagent is completed.

$$\underset{\text{a carboxylic acid}}{\overset{\displaystyle O}{\underset{R}{\parallel}}\underset{}{C}\diagup OH} \xrightarrow[\text{2. H}_3\text{O}^+]{\text{1. LiAlH}_4} \underset{\text{a primary alcohol}}{RCH_2OH} + H_2O$$

$$\underset{\text{an ester}}{\overset{\displaystyle O}{\underset{R}{\parallel}}\underset{}{C}\diagup OCH_3} \xrightarrow[\text{2. H}_3\text{O}^+]{\text{1. LiAlH}_4} \underset{\text{a primary alcohol}}{RCH_2OH} + CH_3OH$$

Replacing some of the hydrogens of $LiAlH_4$ with alkoxy (OR) groups decreases the reactivity of the metal hydride. For example, lithium tri-*tert*-butoxyaluminum hydride reduces an acyl chloride to an aldehyde, whereas $LiAlH_4$ or $NaBH_4$ reduces the acyl chloride all the way to an alcohol.

$$\underset{\text{an acyl chloride}}{\overset{\displaystyle O}{\underset{R}{\parallel}}\underset{}{C}\diagup Cl} \xrightarrow[\text{2. H}_2\text{O}]{\text{1. LiAl[OC(CH}_3)_3]_3\text{H, } -78\ °\text{C}} \underset{\text{an aldehyde}}{\overset{\displaystyle O}{\underset{R}{\parallel}}\underset{}{C}\diagup H}$$

The carbonyl group of an amide is reduced to a methylene group (CH_2) by lithium aluminum hydride (Section 18.6). Primary, secondary, and tertiary amines are formed, depending on the number of substituents bonded to the nitrogen of the amide. To obtain the amine in its neutral basic form, acid is not used in the second step of the reaction.

$$\underset{\text{an amide}}{\overset{\displaystyle O}{\underset{R}{\parallel}}\underset{}{C}\diagup NH_2} \xrightarrow[\text{2. H}_2\text{O}]{\text{1. LiAlH}_4} \underset{\text{a primary amine}}{RCH_2NH_2}$$

The multiply bonded carbon atoms of alkenes and alkynes do not possess a partial positive charge and therefore will not react with reagents that reduce compounds by donating a hydride ion.

$$RCH{=}CH_2 \xrightarrow{\text{NaBH}_4} \text{no reduction reaction}$$

$$RC{\equiv}CH \xrightarrow{\text{NaBH}_4} \text{no reduction reaction}$$

The reducing agents shown in this section are only a fraction of those available to the synthetic chemist.

PROBLEM 3♦

Give the products of the following reactions.

a.
$$CH_3\overset{\displaystyle O}{\overset{\displaystyle \|}{C}}NHCH_3 \xrightarrow[\text{2. H}_2\text{O}]{\text{1. LiAlH}_4}$$

b.
$$CH_3\overset{\displaystyle O}{\overset{\displaystyle \|}{C}}\underset{\underset{\displaystyle CH_3}{|}}{N}CH_3 \xrightarrow[\text{2. H}_2\text{O}]{\text{1. LiAlH}_4}$$

PROBLEM 4♦

Give the products of the following reactions:

a. Ph–C(=O)–NH₂ $\xrightarrow[\text{2. H}_2\text{O}]{\text{1. LiAlH}_4}$

d. cyclohexyl–C(=O)–OCH₂CH₃ $\xrightarrow[\text{2. H}_3\text{O}^+]{\text{1. LiAlH}_4}$

b. Ph–C(=O)–OH $\xrightarrow[\text{2. H}_3\text{O}^+]{\text{1. NaBH}_4}$

e. CH_3CH_2–C(=O)–$NHCH_2CH_3$ $\xrightarrow[\text{2. H}_2\text{O}]{\text{1. NaBH}_4}$

c. CH_3CH_2–C(=O)–CH_2CH_3 $\xrightarrow[\text{2. H}_3\text{O}^+]{\text{1. NaBH}_4}$

f. $CH_3CH_2CH_2$–C(=O)–OH $\xrightarrow[\text{2. H}_3\text{O}^+]{\text{1. LiAlH}_4}$

PROBLEM 5♦

Can carbon–nitrogen double and triple bonds be reduced by lithium aluminum hydride? Explain your answer.

20.3 CHEMOSELECTIVE REACTIONS

A **chemoselective reaction** is a reaction in which a reagent reacts with one functional group in preference to another. For example, $NaBH_4$ in isopropyl alcohol reduces aldehydes faster than it reduces ketones.

$$\xrightarrow[\text{isopropyl alcohol}]{\text{NaBH}_4}$$

In contrast, $NaBH_4$ in aqueous ethanol at $-15\,^{\circ}\text{C}$ in the presence of cerium trichloride reduces ketones faster than it reduces aldehydes.

$$\xrightarrow[\substack{\text{C}_2\text{H}_5\text{OH/H}_2\text{O} \\ -15\,^{\circ}\text{C}}]{\text{NaBH}_4,\ \text{CeCl}_3}$$

Because sodium borohydride cannot reduce an ester, an amide, or a carboxylic acid, it can be used to selectively reduce an aldehyde or a ketone group in a compound that also contains a less reactive carbonyl group. Acid is not used in the second step of the reaction shown here to avoid hydrolyzing the ester:

Because sodium borohydride cannot reduce carbon–carbon double bonds, a carbonyl group in a compound that also has an alkene functional group can be selectively reduced. Acid is not used in the second step of the reaction to avoid addition of the acid to the double bond.

PROBLEM 6♦

What reducing agents should be used to obtain the desired target molecules?

PROBLEM 7♦

Explain why terminal alkynes cannot be reduced by Na in liquid NH_3.

PROBLEM 8

Give the products of the following reactions:

PROBLEM 9   SOLVED

How could you synthesize the following compounds from starting materials containing no more than four carbons?

Solution to 9a   The six-membered ring indicates that the compound can be synthesized by means of a Diels–Alder reaction (Section 7.12).

20.4 OXIDATION OF ALCOHOLS

Oxidation is the reverse of reduction. For example, a ketone is *reduced* to a secondary alcohol; the reverse reaction is the *oxidation* of a secondary alcohol to a ketone.

$$ \text{ketone} \underset{\text{oxidation}}{\overset{\text{reduction}}{\rightleftharpoons}} \text{secondary alcohol} $$

We have seen that chromic acid (H_2CrO_4) is a reagent commonly used to oxidize secondary alcohols to ketones (Section 10.5).

$$ \underset{\textbf{secondary alcohol}}{R-\overset{\overset{\displaystyle OH}{|}}{C}H-R} \xrightarrow{H_2CrO_4} \underset{\textbf{ketone}}{R-\overset{\overset{\displaystyle O}{\|}}{C}-R} $$

Primary alcohols are initially oxidized to aldehydes by chromic acid and other chromium-containing reagents. The reaction does not stop at the aldehyde, however. Instead, the aldehyde is further oxidized to a carboxylic acid (Section 10.5).

$$ \underset{\textbf{a primary alcohol}}{R-CH_2OH} \xrightarrow{H_2CrO_4} \left[\underset{\textbf{an aldehyde}}{\overset{\overset{\displaystyle O}{\|}}{R}\overset{}{\underset{}{C}}H} \right] \xrightarrow[\text{oxidation}]{\text{further}} \underset{\textbf{a carboxylic acid}}{\overset{\overset{\displaystyle O}{\|}}{R}\overset{}{\underset{}{C}}OH} $$

These reactions are easily recognized as oxidations because the number of C—H bonds in the reactant decreases and the number of C—O bonds increases.

The Role of Hydrates in the Oxidation of Primary Alcohols

When a primary alcohol is oxidized to a carboxylic acid, the alcohol is initially oxidized to an aldehyde that is in equilibrium with its hydrate (Section 18.9). It is the hydrate that is subsequently oxidized to a carboxylic acid.

We have seen that if the reaction is carried out with pyridinium chlorochromate (PCC), oxidation can be stopped at the aldehyde (Section 10.5). Because PCC is used in an anhydrous solvent, water is not available to form the hydrate.

$$ CH_3CH_2OH \xrightarrow{H_2CrO_4} \underset{}{CH_3}\overset{\overset{\displaystyle O}{\|}}{C}H \underset{H_2O}{\overset{HCl}{\rightleftharpoons}} CH_3\overset{\overset{\displaystyle OH}{|}}{C}H \underset{\underset{\displaystyle OH}{|}}{} \xrightarrow{H_2CrO_4} CH_3\overset{\overset{\displaystyle O}{\|}}{C}OH $$

Because of the toxicity of chromium-based reagents, other methods for the oxidation of alcohols have been developed. One of the most widely employed because its mild conditions do not affect most other functional groups, called the **Swern oxidation**, uses dimethyl sulfoxide [$(CH_3)_2SO$], oxalyl chloride [$(COCl)_2$], and triethylamine. Since the reaction is *not* carried out in an aqueous solution, the oxidation of a primary alcohol stops at the aldehyde (as in PCC oxidation). Secondary alcohols are oxidized to ketones.

BIOGRAPHY

Daniel Swern (1916–1982) *was born in New York. He received a Ph.D. from the University of Maryland and was a professor of chemistry at Temple University.*

The actual oxidizing agent in the Swern oxidation is dimethylchlorosulfonium ion, which is formed from an S_N2 reaction between dimethyl sulfoxide and oxalyl chloride (see Problem 60).

MECHANISM FOR THE SWERN OXIDATION

- The alcohol displaces the chloride ion from the dimethylchlorosulfonium ion in an S_N2 reaction.
- The product of the first step loses a proton.
- An E2 reaction forms the aldehyde (or the ketone).

chem place Tutorial:
Oxidation of alcohols

Recall that oxidation of an alcohol by chromic acid involves the same three steps: an S_N2 reaction, loss of a proton, and an E2 reaction (Section 10.5).

Treating Alcoholism with Antabuse

Disulfiram, most commonly known by one of its trade names, Antabuse, is used to treat alcoholism. After the drug is taken, it causes violently unpleasant effects if ethanol is consumed within the next two days.

Antabuse®

Antabuse inhibits aldehyde dehydrogenase, the enzyme responsible for oxidizing acetaldehyde (a product of ethanol metabolism) to acetic acid, resulting in a buildup of acetaldehyde. It is the acetaldehyde that causes the unpleasant physiological effects of intoxication: intense flushing, nausea, dizziness, sweating, throbbing headaches, decreased blood pressure, and, ultimately, shock. Consequently, Antabuse should be taken only under strict medical supervision. In some people, aldehyde dehydrogenase does not function properly even under normal circumstances. Their symptoms in response to ingesting alcohol are nearly the same as those of individuals who are medicated with Antabuse.

Antabuse inhibits this enzyme

$$CH_3CH_2OH \xrightarrow{\text{alcohol dehydrogenase}} \underset{\text{acetaldehyde}}{CH_3-\overset{O}{\overset{\|}{C}}-H} \xrightarrow{\text{aldehyde dehydrogenase}} \underset{\text{acetic acid}}{CH_3-\overset{O}{\overset{\|}{C}}-OH}$$

ethanol

Fetal Alcohol Syndrome

The damage done to a human fetus when the mother drinks alcohol during her pregnancy is known as *fetal alcohol syndrome.* The harmful effects—growth retardation, decreased mental func- tioning, and facial and limb abnormalities—are attributable to acetaldehyde, formed from the oxidation of ethanol, crossing the placenta and accumulating in the liver of the fetus.

Secondary alcohols are oxidized to ketones.

Primary alcohols are oxidized to aldehydes or to carboxylic acids.

PROBLEM 10

Give the product formed from the reaction of each of the following alcohols with

a. chromic acid.
b. the reagents required for a Swern oxidation.

1. 3-pentanol	**3.** 2-methyl-2-pentanol	**5.** cyclohexanol
2. 1-pentanol	**4.** 2,4-hexanediol	**6.** 1,4-butanediol

PROBLEM 11

Propose a mechanism for the chromic acid oxidation of 1-propanol to propanal.

20.5 OXIDATION OF ALDEHYDES AND KETONES

Aldehydes are oxidized to carboxylic acids. Because aldehydes are easier to oxidize than primary alcohols, any of the reagents described in the preceding section or in Section 10.5 for oxidizing primary alcohols to carboxylic acids can be used to oxidize aldehydes to carboxylic acids.

$$\underset{\textbf{an aldehyde}}{R-\overset{\overset{\displaystyle O}{\|}}{C}-H} \xrightarrow{\textbf{H}_2\textbf{CrO}_4} \underset{\textbf{a carboxylic acid}}{R-\overset{\overset{\displaystyle O}{\|}}{C}-OH}$$

Silver oxide is a mild oxidizing agent. *Tollens reagent,* a dilute solution of silver oxide in aqueous ammonia, can oxidize an aldehyde, but it is too weak to oxidize an alcohol or any other functional group. An advantage of using Tollens reagent to oxidize an aldehyde is that the reaction occurs under basic conditions. Therefore, you do not have to worry about other functional groups in the molecule that could undergo a reaction in an acidic solution.

$$\underset{}{R-\overset{\overset{\displaystyle O}{\|}}{C}-H} \xrightarrow[\textbf{2. H}_3\textbf{O}^+]{\textbf{1. Ag}_2\textbf{O, NH}_3} \underset{}{R-\overset{\overset{\displaystyle O}{\|}}{C}-OH} + \underset{\substack{\textbf{metallic}\\\textbf{silver}}}{\text{Ag}}$$

The specific oxidizing agent in Tollens reagent is Ag^+, which is reduced to metallic silver. This reaction is the basis of the **Tollens test**; if Tollens reagent is added to a small amount of an aldehyde in a test tube, the inside of the test tube becomes coated with a shiny mirror of metallic silver. Consequently, if a mirror is not formed when Tollens reagent is added to a compound, we can conclude that the compound does not contain an aldehyde group.

Ketones do not react with most of the reagents used to oxidize aldehydes. However, both aldehydes *and* ketones can be oxidized by the conjugate base of a peroxyacid. Aldehydes are oxidized to carboxylic acids, and ketones are oxidized to esters. Recall that a **peroxyacid** contains one more oxygen than a carboxylic acid (Section 4.10), and it is this oxygen that is inserted between the carbonyl carbon and the H of an aldehyde or the R of a ketone. The reaction is called a **Baeyer–Villiger oxidation**. A particularly good reagent for the Baeyer–Villiger reaction is peroxytrifluoroacetate ion.

Baeyer-Villiger oxidations

an aldehyde + CF_3COO^- ⟶ a carboxylic acid + CF_3CO^-

a ketone + CF_3COO^- ⟶ an ester + CF_3CO^-

B I O G R A P H Y

Victor Villiger (1868–1934), *a Swiss chemist, graduated from the University of Geneva. He was Baeyer's student at the University of Munich. The two published the first paper on the Baeyer–Villiger oxidation in Chemische Berichte in 1899.*

Aldehydes are oxidized to carboxylic acids.

Ketones are oxidized to esters.

If the two alkyl substituents attached to the carbonyl group of the ketone are not the same, on what side of the carbonyl carbon is the oxygen inserted? For example, does the oxidation of cyclohexyl methyl ketone form methyl cyclohexanecarboxylate or cyclohexyl acetate?

cyclohexyl methyl ketone $\xrightarrow{CF_3COO^-}$ methyl cyclohexanecarboxylate or cyclohexyl acetate

To answer this question, we need to look at the mechanism for the reaction.

MECHANISM FOR THE BAEYER–VILLIGER OXIDATION

a weak O—O bond

an unstable intermediate

- The ketone and the peroxyacid form an unstable tetrahedral intermediate with a weak O—O bond.
- As the O—O bond breaks heterolytically, one of the alkyl groups migrates to an oxygen. This migration is similar to the 1,2-shifts that occur when carbocations rearrange (Section 4.7).

Studies of the migration tendencies of different groups have established the following order:

relative migration tendencies

most likely to migrate ⟶ H > *tert*-alkyl > *sec*-alkyl = phenyl > primary alkyl > methyl ⟵ least likely to migrate

Therefore, the product of the Baeyer–Villiger oxidation of cyclohexyl methyl ketone will be cyclohexyl acetate because a secondary alkyl group (the cyclohexyl group) is more likely to migrate than a methyl group. Aldehydes are always oxidized to carboxylic acids, since H has the greatest tendency to migrate.

PROBLEM 12

Give the products of the following reactions:

a. phenyl C(=O)CH$_2$CH$_3$ $\xrightarrow{\text{CF}_3\text{COO}^-}$

b. benzaldehyde $\xrightarrow{\text{CF}_3\text{COO}^-}$

c. 2-methylcyclopentanone $\xrightarrow{\text{CF}_3\text{COO}^-}$

d. 2-methyl-4,4-dimethyl-3-pentanone $\xrightarrow{\text{CF}_3\text{COO}^-}$

e. CH$_3$CH$_2$C(=O)H $\xrightarrow[\text{2. H}_3\text{O}^+]{\text{1. Ag}_2\text{O, NH}_3}$

f. CH$_3$CH$_2$C(=O)CH$_3$ $\xrightarrow[\text{2. H}_3\text{O}^+]{\text{1. Ag}_2\text{O, NH}_3}$

20.6 DESIGNING A SYNTHESIS VIII: CONTROLLING STEREOCHEMISTRY

The target molecule of a synthesis may be one of several stereoisomers, in which case a chemist must consider the stereochemical outcome of every step and use highly stereoselective reagents to achieve the desired configuration. If the stereochemistry of the reactions is not controlled, the mixture of stereoisomers obtained as products may be difficult or even impossible to separate.

The number of possible stereoisomers complicating a synthesis depends on the number of double bonds and asymmetric centers in the target molecule because each double bond can exist in an *E* or *Z* configuration (Section 3.5) and each asymmetric center can have an *R* or *S* configuration (Section 5.7). In addition, if the target molecule has rings with a common bond, the rings can be either trans fused or cis fused (Section 2.15). In designing a synthesis, care must be taken to make sure that each double bond, each asymmetric center, and each ring fusion in the product has the appropriate configuration.

We have seen that an enantiomerically pure compound can be obtained if an enzyme is used to catalyze the reaction that forms the compound. Because enzymes are chiral, enzyme-catalyzed reactions result in the exclusive formation of one enantiomer (Section 5.20). For example, ketones are enzymatically reduced to alcohols by enzymes called alcohol dehydrogenases. Whether the *R* or the *S* enantiomer is formed depends on the particular alcohol dehydrogenase used: alcohol dehydrogenase from the bacterium *Lactobacillus kefir* forms *R* alcohols, whereas alcohol dehydrogenases from yeast, horse liver, and the bacterium *Thermoanaerobium brocki* form *S* alcohols. The alcohol dehydrogenases use the biological reducing agent NADPH to carry out the reduction (Section 25.1). These reactions are examples of **enantioselective reactions**—they form more of one enantiomer than of another.

(*R*)-2,2,2-trifluoro-
1-phenyl-1-ethanol

(*S*)-2,2,2-trifluoro-
1-phenyl-1-ethanol

Unfortunately, this method of controlling the configuration of a target molecule is not universally useful because enzymes require substrates of very specific size and shape (Section 24.8).

Chemists now are designing chiral catalysts—catalysts that are not enzymes that can be used to obtain an enantiomerically pure compound. For example, we have seen that an alkene can be oxidized to an epoxide by a peroxyacid (Section 4.9).

Alkenes can be oxidized to epoxides.

$$RCH{=}CH_2 \ + \ R{-}\overset{\overset{O}{\|}}{C}{-}OOH \ \longrightarrow \ RCH{-}CH_2 \ + \ R{-}\overset{\overset{O}{\|}}{C}{-}OH$$

an alkene   **a peroxyacid**   **an epoxide**   **a carboxylic acid**

An enantiomerically pure epoxide of an allylic alcohol can be prepared by treating the alcohol with *tert*-butyl hydroperoxide, titanium isopropoxide, and enantiomerically pure diethyl tartrate (DET). The structure of the epoxide depends on which enantiomer of diethyl tartrate is used.

The 2001 Nobel Prize in Chemistry was awarded to **K. Barry Sharpless, William S. Knowles,** *and* **Ryoji Noyori** *for their work in the field of asymmetric catalysis.*

K. Barry Sharpless *was born in Philadelphia in 1941. He received a B.A. from Dartmouth College in 1963 and a Ph.D. in chemistry from Stanford in 1968. He served as a professor at MIT and Stanford. Currently, he is at the Scripps Research Institute in La Jolla, California.*

This method, developed in 1980 by Barry Sharpless, has proven to be useful for the synthesis of a wide variety of enantiomerically pure compounds, because an epoxide, being very susceptible to attack by nucleophiles, can easily be converted into a compound with two adjacent asymmetric centers. In the following example, an allylic alcohol is converted into an enantiomerically pure epoxide, which is then used to form an enantiomerically pure diol.

What is the product of the reaction of methylmagnesium bromide with either of the enantiomerically pure epoxides that can be prepared from (*E*)-3-methyl-2-penten-1-ol by the method shown immediately above? Assign *R* or *S* configurations to the asymmetric centers of each product.

What stereoisomers are formed from the reaction of cyclohexene oxide with methoxide ion in methanol?

Is the addition of Br₂ to an alkene such as *trans*-2-pentene a stereoselective reaction? Is it a stereospecific reaction? Is it an enantioselective reaction?

William S. Knowles, *was born in 1917. He received a Ph.D. from Columbia University in 1942 and is a scientist at Monsanto Company, St. Louis, Missouri.*

Ryoji Noyori *was born in 1938 in Kobe, Japan. He received a Ph.D. from Kyoto University and is a professor of materials science at Nagoya University in Nagoya, Japan. Knowles and Noyori were cited for their work on chirally catalyzed hydrogenation.*

20.7 OXIDATION OF ALKENES TO 1,2-DIOLS

An alkene can be oxidized to a 1,2-diol by osmium tetroxide (OsO_4). A diol is also called a **glycol**. Because the OH groups are on adjacent carbons, 1,2-diols are also known as **vicinal diols** or **vicinal glycols**. (Recall that vicinal means that two substituents are on adjacent carbons; see Section 4.8.)

Alkenes can be oxidized to 1,2-diols.

$$RCH{=}CHR \xrightarrow[\text{2. } H_2O_2]{\text{1. } OsO_4} \underset{\text{a vicinal diol}}{\overset{\overset{\text{OH} \quad \text{OH}}{|\quad\quad|}}{RCH{-}CHR}}$$

MECHANISM FOR CIS-GLYCOL FORMATION

cyclohexene   a cyclic osmate intermediate   *cis*-1,2-cyclohexanediol   + OsO_4

- Osmium tetroxide forms a cyclic intermediate when it reacts with an alkene. This is a syn addition because both oxygens are delivered to the same side of the double bond. Therefore, the oxidation reaction is stereospecific—a cis alkene forms only a cis diol.

- The intermediate is hydrolyzed with aqueous hydrogen peroxide. Hydrogen peroxide re-oxidizes the osmium reagent back to osmium tetroxide. (Because osmium tetroxide is recycled, only a catalytic amount of this expensive and toxic oxidizing agent is needed.)

chem Tutorial:
place Hydroxylation reactions-synthesis

PROBLEM 16◆

Give the products that would be formed from the reaction of each of the following alkenes with OsO_4 followed by aqueous H_2O_2:

a. $CH_3C{=}CHCH_2CH_3$
$\quad\quad\quad\quad |$
$\quad\quad\quad\quad CH_3$

b. $={=}CH_2$

PROBLEM 17

What stereoisomers would be formed from the reaction of each of the following alkenes with OsO_4 followed by H_2O_2?

a. *trans*-2-butene   **c.** *cis*-2-pentene
b. *cis*-2-butene   **d.** *trans*-2-pentene

20.8 OXIDATIVE CLEAVAGE OF 1,2-DIOLS

1,2-Diols are oxidized to ketones or aldehydes by periodic acid (HIO_4). Periodic acid reacts with the diol to form a cyclic intermediate. When the intermediate breaks down, the bond between the two carbons bonded to the oxygens breaks. If a carbon that was bonded to an OH group is also bonded to two R groups, the product will be a ketone; if the carbon is bonded to an R and an H, the product will be an aldehyde. Because this oxidation reaction cuts the reactant into two pieces, it is called an **oxidative cleavage**.

$$RC-CHR'' \xrightarrow{HIO_4} RC-CHR'' \longrightarrow \underset{R}{\overset{R'}{C}}=O + O=\underset{H}{\overset{R''}{C}} + HIO_3$$

a ketone   an aldehyde

1,2-Diols are oxidized to aldehydes and ketones.

PROBLEM 18♦

An alkene is treated with OsO_4 followed by H_2O_2. When the resulting diol is treated with HIO_4, the only product obtained is an unsubstituted cyclic ketone with molecular formula $C_6H_{10}O$. What is the structure of the alkene?

PROBLEM-SOLVING STRATEGY

Predicting Oxidative Cleavage of 1,2-Diols

Of the following five compounds, explain why only D cannot be cleaved by periodic acid.

A   B   C   D   E

To figure out why one of a series of similar compounds is unreactive, we first need to consider what kinds of compounds undergo the reaction and any stereochemical requirements of the reaction. We know that periodic acid cleaves 1,2-diols. Because the reaction forms a cyclic intermediate, the two OH groups of the diol must be positioned so that they can form the intermediate.

The two OH groups of a 1,2-cyclohexanediol can both be equatorial, they can both be axial, or one can be equatorial and the other axial.

both equatorial   both axial   one equatorial, one axial
trans   trans   cis

In a cis 1,2-cyclohexanediol, one OH is equatorial and the other is axial. Because both cis 1,2-diols (A and E) are cleaved, we know that the cyclic intermediate can be formed when the OH groups are in these positions. In a trans 1,2-diol, both OH groups are equatorial, *or* both are axial (Section 2.14). Two of the trans 1,2-diols can be cleaved (B and C), and one cannot (D). We can conclude that the one that cannot be cleaved must have both OH groups in axial positions because they would be too far from each other to form a cyclic intermediate. Now we need to draw the most stable conformers of B, C, and D to see why only D has both OH groups in axial positions.

B   C   D

The most stable conformer of B is the one with both OH groups in equatorial positions. The steric requirements of the bulky *tert*-butyl group force it into an equatorial position, where there is more room for such a large substituent. This causes both OH groups in compound C to be in equatorial positions and both OH groups in compound D to be in axial positions. Therefore, C can be cleaved by periodic acid, but D cannot.

Now continue on to Problem 19.

PROBLEM 19◆

Which of each pair of diols is cleaved more rapidly by periodic acid?

a. or **b.** or

20.9 OXIDATIVE CLEAVAGE OF ALKENES

We have seen that alkenes can be oxidized to 1,2-diols (Section 20.7), and 1,2-diols can be further oxidized to aldehydes and ketones (Section 20.8). Alkenes can be directly oxidized to carbonyl compounds by ozone (O_3). When an alkene is treated with ozone at low temperatures, the double bond breaks and the carbons that were doubly bonded to each other are now doubly bonded to oxygens instead. This oxidation reaction is known as **ozonolysis**.

Ozone can be produced by passing oxygen gas through an electric discharge. The structure of ozone is represented by the following resonance contributors:

resonance contributors of ozone

Ozone and the alkene undergo a concerted cycloaddition reaction—the two oxygen atoms add to the two sp^2 carbons in a single step. The addition of ozone to an alkene should remind you of the electrophilic addition reactions of alkenes discussed in Chapter 4.

MECHANISM FOR OZONIDE FORMATION

- An electrophile adds to one of the sp^2 carbons, and a nucleophile adds to the other. The electrophile is the oxygen at one end of the ozone molecule, and the nucleophile is the oxygen at the other end. The product of ozone addition to an alkene is a **molozonide**. (The name "molozonide" indicates that one mole of ozone has added to the alkene.)
- The molozonide is unstable because it has two O—O bonds; it immediately rearranges to a more stable **ozonide**.

Because ozonides are explosive, they are seldom isolated. In solution, they are easily cleaved to carbonyl compounds. When an ozonide is cleaved in the presence of a reducing agent, such as zinc or dimethyl sulfide, the products are ketones, aldehydes, or both. The product is a ketone if the sp^2 carbon of the alkene is bonded to two carbon-containing substituents; the product is an aldehyde if at least one of the substituents bonded to the sp^2 carbon is a hydrogen. (The reducing agent prevents aldehydes from being oxidized to carboxylic acids.) Cleaving the ozonide in the presence of zinc or dimethyl sulfide is referred to as "working up the ozonide under reducing conditions."

Alkenes can be oxidized to ketones and to aldehydes (or carboxylic acids).

If the ozonide is cleaved in the presence of an oxidizing agent such as hydrogen peroxide (H_2O_2), the products will be ketones, carboxylic acids, or both. Carboxylic acids are formed instead of aldehydes because any aldehyde that is initially formed will be immediately oxidized to a carboxylic acid by hydrogen peroxide. Cleavage in the presence of H_2O_2 is referred to as "working up the ozonide under oxidizing conditions." The following reactions are examples of the oxidative cleavage of alkenes by ozonolysis:

To determine the product of ozonolysis, replace C=C with C=O O=C. If workup is done under oxidizing conditions, convert any aldehyde products to carboxylic acids.

The one-carbon fragment obtained from the reaction of a terminal alkene with ozone will be oxidized to formaldehyde if the ozonide is worked up under reducing conditions and to formic acid if it is worked up under oxidizing conditions.

Only the side-chain double bond will be oxidized in the following reaction because the stable benzene ring is oxidized only under prolonged exposure to ozone.

PROBLEM 20♦

Give an example of an alkene that forms the same ozonolysis products, regardless of whether the ozonide is worked up under reducing conditions (Zn, H₂O) or oxidizing conditions (H₂O₂).

PROBLEM 21

chem Tutorial:
place Ozonolysis reactions-synthesis

Give the products you would expect to obtain when the following compounds are treated with ozone, followed by workup with

a. Zn, H₂O: **b.** H₂O₂:

1. $CH_3CH_2CH_2\overset{\overset{\displaystyle CH_3}{|}}{C}{=}CHCH_3$ 4.

2. $CH_2{=}CHCH_2CH_2CH_2CH_3$ 5. $CH_3CH_2CH_2CH{=}CHCH_2CH_2CH_3$

3.   6.

Ozonolysis can be used to determine the structure of an unknown alkene. If we know what carbonyl compounds are formed by ozonolysis, we can mentally work backward to deduce the structure of the alkene. For example, if ozonolysis of an alkene followed by a workup under reducing conditions forms acetone and butanal as products, we can conclude that the alkene was 2-methyl-2-hexene.

PROBLEM 22♦

a. What alkene would give only acetone as a product of ozonolysis?
b. What alkenes would give only butanal as a product of ozonolysis?

PROBLEM 23   **SOLVED**

The following products were obtained from ozonolysis of a diene followed by workup under reducing conditions. Give the structure of the diene.

Solution   The five-carbon dicarbonyl compound indicates that the diene must contain five carbons flanked by two double bonds.

$$ \overset{O}{\overset{\|}{H\diagdown C}}\diagdown CH_2CH_2CH_2 \diagdown \overset{O}{\overset{\|}{C}} \diagdown H \quad \Longrightarrow \quad =CHCH_2CH_2CH_2CH= $$

One of the other two carbonyl compounds obtained from ozonolysis has one carbon atom, and the other has three carbon atoms. Therefore, one carbon has to be added to one end of the diene, and three carbons have to be added to the other end.

$$ CH_2=CHCH_2CH_2CH_2CH=CHCH_2CH_3 $$

PROBLEM 24 ◆

What aspect of the structure of the alkene does ozonolysis not tell you?

PROBLEM 25   SOLVED

Describe how the following compound could be prepared, using the given starting material as the only source of carbon. (Perform a retrosynthetic analysis to help you arrive at your answer.)

Solution   In a retrosynthetic analysis, the target molecule can be disconnected to give a five-carbon positively charged fragment and a four-carbon negatively charged fragment (Section 19.22). Pentanal and a butyl magnesium bromide are the synthetic equivalents for these two fragments. 1-Pentene, the five-carbon starting material, can be converted to the required four-carbon compound by ozonolysis.

We can now write the syntheses of pentanal and butyl magnesium bromide from the given starting material in the forward direction, along with the necessary reagents.

The reaction of pentanal with butyl magnesium bromide forms the target molecule.

PROBLEM 26

a. How could you synthesize the following compound from starting materials containing no more than four carbons?
   (*Hint:* A 1,6-diketone can be synthesized by oxidative cleavage of a 1,2-disubstituted cyclohexene.)

b. How could you synthesize the same compound in two steps from starting materials containing no more than six carbons?

20.10 DESIGNING A SYNTHESIS IX: FUNCTIONAL GROUP INTERCONVERSION

Converting one functional group into another is called **functional group interconversion**. Our knowledge of oxidation–reduction reactions has greatly expanded our ability to carry out functional group interconversions. For example, an aldehyde can be converted into a primary alcohol, an alkene, a secondary alcohol, a ketone, a carboxylic acid, an acyl chloride, an ester, an amide, or an amine.

A ketone can be converted into an ester or an alcohol.

As the number of reactions with which you are familiar increases, the number of functional group interconversions you can perform will also grow. As a result, you will find that more than one route is often available when you design a synthesis. The route you actually decide to use will depend on the availability and cost of the starting materials and on the ease with which the reactions in the synthetic pathway can be carried out.

PROBLEM 27

Add the necessary reagents over the reaction arrows.

PROBLEM 28

a. Show two ways to convert an alkyl halide into an alcohol that contains one additional carbon.
b. Show how a primary alkyl halide can be converted into an amine that contains one additional carbon.
c. Show how a primary alkyl halide can be converted into an amine that contains one less carbon.

PROBLEM 29

Show how each of the following compounds could be synthesized from the given starting material:

a.

b.

c.

d.

PROBLEM 30

How many different functional groups can be used to synthesize a primary alcohol?

SUMMARY

Oxidation is always coupled with reduction: a **reducing agent** is oxidized, and an **oxidizing agent** is reduced. A reduction reaction increases the number of C—H bonds or decreases the number of C—O, C—N, or C—X bonds (where X denotes a halogen); an oxidation reaction decreases the number of C—H bonds or increases the number of C—O, C—N, or C—X bonds. Similarly, reduction increases the number of N—H or S—H bonds, and oxidation increases the number of N—O or S—O bonds.

Reduction by the addition of H_2 to an organic compound occurs by one of three mechanisms: **catalytic hydrogenations** add two hydrogen atoms, **dissolving-metal reductions** add two electrons and two protons, and **metal-hydride reductions** add a hydride ion followed by a proton. Carbon–carbon, carbon–nitrogen, and some carbon–oxygen multiple bonds can be reduced by catalytic hydrogenation. An alkyne is reduced by sodium and liquid ammonia to a trans alkene. $NaBH_4$ is used to reduce aldehydes, ketones, and acyl halides; $LiAlH_4$, a stronger reducing agent, is used to reduce carboxylic acids, esters, and amides. Replacing some of the

hydrogens of $LiAlH_4$ with OR groups decreases the reactivity of the metal hydride.

Primary alcohols are oxidized to carboxylic acids by chromium-containing reagents and to aldehydes by PCC or by a **Swern oxidation**. Secondary alcohols are oxidized to ketones. Tollens reagent oxidizes only aldehydes. A **peroxyacid** oxidizes an aldehyde to a carboxylic acid, a ketone to an ester, and an alkene to an epoxide. Alkenes are oxidized to 1,2-diols by osmium tetroxide (OsO_4). 1,2-Diols are **oxidatively cleaved** to ketones and/or aldehydes by periodic acid (HIO_4).

Ozonolysis oxidatively cleaves alkenes to ketones, aldehydes, or both when worked up under reducing conditions and to ketones, carboxylic acids, or both when worked up under oxidizing conditions.

A **chemoselective reaction** is a reaction in which a reagent reacts with one functional group in preference to another. An **enantioselective reaction** forms more of one enantiomer than of another. Converting one functional group into another is called **functional group interconversion**.

SUMMARY OF REACTIONS

1. Catalytic hydrogenation of double and triple bonds (Section 20.2)

a. $RCH=CHR + H_2 \xrightarrow{\text{Pd/C or PtO}_2} RCH_2CH_2R$

  $RC\equiv CR + 2 H_2 \xrightarrow{\text{Pd/C or PtO}_2} RCH_2CH_2R$

  $RCH=NR + H_2 \xrightarrow{\text{Pd/C or PtO}_2} RCH_2NHR$

  $RC\equiv N + 2 H_2 \xrightarrow{\text{Raney Ni}} RCH_2NH_2$

2. Reduction of alkynes to alkenes (Section 20.2)

$$RC{\equiv}CR \xrightarrow[\text{catalyst}]{\underset{\text{Lindlar}}{H_2}} \underset{R}{\overset{H}{\underset{}{}}}C{=}C\underset{R}{\overset{H}{}}$$

$$RC{\equiv}CR \xrightarrow[\text{NH}_3\ \text{(liq)}]{\text{Na or Li}} \underset{R}{\overset{H}{}}C{=}C\underset{H}{\overset{R}{}}$$

3. Reduction of carbonyl compounds with reagents that donate hydride ion (Section 20.2)

a. $\underset{R}{\overset{O}{\underset{H}{\parallel}}}C \xrightarrow[\text{2. H}_3\text{O}^+]{\text{1. NaBH}_4} RCH_2OH$

e. $\underset{R}{\overset{O}{\underset{OH}{\parallel}}}C \xrightarrow[\text{2. H}_3\text{O}^+]{\text{1. LiAlH}_4} RCH_2OH$

b. $\underset{R}{\overset{O}{\underset{R'}{\parallel}}}C \xrightarrow[\text{2. H}_3\text{O}^+]{\text{1. NaBH}_4} \underset{}{\overset{OH}{\underset{}{|}}}RCHR'$

f. $\underset{R}{\overset{O}{\underset{NHR'}{\parallel}}}C \xrightarrow[\text{2. H}_2\text{O}]{\text{1. LiAlH}_4} RCH_2NHR'$

c. $\underset{R}{\overset{O}{\underset{Cl}{\parallel}}}C \xrightarrow[\text{2. H}_3\text{O}^+]{\text{1. NaBH}_4} RCH_2OH$

g. $\underset{R}{\overset{O}{\underset{Cl}{\parallel}}}C \xrightarrow[\text{2. H}_2\text{O}]{\text{1. LiAl[OC(CH}_3)_3]_3\text{H, }-78\ °\text{C}} \underset{R}{\overset{O}{\underset{H}{\parallel}}}C$

d. $\underset{R}{\overset{O}{\underset{OR'}{\parallel}}}C \xrightarrow[\text{2. H}_3\text{O}^+]{\text{1. LiAlH}_4} RCH_2OH\ +\ R'OH$

4. Oxidation of alcohols (Section 20.4)

primary alcohols $RCH_2OH \xrightarrow{H_2CrO_4} \left[\underset{R}{\overset{O}{\underset{H}{\parallel}}}C \right] \xrightarrow[\text{oxidation}]{\text{further}} \underset{R}{\overset{O}{\underset{OH}{\parallel}}}C$

$RCH_2OH \xrightarrow[\text{CH}_2\text{Cl}_2]{\text{PCC}} \underset{R}{\overset{O}{\underset{H}{\parallel}}}C$

$RCH_2OH \xrightarrow[\text{2. triethylamine}]{\text{1. CH}_3\text{SCH}_3,\ \text{ClC}{-}\text{CCl},\ -60\ °\text{C}} \underset{R}{\overset{O}{\underset{H}{\parallel}}}C$

secondary alcohols $\underset{RCHR}{\overset{OH}{|}} \xrightarrow{H_2CrO_4} \underset{R}{\overset{O}{\underset{R}{\parallel}}}C$

$\underset{RCHR}{\overset{OH}{|}} \xrightarrow[\text{2. triethylamine}]{\text{1. CH}_3\text{SCH}_3,\ \text{ClC}{-}\text{CCl},\ -60\ °\text{C}} \underset{R}{\overset{O}{\underset{R}{\parallel}}}C$

5. Oxidation of aldehydes and ketones (Section 20.5)

a. aldehydes

$$RCHO \xrightarrow{H_2CrO_4} RCOOH$$

$$RCHO \xrightarrow[\text{2. } H_3O^+]{\text{1. } Ag_2O, NH_3} RCOOH + Ag \text{ metallic silver}$$

$$RCHO \xrightarrow{CF_3COO^-} RCOOH$$

b. ketones

$$R\overset{O}{C}R \xrightarrow{CF_3COO^-} R\overset{O}{C}OR$$

6. Oxidation of alkenes (Sections 20.7, 20.8, and 20.9)

a.

$$RC(R')=CHR'' \xrightarrow[\text{2. } H_2O_2]{\text{1. } OsO_4} RC(R')(OH)-CHR''(OH) \xrightarrow{RCOOH} R'C(R)-CHR'' \text{ (epoxide)}$$

b.

$$RC(R')=CHR'' \xrightarrow[\substack{\text{2. Zn, } H_2O \\ \text{or} \\ (CH_3)_2S}]{\text{1. } O_3, -78\,°C} R\overset{O}{C}R' + R''CHO$$

$$RC(R')=CHR'' \xrightarrow[\text{2. } H_2O_2]{\text{1. } O_3, -78\,°C} R\overset{O}{C}R' + R''COOH$$

7. Oxidation of 1,2-diols (Section 20.6)

$$RC(R')(OH)-CHR''(OH) \xrightarrow{HIO_4} R\overset{O}{C}R' + R''CHO$$

KEY TERMS

Baeyer–Villiger oxidation (p. 896)
catalytic hydrogenation (p. 889)
chemoselective reaction (p. 892)
dissolving-metal reduction (p. 890)
enantioselective reaction (p. 898)
functional group interconversion (p. 906)
glycol (p. 900)
metal-hydride reduction (p. 890)

molozonide (p. 902)
oxidation (p. 887)
oxidation–reduction reaction (p. 886)
oxidative cleavage (p. 900)
oxidizing agent (p. 886)
ozonide (p. 902)
ozonolysis (p. 902)
peroxyacid (p. 896)

redox reaction (p. 886)
reducing agent (p. 886)
reduction (p. 887)
Rosenmund reduction (p. 889)
Swern oxidation (p. 894)
Tollens test (p. 896)
vicinal diol (p. 900)
vicinal glycol (p. 900)

PROBLEMS

31. Fill in the blank with "oxidized" or "reduced."

a. Secondary alcohols are _____ to ketones.

b. Acyl halides are _____ to aldehydes.

c. Aldehydes are _____ to primary alcohols.

d. Alkenes are _____ to aldehydes and/or ketones.

e. Aldehydes are _____ to carboxylic acids.

f. Alkenes are _____ to 1,2-diols.

g. Alkenes are _____ to alkanes.

32. Give the products of the following reactions. Indicate whether each reaction is an oxidation or a reduction:

a. $\diagup\!\!\diagdown\!\!\diagup\!\!\diagdown$OH $\xrightarrow[\text{H}_2\text{SO}_4]{\text{Na}_2\text{Cr}_2\text{O}_7}$

b. $CH_3CH_2CH_2C{\equiv}CCH_3$ $\xrightarrow[\text{NH}_3\text{ (liq)}]{\text{Na}}$

c.
$$CH_3CH_2\overset{\overset{\displaystyle O}{\|}}{C}Cl \xrightarrow[\substack{\text{partially}\\\text{deactivated Pd}}]{\text{H}_2}$$

d.
$$CH_3CH_2\overset{\overset{\displaystyle O}{\|}}{C}NHCH_3 \xrightarrow[\text{2. H}_2\text{O}]{\text{1. LiAlH}_4}$$

e. $CH_3CH_2C{\equiv}CH$ $\xrightarrow{\substack{\text{1. BH}_3\text{/THF}\\\text{2. H}_2\text{O}_2\text{, HO}^-\text{, H}_2\text{O}\\\text{3. NaBH}_4\\\text{4. H}_3\text{O}^+}}$

f. $CH_3CH_2CH{=}CHCH_2CH_3$ $\xrightarrow[\text{2. Zn, H}_2\text{O}]{\text{1. O}_3\text{, }-78\text{ °C}}$

g. (phenyl)$-CH{=}CHCH_3$ $\xrightarrow{\substack{\text{H}_2\\\text{Pd/C}}}$

h. (cyclopentane)$=CH_2$ $\xrightarrow[\text{2. (CH}_3)_2\text{S}]{\text{1. O}_3\text{, }-78\text{ °C}}$

33. How could each of the following compounds be converted to $CH_3CH_2CH_2\overset{\overset{\displaystyle O}{\|}}{C}OH$?

a. $CH_3CH_2CH_2\overset{\overset{\displaystyle O}{\|}}{C}H$

b. $CH_3CH_2CH_2CH_2OH$

c. $CH_3CH_2CH_2CH_2Br$

d. $CH_3CH_2CH{=}CH_2$

34. Identify A–G:

(benzene) $\xrightarrow[\text{2. H}_2\text{O}]{\substack{\text{1. CH}_3\overset{\overset{\displaystyle O}{\|}}{C}Cl\\\text{AlCl}_3}}$ **A** $\xrightarrow{\text{HO}^-}$ **B** $\xrightarrow[\text{2. H}_3\text{O}^+]{\text{1. CH}_3\text{MgBr}}$ **C** $\xrightarrow[\text{HCl}]{\Delta}$ **D** $\xrightarrow[\text{2. H}_2\text{O}_2]{\text{1. O}_3\text{, }-78\text{ °C}}$ **E** + **F** + **G**

35. Give the products of the following reactions. Indicate whether each reaction is an oxidation or a reduction:

a. (cyclohexene) $\xrightarrow{\substack{\text{1. RCOOH}\\\text{2. CH}_3\text{MgBr}\\\text{3. H}_3\text{O}^+}}$

b.
$$\text{(phenyl)}\overset{\overset{\displaystyle O}{\|}}{C}H \xrightarrow{\substack{\text{H}_2\\\text{Raney Ni}}}$$

c. (cyclohexene) $\xrightarrow[\text{2. H}_2\text{O}_2]{\text{1. OsO}_4}$

d.
$$\text{(phenyl)}\overset{\overset{\displaystyle O}{\|}}{C}OCH_3 \xrightarrow[\text{2. H}_3\text{O}^+]{\text{1. LiAlH}_4}$$

e.
$$\underset{H}{\overset{H_3C}{\diagdown}}C{=}C\underset{CH_3}{\overset{H}{\diagup}} \xrightarrow{\text{CF}_3\overset{\overset{\displaystyle O}{\|}}{C}O^-}$$

f.
$$\text{(phenyl)}\overset{\overset{\displaystyle O}{\|}}{C}H \xrightarrow{\text{CF}_3\overset{\overset{\displaystyle O}{\|}}{C}O^-}$$

g. (cyclohexane) $\xrightarrow[\text{2. H}_2\text{O}_2]{\text{1. O}_3\text{, }-78\text{ °C}}$

36. Identify the alkene that would give each of the following products upon ozonolysis, followed by treatment with hydrogen peroxide:

a. (carboxylic acid structure) + (acetone structure)

b. HO—(C=O)—(C=O)— + (keto-acid structure) OH

c. (cyclohexanone structure) + CH_3CH_2—(C=O)—OH

d. (diketone chain structure)

e. (phenyl ketone) $C(=O)CH_3$ + H—C(=O)—OH

f. (cyclohexane with COOH, COOH) + HO—(C=O)—(C=O)—OH

37. A Hofmann degradation (Section 10.9) of a primary amine forms an alkene that gives butanal and 2-methylpropanal upon ozonolysis and workup under reducing conditions. Identify the amine.

38. Fill in each box with the appropriate reagent:

a. $CH_3CH_2CH=CH_2$ $\xrightarrow[\text{2.}]{\text{1.}}$ $CH_3CH_2CH_2CH_2OH$ $\longrightarrow$ $CH_3CH=CHCH_3$ $\longrightarrow$ CH_3—C(=O)—OH

b. CH_3CH_2Br $\longrightarrow$ ☐ $\xrightarrow[\text{2.}]{\text{1.}}$ $CH_3CH_2CH_2CH_2OH$ $\longrightarrow$ $CH_3CH_2CH_2$—C(=O)—H

c. (cyclohexane) $\longrightarrow$ (bromocyclohexane) $\longrightarrow$ (cyclohexanol) + (cyclohexene) $\longrightarrow$ (cyclohexanone) + HO—(C=O)—(chain)—(C=O)—OH

39. a. Give the products obtained from ozonolysis of each of the following compounds, followed by workup under oxidizing conditions:

1. (cycloheptene with methyl)   2. (cycloheptene with methyl)   3. (cycloheptene with methylene)   4. (cycloheptadiene with methylene)   5. (cycloheptadiene with methylene)

b. What hydrocarbon would form the following products upon reaction with ozone, followed by workup under reducing conditions?

H—(C=O)—(chain)—C(=O)—(C=O)—H + H—(C=O)—(C=O)—H + H—(C=O)—H

40. Show how each of the following compounds can be prepared from cyclohexene:

a. (cyclohexene) $\longrightarrow$ (lactone, 7-membered ring)

b. (cyclohexene) $\longrightarrow$ HO—(chain)—OH

c. (cyclohexene) $\longrightarrow$ HO—(C=O)—(chain)—(C=O)—OH

41. The ¹H NMR spectrum of the product obtained when an unknown alkene reacts with ozone and the ozonolysis product is worked up under oxidizing conditions is shown. Identify the alkene.

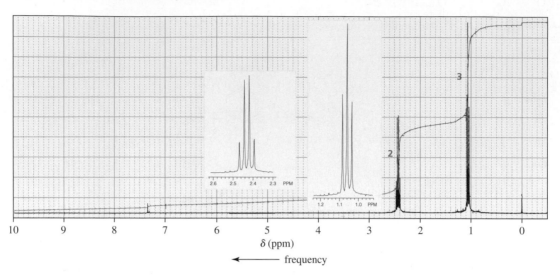

42. Identify A–N:

43. Chromic acid oxidizes 2-propanol six times faster than it oxidizes 2-deuterio-2-propanol. Explain. (*Hint:* See Sections 9.7 and 10.5.)

44. Fill in each box with the appropriate reagent:

45. Show how each of the following compounds could be prepared, using the given starting material:

a.

b.

c.

d.

e.

46. Treatment of an alkene with ozone followed by workup with hydrogen peroxide forms formic acid and a compound that shows three signals (a singlet, a triplet, and a quartet) in its ^{1}H NMR spectrum. Identify the alkene.

47. Which of the following compounds would be more rapidly cleaved by HIO_4?

A   B

48. Show the reagents needed to carry out the following functional group interconversions:

49. The catalytic hydrogenation of 0.50 g of a hydrocarbon at 25 °C consumed about 200 mL of H_2 under 1.0 atm of pressure. Reaction of the hydrocarbon with ozone, followed by treatment with hydrogen peroxide, gave one product, which was found to be a four-carbon carboxylic acid. Identify the hydrocarbon.

50. A student was asked to prepare the compounds shown below from the given starting materials. The reagents he chose to use for each synthesis are shown.
   a. Which of his syntheses were successful?
   b. What products did he obtain from the other syntheses?
   c. In his unsuccessful syntheses, what reagents should he have used to obtain the desired product?

51. The catalytic hydrogenation of compound A formed compound B. The IR spectrum of compound A and the ^{1}H NMR spectrum of compound B are shown. Identify the compounds.

52. A student worked for several days to prepare the following compounds:

$$
\begin{array}{cccccc}
CH_3 & & & & CH_3 & \\
H\!-\!OH & CH_3 & CH_3 & CH_3 & H\!-\!OH & CH_2CH_3 \\
CH_2 & H\!-\!OH & H\!-\!OH & H\!-\!OH & CH_2 & H\!-\!OH \\
H\!-\!OH & H\!-\!OH & HO\!-\!H & HO\!-\!H & HO\!-\!H & H\!-\!OH \\
CH_3 & CH_3 & CH_3 & CH_2CH_3 & CH_3 & CH_2CH_3
\end{array}
$$

She labeled them carefully and went to lunch. To her horror, when she returned, she found that the labels had fallen off the bottles and onto the floor. The friend at the next bench told her that the diols could be easily distinguished by two experiments. All she had to do was determine which ones were optically active and how many products were obtained when each was treated with periodic acid. She did what her friend suggested and learned that:

   1. Compounds A, E, and F are optically active, and B, C, and D are optically inactive.
   2. One product is obtained from the reaction of A, B, and D with periodic acid.
   3. Two products are obtained from the reaction of F with periodic acid.
   4. C and E do not react with periodic acid.

   a. Will she be able to distinguish among the six diols and label them from A to F with only the preceding information?
   b. Provide a systematic name for each structure.

53. Show how propyl propionate could be prepared, using allyl alcohol as the only source of carbon.

54. Compound A has a molecular formula of $C_5H_{12}O$ and is oxidized by an acidic solution of sodium dichromate to give compound B, whose molecular formula is $C_5H_{10}O$. When compound A is heated with H_2SO_4, C and D are obtained. Considerably more D is obtained than C. Reaction of compound C with O_3 followed by treatment with H_2O_2 gives two products: formic acid and compound E, whose molecular formula is C_4H_8O. Reaction of compound D with O_3 followed by treatment with H_2O_2 gives compound F, whose molecular formula is C_3H_6O, and compound G, whose molecular formula is $C_2H_4O_2$. What are the structures of compounds A through G?

55. A compound forms *cis*-1,2-dimethylcyclopropane when it is reduced at room temperature with H_2 and Pd/C. The ^1H NMR spectrum of the compound shows only two singlets. What is the structure of the compound?

56. Show how you could convert

a. maleic acid to (2R,3S)-tartaric acid.

b. fumaric acid to (2R,3S)-tartaric acid.

c. maleic acid to (2R,3R)- and (2S,3S)-tartaric acid.

d. fumaric acid to (2R,3R)- and (2S,3S)-tartaric acid.

maleic acid   fumaric acid   tartaric acid

57. Identify A through O:

58. Show how the following compounds could be prepared from the indicated starting material:

a. CH₃CCH₃ from CH₃CHCH₃

b. CH₃CH=CCH₃ using propane as the only source of carbon

c. CH₃C—CHCH₃ from propane and any molecule with two carbon atoms

d. CH₃CH₂CH from two molecules of ethane

59. Identify the alkene that gives each of the following products upon ozonolysis followed by treatment with dimethyl sulfide:

60. Propose a mechanism to explain how dimethyl sulfoxide and oxalyl chloride react to form the dimethylchlorosulfonium ion used as the oxidizing agent in the Swern oxidation.

$$CH_3-S-CH_3 \;+\; Cl-C-C-Cl \longrightarrow CH_3-S^+-CH_3 + CO_2 + CO + Cl^-$$

dimethyl sulfoxide   oxalyl chloride   dimethylchloro-
                                             sulfonium ion

61. Show how the following compounds could be prepared using only the indicated starting material as the source of carbon:

a.

b.

c.

d.

e.

f.

62. Deduce the structure of the alkene that upon ozonolysis and workup under reducing conditions gave the product shown.

a.

b.

c.

21
More About Amines • Heterocyclic Compounds

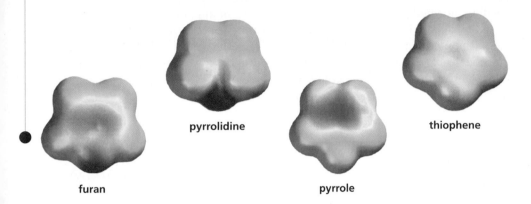

pyrrolidine

thiophene

furan

pyrrole

AMINES, COMPOUNDS IN WHICH ONE OR MORE OF THE HYDROGENS OF AMMONIA (NH$_3$) HAVE been replaced by an alkyl group, are among some of the most abundant compounds in the biological world. We will come to appreciate their biological importance as we explore the structures and properties of amino acids and proteins in Chapter 23; study how enzymes catalyze chemical reactions in Chapter 24; investigate the ways in which coenzymes—compounds derived from vitamins—help enzymes catalyze chemical reactions in Chapter 25; learn about nucleic acids (DNA and RNA) in Chapter 28; and look at how drugs are discovered and designed in Chapter 31.

Amines are also exceedingly important compounds to organic chemists—far too important to leave until the end of a course in organic chemistry. We have, therefore, already studied many aspects of amines and their chemistry. For example, we have seen that the nitrogen in amines is sp^3 hybridized with the lone pair residing in an sp^3 orbital (Section 2.8), and we know that amines invert rapidly at room temperature through a transition state in which the sp^3 nitrogen becomes an sp^2 nitrogen (Section 5.17). We also have examined the physical properties of amines—their hydrogen-bonding properties, boiling points, and solubilities (Section 2.9)—and we learned how amines are named (Section 2.7). Most important, we have seen that the lone-pair electrons of the nitrogen atom cause amines to react as bases, sharing the lone pair with a proton, and as nucleophiles, sharing the lone pair with an atom other than a proton.

an amine is a base

$$R-\ddot{N}H_2 \ + \ H-Br \ \longrightarrow \ R-\overset{+}{N}H_3 \ + \ Br^-$$

an amine is a nucleophile

$$R-\ddot{N}H_2 \ + \ CH_3-Br \ \longrightarrow \ R-\overset{+}{N}H_2-CH_3 \ + \ Br^-$$

In this chapter, we will revisit some of these topics and look at other aspects of amines and their chemistry that we have not considered previously.

Some amines are **heterocyclic compounds** (or **heterocycles**)—cyclic compounds in which one or more of the atoms of the ring are **heteroatoms** (Section 15.4). A variety of atoms, such as N, O, S, Se, P, Si, B, and As, can be incorporated into ring structures.

Heterocycles are an extraordinarily important class of compounds, making up more than half of all known organic compounds. Almost all the compounds we know as drugs (Chapter 31), most vitamins (Chapter 25), and many other natural products are heterocycles. In this chapter, we will consider the most prevalent heterocyclic compounds—the ones containing the heteroatom N, O, or S.

21.1 MORE ABOUT AMINE NOMENCLATURE

In Section 2.7, we saw that amines are classified as primary, secondary, or tertiary, depending on whether one, two, or three hydrogens of ammonia, respectively, have been replaced by an alkyl group. We also saw that amines have both common and systematic names. Common names are obtained by citing the names of the alkyl substituents (in alphabetical order) that have replaced the hydrogens of ammonia. Systematic names employ "amine" as a functional group suffix.

	a primary amine	a secondary amine	a tertiary amine
systematic name:	1-pentanamine	N-ethyl-1-butanamine	N-ethyl-N-methyl-1-propanamine
common name:	pentylamine	butylethylamine	ethylmethylpropylamine

A saturated cyclic amine—a cyclic amine without any double bonds—can be named as a cycloalkane, using the prefix *aza* to denote the nitrogen atom. There are, however, other acceptable names. Some of the more commonly used names are shown here. Notice that heterocyclic rings are numbered so that the heteroatom has the lowest possible number.

azacyclopropane	azacyclobutane	azacyclopentane	azacyclohexane	2-methylazacyclohexane	N-ethylazacyclopentane
aziridine	azetidine	pyrrolidine	piperidine	2-methylpiperidine	N-ethylpyrrolidine

Heterocycles with oxygen and sulfur heteroatoms are named similarly. The prefix for oxygen is *oxa* and that for sulfur is *thia*.

oxacyclopropane	thiacyclopropane	oxacyclobutane	oxacyclopentane	oxacyclohexane	1,4-dioxacyclohexane
oxirane	thiirane	oxetane			
ethylene oxide			tetrahydrofuran	tetrahydropyran	1,4-dioxane

PROBLEM 1 ♦

Name the following compounds:

a.

b.

c.

d.

e.

f.

21.2 MORE ABOUT THE ACID–BASE PROPERTIES OF AMINES

Amines are the most common organic bases. We have seen that ammonium ions have pK_a values of about 10 (Section 1.18) and anilinium ions have pK_a values of about 5 (Sections 7.9 and 16.5). The greater acidity of anilinium ions compared with ammonium ions is due to the greater stability of the conjugate bases of the anilinium ions as a result of electron delocalization. Amines have very high pK_a values. For example, the pK_a of methylamine is 40.

$$CH_3CH_2CH_2\overset{+}{N}H_3 \qquad \text{(ring)}-\overset{+}{N}H_3 \qquad CH_3NH_2$$

an ammonium ion	an anilinium ion	an amine
$pK_a = 10.8$	$pK_a = 4.58$	$pK_a = 40$

Saturated amine heterocycles containing five or more atoms have physical and chemical properties typical of the acyclic amines. For example, pyrrolidine, piperidine, and morpholine are typical secondary amines, and *N*-methylpyrrolidine and quinuclidine are typical tertiary amines. The conjugate acids of these amines have pK_a values expected for ammonium ions. We have seen that the basicity of amines allows them to be easily separated from other organic compounds (Chapter 1, Problems 100 and 101).

the ammonium ions of:	pyrrolidine	piperidine	morpholine	*N*-methylpyrrolidine	quinuclidine
	$pK_a = 11.27$	$pK_a = 11.12$	$pK_a = 9.28$	$pK_a = 10.32$	$pK_a = 11.38$

PROBLEM 2♦

Why is the conjugate acid of morpholine more acidic than the conjugate acid of piperidine?

PROBLEM 3♦

a. Draw the structure of 3-quinuclidinone.
b. What is the approximate pK_a of its conjugate acid?
c. Which has a lower pK_a, the conjugate acid of 3-bromoquinuclidine or the conjugate acid of 3-chloroquinuclidine?

PROBLEM 4   SOLVED

Explain the difference in the pK_a values of the piperidinium and aziridinium ions:

piperidinium ion	aziridinium ion
$pK_a = 11.1$	$pK_a = 8.0$

The piperidinium ion has a pK_a value expected for an ammonium ion. The pK_a value of the aziridinium ion is considerably lower. In this ion, the internal bond angle of the three-membered ring is smaller than usual, causing the external bond angles to be larger than usual. Because of the larger bond angles, the orbital used by nitrogen to overlap the orbital of hydrogen has more *s* character than that of a typical sp^3 nitrogen. This makes nitrogen more electronegative and lowers the pK_a (Section 1.22).

21.3 AMINES REACT AS BASES AND AS NUCLEOPHILES

We have seen that the leaving group of an amine ($^-NH_2$) is such a strong base that amines cannot undergo the substitution and elimination reactions that alkyl halides, alcohols, and ethers undergo (Section 10.8). The relative reactivities of these compounds—each with an electron-withdrawing group bonded to an sp^3 carbon—can be appreciated by comparing the pK_a values of the conjugate acids of their leaving groups, keeping in mind that the weaker the acid, the stronger its conjugate base and the poorer the base is as a leaving group.

relative reactivities

	most reactive					least reactive
	RCH_2F	>	RCH_2OH	~ RCH_2OCH_3	>	RCH_2NH_2

strongest acid, weakest conjugate base	HF	H_2O	RCH_2OH	NH_3	weakest acid, strongest conjugate base
	$pK_a = 3.2$	$pK_a = 15.7$	$pK_a = 15.5$	$pK_a = 36$	

The lone pair on the nitrogen of an amine causes it to be nucleophilic as well as basic. We have seen that amines react as bases in proton transfer reactions and in elimination reactions (Sections 1.18, 9.9, and 10.2).

We have also seen that amines react as nucleophiles in a number of different reactions: in nucleophilic substitution reactions—reactions that *alkylate* the amine (Section 8.3)—such as

$$CH_3CH_2Br + \underset{\text{methylamine}}{CH_3NH_2} \longrightarrow \underset{Br^-}{CH_3CH_2\overset{+}{N}H_2CH_3} \rightleftharpoons \underset{\text{ethylmethylamine}}{CH_3CH_2NHCH_3} + HBr$$

and in nucleophilic addition–elimination reactions—reactions that *acylate* the amine (Sections 17.8, 17.9, and 17.10)—such as

$$\underset{CH_3CH_2}{\overset{\overset{\displaystyle O}{\|}}{C}}{\diagdown}{Cl} + 2\ \underset{\text{methylamine}}{CH_3NH_2} \longrightarrow \underset{\underset{\text{an amide}}{}}{CH_3CH_2}\overset{\overset{\displaystyle O}{\|}}{C}{\diagdown}{NHCH_3} + CH_3\overset{+}{N}H_3Cl^-$$

and in nucleophilic addition–elimination reactions in which water is the species eliminated—the reactions of aldehydes and ketones with primary amines to form imines and with secondary amines to form enamines (Section 18.8)—such as

(cyclopentanone)=O + H₂NCH₂—(benzene) $\underset{\rightleftharpoons}{\overset{\text{trace acid}}{}}$ (cyclopentylidene)=NCH₂—(benzene) + H₂O

primary amine benzylamine   **an imine**

(cyclohexanone)=O + HN(pyrrolidine) $\underset{\rightleftharpoons}{\overset{\text{trace acid}}{}}$ (cyclohexenyl)—N(pyrrolidine) + H₂O

secondary amine pyrrolidine   **an enamine**

and in conjugate addition reactions (Section 18.16)—such as

$$\underset{CH_3CH=CH}{\overset{\overset{\displaystyle O}{\|}}{}}{C}{\diagdown}{H} + CH_3NH_2 \longrightarrow \underset{\underset{NHCH_3}{|}}{CH_3CH}{-}CH_2\overset{\overset{\displaystyle O}{\|}}{C}{\diagdown}{H}$$

We have seen that primary arylamines react with nitrous acid to form stable arenediazonium salts (Section 16.12). Arenediazonium salts are useful to synthetic chemists because the diazonium group can be replaced by a wide variety of nucleophiles. This reaction allows a wider variety of substituted benzenes to be prepared than can be prepared solely from electrophilic aromatic substitution reactions.

an arenediazonium salt

PROBLEM 5

Give the product of each of the following reactions:

a.

b.

c.

d.

21.4 THE SYNTHESIS OF AMINES

The many different ways in which amines can be synthesized, and the mechanisms for the reactions, have already been discussed in several different chapters of this book. These are summarized and the references to where they are discussed can be found on page A-10 of Appendix I.

21.5 AROMATIC FIVE-MEMBERED-RING HETEROCYCLES

We will start the discussion of heterocyclic compounds by looking at heterocycles that have a five-membered aromatic ring.

Pyrrole, Furan, and Thiophene

Pyrrole, **furan**, and **thiophene** are heterocycles with five-membered rings. We have seen that these compounds are aromatic because they are cyclic and planar, every atom in the ring has a p orbital, and the π cloud contains *three* pairs of π electrons (Sections 15.2 and 15.4).

pyrrole　　**furan**　　**thiophene**

orbital structure of pyrrole   **orbital structure of furan**

Pyrrole is an extremely weak base because the electrons shown as a lone pair in the structure are part of the π cloud. Therefore, when pyrrole is protonated, its aromaticity is destroyed. Consequently, the conjugate acid of pyrrole is a very strong acid ($pK_a = -3.8$); it therefore has a strong tendency to lose a proton. The resonance contributors of pyrrole show that nitrogen donates the lone-pair electrons into the five-membered ring.

resonance contributors of pyrrole

resonance hybrid

PROBLEM 6

Draw arrows to show the movement of electrons in going from one resonance contributor to the next in pyrrole.

Pyrrole has a dipole moment of 1.80 D (Section 1.15). The saturated amine with a five-membered ring—pyrrolidine—has a slightly smaller dipole moment of 1.57 D, but as we see from the electrostatic potential maps, the two dipole moments are in opposite directions. (The red areas are on opposite sides of the two molecules.) The dipole moment in pyrrolidine is due to inductive electron withdrawal by the nitrogen. Apparently, the ability of pyrrole's nitrogen to donate electrons into the ring by resonance more than makes up for its inductive electron withdrawal (Section 16.3).

pyrrole $\mu = $ **1.80 D** $\mu = $ **1.57 D**   **pyrrolidine**

In Section 7.6, we saw that the more stable and more nearly equivalent the resonance contributors, the greater is the compound's resonance energy. The resonance energies of pyrrole, furan, and thiophene are not as great as the resonance energies of benzene or the cyclopentadienyl anion, each a compound for which the resonance contributors here all equivalent. Thiophene, with the least electronegative heteroatom, has the greatest delocalization energy of the three, and furan, with the most electronegative heteroatom, has the smallest delocalization energy. This is what we would expect, because the resonance contributors with a positive charge on the heteroatom are the most stable for the compound with the least electronegative heteroatom and the least stable for the compound with the most electronegative heteroatom.

relative delocalization energies of some aromatic compounds

Because pyrrole, furan, and thiophene are aromatic, they undergo electrophilic aromatic substitution reactions. Notice that the mechanism of the reaction is similar to the mechanism for electrophilic aromatic substitution of benzene (Section 15.10).

2-bromofuran

2-bromo-5-methylpyrrole

MECHANISM FOR ELECTROPHILIC AROMATIC SUBSTITUTION

- The electrophile attaches to the pyrrole ring.
- A base (:B) in the reaction mixture removes the proton from the carbon that formed the bond with the electrophile.

Substitution occurs preferentially at C-2 because the intermediate obtained by attaching a substituent at this position is more stable than the intermediate obtained by attaching a substituent at C-3 (Figure 21.1). Both intermediates have a relatively stable resonance contributor in which all the atoms (except H) have complete octets. The intermediate resulting from C-2 substitution of pyrrole has *two* additional resonance contributors, whereas the intermediate resulting from C-3 substitution has only *one* additional resonance contributor.

Pyrrole, furan, and thiophene undergo electrophilic aromatic substitution, preferentially at C-2.

2-position

relatively stable

3-position

relatively stable

◀ **Figure 21.1**
Structures of the possible intermediates that could be formed from the reaction of an electrophile with pyrrole at C-2 and C-3.

If both positions adjacent to the heteroatom are occupied, electrophilic substitution will take place at C-3.

3-bromo-2,5-dimethylthiophene

Pyrrole, furan, and thiophene are all more reactive than benzene toward electrophilic aromatic substitution because they are better able to stabilize the positive charge on the carbocation intermediate, since the lone pair on the heteroatom can donate electrons into the ring by resonance (Figure 21.1).

Furan is not as reactive as pyrrole in electrophilic aromatic substitution reactions. The oxygen of furan is more electronegative than the nitrogen of pyrrole, so oxygen is not as effective as nitrogen in stabilizing the carbocation. Thiophene is less reactive than furan because sulfur's electrons are in a $3p$ orbital, which overlaps less effectively than the $2p$ orbital of nitrogen or oxygen with the $2p$ orbital of carbon. The electrostatic potential maps illustrate the different electron densities of the three rings.

relative reactivity toward electrophilic aromatic substitution

Pyrrole, furan, and thiophene are more reactive than benzene toward electrophilic aromatic substitution.

| pyrrole | furan | thiophene | benzene |

The relative reactivities of pyrrole, furan, and thiophene are reflected in the Lewis acid required to catalyze a Friedel–Crafts acylation reaction (Section 15.14). Benzene requires $AlCl_3$, a relatively strong Lewis acid. Thiophene is more reactive than benzene, so it can undergo a Friedel–Crafts reaction using $SnCl_4$, a weaker Lewis acid. An even weaker Lewis acid, BF_3, can be used when the reactant is furan. Pyrrole is so reactive that an anhydride is used instead of a more reactive acyl chloride, and no catalyst is necessary.

| pyrrole | furan | thiophene |

The resonance hybrid of pyrrole indicates that there is a partial positive charge on the nitrogen. Therefore, pyrrole is protonated on C-2 rather than on nitrogen. This is not unexpected because a proton is an electrophile, and we have just seen that electrophiles attach to the C-2 position of pyrrole.

$pK_a = -3.8$

Pyrrole is unstable in strongly acidic solutions because, once protonated, it can readily polymerize.

The sp^2 nitrogen in pyrrole is more electronegative than the sp^3 nitrogen in a saturated amine (Section 1.21). As a result, pyrrole ($pK_a \sim 17$) is more acidic than the analogous saturated amine ($pK_a \sim 36$). The partial positive charge on the nitrogen atom (apparent in structure of the resonance hybrid) also contributes to pyrrole's increased acidity.

The pK_a values of several nitrogen-containing heterocycles are shown in Table 21.1.

Table 21.1   The pKₐ Values of Several Nitrogen Heterocycles

$pK_a = -3.8$	$pK_a = -2.4$	$pK_a = 1.0$	$pK_a = 2.5$	$pK_a = 4.85$	$pK_a = 5.16$
$pK_a = 6.8$	$pK_a = 8.0$	$pK_a = 11.1$	$pK_a = 14.4$	$pK_a = \sim17$	$pK_a = \sim36$

PROBLEM 7

When pyrrole is added to a dilute solution of D_2SO_4 in D_2O, 2-deuteriopyrrole is formed. Propose a mechanism to account for the formation of this compound.

PROBLEM 8

Use resonance contributors to explain why pyrrole is protonated on C-2 rather than on nitrogen.

PROBLEM-SOLVING STRATEGY

Rank the following compounds in order of increasing basicity.

First, we need to see whether any of the compounds will lose their aromaticity if they are protonated. Such compounds will be very difficult to protonate and therefore will be very weak bases. Pyrrole is such a compound. Next, we need to see whether any of the compounds have a lone pair that can be delocalized. A delocalized lone pair will be harder to protonate than one that is localized. Aniline is such a compound. Finally, we need to look at the hybridization of the nitrogens. The nitrogen of the unsaturated six-membered ring is sp^2 hybridized, whereas the nitrogen of the saturated six-membered ring is sp^3 hybridized. We know that sp^2 nitrogens are more electronegative and therefore harder to protonate than sp^3 nitrogens. Thus, the order of basicity is:

Now continue on to Problem 9.

PROBLEM 9♦

Explain why cyclopentadiene ($pK_a = 15$) is more acidic than pyrrole ($pK_a \sim 17$), even though nitrogen is more electronegative than carbon.

21.6 AROMATIC SIX-MEMBERED-RING HETEROCYCLES

Now we will look at heterocycles that have a six-membered aromatic ring.

Pyridine

When one of the carbons of a benzene ring is replaced by a nitrogen, the resulting compound is called **pyridine**.

pyridine   **orbital structure of pyridine**

these electrons are in an sp^2 orbital perpendicular to the p orbitals

The pyridinium ion is a stronger acid than a typical ammonium ion because its proton is attached to an sp^2 nitrogen, which is more electronegative than an sp^3 nitrogen (Section 1.21).

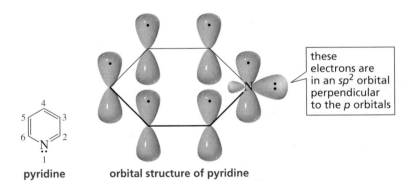

pyridinium ion
$pK_a = 5.16$

pyridine

piperidinium ion
$pK_a = 11.12$

piperidine

The dipole moment of pyridine is 1.57 D. As the resonance contributors and the electrostatic potential map indicate, the electron-withdrawing nitrogen is the negative end of the dipole.

$$\mu = \textbf{1.57 D}$$

benzene

Pyridine undergoes reactions characteristic of tertiary amines. For example, pyridine undergoes an S_N2 reaction with an alkyl halide (Section 8.3).

$$+ \; CH_3{-}I \longrightarrow$$

N-methylpyridinium iodide

pyridine

PROBLEM 10 | **SOLVED**

Will an amide be formed from the reaction of an acyl chloride with an aqueous solution of pyridine? Explain your answer.

Solution An amide will *not* be formed because the positively charged nitrogen causes pyridine to be an excellent leaving group. Therefore, the intermediate hydrolyzes rapidly. As a result, the final product of the reaction is a carboxylic acid. (If the final pH of the solution is greater than the pK_a of the carboxylic acid, the carboxylic acid will be predominantly in its basic form.)

Pyridine is aromatic. Like benzene, it has two uncharged resonance contributors. Because of the electron-withdrawing nitrogen, pyridine has three charged resonance contributors that benzene does not have.

resonance contributors of pyridine

Being aromatic, pyridine (like benzene) undergoes electrophilic aromatic substitution reactions. The mechanism for the reaction is shown below.

MECHANISM FOR ELECTROPHILIC AROMATIC SUBSTITUTION

- The electrophile attaches to the pyridine ring.

- A base (:B) in the reaction mixture removes the proton from the carbon that formed the bond with the electrophile.

Electrophilic aromatic substitution of pyridine takes place at C-3 because the most stable intermediate is obtained by placing an electrophilic substituent at that position (Figure 21.2). When the substituent is placed at C-2 or C-4, one of the resulting resonance contributors is particularly unstable because its nitrogen atom has an incomplete octet *and* a positive charge.

▶ **Figure 21.2**
Structures of the possible intermediates that could be formed from the reaction of an electrophile with pyridine.

The electron-withdrawing nitrogen atom makes the intermediate obtained from electrophilic aromatic substitution of pyridine less stable than the carbocation intermediate obtained from electrophilic aromatic substitution of benzene. Pyridine, therefore, is less reactive than benzene. Indeed, it is even less reactive than nitrobenzene. (Recall from Section 16.3 that an electron-withdrawing nitro group strongly deactivates a benzene ring toward electrophilic aromatic substitution.)

relative reactivity toward electrophilic aromatic substitution

Pyridine, therefore, undergoes electrophilic aromatic substitution reactions only under vigorous conditions, and the yields of these reactions are often quite low. If the nitrogen becomes protonated under the reaction conditions, the reactivity decreases further because a positively charged nitrogen would make the carbocation intermediate even less stable.

Pyridine undergoes electrophilic aromatic substitution at C-3.

We have seen that highly deactivated benzene rings do not undergo Friedel–Crafts alkylation or acylation reactions. Therefore, pyridine, whose reactivity is similar to that of a highly deactivated benzene, does not undergo these reactions either.

PROBLEM 11◆

Give the product formed when pyridine reacts with ethyl bromide.

Since pyridine is *less* reactive than benzene in *electrophilic* aromatic substitution reactions, it is not surprising that pyridine is *more* reactive than benzene in *nucleophilic* aromatic substitution reactions. The electron-withdrawing nitrogen atom that destabilizes the intermediate in electrophilic aromatic substitution stabilizes it in nucleophilic aromatic substitution.

Pyridine is *less* reactive than benzene toward electrophilic aromatic substitution and *more* reactive than benzene toward nucleophilic aromatic substitution.

MECHANISM FOR NUCLEOPHILIC AROMATIC SUBSTITUTION

- The nucleophile adds to the ring carbon attached to the leaving group.
- The leaving group is eliminated.

Nucleophilic aromatic substitution of pyridine takes place at C-2 and C-4 because attack at these positions leads to the most stable intermediate. Only when nucleophilic attack occurs at these positions is a resonance contributor obtained that has the greatest electron density on nitrogen, the most electronegative of the ring atoms (Figure 21.3).

◄ **Figure 21.3**
Structures of the possible intermediates that could be formed from the reaction of a nucleophile with a substituted pyridine.

If the leaving groups at C-2 and C-4 are different, the incoming nucleophile will preferentially substitute for the weaker base (the better leaving group).

Pyridine undergoes nucleophilic aromatic substitution at C-2 and C-4.

PROBLEM 12

Compare the mechanisms of the following reactions:

PROBLEM 13

a. Propose a mechanism for the following reaction:

b. What other product is formed?

Substituted pyridines undergo many of the side-chain reactions that substituted benzenes undergo. For example, alkyl-substituted pyridines can be brominated and oxidized.

When 2- or 4-aminopyridine is diazotized, α-pyridone or γ-pyridone is formed. Apparently, the diazonium salt reacts immediately with water to form a hydroxypyridine (Section 16.10). The product of the reaction is a pyridone because the keto form of a hydroxypyridine is more stable than the enol form. (The mechanism for the conversion of a primary amino group into a diazonium group is shown in Section 16.12.)

2-aminopyridine   **2-hydroxypyridine enol form**   **α-pyridone keto form**

4-aminopyridine   **4-hydroxypyridine enol form**   **γ-pyridone keto form**

The electron-withdrawing nitrogen and the ability to delocalize the negative charge causes the hydrogens on carbons attached to the 2- and 4-positions of the pyridine ring to have about the same acidity as the α-hydrogens of ketones (Section 19.1).

Consequently, the α-hydrogens of alkyl substituents can be removed by base, and the resulting carbanions can react as nucleophiles.

an aldol condensation

$$+ \ H_2O$$

CH_3Br
an S_N2 reaction

$$+ \ Br^-$$

PROBLEM 14♦

Rank the following compounds in order of decreasing ease of removing a proton from a methyl group:

---

chem place   Tutorial:
Lone pair electrons on nitrogen heterocycles

Tutorial:
Basic sites in nitrogen heterocycles

21.7 SOME AMINE HETEROCYCLES HAVE IMPORTANT ROLES IN NATURE

Proteins are naturally occurring polymers of α-amino acids (Chapter 23). Three of the 20 most common naturally occurring amino acids contain heterocyclic rings. Proline has a pyrrolidine ring; typtophan has an indole ring; and histidine has an imidazole ring.

proline   tryptophan   histidine

Imidazole

Imidazole, the heterocyclic ring of histidine, is an aromatic compound because it is cyclic and planar, every atom in the ring has a p orbital, and the cloud contains *three* pairs of π electrons (Section 15.2). The electrons drawn as lone-pair electrons on N-1 are part of the π cloud because they are in a p orbital, whereas the lone-pair electrons on

N-3 are not part of the π cloud because they are in an sp^2 orbital that is perpendicular to the p orbitals.

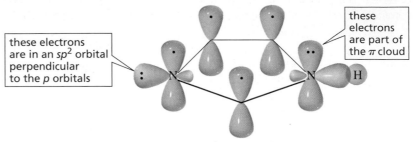

resonance contributors of imidazole

these electrons are in an sp^2 orbital perpendicular to the p orbitals

these electrons are part of the π cloud

orbital structure of imidazole

Because the lone-pair electrons in the sp^2 orbital are not part of the π cloud, imidazole is protonated in acidic solutions. The conjugate acid of imidazole has a pK_a value of 6.8. Thus, imidazole exists in both the protonated and unprotonated forms at physiological pH (7.3). This is one of the reasons that histidine, the imidazole-containing amino acid, is an important catalytic component of many enzymes (Section 24.9).

$$pK_a = 6.8$$

Notice that both protonated imidazole and the imidazole anion have two equivalent resonance contributors. Thus, the two nitrogens become equivalent when imidazole is either protonated or deprotonated.

protonated imidazole   **imidazole anion**

resonance hybrid   resonance hybrid

PROBLEM 15

Why is imidazole a stronger acid ($pK_a = 14.4$) than pyrrole ($pK_a = 17$)?

PROBLEM 16♦

Give the major product of the following reaction:

$$\text{N} \quad \text{NCH}_3 + \text{Br}_2 \xrightarrow{\text{FeBr}_3}$$

chem Tutorial:
place Recognizing heterocyclic rings.

PROBLEM 17♦

List imidazole, pyrrole, and benzene in order of decreasing reactivity toward electrophilic aromatic substitution.

PROBLEM 18♦

Imidazole boils at 257 °C, whereas N-methylimidazole boils at 199 °C. Explain this difference in boiling points.

PROBLEM 19♦

What percent of imidazole will be protonated at physiological pH (7.3)?

Purine and Pyrimidine

Nucleic acids (DNA and RNA) contain substituted **purines** and substituted **pyrimidines** (Section 28.1); DNA contains adenine, guanine, cytosine, and thymine (abbreviated A, G, C, and T); RNA contains adenine, guanine, cytosine, and uracil (A, G, C, and U). Why DNA contains T instead of U is explained in Section 28.10. Unsubstituted purine and pyrimidine are not found in nature. Notice that hydroxypurines and hydroxypyrimidines are more stable in the keto form than in the enol form. We will see that the preference for the keto form is crucial for proper base pairing in DNA (Section 28.3).

purine   pyrimidine

adenine   guanine   cytosine   uracil   thymine

PROBLEM 20

Why is protonated pyrimidine ($pK_a = 1.0$) more acidic than protonated pyridine ($pK_a = 5.2$)?

Porphyrin

Substituted *porphyrins* are another group of important naturally occurring heterocyclic compounds. A **porphyrin ring system** consists of four pyrrole rings joined by one-carbon bridges. Heme, which is found in hemoglobin and myoglobin, contains an iron ion (Fe) ligated by the four nitrogens of a porphyrin ring system. **Ligation** is the sharing of lone-pair electrons with a metal ion.

a porphyrin ring system   heme

Hemoglobin has four polypeptide chains and four heme groups (Figure 23.13 on page 1016); myoglobin has one polypeptide chain and one heme group. Hemoglobin is responsible for transporting oxygen to cells and carbon dioxide away from cells, whereas myoglobin is responsible for storing oxygen in cells. The iron atoms in hemoglobin and myoglobin, in addition to being ligated to the four nitrogens of the porphyrin ring, are also ligated to a histidine of the protein component (globin), and the sixth ligand is oxygen or carbon dioxide. Carbon monoxide is about the same size and shape as O_2, but CO binds more tightly than O_2 to iron. In addition, once a hemoglobin molecule has bound two CO molecules, it cannot get into the configuration necessary to bind O_2. Consequently, breathing carbon monoxide can be fatal because it interferes with the transport of oxygen through the bloodstream.

The extensive conjugated system of heme gives blood its characteristic red color. Its high molar absorptivity (about $160,000 \, M^{-1} \, cm^{-1}$) allows concentrations as low as $1 \times 10^{-8} \, M$ to be detected by UV spectroscopy (Section 13.18).

The ring system in chlorophyll *a*, the substance responsible for the green color of plants (its structure is on page 539), is similar to porphyrin but contains a cyclopentanone ring and one of its pyrrole rings is partially reduced. The metal ion in chlorophyll *a* is magnesium (Mg).

Vitamin B_{12} also has a ring system similar to porphyrin, but in this case, the metal ion is cobalt (Co). Other aspects of vitamin B_{12}'s structure and chemistry are discussed in Section 25.6.

PROBLEM 21 ◆

Is porphyrin aromatic?

Porphyrin, Bilirubin, and Jaundice

The average human body breaks down about 6 g of hemoglobin each day. The protein portion (globin) and the iron are reutilized, but the porphyrin ring is broken down, being reduced first to biliverdin, a green compound, and then to bilirubin, a yellow compound. If more bilirubin is formed than can be excreted by the liver, it accumulates in the blood. When its concentration there reaches a certain level, it diffuses into the tissues, giving them a yellow appearance. This condition is known as jaundice.

SUMMARY

Amines are classified as primary, secondary, or tertiary, depending on whether one, two, or three hydrogens of ammonia have been replaced by alkyl groups. Some amines are **heterocyclic compounds**—cyclic compounds in which one or more of the atoms of the ring is an atom other than carbon. Heterocyclic rings are numbered so that the **heteroatom** has the lowest possible number.

The lone pair on the nitrogen causes amines to be both bases and nucleophiles. Amines react as nucleophiles in - nucleophilic substitution reactions, in nucleophilic addition–elimination reactions, and in conjugate addition reactions. Amines react as bases in acid–base reactions and in elimination reactions.

Saturated heterocycles have physical and chemical properties typical of acyclic compounds that contain the same heteroatom. **Pyrrole, furan,** and **thiophene** are heterocyclic aromatic compounds that undergo electrophilic aromatic substitution reactions preferentially at C-2. They are more reactive than benzene toward electrophilic aromatic substi-

tution. When pyrrole is protonated, its aromaticity is destroyed. Pyrrole polymerizes in strongly acidic solutions.

Replacing one of benzene's carbons with a nitrogen forms **pyridine**, a heterocyclic aromatic compound that undergoes electrophilic aromatic substitution reactions at C-3 and nucleophilic aromatic substitution reactions at C-2 and C-4. Pyridine is less reactive than benzene toward electrophilic aromatic substitution and more reactive than benzene toward nucleophilic aromatic substitution.

Imidazole is the heterocyclic ring of the amino acid histidine. The conjugate acid of imidazole has a pK_a of 6.8, allowing it to exist in both the protonated and unprotonated forms at physiological pH (pH 7.3). Nucleic acids (DNA and RNA) contain substituted **purines** and substituted **pyrimidines**. Hydroxypurines and hydroxypyrimidines are more stable in the keto form. A **porphyrin ring system** consists of four pyrrole rings joined by one-carbon bridges; in hemoglobin and myoglobin, the four nitrogen atoms are ligated to Fe. The metal ion in chlorophyll *a* is Mg, and the metal ion in vitamin B_{12} is Co.

SUMMARY OF REACTIONS

1. Reactions of amines as nucleophiles (Section 21.3)
   a. In alkylation reactions:

$$R' - \ddot{N}H_2 \xrightarrow{RBr} R' - \overset{+}{N}H_2 \; Br^- \rightleftharpoons R' - \ddot{N}H \xrightarrow{RBr} R' - \overset{+}{N}H \; Br^- \rightleftharpoons R' - \ddot{N}: \xrightarrow{RBr} R' - \overset{+}{N} - R$$

(with R substituents and + HBr shown)

b. In nucleophilic addition–elimination reactions:
  i. Reaction of an amine with a carbonyl group that has a leaving group:

  ii. Reaction of a primary amine with an aldehyde or ketone to form an imine:

  iii. Reaction of a secondary amine with an aldehyde or ketone to form an enamine:

c. In conjugate addition reactions:

2. Primary arylamines react with nitrous acid to form stable arenediazonium salts (Section 21.3).

3. Electrophilic aromatic substitution reactions
  a. Pyrrole, furan, and thiophene (Section 21.8):

  b. Pyridine (Section 21.9):

4. Nucleophilic aromatic substitution reactions of pyridine (Section 21.9)

KEY TERMS

amines (p. 917)
furan (p. 921)
heteroatom (p. 918)
heterocycle (p. 918)
heterocyclic compound (p. 918)

imidazole (p. 931)
ligation (p. 933)
porphyrin ring system (p. 933)
purine (p. 933)
pyridine (p. 926)

pyrimidine (p. 933)
pyrrole (p. 921)
thiophene (p. 921)

PROBLEMS

22. Name each of the following:

a. [structure: azetidine with NH and CH₃]   b. [structure: piperidine with CH₃ groups]   c. [structure: pyrrole with Cl]   d. [structure: piperidine with CH₃ and CH₃CH₂]

23. Give the product of each of the following reactions:

a. [pyrrolidine N-H] + [benzoyl chloride, O=C–Cl] ⟶

d. [furan with CH₃] + [CH₃C(=O)Cl] ⟶

g. [pyrrole N-H] + C₆H₅N⁺≡N ⟶

b. [2-bromopyridine] + HO⁻ ⟶

e. [2-chloropyridine] $\xrightarrow{C_6H_5Li}$

h. [2-methylpyridine] $\xrightarrow[\text{2. CH}_3\text{CH}_2\text{CH}_2\text{Br}]{\text{1. } \bar{N}H_2}$

c. $CH_3CH_2CH_2CH_2Br \xrightarrow[\text{2. H}_2\text{, Raney Ni}]{\text{1. } \bar{C}\equiv N}$

f. [cyclohexylamine, NH₂] + CH₃CH₂CH₂Br ⟶

i. [2-bromothiophene] $\xrightarrow[\text{2. CO}_2 \\ \text{3. HCl}]{\text{1. Mg/Et}_2\text{O}}$

24. List the following compounds in order of decreasing acidity:

25. Which of the following compounds is easier to decarboxylate?

[pyridine-2-carboxylic acid, COOH] or [pyridine with CH₂COOH]

26. Rank the following compounds in order of decreasing reactivity in an electrophilic aromatic substitution reaction:

[benzene–OCH₃]   [benzene–NHCH₃]   [benzene–SCH₃]

27. One of the following compounds undergoes electrophilic aromatic substitution predominantly at C-3, and one undergoes electrophilic aromatic substitution predominantly at C-4. Which is which?

[pyridine with CCH₂CH₃ (=O)]   [pyridine with NHCH₂CH₃]

28. Benzene undergoes electrophilic aromatic substitution reactions with aziridines in the presence of a Lewis acid such as AlCl₃.

a. What are the major and minor products of the following reaction?

[benzene] + [N-methyl-2-methylaziridine] $\xrightarrow{\text{AlCl}_3}$

b. Would you expect epoxides to undergo similar reactions?

29. The dipole moments of furan and tetrahydrofuran are in the same direction. One compound has a dipole moment of 0.70 D, and the other has a dipole moment of 1.73 D. Which is which?

30. A tertiary amine reacts with hydrogen peroxide to form a tertiary amine oxide.

a tertiary amine   a tertiary amine oxide

Tertiary amine oxides undergo a reaction similar to the Hofmann elimination reaction (Section 10.9), called a **Cope elimination reaction**. In this reaction, a tertiary amine oxide, rather than a quaternary ammonium ion, undergoes elimination. A strong base is not needed for a Cope elimination because the amine oxide acts as its own base.

Does the Cope elimination have an alkene-like transition state or a carbanion-like transition state?

31. Give the products that would be obtained by treating the following tertiary amines with hydrogen peroxide followed by heat:

32. The chemical shifts of the C-2 hydrogen in the spectra of pyrrole, pyridine, and pyrrolidine are 2.82 ppm, 6.42 ppm, and 8.50 ppm. Match each heterocycle with its chemical shift.

33. Explain why protonation of aniline has a dramatic effect on the compound's UV spectrum, whereas protonation of pyridine has only a small effect on that compound's UV spectrum.

34. Explain why pyrrole (pK_a 17) is a much stronger acid than ammonia (pK_a 36).

35. Propose a mechanism for the following reaction:

36. Quinolines, heterocyclic compounds that contain a pyridine ring fused to a benzene ring, are commonly synthesized by a method known as the Skraup synthesis, in which aniline reacts with glycerol under acidic conditions. Nitrobenzene is added to the reaction mixture to serve as an oxidizing agent. The first step in the synthesis is the dehydration of glycerol to propenal.

quinoline   glycerol

a. What product would be obtained if *para*-ethylaniline were used instead of aniline?
b. What product would be obtained if 3-hexen-2-one were used instead of glycerol?
c. What starting materials are needed for the synthesis of 2,7-diethyl-3-methylquinoline?

37. Propose a mechanism for each of the following reactions:

38. Give the major product of each of the following reactions:

a. [structure: 3-acetylfuran] + HNO₃ $\xrightarrow{H_2SO_4}$

d. [structure: 2-pyridone] + PCl₃ ⟶

b. [structure: 2-nitrothiophene] + Br₂ ⟶

e. [structure: 4-methyl-N-methylpyridinium] $\xrightarrow[\substack{\text{2. } H_2C=O \\ \text{3. HCl}}]{\text{1. HO}^-}$

c. [structure: 4-(dimethylamino)pyridine] + CH₃I ⟶

f. [structure: pyrrole] + CH₃CH₂MgBr ⟶

39. a. Draw resonance contributors to show why pyridine-*N*-oxide is more reactive than pyridine toward electrophilic aromatic substitution

b. At what position does pyridine-*N*-oxide undergo electrophilic aromatic substitution?

40. Propose a mechanism for the following reaction:

[structure: 2-methylpyridine N-oxide] + [acetic anhydride CH₃COOCCH₃] ⟶ [structure: 2-(acetoxymethyl)pyridine] + [CH₃COOH]

41. Pyrrole reacts with excess *para*-(*N,N*-dimethylamino)benzaldehyde to form a highly colored compound. Draw the structure of the colored compound.

42. 2-Phenylindole is prepared from the reaction of acetophenone and phenylhydrazine, a method known as the Fischer indole synthesis. Propose a mechanism for this reaction. (*Hint:* The reactive species is the enamine tautomer of the phenylhydrazone.)

[structure: acetophenone] + [structure: phenylhydrazine]—NHNH₂ $\xrightarrow[\Delta]{\text{trace acid}}$ [structure: 2-phenylindole] + NH₃ + H₂O

phenylindole

43. What starting materials are required to synthesize the following compounds, using the Fischer indole synthesis? (*Hint:* See Problem 42.)

a. [structure: 2-ethylindole] —CH₂CH₃

b. [structure: 3-ethylindole] CH₂CH₃

c. [structure: tetrahydrocarbazole]

44. Organic chemists work with tetraphenylporphyrins rather than with porphyrins because tetraphenylporphyrins are much more resistant to air oxidation. Tetraphenylporphyrin can be prepared by the reaction of benzaldehyde with pyrrole. Propose a mechanism for the formation of the ring system shown here:

[structure: acetophenone] + [structure: pyrrole] $\xrightarrow{\text{BH}_3/\text{THF}}$ [structure: porphyrin ring system] $\xrightarrow{\text{oxidation}}$ tetraphenylporphyrin

Bioorganic Compounds

Chapters 22 through 28 discuss the chemistry of organic compounds found in biological systems. Many of these compounds are larger than the organic compounds you have seen up to this point, and they often have more than one functional group, but the principles that govern their structure and reactivity are essentially the same as those that govern the structure and reactivity of the compounds that you have been studying. These chapters, therefore, will give you the opportunity to review much of the organic chemistry you have learned as you apply it to compounds found in the biological world.

CHAPTER 22
The Organic Chemistry of Carbohydrates

Chapter 22 introduces you to the organic chemistry of carbohydrates, the most abundant class of compounds in the biological world. First you will learn about the structures and reactions of monosaccharides. Then you will see how they are linked to form disaccharides and polysaccharides. Many examples of carbohydrates found in nature will be discussed.

CHAPTER 23
The Organic Chemistry of Amino Acids, Peptides, and Proteins

Chapter 23 starts by looking at the physical properties of amino acids. Then you will see how amino acids are linked to form peptides and proteins. You will also see how proteins are made in the laboratory. Later, when you read Chapter 28, you will be able to compare the laboratory synthesis with how they are synthesized in nature. What you learn about protein structure in this chapter will prepare you for understanding how enzymes catalyze chemical reactions, which is discussed in Chapter 24.

CHAPTER 24
Catalysis

Chapter 24 first describes the various ways that organic reactions can be catalyzed and then shows how enzymes employ these same methods to catalyze reactions in biological systems.

CHAPTER 25
The Organic Chemistry of the Coenzymes, Compounds Derived from Vitamins

Chapter 25 describes the chemistry of the coenzymes— organic compounds that some enzymes need to catalyze biological reactions. Coenzymes play a variety of chemical roles: some function as oxidizing and reducing agents, some allow electrons to be delocalized, some activate groups for further reaction, and some provide good nucleophiles or strong bases needed for reactions. Because coenzymes are derived from vitamins, you will see why vitamins are necessary for many of the organic reactions that occur in biological systems.

CHAPTER 26
The Organic Chemistry of Metabolic Pathways

Chapter 26 looks at the organic reactions that living organisms carry out to obtain the energy they need and to synthesize the compounds they require. You will also see why many reactions in biological systems could not occur without ATP.

CHAPTER 27
The Organic Chemistry of Lipids

Chapter 27 discusses the organic chemistry of lipids. Lipids are water-insoluble compounds found in animals and plants. First you will study the structure and function of different kinds of lipids. You will then be able to understand such things as the difference in structure that causes fats to be solid and liquids to be oils, what causes butter to become rancid, and how cholesterol and other terpenes are synthesized in nature.

CHAPTER 28
The Chemistry of the Nucleic Acids

Chapter 28 covers the structures and chemistry of nucleosides, nucleotides, and nucleic acids (RNA and DNA). You will see how nucleotides are linked to form nucleic acids, why DNA contains thymine instead of uracil, and how the genetic messages encoded in DNA are transcribed into mRNA and then translated into proteins. Also explained are how the sequence of bases in DNA is determined and how DNA with specific base sequences can be synthesized.

22

The Organic Chemistry of Carbohydrates

oligosaccharide

cell surface

D-glucose

D-fructose

BIOORGANIC COMPOUNDS ARE ORGANIC COMPOUNDS FOUND IN BIOLOGICAL SYSTEMS. Their structures can be quite complex, yet their reactivity is governed by the same principles as the comparatively simple organic molecules we have discussed so far. The organic reactions that chemists carry out in the laboratory are in many ways just the same as those performed by nature inside a living cell. In other words, bioorganic reactions can be thought of as organic reactions that take place in tiny flasks called cells.

Although most bioorganic compounds have more complicated structures than those of the organic compounds you are now used to seeing, do not let the structures fool you into thinking that their chemistry must be equally complicated. One reason the structures of bioorganic compounds are more complicated is that bioorganic compounds must be able to recognize each other. Much of their structure is for that very purpose, a function called **molecular recognition**.

The first group of bioorganic compounds we will look at are *carbohydrates*—the most abundant class of compounds in the biological world, making up more than 50% of the dry weight of the Earth's biomass. Carbohydrates are important constituents of all living organisms and have a variety of different functions. Some are important structural components of cells; others act as recognition sites on cell surfaces. For example, the first event in any of our lives was a sperm recognizing a carbohydrate on the outer surface of an egg. Other carbohydrates serve as a major source of metabolic energy. The leaves, fruits, seeds, stems, and roots of plants, for instance, contain carbohydrates that plants use for their own metabolic needs but that can also serve the metabolic needs of the animals that eat the plants.

Early chemists noted that carbohydrates have molecular formulas that make them appear to be hydrates of carbon, $C_n(H_2O)_n$—hence the name. Later structural studies revealed, however, that these compounds are *not* hydrates because they do not contain intact water molecules. Nevertheless, the term *carbohydrate* persists.

Carbohydrates are polyhydroxy aldehydes such as D-glucose, polyhydroxy ketones such as D-fructose, and compounds such as sucrose formed by linking polyhydroxy aldehydes or polyhydroxy ketones together (Section 22.16). The chemical structures of carbohydrates are commonly represented by wedge-and-dash structures or by Fischer projections. Notice that both D-glucose and D-fructose have the molecular formula $C_6H_{12}O_6$, consistent with the general formula $C_6(H_2O)_6$ that made early chemists think that those compounds were hydrates of carbon.

D-glucose
a polyhydroxy aldehyde

D-fructose
a polyhydroxy ketone

wedge-and-dash structure   Fischer projection   wedge-and-dash structure   Fischer projection

Recall from Section 5.6 that horizontal bonds point toward the viewer and vertical bonds point away from the viewer in Fischer projections.

The most abundant carbohydrate in nature is D-glucose. Animals obtain D-glucose from food that contains D-glucose, such as plants. Plants produce D-glucose by *photosynthesis*. During photosynthesis, plants take up water through their roots and use carbon dioxide from the air to synthesize D-glucose and oxygen. Because photosynthesis is the reverse of the process used by organisms to obtain energy—specifically, the oxidation of D-glucose to carbon dioxide and water—plants require energy to carry out photosynthesis. Plants obtain the energy they need for photosynthesis from sunlight, captured by chlorophyll molecules in green plants. Photosynthesis uses the CO_2 that animals exhale as waste and generates the O_2 that animals inhale to sustain life. Nearly all the oxygen in the atmosphere has been released by photosynthetic processes.

$$C_6H_{12}O_6 + 6\,O_2 \underset{\text{photosynthesis}}{\overset{\text{oxidation}}{\rightleftharpoons}} 6\,CO_2 + 6\,H_2O$$
glucose

22.1 CLASSIFICATION OF CARBOHYDRATES

The terms *carbohydrate, saccharide*, and *sugar* are used interchangeably. *Saccharide* comes from the word for *sugar* in several early languages (*sarkara* in Sanskrit, *sakcharon* in Greek, and *saccharum* in Latin).

There are two classes of carbohydrates: *simple carbohydrates* and *complex carbohydrates*. **Simple carbohydrates** are **monosaccharides** (single sugars), whereas **complex carbohydrates** contain 2 or more monosaccharides linked together. **Disaccharides** have 2 monosaccharides linked together, **oligosaccharides** have 3 to 10 (*oligos* is Greek for "few"), and **polysaccharides** have 10 or more. Disaccharides, oligosaccharides, and polysaccharides can be broken down to monosaccharides by hydrolysis.

a monosaccharide subunit

$$-M-M-M-M-M-M-M-M-M- \xrightarrow{\text{hydrolysis}} x\,M$$
polysaccharide   monosaccharide

A *monosaccharide* can be a polyhydroxy aldehyde such as D-glucose or a polyhydroxy ketone such as D-fructose. Polyhydroxy aldehydes are called **aldoses** ("ald" is for aldehyde; "ose" is the suffix for a sugar), whereas polyhydroxy ketones are called **ketoses**. Monosaccharides are also classified according to the number of carbons they contain: those with three carbons are **trioses**, those with four carbons are **tetroses**, those with five carbons are **pentoses**, and those with six and seven carbons are **hexoses** and **heptoses**, respectively. Therefore, a six-carbon polyhydroxy aldehyde such as D-glucose is an aldohexose, whereas a six-carbon polyhydroxy ketone such as D-fructose is a ketohexose.

Classify the following monosaccharides:

D-ribose   D-sedoheptulose   D-mannose

22.2 THE D AND L NOTATION

The smallest aldose, and the only one whose name does not end in "ose," is glyceraldehyde, an aldotriose.

A carbon to which four different groups are attached is an asymmetric center.

asymmetric center

$HOCH_2CH$ C H
        OH
glyceraldehyde

Because glyceraldehyde has an asymmetric center, it can exist as a pair of enantiomers. We know that the isomer on the left below has the R configuration because an arrow drawn from the highest priority substituent (OH) to the next highest priority substituent (CH=O) is clockwise and the lowest priority group is on a hatched wedge (Section 5.7).

clockwise is **R**

(**R**)-(+)-glyceraldehyde   (**S**)-(−)-glyceraldehyde

perspective formulas

H is on a horizontal bond so counter-clockwise is **R**

(**R**)-(+)-glyceraldehyde   (**S**)-(−)-glyceraldehyde

Fischer projections

The notations D and L are used to describe the configurations of carbohydrates. In a Fischer projection of a monosaccharide, the carbonyl group is always placed on top (in the case of aldoses) or as close to the top as possible (in the case of ketoses). Examine the Fischer projection of galactose shown below and note that the compound has four asymmetric centers (C-2, C-3, C-4, and C-5). *If the OH group attached to the bottom-most asymmetric center (the carbon second from the bottom) is on the right, the compound is a D-sugar. If that OH group is on the left, the compound is an L-sugar.* Almost all sugars found in nature are D-sugars. Notice that the mirror image of a D-sugar is an L-sugar.

D-glyceraldehyde   L-glyceraldehyde

the OH group is on the right

D-galactose

the OH group is on the right

L-galactose
mirror image of D-galactose

The common name of the monosaccharide, together with the D or L designation, completely defines its structure, because the configurations of all the asymmetric centers are implicit in the common name.

Emil Fischer and his colleagues studied carbohydrates in the late nineteenth century, when techniques for determining the absolute configurations of compounds were not available. Fischer arbitrarily assigned the *R*-configuration to the dextrorotatory isomer of glyceraldehyde that we call D-glyceraldehyde. He turned out to be correct: D-glyceraldehyde is (*R*)-(+)-glyceraldehyde, and L-glyceraldehyde is (*S*)-(−)-glyceraldehyde (Section 5.15).

Like *R* and *S*, the symbols D and L indicate the configuration of an asymmetric center, but they do not indicate whether the compound rotates the plane of polarization of polarized light to the right (+) or to the left (−) (Section 5.7). For example, D-glyceraldehyde is dextrorotatory, whereas D-lactic acid is levorotatory. In other words, optical rotation, like melting or boiling points, is a physical property of a compound, whereas "*R*, *S*, D, and L" are conventions humans use to indicate the configuration about an asymmetric center.

D-(+)-glyceraldehyde   D-(−)-lactic acid

PROBLEM 2

Draw Fischer projections of L-glucose and L-fructose.

PROBLEM 3 ♦

Indicate whether each of the following is D-glyceraldehyde or L-glyceraldehyde, assuming that the horizontal bonds point toward you and the vertical bonds point away from you (Section 5.7):

chem Tutorial:
place   D and L Notation

22.3 THE CONFIGURATIONS OF ALDOSES

Aldotetroses have two asymmetric centers and therefore four stereoisomers. Two of the stereoisomers are D-sugars and two are L-sugars. The names of the aldotetroses—erythrose and threose—were used to name the erythro and threo pairs of enantiomers described in Section 5.11.

D-erythrose   L-erythrose   D-threose   L-threose

Aldopentoses have three asymmetric centers and therefore eight stereoisomers (four pairs of enantiomers); aldohexoses have four asymmetric centers and 16 stereoisomers (eight pairs of enantiomers). The four D-aldopentoses and the eight D-aldohexoses are shown in Table 22.1.

Table 22.1   Configurations of the D-Aldoses

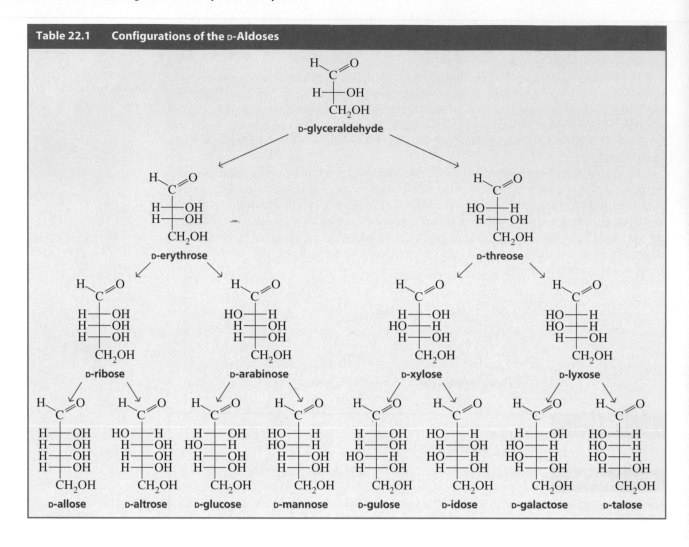

Diastereomers that differ in configuration at only one asymmetric center are called **epimers**. For example, D-ribose and D-arabinose are C-2 epimers because they differ in configuration only at C-2; D-idose and D-talose are C-3 epimers.

D-ribose   D-arabinose
C-2 epimers

D-idose   D-talose
C-3 epimers

D-Mannose is the C-2 epimer of D-glucose.

D-Galactose is the C-4 epimer of D-glucose.

Diastereomers are stereoisomers that are not enantiomers.

An epimer is a particular kind of diastereomer. (Recall that diastereomers are stereoisomers that are not enantiomers; Section 5.11.) D-Glucose, D-mannose, and D-galactose are the most common aldohexoses in biological systems. An easy way to learn their structures is to memorize the structure of D-glucose and then remember that D-mannose is the C-2 epimer of D-glucose and D-galactose is the C-4 epimer of D-glucose.

PROBLEM 4 ◆

a. Are D-erythrose and L-erythrose enantiomers or diastereomers?

b. Are L-erythrose and L-threose enantiomers or diastereomers?

chem Tutorial:
place Configurations of the D-aldoses

PROBLEM 5♦

a. What sugar is the C-3 epimer of D-xylose?
b. What sugar is the C-5 epimer of D-allose?
c. What sugar is the C-4 epimer of L-gulose?

PROBLEM 6♦

What are the systematic names of the following compounds? Indicate the configuration (*R* or *S*) of each asymmetric center:

a. D-glucose   **b.** D-mannose   **c.** D-galactose   **d.** L-glucose

22.4 THE CONFIGURATIONS OF KETOSES

Naturally occurring ketoses have the ketone group in the 2-position. The configurations of the naturally occurring ketoses are shown in Table 22.2. A ketose has one less asymmetric center than does an aldose with the same number of carbons. Therefore, a ketose has only half as many stereoisomers as an aldose with the same number of carbons.

Table 22.2   Configurations of the D-Ketoses

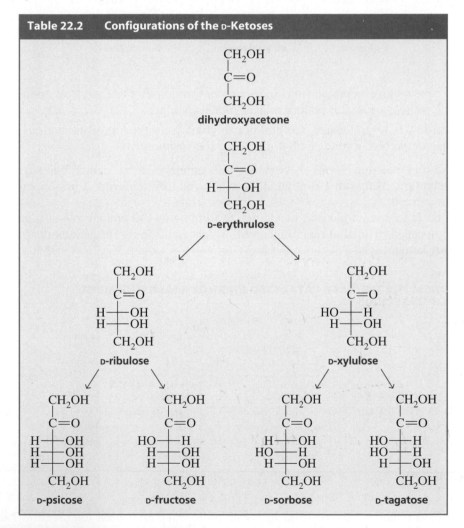

PROBLEM 7♦

What sugar is the C-3 epimer of D-fructose?

PROBLEM 8♦

How many stereoisomers are possible for
a. a 2-ketoheptose?   **b.** an aldoheptose?   **c.** a ketotriose?

22.5 THE REACTIONS OF MONOSACCHARIDES IN BASIC SOLUTIONS

Monosaccharides cannot undergo reactions with basic reagents because in a basic solution, a monosaccharide is converted to a complex mixture of polyhydroxy aldehydes and polyhydroxy ketones. Let's first look at what happens to D-glucose in a basic solution, beginning with its conversion to its C-2 epimer.

MECHANISM FOR THE BASE-CATALYZED EPIMERIZATION OF A MONOSACCHARIDE

- The base removes a proton from an α-carbon, forming an enolate ion (Section 19.3). In the enolate ion, C-2 is no longer an asymmetric center.

- When C-2 is re-protonated, the proton can come from the top or the bottom of the planar sp^2 carbon, forming both D-glucose and D-mannose.

Because the reaction forms a pair of C-2 epimers, it is called epimerization. **Epimerization** changes the configuration of a carbon by removing a proton and then re-protonating it.

In a basic solution D-glucose, in addition to forming its C-2 epimer, can also undergo a reaction called an **enediol rearrangement**, which results in the formation of D-fructose and other ketohexoses.

MECHANISM FOR THE BASE-CATALYZED ENEDIOL REARRANGEMENT OF A MONOSACCHARIDE

- The base removes a proton from an α-carbon, forming an enolate ion (Section 19.3).

- The enolate ion is protonated to form an enediol.

- The enediol has two OH groups that can form a carbonyl group. Tautomerization of the OH at C-1 (as in base-catalyzed epimerization above) re-forms D-glucose or forms D-mannose; tautomerization of the OH group at C-2 forms D-fructose.

Another enediol rearrangement, initiated by a base removing a proton from C-3 of D-fructose, forms an enediol that can tautomerize to give a ketose with the carbonyl group at C-2 or C-3. Thus, the carbonyl group can be moved up and down the chain.

In a basic solution an aldose forms a C-2 epimer and one or more ketoses.

PROBLEM 9

Show how an enediol rearrangement can move the carbonyl carbon of fructose from C-2 to C-3.

PROBLEM 10

Write the mechanism for the base-catalyzed conversion of D-fructose into D-glucose and D-mannose.

PROBLEM 11◆

When D-tagatose is added to a basic aqueous solution, an equilibrium mixture of three monosaccharides is obtained. What are these monosaccharides?

22.6 THE OXIDATION–REDUCTION REACTIONS OF MONOSACCHARIDES

Because they contain *alcohol* functional groups and *aldehyde* or *ketone* functional groups, the reactions of monosaccharides are an extension of what you have already learned about the reactions of alcohols, aldehydes, and ketones. For example, an aldehyde group in a monosaccharide can be oxidized or reduced and can react with nucleophiles to form imines, hemiacetals, and acetals. As you read this section and those that follow, dealing with the reactions of monosaccharides, you will find cross-references to earlier discussions of simpler organic compounds undergoing the same reactions. Go back and look at these earlier discussions when they are mentioned; they will make learning about carbohydrates a lot easier.

Reduction

The carbonyl group in aldoses and ketoses can be reduced by $NaBH_4$ (Section 20.2). The product of the reduction is a polyalcohol, known as an **alditol**. Reduction of an aldose forms one alditol. For example, the reduction of D-mannose forms D-mannitol, the alditol found in mushrooms, olives, and onions. Reduction of a ketose forms two alditols because the reaction creates a new asymmetric center in the product. For example, the reduction of D-fructose forms D-mannitol and D-glucitol, the C-2 epimer of D-mannitol. D-Glucitol—also called sorbitol—is about 60% as sweet as sucrose. It is found in plums, pears, cherries, and berries. It is also used as a sugar substitute in the manufacture of candy; we will see why in Section 22.17.

PROBLEM 12◆

What products are obtained from the reduction of

a. D-idose?   **b.** D-sorbose?

PROBLEM 13◆

a. What other monosaccharide is reduced only to the alditol obtained from the reduction of

   1. D-talose?   **2.** D-glucose?   **3.** D-galactose?

b. What monosaccharide is reduced to two alditols, one of which is the alditol obtained from the reduction of

   1. D-talose?   **2.** D-allose?

Oxidation

Aldoses can be distinguished from ketoses by observing what happens to the color of an aqueous solution of Br_2 when it is added to the sugar. Br_2 is a mild oxidizing agent and easily oxidizes the aldehyde group, but it cannot oxidize ketones or alcohols. Consequently, if a small amount of an aqueous solution of Br_2 is added to an unknown monosaccharide, the reddish-brown color of Br_2 will disappear if the monosaccharide is an aldose because Br_2 will be reduced to Br^-, which is colorless. If the red color persists, indicating no reaction with Br_2, the monosaccharide is a ketose. The product of the oxidation reaction is an **aldonic acid**.

D-glucose + Br₂ (red) → (H₂O) → D-gluconic acid, an aldonic acid + 2 Br⁻ (colorless)

Both aldoses and ketoses are oxidized to aldonic acids by Tollens reagent (Ag^+, NH_3, HO^-), which therefore cannot be used to distinguish them. We saw, however, in Section 20.3, that Tollens reagent oxidizes aldehydes but not ketones. Why, then, are ketoses oxidized by Tollens reagent, if ketones are not? Ketoses are oxidized because the oxidation reaction is carried out under basic conditions, and in a basic solution, a ketose can be converted into an aldose by an enediol rearrangement (Section 22.5).

a ketose $\xrightarrow{HO^-}$ an aldose $\xrightarrow[HO^-]{Ag^+, NH_3}$ a carboxylate ion

Dilute nitric acid (HNO_3) is a stronger oxidizing agent than those discussed above. It oxidizes aldehydes *and* primary alcohols, but it does not oxidize secondary alcohols. The product obtained when both the aldehyde and the primary alcohol groups of an aldose are oxidized is called an **aldaric acid**. (In an ald*on*ic acid, *on*e end is oxidized. In an ald*aric* acid, both ends *are* oxidized.)

D-glucose $\xrightarrow[\Delta]{HNO_3}$ D-glucaric acid, an aldaric acid

---

PROBLEM 14 ◆

a. Name an aldohexose other than D-glucose that is oxidized to D-glucaric acid by nitric acid.

b. What is another name for D-glucaric acid?

c. Name another pair of aldohexoses that are oxidized to identical aldaric acids.

22.7 MONOSACCHARIDES FORM CRYSTALLINE OSAZONES

The tendency of monosaccharides to form syrups that do not crystallize made the purification and isolation of monosaccharides difficult. However, Emil Fischer found that when phenylhydrazine is added to an aldose or a ketose, a yellow crystalline solid that is insoluble in water is formed. He called this derivative an **osazone** ("os" for sugar; "azone" for hydrazone). Osazones are easily isolated and purified and were once used extensively to identify monosaccharides.

Aldehydes and ketones react with one equivalent of phenylhydrazine, forming phenylhydrazones (Section 18.8). Aldoses and ketoses, in contrast, react with three equivalents of phenylhydrazine, forming osazones: one equivalent oxidizes the OH group at C-2 to a carbonyl group (and is reduced to aniline and ammonia), and two equivalents form imines with carbonyl groups. The reaction stops at this point, regardless of how much phenylhydrazine is present.

Because the configuration at C-2 is lost during osazone formation, C-2 epimers form identical osazones. For example, D-idose and D-gulose, which are C-2 epimers, both form the same osazone.

C-2 epimers form identical osazones.

The C-1 and C-2 carbons of ketoses react with phenylhydrazine. Consequently, D-fructose, D-glucose, and D-mannose all form the same osazone.

Measuring the Blood Glucose Levels in Diabetes

Glucose in the bloodstream reacts with an NH_2 group of hemoglobin to form an imine (Section 18.8) that subsequently undergoes an irreversible rearrangement to a more stable α-aminoketone known as hemoglobin-A_{Ic}.

D-glucose → NH₂-hemoglobin, trace acid → rearrangement → hemoglobin-A_{Ic}

Insulin is the hormone that regulates the level of glucose—and thus the amount of hemoglobin-A_{Ic}—in the blood. Diabetes is a condition in which the body does not produce sufficient insulin, or in which the insulin it produces does not function properly. Because people with untreated diabetes have increased blood glucose levels, they also have a higher concentration of hemoglobin-A_{Ic} than people without diabetes. Thus, measuring the hemoglobin-A_{Ic} level is a way to determine whether the blood glucose level of a diabetic patient is being controlled.

Cataracts, a common complication in diabetes, are caused by the reaction of glucose with the NH_2 group of proteins in the lens of the eye. Some think the arterial rigidity common in old age may be attributable to a similar reaction of glucose with the NH_2 group of proteins.

PROBLEM 15♦

Name a ketose and another aldose that form the same osazone as

a. D-ribose   **b.** D-altrose   **c.** L-idose   **d.** D-galactose

PROBLEM 16♦

What monosaccharides form the same osazone as D-sorbose?

22.8 LENGTHENING THE CHAIN: THE KILIANI–FISCHER SYNTHESIS

The carbon chain of an aldose can be increased by one carbon in a **Kiliani–Fischer synthesis**. In other words, tetroses can be converted into pentoses, and pentoses can be converted into hexoses.

the modified Kiliani–Fischer synthesis

D-erythrose + ⁻C≡N → new asymmetric center → H_2 Pd/BaSO₄ → HCl / H_2O → D-ribose + ⁺NH₄

→ H_2 Pd/BaSO₄ → HCl / H_2O → D-arabinose + ⁺NH₄

products are C-2 epimers

- Hydrogen cyanide adds to the carbonyl group in the first step of the synthesis. This reaction converts the carbonyl carbon in the starting material to an asymmetric center. Consequently, two products are formed that differ only in their configuration at C-2. The configurations of the other asymmetric centers do not change because no bond to any of the asymmetric centers is broken during the course of the reaction (Section 5.14).

The Kiliani–Fischer synthesis leads to a pair of C-2 epimers.

- The C≡N bond is reduced to an imine, using a partially deactivated palladium catalyst so that the imine is not further reduced to an amine (Section 6.9).
- The two imines are hydrolyzed to aldoses (Section 18.8).

Notice that the synthesis leads to a pair of C-2 epimers. The two epimers are not obtained in equal amounts because the first step of the reaction produces a pair of diastereomers and diastereomers are generally formed in unequal amounts (Section 5.18).

PROBLEM 17♦

What monosaccharides would be formed in a Kiliani–Fischer synthesis starting with each of the following compounds?

a. D-xylose   **b.** L-threose

B I O G R A P H Y

Heinrich Kiliani (1855–1945) *was born in Germany. He received a Ph.D. from the University of Munich, studying under Professor Emil Erlenmeyer. Kiliani became a professor of chemistry at the University of Freiburg.*

22.9 SHORTENING THE CHAIN: THE WOHL DEGRADATION

The **Wohl degradation**—the opposite of the Kiliani–Fischer synthesis—shortens an aldose chain by one carbon: hexoses are converted to pentoses, and pentoses are converted to tetroses.

the Wohl degradation

Ac_2O =

- In the first step, the aldehyde reacts with hydroxylamine to form an oxime (Section 18.8).
- Heating with acetic anhydride dehydrates the oxime, forming a nitrile; all the OH groups are converted to esters.
- Treatment with base hydrolyzes the ester groups (Section 17.12) and eliminates the cyano group (Section 18.7).

B I O G R A P H Y

Alfred Wohl (1863–1933) *was born in West Prussia, now part of Poland. He received a Ph.D. from the University of Berlin, where he worked with August von Hofmann (Section 10.9). He was a professor of chemistry at Technical University of Danzig.*

PROBLEM 18♦

What two monosaccharides can be degraded to

a. D-ribose   **b.** D-arabinose?   **c.** L-ribose?

22.10 THE STEREOCHEMISTRY OF GLUCOSE: THE FISCHER PROOF

Emil Fischer determined the stereochemistry of glucose in 1891, using one of the most brilliant examples of reasoning in the history of chemistry. He chose (+)-glucose for his study because it is the most common monosaccharide found in nature.

Fischer knew that (+)-glucose is an aldohexose, but 16 different structures can be written for an aldohexose. Which of them represents the structure of (+)-glucose? The 16 stereoisomers of an aldohexose are actually eight pairs of enantiomers, so if we know the structures of one set of eight, we automatically know the structures of the other set of eight. Therefore, Fischer needed to consider only one set of eight. He considered the eight stereoisomers that have their C-5 OH group on the right in the Fischer projection (the stereoisomers shown below that we now call the D-sugars).

One of these is (+)-glucose, and its mirror image is (−)-glucose. It would not be possible to determine whether (+)-glucose was D-glucose or L-glucose until 1951. Fischer used the following information to determine glucose's stereochemistry—that is, to determine the configuration of each of its asymmetric centers.

1. When the Kiliani–Fischer synthesis is performed on the sugar known as (−)-arabinose, the two sugars known as (+)-glucose and (+)-mannose are obtained. This means that (+)-glucose and (+)-mannose are C-2 epimers. Consequently, (+)-glucose and (+)-mannose have to be one of the following pairs: sugars 1 and 2, 3 and 4, 5 and 6, or 7 and 8.

2. (+)-Glucose and (+)-mannose are both oxidized by nitric acid to optically active aldaric acids. The aldaric acids of sugars 1 and 7 would not be optically active because each has a plane of symmetry. (We saw in Section 5.12 that a compound containing a plane of symmetry is achiral.) Excluding sugars 1 and 7 means that (+)-glucose and (+)-mannose must be sugars 3 and 4 or 5 and 6.

3. Because (+)-glucose and (+)-mannose are the products obtained when the Kiliani–Fischer synthesis is carried out on (−)-arabinose, Fischer knew that if (−)-arabinose has the structure shown below on the left, (+)-glucose and (+)-mannose are sugars 3 and 4. On the other hand, if (−)-arabinose has the structure shown on the right, (+)-glucose and (+)-mannose are sugars 5 and 6:

When (−)-arabinose is oxidized with nitric acid, the aldaric acid that results is optically active. This means that the aldaric acid does *not* have a plane of symmetry. Therefore, (−)-arabinose must have the structure shown above on the left because the aldaric acid of the sugar on the right has a plane of symmetry. Thus, (+)-glucose and (+)-mannose are represented by sugars 3 and 4.

4. Now the only question remaining was whether (+)-glucose is sugar 3 or sugar 4. To answer this question, Fischer had to develop a chemical method for interchanging the aldehyde and primary alcohol groups of an aldohexose. When he chemically interchanged those groups on the sugar known as (+)-glucose, he obtained an aldohexose that was different from (+)-glucose; when he interchanged those groups on (+)-mannose, he still had (+)-mannose. Therefore, he concluded that (+)-glucose is sugar 3 because interchanging its aldehyde and primary alcohol groups leads to a different sugar (L-gulose).

reverse the aldehyde and hydroxymethyl groups

D-glucose

L-gulose
drawn upside down

= L-gulose

If (+)-glucose is sugar 3, (+)-mannose must be sugar 4. As predicted, when the aldehyde and hydroxymethyl groups of sugar 4 are interchanged, the same sugar is obtained.

reverse the aldehyde and hydroxymethyl groups

D-mannose

D-mannose
drawn upside down

= D-mannose

Using similar reasoning, Fischer went on to determine the stereochemistry of the other aldohexoses. He received the Nobel Prize in Chemistry in 1902 for this achievement. His original guess that (+)-glucose is a D-sugar was later shown to be correct, so all of his structures are correct (Section 5.15). If he had been wrong and (+)-glucose had been an L-sugar, his contribution to the stereochemistry of aldoses would still have had the same importance, but all his stereochemical assignments would have had to be reversed.

PROBLEM 19 — SOLVED

Aldohexoses A and B form the same osazone. Compound A is oxidized by nitric acid to an optically active aldaric acid, and compound B is oxidized to an optically inactive aldaric acid. Wohl degradation of either A or B forms aldopentose C, which is oxidized by nitric acid to an optically active aldaric acid. Wohl degradation of C forms D, which is oxidized by nitric acid to an optically active aldaric acid. Wohl degradation of D forms (+)-glyceraldehyde. Identify A, B, C, and D.

Solution   This is the kind of problem that should be solved by working backward. The bottom-most asymmetric center in D must have the OH group on the right because D is degraded to (+)-glyceraldehyde. Since D is oxidized to an optically active aldaric acid, D must be D-threose. The two bottom-most asymmetric centers in C and D have the same configuration because C is degraded to D. Since C is oxidized to an optically active aldaric acid, C must be D-lyxose. Compounds A and B, therefore, must be D-galactose and D-talose. Because A is oxidized to an optically active aldaric acid, it must be D-talose and B must be D-galactose.

PROBLEM 20 ◆

Identify A, B, C, and D in the preceding problem if D is oxidized to an optically *inactive* aldaric acid, if A, B, and C are oxidized to optically active aldaric acids, and if interchanging the aldehyde and alcohol groups of A leads to a different sugar.

Glucose/Dextrose

André Dumas first used the term *glucose* in 1838 to refer to the sweet compound that comes from honey and grapes. Later, Kekulé (Section 7.1) decided that it should be called dextrose because it was dextrorotatory. When Fischer studied the sugar, he called it glucose, and chemists have called it glucose ever since, although dextrose is often found on food labels.

22.11 MONOSACCHARIDES FORM CYCLIC HEMIACETALS

D-Glucose exists in three different forms: the open-chain form of D-glucose that we have been discussing and two cyclic forms—α-D-glucose and β-D-glucose. We know that the two cyclic forms are different because they have different melting points and different specific rotations (Section 5.8).

How can D-glucose exist in a cyclic form? In Section 18.10, we saw that an aldehyde reacts with an alcohol to form a hemiacetal. A monosaccharide such as D-glucose has an aldehyde group and several alcohol groups. The alcohol group bonded to C-5 of D-glucose reacts with the aldehyde group. The reaction forms two cyclic (six-membered ring) hemiacetals. At equilibrium, there is almost twice as much β-D-glucose (64%) as α-D-glucose (36%).

To see that the OH group on C-5 is in the proper position to attack the aldehyde group, we need to convert the Fischer projection of D-glucose to a flat ring structure. To do this, draw the primary alcohol group *up* from the back left-hand corner. Groups on the *right* in a Fischer projection are *down* in the cyclic structure, whereas groups on the *left* in a Fischer projection are *up* in the cyclic structure.

Groups on the *right* in a Fischer projection are *down* in a Haworth projection.

Groups on the *left* in a Fischer projection are *up* in a Haworth projection.

The six-membered ring hemiacetals shown here are drawn as Haworth projections. In a **Haworth projection**, the six-membered ring is represented as flat and is viewed edge-on. The ring oxygen is always placed in the back right-hand corner of the ring, with the anomeric carbon (C-1) on the right-hand side and the primary alcohol group drawn *up* from the back left-hand corner (C-5).

Why are there two different cyclic forms? Two different hemiacetals are formed because the carbonyl carbon of the open-chain aldehyde becomes a new asymmetric center in the cyclic hemiacetal. If the OH group bonded to the new asymmetric center is down (trans to the primary alcohol group at C-5), the hemiacetal is α-D-glucose; if the OH group is up (cis to the primary alcohol group at C-5), the hemiacetal is β-D-glucose. The mechanism for cyclic hemiacetal formation is the same as the mechanism for hemiacetal formation between individual aldehyde and alcohol molecules (Section 18.10).

α-D-Glucose and β-D-glucose are anomers. **Anomers** are two sugars that differ in configuration only at the carbon that was the carbonyl carbon in the open-chain form. This carbon is called the **anomeric carbon**. (*Ano* is Greek for "upper"; thus, anomers differ in configuration at the asymmetric center that would be uppermost in a Fischer projection.) The prefixes α- and β- denote the configuration about the anomeric carbon. Because anomers, like epimers, differ in configuration at only one carbon atom, they too are a particular kind of diastereomer. Notice that the anomeric carbon is the only carbon in the molecule that is bonded to two oxygens.

In an aqueous solution, the open-chain form of D-glucose is in equilibrium with the two cyclic hemiacetals. Because formation of the cyclic hemiacetals proceeds nearly to completion (unlike formation of acyclic hemiacetals), very little of the glucose is in the open-chain form (about 0.02%). Even so, the sugar still undergoes the reactions discussed in previous sections (oxidation, reduction, and osazone formation) because the reagents react with the small amount of open-chain aldehyde that is present. As the open-chain compound reacts, the equilibrium shifts to produce more open-chain compound, which can then undergo reaction. Eventually, all the glucose molecules react by way of the open-chain aldehyde.

When crystals of pure α-D-glucose are dissolved in water, the specific rotation gradually changes from +112.2 to +52.7. When crystals of pure β-D-glucose are dissolved in water, the specific rotation gradually changes from +18.7 to +52.7. This change in rotation occurs because in water, the hemiacetal opens to form the aldehyde, and when the aldehyde recyclizes, both α-D-glucose and β-D-glucose are formed. Eventually, the three forms of glucose reach equilibrium concentrations. The specific rotation of the equilibrium mixture is +52.7. This is why the same specific rotation results whether the crystals originally dissolved in water are α-D-glucose or β-D-glucose or any mixture of the two. A slow change in optical rotation to an equilibrium value is called **mutarotation**.

If an aldose can form a five- or a six-membered-ring, it will exist predominantly as a cyclic hemiacetal in solution. Whether a five- or a six-membered-ring is formed depends on their relative stabilities. D-Ribose is an example of an aldose that forms five-membered-ring hemiacetals: α-D-ribose and β-D-ribose. The Haworth projection of a five-membered-ring sugar is viewed edge-on, with the ring oxygen pointing away from the viewer. The anomeric carbon is again on the right-hand side of the molecule, and the primary alcohol group is drawn up from the back left-hand corner.

Six-membered-ring sugars are called **pyranoses**, and five-membered-ring sugars are called **furanoses**. These names come from *pyran* and *furan,* the names of the cyclic ethers shown in the margin. Consequently, α-D-glucose is also called α-D-glucopyranose, and α-D-ribose is also called α-D-ribofuranose The prefix α- indicates the configuration about the anomeric carbon, and *pyranose* or *furanose* indicates the size of the ring.

pyran

furan

α-D-glucose
α-D-glucopyranose

α-D-ribose
α-D-ribofuranose

Ketoses also exist in solution predominantly in cyclic forms. For example, D-fructose forms a five-membered-ring hemiketal as a result of the reaction of its C-5 OH group with its ketone carbonyl group. If the OH group bonded to the new asymmetric center is trans to the primary alcohol group, the compound is α-D-fructofuranose; if it is cis to the primary alcohol group, the compound is β-D-fructofuranose. Notice that in ketoses the anomeric carbon is C-2, not C-1 as in aldoses.

α-D-fructofuranose   β-D-fructofuranose   α-D-fructopyranose   β-D-fructopyranose

D-Fructose can also form a six-membered ring by using the C-6 OH group. The pyranose form predominates in the monosaccharide, whereas the furanose form predominates when the sugar is part of a disaccharide. (See the structure of sucrose on page 963.)

Haworth projections are useful because they show clearly whether the OH groups on the ring are cis or trans to each other. Five-membered rings are nearly planar, so furanoses are represented fairly accurately by Haworth projections. Haworth projections, however, are structurally misleading for pyranoses because a six-membered ring is not flat but exists preferentially in a chair conformation (Section 2.12).

chem Tutorial:
place Cyclization of a monosaccharide

PROBLEM 21   SOLVED

4-Hydroxy- and 5-hydroxyaldehydes exist primarily as cyclic hemiacetals. Draw the structure of the cyclic hemiacetal formed by each of the following:

a. 4-hydroxybutanal
b. 5-hydroxypentanal

c. 4-hydroxypentanal
d. 4-hydroxyheptanal

Solution to 21a   Draw the reactant with its alcohol and carbonyl groups on the same side of the molecule. Then look to see what size ring will form. Two cyclic products are obtained because the carbonyl carbon of the reactant has been converted into a new asymmetric center in the product.

PROBLEM 22

Draw the following sugars using Haworth projections:

a. β-D-galactopyranose
b. α-D-tagatopyranose
c. α-L-glucopyranose

PROBLEM 23

D-Glucose most often exists as a pyranose, but it can also exist as a furanose. Draw the Haworth projection of α-D-glucofuranose.

22.12 GLUCOSE IS THE MOST STABLE ALDOHEXOSE

Drawing D-glucose in its chair conformation shows why it is the most common aldohexose in nature. To convert the Haworth projection of D-glucose into a chair conformer, start by drawing the chair so that the backrest is on the left and the footrest is on the right. Then place the ring oxygen at the back right-hand corner and the primary alcohol group in the equatorial position. The primary alcohol group is the largest of all the substituents, and we know that large substituents are more stable in the equatorial position because there is less steric strain in that position (Section 2.13). Because the OH group bonded to C-4 is trans to the primary alcohol group (this is easily seen in the Haworth projection), the C-4 OH group is also in the equatorial position. (Recall from Section 2.14 that 1,2-diequatorial substituents are trans to one another.) The C-3 OH group is trans to the C-4 OH group, so the C-3 OH group is also in the equatorial position. As you move around the ring, you will find that all the OH substituents in β-D-glucose are in equatorial positions. The axial positions are all occupied by hydrogens, which require little space and therefore experience little steric strain. No other aldohexose exists in such a strain-free conformation. This means that β-D-glucose is the most stable of all the aldohexoses, so we should not be surprised that it is the most prevalent aldohexose in nature.

α-D-glucose
chair conformer

The α-position is down in a Haworth projection and axial in a chair conformation.

The β-position is up in a Haworth projection and equatorial in a chair conformation.

β-D-glucose
chair conformer

The chair conformers show why there is more β-D-glucose than α-D-glucose in an aqueous solution at equilibrium. The OH group bonded to the anomeric carbon is in the equatorial position in β-D-glucose, whereas it is in the axial position in α-D-glucose. Therefore, β-D-glucose is more stable than α-D-glucose, so β-D-glucose predominates at equilibrium in an aqueous solution.

α-D-glucose
36%

β-D-glucose
64%

If you remember that all the OH groups in β-D-glucose are in equatorial positions, you will find it easy to draw the chair conformer of any other pyranose. For example, if you want to draw α-D-galactose, you would put all the OH groups in equatorial positions except the OH groups at C-4 (because galactose is a C-4 epimer of glucose) and at C-1 (because you want the α-anomer). You would put these two OH groups in axial positions.

the OH at C-4 is axial

HO CH$_2$OH

HO OH OH

the OH at C-1 is axial (α)

α-D-**galactose**

To draw an L-pyranose, draw the D-pyranose first, and then draw its mirror image. For example, to draw β-L-gulose, first draw β-D-gulose. (Gulose differs from glucose at C-3 and C-4, so the OH groups at these positions are in axial positions.) Then draw the mirror image of β-D-gulose to get β-L-gulose.

the OH at C-4 is axial

HO CH$_2$OH

the OH at C-1 is equatorial (β)

OH OH HO

β-D-**gulose**

the OH at C-3 is axial

HO HOCH$_2$ OH

HO OH

β-L-**gulose**

PROBLEM 24◆　SOLVED

Which OH groups are in the axial position in

a. β-D-mannopyranose?　　　**b.** β-D-idopyranose?　　　**c.** α-D-allopyranose?

Solution to 24a　All the OH groups in β-D-glucose are in equatorial positions. Because β-D-mannose is a C-2 epimer of β-D-glucose, only the C-2 OH group of β-D-mannose is in the axial position.

22.13　FORMATION OF GLYCOSIDES

In the same way that a hemiacetal (or hemiketal) reacts with an alcohol to form an acetal (or ketal) (Section 18.10), the cyclic hemiacetal (or hemiketal) formed by a monosaccharide can react with an alcohol to form an acetal (or ketal). The acetal or ketal of a sugar is called a **glycoside**, and the bond between the anomeric carbon and the alkoxy oxygen is called a **glycosidic bond**. Glycosides are named by replacing the "e" ending of the sugar's name with "ide." Thus, a glycoside of glucose is a glucoside, a glycoside of galactose is a galactoside, and so on. If the pyranose or furanose name is used, the acetal (or ketal) is called a **pyranoside** or a **furanoside**.

CH$_2$OH
HO
HO OH H
β-D-glucose
β-D-glucopyranose

$\xrightarrow{\text{CH}_3\text{CH}_2\text{OH}}$
HCl

a glycosidic bond

CH$_2$OH
HO
HO OCH$_2$CH$_3$
OH H
ethyl β-D-glucoside
ethyl β-D-glucopyranoside

acetal

+

CH$_2$OH
HO
HO H
OH OCH$_2$CH$_3$
ethyl α-D-glucoside
ethyl α-D-glucopyranoside

Notice that the reaction of a single anomer with an alcohol leads to the formation of both the α- and β-glycosides. The mechanism of the reaction shows why both glycosides are formed.

MECHANISM FOR GLYCOSIDE FORMATION

an oxocarbenium ion

alcohol approaches from the top

alcohol approaches from the bottom

a β-glycoside

an α-glycoside
major product

- The OH group bonded to the anomeric carbon becomes protonated in the acidic solution.

- A lone pair on the ring oxygen helps eliminate a molecule of water. The anomeric carbon in the resulting oxocarbenium ion is sp^2 hybridized, so that part of the molecule is planar. (An **oxocarbenium ion** has a positive charge that is shared by a carbon and an oxygen.)

- When the alcohol approaches from the top of the plane, the β-glycoside is formed; when it approaches from the bottom of the plane, the α-glycoside is formed.

Notice that the mechanism is the same as that shown for acetal formation in Section 18.10. Surprisingly, D-glucose forms more of the α-glycoside than the β-glycoside. The reason for this is explained in the next section.

Similar to the reaction of a monosaccharide with an alcohol is the reaction of a monosaccharide with an amine in the presence of a trace amount of acid. The product of the reaction is an *N*-glycoside. An **N-glycoside** has a nitrogen in place of the oxygen at the glycosidic linkage. The subunits of DNA and RNA are β-*N*-glycosides (Section 28.1).

chem place Tutorial: Identifying glycosidic linkages and numbering pyranose and furanose rings

N-phenyl α-D-ribosylamine
an α-*N*-glycoside

N-phenyl β-D-ribosylamine
a β-*N*-glycoside

PROBLEM 25◆

Why is only a trace amount of acid used in the formation of an *N*-glycoside?

22.14 THE ANOMERIC EFFECT

We have seen that *β*-D-glucose is more stable than *α*-D-glucose because there is more room for a substituent in the equatorial position. However, the preference of the OH group for the equatorial position is not as large as one might expect. For example, the relative amounts of *β*-D-glucose and *α*-D-glucose are 2 : 1 (Section 22.10), but the relative amounts of the OH group of cyclohexanol in the equatorial and axial positions is 5.4 : 1 (Table 2.10 on page 107).

However, when glucose reacts with an alcohol to form a glucoside, the major product is the *α*-glucoside. Because acetal formation is reversible, the *α*-glucoside must be more stable than the *β*-glucoside. The preference of certain substituents bonded to the anomeric carbon for the axial position is called the **anomeric effect**.

What is responsible for the anomeric effect? The C—Z bond has a *σ** antibonding orbital. If one of the ring oxygen's lone pairs is in an orbital that is parallel to the *σ** antibonding orbital, the molecule can be stabilized by electron delocalization—some of the electron density moves from the sp^3 orbital of oxygen into the *σ** antibonding orbital. Oxygen's orbital can overlap the *σ** antibonding orbital only if the substituent is axial. If the substituent is equatorial, neither of the orbitals that contain a lone pair is aligned correctly for overlap.

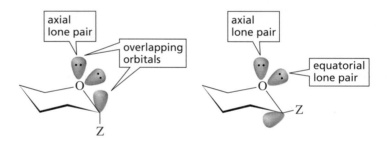

22.15 REDUCING AND NONREDUCING SUGARS

Because glycosides are acetals (or ketals), they are not in equilibrium with the open-chain aldehyde (or ketone) in aqueous solutions. Without being in equilibrium with a compound that has a carbonyl group, they cannot be oxidized by reagents such as Ag^+ or Br_2. Glycosides, therefore, are nonreducing sugars—they cannot reduce Ag^+ or Br_2.

In contrast, hemiacetals (or hemiketals) are in equilibrium with the open-chain sugars in aqueous solution, so they can reduce Ag^+ or Br_2. In summary, as long as a sugar has an aldehyde, a ketone, a hemiacetal, or a hemiketal group, it is able to reduce an oxidizing agent and therefore is classified as a **reducing sugar**. Without one of these groups, it is a **nonreducing sugar**.

A sugar with an aldehyde, a ketone, a hemiacetal, or a hemiketal group is a reducing sugar. A sugar without one of these groups is a nonreducing sugar.

PROBLEM 26   **SOLVED**

Name the following compounds, and indicate whether each is a reducing sugar or a nonreducing sugar:

a.

b.

c.

d.

Solution to 26a   The only OH group in an axial position in part a is the one at C-3. Therefore, this sugar is the C-3 epimer of D-glucose, which is D-allose. The substituent at the anomeric carbon is in the β-position. Thus, the sugar's name is propyl β-D-alloside or propyl β-D-allopyranoside. Because the sugar is an acetal, it is a nonreducing sugar.

chem place   Tutorial:
Common terms in carbohydrate chemistry

22.16 DISACCHARIDES

If the hemiacetal group of a monosaccharide forms an acetal by reacting with an alcohol group of another monosaccharide, the glycoside that is formed is a disaccharide. **Disaccharides** are compounds consisting of two monosaccharide subunits hooked together by a glycosidic linkage. For example, maltose is a disaccharide obtained from the hydrolysis of starch. It contains two D-glucose subunits connected by a glycosidic linkage. This particular linkage is called an **α-1,4′-glycosidic linkage** because the linkage is between C-1 of one sugar subunit and C-4 of the other, and the oxygen bonded to the anomeric carbon in the glycosidic linkage is in the α-position. The prime superscript indicates that C-4 is not in the same ring as C-1. *Remember that the α-position is axial and the β-position is equatorial when a sugar is shown in a chair conformation.*

an α-1,4′-glycosidic linkage

the configuration of this carbon is not specified

maltose

Notice that the structure of maltose does not specify the configuration of the anomeric carbon that is not an acetal (the anomeric carbon of the subunit on the right marked with a wavy line) because maltose can exist in both the α and β forms. In α-maltose, the OH group bonded to this anomeric carbon is in the axial position. In β-maltose, the OH group is in the equatorial position. Because maltose can exist in both α and β forms, mutarotation occurs when crystals of one form are dissolved in a solvent. Maltose is a reducing sugar because the right-hand subunit is a hemiacetal and therefore is in equilibrium with the open-chain aldehyde that is easily oxidized.

Cellobiose, a disaccharide obtained from the hydrolysis of cellulose, also contains two D-glucose subunits. Cellobiose differs from maltose in that the two glucose subunits are hooked together by a **β-1,4′-glycosidic linkage**. Thus, the only difference in the structures of maltose and cellobiose is the configuration of the glycosidic linkage. Like maltose, cellobiose exists in both α and β forms because the OH group bonded to the anomeric carbon not involved in acetal formation can be in either the axial position (in α-cellobiose) or the equatorial position (in β-cellobiose). Cellobiose is a reducing sugar because the subunit on the right is a hemiacetal.

cellobiose

Lactose is a disaccharide found in milk. It constitutes 4.5% of cow's milk and 6.5% of human milk by weight. One of the subunits of lactose is D-galactose, and the other is D-glucose. The D-galactose subunit is an acetal, and the D-glucose subunit is a hemiacetal. The subunits are joined by a β-1,4'-glycosidic linkage. Because one of the subunits is a hemiacetal, lactose is a reducing sugar and undergoes mutarotation.

lactose

A simple experiment can prove that the hemiacetal group in lactose belongs to the glucose residue and not to the galactose residue. The disaccharide is treated with excess methyl iodide in the presence of Ag₂O, a reaction that methylates all the OH groups via S_N2 reactions. Because the OH group is a relatively poor nucleophile, silver oxide is used to increase the leaving propensity of the iodide ion. The product is then hydrolyzed under acidic conditions. This treatment causes the two acetals to be hydrolyzed, but all the ethers, formed by methylating the OH groups, are untouched. Identification of the products shows that the glucose residue contained the hemiacetal group in the disaccharide because its C-4 OH group was not able to react with methyl iodide (since it was used to form the acetal with galactose). The C-4 OH of galactose, on the other hand, was able to react with methyl iodide.

2,3,4,6-tetra-O-methylgalactose   **2,3,6-tri-O-methylglucose**

Lactose Intolerance

Lactase is an enzyme that specifically breaks the β-1,4′-glycosidic linkage of lactose. Cats and dogs lose their intestinal lactase when they become adults; they are then no longer able to digest lactose. Consequently, when they are fed milk or milk products, the undegraded lactose causes digestive problems such as bloating, abdominal pain, and diarrhea. These problems occur because only monosaccharides can pass into the bloodstream, so lactose has to pass undigested into the large intestine. When humans have stomach flu or other intestinal disturbances, they can temporarily lose their lactase, thereby becoming lactose intolerant. Some humans lose their lactase permanently as they mature. Lactose intolerance is much more common in people whose ancestors came from nondairy-producing countries. For example, only 3% of Danes are lactose intolerant, compared with 90% of all Chinese and Japanese and 97% of Thais. This is why you are not likely to find dairy items on Chinese menus.

Galactosemia

After lactose is degraded into glucose and galactose, the galactose must be converted into glucose before it can be used by cells. Individuals who do not have the enzyme that converts galactose into glucose have the genetic disease known as galactosemia. Without this enzyme, galactose accumulates in the bloodstream. This condition can cause mental retardation and even death in infants. Galactosemia is treated by excluding galactose from the diet.

The most common disaccharide, sucrose, is the substance we know as table sugar. Obtained from sugar beets and sugar cane, sucrose consists of a D-glucose subunit and a D-fructose subunit linked by a glycosidic bond between C-1 of glucose (in the α-position) and C-2 of fructose (in the β-position). About 90 million tons of sucrose are produced commercially throughout the world each year.

Unlike the other disaccharides that we have looked at, sucrose is not a reducing sugar and does not exhibit mutarotation because its glycosidic bond is between the anomeric carbon of glucose and the anomeric carbon of fructose. Sucrose, therefore, does not have a hemiacetal or hemiketal group, so it is not in equilibrium with the readily oxidized open-chain aldehyde or ketone form in aqueous solution.

sucrose

Sucrose has a specific rotation of +66.5. When it is hydrolyzed, the resulting 1 : 1 mixture of glucose and fructose has a specific rotation of −22.0. Because the sign of the rotation changes when sucrose is hydrolyzed, a 1 : 1 mixture of glucose and fructose is called *invert sugar.* The enzyme that catalyzes the hydrolysis of sucrose is called *invertase.* Honeybees have invertase, so the honey they produce is a mixture of sucrose, glucose, and fructose. Because fructose is sweeter than sucrose, invert sugar is sweeter than sucrose. Some foods are advertised as containing fructose instead of sucrose, which means that they achieve the same level of sweetness with a lower sugar (lower calorie) content.

chem place Tutorial: Identifying glycosidic linkages and numbering pyranose and furanose rings

---

PROBLEM 27 ♦

What is the specific rotation of an equilibrium mixture of fructose? (*Hint*: The specific rotation of an equilibrium mixture of glucose is +52.7.)

22.17 POLYSACCHARIDES

Polysaccharides contain as few as 10 or as many as several thousand monosaccharide units joined together by glycosidic linkages. The most common polysaccharides are starch and cellulose.

Starch is the major component of flour, potatoes, rice, beans, corn, and peas. It is a mixture of two different polysaccharides: amylose (about 20%) and amylopectin (about 80%). Amylose is composed of unbranched chains of D-glucose units joined by α-1,4′-glycosidic linkages.

three subunits of amylose

Amylopectin is a branched polysaccharide. Like amylose, it is composed of chains of D-glucose units joined by α-1,4′-glycosidic linkages. Unlike amylose, however, amylopectin also contains **α-1,6′-glycosidic linkages**. These linkages create branches in the polysaccharide (Figure 22.1). Amylopectin can contain up to 10^6 glucose units, making it one of the largest molecules found in nature.

five subunits of amylopectin

an α-1,4'-glycosidic bond

an α-1,6'-glycosidic bond

◄ **Figure 22.1**
◄ **Figure 22.1**
Branching in amylopectin.
The hexagons represent glucose
units. They are joined by α-1,4'-
and α-1,6'-glycosidic bonds.

Living cells oxidize D-glucose in the first of a series of processes that provide them with energy (Section 26.7). When animals have more D-glucose than they need for energy, they convert the excess D-glucose into a polymer called glycogen. Glycogen has a structure similar to that of amylopectin, but glycogen has more branches (Figure 22.2). The branch points in glycogen occur about every 10 residues, whereas those in amylopectin occur about every 25 residues. The high degree of branching in glycogen has important physiological consequences. When an animal needs energy, many individual glucose units can be simultaneously removed from the ends of many branches. Plants convert excess D-glucose into starch.

amylopectin   **glycogen**

◄ **Figure 22.2**
A comparison of the branching in
amylopectin and glycogen.

Why the Dentist Is Right

Bacteria found in the mouth have an enzyme that converts sucrose into a polysaccharide called dextran. Dextran is made up of glucose units joined mainly through α-1,3'- and α-1,6'-glycosidic linkages. About 10% of dental plaque is composed of dextran, and bacteria hidden in the plaque attack tooth enamel. This is the chemical basis for your dentist's warning not to eat candy. This is also why sorbitol and mannitol are the saccharides added to gum—they cannot be converted to dextran.

Cellulose is the major structural component of plants. Cotton, for example, is composed of about 90% cellulose, and wood is about 50% cellulose. Like amylose, cellulose is composed of unbranched chains of D-glucose units. Unlike amylose, however, the glucose units in cellulose are joined by β-1,4'-glycosidic linkages rather than by α-1,4'-glycosidic linkages.

a β-1,4'-glycosidic linkage

three subunits of cellulose

▲ Figure 22.3
The α-1,4'-glycosidic linkages in amylose cause it to form a left-handed helix. Many of its OH groups form hydrogen bonds with water molecules.

All mammals have the enzyme (α-glucosidase) that hydrolyzes the α-1,4'-glycosidic linkages that join glucose units in amylose, amylopectin, and glycogen, but they do not have the enzyme (β-glucosidase) that hydrolyzes β-1,4'-glycosidic linkages. As a result, mammals *cannot* obtain the glucose they need by eating cellulose. However, bacteria that possess β-glucosidase inhabit the digestive tracts of grazing animals, so cows can eat grass and horses can eat hay to meet their nutritional requirements for glucose. Termites also harbor bacteria that break down the cellulose in the wood they eat.

The different glycosidic linkages in starch and cellulose give these compounds very different physical properties. The α-linkages in starch cause amylose to form a helix that promotes hydrogen bonding of its OH groups to water molecules (Figure 22.3). As a result, starch is soluble in water.

On the other hand, the β-linkages in cellulose promote the formation of intramolecular hydrogen bonds. Consequently, these molecules arrange themselves in linear arrays (Figure 22.4), held together by intermolecular hydrogen bonds between adjacent chains. (Also compare the molecular models of maltose and cellobiose on pages 961 and 962.) These large aggregates cause cellulose to be insoluble in water. The strength of these bundles of polymer chains makes cellulose an effective structural material. Processed cellulose is also used for the production of paper and cellophane.

Strands of cellulose in a plant cell wall

intramolecular hydrogen bond

note that this ring is inverted compared to that in the structure of cellulose on page 965

▲ Figure 22.4
The β-1,4'-glycosidic linkages in cellulose form intramolecular hydrogen bonds, which cause the molecules to assemble in linear arrays.

The shell of this bright orange crab from Australia is composed largely of chitin.

Chitin (KY-tin) is a polysaccharide that is structurally similar to cellulose. It is the major structural component of the shells of crustaceans (such as lobsters, crabs, and shrimps) and the exoskeletons of insects and other arthropods, and it is also the structural material of fungi. Like cellulose, chitin has β-1,4'-glycosidic linkages. It differs from cellulose in that it has an *N*-acetylamino group instead of an OH group at the C-2 position. The β-1,4'-glycosidic linkages give chitin its structural rigidity.

an *N*-acetylamino group

three subunits of chitin

Controlling Fleas

Several different drugs have been developed to help pet owners control fleas. One of these drugs is lufenuron, the active ingredient in Program. Lufenuron interferes with the flea's production of chitin. The consequences are fatal for the flea because its exoskeleton is composed primarily of chitin.

lufenuron

PROBLEM 28

What is the main structural difference between

a. amylose and cellulose?

b. amylose and amylopectin?

c. amylopectin and glycogen?

d. cellulose and chitin?

22.18 SOME NATURALLY OCCURRING PRODUCTS DERIVED FROM CARBOHYDRATES

Deoxy sugars are sugars in which one of the OH groups is replaced by a hydrogen (*deoxy* means "without oxygen"). 2-Deoxyribose is an important example of a deoxy sugar; it is missing the oxygen at the C-2 position. D-Ribose is the sugar component of ribonucleic acid (RNA), whereas 2-deoxyribose is the sugar component of deoxyribonucleic acid (DNA); (see Section 28.1).

β-D-**ribose** β-D-**2-deoxyribose**

In **amino sugars**, one of the OH groups is replaced by an amino group. *N*-Acetylglucosamine—the subunit of chitin and one of the subunits of bacterial cell walls—is an example of an amino sugar (Sections 22.17 and 24.9). Some important antibiotics contain amino sugars. For example, the three subunits of the antibiotic gentamicin are deoxyamino sugars. Notice that the middle subunit is missing the ring oxygen, so it is not a sugar.

gentamicin
an antibiotic

Heparin

Heparin—a natural anticoagulant—is a polysaccharide found principally in cells that line arterial walls. Some of its alcohol and amino groups are sulfonated, some of its alcohol groups are oxidized, and some of its amino groups are acetylated. Heparin is released when an injury occurs in order to prevent excessive blood clot formation. Heparin is widely used clinically as an anticoagulant.

heparin

L-Ascorbic acid (vitamin C) is synthesized from D-glucose in plants and in the livers of most vertebrates. Humans, monkeys, and guinea pigs do not have the enzymes necessary for the biosynthesis of vitamin C, so they must obtain the vitamin from their diets. The biosynthesis of vitamin C involves the enzymatic conversion of D-glucose to L-gulonic acid, reminiscent of the last step in the Fischer proof. L-Gulonic acid is converted into a γ-lactone by the enzyme lactonase, and then an enzyme called oxidase oxidizes the lactone to L-ascorbic acid. The L-designation of ascorbic acid refers to the configuration at C-5, which was C-2 in D-glucose.

the synthesis of L-ascorbic acid

D-glucose → (oxidizing enzyme) → (reducing enzyme) → (rotate 180°) = L-gulonic acid → (lactonase) → a γ-lactone → (oxidase) → L-ascorbic acid / vitamin C → (oxidation) → L-dehydroascorbic acid

L-configuration

$pK_a = 4.17$

Although L-ascorbic acid does not have a carboxylic acid group, it is an acidic compound because the pK_a of the C-3 OH group is 4.17. L-Ascorbic acid is readily oxidized—notice that when it is oxidized, it loses hydrogens—to L-dehydroascorbic acid, which is also physiologically active. If the lactone ring is opened by hydrolysis, all vitamin C activity is lost. Therefore, not much intact vitamin C survives in food that has been thoroughly cooked. Worse, if the food is cooked in water and then drained, the water-soluble vitamin is thrown out with the water!

Vitamin C

Vitamin C is an antioxidant because it prevents oxidation reactions by radicals. It traps radicals formed in aqueous environments (Section 12.11), preventing harmful oxidation reactions the radicals would cause. Not all the physiological functions of vitamin C are known. However, we do know it is required for the synthesis of collagen, which is the structural protein of skin, tendons, connective tissue, and bone. Vitamin C is abundant in citrus fruits and tomatoes. When the vitamin is not present in the diet, lesions appear on the skin, severe bleeding occurs about the gums, in the joints, and under the skin, and any wound heals slowly. The condition, known as *scurvy*, was the first disease to be treated by adjusting the diet. British sailors who shipped out to sea after the late 1700s were required to eat limes to prevent scurvy (which is how they came to be called "limeys"). Not until 200 years later did it become known that the substance preventing scurvy was vitamin C. *Scorbutus* is Latin for "scurvy"; *ascorbic*, therefore, means "no scurvy."

PROBLEM 29

Explain why the C-3 OH group of vitamin C is more acidic than the C-2 OH group.

22.19 CARBOHYDRATES ON CELL SURFACES

Many cells have short oligosaccharide chains on their surface that enable the cells to recognize and interact with other cells and with invading viruses and bacteria. These oligosaccharides are linked to the surface of the cell by the reaction of an OH or an NH_2 group of a cell-membrane protein with the anomeric carbon of a cyclic sugar. Proteins bonded to oligosaccharides are called **glycoproteins**. The percentage of carbohydrate in glycoproteins is variable; some glycoproteins contain as little as 1% carbohydrate by weight, whereas others contain as much as 80%.

An English sailor circa 1829

Carbohydrates on the surfaces of cells provide a way for cells to recognize one another, serving as points of attachment for other cells, viruses, and toxins. Therefore, surface carbohydrates have been found to play a role in activities as diverse as infection, prevention of infection, fertilization, inflammatory diseases such as rheumatoid arthritis and septic shock, and blood clotting. The fact that several known antibiotics contain amino sugars (Section 22.18) suggests that the antibiotics function by recognizing target cells. Carbohydrate interactions also are involved in the regulation of cell growth, so changes in membrane glycoproteins are thought to be correlated with malignant transformations.

Differences in blood type (A, B, or O) are actually differences in the sugars bound to the surfaces of red blood cells. Each type of blood is associated with a different carbohydrate structure (Figure 22.5). Type AB blood is a mixture of type A blood and type B blood.

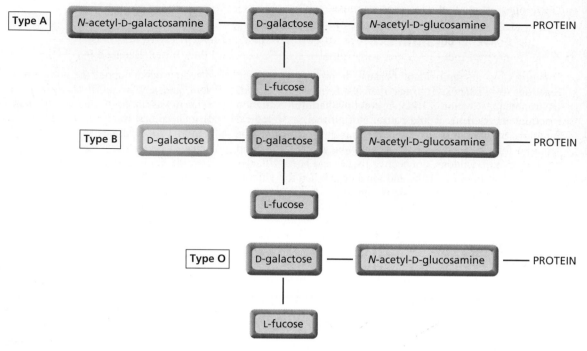

▲ **Figure 22.5**
Blood type is determined by the nature of the sugar on the surfaces of red blood cells. Fucose is 6-deoxygalactose.

Antibodies are proteins that are synthesized by the body in response to foreign substances called *antigens.* Interaction with the antibody causes the antigen to either precipitate or be flagged for destruction by immune system cells. This is why, for example, blood cannot be transferred from one person to another unless the blood types of the donor and acceptor are compatible. Otherwise the donated blood will be considered a foreign substance and provoke an immune response.

Looking at Figure 22.5, we can see why the immune system of type A people recognizes type B blood as foreign and vice versa. The immune system of people with type A, B, or AB blood does not, however, recognize type O blood as foreign because the carbohydrate in type O blood is also a component of types A, B, and AB. Thus, anyone can accept type O blood, so people with type O blood are called universal donors. People with type AB blood can accept types AB, A, B, and O blood, so they are referred to as universal acceptors.

PROBLEM 30♦

Refer to Figure 22.5 to answer the following questions:
a. People with type O blood can donate blood to anyone, but they cannot receive blood from everyone. From whom can they *not* receive blood?
b. People with type AB blood can receive blood from anyone, but they cannot give blood to everyone. To whom can they *not* give blood?

22.20 SYNTHETIC SWEETENERS

For a molecule to taste sweet, it must bind to a receptor on a taste bud cell of the tongue. The binding of this molecule causes a nerve impulse to pass from the taste bud to the brain, where the molecule is interpreted as being sweet. Sugars differ in their degree of "sweetness." Compared with the sweetness of glucose, which is assigned a relative value of 1.00, the sweetness of sucrose is 1.45, and that of fructose, the sweetest of all sugars, is 1.65.

Developers of synthetic sweeteners must evaluate potential products in terms of several factors—such as toxicity, stability, and cost—in addition to taste. Saccharin (Sweet'N Low), the first synthetic sweetener, was discovered accidentally by Ira Remsen. One evening he noticed that the dinner rolls initially tasted sweet and then bitter. Because his wife did not notice that the rolls had an unusual taste, Remsen tasted his fingers and found they had the same odd taste. The next day he tasted the chemicals he had been working with the day before and found one that had an extremely sweet taste. (As strange as it may seem today, at one time it was common for chemists to taste compounds in order to characterize them.) He called this compound saccharin; it was eventually found to be about 300 times sweeter than glucose. Notice that, in spite of its name, saccharin is *not* a saccharide.

Ira Remsen (1846–1927) *was born in New York. After receiving an M.D. from Columbia University in 1867 to please his parents, he decided to become a chemist. He earned a Ph.D. from the University of Gottingen in 1870, did research at the University of Tubingen, and returned to the United States in 1875 to accept a faculty position at Williams College. In 1876, he became a professor of chemistry at the newly established Johns Hopkins University, where he initiated the first center for chemical research in the United States. He later became the second president of Johns Hopkins University.*

saccharin   dulcin   acesulfame potassium

aspartame   sucralose

sodium cyclamate

Because it has little caloric value, saccharin became an important substitute for sucrose after becoming commercially available in 1885. The chief nutritional problem in the West was—and still is—the overconsumption of sugar and its consequences: obesity, heart disease, and dental decay. Saccharin is also a boon to people with diabetes, who must limit their consumption of sucrose and glucose. Although the toxicity of saccharin had not been studied carefully when the compound was first marketed (our current concern with toxicity is a fairly recent development), extensive studies since then have shown saccharin to be harmless. In 1912, saccharin was temporarily banned in the United States, not because of any concern about its toxicity, but because of a concern that people would miss out on the nutritional benefits of sugar.

The Wonder of Discovery

Ira Remsen gave the following account of why he became a scientist.* He was working as a physician and came across the statement "Nitric acid acts upon copper" in a chemistry book. He decided to see what "acts on" meant. He poured nitric acid on a penny sitting on a table. "But what was this wonderful thing which I beheld? The cent had already changed and it was not a small change either. A greenish blue liquid foamed and fumed over the cent and over the table. The air in the neighborhood of the performance became dark red. A great colored cloud arose. This was disagreeable and suffocating—how should I stop this? I tried to get rid of the objectionable mess by picking it up and throwing it out of the window, which I had meanwhile opened. I learned another fact—nitric acid not only acts upon copper but it

acts upon my fingers. The pain led to another unpremeditated experiment. I drew my fingers across my trousers and another fact was discovered. Nitric acid also acts upon trousers. Taking everything else into consideration, that was the most impressive experiment, and, relatively, probably the most expensive experiment I ever performed. I tell of it even now with interest. It was a revelation to me. It resulted in a desire on my part to learn even more about that remarkable kind of action. Plainly the only way to learn about it was to see its results, to experiment, to work in a laboratory."

* L. R. Summerlin, C. L. Bordford, and J. B. Ealy, *Chemical Demonstrations*, 2nd ed. (Washington, D.C.: American Chemical Society, 1988).

Dulcin was the second synthetic sweetener to be discovered (in 1884). Even though it did not have the bitter, metallic aftertaste associated with saccharin, it never achieved much popularity. Dulcin was taken off the market in 1951 in response to concerns about its toxicity.

Sodium cyclamate became a widely used nonnutritive sweetener in the 1950s, but was banned in the United States some 20 years later in response to two studies that appeared to show that large amounts of sodium cyclamate cause liver cancer in mice.

Aspartame (NutraSweet, Equal), about 200 times sweeter than sucrose, was approved by the U.S. Food and Drug Administration (FDA) in 1981. Because aspartame contains a phenylalanine subunit, it should not be used by people with the genetic disease known as phenylketonuria (PKU) (Section 26.9).

Acesulfame potassium (Sweet and Safe, Sunette, Sweet One) was approved in 1988. Also called acesulfame-K, it too is about 200 times sweeter than glucose. It has less aftertaste than saccharine and is more stable than aspartame at high temperatures.

Sucralose (Splenda), 600 times sweeter than glucose, is the most recently approved (1991) synthetic sweeter. It maintains its sweetness in foods stored for long periods and at temperatures used in baking. Sucralose is made from sucrose by selectively replacing three of sucrose's OH groups with chlorines. During the chlorination, the 4-position of the glucose ring becomes inverted, so sucralose is a galactopyranoside, not a glucopyranoside. The body does not recognize sucralose as a carbohydrate, so instead of being metabolized it is eliminated from the body unchanged.

The fact that these synthetic sweeteners have such different structures shows that the sensation of sweetness is not induced by a single molecular shape.

Acceptable Daily Intake

The FDA has established an acceptable daily intake (ADI) value for many of the food ingredients it clears for use. The ADI is the amount of the substance a person can consume safely, each day of his or her life. For example, the ADI for acesulfame-K is 15 mg/kg/day. This means each day a 132-lb person can consume the amount of acesulfame-K that would be found in two gallons of an artificially sweetened beverage. The ADI for sucralose is also 15 mg/kg/day.

SUMMARY

Bioorganic compounds—organic compounds found in biological systems—obey the same chemical principles that smaller organic molecules do. Much of the structure of bioorganic compounds exists for the purpose of **molecular recognition**.

Carbohydrates are the most abundant class of compounds in the biological world. They are polyhydroxy aldehydes (**aldoses**) and polyhydroxy ketones (**ketoses**), or compounds formed by linking up aldoses and ketoses. The notations D and L describe the configuration of the bottom-most asymmetric center of a **monosaccharide** in a Fischer projection; the configurations of the other carbons are implicit in the common name. Most naturally occurring sugars are D-sugars. Naturally occurring ketoses have the ketone group in the 2-position. **Epimers** differ in configuration at only one asymmetric center: D-mannose is the C-2 epimer of D-glucose and D-galactose is the C-4 epimer of D-glucose.

In a basic solution, a monosaccharide is converted to a complex mixture of polyhydroxy aldehydes and polyhydroxy ketones. Reduction of an aldose forms one **alditol**; reduction of a ketose forms two alditols. Br_2 oxidizes aldoses but not ketoses; Tollens reagent oxidizes both. Aldoses are oxidized to **aldonic acids** or to **aldaric acids**. Aldoses and ketoses react with three equivalents of phenylhydrazine, forming **osazones**. C-2 epimers form identical osazones. The **Kiliani–Fischer synthesis** increases the carbon chain of an aldose by one carbon; it forms C-2 epimers. The **Wohl degradation** decreases the carbon chain by one carbon. The OH groups of monosaccharides react with methyl iodide/silver oxide to form ethers.

The aldehyde or keto group of a **monosaccharide** reacts with one of its OH groups to form cyclic hemiacetals or hemiketals: glucose forms α-D-glucose and β-D-glucose. The α-position is axial when a sugar is shown in a chair conformation and down when the sugar is shown in a Haworth projection; the β-position is equatorial when a sugar is shown in a chair conformation and up when the sugar is shown in a Haworth projection. α-D-Glucose and β-D-glucose are **anomers**—they differ in configuration only at the **anomeric carbon**, which is the carbon that was the carbonyl carbon in the open-chain form. Anomers have different physical properties. More β-D-glucose is present than α-D-glucose in a solution at equilibrium. Six-membered-ring sugars are **pyranoses**; five-membered-ring sugars are **furanoses**. The most abundant monosaccharide in nature is D-glucose. All the OH groups in β-D-glucose are in equatorial positions. A slow change in optical rotation to an equilibrium value is called **mutarotation**.

A cyclic hemiacetal (or hemiketal) can react with an alcohol to form an acetal (or ketal), called a **glycoside**. If the name "pyranose" or "furanose" is used, the acetal is called a **pyranoside** or a **furanoside**. The bond between the anomeric carbon and the alkoxy oxygen is called a **glycosidic bond**. The preference for the axial position by certain substituents bonded to the anomeric carbon is called the **anomeric effect**. If a sugar has an aldehyde, ketone, hemiacetal, or hemiketal group, it is a reducing sugar.

Disaccharides consist of two monosaccharides hooked together by a glycosidic linkage. Maltose has an α-**1,4'-** glycosidic **linkage** between two glucose subunits; cellobiose has a β-**1,4'-glycosidic linkage** between two glucose subunits. The most common disaccharide is sucrose; it has a D-glucose subunit and a D-fructose subunit linked by their anomeric carbons.

Polysaccharides contain as few as 10 or as many as several thousand monosaccharides joined together by glycosidic linkages. Starch is composed of amylose and amylopectin. Amylose has unbranched chains of D-glucose units joined by α-1,4'-glycosidic linkages. Amylopectin, too, has chains of D-glucose units joined by α-1,4'-glycosidic linkages, but it also has α-1,6'-glycosidic linkages that create branches. Glycogen is similar to amylopectin but has more branches. Cellulose has unbranched chains of D-glucose units joined by β-1,4'-glycosidic linkages. The α-linkages cause amylose to form a helix; the β-linkages allow the molecules of cellulose to form intramolecular hydrogen bonds.

The surfaces of many cells contain short oligosaccharide chains that allow the cells to interact with each other. These oligosaccharides are linked to the cell surface by protein groups. Proteins bonded to oligosaccharides are called **glycoproteins**.

SUMMARY OF REACTIONS

1. Epimerization (Section 22.5)

2. Enediol rearrangement (Section 22.5)

3. Reduction (Section 22.6)

4. Oxidation (Section 22.6)

a.

$$\begin{array}{c} \text{H}\!\!-\!\!\text{C}\!\!=\!\!\text{O} \\ | \\ (\text{CHOH})_n \\ | \\ \text{CH}_2\text{OH} \end{array} \xrightarrow[\text{HO}^-]{\text{Ag}^+, \text{NH}_3} \begin{array}{c} \text{}^-\text{O}\!\!-\!\!\text{C}\!\!=\!\!\text{O} \\ | \\ (\text{CHOH})_n \\ | \\ \text{CH}_2\text{OH} \end{array} + \ \text{Ag}$$

c.

$$\begin{array}{c} \text{H}\!\!-\!\!\text{C}\!\!=\!\!\text{O} \\ | \\ (\text{CHOH})_n \\ | \\ \text{CH}_2\text{OH} \end{array} \xrightarrow[\text{H}_2\text{O}]{\text{Br}_2} \begin{array}{c} \text{HO}\!\!-\!\!\text{C}\!\!=\!\!\text{O} \\ | \\ (\text{CHOH})_n \\ | \\ \text{CH}_2\text{OH} \end{array} + \ 2\ \text{Br}^-$$

b.

$$\begin{array}{c} \text{CH}_2\text{OH} \\ | \\ \text{C}\!\!=\!\!\text{O} \\ | \\ (\text{CHOH})_n \\ | \\ \text{CH}_2\text{OH} \end{array} \xrightarrow[\text{HO}^-]{\text{Ag}^+, \text{NH}_3} \begin{array}{c} \text{}^-\text{O}\!\!-\!\!\text{C}\!\!=\!\!\text{O} \\ | \\ \text{CHOH} \\ | \\ (\text{CHOH})_n \\ | \\ \text{CH}_2\text{OH} \end{array} + \ \text{Ag}$$

d.

$$\begin{array}{c} \text{H}\!\!-\!\!\text{C}\!\!=\!\!\text{O} \\ | \\ (\text{CHOH})_n \\ | \\ \text{CH}_2\text{OH} \end{array} \xrightarrow[\Delta]{\text{HNO}_3} \begin{array}{c} \text{HO}\!\!-\!\!\text{C}\!\!=\!\!\text{O} \\ | \\ (\text{CHOH})_n \\ | \\ \text{C} \\ \text{O} \ \ \text{OH} \end{array}$$

5. Osazone formation (Section 22.7)

$$\begin{array}{c} \text{H}\!\!-\!\!\text{C}\!\!=\!\!\text{O} \\ | \\ \text{CHOH} \\ | \\ (\text{CHOH})_n \\ | \\ \text{CH}_2\text{OH} \end{array} + \ 3\ \text{NH}_2\text{NH}\!\!-\!\!\text{C}_6\text{H}_5 \xrightarrow[]{\text{trace} \\ \text{acid}} \begin{array}{c} \text{H}\!\!-\!\!\text{C}\!\!=\!\!\text{NNHC}_6\text{H}_5 \\ | \\ \text{C}\!\!=\!\!\text{NNHC}_6\text{H}_5 \\ | \\ (\text{CHOH})_n \\ | \\ \text{CH}_2\text{OH} \end{array} + \ \text{C}_6\text{H}_5\text{NH}_2 + \ \text{NH}_3 + \ 2\ \text{H}_2\text{O}$$

6. Chain elongation: the Kiliani–Fischer synthesis (Section 22.8)

$$\begin{array}{c} \text{H}\!\!-\!\!\text{C}\!\!=\!\!\text{O} \\ | \\ (\text{CHOH})_n \\ | \\ \text{CH}_2\text{OH} \end{array} \xrightarrow[\begin{array}{l} \text{1. NaC}\!\equiv\!\text{N/HCl} \\ \text{2. H}_2, \text{Pd/BaSO}_4 \\ \text{3. HCl/H}_2\text{O} \end{array}]{} \begin{array}{c} \text{H}\!\!-\!\!\text{C}\!\!=\!\!\text{O} \\ | \\ (\text{CHOH})_{n+1} \\ | \\ \text{CH}_2\text{OH} \end{array}$$

7. Chain shortening: the Wohl degradation (Section 22.9)

$$\begin{array}{c} \text{H}\!\!-\!\!\text{C}\!\!=\!\!\text{O} \\ | \\ (\text{CHOH})_n \\ | \\ \text{CH}_2\text{OH} \end{array} \xrightarrow[\begin{array}{l} \text{1. NH}_2\text{OH/trace acid} \\ \text{2. Ac}_2\text{O, 100 °C} \\ \text{3. HO}^-, \text{H}_2\text{O} \end{array}]{} \begin{array}{c} \text{H}\!\!-\!\!\text{C}\!\!=\!\!\text{O} \\ | \\ (\text{CHOH})_{n-1} \\ | \\ \text{CH}_2\text{OH} \end{array}$$

8. Acetal (and ketal) formation (Section 22.13)

KEY TERMS

hexose (p. 941)
ketose (p. 941)
Kiliani–Fischer synthesis (p. 951)
molecular recognition (p. 941)
monosaccharide (p. 941)
mutarotation (p. 955)
nonreducing sugar (p. 960)

oligosaccharide (p. 941)
osazone (p. 949)
oxocarbenium ion (p. 959)
pentose (p. 941)
polysaccharide (p. 941)
pyranose (p. 955)

pyranoside (p. 958)
reducing sugar (p. 960)
simple carbohydrate (p. 941)
tetrose (p. 941)
triose (p. 941)
Wohl degradation (p. 951)

PROBLEMS

31. Give the product or products that are obtained when D-galactose reacts with each of the following substances:

a. nitric acid $+ \Delta$
b. Tollens reagent
c. NaBH$_4$, followed by H$_3$O$^+$
d. three equivalents of phenylhydrazine $+$ trace acid

e. Br$_2$ in water
f. ethanol $+$HCl
g. 1. hydroxylamine/trace acid   2. acetic anhydride/Δ
   3. HO$^-$/H$_2$O

32. Identify the sugar in each description:
   a. An aldopentose that is not D-arabinose forms D-arabinitol when it is reduced with NaBH$_4$.
   b. A sugar forms the same osazone as D-galactose with phenylhydrazine, but it is not oxidized by an aqueous solution of Br$_2$.
   c. A sugar that is not D-altrose forms D-altraric acid when it is oxidized with nitric acid.
   d. A ketose that, when reduced with NaBH$_4$, forms D-altritol and D-allitol.

33. D-Xylose and D-lyxose are formed when D-threose undergoes a Kiliani–Fischer synthesis. D-Xylose is oxidized to an optically inactive aldaric acid, whereas D-lyxose forms an optically active aldaric acid. What are the structures of D-xylose and D-lyxose?

34. Answer the following questions about the eight aldopentoses:
   a. Which are enantiomers?
   b. Which give identical osazones?
   c. Which form an optically active compound when oxidized with nitric acid?

35. The reaction of D-ribose with one equivalent of methanol plus HCl forms four products. Give the structures of the products.

36. Compounds A, B, and C are three different D-aldohexoses. Compounds A and B are reduced to the same optically active alditol, but form different osazones when treated with phenylhydrazine. Compounds B and C form the same osazone but are reduced to different alditols. Give the structures of A, B, and C.

37. Determine the structure of D-galactose, using arguments similar to those used by Fischer to prove the structure of D-glucose.

38. A student isolated a monosaccharide and determined that it had a molecular weight of 150. Much to his surprise, he found that it was not optically active. What is the structure of the monosaccharide?

39. The ^{1}H NMR spectrum of D-glucose in D$_2$O exhibits two high-frequency doublets. What is responsible for these doublets?

40. Treatment with sodium borohydride converts aldose A into an optically inactive alditol. Wohl degradation of A forms B, whose alditol is optically inactive. Wohl degradation of B forms D-glyceraldehyde. Identify A and B.

41. A hexose was obtained after $(+)$-glyceraldehyde underwent three successive Kiliani–Fischer syntheses. Identify the hexose from the following experimental information: oxidation with nitric acid forms an optically active aldaric acid; a Wohl degradation followed by oxidation with nitric acid forms an optically inactive aldaric acid; and a second Wohl degradation forms erythrose.

42. D-Glucuronic acid is found widely in plants and animals. One of its functions is to detoxify poisonous HO-containing compounds by reacting with them in the liver to form glucuronides. Glucuronides are water soluble and therefore readily excreted. After ingestion of a poison such as turpentine, morphine, or phenol, the glucuronides of these compounds are found in the urine. Give the structure of the glucuronide formed by the reaction of β-D-glucuronic acid and phenol.

β-D-glucuronic acid

43. A D-aldopentose is oxidized by nitric acid to an optically active aldaric acid. A Wohl degradation of the aldopentose leads to a monosaccharide that is oxidized by nitric acid to an optically inactive aldaric acid. Identify the D-aldopentose.

44. Hyaluronic acid, a component of connective tissue, is the fluid that lubricates the joints. It is a polymer of alternating *N*-acetyl-D-glucosamine and D-glucuronic acid subunits joined by β-1,3'-glycosidic linkages. Draw a short segment of hyaluronic acid.

45. In order to synthesize D-galactose, a student went to the stockroom to get some D-lyxose to use as a starting material. She found that the labels had fallen off the bottles containing D-lyxose and D-xylose. How could she determine which bottle contains D-lyxose?

46. The aldonic acid of D-glucose forms a five-membered ring lactone. Draw its structure.

47. The aldaric acid of D-glucose forms two five-membered ring lactones. Draw their structures.

48. How many aldaric acids are obtained from the 16 aldohexoses?

49. A hexose was obtained when the residue of a shrub *Sterculia setigeria* undergoes acid-catalyzed hydrolysis. Identify the hexose from the following experimental information: it undergoes mutarotation; it does not react with Br_2; and D-galactonic acid and D-talonic acid are formed when it reacts with Tollens reagent.

50. When D-fructose is dissolved in D_2O and the solution is made basic, the D-fructose recovered from the solution has an average of 1.7 deuterium atoms attached to the C-1 carbon per molecule. Show the mechanism that accounts for the incorporation of these deuterium atoms into D-fructose.

51. Draw β-D-talopyranose and α-D-idopyranose.

52. Calculate the percentages of α-D-glucose and β-D-glucose present at equilibrium from the specific rotations of α-D-glucose, β-D-glucose, and the equilibrium mixture. Compare your values with those given in Section 22.11. (*Hint:* The specific rotation of the mixture equals the specific rotation of α-D-glucose times the fraction of glucose present in the α-form plus the specific rotation of β-D-glucose times the fraction of glucose present in the β-form.)

53. An unknown disaccharide gives a positive Tollens test. A β-1,4'-glycosidase hydrolyzes it to D-galactose and D-mannose. When the disaccharide is treated with methyl iodide and Ag_2O (Section 22.16) and then hydrolyzed with dilute HCl, the products are 2,3,4,6-tetra-*O*-methylgalactose and 2,3,4-tri-*O*-methylmannose. Propose a structure for the disaccharide.

54. Predict whether D-altrose exists preferentially as a pyranose or a furanose. (*Hint:* In the most stable arrangement for a five-membered ring, all the adjacent substituents are trans.)

55. Trehalose, $C_{12}H_{22}O_{11}$, is a nonreducing sugar that is only 45% as sweet as sugar but does not attract moisture and so remains free-flowing and dry. When hydrolyzed by aqueous acid or the enzyme maltase, it forms only D-glucose. When it is treated with excess methyl iodide in the presence of Ag_2O and then hydrolyzed with water under acidic conditions, only 2,3,4,6-tetra-*O*-methyl-D-glucose is formed.
a. Draw the structure for trehalose.   **b.** What is the function of Ag_2O?

56. Propose a mechanism for the rearrangement that converts an α-hydroxyimine into an α-aminoketone in the presence of a trace amount of acid (page 950).

57. All the glucose units in dextran have six-membered rings. When a sample of dextran is treated with methyl iodide and Ag_2O and the product is hydrolyzed under acidic conditions, the final products are 2,3,4,6-tetra-*O*-methyl-D-glucose, 2,4,6-tri-*O*-methyl-D-glucose, 2,3,4-tri-*O*-methyl-D-glucose, and 2,4-di-*O*-methyl-D-glucose. Draw a short segment of dextran.

58. When a pyranose is in the chair conformation in which the CH_2OH group and the C-1 OH group are both in axial positions, the two groups can react to form an acetal. This is called the anhydro form of the sugar (it has "lost water"). The anhydro form of D-idose is shown here. In an aqueous solution at 100 °C, about 80% of D-idose exists in the anhydro form. Under the same conditions, only about 0.1% of D-glucose exists in the anhydro form. Explain.

anhydro form of D-idose

59. Devise a method to convert D-glucose into D-allose.

23

The Organic Chemistry of Amino Acids, Peptides, and Proteins

oxidized glutathione

THE THREE KINDS OF POLYMERS PREVALENT IN NATURE ARE POLYSACCHARIDES, proteins, and nucleic acids. We have already looked at polysaccharides (Section 22.17), and nucleic acids will be discussed in Chapter 28. Now we will turn our attention to proteins and the structurally similar, but shorter, peptides.

Peptides and **proteins** are polymers of amino acids. The amino acids are linked together by amide bonds. An **amino acid** is a carboxylic acid with a protonated amino group on the α-carbon.

**a protonated
α-aminocarboxylic acid
an amino acid**

amide bonds

amino acids are linked together by amide bonds

a tripeptide

Amino acid polymers can be composed of any number of amino acids. A **dipeptide** contains 2 amino acids linked together, a **tripeptide** contains 3, an **oligopeptide** contains 3 to 10, and a **polypeptide** contains many. Proteins are naturally occurring polypeptides made up of 40 to 4000 amino acids. Proteins and peptides serve many functions in biological systems (Table 23.1).

Proteins can be divided roughly into two classes. **Fibrous proteins** contain long chains of polypeptides arranged in bundles; these proteins are insoluble in water. **Globular proteins** tend to have roughly spherical shapes and are soluble in water. All structural proteins are fibrous proteins; most enzymes are globular proteins.

Table 23.1	Examples of the Diverse Functions of Proteins in Biological Systems
Structural proteins	These proteins impart strength to biological structures or protect organisms from their environment. For example, collagen is the major component of bones, muscles, and tendons; keratin is the major component of hair, hooves, feathers, fur, and the outer layer of skin.
Protective proteins	Snake venoms and plant toxins protect their owners from predators. Blood-clotting proteins protect the vascular system when it is injured. Antibodies and peptide antibiotics protect us from disease.
Enzymes	Enzymes are proteins that catalyze the reactions that occur in biological systems.
Hormones	Some of the hormones, such as insulin, that regulate the reactions that occur in bological systems are proteins.
Proteins with physiological functions	These proteins are responsible for physiological functions such as the transport and storage of oxygen in the body, the storage of oxygen in the muscles, and the contraction of muscles.

glycine

leucine

aspartate

lysine

23.1 CLASSIFICATION AND NOMENCLATURE OF AMINO ACIDS

The structures of the 20 most common naturally occurring amino acids and the frequency with which each occurs in proteins are shown in Table 23.2. Other amino acids occur in nature but only infrequently. Notice that the amino acids differ only in the substituent (R) attached to the α-carbon. The wide variation in these substituents (called **side chains**) is what gives proteins their great structural diversity and, as a consequence, their great functional diversity. Notice too that all amino acids except proline contain a primary amino group. Proline contains a secondary amino group incorporated into a five-membered ring.

The amino acids are almost always called by their common names. Often, the name tells you something about the amino acid. For example, glycine got its name as a result of its sweet taste (*glykos* is Greek for "sweet"), and valine, like valeric acid, has five carbons. Asparagine was first found in asparagus, and tyrosine was isolated from cheese (*tyros* is Greek for "cheese").

Dividing the amino acids into classes, as in Table 23.2, makes them easier to learn. The aliphatic side-chain amino acids include glycine, the amino acid in which R = H, and four amino acids with alkyl side chains. Alanine is the amino acid with a methyl side chain, and valine has an isopropyl side chain. Notice that, in spite of its name, isoleucine does not have an isobutyl substituent; it has a *sec*-butyl substituent. Leucine is the amino acid that has an isobutyl substituent. Each of the amino acids has both a three-letter abbreviation (in most cases, the first three letters of the name) and a single-letter abbreviation.

Two amino acid side chains—serine and threonine—contain alcohol groups. Serine is an HO-substituted alanine, and threonine has a branched ethanol substituent. There are also two sulfur-containing amino acids: cysteine is an HS-substituted alanine, and methionine has a 2-(methylthio)ethyl substituent.

There are two acidic amino acids (amino acids with two carboxylic acid groups): aspartate and glutamate. Aspartate is a carboxy-substituted alanine, and glutamate has one more methylene group than aspartate. (If their carboxyl groups are protonated, they are called aspartic acid and glutamic acid, respectively.) Two amino acids—asparagine and glutamine—are amides of the acidic amino acids; asparagine is the amide of aspartate, and glutamine is the amide of glutamate. Notice that the obvious one-letter abbreviations cannot be used for these four amino acids because A and G are used for alanine and glycine. Aspartate and glutamate are abbreviated D and E; asparagine and glutamine are abbreviated N and Q.

Table 23.2 The Most Common Naturally Occurring Amino Acids.
The amino acids are shown in the form that predominates at physiological pH (7.3).

	Formula	Name	Abbreviations		Average relative abundance in proteins
Aliphatic side-chain amino acids	$H-CH-C\begin{smallmatrix}O\\O^-\end{smallmatrix}$ $^+NH_3$	Glycine	Gly	G	7.5%
	$CH_3-CH-C\begin{smallmatrix}O\\O^-\end{smallmatrix}$ $^+NH_3$	Alanine	Ala	A	9.0%
	$CH_3CH-CH-C\begin{smallmatrix}O\\O^-\end{smallmatrix}$ CH_3 $^+NH_3$	Valine*	Val	V	6.9%
	$CH_3CHCH_2-CH-C\begin{smallmatrix}O\\O^-\end{smallmatrix}$ CH_3 $^+NH_3$	Leucine*	Leu	L	7.5%
	$CH_3CH_2CH-CH-C\begin{smallmatrix}O\\O^-\end{smallmatrix}$ CH_3 $^+NH_3$	Isoleucine*	Ile	I	4.6%
Hydroxy-containing amino acids	$HOCH_2-CH-C\begin{smallmatrix}O\\O^-\end{smallmatrix}$ $^+NH_3$	Serine	Ser	S	7.1%
	$CH_3CH-CH-C\begin{smallmatrix}O\\O^-\end{smallmatrix}$ OH $^+NH_3$	Threonine*	Thr	T	6.0%
Sulfur-containing amino acids	$HSCH_2-CH-C\begin{smallmatrix}O\\O^-\end{smallmatrix}$ $^+NH_3$	Cysteine	Cys	C	2.8%

(Continued)

Table 23.2 Continued

	Formula	Name	Abbreviations		Average relative abundance in proteins
	$CH_3SCH_2CH_2-CH$ with $C(=O)O^-$ and $^+NH_3$	Methionine*	Met	M	1.7%
Acidic amino acids	$^-O-C(=O)-CH_2-CH$ with $C(=O)O^-$ and $^+NH_3$	Aspartate (aspartic acid)	Asp	D	5.5%
	$^-O-C(=O)-CH_2CH_2-CH$ with $C(=O)O^-$ and $^+NH_3$	Glutamate (glutamic acid)	Glu	E	6.2%
Amides of acidic amino acids	$H_2N-C(=O)-CH_2-CH$ with $C(=O)O^-$ and $^+NH_3$	Asparagine	Asn	N	4.4%
	$H_2N-C(=O)-CH_2CH_2-CH$ with $C(=O)O^-$ and $^+NH_3$	Glutamine	Gln	Q	3.9%
Basic amino acids	$H_3\overset{+}{N}CH_2CH_2CH_2CH_2-CH$ with $C(=O)O^-$ and $^+NH_3$	Lysine*	Lys	K	7.0%
	$H_2N-C(=\overset{+}{N}H_2)-NHCH_2CH_2CH_2-CH$ with $C(=O)O^-$ and $^+NH_3$	Arginine*	Arg	R	4.7%
Benzene-containing amino acids	$C_6H_5-CH_2-CH$ with $C(=O)O^-$ and $^+NH_3$	Phenylalanine*	Phe	F	3.5%
	$HO-C_6H_4-CH_2-CH$ with $C(=O)O^-$ and $^+NH_3$	Tyrosine	Tyr	Y	3.5%

Table 23.2 Continued

	Formula	Name	Abbreviations		Average relative abundance in proteins
Heterocyclic amino acids		Proline	Pro	P	4.6%
		Histidine*	His	H	2.1%
		Tryptophan*	Trp	W	1.1%

* Essential amino acid

There are two basic amino acids (amino acids with two basic nitrogen-containing groups): lysine and arginine. Lysine has an ϵ-amino group, and arginine has a δ-guanidino group. At physiological pH, these groups are protonated. The ϵ and δ can remind you how many methylene groups each amino acid has.

Two amino acids—phenylalanine and tyrosine—contain benzene rings. As its name indicates, phenylalanine is phenyl-substituted alanine. Tyrosine is phenylalanine with a *para*-hydroxy substituent.

Proline, histidine, and tryptophan are heterocyclic amino acids. We have noted that proline, with its nitrogen incorporated into a five-membered ring, is the only amino acid that contains a secondary amino group. Histidine is an imidazole-substituted alanine. Imidazole is an aromatic compound because it is cyclic and planar, each of its ring atoms has a *p* orbital, and it has three pairs of delocalized π electrons (Section 21.7). The pK_a of a protonated imidazole ring is 6.0, so the ring will be protonated in acidic solutions and nonprotonated in basic solutions (see page 986).

Tryptophan is an indole-substituted alanine. Like imidazole, indole is an aromatic compound. Because the lone pair on the nitrogen of indole is needed for the compound's aromaticity, indole is a very weak base. (The pK_a of protonated indole is -2.4.) Therefore, the ring nitrogen in tryptophan is never protonated under physiological conditions.

indole

chem
place

Tutorial:
Basic nitrogens in histidine and arginine

Ten amino acids are **essential amino acids**; they are denoted in Table 23.2 by asterisks (*). Humans must obtain these 10 essential amino acids from their diets because they either cannot synthesize them at all or cannot synthesize them in adequate amounts. For example, humans must have a dietary source of phenylalanine because they cannot synthesize benzene rings. However, they do not need tyrosine in their diet because they can synthesize the necessary amounts from phenylalanine (Section 26.9). Although humans can synthesize arginine, it is needed for growth in greater amounts than can be synthesized. So arginine is considered an essential amino acid for children but not an essential amino acid for adults.

Proteins and Nutrition

Proteins are an important component of our diets. Dietary protein is hydrolyzed in the body to individual amino acids. Some of these amino acids are used to synthesize proteins needed by the body, some are broken down further to supply energy to the body, and some are used as starting materials for the synthesis of nonprotein compounds that the body needs, such as thyroxine (Section 15.11), adrenaline, and melanin (Section 26.9).

Not all proteins contain the same amino acids. Most proteins from meat and dairy products contain all the amino acids needed by the body. However, most proteins from vegetable sources are *incomplete* proteins; they contain too little of one or more essential amino acids to support human growth. For example, bean protein is deficient in methionine and wheat protein is deficient in lysine. Therefore, a balanced diet must include proteins from different sources.

PROBLEM 1

a. Explain why, when the imidazole ring of histidine is protonated, the double-bonded nitrogen is the nitrogen that accepts the proton.

b. Explain why, when the guanidino group of arginine is protonated, the double-bonded nitrogen is the nitrogen that accepts the proton.

23.2 THE CONFIGURATION OF THE AMINO ACIDS

The α-carbon of all the naturally occurring amino acids except glycine is an asymmetric center. Therefore, 19 of the 20 amino acids listed in Table 23.2 can exist as enantiomers. The D and L notation used for monosaccharides (Section 22.2) is also used for amino acids. An amino acid drawn in a Fischer projection with the carboxyl group on the top and the R group on the bottom of the vertical axis is a **D-amino acid** if the amino group is on the right, and an **L-amino acid** if the amino group is on the left. Unlike monosaccharides, where the D isomer is the one found in nature, most amino acids found in nature have the L configuration. To date, D-amino acids have been found only in a few peptide antibiotics and in some small peptides attached to the cell walls of bacteria.

> **Naturally occurring monosaccharides have the D configuration.**
>
> **Naturally occurring amino acids have the L configuration.**

D-glyceraldehyde

L-glyceraldehyde

D-amino acid

L-amino acid

L-alanine
an amino acid

Why D-sugars and L-amino acids? Although it made no difference which isomer nature "selected" to be synthesized, it was important that only one was selected. For example, proteins that contain both D- and L-amino acids do not fold, and without folding there can be no catalysis (Section 24.8). It was also important that the same isomer be synthesized by all organisms. For example, since mammals ended up having L-amino acids, L-amino acids must be the isomers synthesized by the organisms that mammals depend on for food.

Amino Acids and Disease

The Chamorro people of Guam have a high incidence of a syndrome that resembles amyotrophic lateral sclerosis (ALS or Lou Gehrig's disease) with elements of Parkinson's disease and dementia. This syndrome developed during World War II when, as a result of food shortages, the tribe ate large quantities of *Cycas circinalis* seeds. These seeds contain β-methyl-amino-L-alanine, an amino acid that binds to cell receptors that bind L-glutamate (Section 31.6). When monkeys are given β-methylamino-L-alanine, they develop some of the features of this syndrome. There is hope that, by studying the mechanism of action of β-methylamino-L-alanine, we may gain an understanding of how ALS and Parkinson's disease arise.

L-alanine

β-methylamino-L-alanine

L-glutamate

PROBLEM 2♦

  a. Which isomer—(R)-alanine or (S)-alanine—is D-alanine?
  b. Which isomer—(R)-aspartate or (S)-aspartate—is D-aspartate?
  c. Can a general statement be made relating R and S to D and L?

A Peptide Antibiotic

Gramicidin S, an antibiotic produced by a strain of bacteria, is a cyclic decapeptide. Notice that one of its amino acids is ornithine, an amino acid not listed in Table 23.2 because it occurs rarely in nature. Ornithine resembles lysine but has one less methylene group in its side chain. Notice also that the antibiotic contains two D-amino acids.

```
              ─L-Val─
       L-Pro          L-Orn
   L-Phe                  L-Leu

   L-Leu                  D-Phe ◄─── D-phenylalanine
D-ornithine ───► D-Orn    L-Pro
              ─L-Val─
           gramicidin S
```

$$H_3\overset{+}{N}CH_2CH_2CH_2\underset{\underset{\overset{+}{N}H_3}{|}}{CH}\overset{\displaystyle O}{\overset{\|}{C}}O^-$$

ornithine

PROBLEM 3   SOLVED

Threonine has two asymmetric centers and therefore has four stereoisomers.

```
      COO⁻              COO⁻              COO⁻              COO⁻
  H──┼──⁺NH₃      H₃⁺N──┼──H        H──┼──⁺NH₃       H₃⁺N──┼──H
  H──┼──OH        HO──┼──H          HO──┼──H         H──┼──OH
      CH₃              CH₃               CH₃              CH₃
       1                2                 3                4
```

Naturally occurring L-threonine is (2S,3R)-threonine. Which of the stereoisomers is L-threonine?

Solution   Stereoisomer 1 has the R configuration at both C-2 and C-3 because in both cases the arrow drawn from the highest to the next-highest-priority substituent is counterclockwise. In both cases, counterclockwise signifies R because the lowest priority substituent (H) is on a horizontal bond (Section 5.7). Therefore, the configuration of (2S,3R)-threonine is the opposite of that in stereoisomer 1 at C-2 and the same as that in stereoisomer 1 at C-3. Thus, L-threonine is stereoisomer 4. Notice that the ⁺NH₃ group is on the left, just as we would expect for the Fischer projection of a naturally ocurring amino acid.

PROBLEM 4♦

Do any other amino acids in Table 23.2 have more than one asymmetric center?

23.3 THE ACID–BASE PROPERTIES OF AMINO ACIDS

Every amino acid has a carboxyl group and an amino group, and each group can exist in an acidic form or a basic form, depending on the pH of the solution in which the amino acid is dissolved.

We have seen that compounds exist primarily in their acidic forms (that is, with their protons attached) in solutions that are more acidic than their pK_a values and primarily in their basic forms (that is, without their protons) in solutions that are more basic than their pK_a values (Section 1.25). The carboxyl groups of the amino acids have pK_a values of approximately 2, and the protonated amino groups have pK_a values near 9 (Table 23.3). Both groups, therefore, will be in their acidic forms in a very acidic solution (pH ∼ 0).

At pH $= 7$, the pH of the solution is greater than the pK_a of the carboxyl group, but less than the pK_a of the protonated amino group. The carboxyl group, therefore, will be in its basic form and the amino group will be in its acidic form. In a strongly basic solution (pH $\sim$ 11), both groups will be in their basic forms.

The acidic form (with the proton) predominates if the pH of the solution is less than the pK_a of the ionizable group, and the basic form (without the proton) predominates if the pH of the solution is greater than the pK_a of the ionizable group.

Table 23.3 The pK_a Values of Amino Acids			
Amino acid	pK_a α-COOH	pK_a α-$\overset{+}{\text{NH}}_3$	pK_a Side chain
Alanine	2.34	9.69	—
Arginine	2.17	9.04	12.48
Asparagine	2.02	8.84	—
Aspartic acid	2.09	9.82	3.86
Cysteine	1.92	10.46	8.35
Glutamic acid	2.19	9.67	4.25
Glutamine	2.17	9.13	—
Glycine	2.34	9.60	—
Histidine	1.82	9.17	6.04
Isoleucine	2.36	9.68	—
Leucine	2.36	9.60	—
Lysine	2.18	8.95	10.79
Methionine	2.28	9.21	—
Phenylalanine	2.16	9.18	—
Proline	1.99	10.60	—
Serine	2.21	9.15	—
Threonine	2.63	9.10	—
Tryptophan	2.38	9.39	—
Tyrosine	2.20	9.11	10.07
Valine	2.32	9.62	—

Notice that an amino acid can never exist as an uncharged compound, regardless of the pH of the solution. To be uncharged, an amino acid would have to lose a proton from an $^+$NH$_3$ group with a pK_a of about 9 before it would lose a proton from a COOH group with a pK_a of about 2. This clearly is impossible: a weak acid (p$K_a = 9$) cannot be more acidic than a strong acid (p$K_a = 2$). Therefore, at physiological pH (7.3) an amino acid such as alanine exists as a dipolar ion, called a zwitterion. A **zwitterion** is a compound that has a negative charge on one atom and a positive charge on a nonadjacent atom. (The name comes from *zwitter*, German for "hermaphrodite" or "hybrid.")

A few amino acids have side chains with ionizable hydrogens (Table 23.3). The protonated imidazole side chain of histidine, for example, has a pK_a of 6.04. Histidine, therefore, can exist in four different forms, and the form that predominates depends on the pH of the solution.

pH = 0   pH = 4   pH = 8   pH = 12

histidine

PROBLEM 5 ◆

Why are the carboxylic acid groups of the amino acids so much more acidic ($pK_a \sim 2$) than a carboxylic acid such as acetic acid ($pK_a = 4.76$)?

PROBLEM 6   SOLVED

Draw the predominant form for each of the following amino acids at physiological pH (7.3):

a. aspartate   **c.** glutamine   **e.** arginine
b. histidine   **d.** lysine   **f.** tyrosine

Solution to 6a   Both carboxyl groups are in their basic forms because the pH of the solution is greater than their pK_a values. The protonated amino group is in its acidic form because the pH of the solution is less than its pK_a value.

PROBLEM 7 ◆

Draw the predominant form for glutamate in a solution with the following pH:

a. 0   **b.** 3   **c.** 6   **d.** 11

PROBLEM 8

a. Why is the pK_a of the glutamate side chain greater than the pK_a of the aspartate side chain?
b. Why is the pK_a of the arginine side chain greater than the pK_a of the lysine side chain?

23.4 THE ISOELECTRIC POINT

The **isoelectric point** (pI) of an amino acid is the pH at which it has no net charge. In other words, it is the pH at which the amount of positive charge on an amino acid exactly balances the amount of negative charge:

$$pI = pH \text{ at which there is no net charge}$$

Recall from the Henderson–Hasselbalch equation (Section 1.25) that when $pH = pK_a$, half the group is in its acidic form and half is in its basic form.

An amino acid will be positively charged if the pH of the solution is less than the pI of the amino acid and will be negatively charged if the pH of the solution is greater than the pI of the amino acid.

The pI of an amino acid that does *not have an ionizable side chain*—such as alanine—is midway between its two pK_a values. This is because at pH = 2.34, half the molecules have a negatively charged carboxyl group and half have an uncharged carboxyl group, and at pH = 9.69, half the molecules have a positively charged amino group and half have an uncharged amino group. As the pH increases from 2.34, the carboxyl group of more molecules becomes negatively charged; as the pH decreases from 9.69, the amino group of more molecules becomes positively charged. Therefore, at the average of the two pK_a values, the number of negatively charged groups equals the number of positively charged groups.

The pI of most amino acids that *have an ionizable side chain* (see Problem 12) is the average of the pK_a values of the similarly ionizing groups (either positively charged groups ionizing to uncharged groups or uncharged groups ionizing to negatively charged groups). For example, the pI of lysine is the average of the pK_a values of the two groups that are positively charged in their acidic form and uncharged in their basic form. The pI of glutamic acid, on the other hand, is the average of the pK_a values of the two groups that are uncharged in their acidic form and negatively charged in their basic form.

alanine

$$pI = \frac{2.34 + 9.69}{2} = \frac{12.03}{2} = 6.02$$

lysine

$$pI = \frac{8.95 + 10.79}{2} = \frac{19.74}{2} = 9.87$$

glutamic acid

$$pI = \frac{2.19 + 4.25}{2} = \frac{6.44}{2} = 3.22$$

PROBLEM 9

Explain why the pI of lysine is the average of the pK_a values of its two protonated amino groups.

PROBLEM 10♦

Calculate the pI of each of the following amino acids:

a. asparagine   **b.** arginine   **c.** serine   **d.** aspartate

PROBLEM 11♦

a. Which amino acid has the lowest pI value?
b. Which amino acid has the highest pI value?
c. Which amino acid has the greatest amount of negative charge at pH = 6.20?
d. Which amino acid has a greater negative charge at pH = 6.20, glycine or methionine?

PROBLEM 12

Explain why the pI values of tyrosine and cysteine cannot be determined by the method just described.

23.5 SEPARATING AMINO ACIDS

A mixture of amino acids can be separated by several different techniques.

Electrophoresis

Electrophoresis separates amino acids on the basis of their pI values. A few drops of a solution of an amino acid mixture are applied to the middle of a piece of filter paper or to a gel. When the paper or the gel is placed in a buffered solution between two electrodes and an electric field is applied (Figure 23.1), an amino acid with a pI greater than the pH of the solution will have an overall positive charge and will migrate toward the cathode (the negative electrode). The farther the amino acid's pI is from the pH of the buffer, the more positive the amino acid will be and the farther it will migrate toward the cathode in a given amount of time. An amino acid with a pI less than the pH of the buffer will have an overall negative charge and will migrate toward the anode (the positive electrode). If two molecules have the same charge, the larger one will move more slowly during electrophoresis because the same charge has to move a greater mass.

Considering that amino acids are colorless, how can we detect them after they have been separated? After the amino acids have been separated by electrophoresis, the filter paper is sprayed with ninhydrin and dried in a warm oven. Most amino acids form a purple product when heated with ninhydrin. The number of different kinds of amino acids in the mixture is determined by the number of colored spots on the filter paper (Figure 23.1). The individual amino acids are identified by their location on the paper compared with a standard.

▲ **Figure 23.1**
Arginine, alanine, and aspartate separated by electrophoresis at pH = 5.

The mechanism for formation of the colored product is shown below, omitting the mechanisms for the steps involving dehydration, imine formation, and imine hydrolysis. (These mechanisms are shown in Sections 18.8 and 18.9.)

MECHANISM FOR THE REACTION OF AN AMINO ACID WITH NINHYDRIN TO FORM A COLORED PRODUCT

chem
place Tutorial:
Electrophoresis and pI

Paper Chromatography and Thin-Layer Chromatography

Paper chromatography once played an important role in biochemical analysis because it provided a method for separating amino acids using very simple equipment. Although more modern techniques are generally employed today, we will describe the principles behind paper chromatography because many of the same principles are employed in modern separation techniques.

Paper chromatography separates amino acids on the basis of polarity. A few drops of a solution of an amino acid mixture are applied to the bottom of a strip of filter paper. The edge of the paper is then placed in a solvent (typically a mixture of water, acetic acid, and butanol). The solvent moves up the paper by capillary action, carrying the amino acids with it. Depending on their polarities, the amino acids have different affinities for the mobile (solvent) and stationary (paper) phases and therefore travel up the paper at different rates. When a solvent that is less polar than the paper is employed, the more polar the amino acid, the more strongly it is adsorbed onto the relatively polar paper. The less polar amino acids travel up the paper more rapidly, since they have a greater affinity for the mobile phase. Therefore, when the paper is developed with ninhydrin, the colored spot closest to the origin is the most polar amino acid and the spot farthest away from the origin is the least polar amino acid (Figure 23.2).

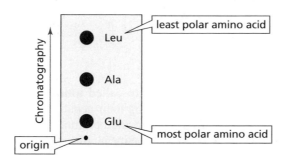

Less polar amino acids travel more rapidly.

◀ **Figure 23.2**
Separation of glutamate, alanine, and leucine by paper chromatography.

The most polar amino acids are those with charged side chains, the next most polar are those with side chains that can form hydrogen bonds, and the least polar are those with hydrocarbon side chains. For amino acids with hydrocarbon side chains, the larger the alkyl group, the less polar the amino acid. In other words, leucine is less polar than valine.

Paper chromatography has largely been replaced by **thin-layer chromatography** (TLC), which differs from paper chromatography in that TLC uses a plate with a coating of solid material instead of filter paper. The physical property on which the separation is based depends on the solid material and the solvent chosen for the mobile phase.

PROBLEM 13♦

What aldehyde is formed when valine is treated with ninhydrin?

PROBLEM 14♦

A mixture of seven amino acids (glycine, glutamate, leucine, lysine, alanine, isoleucine, and aspartate) is separated by TLC. Explain why only six spots show up when the chromatographic plate is sprayed with ninhydrin and heated.

Ion-Exchange Chromatography

A technique called **ion-exchange chromatography** can not only identify amino acids, but also determine the relative amounts of different amino acids present in a mixture. This technique employs a column packed with an insoluble resin. A solution of a mixture of amino acids is loaded onto the top of the column, and a series of buffer solutions of increasing pH are poured through the column. The amino acids separate because they flow through the column at different rates, as explained on page 990.

The resin is a chemically inert material with charged groups. The structure of a commonly used resin is shown in Figure 23.3. If a mixture of lysine and glutamate in a solution with a pH = 6 were to be loaded onto the column, glutamate would travel down the column rapidly because its negatively charged side chain would be repelled by the negatively charged sulfonic acid groups of the resin. The positively charged side chain of lysine, on the other hand, would cause that amino acid to be retained on the column. This kind of resin is called a **cation-exchange resin** because it exchanges the Na^+ counterions of the SO_3^- groups for the positively charged species traveling through the column. In addition, the relatively nonpolar nature of the column causes it to retain nonpolar amino acids longer than polar amino acids.

▶ **Figure 23.3**
A section of a cation-exchange resin. This particular resin is called Dowex 50.

Cations bind most strongly to cation-exchange resins.

Anions bind most strongly to anion-exchange resins.

Resins with positively charged groups are called **anion-exchange resins** because they impede the flow of anions by exchanging their negatively charged counterions for negatively charged species traveling through the column. A common anion-exchange resin, Dowex 1, has $CH_2N^+(CH_3)_3Cl^-$ groups in place of the $SO_3^-Na^+$ groups in Figure 23.3.

An **amino acid analyzer** is an instrument that automates ion-exchange chromatography. When a solution of amino acids passes through the column of an amino acid analyzer containing a cation-exchange resin, the amino acids move through the column at different rates, depending on their overall charge. The solution that flows out of the column (the effluent) is collected in fractions, and these are collected often enough that a different amino acid ends up in each one (Figure 23.4).

▶ **Figure 23.4**
Separation of amino acids by ion-exchange chromatography.

Fractions are sequentially collected

If ninhydrin is added to each of the fractions, the concentration of amino acid in each fraction can be determined by the amount of absorbance at 570 nm because the colored compound formed by the reaction of an amino acid with ninhydrin has a λ_{max} of 570 nm (Section 13.18). This information combined with each fraction's rate of passage through the column allow the identity and relative amount of each amino acid in the mixture to be determined (Figure 23.5).

◀ **Figure 23.5**
A typical chromatogram obtained from the separation of a mixture of amino acids using an automated amino acid analyzer.

Water Softeners: Examples of Cation-Exchange Chromatography

Water-softening systems contain a column packed with a cation-exchange resin that has been flushed with concentrated sodium chloride. When "hard water" (water with high levels of calcium and magnesium ions; Section 17.14) passes through the column, the resin binds the magnesium and calcium ions more tightly than it binds sodium ions. Thus, the water-softening system removes magnesium and calcium ions from the water and replaces them with sodium ions. The resin must be recharged from time to time by being flushed with concentrated sodium chloride, thereby replacing the bound magnesium and calcium ions with sodium ions.

PROBLEM 15

Why are buffer solutions of increasingly higher pH used to elute the column that generates the chromatogram shown in Figure 23.5? (*Elute* means wash out with a solvent.)

PROBLEM 16

Explain the order of elution (with a buffer of pH 4) of each of the following pairs of amino acids through a column packed with Dowex 50 (Figure 23.3):

a. aspartate before serine
b. glycine before alanine
c. valine before leucine
d. tyrosine before phenylalanine

PROBLEM 17 ♦

Give the order in which the following amino acids would be eluted with a buffer of pH 4 from a column containing an anion-exchange resin (Dowex 1):

histidine, serine, aspartate, valine.

chem Tutorial:
place Column chromotography

23.6 THE SYNTHESIS OF AMINO ACIDS

Chemists do not have to rely on nature to produce amino acids; they can synthesize them in the laboratory, using a variety of methods.

HVZ Reaction Followed by Reaction with Ammonia

One of the oldest methods used to synthesize an amino acid is to employ an HVZ reaction to replace an α-hydrogen of a carboxylic acid with a bromine (Section 19.6).

The resulting α-bromocarboxylic acid can then undergo an S_N2 reaction with ammonia to form the amino acid (Section 8.3).

PROBLEM 18◆

Why is excess ammonia used in the preceding reaction?

Reductive Amination

Amino acids can also be synthesized by reductive amination of an α-keto acid (Section 18.8).

PROBLEM 19◆

Biological organisms can also convert α-keto acids into amino acids, but because the reagents organic chemists use for this reaction are not available in living cells, cells carry out this reaction by a different mechanism (Section 25.6).

a. What amino acid is obtained from the reductive amination of each of the following metabolic intermediates in the cell?

pyruvic acid   oxaloacetic acid α-ketoglutaric acid

b. What amino acids are obtained from the same metabolic intermediates when the amino acids are synthesized in the laboratory?

N-Phthalimidomalonic Ester Synthesis

Amino acids can be synthesized with much better yields than those obtained by the previous two methods via an *N*-phthalimidomalonic ester synthesis, a method that combines the malonic ester synthesis (Section 19.20) and the Gabriel synthesis (Section 17.18). The mechanism for the reaction is shown below.

MECHANISM FOR THE N-PHTHALIMIDOMALONIC ESTER SYNTHESIS

- α-Bromomalonic ester and potassium phthalimide undergo an S_N2 reaction.
- A proton is easily removed from the α-carbon of *N*-phthalimidomalonic ester since it is flanked by two ester groups.
- The resulting carbanion undergoes an S_N2 reaction with an alkyl halide.

- Heating in an acidic aqueous solution hydrolyzes the two ester groups and the two amide bonds and decarboxylates the 3-oxocarboxylic acid.

α-bromomalonic ester   potassium phthalimide   *N*-phthalimidomalonic ester

phthalic acid   + CO_2 +   an amino acid

A variation of the *N*-phthalimidomalonic ester synthesis uses acetamidomalonic ester in place of *N*-phthalimidomalonic ester.

acetamidomalonic ester

acetic acid   + CO_2 +   an amino acid

Strecker Synthesis

Amino acids can be prepared by a method known as the Strecker synthesis. In this synthesis, an aldehyde reacts with ammonia forming an imine. An addition reaction with cyanide ion forms an intermediate, which, when hydrolyzed, forms the amino acid (Section 17.19). Compare this reaction with the Kiliani–Fischer synthesis of aldoses in Section 22.8.

an aldehyde   an imine   an amino acid

PROBLEM 20◆

What amino acid would be formed using the *N*-phthalimidomalonic ester synthesis when the following alkyl halides are used in the third step?

a. CH$_3$CHCH$_2$Br
  |
  CH$_3$

b. CH$_3$SCH$_2$CH$_2$Br

PROBLEM 21◆

What alkyl halide would you use in the acetamidomalonic ester synthesis to prepare

a. lysine? **b.** phenylalanine?

PROBLEM 22◆

What amino acid would be formed when the aldehyde used in the Strecker synthesis is

a. acetaldehyde? **b.** 2-methylbutanal? **c.** 3-methylbutanal?

23.7 THE RESOLUTION OF RACEMIC MIXTURES OF AMINO ACIDS

When amino acids are synthesized in nature, only the L-enantiomer is formed (Section 5.20). However, when amino acids are synthesized in the laboratory, the product is usually a racemic mixture of D and L enantiomers. If only one isomer is desired, the enantiomers must be separated, which can be accomplished by means of an enzyme-catalyzed reaction. Because an enzyme is chiral, it will react at a different rate with each of the enantiomers (Section 5.21). For example, pig kidney aminoacylase is an enzyme that catalyzes the hydrolysis of *N*-acetyl-L-amino acids, but not *N*-acetyl-D-amino acids. Therefore, if the racemic amino acid is converted to a pair of *N*-acetylamino acids and the *N*-acetylated mixture is hydrolyzed with pig kidney aminoacylase, the products will be the L-amino acid and *N*-acetyl-D-amino acid, which are easily separated. Because the resolution (separation) of the enantiomers depends on the difference in the rates of reaction of the enzyme with the two *N*-acetylated compounds, this technique is known as a **kinetic resolution**.

PROBLEM 23

Pig liver esterase is an enzyme that catalyzes the hydrolysis of esters. It hydrolyzes esters of L-amino acids more rapidly than esters of D-amino acids. How can this enzyme be used to separate a racemic mixture of amino acids?

23.8 PEPTIDE BONDS AND DISULFIDE BONDS

Peptide bonds and disulfide bonds are the only covalent bonds that join amino acids together in a peptide or a protein.

Peptide Bonds

The amide bonds that link amino acids are called **peptide bonds**. By convention, peptides and proteins are written with the free amino group (of the **N-terminal amino acid**) on the left and the free carboxyl group (of the **C-terminal amino acid**) on the right.

When the identities of the amino acids in a peptide are known but their sequence is not known, the amino acids are written separated by commas. When their sequence is known, the amino acids are written connected by hyphens. In the pentapeptide represented below, valine is the N-terminal amino acid and histidine is the C-terminal amino acid. The amino acids are numbered starting with the N-terminal end. Alanine is therefore referred to as Ala 3 because it is the third amino acid from the N-terminal end. In naming the peptide, adjective names (ending in "yl") are used for all the amino acids except the C-terminal amino acid. Thus, this pentapeptide is named valylcysteinylalanylglutamylhistidine. Each amino acid has an L configuration unless otherwise specified.

Glu, Cys, His, Val, Ala

the pentapeptide contains the indicated amino acids, but their sequence is not known

Val-Cys-Ala-Glu-His

the amino acids in the pentapeptide have the indicated sequence

A peptide bond has about 40% double-bond character because of electron delocalization (Section 17.2). Steric hindrance in the cis configuration causes the trans configuration about the amide linkage to be more stable, so the α-carbons of adjacent amino acids are trans to each other (Section 4.11).

resonance contributors

The partial double-bond character prevents free rotation about the peptide bond, so the carbon and nitrogen atoms of the peptide bond and the two atoms to which each is attached are held rigidly in a plane (Figure 23.6). This regional planarity affects the way a chain of amino acids can fold, so electron delocalization has important implications for the three-dimensional shapes of peptides and proteins (Section 23.14).

◀ **Figure 23.6**
A segment of a polypeptide chain. Colored squares indicate the plane defined by each peptide bond. Notice that the R groups bonded to the α-carbons are on alternate sides of the peptide backbone.

PROBLEM 24

Draw the tetrapeptide Ala-Thr-Asp-Asn and indicate the peptide bonds.

PROBLEM 25♦

Using the three-letter abbreviations, write the six tripeptides consisting of Ala, Gly, and Met.

PROBLEM 26

Draw a peptide bond in the cis configuration.

PROBLEM 27♦

Which bonds in the backbone of a peptide can rotate freely?

Disulfide Bonds

When thiols are oxidized under mild conditions, they form disulfides. A **disulfide** is a compound with an S—S bond. (Recall that the number of S—H bonds decreases in an oxidation reaction and increases in a reduction reaction; see Section 20.1.)

$$2\ R\text{—SH} \xrightarrow{\text{mild oxidation}} RS\text{—SR}$$

$$\text{a thiol} \qquad\qquad\qquad \text{a disulfide}$$

An oxidizing agent commonly used for this reaction is Br_2 (or I_2) in a basic solution.

MECHANISM FOR OXIDATION OF A THIOL TO A DISULFIDE

$$R\text{—}\ddot{S}H \underset{H_2O}{\overset{HO^-}{\rightleftharpoons}} R\text{—}\ddot{\underset{..}{S}}{}^- \quad \overset{Br\text{—}Br}{\longrightarrow} \quad R\text{—}S\text{—}Br \quad \overset{R\text{—}\ddot{S}{}^-}{\longrightarrow} \quad R\text{—}\ddot{\underset{..}{S}}\text{—}\ddot{\underset{..}{S}}\text{—}R \ + \ Br^- $$

$$+ \ Br^-$$

Because thiols can be oxidized to disulfides, disulfides can be reduced to thiols.

$$RS\text{—}SR \xrightarrow{\text{reduction}} 2\ R\text{—SH}$$

$$\text{a disulfide} \qquad\qquad \text{a thiol}$$

Disulfides are reduced to thiols.

Thiols are oxidized to disulfides.

Cysteine is an amino acid that contains a thiol group. Two cysteine molecules therefore can be oxidized to a disulfide. This disulfide is called cystine.

$$2\ HSCH_2CH \underset{{}^+NH_3}{\overset{O}{\underset{||}{\overset{C}{-}}}}O^- \xrightarrow{\text{mild oxidation}} {}^-O\underset{{}^+NH_3}{\overset{O}{\underset{||}{\overset{C}{-}}}}CHCH_2S\text{—}SCH_2CH\underset{{}^+NH_3}{\overset{O}{\underset{||}{\overset{C}{-}}}}O^-$$

$$\text{cysteine} \qquad\qquad\qquad\qquad \text{cystine}$$

Two cysteines in a protein can be oxidized to a disulfide, creating a bond known as a **disulfide bridge**. Disulfide bridges are the only covalent bonds that are found between nonadjacent amino acids in peptides and proteins. They contribute to the overall shape of a protein by linking cysteines found in different parts of the peptide backbone, as shown in Figure 23.7.

▶ **Figure 23.7**
Disulfide bridges cross-linking portions of a peptide.

polypeptide

disulfide bridges cross-linking portions of a polypeptide

The hormone insulin, secreted by the pancreas, controls the level of glucose in the blood by regulating glucose metabolism. Insulin is a polypeptide with two peptide chains. The short chain (the A-chain) contains 21 amino acids, and the long chain (the B-chain) contains 30 amino acids. The A- and B-chains are connected to each other by two disulfide bridges. These are **interchain disulfide bridges** (between two chains). Insulin also has an **intrachain disulfide bridge** (within a chain).

insulin

Hair: Straight or Curly?

Hair is made up of a protein called keratin that contains an unusually large number of cysteines (about 8% of the amino acids compared with an average of 2.8% for other proteins). These cysteines furnish keratin with many disulfide bridges that preserve its three-dimensional structure. People can alter the structure of their hair (if they think it is either too straight or too curly) by changing the location of these disulfide bridges. This can be accomplished by first applying a reducing agent to the hair to reduce all the disulfide bridges in the protein strands. Then, after rearranging the hair into the desired shape (using curlers to curl it or combing it straight to uncurl it), an oxidizing agent is applied to form new disulfide bridges. The new disulfide bridges hold the hair in its new shape. When this treatment is applied to straight hair, it is called a "permanent." When it is applied to curly hair, it is called "hair straightening."

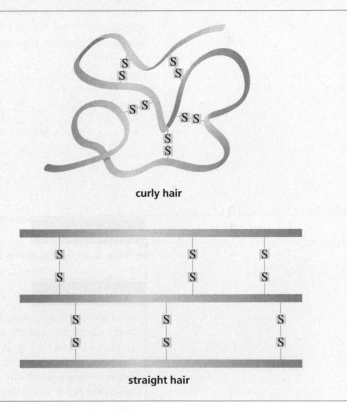

curly hair

straight hair

23.9 SOME INTERESTING PEPTIDES

Enkephalins are pentapeptides synthesized by the body to control pain. They decrease the body's sensitivity to pain by binding to receptors in certain brain cells. Part of the three-dimensional structures of enkephalins must be similar to those of morphine and related painkillers such as Demerol because they bind to the same receptors (Sections 31.3 and 31.6).

Tyr-Gly-Gly-Phe-Leu   Tyr-Gly-Gly-Phe-Met
leucine enkephalin   **methionine enkephalin**

Bradykinin, vasopressin, and oxytocin are peptide hormones. They are all nonapeptides. Bradykinin inhibits the inflammation of tissues. Vasopressin controls blood pressure by regulating the contraction of smooth muscle; it is also an antidiuretic.

Oxytocin induces labor in pregnant women by stimulating the uterine muscle to contract, and it also stimulates milk production in nursing mothers. Vasopressin and oxytocin both have an intrachain disulfide bridge, and their C-terminal amino acids contain amide rather than carboxyl groups. Notice that the C-terminal amide group is indicated by writing "NH$_2$" after the name of the C-terminal amino acid. Vasopressin and oxytocin also act on the brain. Vasopressin is a "fight-or-flight" hormone, whereas oxytocin has the opposite effect; it calms the body and promotes social bonding. In spite of their very different physiological effects, vasopressin and oxytocin differ only by two amino acids.

bradykinin   Arg-Pro-Pro-Gly-Phe-Ser-Pro-Phe-Arg

vasopressin   Cys-Tyr-Phe-Gln-Asn-Cys-Pro-Arg-Gly-NH$_2$
                  | |
                  S————————————————————S

oxytocin   Cys-Tyr-Ile-Gln-Asn-Cys-Pro-Leu-Gly-NH$_2$
               | |
               S————————————————————S

The synthetic sweetener aspartame (or Equal or NutraSweet; see Section 22.20) is the methyl ester of a dipeptide of L-aspartate and L-phenylalanine. Aspartame is about 200 times sweeter than sucrose. The ethyl ester of the same dipeptide is not sweet. If a D-amino acid is substituted for either of the L-amino acids of aspartame, the resulting dipeptide is bitter rather than sweet.

aspartame
NutraSweet®

PROBLEM 28◆

What is the configuration about each of the asymmetric centers in aspartame?

PROBLEM 29

Glutathione is a tripeptide whose function is to destroy harmful oxidizing agents in the body. Oxidizing agents are thought to be responsible for some of the effects of aging and to play a causative role in cancer. Glutathione removes oxidizing agents by reducing them. In the process, glutathione is oxidized, resulting in the formation of a disulfide bond between two glutathione molecules (see page 997). An enzyme subsequently reduces the disulfide bond, returning glutathione to its original condition so it can react with more oxidizing agents.

glutathione

oxidizing agent / reducing agent

oxidized glutathione

> **a.** What amino acids make up glutathione?
> **b.** What is unusual about glutathione's structure? (If you cannot answer this question, draw the structure you would expect for the tripeptide, and compare your structure with the structure of glutathione.)

23.10 THE STRATEGY OF PEPTIDE BOND SYNTHESIS: N-PROTECTION AND C-ACTIVATION

One difficulty in synthesizing a polypeptide is that the amino acids have two functional groups, enabling them to combine in different ways. For example, suppose you wanted to make the dipeptide Gly-Ala. That dipeptide is only one of four possible dipeptides that could be formed from a mixture of alanine and glycine.

| Gly-Ala | Ala-Ala | Gly-Gly | Ala-Gly |

If the amino group of the amino acid that is to be on the N-terminal end (in this case, Gly) is protected (Section 18.11), it will not be available to form a peptide bond. If its group is activated before the second amino acid is added, the amino group of the added amino acid (in this case, Ala) will react with the activated carboxyl group of glycine in preference to reacting with a nonactivated carboxyl group of another alanine molecule.

The N-terminal amino acid must have its amino group protected and its carboxyl group activated.

The reagent most often used to protect the amino group of an amino acid is di-*tert*-butyl dicarbonate, known by the acronym *t*-BOC (pronounced "tee-bok"). Its popularity is due to the ease with which the protecting group can be removed when the need for protection is over. Notice that the amino group rather than the carboxy group of the amino acid reacts with *t*-BOC because the amino group is a better nucleophile (Section 18.18).

| di-*tert*-butyl dicarbonate | glycine | N-protected glycine |

The reagent most often used to activate the carboxyl group is dicyclohexylcarbodi-imide (DCC). DCC activates a carboxyl group by putting a good leaving group on the carbonyl carbon.

N-protected Gly

**dicyclohexylcarbodiimide
DCC**

**proton
transfer**

activating
group

protected

activated

After the amino acid's N-terminal group is protected and its C-terminal group is acti-vated, the second amino acid is added. The unprotected amino group of the second amino acid attacks the activated carboxyl group, forming a tetrahedral intermediate. The C—O bond of the tetrahedral intermediate is easily broken because the bonding electrons are delocalized; breaking this bond forms dicyclohexylurea, a stable diamide.

Ala

tetrahedral
intermediate

new peptide bond

dicyclohexylurea
a diamide

Amino acids can be added to the growing C-terminal end by repeating the same two steps: activating the carboxyl group of the C-terminal amino acid of the peptide by treating it with DCC and then adding a new amino acid.

N-protected Gly–Ala   **N-protected Gly–Ala–Val**

When the desired number of amino acids has been added to the chain, the protecting group on the N-terminal amino acid is removed. As mentioned above, *t*-BOC is an ideal protecting group because it can be removed with trifluoroacetic acid in dichloromethane, a reagent that will not break any other covalent bonds. The protecting group is removed by an elimination reaction, forming isobutylene and carbon dioxide. Because these products are gases, they escape, driving the reaction to completion.

N-protected Gly–Ala–Val

Gly–Ala–Val

Theoretically, one should be able to make as long a peptide as desired with this technique. Reactions never produce 100% yields, however, and the yields are further decreased during the purification process. (After each step of the synthesis, the peptide must be purified to prevent subsequent unwanted reactions with leftover reagents.) Assuming that each amino acid can be added to the growing end of the peptide chain with an 80% yield (a relatively high yield, as you can probably appreciate from your own experience in the laboratory), the overall yield of the synthesis of a nonapeptide such as bradykinin would be only 17%. It is clear that large polypeptides could never be synthesized this way.

Number of amino acids

	2	3	4	5	6	7	8	9
Overall yield	80%	64%	51%	41%	33%	26%	21%	17%

PROBLEM 30◆

What dipeptides would be formed by heating a mixture of valine and N-protected leucine?

PROBLEM 31

Suppose you are trying to synthesize the dipeptide Val-Ser. Compare the product that would be obtained if thionyl chloride were used to activate the carboxyl group of N-protected valine with the product that would be obtained if it were activated with DCC.

PROBLEM 32

Show the steps in the synthesis of the tetrapeptide Leu-Phe-Lys-Val.

PROBLEM 33◆

a. Calculate the overall yield of bradykinin when the yield for the addition of each amino acid to the chain is 70%.

b. What would be the overall yield of a peptide containing 15 amino acids if the yield for the incorporation of each is 80%?

23.11 AUTOMATED PEPTIDE SYNTHESIS

In addition to producing low overall yields, the method of peptide synthesis described in Section 23.10 is extremely time-consuming because the product must be purified at each step of the synthesis. In 1969, Bruce Merrifield described a method that revolutionized the synthesis of peptides because it provided a much faster way to produce peptides in much higher yields. Furthermore, because it is automated, the synthesis requires fewer hours of direct attention. With this technique, bradykinin was synthesized in 27 hours with an 85% yield. Subsequent refinements in the technique now allow a reasonable yield of a peptide containing 100 amino acids to be synthesized in four days.

In the Merrifield method, the C-terminal amino acid is covalently attached to a solid support in a column. Each N-terminal-protected amino acid is added one at a time, along with other needed reagents. Thus, the protein is synthesized from the C-terminal end to the N-terminal end. (Proteins are synthesized in nature from the N-terminal end to the C-terminal end; Section 28.9.) Because the process uses a solid support and is automated, Merrifield's method of protein synthesis is called **automated solid-phase peptide synthesis**.

Merrifield automated solid-phase synthesis of a tripeptide

The solid support to which the C-terminal amino acid is attached is a resin similar to the one used in ion-exchange chromatography (Section 23.5), except that the benzene rings have chloromethyl substituents instead of sulfonic acid substituents. Before the C-terminal amino acid is attached to the resin, its amino group is protected with *t*-BOC to prevent the amino group from reacting with the resin. The C-terminal amino acid is attached to the resin by means of an S_N2 reaction: its carboxyl group attacks a benzyl carbon of the resin, displacing a chloride ion (Section 8.3).

After the C-terminal amino acid is attached to the resin, the *t*-BOC protecting group is removed (Section 23.10). The next amino acid, with its amino group protected with *t*-BOC and its carboxyl group activated with DCC, is added to the column.

A huge advantage of the Merrifield method of peptide synthesis is that the growing peptide can be purified by washing the column with an appropriate solvent after each step of the procedure. The impurities are washed out of the column because they are not attached to the solid support. Because the peptide is covalently attached to the resin, none of it is lost in the purification step, leading to high yields of purified product.

After the required amino acids have been added one by one, the peptide can be removed from the resin by treatment with HF under mild conditions that do not break any peptide bonds.

Over time, Merrifield's technique has been improved so that peptides can be made more rapidly and more efficiently. However, it still cannot begin to compare with nature. A bacterial cell is able to synthesize a protein containing thousands of amino acids in seconds and can simultaneously synthesize thousands of different proteins with no mistakes.

Since the early 1980s, it has been possible to synthesize proteins by genetic engineering techniques. Strands of DNA, introduced into bacterial cells, cause cells to produce large amounts of a desired protein (Section 28.13). Until genetic engineering techniques became available, cattle and pigs were the sources of insulin for people with diabetes. The insulin was effective, but there were concerns about whether enough could be obtained over the long term for the growing population of diabetics. In addition, this insulin did not have exactly the same sequence of amino acids as human insulin, so allergic reactions could occur. Now, however, mass quantities of synthetic insulin, chemically identical to human insulin, are produced from genetically modified *E. coli*. Genetic engineering techniques also have been useful in synthesizing proteins that differ in one or a few amino acids from a natural protein. Such synthetic proteins have been used, for example, to learn how a change in a single amino acid affects the properties of a protein (Section 24.9).

chem place Tutorial: Merrifield automated solid-phase peptide synthesis

---

PROBLEM 34

Show the steps in the synthesis of the tetrapeptide in Problem 32, using Merrifield's method.

23.12 AN INTRODUCTION TO PROTEIN STRUCTURE

Proteins are described by four levels of structure. The **primary structure** of a protein is the sequence of amino acids in the chain and the location of all the disulfide bridges. **Secondary structures** are regular conformations assumed by segments of the protein's backbone when it folds. The **tertiary structure** is the three-dimensional structure of the entire polypeptide. If a protein has more than one polypeptide chain, it also has a quaternary structure. The **quaternary structure** is the way the individual polypeptide chains are arranged with respect to one another.

Primary Structure and Evolution

When scientists examine the primary structures of proteins that carry out the same function in different organisms, they can correlate the number of amino acid differences in the proteins to the closeness of the taxonomic relationship between the species. For example, cytochrome *c*, a protein that transfers electrons in biological oxidations, has about 100 amino acids. Yeast cytochrome *c* differs by 48 amino acids from horse cytochrome *c*,

whereas duck cytochrome *c* differs by only two amino acids from chicken cytochrome *c*. Clearly, ducks and chickens have a much closer taxonomic relationship than horses and yeast. Likewise, the cytochrome *c* in chickens and turkeys have identical primary structures. Human cytochrome *c* and chimpanzee cytochrome *c* are also identical and differ by one amino acid from the cytochrome *c* of the rhesus monkey.

23.13 HOW TO DETERMINE THE PRIMARY STRUCTURE OF A POLYPEPTIDE OR PROTEIN

The first step in determining the sequence of amino acids in a polypeptide (or protein) is to reduce the disulfide bridges in order to obtain a single polypeptide chain. A commonly used reducing agent is 2-mercaptoethanol. Notice that when it reduces a disulfide bridge, 2-mercaptoethanol is oxidized to a disulfide (Section 23.8). Reaction of the protein thiol groups with iodoacetic acid prevents the disulfide bridges from re-forming as a result of oxidation by O_2.

cleaving disulfide bridges

PROBLEM 35

Write the mechanism for the reaction of a cysteine side chain with iodoacetic acid.

Now we need to determine the number and kinds of amino acids in the polypeptide chain. To do this, a sample of the polypeptide is dissolved in 6 M HCl and heated at 100 °C for 24 hours. This treatment hydrolyzes all the amide bonds in the polypeptide, including the amide bonds in the side chains of asparagine and glutamine.

$$\text{protein} \xrightarrow[\substack{100\ °C \\ 24\ h}]{6\ \text{M HCl}} \text{amino acids}$$

The mixture of amino acids is then passed through an amino acid analyzer to identify the amino acids and determine how many of each kind are in the polypeptide (Section 23.5).

Because all the asparagines and glutamines have been hydrolyzed to aspartates and glutamates, the number of aspartates or glutamates in the amino acid mixture tells us the number of aspartates plus asparagines or glutamates plus glutamines in the original protein. A separate test must be conducted to distinguish between aspartate and asparagine or between glutamate and glutamine in the original polypeptide.

*Insulin was the first protein to have its primary sequence determined. This was done in 1953 by **Frederick Sanger** who was awarded the 1958 Nobel Prize in Chemistry for his work. Sanger was born in England in 1918 and received a Ph.D. from Cambridge University, where he has worked for his entire career. He also received a share of the 1980 Nobel Prize in Chemistry (Section 28.11) for being the first to sequence a DNA molecule (with 5375 nucleotide pairs).*

The strongly acidic conditions used for hydrolysis destroy all the tryptophans because the indole ring is unstable in acid (Section 21.5). However, the tryptophan content can be determined by hydroxide-ion-promoted hydrolysis of the peptide. This is not a general method for peptide bond hydrolysis because the strongly basic conditions destroy several other amino acids.

One of the most widely used methods to identify the N-terminal amino acid of a polypeptide is to treat the polypeptide with phenyl isothiocyanate (PITC), more commonly known as **Edman's reagent**. This reagent reacts with the N-terminal amino group, and the resulting thiazolinone derivative is cleaved from the polypeptide under mildly acidic conditions, leaving behind a polypeptide with one fewer amino acid.

**phenyl isothiocyanate
PITC
Edman's reagent**

**peptide without the
original N-terminal
amino acid**

a thiazolinone

The thiazolinone rearranges in dilute acid to a more stable phenylthiohydantoin (PTH) (see Problem 72).

a thiazolinone   **a PTH-amino acid**

Because each amino acid has a different side chain (R), each amino acid forms a different PTH–amino acid. The particular PTH–amino acid can be identified by chromatography using known standards. Several successive Edman degradations can be carried out on a peptide. An automated instrument known as a *sequenator* allows about 50 successive Edman degradations of a polypeptide to be performed. The entire primary sequence cannot be determined in this way, however, because side products accumulate that interfere with the results.

The C-terminal amino acid of the polypeptide can be identified using a peptidase called carboxypeptidase A. A **peptidase** is an enzyme that catalyzes the hydrolysis of a peptide bond. Carboxypeptidase A catalyzes the hydrolysis of the C-terminal peptide bond, cleaving off the C-terminal amino acid, as long as it is *not* arginine or lysine (Section 24.9). On the other hand, carboxypeptidase B cleaves off the C-terminal amino acid *only* if it is arginine or lysine. Carboxypeptidase A and B are exopeptidases; an **exopeptidase** is an enzyme that catalyzes the hydrolysis of a peptide bond at the end of a peptide chain.

site where carboxypeptidase cleaves

Once the N-terminal and C-terminal amino acids have been identified, a sample of the polypeptide is hydrolyzed with dilute acid. This treatment, called **partial hydrolysis**, hydrolyzes only some of the peptide bonds. The resulting fragments are separated, and the amino acid composition of each is determined by using electrophoresis or an amino acid analyzer. The sequence of the original protein can then be deduced by lining up the peptides and looking for regions of overlap. (The N-terminal and C-terminal amino acids of each fragment can also be identified, if needed.)

PROBLEM 36◆

In determining the primary structure of insulin, what would lead you to conclude that insulin had more than one polypeptide chain?

PROBLEM-SOLVING STRATEGY

Sequencing an Oligopeptide

When a nonapeptide undergoes partial hydrolysis, it forms dipeptides, tripeptides, and a tertrapeptide whose amino acid compositions are shown below. Reaction of the intact nonapeptide with Edman's reagent releases PTH-Leu. What is the sequence of the nonapeptide?

1. Pro, Ser   **3.** Met, Ala, Leu   **5.** Glu, Ser, Val, Pro   **7.** Met, Leu
2. Gly, Glu   **4.** Gly, Ala   **6.** Glu, Pro, Gly   **8.** His, Val

- Because we know that the N-terminal amino acid is Leu, we need to look for a fragment that contains Leu. Fragment (7) tells us that Met is next to Leu, and fragment (3) tells us that Ala is next to Met.

- Now we look for another fragment that contains Ala. Fragment (4) contains Ala and tells us that Gly is next to Ala.

- From fragment (2), we know that Glu comes next; Glu is in both fragments (5) and (6).

- Fragment (5) has three amino acids we have yet to place in the growing peptide (Ser, Val, Pro), but fragment (6) has only one, so from fragment (6), we know that Pro is the next amino acid.

- Fragment (1) tells us that the next amino acid is Ser; now we can use fragment (5). Fragment (5) tells us that the next amino acid is Val, and fragment (8) tells us that His is the last (C-terminal) amino acid.

- Thus, the amino acid sequence of the nonapeptide is

    Leu-Met-Ala-Gly-Glu-Pro-Ser-Val-His

Now continue on to Problem 37.

PROBLEM 37◆

A decapeptide undergoes partial hydrolysis to give peptides whose amino acid compositions are shown. Reaction of the intact decapeptide with Edman's reagent releases PTH-Gly. What is the sequence of the decapeptide?

1. Ala, Trp   **3.** Pro, Val   **5.** Trp, Ala, Arg   **7.** Glu, Ala, Leu
2. Val, Pro, Asp   **4.** Ala, Glu   **6.** Arg, Gly   **8.** Met, Pro, Leu, Glu

A polypeptide can also be partially hydrolyzed using endopeptidases. An **endopeptidase** is an enzyme that catalyzes the hydrolysis of a peptide bond that is not at the end of a peptide chain. Trypsin, chymotrypsin, and elastase are endopeptidases that catalyze the hydrolysis of only the specific peptide bonds listed in Table 23.4. Trypsin, for example, catalyzes the hydrolysis of the peptide bond on the C-side of arginine or lysine.

Table 23.4	Specificity of Peptide or Protein Cleavage
Reagent	**Specificity**
Chemical reagents	
Edman's reagent	removes the N-terminal amino acid
Cyanogen bromide	hydrolyzes on the C-side of Met
Exopeptidases*	
Carboxypeptidase A	removes the C-terminal amino acid (not Arg or Lys)
Carboxypeptidase B	removes the C-terminal amino acid (only Arg or Lys)
Endopeptidases*	
Trypsin	hydrolyzes on the C-side of Arg and Lys
Chymotrypsin	hydrolyzes on the C-side of amino acids that contain aromatic six-membered rings (Phe, Tyr, Trp)
Elastase	hydrolyzes on the C-side of small amino acids (Gly and Ala)
* Cleavage will not occur if Pro is at the hydrolysis site.	

Thus, trypsin will catalyze the hydrolysis of three peptide bonds in the following polypeptide, creating a hexapeptide, a dipeptide, and two tripeptides.

Ala-Lys-Phe-Gly-Asp-Trp-Ser-Arg-Glu-Val-Arg-Tyr-Leu-His

cleavage by trypsin

Chymotrypsin catalyzes the hydrolysis of the peptide bond on the C-side of amino acids that contain aromatic six-membered rings (Phe, Tyr, Trp).

Ala-Lys-Phe-Gly-Asp-Trp-Ser-Arg-Glu-Val-Arg-Tyr-Leu-His

cleavage by chymotrypsin

Elastase catalyzes the hydrolysis of peptide bonds on the C-side of the two smallest amino acids (Gly, Ala). Chymotrypsin and elastase are much less specific than trypsin. (An explanation for the specificity of these enzymes is given in Section 24.9.)

Ala-Lys-Phe-Gly-Asp-Trp-Ser-Arg-Glu-Val-Arg-Tyr-Leu-His

cleavage by elastase

None of the exopeptidases or endopeptidases that we have mentioned will catalyze the hydrolysis of a peptide bond if proline is at the hydrolysis site. These enzymes recognize the appropriate hydrolysis site by its shape and charge, and the cyclic structure of proline causes the hydrolysis site to have an unrecognizable three-dimensional shape.

Ala-Lys-Pro

trypsin will not cleave

Leu-Phe-Pro

chymotrypsin will not cleave

Pro-Phe-Val

chymotrypsin will cleave

Cyanogen bromide (BrC≡N) causes the hydrolysis of the peptide bond on the C-side of methionine. The mechanism of the reaction is shown below. Cyanogen bromide is more specific about what peptide bonds it cleaves than are the endopeptidases, so cyanogen bromide provides more reliable information about the primary structure (the sequence of amino acids). Because cyanogen bromide is not a protein, it does not recognize the substrate by its shape. Therefore, it will still cleave the peptide bond if proline is at the hydrolysis site.

Ala-Lys-Phe-Gly-Met-Pro-Ser-Arg-Met-Val-Arg-Tyr-Leu-His

cleavage by cyanogen bromide

MECHANISM FOR CLEAVAGE OF A PEPTIDE BOND BY CYANOGEN BROMIDE

- The highly nucleophilic sulfur of methionine attacks the carbon of cyanogen bromide and eliminates a bromide ion.
- Nucleophilic attack by oxygen on the methylene group, resulting in departure of the weakly basic leaving group, forms a five-membered ring.
- Acid-catalyzed hydrolysis of the imine cleaves the protein (Section 18.8).
- Further hydrolysis causes the lactone (a cyclic ester) to open to a carboxyl group and an alcohol group (Section 17.11).

The last step in determining the primary structure of a protein is to figure out the location of any disulfide bonds. This is done by hydrolyzing a sample of the protein that has intact disulfide bonds. From a determination of the amino acids in the cysteine-containing fragments, the locations of the disulfide bonds in the protein can be established (Problem 60).

PROBLEM 38

Why does cyanogen bromide not cleave on the C-side of cysteine?

PROBLEM 39♦

Indicate the peptides that would result from cleavage by the indicated reagent:
a. His-Lys-Leu-Val-Glu-Pro-Arg-Ala-Gly-Ala by trypsin
b. Leu-Gly-Ser-Met-Phe-Pro-Tyr-Gly-Val by chymotrypsin

PROBLEM 40   **SOLVED**

Determine the amino acid sequence of a polypeptide from the following data:
  Acid-catalyzed hydrolysis gives Ala, Arg, His, 2 Lys, Leu, 2 Met, Pro, 2 Ser, Thr, Val.
  Carboxypeptidase A releases Val.
  Edman's reagent releases PTH-Leu.
  Cleavage with cyanogen bromide gives three peptides with the following amino acid compositions:
1. His, Lys, Met, Pro, Ser   **3.** Ala, Arg, Leu, Lys, Met, Ser
2. Thr, Val

  Trypsin-catalyzed hydrolysis gives three peptides and a single amino acid:
1. Arg, Leu, Ser   **3.** Lys
2. Met, Pro, Ser, Thr, Val   **4.** Ala, His, Lys, Met

Solution   Acid-catalyzed hydrolysis shows that the polypeptide has 13 amino acids. The N-terminal amino acid is Leu (revealed by Edman's reagent), and the C-terminal amino acid is Val (revealed by carboxypeptidase A).

Leu   __ __ __ __ __ __ __ __ __ __ __   Val

- Because cyanogen bromide cleaves on the C-side of Met, any peptide containing Met must have Met as its C-terminal amino acid. Thus, the peptide that does not contain Met must be the C-terminal peptide. We know that peptide 3 is the N-terminal peptide because it contains Leu. Because peptide 3 is a hexapeptide, we know that the sixth amino acid in the 13-amino-acid polypeptide is Met. We also know that the eleventh amino acid is Met because cyanogen bromide cleavage gave the dipeptide Thr, Val. The cyanogen bromide data also tell us that Thr is the twelfth amino acid.

    Ala, Arg, Lys, Ser   His, Lys, Pro, Ser
Leu __ __ __ __   Met __ __ __ __   Met   Thr   Val

- Because trypsin cleaves on the C-side of Arg and Lys, any peptide containing Arg or Lys must have that amino acid as its C-terminal amino acid. Therefore, Arg is the C-terminal amino acid of peptide 1, so we now know that the first three amino acids are Leu-Ser-Arg. We also know that the next two are Lys-Ala because if they were Ala-Lys, trypsin cleavage would give an Ala, Lys dipeptide. The trypsin data also identify the positions of His and Lys.

                            Pro, Ser
Leu   Ser   Arg   Lys   Ala   Met   His   Lys __ __   Met   Thr   Val

- Finally, because trypsin successfully cleaves on the C-side of Lys, Pro cannot be adjacent to Lys. Thus, the amino acid sequence of the polypeptide is

Leu   Ser   Arg   Lys   Ala   Met   His   Lys   Ser   Pro   Met   Thr   Val

PROBLEM 41◆

Determine the primary structure of an octapeptide from the following data:

Acid-catalyzed hydrolysis gives 2 Arg, Leu, Lys, Met, Phe, Ser, Tyr.

Carboxypeptidase A releases Ser.

Edman's reagent releases Leu.

Cyanogen bromide forms two peptides with the following amino acid compositions:

1. Arg, Phe, Ser   **2.** Arg, Leu, Lys, Met, Tyr

Trypsin forms the following two amino acids and two peptides:

1. Arg   **3.** Arg, Met, Phe
2. Ser   **4.** Leu, Lys, Tyr

PROBLEM 42

Following are the structures of the peptides obtained from a trypsin digestion of two different polypeptides. In each case, indicate the possible sequences from the given data and tell what further experiment should be carried out in order to determine the primary structure of the polypeptide.

a. 1. Val-Gly-Asp-Lys   **b. 1.** Val-Leu-Gly-Glu
2. Leu-Glu-Pro-Ala-Arg   **2.** Ala-Glu-Pro-Arg
3. Ala-Leu-Gly-Asp   **3.** Ala-Met-Gly-Lys

23.14 THE SECONDARY STRUCTURE OF PROTEINS

Secondary structure describes the repetitive conformations assumed by segments of the backbone chain of a peptide or protein. In other words, the secondary structure describes how segments of the backbone fold. Three factors determine the secondary structure of a stretch of protein:

- The regional planarity about each peptide bond (as a result of the partial double-bond character of the amide bond), which limits the possible conformations of the peptide chain (Section 23.8)
- Maximizing the number of peptide groups that engage in hydrogen bonding (that is, form a hydrogen bond between the carbonyl oxygen of one amino acid and the amide hydrogen of another) to minimize energy

- The need for adequate separation between neighboring R groups to avoid steric strain and repulsion of like charges

α-Helix

One type of secondary structure is the **α-helix**. In an α-helix, the backbone of the polypeptide coils around the long axis of the protein molecule. The α-helical configuration allows the amino acids to have the bond lengths and bond angles required for maximum stability. The substituents on the α-carbons of the amino acids protrude outward from the helix, thereby minimizing steric strain (Figure 23.8a). The helix is stabilized by hydrogen bonds: each hydrogen attached to an amide nitrogen is hydrogen bonded to a carbonyl oxygen of an amino acid four amino acids away (Figure 23.8b). Because the amino acids have the L-configuration, the α-helix is a right-handed helix; that is, it rotates in a clockwise direction as it spirals down (Figure 23.8c). Each turn of the helix contains 3.6 amino acids, and the repeat distance of the helix is 5.4 Å.

▲ **Figure 23.8**
(a) A segment of a protein in an α-helix. (b) The helix is stabilized by hydrogen bonding between peptide groups. (c) Looking at the longitudinal axis of an α-helix.

Not all amino acids are able to fit into an α-helix. Proline, for example, causes a distortion in a helix because the bond between the proline nitrogen and the α-carbon cannot rotate to let proline fit into a helix properly. Similarly, two adjacent amino acids that have more than one substituent on a β-carbon (valine, isoleucine, or threonine) cannot fit into a helix because of steric crowding between the R groups. Finally, two adjacent amino acids with like-charged substituents cannot fit into a helix because of electrostatic repulsion between the R groups. The percentage of amino acids coiled into an α-helix varies from protein to protein, but on average about 25% of the amino acids in a globular protein are in α-helices.

Right-Handed and Left-Handed Helices

The α-helix, composed of a chain of L-amino acids, is a right-handed helix. When scientists synthesized a chain of D-amino acids, they found that it folded into a left-handed helix that was the mirror image of the right-handed α-helix. When they synthesized a peptidase that contained only D-amino acids, they found

that the enzyme was just as catalytically active as the naturally occurring enzyme with L-amino acids. However, the peptidase that contained D-amino acids would cleave peptide bonds only in polypeptide chains composed of D-amino acids.

β-Pleated Sheet

The second type of secondary structure is the **β-pleated sheet**. In a β-pleated sheet, the polypeptide backbone is extended in a zigzag structure resembling a series of pleats. A β-pleated sheet is almost fully extended—the average two amino acid repeat distance is 7.0 Å. The hydrogen bonding in a β-pleated sheet occurs between neighboring peptide chains, and these chains can run in the same direction or in opposite directions. In a **parallel β-pleated sheet**, the adjacent chains run in the same direction. In an **antiparallel β-pleated sheet**, the adjacent chains run in opposite directions (Figure 23.9).

N-terminal   N-terminal

R—CH   R—CH

C=O   C=O

H—N   H—N

HC—R   HC—R

O=C   O=C

N—H   N—H

R—CH   R—CH

C=O   C=O

H—N   H—N

HC—R   HC—R

C-terminal   C-terminal

Parallel

N-terminal   C-terminal

R—CH   HC—R

C=O····H—N

H—N   C=O

HC—R   R—CH

O=C   N—H

N—H····O=C

R—CH   HC—R

C=O····H—N

H—N   C=O

HC—R   R—CH

C-terminal   N-terminal

Antiparallel

◀ **Figure 23.9**
Segments of β-pleated sheets drawn to illustrate their pleated character. Note that the first is a parallel β-pleated sheet, and the second is an antiparallel β-pleated sheet.

Because the substituents (R) on the α-carbons of the amino acids on adjacent chains are close to each other, the substituents must be small if the chains are to nestle closely enough together to maximize hydrogen-bonding interactions. Silk, for example, contains a large proportion of relatively small amino acids (glycine and alanine) and therefore has large segments of β-pleated sheet. The number of side-by-side strands in a β-pleated sheet ranges from 2 to 15 in a globular protein. The average strand in a β-pleated sheet section of a globular protein contains six amino acids.

Wool and the fibrous protein of muscle are examples of proteins with secondary structures that are almost all α-helices. Consequently, these proteins can be stretched. In contrast, proteins with secondary structures that are predominantly β-pleated sheets, such as silk and spider webs, cannot be stretched because a β-pleated sheet is almost fully extended.

Coil Conformation

Generally, less than half of the protein's backbone is arranged in a defined secondary structure—an α-helix or a β-pleated sheet (Figure 23.10). Most of the rest of the protein, though highly ordered, is difficult to describe. Many of these ordered polypeptide fragments are said to be in **coil** or **loop conformations**.

◀ **Figure 23.10**
The backbone structure of carboxypeptidase A: α-helical segments are purple; β-pleated sheets are indicated by flat green arrows pointing in the N → C direction.

> **PROBLEM 43 ♦**
>
> How long is an α-helix that contains 74 amino acids? Compare the length of this α-helix with the length of a fully extended peptide chain containing the same number of amino acids. (The distance between consecutive amino acids in a fully extended chain is 3.5 Å.)

β-Peptides: An Attempt to Improve on Nature

Chemists are currently studying β-peptides, which are polymers of β-amino acids. These peptides have backbones one carbon longer than the peptides nature synthesizes using α-amino acids. Therefore, each β-amino acid has two carbons to which side chains can be attached.

Like α-polypeptides, β-polypeptides fold into relatively stable helical and pleated sheet conformations, causing scientists to wonder whether biological activity might be possible with such peptides. Recently, a β-peptide with biological activity has been synthesized that mimics the activity of the hormone somatostatin. There is hope that β-polypeptides will provide a source of new drugs and catalysts. Surprisingly, the peptide bonds in β-polypeptides are resistant to the enzymes that catalyze the hydrolysis of peptide bonds in α-polypeptides. This resistance to hydrolysis means that a β-polypeptide drug would have a longer duration of action in the bloodstream.

23.15 THE TERTIARY STRUCTURE OF PROTEINS

The *tertiary structure* of a protein is the three-dimensional arrangement of all the atoms in the protein (Figure 23.11). Proteins fold spontaneously in solution to maximize their stability. Every time there is a stabilizing interaction between two atoms, free energy is released. The more free energy released (the more negative the $\Delta G°$), the more stable the protein. Consequently, a protein tends to fold in a way that maximizes the number of stabilizing interactions.

▶ **Figure 23.11**
The three-dimensional structure of carboxypeptidase A.

The stabilizing interactions in a protein include disulfide bonds, hydrogen bonds, electrostatic attractions (attractions between opposite charges), and hydrophobic (van der

Waals) interactions. Stabilizing interactions can occur between peptide groups (atoms in the backbone of the protein), between side-chain groups (α-substituents), and between peptide and side-chain groups (Figure 23.12). Because the side-chain groups help determine how a protein folds, the tertiary structure of a protein is determined by its primary structure.

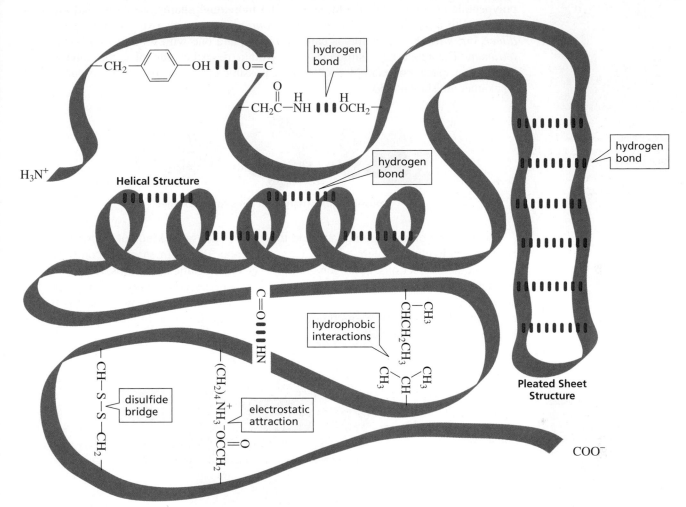

▲ **Figure 23.12**
Stabilizing interactions responsible for the tertiary structure of a protein.

Disulfide bonds are the only covalent bonds that can form when a protein folds. The other bonding interactions that occur in folding are much weaker, but because there are so many of them, they are important interactions in determining how a protein folds.

Most proteins exist in aqueous environments. Therefore, they tend to fold in a way that exposes the maximum number of polar groups to the surrounding water and that buries the nonpolar groups in the protein's interior, away from water.

The **hydrophobic interactions** between nonpolar groups in the protein increase its stability by increasing the entropy of water molecules. Water molecules that surround nonpolar groups are highly structured. When two nonpolar groups come together, the surface area in contact with water diminishes, decreasing the amount of structured water. Decreasing structure increases entropy, which in turn decreases the free energy, which increases the stability of the protein. (Recall that $\Delta G° = \Delta H° - T\Delta S°$.)

PROBLEM 44◆

How would a protein that resides in the nonpolar interior of a membrane fold compare with the water-soluble protein just discussed? (*Hint:* See Section 27.4.)

Max Ferdinand Perutz (1914–2002) *was born in Austria. In 1936, because of the rise of Nazism, he moved to England, where he received a Ph.D. from Cambridge University and became a professor there. He and John Kendrew shared the 1962 Nobel Prize in Chemistry. They had used X-ray diffraction to determine, for the first time, the tertiary structure of a protein.*

John Kendrew (1917–1997) *was born in England and educated at Cambridge University, where Max Perutz was working on the structure of hemoglobin (completed in 1959). Perutz assigned the work on myoglobin, a smaller protein, to Kendrew, who completed it in 1957.*

23.16 THE QUATERNARY STRUCTURE OF PROTEINS

Not all proteins consist of a single polypeptide chain. Proteins that have more than one polypeptide chain are called **oligomers**. The individual chains are called **subunits**. A protein with a single subunit is called a *monomer*; one with two subunits is called a *dimer*; one with three subunits is called a *trimer*; and one with four subunits is called a *tetramer*. The quaternary structure of a protein describes the way the subunits are arranged in space. For example, some of the possible arrangements of the six subunits of a hexamer are shown below.

possible quaternary structures for a hexamer

The subunits of an oligomer are held together by the same kinds of interactions that hold the individual protein chains in a particular three-dimensional conformation: hydrophobic interactions, hydrogen bonding, and electrostatic attractions. Hemoglobin is an example of a tetramer: it is made up of two different kinds of subunits, one with 141 amino acids and one with 146 amino acids, and each hemoglobin molecule has two of each kind. The quaternary structure of hemoglobin is shown in Figure 23.13. Also see Figure 14.45 on page 602 that shows a protein with seven subunits.

▲ **Figure 23.13**
A representation of the quaternary structure of hemoglobin generated by computer graphics. The orange and green represent the four polypeptide chains; there are two identical orange subunits and two identical green subunits. Two of the porphyrin rings (gray beads; Section 21.7) are visible, ligated to iron (pink) and bonded to oxygen (red).

PROBLEM 45 ◆

a. Which would have the greatest percentage of polar amino acids, a spherical protein, a cigar-shaped protein, or a subunit of a hexamer?
b. Which would have the smallest percentage of polar amino acids?

23.17 PROTEIN DENATURATION

Destroying the highly organized tertiary structure of a protein is called **denaturation**. Anything that breaks the bonds maintaining the three-dimensional shape of the protein will cause the protein to denature (unfold). Because these bonds are weak, proteins are easily denatured. The totally random conformation of a denatured protein is called a **random coil**. Here are some of the ways that proteins can be denatured:

- Changing the pH denatures proteins because it changes the charges on many of the side chains. This disrupts electrostatic attractions and hydrogen bonds.
- Certain reagents such as urea and guanidine hydrochloride denature proteins by forming hydrogen bonds to protein groups that are stronger than the hydrogen bonds formed between the groups.
- Detergents such as sodium dodecyl sulfate denature proteins by associating with the nonpolar groups of the protein, thereby interfering with normal hydrophobic interactions.
- Organic solvents denature proteins by disrupting hydrophobic interactions.
- Proteins can also be denatured by heat or by agitation. Both increase molecular motion, which can disrupt the attractive forces. A well-known example is the change that occurs to the white of an egg when it is heated or whipped.

SUMMARY

Peptides and **proteins** are polymers of **amino acids** linked together by **peptide** (amide) bonds. A **dipeptide** contains 2 amino acids linked together, a **tripeptide** contains 3, an **oligopeptide** contains 3 to 10, and a **polypeptide** contains many amino acids. Proteins have 40 to 4000 amino acids. The **amino acids** differ only in the substituent attached to the α-carbon. Almost all amino acids found in nature have the L configuration.

The carboxyl groups of the amino acids have pK_a values of ~ 2, and the protonated amino groups have pK_a values of ~ 9. At physiological pH, an amino acid exists as a **zwitterion**. A few amino acids have side chains with ionizable hydrogens. The **isoelectric point** (pI) of an amino acid is the pH at which the amino acid has no net charge. A mixture of amino acids can be separated based on their pI values by **electrophoresis** or based on their polarities by **paper chromatography** or **thin-layer chromatography**. Separation can also be achieved using **ion-exchange chromatography** employing an **anion-** or a **cation-exchange resin**. An **amino acid analyzer** is an instrument that automates ion-exchange chromatography. A racemic mixture of amino acids can be separated by a **kinetic resolution** using an enzyme-catalyzed reaction.

Rotation about a peptide bond is restricted because of its partial double-bond character. Two cysteine side chains can be oxidized to a **disulfide bridge**, the only kind of covalent bond that is found between nonadjacent amino acids. By convention, peptides and proteins are written with the free amino group (the **N-terminal amino acid**) on the left and the free carboxyl group (the **C-terminal amino acid**) on the right.

To synthesize a peptide bond, the amino group of the N-terminal amino acid must be protected (for example, by t-BOC) and its carboxyl group activated (with DCC). A second amino acid is added to form a dipeptide. Amino acids can be added to the growing C-terminal end by repeating the same two steps: activating the carboxyl group of the C-terminal amino acid with DCC and adding a new amino acid. **Automated solid-phase peptide synthesis** allows peptides to be made more rapidly and in higher yields.

The **primary structure** of a protein is the sequence of its amino acids and the location of all its disulfide bridges. The N-terminal amino acid of a peptide or protein can be determined with **Edman's reagent**. The C-terminal amino acid can be identified with a carboxypeptidase. An **exopeptidase** catalyzes the hydrolysis of a peptide bond at the end of a peptide chain. An **endopeptidase** catalyzes the hydrolysis of a peptide bond that is not at the end of a peptide chain. **Partial hydrolysis** hydrolyzes only some of the peptide bonds.

The **secondary structure** of a protein describes how local segments of the protein's backbone fold. A protein folds so as to maximize the number of stabilizing interactions: disulfide bonds, hydrogen bonds, electrostatic attractions (attraction between opposite charges), and **hydrophobic interactions** (interactions between nonpolar groups). An α-**helix** and a β-**pleated sheet** are types of secondary structure.

The **tertiary structure** of a protein is the three-dimensional arrangement of all the atoms in the protein. Proteins with more than one peptide chain are called **oligomers**. The individual chains are called **subunits**. The **quaternary structure** of a protein describes the way the **subunits** are arranged with respect to each other in space.

KEY TERMS

PROBLEMS

46. Explain why, unlike most amines and carboxylic acids, amino acids are insoluble in diethyl ether.

47. Alanine has pK_a values of 2.34 and 9.69. At what pH will alanine exist as indicated?

a. (50%) (50%)   **b.** (100%)   **c.** (50%) (50%)

48. Show the peptides that would result from cleavage by the indicated reagent:
a. Val-Arg-Gly-Met-Arg-Ala-Ser by carboxypeptidase A
b. Ser-Phe-Lys-Met-Pro-Ser-Ala-Asp by cyanogen bromide
c. Arg-Ser-Pro-Lys-Lys-Ser-Glu-Gly by trypsin

49. Which would have a higher percentage of negative charge at physiological pH (7.3), leucine with pI = 5.98 or asparagine with pI = 5.43?

50. Aspartame has a pI of 5.9. Draw its prevailing form at physiological pH.

51. Draw the form of aspartate that predominates at
a. pH = 1.0   **b.** pH = 2.6   **c.** pH = 6.0   **d.** pH = 11.0

52. A professor was preparing a manuscript for publication in which she reported that the pI of the tripeptide Lys-Lys-Lys was 10.6. One of her students pointed out that there must be an error in her calculations because the pK_a of the ε-amino group of lysine is 10.8 and the pI of the tripeptide has to be greater than any of its individual pK_a values. Was the student correct?

53. A mixture of amino acids that do not separate sufficiently when a single technique is used can often be separated by two-dimensional chromatography. In this technique, the mixture of amino acids is applied to a piece of filter paper and separated by chromatographic techniques. The paper is then rotated 90°, and the amino acids are further separated by electrophoresis, producing a type of chromatogram called a *fingerprint*. Identify the spots in the fingerprint obtained from a mixture of Ser, Glu, Leu, His, Met, and Thr.

54. Determine the amino acid sequence of a polypeptide from the following data:

Complete hydrolysis of the peptide yields the following amino acids: Arg, 2 Gly, Ile, 3 Leu, 2 Lys, 2 Met, 2 Phe, Pro, Ser, 2 Tyr, Val.
Treatment with Edman's reagent gives PTH-Gly.
Carboxypeptidase A releases Phe.

Treatment with cyanogen bromide yields the following three peptides:

1. Gly-Leu-Tyr-Phe-Lys-Ser-Met   **2.** Gly-Leu-Tyr-Lys-Val-Ile-Arg-Met   **3.** Leu-Pro-Phe

Treatment with trypsin yields the following four peptides:

1. Gly-Leu-Tyr-Phe-Lys   **2.** Ser-Met-Gly-Leu-Tyr-Lys   **3.** Val-Ile-Arg   **4.** Met-Leu-Pro-Phe

55. Explain the difference in the pK_a values of the carboxyl groups of alanine, serine, and cysteine.

56. Which would be a more effective buffer at physiological pH, a solution of 0.1 M glycylglycylglycylglycine or a solution of 0.2 M glycine?

57. Identify the location and type of charge on the hexapeptide Lys-Ser-Asp-Cys-His-Tyr at each of the following pH values:
   a. pH = 5   **b.** pH = 7   **c.** pH = 9   **d.** pH = 12

58. Give the product obtained when a lysine side chain in a polypeptide reacts with maleic anhydride.

lysine residue   maleic anhydride

59. After the following polypeptide was treated with maleic anhydride, it was hydrolyzed by trypsin. (After a polypeptide is treated with maleic anhydride, trypsin will cleave the polypeptide only on the C-side of arginine.)

Gly-Ser-Asp-Ala-Leu-Pro-Gly-Ile-Thr-Ser-Arg-Asp-Val-Ser-Lys-Val-Glu-Tyr-Phe-
        Glu-Ala-Gly-Arg-Ser-Glu-Phe-Lys-Glu-Pro-Arg-Leu-Tyr-Met-Lys-Val-Glu-Gly-Arg-Pro-Val-Ser-Ala-Gly-Leu-Trp

   a. After a polypeptide is treated with maleic anhydride, why does trypsin no longer cleave it on the C-side of lysine?
   b. How many fragments are obtained from the polypeptide?
   c. In what order would the fragments be eluted from an anion-exchange column using a buffer of pH = 5.

60. Treatment of a polypeptide with 2-mercaptoethanol yields two polypeptides with the following primary sequences:

Val-Met-Tyr-Ala-Cys-Ser-Phe-Ala-Glu-Ser

Ser-Cys-Phe-Lys-Cys-Trp-Lys-Tyr-Cys-Phe-Arg-Cys-Ser

Treatment of the original intact polypeptide with chymotrypsin yields the following peptides:

1. Ala, Glu, Ser   **3.** Tyr, Val, Met   **5.** Ser, Phe, 2 Cys, Lys, Ala, Trp
2. 2 Phe, 2 Cys, Ser   **4.** Arg, Ser, Cys   **6.** Tyr, Lys

Determine the positions of the disulfide bridges in the original polypeptide.

61. Show how aspartame can be synthesized using DCC.

62. Show how valine can be prepared by
   a. a Hell–Volhard–Zelinski reaction.   **d.** a N-phthalimidomalonic ester synthesis.
   b. a Strecker synthesis.   **e.** an acetamidomalonic ester synthesis.
   c. a reductive amination.

63. Reaction of a polypeptide with carboxypeptidase A releases Met. The polypeptide undergoes partial hydrolysis to give the following peptides. What is the sequence of the polypeptide?
   1. Ser, Lys, Trp   **5.** Met, Ala, Gly   **9.** Lys, Ser
   2. Gly, His, Ala   **6.** Ser, Lys, Val   **10.** Glu, His, Val
   3. Glu, Val, Ser   **7.** Glu, His   **11.** Trp, Leu, Glu
   4. Leu, Glu, Ser   **8.** Leu, Lys, Trp   **12.** Ala, Met

64. a. How many different octapeptides can be made from the 20 naturally occurring amino acids?
   b. How many different proteins containing 100 amino acids can be made from the 20 naturally occurring amino acids?

65. Glycine has pK_a values of 2.3 and 9.6. Would you expect the pK_a values of glycylglycine to be higher or lower than these values?

66. A mixture of 15 amino acids gave the fingerprint shown below (see Problem 53). Identify the spots. (*Hint 1:* Pro reacts with ninhydrin to produce a yellow color; Phe and Tyr produce a yellow-green color. *Hint 2:* Count the number of spots before you start.)

67. Write the mechanism for the reaction of an amino acid with di-*tert*-butyl dicarbonate.

68. Dithiothreitol reacts with disulfide bridges in the same way that 2-mercaptoethanol does. With dithiothreitol, however, the equilibrium lies much more to the right. Explain.

69. α-Amino acids can be prepared by treating an aldehyde with ammonia/trace acid, followed by hydrogen cyanide, followed by acid-catalyzed hydrolysis.
   a. Give the structures of the two intermediates formed in this reaction.
   b. What amino acid is formed when the aldehyde that is used is 3-methylbutanal?
   c. What aldehyde would be needed to prepare valine?

70. The UV spectra of tryptophan, tyrosine, and phenylalanine are shown here. Each spectrum is that of a 1.0×10^{-3} M solution of the amino acid, buffered at pH = 6.0, in a cell with a light path of 1.0 cm. Calculate the approximate molar absorptivity of each of the three amino acids at 280 nm.

71. A chemist wanted to test his hypothesis that the disulfide bridges that form in many proteins do so after the minimum energy conformation of the protein has been achieved. He treated a sample of lysozyme, an enzyme containing four disulfide bridges, with 2-mercaptoethanol and then added urea to denature the enzyme. He slowly removed these reagents so that the enzyme could re-fold and re-form the disulfide bridges. The lysozyme he recovered had 80% of its original activity. What would be the percent activity in the recovered enzyme if disulfide bridge formation were entirely random rather than determined by the tertiary structure? Does this experiment support his hypothesis?

72. Propose a mechanism for the rearrangement of the thiazoline obtained from reaction of Edman's reagent with a peptide to a PTH-amino acid (page 1006). (*Hint:* Thioesters are susceptible to hydrolysis.)

73. A normal polypeptide and a mutant of the polypeptide were hydrolyzed by an endopeptidase under the same conditions. The normal and mutant polypeptide differ by one amino acid. The fingerprints of the peptides obtained from the two polypeptides are shown below. What kind of amino acid substitution occurred as a result of the mutation? (That is, is the substituted amino acid more or less polar than the original amino acid? Is its pI lower or higher?) (*Hint:* You might find it convenient to photocopy the fingerprints, cut them out, and overlay them.)

74. Determine the amino acid sequence of a polypeptide from the following data:

Complete hydrolysis of the peptide yields the following amino acids: Ala, Arg, Gly, 2 Lys, Met, Phe, Pro, 2 Ser, Tyr, Val.

Treatment with Edman's reagent gives PTH-Val.

Carboxypeptidase A releases Ala.

Treatment with cyanogen bromide yields the following two peptides:
1. Ala, 2 Lys, Phe, Pro, Ser, Tyr   **2.** Arg, Gly, Met, Ser, Val

Treatment with trypsin yields the following three peptides:
1. Gly, Lys, Met, Tyr   **2.** Ala, Lys, Phe, Pro, Ser   **3.** Arg, Ser, Val

Treatment with chymotrypsin yields the following three peptides:
1. 2 Lys, Phe, Pro   **2.** Arg, Gly, Met, Ser, Tyr, Val   **3.** Ala, Ser

24
Catalysis

an RNA catalyst

A **CATALYST** IS A SUBSTANCE THAT *INCREASES THE RATE OF A CHEMICAL REACTION without itself being consumed or changed in the reaction* (Section 3.7). We have seen that the rate of a chemical reaction depends on the energy barrier of the rate-determining step that must be overcome in the process of converting reactants into products. The height of the "energy hill" is indicated by the free energy of activation ($\Delta G^{\ddagger}$). A catalyst increases the rate of a chemical reaction by providing a pathway with a lower $\Delta G^{\ddagger}$ (Section 3.7). A catalyst can decrease $\Delta G^{\ddagger}$ in one of three ways:

1. The catalyzed and uncatalyzed reactions can have different, but similar, mechanisms, with the catalyst providing a way to provide a *more reactive species* (Figure 24.1a).

2. The catalyzed and uncatalyzed reactions can have different, but similar, mechanisms, with the catalyst providing a way to make *the transition state more stable* (Figure 24.1b).

3. The catalyst can completely *change the mechanism* of the reaction, providing an alternative pathway with a smaller $\Delta G^{\ddagger}$ than that for the uncatalyzed reaction (Figure 24.2).

When we say that a catalyst is neither consumed nor changed by a reaction, we do not mean that it does not participate in the reaction. A catalyst *must* participate in the reaction if it is going to make it go faster. What we mean is that a catalyst has the same form after the reaction as it had before the reaction. Because the catalyst is not used up during the reaction, only a small amount of the catalyst is needed. (If a catalyst is used up in one step of the reaction, it must be regenerated in a subsequent step.) Therefore, a catalyst is added to a reaction mixture in small *catalytic* amounts, much smaller than the number of moles of reactant (typically .01 to 10% of the number of moles of reactant).

28

The Chemistry of the Nucleic Acids

DNA

IN PREVIOUS CHAPTERS, WE STUDIED TWO OF THE THREE MAJOR KINDS OF BIOPOLYMERS: polysaccharides in Chapter 22 and proteins in Chapter 23. Now we will look at the third—nucleic acids. There are two types of nucleic acids: **deoxyribonucleic acid (DNA)** and **ribonucleic acid (RNA)**. DNA encodes an organism's entire hereditary information and controls the growth and division of cells. In all organisms (except certain viruses), the genetic information stored in DNA is transcribed into RNA. This information can then be translated for the synthesis of all the proteins needed for cellular structure and function.

DNA was first isolated in 1869 from the nuclei of white blood cells. Because it was found in the nucleus and was acidic, it was called *nucleic acid.* Eventually, scientists found that the nuclei of all cells contain DNA, but until experiments were reported in 1944 in which DNA was transferred from one species to another, along with inheritable traits, they did not realize that nucleic acids are the carriers of genetic information. In 1953, James Watson and Francis Crick described the three-dimensional structure of DNA—the famed double helix.

28.1 NUCLEOSIDES AND NUCLEOTIDES

Nucleic acids are chains of five-membered-ring sugars linked by phosphate groups. Notice that the linkages are **phosphodiesters** (Figure 28.1). The anomeric carbon of each sugar is bonded to a nitrogen of a heterocyclic compound in a β-glycosidic linkage. (Recall from Section 22.11 that a β-linkage is one in which the substituents at C-1 and C-4 are on the same side of the furanose ring.) Because the heterocyclic compounds are amines, they are commonly referred to as **bases**. In RNA the five-membered-ring sugar is D-ribose. In DNA it is 2′-deoxy-D-ribose (D-ribose without an OH group in the 2′-position).

▲ **Figure 28.1**
Nucleic acids consist of a chain of five-membered-ring sugars linked by phosphate groups. Each sugar (D-ribose in RNA, 2′-deoxy-D-ribose in DNA) is bonded to a heterocyclic amine (a base) in a β-glycosidic linkage.

The vast differences in heredity between different species and between different members of the same species are determined by the sequence of the bases in DNA. Surprisingly, there are only four bases in DNA: two are substituted purines (adenine and guanine), and two are substituted pyrimidines (cytosine and thymine).

Rosalind Franklin (1920–1958) was born in London. She graduated from Cambridge University and studied X-ray diffraction techniques in Paris. In 1951 she returned to England and accepted a position to develop an X-ray diffraction unit in the biophysics department at King's College. Her X-ray studies showed that DNA was a helix with phosphate groups on the outside of the molecule. Tragically, Franklin never protected herself from her X-ray source and died without knowing the role her work had played in determining the structure of DNA and without being recognized for her contribution.

Watson and Crick shared the 1962 Nobel Prize in Medicine or Physiology with Maurice Wilkins for determining the double helical structure of DNA. Wilkins (1916–2004), who contributed X-ray studies that confirmed the double helical structure, was born in New Zealand to Irish immigrants and moved to England six years later with his parents. He received a Ph.D. from Birmingham University. During World War II he joined other British scientists who were working with American scientists on the development of the atomic bomb. He returned to England in 1945 and, having lost interest in physics, turned his attention to biology.

Francis Crick (*left*) and James Watson (*right*)

Rosalind Franklin (By courtesy of the National Portrait Gallery, London)

RNA also contains only four bases. Three (adenine, guanine, and cytosine) are the same as those in DNA, but the fourth base in RNA is uracil instead of thymine. Notice that thymine and uracil differ only by a methyl group. (Thymine is 5-methyluracil.) The reason DNA contains thymine instead of uracil is explained in Section 28.10.

The purines and pyrimidines are bonded to the anomeric carbon of the furanose ring—purines at N-9 and pyrimidines at N-1—in a β-glycosidic linkage. A compound containing a base bonded to D-ribose or to 2′-deoxy-D-ribose is called a **nucleoside**. The ring positions of the sugar component of a nucleoside are indicated by primed numbers to distinguish them from the ring positions of the base. This is why the sugar component of DNA is referred to as 2′-deoxy-D-ribose.

Notice the difference in the base names and their corresponding nucleoside names in Table 28.1. For example, adenine is the base, whereas adenosine is the nucleoside; similarly, cytosine is the base, whereas cytidine is the nucleoside, and so forth. Because uracil is found only in RNA, it is shown attached to D-ribose but not to 2′-deoxy-D-ribose; because thymine is found only in DNA, it is shown attached to 2′-deoxy-D-ribose but not to D-ribose.

Table 28.1 The Names of the Bases, the Nucleosides, and the Nucleotides

Base	Ribonucleoside	Deoxyribonucleoside	Ribonucleotide	Deoxyribonucleotide
Adenine	Adenosine	2′-Deoxyadenosine	Adenosine 5′-phosphate	2′-Deoxyadenosine 5′-phosphate
Guanine	Guanosine	2′-Deoxyguanosine	Guanosine 5′-phosphate	2′-Deoxyguanosine 5′-phosphate
Cytosine	Cytidine	2′-Deoxycytidine	Cytidine 5′-phosphate	2′-Deoxycytidine 5′-phosphate
Thymine	—	Thymidine	—	Thymidine 5′-phosphate
Uracil	Uridine	—	Uridine 5′-phosphate	

nucleosides

adenosine   guanosine   cytidine   uridine

2′-deoxyadenosine   2′-deoxyguanosine   2′-deoxycytidine   thymidine

---

PROBLEM 1

In acidic solutions, nucleosides are hydrolyzed to a sugar and a heterocyclic base. Propose a mechanism for this reaction.

A **nucleotide** is a nucleoside with either the 5′- or the 3′-OH group bonded in an ester linkage to phosphoric acid. The nucleotides of RNA—where the sugar is D-ribose—are more precisely called **ribonucleotides**, whereas the nucleotides of DNA—where the sugar is 2′-deoxy-D-ribose—are called **deoxyribonucleotides**.

nucleoside = base + sugar
nucleotide = base + sugar + phosphate

nucleotides

adenosine 5′-monophosphate
a ribonucleotide

2′-deoxycytidine 3′-monophosphate
a deoxyribonucleotide

Because phosphoric acid can form an anhydride (Section 26.1), nucleotides can exist as monophosphates, diphosphates, and triphosphates. They are named by adding *monophosphate* or *diphosphate* or *triphosphate* to the name of the nucleoside.

adenosine
5′-monophosphate
AMP

adenosine
5′-diphosphate
ADP

adenosine
5′-triphosphate
ATP

2′-deoxyadenosine
5′-monophosphate
dAMP

2′-deoxyadenosine
5′-diphosphate
dADP

2′-deoxyadenosine
5′-triphosphate
dATP

Notice that nucleotide names are abbreviated (A, G, C, T, U—followed by MP, DP, or TP, depending on whether it is a monophosphate, diphosphate, or triphosphate—with a d in front if it contains a 2′-deoxy-D-ribose).

PROBLEM 2

Draw the structure for each of the following:

a. dCDP   **c.** dUMP   **e.** guanosine-triphosphate
b. dTTP   **d.** UDP   **f.** adenosine-monophosphate

28.2 OTHER IMPORTANT NUCLEOTIDES

We have seen that ATP is the most important source of chemical energy (Section 26.1). ATP, however, is not the only biologically important nucleotide. Guanosine 5′-triphosphate (GTP) is used in place of ATP in some phosphoryl transfer reactions. We have also seen in Sections 25.1 and 25.2 that dinucleotides are used as oxidizing agents (NAD^+, $NADP^+$, FAD, FMN) and reducing agents (NADH, NADPH, $FADH_2$, $FMNH_2$).

Another important nucleotide is adenosine 5′,3′-monophosphate, commonly known as cyclic AMP. Cyclic AMP is called a "second messenger" because it serves as a link between several hormones (the first messengers) and enzymes that regulate cellular function. Secretion of certain hormones, such as adrenaline, activates adenylate cyclase, the enzyme responsible for the synthesis of cyclic AMP from ATP. Cyclic

AMP then activates an enzyme, generally by phosphorylating it. Cyclic nucleotides are so important in regulating cellular reactions that an entire scientific journal is devoted to these processes.

ATP   adenylate cyclase   cyclic AMP

PROBLEM 3

What products would be obtained from the hydrolysis of cyclic AMP?

28.3 NUCLEIC ACIDS ARE COMPOSED OF NUCLEOTIDE SUBUNITS

We have seen that **nucleic acids** are composed of long strands of nucleotide subunits (Figure 28.1). A **dinucleotide** contains two nucleotide subunits, an **oligonucleotide** contains three to ten subunits, and a **polynucleotide** contains many subunits. DNA and RNA are polynucleotides.

Nucleotide triphosphates are the starting materials for the biosynthesis of nucleic acids. DNA is synthesized by enzymes called *DNA polymerases*; RNA is synthesized by enzymes called *RNA polymerases*. The nucleotides are linked as a result of nucleophilic attack by a $3'$-OH group of one nucleotide triphosphate on the α-phosphorus of another nucleotide triphosphate, breaking a phosphoanhydride bond and eliminating pyrophosphate (Figure 28.2). This means that the phosphodiester bonds join the $3'$-OH group of one nucleotide to the $5'$-OH group of the next nucleotide, and the growing polymer is synthesized in the $5' \longrightarrow 3'$ direction. In other words, new nucleotides are added to the $3'$-end. Pyrophosphate is subsequently hydrolyzed, which makes the reaction irreversible (Section 26.3). RNA strands are biosynthesized in the same way, using ribonucleotides instead of $2'$-deoxyribonucleotides.

The **primary structure** of a nucleic acid is the sequence of bases in the strand. By convention, the sequence of bases in a polynucleotide is written in the $5' \longrightarrow 3'$ direction (the $5'$-end is on the left). Remember that the nucleotide at the $5'$-end of the strand has an unlinked $5'$-triphosphate group, and the nucleotide at the $3'$-end has an unlinked $3'$-hydroxyl group.

ATGAGCCATGTAGCCTAATCGGC

5′-end   3′-end

Watson and Crick concluded that DNA consists of two strands of nucleotides, with the sugar–phosphate backbone on the outside and the bases on the inside. The strands are antiparallel (they run in opposite directions) and are held together by hydrogen bonds between the bases on one strand and the bases on the other strand (Figure 28.3).

Experiments carried out by Erwin Chargaff were critical to Watson and Crick's proposal for the secondary structure of DNA. These experiments showed that the number of adenines in DNA equals the number of thymines and the number of guanines equals the number of cytosines. Chargaff also noted that the number of adenines and thymines relative to the number of guanines and cytosines is characteristic of a given species but

5′-end

a phosphoester bond

a phosphoester bond

5′

3′

base

base

3′ :OH

base

the 3′-OH group attacks the α-phosphorus of the next nucleotide to be incorporated into the chain

5′

:OH

base

OH

3′-end

DNA is synthesized in the 5′ ⟶ 3′ direction.

◄ **Figure 28.2**
Addition of nucleotides to a growing strand of DNA. Biosynthesis occurs in the 5′ ⟶ 3′ direction.

varies from species to species. In human DNA, for example, 60.4% of the bases are adenines and thymines, whereas 74.2% of the bases are adenines and thymines in the DNA of the bacterium *Sarcina lutea.*

Chargaff's data showing that [adenine] = [thymine] and [guanine] = [cytosine] could be explained if adenine (A) always paired with thymine (T) and guanine (G) always paired with cytosine (C). This means the two strands are *complementary:* where there is an A in one strand, there is a T in the opposing strand, and where there is a G in one strand there is a C in the other strand (Figure 28.3). Thus, if you know the sequence of bases in one strand, you can figure out the sequence of bases in the other strand.

Why does A pair with T? Why does G pair with C? First of all, the width of the double-stranded molecule is relatively constant, so a purine must pair with a pyrimidine. If the larger purines paired, the strands would bulge; if the smaller pyrimidines paired, the strands would have to pull in to bring the two pyrimidines close enough to form hydrogen bonds. But what causes A to pair with T rather than with C (the other pyrimidine)? The base pairing is dictated by hydrogen bonding. Learning that the bases exist in the keto form (Section 19.2) allowed Watson to explain the pairing.* Adenine forms two hydrogen bonds with thymine but would form only one hydrogen bond with cytosine. Guanine forms three hydrogen bonds with cytosine but would form only one hydrogen bond with thymine (Figure 28.4).

The two antiparallel DNA strands are not linear but are twisted into a helix around a common axis (see Figure 28.5a). The base pairs are planar and parallel to each other on the inside of the helix (Figures 28.5c). The secondary structure is therefore known as a **double helix**. The double helix resembles a circular staircase: the base pairs are the rungs, and the sugar–phosphate backbone represents the handrails. The OH group

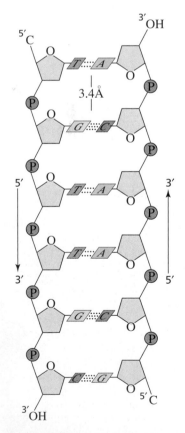

5′C   3′OH

3.4Å

5′   3′

3′   5′

3′OH   5′C

▲ **Figure 28.3**
The sugar–phosphate backbone of DNA is on the outside and the bases are on the inside, A's paring with T's and G's pairing with C's. The two strands are antiparallel— they run in opposite directions.

*Watson was having difficulty understanding the base pairing in DNA because he thought the bases existed in the enol form (see Problem 5). When Jerry Donohue, an American crystallographer, informed him that the bases more likely existed in the keto form, Chargaff's data could easily be explained by hydrogen bonding between adenine and thymine and between guanine and cytosine.

▲ **Figure 28.4**
Base pairing in DNA: adenine and thymine form two hydrogen bonds; cytosine and guanine form
three hydrogen bonds.

of the phosphate linkages has a pK_a of about 2, so it is in its basic form (negatively charged) at physiological pH (Figure 28.2). The negatively charged backbone repels nucleophiles, thereby preventing cleavage of the phosphodiester bonds.

Hydrogen bonding between base pairs is just one of the forces holding the two strands of the DNA double helix together. The bases are planar aromatic molecules that stack on top of one another, each pair slightly rotated with respect to the next pair, like a partially spread-out hand of cards. In this arrangement, there are favorable van der Waals interactions between the mutually induced dipoles of adjacent pairs of bases. These interactions, known as **stacking interactions**, are weak attractive forces, but when added together they contribute significantly to the stability of the double helix. Stacking interactions are strongest between two purines and weakest between two pyrimidines. Confinement of the bases to the inside of the helix has an additional stabilizing effect—it reduces the surface area of the relatively nonpolar residues that is exposed to water, which increases the entropy of the surrounding water molecules (Section 23.15).

▲ **Figure 28.5**
(a) The DNA double helix.
(b) The view looking down the long axis of the helix.
(c) The bases are planar and parallel on the inside of the helix.

There are two different alternating grooves in a DNA helix; a **major groove** and a narrower **minor groove**. Proteins and other molecules can bind to the grooves. The hydrogen-bonding properties of the functional groups facing into each groove determine what kind of molecules will bind to the groove. For example, netropsin is an antibiotic that works by binding to the minor groove of DNA (Section 31.10).

PROBLEM 4

Indicate whether each functional group of the five heterocyclic bases in nucleic acids can function as a hydrogen bond acceptor (A), a hydrogen bond donor (D), or both (D/A).

PROBLEM 5

Using the D, A, and D/A designations in Problem 4, indicate how base pairing would be affected if the bases existed in the enol form.

PROBLEM 6♦

If one of the strands of DNA has the following sequence of bases running in the 5' ⟶ 3' direction

$$5'—G—G—A—C—A—A—T—C—T—G—C—3'$$

a. what is the sequence of bases in the complementary strand?
b. what base is closest to the 5'-end in the complementary strand?

28.4 WHY DNA DOES NOT HAVE A 2'-OH GROUP

Unlike DNA, RNA is not stable because the 2'-OH group of ribose is a nucleophile and causes RNA to be easily cleaved (Figure 28.6). This explains why the 2'-OH group is absent in DNA. DNA must remain intact throughout the life span of a cell to preserve the genetic information. Easy cleavage of DNA would have disastrous consequences for the cell and for life itself. RNA, in contrast, is synthesized as it is needed and is degraded once it has served its purpose.

▲ **Figure 28.6**
Cleavage of RNA by the 2'-OH group. RNA is thought to undergo cleavage 3 billion times faster than DNA.

PROBLEM 7

The 2', 3'-cyclic phosphodiester that is formed when RNA is hydrolyzed (Figure 28.6) reacts with water, forming a mixture of nucleotide 2'- and 3'-phosphates. Propose a mechanism for this reaction.

28.5 THE BIOSYNTHESIS OF DNA IS CALLED REPLICATION

The genetic information of a human cell is contained in 23 pairs of chromosomes. Each chromosome is composed of several thousand **genes** (segments of DNA). The total DNA from a human cell—the **human genome**—contains 3.1 billion base pairs.

Part of the excitement created by Watson and Crick's proposed structure for DNA was due to the fact that the structure immediately suggested how DNA is able to pass on genetic information to succeeding generations. Because the two strands are complementary, both carry the same genetic information. Thus, when organisms reproduce, DNA molecules can be copied using the same base-pairing principle that is fundamental to their structure: Each strand can serve as the template for the synthesis of a complementary new strand (Figure 28.7). The new (daughter) DNA molecules are identical to the original (parent) molecule—they contain all the original genetic information. The synthesis of identical copies of DNA is called **replication**.

B I O G R A P H Y

Arthur Kornberg (1918–2007) *was born in New York. He graduated from the College of the City of New York and received an M.D. from the University of Rochester. He is a professor of biochemistry at Stanford University. Kornberg prepared synthetic strands of DNA in a manner similar to that used by Ochoa. For this work, Ochoa and Kornberg shared the 1959 Nobel Prize in Physiology or Medicine.*

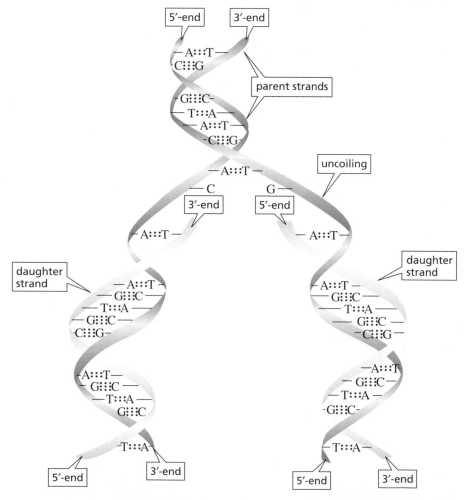

▶ **Figure 28.7**
Replication of DNA. The green daughter strand on the left is synthesized continuously in the 5′ ⟶ 3′ direction; the green daughter strand on the right is synthesized discontinuously in the 5′ ⟶ 3′ direction.

B I O G R A P H Y

Severo Ochoa (1905–1993) *was born in Spain. He graduated from the University of Malaga in 1921 and received an M.D. from the University of Madrid. He spent the next four years studying in Germany and England and then joined the faculty at New York University College of Medicine. Ochoa became a U.S. citizen in 1956. He was the first to prepare synthetic strands of RNA by incubating nucleotides in the presence of enzymes that catalyze the biosynthesis of RNA.*

All the reactions involved in nucleic acid synthesis are catalyzed by enzymes. The synthesis of DNA takes place in a region of the molecule where the strands have started to separate. Because a nucleic acid can be synthesized only in the 5′ ⟶ 3′ direction, only the daughter strand on the left in Figure 28.7 is synthesized continuously in a single piece (because it is synthesized in the 5′ ⟶ 3′ direction). The other daughter strand needs to grow in a 3′ ⟶ 5′ direction, so it is synthesized discontinuously in small pieces. Each piece is synthesized in the 5′ ⟶ 3′ direction, and the fragments are joined together by an enzyme called DNA ligase. Each of the two new molecules of DNA—called daughter molecules—contains one of the original parent strands (blue strand in Figure 28.7) plus a newly synthesized strand (green strand). This process is called **semiconservative replication**.

PROBLEM 8

Using a dark line for the original parental DNA and a wavy line for DNA synthesized from parental DNA, show what the population of DNA molecules would look like in the fourth generation of replicated molecules.

28.6 DNA AND HEREDITY

If DNA contains hereditary information, there must be a method to decode that information. The decoding occurs in two steps.

1. The sequence of bases in DNA provides a blueprint for the synthesis of RNA; the synthesis of RNA from a DNA blueprint is called **transcription** (Section 28.7).
2. The sequence of bases in RNA determines the sequence of amino acids in a protein; the synthesis of a protein from an RNA blueprint is called **translation** (Section 28.8).

Transcription: DNA $\longrightarrow$ RNA

Translation: mRNA $\longrightarrow$ protein

Don't confuse transcription and translation: these words are used just as they are used in English. Transcription (DNA to RNA) is copying *within the same language*—in this case the language of nucleotides. Translation (RNA to protein) is *changing to another language*—the language of amino acids. First we will look at transcription.

Natural Products that Modify DNA

More than three-quarters of clinically approved anticancer drugs are natural products—compounds derived from plants, marine organisms, or microbes—that interact with DNA. Because cancer is characterized by the uncontrolled growth and proliferation of cells, compounds that interfere with the replication or transcription of DNA stop the growth of cancer cells. These drugs can interact with DNA by intercalation or by binding to either its major or minor groove (Section 28.4). The three compounds discussed below were isolated from *Streptomyces* bacteria found in soil.

Intercalating compounds become sandwiched between the stacked bases in DNA. These compounds therefore are planar and often aromatic; their binding to DNA is stabilized by stacking interactions with neighboring base pairs. Actinomycin D is an example of an intercalator. When this drug binds to DNA, it distorts the double helix, inhibiting both the replication and transcription of DNA. Actinomycin D has been used to treat a variety of cancers.

Drugs that bind to the major and minor grooves of DNA do so by a combination of hydrogen bonding, van der Waals interactions, and electrostatic attractions—the same forces proteins use to bind their substrates and to hold their amino acid chains in the correct three-dimensional conformation. Leinamycin is an example of an anticancer drug that binds to the major groove. Once leinamycin is bound, it alkylates the N-7 position of the purine ring.

Bleomycin binds to the minor groove of DNA. Once in the minor groove, it uses a bound iron atom to remove a hydrogen atom from DNA, the first step in cleaving DNA. This drug has been approved for the treatment of Hodgkin lymphoma.

actinomycin D   leinamycin   bleomycin

28.7 THE BIOSYNTHESIS OF RNA IS CALLED TRANSCRIPTION

Transcription starts when DNA unwinds at a particular site—called a *promoter site*—to form two single strands. One of the strands is called the **sense strand**. The complementary strand is called the **template strand**. The template strand is read in the $3' \longrightarrow 5'$ direction, so that RNA can be synthesized in the $5' \longrightarrow 3'$ direction (Figure 28.8). The bases in the template strand specify the bases that need to be incorporated into RNA, following the same base-pairing principle that allows replication of DNA. For example, each guanine in the template strand specifies the incorporation of a cytosine into RNA, and each adenine in the template strand specifies the incorporation of a uracil into RNA. (Recall that in RNA, uracil is used instead of thymine.) Because both RNA and the sense strand of DNA are complementary to the template strand, RNA and the sense strand of DNA have the same base sequence, except that RNA has a uracil wherever the sense strand has a thymine. Just as there are promoter sites in DNA that signal where to start RNA synthesis, there are sites signaling that no more bases should be added to the growing RNA chain.

RNA is synthesized in the 5′ ⟶ 3′ direction.

▶ **Figure 28.8**
Transcription: using DNA as a blueprint for the synthesis of RNA.

B I O G R A P H Y

Sidney Altman *and* **Thomas R. Cech** *received the 1989 Nobel Prize in Chemistry for their discovery of the catalytic properties of RNA.* **Sidney Altman** *was born in Montreal in 1939. He received a B.S. from MIT and a Ph.D. from the University of Colorado, Boulder. He was a postdoctoral fellow in Francis Crick's laboratory at Cambridge University. He is now a professor of biology at Yale University.* **Thomas Cech** *was born in Chicago in 1947. He received a B.A. from Grinnell College and a Ph.D. from the University of California, Berkeley. He was a postdoctoral fellow at MIT and is now a professor of chemistry at the University of Colorado, Boulder.*

Surprisingly, a gene is not necessarily a continuous sequence of bases. Often the bases of a gene are interrupted by bases that appear to have no informational content. A stretch of bases representing a portion of a gene is called an **exon**, whereas a stretch of bases that contains no genetic information is called an **intron**. The RNA that is synthesized is complementary to the entire sequence of DNA bases—exons and introns—between the promoter site and the stop signal. So, after the RNA is synthesized, but before it leaves the nucleus, the so-called nonsense bases (encoded by the introns) are cut out and the informational fragments are spliced together, resulting in a much shorter RNA molecule. This RNA-processing step is known as **RNA splicing**. Scientists have found that only about 2% of DNA contains genetic information; 98% consists of introns.

It has been suggested that the purpose of introns is to make RNA more versatile. The originally synthesized long strand of RNA can be spliced in different ways to create a variety of shorter RNAs.

PROBLEM 9◆

Why do both thymine and uracil specify the incorporation of adenine?

28.8 THERE ARE THREE KINDS OF RNA

RNA molecules are much shorter than DNA molecules and are generally single-stranded. Although DNA molecules can have billions of base pairs, RNA molecules rarely have more than 10,000 nucleotides. There are three kinds of RNA:

- **messenger RNA (mRNA)**, whose sequence of bases determines the sequence of amino acids in a protein
- **ribosomal RNA (rRNA)**, a structural component of ribosomes, which are the particles on which the biosynthesis of proteins takes place
- **transfer RNA (tRNA)**, the carrier of amino acids for protein synthesis.

tRNA molecules are much smaller than mRNA or rRNA molecules; a tRNA contains only 70 to 90 nucleotides. The single strand of tRNA is folded into a characteristic cloverleaf structure, with three loops and a little bulge next to the right-hand loop (Figure 28.9a). There are at least four regions with complementary base pairing. All tRNAs have a CCA sequence at the 3′-end. The three bases at the bottom of the loop directly opposite the 5′- and 3′-ends are called an **anticodon** (Figures 28.9a and b).

◀ **Figure 28.9**
(a) A transfer RNA. Compared with other RNAs, tRNA contains a high percentage of unusual bases (shown as empty circles). These bases result from enzymatic modification of the four normal bases.
(b) A transfer RNA: the anticodon is green; the CCA at the 3′-end is red.

Each tRNA can carry an amino acid bound as an ester to its terminal 3′-OH group. The amino acid will be inserted into a protein during protein biosynthesis. Each tRNA can carry only one particular amino acid. A tRNA that carries alanine is designated as tRNA^{Ala}.

The attachment of an amino acid to a tRNA is catalyzed by an enzyme called aminoacyl-tRNA synthetase. The mechanism for the reaction is shown below.

MECHANISM FOR THE ATTACHMENT OF AN AMINO ACID TO A tRNA

• The carboxylate group of the amino acid is activated by forming an acyl adenylate; now the amino acid has a good leaving group (Section 26.2).

• The pyrophosphate that is eliminated is subsequently hydrolyzed, ensuring the irreversibility of the phosphoryl transfer reaction (Section 26.2).

• A nucleophilic addition–elimination reaction occurs in which the 3′-OH group of tRNA adds to the carbonyl carbon of the acyl adenylate, forming a tetrahedral intermediate.

• The aminoacyl tRNA is formed when AMP is eliminated from the tetrahedral intermediate.

All the steps take place at the active site of the enzyme. Each amino acid has its own aminoacyl-tRNA synthetase. Each synthetase has two specific binding sites, one for the amino acid and one for the tRNA that carries that amino acid (Figure 28.10).

▲ **Figure 28.10**
An aminoacyl-tRNA synthetase has a binding site for tRNA and a binding site for the particular amino acid that is to be attached to that tRNA. Histidine is the amino acid, and tRNA^His is the tRNA in this example.

It is critical that the correct amino acid be attached to the tRNA. Otherwise, the protein will not be synthesized correctly. Fortunately, the synthetases correct their own mistakes. For example, valine and threonine are approximately the same size, but threonine has an OH group in place of a CH_3 group of valine. Both amino acids, therefore, can bind at the amino acid binding site of the aminoacyl-tRNA synthetase for valine, and both can then be activated by reacting with ATP to form an acyl adenylate. The aminoacyl-tRNA synthetase for valine has two adjacent catalytic sites, one for attaching the acyl adenylate to tRNA and one for hydrolyzing the acyl adenylate.

$$CH_3CH-CH \quad \begin{matrix} O \\ \| \\ C \end{matrix} \quad O^- \qquad CH_3CH-CH \quad \begin{matrix} O \\ \| \\ C \end{matrix} \quad O^-$$
$$\underset{\text{valine}}{CH_3 \quad {}^+NH_3} \qquad\qquad \underset{\text{threonine}}{OH \quad {}^+NH_3}$$

The site for acylating tRNA is hydrophobic, so valine is preferred over threonine for the tRNA acylation reaction. The hydrolytic site is polar, so threonine is preferred over valine for the hydrolysis reaction. Thus, if threonine is activated by the aminoacyl-tRNA synthetase for valine, it will be hydrolyzed rather than transferred to the tRNA.

28.9 THE BIOSYNTHESIS OF PROTEINS IS CALLED TRANSLATION

A protein is synthesized from its N-terminal end to its C-terminal end by a process that reads the bases along the mRNA strand in the 5′ ⟶ 3′ direction. Each amino acid that is to be incorporated into a protein is specified by one or more three-base sequences called **codons**. The bases are read consecutively and are never skipped. The three-base sequences and the amino acid each sequence codes for are known as the **genetic code** (Table 28.2). A codon is written with the 5′-nucleotide on the left. For example, the codon UCA on mRNA codes for the amino acid serine, whereas CAG codes for glutamine.

Table 28.2	The Genetic Code				
5′-Position	**Middle position**				**3′-Position**
	U	C	A	G	
U	Phe	Ser	Tyr	Cys	U
	Phe	Ser	Tyr	Cys	C
	Leu	Ser	Stop	Stop	A
	Leu	Ser	Stop	Trp	G
C	Leu	Pro	His	Arg	U
	Leu	Pro	His	Arg	C
	Leu	Pro	Gln	Arg	A
	Leu	Pro	Gln	Arg	G
A	Ile	Thr	Asn	Ser	U
	Ile	Thr	Asn	Ser	C
	Ile	Thr	Lys	Arg	A
	Met	Thr	Lys	Arg	G
G	Val	Ala	Asp	Gly	U
	Val	Ala	Asp	Gly	C
	Val	Ala	Glu	Gly	A
	Val	Ala	Glu	Gly	G

Because there are four bases and the codons are triplets, 4^3 (or 64) different codons are possible. This is many more than are needed to specify the 20 different amino acids, so all the amino acids—except methionine and tryptophan—have more than one codon. It is not surprising, therefore, that methionine and tryptophan are the least abundant amino acids in proteins. Actually, 61 of the codons specify amino acids, and three codons are stop codons. **Stop codons** tell the cell to "stop protein synthesis here."

How the information in mRNA is translated into a polypeptide is shown in Figure 28.11. In this figure, serine was the last amino acid incorporated into the growing polypeptide chain.

- Serine was specified by the AGC codon in the mRNA because the anticodon of the tRNA that carries serine is GCU (3′-UCG-5′). (Remember that a base sequence is read in the 5′ $\longrightarrow$ 3′ direction, so the sequence of bases in an anticodon must be read from right to left.)
- The next codon, CUU, signals for a tRNA with an anticodon of AAG (3′-GAA-5′). That particular tRNA carries leucine. The amino group of leucine reacts in an enzyme-catalyzed nucleophilic addition–elimination reaction with the ester on the adjacent serine tRNA, displacing that tRNA (Section 17.7).
- The next codon (GCC) specifies a tRNA carrying alanine. The amino group of alanine reacts in an enzyme-catalyzed nucleophilic addition-elimination reaction with the ester group on the adjacent leucine-carrying tRNA, displacing the tRNA that brought in leucine.

Subsequent amino acids are brought in one at a time in the same way, with the codon in mRNA specifying the amino acid to be incorporated by complementary base pairing with the anticodon of the tRNA that carries that amino acid.

A protein is synthesized in the N-terminal $\longrightarrow$ C-terminal direction.

▶ **Figure 28.11**
Translation. The sequence of bases in mRNA determines the sequence of amino acids in a protein.

PROBLEM 10◆

If methionine is the first amino acid incorporated into an oligopeptide, what oligopeptide is coded for by the following stretch of mRNA?

5′—G—C—A—U—G—G—A—C—C—C—C—G—U—U—A—U—U—
A—A—A—C—A—C—3′

PROBLEM 11 ♦

Four C's occur in a row in the segment of mRNA in Problem 10. What oligopeptide would be formed from the mRNA if one of the four C's were cut out of the strand?

PROBLEM 12

UAA is a stop codon. Why does the UAA sequence in mRNA in Problem 10 not cause protein synthesis to stop?

Protein synthesis takes place on the ribosomes (Figure 28.12). The smaller of the two subunits in the ribosome has three binding sites for RNA molecules. It binds the mRNA whose base sequence is to be read, the tRNA carrying the growing peptide chain, and the tRNA carrying the next amino acid to be incorporated into the protein. The larger subunit of the ribosome catalyzes peptide bond formation.

B I O G R A P H Y

A sculpture done by Robert Holley.

Robert W. Holley (1922–1993) *was born in Illinois and received a bachelor's degree from the University of Illinois and a Ph.D. from Cornell University. During World War II he worked on the synthesis of penicillin at Cornell Medical School. He was a professor at Cornell and later at the University of California, San Diego. He was also a noted sculptor.*

▲ **Figure 28.12**
Transcription and translation.
1. Transcription of DNA occurs in the nucleus of the cell. The initial RNA transcript is the precursor of all RNA: tRNA, rRNA, and mRNA.
2. The initially formed RNA often must be chemically modified before it acquires biological activity. Modification can entail removing nucleotide segments, adding nucleotides to the 5'- or 3'-ends, or chemically altering certain nucleotides.
3. Proteins are added to rRNA to form ribosomal subunits. tRNA, mRNA, and ribosomal subunits leave the nucleus.
4. Each tRNA binds the appropriate amino acid.
5. tRNA, mRNA, and a ribosome work together to translate the mRNA information into a protein.

Sickle Cell Anemia

Sickle cell anemia is an example of the damage that can be caused by a change in a single base of DNA (Problem 71 in Chapter 23). It is a hereditary disease caused when a GAG triplet becomes a GTG triplet in the sense strand of a section of DNA that codes for the β-subunit of hemoglobin (Section 23.16). As a consequence, the mRNA codon becomes GUG—which signals for incorporation of valine—rather than GAG, which would have signaled for incorporation of glutamate. The change from a polar glutamate to a nonpolar valine is sufficient to change the shape of the deoxyhemoglobin molecule, which induces aggregation and subsequent precipitation of deoxyhemoglobin in red blood cells. This stiffens the cells, making it difficult for them to squeeze through capillaries. Blockage of capillaries causes severe pain and can be fatal.

Normal red blood cells

Sickle red blood cells

Antibiotics that Act by Inhibiting Translation

Puromycin is a naturally occurring antibiotic, one of several that acts by inhibiting translation. It does so by mimicking the 3'-CCA-aminoacyl portion of a tRNA, fooling the enzyme into transferring the growing peptide chain to the amino group of puromycin rather than to the amino group of the incoming 3'-CCA-aminoacyl tRNA. As a result, protein synthesis stops. Because puromycin blocks protein synthesis in eukaryotes as well as in prokaryotes, it is poisonous to humans and therefore is not a clinically useful antibiotic. To be clinically useful, an antibiotic must affect protein synthesis only in prokaryotic cells.

puromycin

Clinically useful antibiotics	Mode of action
Tetracycline	Prevents the aminoacyl-tRNA from binding to the ribosome
Erythromycin	Prevents the incorporation of new amino acids into the protein
Streptomycin	Inhibits the initiation of protein synthesis
Chloramphenicol	Prevents the new peptide bond from being formed

PROBLEM 13 ◆

Write the sequences of bases in the sense strand of DNA that resulted in the mRNA in Problem 10.

PROBLEM 14

List the possible codons on mRNA that specify each amino acid in Problem 10 and the anticodon on the tRNA that carries that amino acid.

28.10 WHY DNA CONTAINS THYMINE INSTEAD OF URACIL

In Section 24.8 we saw that dTMP is formed by methylating dUMP, with coenzyme N^5,N^{10}-methylenetetrahydrofolate supplying the methyl group.

dUMP

R′ = 2′-deoxyribose-5-P

dTMP

Because the incorporation of the methyl group into uracil oxidizes tetrahydrofolate to dihydrofolate, dihydrofolate must be reduced back to tetrahydrofolate to prepare the coenzyme for another catalytic cycle. The reducing agent is NADPH.

$$\text{dihydrofolate} + \text{NADPH} + \text{H}^+ \xrightarrow{\text{dihydrofolate reductase}} \text{tetrahydrofolate} + \text{NADP}^+$$

Every NADPH formed in a biological organism can result in the formation of three ATPs (Section 26.11). Therefore, using an NADPH to reduce dihydrofolate comes at the expense of ATP. This means that the synthesis of thymine is energetically expensive, so there must be a good reason for DNA to contain thymine instead of uracil.

The presence of thymine instead of uracil in DNA prevents potentially lethal mutations. Cytosine can tautomerize to form an imine (Section 19.2), which can be hydrolyzed to uracil (Section 18.8). The overall reaction is called a **deamination** because it removes an amino group.

cytosine amino tautomer

imino tautomer

uracil

If a C in DNA is deaminated to a U, the U will specify incorporation of an A into the daughter strand during replication instead of the G that would have been specified by C. Fortunately, there is an enzyme that recognizes a U in DNA as a "mistake" and replaces it with a C before an incorrect base can be inserted into the daughter strand. The enzyme cuts out the U and replaces it with a C. If U's were normally found in DNA, the enzyme could not distinguish between a normal U and a U formed by deamination of cytosine. Having T's in place of U's in DNA allows the U's that are found in DNA to be recognized as mistakes.

Unlike DNA, which replicates itself, any mistake in RNA does not survive for long because RNA is constantly being degraded and then resynthesized from the DNA template. Therefore, it is not worth spending the extra energy to incorporate T's into RNA.

PROBLEM 15

Adenine can be deaminated to hypoxanthine, and guanine can be deaminated to xanthine. Draw structures for hypoxanthine and xanthine.

PROBLEM 16

Explain why thymine cannot be deaminated.

28.11 HOW THE BASE SEQUENCE OF DNA IS DETERMINED

In June 2000, two teams of scientists (one from a private biotechnology company and one from the publicly funded Human Genome Project) announced that they had completed the first draft of the sequence of the 3.1 billion base pairs in human DNA. This is an enormous accomplishment. Consider, for example, that if the sequence of 1 million base pairs were determined each day, it would take more than 10 years to complete the sequence of the human genome.

Clearly, DNA molecules are too large to sequence as a unit. Therefore, DNA is first cleaved at specific base sequences, and the resulting DNA fragments are then sequenced individually.

The enzymes that cleave DNA at specific base sequences are called **restriction endonucleases**, and the DNA fragments they produce are called **restriction fragments**. Several hundred restriction endonucleases are now known; a few examples, the base sequence each recognizes, and the point of cleavage in that base sequence are shown here.

restriction enzyme	recognition sequence
*Alu*I	AGCT TCGA
*Fnu*DI	GGCC CCGG
*Pst*I	CTGCAG GACGTC

The base sequences that most restriction endonucleases recognize are *palindromes*. A palindrome is a word or a group of words that reads the same forward and backward. "Toot" and "race car" are examples of palindromes, as is "Was it a car or a rat I saw?" A restriction endonuclease recognizes a piece of DNA in which *the template strand is a palindrome of the sense strand*. In other words, the sequence of bases in the template strand (reading from right to left) is identical to the sequence of bases in the sense strand (reading from left to right).

PROBLEM 17♦

Which of the following base sequences would most likely be recognized by a restriction endonuclease?

a. ACGCGT   **c.** ACGGCA   **e.** ACATCGT
b. ACGGGT   **d.** ACACGT   **f.** CCAACC

Frederick Sanger (who received the 1953 Nobel Prize in Chemistry for being the first to determine the primary sequence of a protein; see Section 23.11) and Walter Gilbert shared the 1980 Nobel Prize in Chemistry for their work on DNA sequencing. Over the years, their procedure has been replaced by other methods. The technique currently used is an automated procedure called **pyrosequencing**. In this method, a small piece of DNA primer is added to the restriction fragment whose sequence is to be determined; this is called a *restriction fragment:primer hybrid*. Nucleotides are then added to the primer by base pairing with the restriction fragment. This method—known as *sequencing-by-synthesis*—detects the identity of each base that adds to the primer.

Pyrosequencing requires DNA polymerase—the enzyme that adds nucleotides to a strand of DNA—and two additional enzymes that cause light to be emitted when pyrophosphate is detected.

DNA to be sequenced

3′—AGGCTCCAGTGATCCG—5′ $\xrightarrow[\substack{\text{3′-protected}\\ \text{2′-deoxyribonucleotide}\\ \text{5′-triphosphate}}]{\substack{\text{DNA polymerase}\\ \text{2 additional enzymes}}}$

P—TC

a restriction fragment: primer hybrid

primer

Pyrosequencing also requires the four 2′-deoxyribonucleotide 5′-triphosphates, each with a protected 3′-OH group.

a 3′-protected 2′-deoxyribonucleotide triphosphate

The restriction fragment:primer hybrids are attached to a solid support, similar to the solid support used in the automated synthesis of polypeptides (Section 23.11). The steps involved in pyrosequencing are:

- The enzymes and one of the four 3′-protected 2′-deoxyribonucleotide 5′-triphosphates (for example, 3′-protected dATP) are added to the column.
- The reagents are washed from the solid support.
- The process is repeated with a different 3′-protected 2′-deoxynucleotide 5′-triphosphate (for example, 3′-protected dGTP).
- The process is repeated with 3′-protected dCTP and then repeated again with 3′-protected dTTP.
- The sequencer keeps track of which of the four nucleotides caused light to be observed—in other words, which nucleotide released pyrophosphate as a result of being added to the primer.
- The protecting group on the 3′OH is removed.

The steps are repeated in order to determine the identity of the next nucleotide that adds to the primer. Pyrosequencing can determine the base sequence of a restriction fragment with as many as 500 nucleotides.

Once the sequence of bases in a restriction fragment is determined, the results can be checked by using the same process to obtain the base sequence of the fragment's complementary strand. The base sequence of the original piece of DNA can be determined by repeating the entire procedure with a different restriction endonuclease and noting overlapping fragments.

 The X PRIZE

The successful sequencing of the human genome, with 3.1 million base pairs, took nine months and cost $100 million, in addition to the hundreds of millions of dollars it cost to develop the required instrumentation. To stimulate the development of new technology that will increase the speed and decrease the cost of sequencing human genomes in order to accelerate the development of a new era of personalized medicine, the X PRIZE (worth $10 million) has been created. It will be given to the first team that can build a device that can sequence 100 human genomes in 10 days or less with the following criteria:

- It must have an accuracy of no more than one error for every 100,000 bases sequenced.
- At least 98% of the genome must be sequenced.
- It must cost no more than $10,000 per genome.

Kary B. Mullis *received the Nobel Prize in Chemistry in 1993 for his invention of PCR. He was born in North Carolina in 1944 and received a B.S. from the Georgia Institute of Technology in 1966 and a Ph.D. from the University of California, Berkeley. After holding several postdoctoral positions, he joined the Cetus Corporation in Emeryville, California. He conceived the idea of PCR while driving from Berkeley to Mendocino. Currently, he consults and lectures about biotechnology.*

28.12 THE POLYMERASE CHAIN REACTION (PCR)

The PCR (**polymerase chain reaction**) technique, developed in 1983, allows scientists to amplify DNA—that is, to make billions of copies—in a very short time. With PCR, sufficient DNA for analysis can be obtained from a single hair follicle or sperm.

PCR is done by adding the following to a solution containing the segment of DNA to be amplified (the target DNA):

- a large excess of primers (short pieces of DNA) that base pair (anneal) with the short nucleotide sequence at the two ends of the piece of DNA to be amplified
- the four deoxyribonucleotide triphosphates (dATP, dGTP, dCTP, dTTP)
- a heat-stable DNA polymerase

The following three steps are then carried out (Figure 28.13):

▶ **Figure 28.13**
Two cycles of the polymerase chain reaction.

The DNA from a 40-million-year-old leaf preserved in amber was amplified by PCR and then sequenced.

- *Strand separation:* The solution is heated to 95 °C, which causes double-stranded DNA to separate into two single strands.
- *Base pairing of the primers:* The solution is cooled to 54 °C, a temperature at which the primers (red and yellow boxes in Figure 28.13) can pair with the bases at the 3′-end of the target (green) DNA.
- *DNA synthesis:* The solution is heated to 72 °C, a temperature at which DNA polymerase catalyzes the addition of nucleotides to the primer. Notice that because the primers attach to the 3′-end of the target DNA, copies of the target DNA are synthesized in the required 5′ ⟶ 3′ direction.

The solution is then heated to 95 °C to begin a second cycle; the second cycle produces four copies of double-stranded DNA. The third cycle therefore starts with eight single strands of DNA and produces 16 single strands. It takes about an hour to complete 30 cycles, at which point DNA has been amplified a billionfold.

PCR has a wide range of clinical uses. It can be used to detect mutations that lead to cancer, to diagnose genetic diseases, to reveal the presence of HIV that would be missed by an antibody assay, to monitor cancer chemotherapy, and to rapidly identify an infectious disease.

DNA Fingerprinting

Forensic chemists use PCR to compare DNA samples collected at the scene of a crime with the DNA of the suspected perpetrator. The base sequences of segments of noncoding DNA vary from individual to individual. Forensic laboratories have identified 13 of these segments that are the most accurate for identification purposes. If the sequences of bases from two DNA samples are the same, the chance is about 80 billion to one that they are from the same individual. DNA fingerprinting is also used to establish paternity, accounting for about 100,000 DNA profiles a year.

28.13 GENETIC ENGINEERING

Recombinant DNA molecules are DNA molecules (natural or synthetic) that have been attached to a small piece of carrier DNA in a compatible host cell and allowed to replicate millions of times. Recombinant DNA technology—also known as **genetic engineering**—has many practical applications. For example, replicating the DNA for human insulin in this way makes it possible to synthesize large amounts of human insulin (Section 23.8).

Agriculture is benefiting from genetic engineering as crops are being produced with new genes that increase their resistance to drought and insects. For example, genetically engineered cotton crops are resistant to the cotton bollworm, and genetically engineered corn is resistant to the corn rootworm. Genetically modified organisms (GMOs) have been responsible for a nearly 50% reduction in agricultural chemical sales in the United States. At the same time, many people worry about the potential consequences of changing the genes of any species.

Resisting Herbicides

Glyphosate, the active ingredient in a well-known herbicide called Roundup, kills weeds by inhibiting an enzyme that plants need to synthesize phenylalanine and tryptophan, amino acids required for growth. Corn and cotton have been genetically engineered to tolerate the herbicide. Then, when fields are sprayed with glyphosate, the weeds are killed but not the crops. These crops have been given a gene that produces an enzyme that inactivates glyphosate by acetylating it with acetyl-CoA in a nucleophilic addition–elimination reaction (Section 17.16).

Corn genetically engineered to resist the herbicide glyphosate by acetylating it.

glyphosate
an herbicide

N-acetylglyphosate
harmless to plants

28.14 THE LABORATORY SYNTHESIS OF DNA STRANDS

There are many reasons why scientists have developed methods for synthesizing oligonucleotides with specific base sequences. One is to make the primers used for pyrosequencing and PCR (Sections 28.11 and 28.12). Another is to make fragments that can ultimately be pieced together to form a gene. A synthetic gene could be inserted into the

DNA of microorganisms, causing the organisms to synthesize a particular protein. Alternatively, a synthetic gene could be inserted into the DNA of an organism defective in that gene, thus correcting the defect; this treatment strategy is known as **gene therapy**.

Synthesizing an oligonucleotide with a particular base sequence is an even more challenging task than synthesizing a polypeptide with a specific amino acid sequence because each nucleotide has several groups that must be protected and then deprotected at the proper times. Oligonucleotide synthesis is carried out in an automated method similar to automated peptide synthesis (Section 23.11); the growing nucleotide is attached to a solid support so that purification can be carried out by flushing the reaction container with an appropriate solvent. With this technique, none of the synthesized product is lost during purification.

Phosphoramidite Monomers

One current method synthesizes oligonucleotides using phosphoramidite monomers. The 5′-OH group of each phosphoramidite monomer is attached to a *para*-dimethoxytrityl (DMTr) protecting group. The particular group (Pr) used to protect the base depends on the base.

a phosphoramidite

a phosphoramidite monomer
used for
oligonucleotide synthesis

$DMTr = CH_3O$—

The 3′-nucleoside of the oligonucleotide to be synthesized is attached to a controlled-pore glass solid support, and the oligonucleotide is synthesized from the 3′-end. When a monomer is added to the nucleoside attached to the solid support, the only nucleophile in the reaction mixture is the 5′-OH group of the sugar bonded to the solid support. This nucleophile attacks the phosphorus of the phosphoramidite, displacing the amine and forming a phosphite. The amine is too strong a base to be eliminated without being protonated. Protonated tetrazole is the acid used for protonation because it is strong enough to protonate the diisopropylamine leaving group, but not strong enough to remove the DMTr protecting group. The phosphite is oxidized to a phosphate using I_2 or *tert*-butylhydroperoxide. The DMTr protecting group on the 5′-end of the dinucleotide is removed with mild acid. The cycle of (1) monomer addition, (2) oxidation, and (3) deprotection with acid is repeated over and over until a polymer of the desired length and sequence is obtained. Notice that the DNA polymer is synthesized in the 3′ ⟶ 5′ direction, opposite to the direction (5′ ⟶ 3′) in which DNA is synthesized in nature.

DMTr—O

base₂—Pr

a phosphate

base₁—Pr

solid support

mild acid

1. new monomer H⁺—tetrazole
2. I₂
3. mild acid

chain extension

solid support

The NH$_2$ groups of cytosine, adenine, and guanine are nucleophiles and therefore must be protected to prevent them from reacting with a newly added monomer; they are protected as amides. Thymine does not contain any nucleophilic groups, so it does not have to be protected.

unprotected bases   **protected bases**

cytosine

adenine

guanine

After the oligonucleotide is synthesized, the protecting groups on the phosphates and the protecting groups on the bases must be removed, and the oligonucleotide has to be detached from the solid support. This can all be done in a single step using aqueous ammonia. Because a hydrogen bonded to a carbon adjacent to a cyano group is relatively acidic (Section 19.1), ammonia can be used as the base in the elimination reaction that removes the phosphate protecting group.

Currently, automated DNA synthesizers can synthesize nucleic acids containing as many as 130 nucleotides in acceptable yields, adding one nucleotide every 2 to 3 minutes. (Imagine doing ~390 reactions—130 couplings, 130 oxidations, and 130 DMT removals—plus final deprotections, and having to isolate the product after each one!) Longer nucleic acids can be prepared by splicing together two or more individually prepared strands. To ensure a good overall yield of oligonucleotide, the addition of each monomer must occur in high yield (98%). This can be accomplished by using a large excess of monomer. This, however, makes oligonucleotide synthesis very expensive because the unreacted monomers are wasted.

H-Phosphonate Monomers

A second method employed to synthesize oligonucleotides with specific base sequences—one using H-phosphonate monomers—improves on the phosphoramidite method in that the monomers are easier to handle and phosphate protecting groups are not needed. However, the yields are not as good. The H-phosphonate monomers are activated by reacting with an acyl chloride, which converts them into phosphoanhydrides. The 5′-OH group of the nucleoside attached to the solid support by its 3′-OH group reacts with the phosphoanhydride, forming a dimer. The DMTr protecting group is removed with acid under mild conditions, and a second activated monomer is added. Monomers are added one at a time in this way until the strand is complete. Oxidation with I_2 (or with *tert*-butyl hydroperoxide) converts the H-phosphonate groups to phosphate groups. The base-protecting groups are removed by aqueous ammonia as in the phosphoramidite method.

Notice that in the phosphoramidite method, an oxidation takes place each time a monomer is added, whereas in the H-phosphonate method, a single oxidation is carried out after the entire strand has been synthesized.

PROBLEM 18

Propose a mechanism for removal of the DMTr protecting group by treatment with acid.

SUMMARY

There are two types of nucleic acids: **deoxyribonucleic acid (DNA)** and **ribonucleic acid (RNA)**. DNA encodes an organism's hereditary information and controls the growth and division of cells. In most organisms, the genetic information stored in DNA is **transcribed** into RNA. The information thus contained in the RNA strand can then be **translated** for the synthesis of all the proteins needed for cellular structure and function.

A **nucleoside** contains a base bonded to D-ribose or to 2′-deoxy-D-ribose. A **nucleotide** is a nucleoside with either the 5′- or the 3′-OH group bonded to phosphoric acid by an ester linkage. **Nucleic acids** are composed of long strands of nucleotide subunits linked by phosphodiester bonds. These linkages join the 3′-OH group of one nucleotide to the 5′-OH group of the next nucleotide. A **dinucleotide** contains two nucleotide subunits, an **oligonucleotide** contains 3 to 10 subunits, and a **polynucleotide** contains many subunits. DNA contains 2′-deoxy-D-ribose, whereas RNA contains D-ribose. The difference in the sugars causes DNA to be stable and RNA to be easily cleaved.

The **primary structure** of a nucleic acid is the sequence of bases in its strand. DNA contains **A, G, C,** and **T**; RNA contains **A, G, C,** and **U**. The presence of **T** instead of **U** in DNA prevents mutations caused by imine hydrolysis of **C** to form **U**. DNA is double-stranded. The strands run in

opposite directions and are twisted into a double helix, giving DNA a major groove and a minor groove. The bases are confined to the inside of the helix, and the sugar and phosphate groups are on the outside. The strands are held together by hydrogen bonds between bases of opposing strands as well as by **stacking interactions**; these are van der Waals attractions between adjacent bases on the same strand. The two strands—one is called a **sense strand** and the other a **template strand**—are complementary: **A** pairs with **T**, and **G** pairs with **C**. DNA is synthesized in the 5′ ⟶ 3′ direction by a process called **semiconservative replication.**

The sequence of bases in DNA provides the blueprint for the synthesis (**transcription**) of RNA. RNA is synthesized in the 5′ ⟶ 3′ direction by reading the bases along the DNA template strand in the 3′ ⟶ 5′ direction. There are three kinds of RNA: messenger RNA, ribosomal RNA, and transfer RNA. Protein synthesis (**translation**) proceeds from the N-terminal end to the C-terminal end by a process that reads the bases along the mRNA strand in the 5′ ⟶ 3′ direction. Each three-base sequence—a **codon**—specifies the particular amino acid to be incorporated into a protein. A tRNA carries the amino acid bound as an ester to its terminal 3′-position. The codons and the amino acids they specify are known as the **genetic code.**

Restriction endonucleases cleave DNA at specific palindromes forming **restriction fragments**. **Pyrosequencing** is the method currently preferred to determine the sequence of bases in the restriction fragments. The **polymerase chain reaction (PCR)** amplifies segments of DNA, making billions of copies in a very short time. Oligonucleotides with specific base sequences can be synthesized using phosphoramidite monomers or H-phosphonate monomers.

KEY TERMS

anticodon (p. 1155)
base (p. 1147)
codon (p. 1161)
deamination (p. 1165)
deoxyribonucleic acid (DNA) (p. 1147)
deoxyribonucleotide (p. 1150)
dinucleotide (p. 1152)
double helix (p. 1153)
exon (p. 1158)
gene (p. 1156)
gene therapy (p. 1170)
genetic code (p. 1161)
genetic engineering (p. 1169)
human genome (p. 1156)
intron (p. 1158)

major groove (p. 1155)
messenger RNA (mRNA) (p. 1158)
minor groove (p. 1155)
nucleic acid (p. 1147)
nucleoside (p. 1149)
nucleotide (p. 1150)
oligonucleotide (p. 1152)
phosphodiester (p. 1147)
polymerase chain reaction (PCR) (p. 1168)
polynucleotide (p. 1152)
primary structure of DNA (p. 1152)
pyrosequencing (p. 1166)
recombinant DNA (p. 1169)
replication (p. 1156)
restriction endonuclease (p. 1166)

restriction fragment (p. 1166)
ribonucleic acid (RNA) (p. 1147)
ribonucleotide (p. 1150)
ribosomal RNA (rRNA) (p. 1158)
RNA splicing (p. 1158)
semiconservative replication (p. 1156)
sense strand (p. 1157)
stacking interactions (p. 1154)
stop codon (p. 1161)
template strand (p. 1157)
transcription (p. 1157)
transfer RNA (tRNA) (p. 1158)
translation (p. 1157)

PROBLEMS

19. Name the following compounds:

20. What nonapeptide is coded for by the following fragment of mRNA?

$$5' — AAA — GUU — GGC — UAC — CCC — GGA — AUG — GUG — GUC — 3'$$

21. What is the sequence of bases in the template strand of DNA that codes for the mRNA in Problem 20?

22. What is the sequence of bases in the sense strand of DNA that codes for the mRNA in Problem 20?

23. What would be the C-terminal amino acid if the codon at the 3′-end of the mRNA in Problem 20 underwent the following mutation:
   a. if the first base was changed to A?
   b. if the second base was changed to A?
   c. if the third base was changed to A?
   d. if the third base was changed to G?

24. What would be the base sequence of the segment of DNA responsible for the biosynthesis of the following hexapeptide?

Gly-Ser-Arg-Val-His-Glu

25. Propose a mechanism for the following reaction:

26. Match the codon with the anticodon:

Codon	Anticodon
AAA	ACC
GCA	CCU
CUU	UUU
AGG	AGG
CCU	UGA
GGU	AAG
UCA	GUC
GAC	UGC

27. Using the single-letter abbreviations for the amino acids in Table 23.1, write the sequence of amino acids in a tetrapeptide represented by the first four different letters in your first name. Do not use any letter twice. (Because not all letters are assigned to amino acids, you might have to use one or two letters in your last name.) Write one of the sequences of bases in mRNA that would result in the synthesis of that tetrapeptide. Write the sequence of bases in the sense strand of DNA that would result in formation of that fragment of mRNA.

28. Which of the following pairs of dinucleotides are present in equal amounts in DNA?
  a. CC and GG   **c.** CA and TG   **e.** GT and CA
  b. CG and GT   **d.** CG and AT   **f.** TA and AT

29. Human immunodeficiency virus (HIV) is the retrovirus that causes AIDS. AZT is the best known of the drugs designed to interfere with retroviral DNA synthesis. When cells take up AZT, they convert it to AZT-triphosphate. Explain how AZT interferes with DNA synthesis.

**3′-azido-2′-deoxythymidine
AZT**

30. Why is the codon a triplet rather than a doublet or a quartet?

31. RNAase, the enzyme that catalyzes the hydrolysis of RNA, has two catalytically active histidine residues at its active site. One of the histidine residues is catalytically active in its acidic form, and the other is catalytically active in its basic form. Propose a mechanism for RNAase.

32. The amino acid sequences of peptide fragments obtained from a normal protein were compared with those obtained from the same protein synthesized by a defective gene. They were found to differ in only one peptide fragment. Their amino acid sequences are shown here:

Normal: Gln-Tyr-Gly-Thr-Arg-Tyr-Val
Mutant: Gln-Ser-Glu-Pro-Gly-Thr

  a. What is the defect in DNA?
  b. It was later determined that the normal peptide fragment is an octapeptide with a C-terminal Val-Leu. What is the C-terminal amino acid of the mutant peptide?

33. Which cytosine in the following sense strand of DNA could cause the most damage to the organism if it were deaminated?

A—T—G—T—C—G—C—T—A—A—T—C

34. 5-Bromouracil, a highly mutagenic compound (that is, a compound that causes changes in DNA), is used in cancer chemotherapy. When administered to a patient, it is converted to the triphosphate and incorporated into DNA in place of thymine, which it resembles sterically. Why does it cause mutations? (*Hint:* The bromo substituent increases the stability of the enol tautomer.)

35. Sodium nitrite, a common food preservative (page 690), is capable of causing mutations in an acidic environment by converting cytosines to uracils. Explain how this occurs.

36. *Staphylococcus* nuclease is an enzyme that catalyzes the hydrolysis of DNA.

The reaction is catalyzed by Ca^{2+}, Glu 43, and Arg 87. Propose a mechanism for this reaction. Recall that the nucleotides in DNA have phosphodiester linkages.

37. The first amino acid incorporated into a polypeptide chain during its biosynthesis in prokaryotes is *N*-formylmethionine. Explain the purpose of the formyl group. (*Hint:* The risosome has a binding site for the growing peptide chain and a binding site for the incoming amino acid.)

38. Why does DNA not unravel completely before replication begins?

Physical Properties of Organic Compounds

Physical Properties of Alkenes

Name	mp (°C)	bp (°C)	Density (g/mL)
Ethene	−169	−104	
Propene	−185	−47	
1-Butene	−185	−6.3	
1-Pentene		30	0.641
1-Hexene	−138	64	0.673
1-Heptene	−119	94	0.697
1-Octene	−101	122	0.715
1-Nonene	−81	146	0.730
1-Decene	−66	171	0.741
cis-2-Butene	−180	37	0.650
trans-2-Butene	−140	37	0.649
Methylpropene	−140	−6.9	0.594
cis-2-Pentene	−180	37	0.650
trans-2-Pentene	−140	37	0.649
Cyclohexene	−104	83	0.811

Physical Properties of Alkynes

Name	mp (°C)	bp (°C)	Density (g/mL)
Ethyne	−82	−84.0	
Propyne	−101.5	−23.2	
1-Butyne	−122	8.1	
2-Butyne	−24	27	0.694
1-Pentyne	−98	39.3	0.695
2-Pentyne	−101	55.5	0.714
3-Methyl-1-butyne		29	0.665
1-Hexyne	−132	71	0.715
2-Hexyne	−92	84	0.731
3-Hexyne	−101	81	0.725
1-Heptyne	−81	100	0.733
1-Octyne	−80	127	0.747
1-Nonyne	−50	151	0.757
1-Decyne	−44	174	0.766

Physical Properties of Cyclic Saturated Alkanes

Name	mp (°C)	bp (°C)	Density (g/mL)
Cyclopropane	−128	−33	
Cyclobutane	−80	−12	
Cyclopentane	−94	50	0.751
Cyclohexane	6.5	81	0.779
Cycloheptane	−12	118	0.811
Cyclooctane	14	149	0.834
Methylcyclopentane	−142	72	0.749
Methylcyclohexane	−126	100	0.769
cis-1,2-Dimethylcyclopentane	−62	99	0.772
trans-1,2-Dimethylcyclopentane	−120	92	0.750

Physical Properties of Ethers

Name	mp (°C)	bp (°C)	Density (g/mL)
Dimethyl ether	−141	−24.8	
Diethyl ether	−116	34.6	0.706
Dipropyl ether	−123	88	0.736
Diisopropyl ether	−86	69	0.725
Dibutyl ether	−98	142	0.764
Divinyl ether		35	
Diallyl ether		94	0.830
Tetrahydrofuran	−108	66	0.889
Dioxane	12	101	1.034

Physical Properties of Alcohols

Name	mp (°C)	bp (°C)	Solubility (g/100 g H_2O at 25 °C)
Methanol	−97.8	64	∞
Ethanol	−114.7	78	∞
1-Propanol	−127	97.4	∞
1-Butanol	−90	118	7.9
1-Pentanol	−78	138	2.3
1-Hexanol	−52	157	0.6
1-Heptanol	−36	176	0.2
1-Octanol	−15	196	0.05
2-Propanol	−89.5	82	∞
2-Butanol	−115	99.5	12.5
2-Methyl-1-propanol	−108	108	10.0
2-Methyl-2-propanol	25.5	83	∞
3-Methyl-1-butanol	−117	130	2
2-Methyl-2-butanol	−12	102	12.5
2,2-Dimethyl-1-propanol	55	114	∞
Allyl alcohol	−129	97	∞
Cyclopentanol	−19	140	s. sol.
Cyclohexanol	24	161	s. sol.
Benzyl alcohol	−15	205	4

Physical Properties of Amines

Name	mp (°C)	bp (°C)	Solubility (g/100 g H_2O at 25 °C)
Primary Amines			
Methylamine	−93	−6.3	v. sol.
Ethylamine	−81	17	∞
Propylamine	−83	48	∞
Isopropylamine	−95	33	∞
Butylamine	−49	78	v. sol.
Isobutylamine	−85	68	∞
sec-Butylamine	−72	63	∞
tert-Butylamine	−67	46	∞
Cyclohexylamine	−18	134	s. sol.
Secondary Amines			
Dimethylamine	−93	7.4	v. sol.
Diethylamine	−50	55	10.0
Dipropylamine	−63	110	10.0
Dibutylamine	−62	159	s. sol.
Tertiary Amines			
Trimethylamine	−115	2.9	91
Triethylamine	−114	89	14
Tripropylamine	−93	157	s. sol.

Physical Properties of Alkyl Halides

Name	bp (°C) Fluoride	Chloride	Bromide	Iodide
Methyl	−78.4	−24.2	3.6	42.4
Ethyl	−37.7	12.3	38.4	72.3
Propyl	−2.5	46.6	71.0	102.5
Isopropyl	−9.4	34.8	59.4	89.5
Butyl	32.5	78.4	100	130.5
Isobutyl		68.8	90	120
sec-Butyl		68.3	91.2	120.0
tert-Butyl		50.2	73.1	dec.
Pentyl	62.8	108	130	157.0
Hexyl	92	133	154	179

Physical Properties of Benzene and Substituted Benzenes

Name	mp (°C)	bp (°C)	Solubility (g/100 g H_2O at 25 °C)
Aniline	−6	184	3.7
Benzene	5.5	80.1	s. sol.
Benzaldehyde	−26	178	s. sol.
Benzamide	132	290	s. sol.
Benzoic acid	122	249	0.34
Bromobenzene	−30.8	156	insol.
Chlorobenzene	−45.6	132	insol.
Nitrobenzene	5.7	210.8	s. sol.
Phenol	43	182	s. sol.
Styrene	−30.6	145.2	insol.
Toluene	−95	110.6	insol.

Physical Properties of Carboxylic Acids

Name	mp (°C)	bp (°C)	Solubility (g/100 g H$_2$O at 25 °C)
Formic acid	8.4	101	∞
Acetic acid	16.6	118	∞
Propionic acid	−21	141	∞
Butanoic acid	−5	162	∞
Pentanoic acid	−34	186	4.97
Hexanoic acid	−4	202	0.97
Heptanoic acid	−8	223	0.24
Octanoic acid	17	237	0.068
Nonanoic acid	15	255	0.026
Decanoic acid	32	270	0.015

Physical Properties of Dicarboxylic Acids

Name	mp (°C)	Solubility (g/100 g H$_2$O at 25 °C)
Oxalic acid	189	S
Malonic acid	136	v. sol.
Succinic acid	185	s. sol.
Glutaric acid	98	v. sol.
Adipic acid	151	s. sol.
Pimelic acid	106	s. sol.
Phthalic acid	231	s. sol.
Maleic acid	130.5	v. sol.
Fumaric acid	302	s. sol.

Physical Properties of Acyl Chlorides and Acid Anhydrides

Name	mp (°C)	bp (°C)
Acetyl chloride	−112	51
Propionyl chloride	−94	80
Butyryl chloride	−89	102
Valeryl chloride	−110	128
Acetic anhydride	−73	140
Succinic anhydride		120

Physical Properties of Amides

Name	mp (°C)	bp (°C)
Formamide	3	200 d*
Acetamide	82	221
Propanamide	80	213
Butanamide	116	216
Pentanamide	106	232

* d means the substance decomposes.

Physical Properties of Esters

Name	mp (°C)	bp (°C)
Methyl formate	−100	32
Ethyl formate	−80	54
Methyl acetate	−98	57.5
Ethyl acetate	−84	77
Propyl acetate	−92	102
Methyl propionate	−87.5	80
Ethyl propionate	−74	99
Methyl butyrate	−84.8	102.3
Ethyl butyrate	−93	121

Physical Properties of Aldehydes

Name	mp (°C)	bp (°C)	Solubility (g/100 g H$_2$O at 25 °C)
Formaldehyde	−92	−21	v. sol.
Acetaldehyde	−121	21	∞
Propionaldehyde	−81	49	16
Butyraldehyde	−96	75	7
Pentanal	−92	103	s. sol.
Hexanal	−56	131	s. sol.
Heptanal	−43	153	0.1
Octanal		171	insol.
Nonanal		192	insol.
Decanal	−5	209	insol.
Benzaldehyde	−26	178	0.3

Physical Properties of Ketones

Name	mp (°C)	bp (°C)	Solubility (g/100 g H$_2$O at 25 °C)
Acetone	−95	56	∞
2-Butanone	−86	80	25.6
2-Pentanone	−78	102	5.5
2-Hexanone	−57	127	1.6
2-Heptanone	−36	151	0.4
2-Octanone	−16	173	insol.
2-Nonanone	−7	195	insol.
2-Decanone	14	210	insol.
3-Pentanone	−40	102	4.8
3-Hexanone		123	1.5
3-Heptanone	−39	149	0.3
Acetophenone	19	202	insol.
Propiophenone	18	218	insol.

pKa Values

Compound	pK_a	Compound	pK_a	Compound	pK_a
$CH_3C{\equiv}\overset{+}{N}H$	−10.1	O_2N—C₆H₄—$\overset{+}{N}H_3$	1.0	CH_3—C₆H₄—$\overset{O}{\overset{\|}{C}}OH$	4.3
HI	−10	pyrimidinium ($\overset{+}{N}H$)	1.0	CH_3O—C₆H₄—$\overset{O}{\overset{\|}{C}}OH$	4.5
HBr	−9	$Cl_2CH\overset{O}{\overset{\|}{C}}OH$	1.3	C₆H₅—$\overset{+}{N}H_3$	4.6
$CH_3\overset{+OH}{\overset{\|\|}{C}}H$	−8	HSO_4^-	2.0	$CH_3\overset{O}{\overset{\|}{C}}OH$	4.8
$CH_3\overset{+OH}{\overset{\|\|}{C}}CH_3$	−7.3	H_3PO_4	2.1	quinolinium ($\overset{+}{N}H$)	4.9
HCl	−7	purine ($H\overset{+}{N}$)	2.5	CH_3—C₆H₄—$\overset{+}{N}H_3$	5.1
C₆H₅—SO_3H	−6.5	$FCH_2\overset{O}{\overset{\|}{C}}OH$	2.7	pyridinium ($\overset{+}{N}H$)	5.2
$CH_3\overset{+OH}{\overset{\|\|}{C}}OCH_3$	−6.5	$ClCH_2\overset{O}{\overset{\|}{C}}OH$	2.8	CH_3O—C₆H₄—$\overset{+}{N}H_3$	5.3
$CH_3\overset{+OH}{\overset{\|\|}{C}}OH$	−6.1	$BrCH_2\overset{O}{\overset{\|}{C}}OH$	2.9	$CH_3\overset{+}{C}{=}NHCH_3$, CH_3	5.5
H_2SO_4	−5	$ICH_2\overset{O}{\overset{\|}{C}}OH$	3.2	$CH_3\overset{O}{\overset{\|}{C}}CH_2\overset{O}{\overset{\|}{C}}H$	5.9
pyrrolium ($\overset{+}{N}H$)	−3.8	HF	3.2	$HO\overset{+}{N}H_3$	6.0
$CH_3CH_2\overset{H}{\overset{+}{O}}CH_2CH_3$	−3.6	HNO_2	3.4	H_2CO_3	6.4
$CH_3CH_2\overset{H}{\overset{+}{O}}H$	−2.4	O_2N—C₆H₄—$\overset{O}{\overset{\|}{C}}OH$	3.4	imidazolium ($HN\overset{+}{}NH$)	6.8
$CH_3\overset{H}{\overset{+}{O}}H$	−2.5	$H\overset{O}{\overset{\|}{C}}OH$	3.8	H_2S	7.0
H_3O^+	−1.7	Br—C₆H₄—$\overset{+}{N}H_3$	3.9	O_2N—C₆H₄—OH	7.1
HNO_3	−1.3	Br—C₆H₄—$\overset{O}{\overset{\|}{C}}OH$	4.0	$H_2PO_4^-$	7.2
CH_3SO_3H	−1.2	pyridine—$\overset{O}{\overset{\|}{C}}OH$	4.2	C₆H₅—SH	7.8
$CH_3\overset{+OH}{\overset{\|\|}{C}}NH_2$	0.0				
$F_3C\overset{O}{\overset{\|}{C}}OH$	0.2				
$Cl_3C\overset{O}{\overset{\|}{C}}OH$	0.64				
pyridine $\overset{+}{N}$—OH	0.79				

[a]pK_a values are for the red H in each structure

pK_a Values (continued)

Compound	pK_a	Compound	pK_a	Compound	pK_a
aziridinium (ring, $\overset{+}{N}H_2$)	8.0	$CH_3CCH_2COCH_2CH_3$ (diketone)	10.7	pyrrole (ring, NH)	~17
$H_2N\overset{+}{N}H_3$	8.1	$CH_3\overset{+}{N}H_3$	10.7	CH_3CH (O)	17
CH_3COOH	8.2	cyclohexyl–$\overset{+}{N}H_3$	10.7	$(CH_3)_3COH$	18
phthalimide (NH)	8.3	$(CH_3)_2\overset{+}{N}H_2$	10.7	CH_3CCH_3 (O)	20
$CH_3CH_2NO_2$	8.6	piperidinium (ring, $\overset{+}{N}$, H H)	11.1	$CH_3COCH_2CH_3$ (O)	24.5
$CH_3CCH_2CCH_3$ (diketone)	8.9	$CH_3CH_2\overset{+}{N}H_3$	11.0	$HC\equiv CH$	25
$HC\equiv N$	9.1	pyrrolidinium (ring, $\overset{+}{N}$, H H)	11.3	$CH_3C\equiv N$	25
morpholinium (ring, O, $\overset{+}{N}$, H H)	9.3	$HOOH$	11.6	$CH_3CN(CH_3)_2$ (O)	30
		HPO_4^{2-}	12.3	H_2	35
Cl–◯–OH	9.4	CF_3CH_2OH	12.4	NH_3	36
$\overset{+}{N}H_4$	9.4	$CH_3CH_2OCCH_2COCH_2CH_3$	13.3	pyrrolidine (ring, NH)	36
$HOCH_2CH_2\overset{+}{N}H_3$	9.5	$HC\equiv CCH_2OH$	13.5	CH_3NH_2	40
$H_3\overset{+}{N}CH_2CO^-$ (O)	9.8	H_2NCNH_2 (O)	13.7	◯–CH_3	41
◯–OH	10.0	$CH_3\overset{+}{N}(CH_3)CH_2CH_2OH$ (CH_3)	13.9	◯	43
CH_3–◯–OH	10.2	imidazole (ring N, NH)	14.4	$CH_2=CHCH_3$	43
HCO_3^-	10.2	CH_3OH	15.5	$CH_2=CH_2$	44
CH_3NO_2	10.2	H_2O	15.7	△ (cyclopropane)	46
H_2N–◯–OH	10.3	CH_3CH_2OH	16.0	CH_4	60
CH_3CH_2SH	10.5	CH_3CNH_2 (O)	16	CH_3CH_3	> 60
$(CH_3)_3\overset{+}{N}H$	10.6	(cyclohexadienyl)–CCH_3 (O)	16.0		

Derivations of Rate Laws

How to Determine Rate Constants

A **reaction mechanism** is a detailed analysis of how the chemical bonds (or the electrons) in the reactants rearrange to form the products. The mechanism for a given reaction must obey the observed rate law for the reaction. A **rate law** tells how the rate of a reaction depends on the concentration of the species involved in the reaction.

First-Order Reaction

The rate is proportional to the concentration of one reactant:

$$A \xrightarrow{k_1} \text{products}$$

Rate law: $\text{rate} = k_1[A]$

To determine the first-order rate constant (k_1):

Change in the concentration of A with respect to time:

$$\frac{-d[A]}{dt} = k_1[A]$$

Let $a =$ the initial concentration of A;
let $x =$ concentration of A that has reacted up to time t.
Therefore, the concentration of A left at time t is $(a - x)$
Substituting into the previous equation gives

$$\frac{-d(a - x)}{dt} = k_1(a - x)$$

$$\frac{-da}{dt} + \frac{dx}{dt} = k_1(a - x)$$

$$0 + \frac{dx}{dt} = k_1(a - x)$$

$$\frac{dx}{(a - x)} = k_1 dt$$

Integrating the previous equation yields

$$-\ln(a - x) = k_1 t + \text{constant}$$

At $t = 0$, $x = 0$; therefore,

$$\text{constant} = -\ln a$$

$$-\ln(a - x) = k_1 t - \ln a$$

$$\ln \frac{a}{a - x} = k_1 t$$

$$\ln \frac{a - x}{a} = -k_1 t$$

$\ln \frac{(a - x)}{a}$ slope $= -k_1$

Half-Life of a First-Order Reaction

The **half-life** ($t_{1/2}$) of a reaction is the time it takes for half the reactant to react (or for half the product to form). To derive the half-life of a reactant in a first-order reaction, we begin with the equation

$$\ln \frac{a}{(a - x)} = k_1 t$$

At $t_{1/2}$, $x = \dfrac{a}{2}$; therefore,

$$\ln \frac{a}{\left(a - \dfrac{a}{2}\right)} = k_1 t_{1/2}$$

$$\ln \frac{a}{\dfrac{a}{2}} = k_1 t_{1/2}$$

$$\ln 2 = k_1 t_{1/2}$$

$$0.693 = k_1 t_{t/2}$$

$$t_{1/2} = \frac{0.693}{k_1}$$

Notice that the half-life of a first-order reaction is independent of the concentration of the reactant.

Second-Order Reaction

The rate is proportional to the concentration of two reactants:

$$A + B \xrightarrow{k_2} \text{products}$$

Rate law: rate $= k_2[A][B]$

To determine the second-order rate constant (k_2):

Change in the concentration of A with respect to time:

$$\frac{-d[A]}{dt} = k_2[A][B]$$

Let a = the initial concentration of A;
let b = the initial concentration of B;
let x = the concentration of A that has reacted at time t.

Therefore, the concentration of A left at time $t = (a - x)$, and the concentration of B left at time $t = (b - x)$.
Substitution gives

$$\frac{dx}{dt} = k_2(a - x)(b - x)$$

For the case where $a = b$ (this condition can be arranged experimentally),

$$\frac{dx}{dt} = k_2(a - x)^2$$

$$\frac{dx}{(a - x)^2} = k_2 \, dt$$

Integrating the equation gives

$$\frac{1}{(a - x)} = k_2 t + \text{constant}$$

At $t = 0$, $x = 0$; therefore,

$$\text{constant} = \frac{1}{a}$$

$$\frac{1}{(a - x)} - \frac{1}{a} = k_2 t$$

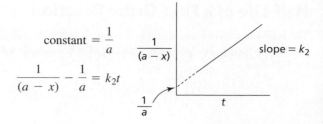

Half-Life of a Second-Order Reaction

$$\frac{1}{(a - x)} - \frac{1}{a} = k_2 t$$

At $t_{1/2}$, $x = \dfrac{a}{2}$; therefore,

$$\frac{1}{a} = k_2 t_{1/2}$$

$$t_{1/2} = \frac{1}{k_2 a}$$

Pseudo-First-Order Reaction

It is easier to determine a first-order rate constant than a second-order rate constant because the kinetic behavior of a first-order reaction is independent of the initial concentration of the reactant. Therefore, a first-order rate constant can be determined without knowing the initial concentration of the reactant. The determination of a second-order rate constant requires not only that the initial concentration of the reactants be known but also that the initial concentrations of the two reactants be identical in order to simplify the kinetic equation.

However, if the concentration of one of the reactants in a second-order reaction is much greater than the concentration of the other, the reaction can be treated as a first-order reaction. Such a reaction is known as a **pseudo-first-order reaction** and is given by

$$\frac{-d[A]}{dt} = k_2 [A][B]$$

If $[B] \gg [A]$, then

$$\frac{-d[A]}{dt} = k_2'[A]$$

The rate constant obtained for a pseudo-first-order reaction (k_2') includes the concentration of B, but k_2 can be determined by carrying out the reaction at several different concentrations of B and determining the slope of a plot of the observed rate versus [B].

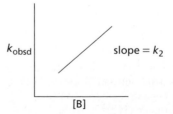

Summary of Methods Used to Synthesize a Particular Functional Group

SYNTHESIS OF ACETALS
1. Acid-catalyzed reaction of an aldehyde with two equivalents of an alcohol (18.10).

SYNTHESIS OF ACID ANHYDRIDES
1. Reaction of an acyl halide with a carboxylate ion (17.8).
2. Preparation of a cyclic anhydride by heating a dicarboxylic acid (17.23).

SYNTHESIS OF ACYL CHLORIDES OR ACYL BROMIDES
1. Reaction of a carboxylic acid with $SOCl_2$, PCl_3 or PBr_3 (17.21).

SYNTHESIS OF ALCOHOLS
1. Acid-catalyzed hydration of an alkene (4.5).
2. Oxymercuration–demercuration of an alkene (4.9).
3. Hydroboration–oxidation of an alkene (4.11).
4. Reaction of an alkyl halide with HO^- (8.1, 8.4).
5. Reaction of a Grignard reagent with an epoxide (11.2).
6. Reduction of an aldehyde, a ketone, an acyl chloride, an anhydride, an ester, or a carboxylic acid (18.6, 20.2).
7. Reaction of a Grignard reagent with an aldehyde, a ketone, an acyl chloride, or an ester (18.4).
8. Reduction of a ketone with $NaBH_4$ in cold aqueous ethanol in the presence of cerium trichloride (20.3).
9. Cleavage of an ether with HI or HBr (10.6).
10. Reaction of an organozinc reagent with an aldehyde or a ketone (p. 880).

SYNTHESIS OF ALDEHYDES
1. Hydroboration-oxidation of a terminal alkyne (6.8).
2. Oxidation of a primary alcohol with pyridinium chlorochromate (10.5, 20.4).
3. Swern oxidation of a primary alcohol with dimethyl sulfoxide, oxalyl chloride, and triethylamine (20.4).
4. Rosenmund reduction: catalytic hydrogenation of an acyl chloride (20.2).
5. Reaction of an acyl chloride with lithium tri(*tert*-butoxy)aluminum hydride (20.2).
6. Reaction of an ester with diisobutylaluminum hydride (DIBALH) (18.6).
7. Cleavage of a 1,2-diol with periodic acid (20.8).
8. Ozonolysis of an alkene, followed by workup under reducing conditions (20.9).

SYNTHESIS OF ALKANES
1. Catalytic hydrogenation of an alkene or an alkyne (4.11, 6.9, 20.2).
2. Reaction of a Grignard reagent with a source of protons (11.1).
3. Wolff–Kishner or Clemmensen reduction of an aldehyde or a ketone (15.16, 18.8).
4. Reduction of a thioacetal or thioketal with H_2 and Raney nickel (18.12).
5. Reaction of a Gilman reagent with an alkyl halide (11.4).
6. Preparation of a cyclopropane by the reaction of an alkene with a carbene (p. 192).

SYNTHESIS OF ALKENES
1. Elimination of hydrogen halide from an alkyl halide (9.1, 9.2, 9.3).
2. Acid-catalyzed dehydration of an alcohol (10.4).
3. Hofmann elimination reaction: elimination of a proton and a tertiary amine from a quaternary ammonium hydroxide (10.9).
4. Exhaustive methylation of an amine, followed by a Hofmann elimination reaction (10.9).
5. Hydrogenation of an alkyne with Lindlar catalyst to form a cis alkene (6.9, 20.2).
6. Reduction of an alkyne with Na (or Li) and liquid ammonia to form a trans alkene (6.9, 20.2).
7. Formation of a cyclic alkene using a Diels–Alder reaction (7.12, 30.4).
8. Wittig reaction: reaction of an aldehyde or a ketone with a phosphonium ylide (18.13).
9. Reaction of a Gilman reagent with a halogenated alkene (11.4).
10. Heck reaction couples a vinyl halide with an alkene in a basic solution in the presence of PdL_2 (11.5).
11. Suzuki reaction couples a vinyl halide with an organoborane in the presence of (PdL_2) (11.5).
12. Alkene metathesis (11.6).

SYNTHESIS OF ALKYL HALIDES

1. Addition of hydrogen halide (HX) to an alkene (4.1).
2. Addition of HBr + peroxide to an alkene (12.7).
3. Addition of halogen to an alkene (4.8).
4. Addition of hydrogen halide or a halogen to an alkyne (6.6).
5. Radical halogenation of an alkane, an alkene, or an alkyl benzene (12.2, 12.9).
6. Reaction of an alcohol with hydrogen halide, $SOCl_2$, PCl_3, or PBr_3 (10.1, 10.2).
7. Reaction of a sulfonate ester with halide ion (10.3).
8. Cleavage of an ether with HI or HBr (10.7).
9. Halogenation of an a-carbon of an aldehyde, a ketone, or a carboxylic acid (19.5, 19.6).

SYNTHESIS OF ALKYNES

1. Elimination of hydrogen halide from a vinyl halide (9.9).
2. Two successive eliminations of hydrogen halide from a vicinal dihalide or a geminal dihalide (9.9).
3. Reaction of an acetylide ion (formed by removing a proton from a terminal alkyne) with an alkyl halide (6.11).
4. Alkyne metathesis (11.6).

SYNTHESIS OF AMIDES

1. Reaction of an acyl chloride, an acid anhydride, or an ester with ammonia or with an amine (17.8, 17.9, 17.10).
2. Reaction of a carboxylic acid and an amine with dicyclohexylcarbodiimide (23.10).
3. Reaction of a nitrile with a secondary or tertiary alcohol (p. 768).

SYNTHESIS OF AMINES

1. Reaction of an alkyl halide with NH_3, RNH_2, or R_2NH (8.3).
2. Reaction of an alkyl halide with azide ion, followed by reduction of the alkyl azide (8.3).
3. Reduction of an imine, a nitrile, or an amide (17.19, 18.6, 20.2).
4. Reductive amination of an aldehyde or a ketone (18.8).
5. Gabriel synthesis of primary amines: reaction of a primary alkyl halide with potassium phthalimide (17.18).
6. Reduction of a nitro compound (16.1).
7. Condensation of a secondary amine and formaldehyde with a carbon acid (p. 882).

SYNTHESIS OF AMINO ACIDS

1. Hell–Volhard–Zelinski reaction: halogenation of a carboxylic acid, followed by treatment with excess NH_3 (19.6).
2. Reductive amination of an a-keto acid (23.6).
3. The *N*-phthalimidomalonic ester synthesis (Section 23.6).
4. The acetamidomalonic ester synthesis (Section 23.6).
5. The Strecker synthesis: reaction of an aldehyde with ammonia, followed by addition of cyanide ion and hydrolysis (Section 23.6).

SYNTHESIS OF CARBOXYLIC ACIDS

1. Oxidation of a primary alcohol (10.5, 20.4).
2. Oxidation of an aldehyde (10.5, 20.4).
3. Ozonolysis of a monosubstituted alkene or a 1,2-disubstituted alkene, followed by workup under oxidizing conditions (20.9).
4. Oxidation of an alkyl benzene (16.1).
5. Hydrolysis of an acyl halide, an acid anhydride, an ester, an amide, or a nitrile (17.8, 17.9, 17.10, 17.16, 17.19).
6. Haloform reaction: reaction of a methyl ketone with excess Br_2 (or Cl_2 or I_2) $+$ HO^- (19.5).
7. Reaction of a Grignard reagent with CO_2 (18.4).
8. Malonic ester synthesis (19.20).
9. Favorskii reaction: reaction of an a-haloketone with hydroxide ion (p. 880).

SYNTHESIS OF CYANOHYDRINS

1. Reaction of an aldehyde or a ketone with sodium cyanide and HCl (18.7).

SYNTHESIS OF 1,2-DIOLS

1. Reaction of an epoxide with water (10.7).
2. Reaction of an alkene with osmium tetroxide or potassium permanganate (20.7).

SYNTHESIS OF DISULFIDES

1. Mild oxidation of a thiol (23.8).

SYNTHESIS OF ENAMINES

1. Reaction of an aldehyde or a ketone with a secondary amine (18.8).

SYNTHESIS OF EPOXIDES

1. Reaction of an alkene with a peroxyacid (4.10).
2. Reaction of a halohydrin with hydroxide ion (p. 448).
3. Reaction of an aldehyde or a ketone with a sulfonium ylide (p. 827).

SYNTHESIS OF ESTERS

1. Reaction of an acyl halide or an acid anhydride with an alcohol (17.8, 17.9).
2. Acid-catalyzed reaction of an ester or a carboxylic acid with an alcohol (17.10, 17.15).
3. Reaction of an alkyl halide with a carboxylate ion (9.8).
4. Reaction of a sulfonate ester with a carboxylate ion (10.3).
5. Oxidation of a ketone (20.5).
6. Preparation of a methyl ester by the reaction of a carboxylate ion with diazomethane (16.12).

SYNTHESIS OF ETHERS

1. Acid-catalyzed addition of an alcohol to an alkene (4.6).
2. Alkoxymercuration–demercuration of an alkene (4.9).
3. Williamson ether synthesis: reaction of an alkoxide ion with an alkyl halide (9.9).
4. Formation of symmetrical ethers by heating an acidic solution of a primary alcohol (10.4).

SYNTHESIS OF HALOHYDRINS

1. Reaction of an alkene with Br_2 (or Cl_2) and H_2O (4.8).
2. Reaction of an epoxide with a hydrogen halide (10.6).

SYNTHESIS OF IMINES

1. Reaction of an aldehyde or a ketone with a primary amine (18.8).

SYNTHESIS OF KETALS

1. Acid-catalyzed reaction of a ketone with two equivalents of an alcohol (18.10).

SYNTHESIS OF KETONES

1. Addition of water to an alkyne (6.7).
2. Hydroboration–oxidation of an alkyne (6.8).
3. Oxidation of a secondary alcohol (10.5, 20.4).
4. Cleavage of a 1,2-diol with periodic acid (20.8).
5. Ozonolysis of an alkene (20.9).
6. Friedel–Crafts acylation of an aromatic ring (15.15).
7. Preparation of a methyl ketone by the acetoacetic ester synthesis (19.21).
8. Preparation of a cyclic ketone by the reaction of the next-size-smaller cyclic ketone with diazomethane (p. 829).

SYNTHESIS OF α, β-UNSATURATED KETONES

1. Elimination from an a-haloketone (19.7).
2. Selenenylation of a ketone, followed by oxidative elimination (p. 883).

SYNTHESIS OF NITRILES

1. Reaction of an alkyl halide with cyanide ion (8.3).

SYNTHESIS OF SUBSTITUTED BENZENES

1. Halogenation with Br_2 or Cl_2 and a Lewis acid (15.11).
2. Nitration with $HNO_3 + H_2SO_4$ (15.12).
3. Sulfonation: reaction with H_2SO_4 (15.13).
4. Friedel–Crafts acylation (15.14).
5. Friedel–Crafts alkylation (15.15, 15.16).
6. Sandmeyer reaction: reaction of an arenediazonium salt with CuBr, CuCl, or CuCN (16.10).
7. Formation of a phenol by reaction of an arenediazonium salt with water (16.13).
8. Formation of an aniline by reaction of a benzyne intermediate with $^-NH_2$ (16.13).
9. Reaction of a Gilman reagent with an aryl halide (11.4).
10. Heck reaction: couples a benzyl halide or an aryl halide or a triflate with an alkene in a basic solution in the presence of PdL_2 (11.5).
11. Suzuki reaction: couples a benzyl or aryl halide with an organoborane in the presence of PdL_2 (11.5).

SYNTHESIS OF SULFIDES

1. Reaction of a thiol with an alkyl halide (10.11).
2. Reaction of a thiol with a sulfonate ester (10.3).

SYNTHESIS OF THIOLS

1. Reaction of an alkyl halide with hydrogen sulfide (8.3).
2. Catalytic hydrogenation of a disulfide (23.8).

A P P E N D I X   V

Summary of Methods Employed to Form Carbon–Carbon Bonds

1. Alkene metathesis (11.6).
2. Reaction of an acetylide ion with an alkyl halide or a sulfonate ester (6.11, 8.3, 10.3).
3. Diels–Alder and other cycloaddition reactions (7.12, 30.4).
4. Reaction of a Grignard reagent with an epoxide (10.7).
5. Friedel–Crafts alkylation and acylation (15.14–15.16).
6. Reaction of a cyanide ion with an alkyl halide or a sulfonate ester (8.3, 10.3).
7. Reaction of a cyanide ion with an aldehyde or a ketone (18.7).
8. Reaction of a Grignard reagent with an epoxide, an aldehyde, a ketone, an ester, an amide, or CO_2 (11.12, 18.4).
9. Reaction of an organozinc reagent with an aldehyde or a ketone (p. 880).
10. Reaction of an alkene with a carbene (p. 192).
11. Reaction of a Giman reagent (lithium dialkylcuprate) with an a,b-unsaturated ketone or an a,b-unsaturated aldehyde (18.16).
12. Aldol addition (19.12–19.14, 19.17).
13. Claisen condensation (19.15–19.17).
14. Perkin condensation (p. 880).
15. Knoevenagel condensation (p. 880).
16. The benzoin condensation (p. 884).
17. Malonic ester synthesis and acetoacetic ester synthesis (19.20, 19.21).
18. Michael addition reaction (19.11).
19. Alkylation of an enamine (19.10).
20. Alkylation of the a-carbon of a carbonyl compound (19.9).
21. Reaction of a Gilman reagent with an aryl halide or a halogenated alkene (11.2).
22. Heck reaction: couples a vinyl, a benzyl, or an aryl halide, or a triflate with an alkene in a basic solution in the presence of PdL_2 (11.5).
23. Suzuki reaction: couples a vinyl, a benzyl, or an aryl halide with an organoborane in the presence of PdL_2 (11.5).

Spectroscopy Tables

Mass Spectrometry

Common fragment ions*

m/z	Ion	m/z	Ion
14	CH_2	46	NO_2
15	CH_3	47	CH_2SH, CH_3S
16	O	48	$CH_3S + H$
17	OH	49	CH_2Cl
18	H_2O, NH_4	51	CHF_2
19	F, H_3O	53	C_4H_5
26	$C{\equiv}N$	54	$CH_2CH_2C{\equiv}N$
27	C_2H_3	55	C_4H_7, $CH_2{=}CHC{=}O$
28	C_2H_4, CO, N_2, $CH{=}NH$	56	C_4H_8
29	C_2H_5, CHO	57	C_4H_9, $C_2H_5C{=}O$
30	CH_2NH_2, NO	58	$CH_3\overset{O}{\overset{\|}{C}}CH_2 + H$, $C_2H_5CHNH_2$, $(CH_3)_2NCH_2$, $C_2H_5NHCH_2$, C_2H_2S
31	CH_2OH, OCH_3	59	$(CH_3)_2COH$, $CH_2OC_2H_5$, $\overset{O}{\overset{\|}{C}}OCH_3$, $CH_2C{=}O + H$, CH_3OCHCH_3, $\underset{NH_2}{\|}$
32	O_2 (air)	60	CH_3CHCH_2OH $CH_2COOH + H$, CH_2ONO
33	SH, CH_2F		
34	H_2S		
35	Cl		
36	HCl		
39	C_3H_3		
40	$CH_2C{=}N$		
41	C_3H_5, $CH_2C{\equiv}N + H$, C_2H_2NH		
42	C_3H_6		
43	C_3H_7, $CH_3C{=}O$, C_2H_5N		
44	$CH_2CH{=}O + H$, CH_3CHNH_2, CO_2, $NH_2C{=}O$, $(CH_3)_2N$		
45	CH_3CHOH, CH_2CH_2OH, CH_2OCH_3, COOH, $CH_3CHO + H$		

* All of these ions have a single positive charge.

Mass Spectrometry

Common fragment lost

Molecular ion minus	Fragment lost	Molecular ion minus	Fragment lost
1	H	41	$CH_2\!\!=\!\!CHCH_2$
15	CH_3	42	$CH_2\!\!=\!\!CHCH_3$, $CH_2\!\!=\!\!C\!\!=\!\!O$, $\overset{\displaystyle CH_2}{CH_2\!\!-\!\!CH_2}$, NCO
17	HO	43	C_3H_7, $CH_3\overset{O}{\overset{\|}{C}}$, $CH_2\!\!=\!\!CHO$, HCNO, $CH_3 + CH_2\!\!=\!\!CH_2$
18	H_2O	44	$CH_2\!\!=\!\!CHOH$, CO_2, N_2O, $CONH_2$, $NHCH_2CH_3$
19	F	45	CH_3CHOH, CH_3CH_2O, CO_2H, $CH_3CH_2NH_2$
20	HF	46	$H_2O + CH_2\!\!=\!\!CH_2$, CH_3CH_2OH, NO_2
26	$CH\!\!\equiv\!\!CH$, $C\!\!\equiv\!\!N$	47	CH_3S
27	$CH_2\!\!=\!\!CH$, $HC\!\!\equiv\!\!N$	48	CH_3SH, SO, O_3
28	$CH_2\!\!=\!\!CH_2$, CO, (HCN + H)	49	CH_2Cl
29	CH_3CH_2, CHO	51	CHF_2
30	NH_2CH_2, CH_2O, NO	52	C_4H_4, C_2N_2
31	OCH_3, CH_2OH, CH_3NH_2	53	C_4H_5
32	CH_3OH,S	54	$CH_2\!\!=\!\!CHCH\!\!=\!\!CH_2$
33	HS, (CH_3 and H_2O)	55	$CH_2\!\!=\!\!CHCHCH_3$
34	H_2S	56	$CH_2\!\!=\!\!CHCH_2CH_3$, $CH_3CH\!\!=\!\!CHCH_3$
35	Cl	57	C_4H_9
36	HCl, $2H_2O$	58	NCS, NO + CO, CH_3COCH_3
37	HCl + H	59	$CH_3O\overset{O}{\overset{\|}{C}}$, $CH_3\overset{O}{\overset{\|}{C}}NH_2$
38	C_3H_2, C_2N, F_2	60	C_3H_7OH
39	C_3H_3, HC_2N		
40	$CH_3C\!\!\equiv\!\!CH$		

¹H NMR Chemical Shifts

Legend: $\mathrm{X = CH_3}$ $\mathrm{X = CH_2{-}}$ $\mathrm{X = \overset{|}{C}H{-}}$

(ppm) scale: 5 — 4 — 3 — 2 — 1 — 0

Functional groups (X groups):

- $RCH_2{-}X$
- $RCH{=}CH{-}X$
- $RC{\equiv}C{-}X$
- $C_6H_5{-}X$ (benzene ring — X)
- $F{-}X$
- $Cl{-}X$
- $Br{-}X$
- $I{-}X$
- $HO{-}X$
- $RO{-}X$
- $C_6H_5{-}O{-}X$ (phenoxy — X)
- $R{-}\overset{O}{\overset{\|}{C}}{-}O{-}X$
- $C_6H_5{-}\overset{O}{\overset{\|}{C}}{-}O{-}X$
- $H{-}\overset{O}{\overset{\|}{C}}{-}X$
- $R{-}\overset{O}{\overset{\|}{C}}{-}X$
- $C_6H_5{-}\overset{O}{\overset{\|}{C}}{-}X$
- $HO{-}\overset{O}{\overset{\|}{C}}{-}X$
- $RO{-}\overset{O}{\overset{\|}{C}}{-}X$
- $R_2N{-}\overset{O}{\overset{\|}{C}}{-}X$
- $N{\equiv}C{-}X$
- $H_2N{-}X$
- $R_2N{-}X$
- $C_6H_5{-}\overset{\underset{|}{R}}{N}{-}X$
- $R_3\overset{+}{N}{-}X$
- $R{-}\overset{O}{\overset{\|}{C}}{-}NH{-}X$
- $O_2N{-}X$

Characteristic Infrared Group Frequencies (S = strong, M = medium, W = weak). (Courtesy of N.B. Colthup, Stamford Research Laboratories, American Cyanamid Company, and the editor of the *Journal of the Optical Society*.) Overtone bands are marked 2ν.

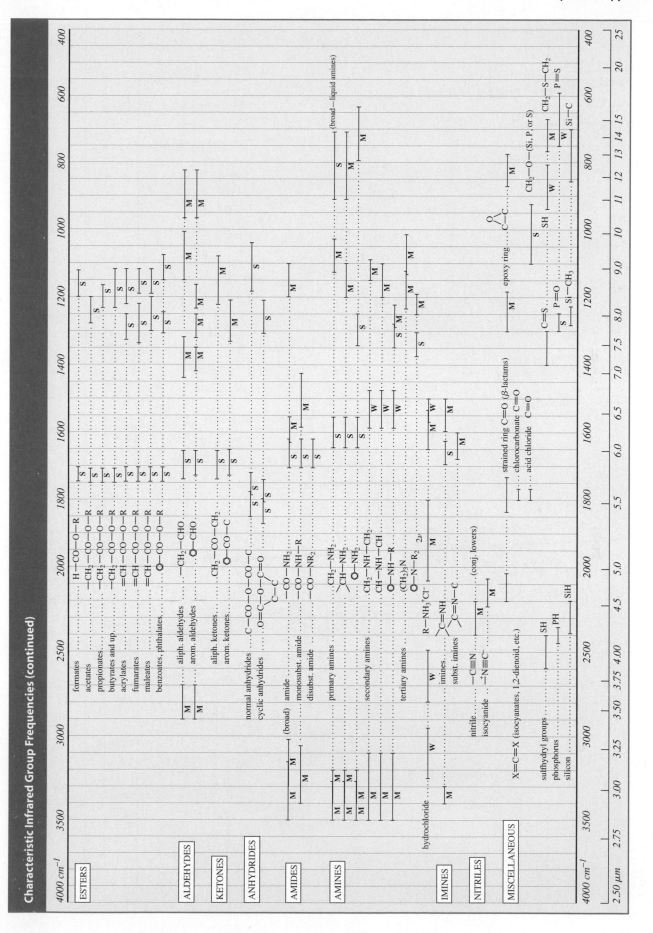

Characteristic Infrared Group Frequencies (continued)

Characteristic Infrared Group Frequencies (continued)

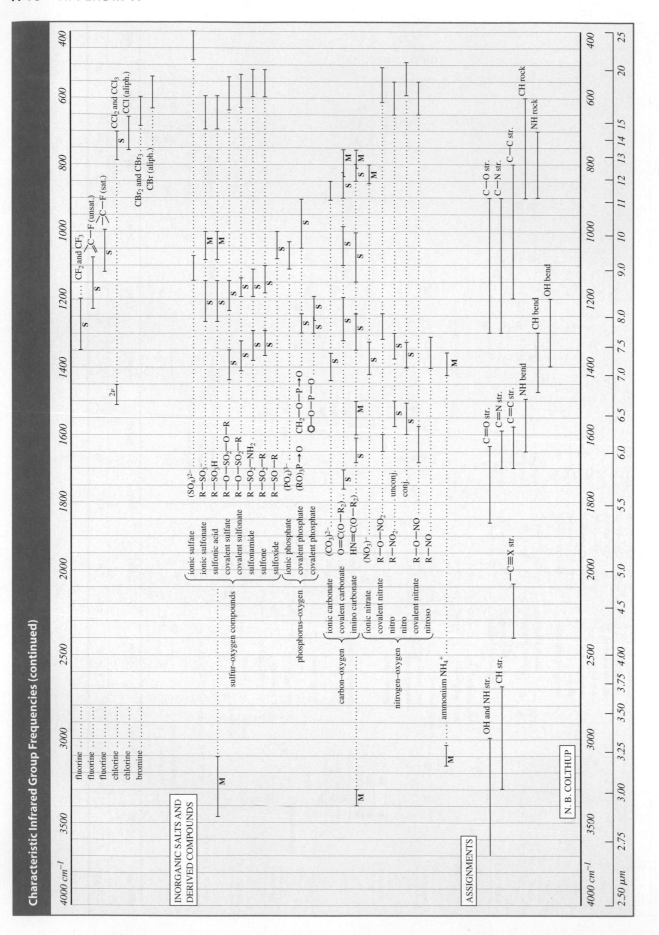

INORGANIC SALTS AND
DERIVED COMPOUNDS

ASSIGNMENTS

N. B. COLTHUP

Chapter 1

1-1. $8 + 8, 8 + 9, 8 + 10$

1-2. a. 3 **b.** 5 **c.** 6 **d.** 7

1-3. a. Cl $1s^2 2s^2 2p^6 3s^2 3p^5$; Br $1s^2 2s^2 2p^6 3s^2 3p^6 4s^2 3d^{10} 4p^5$; I $1s^2 2s^2 2p^6 3s^2 3p^6 4s^2 3d^{10} 4p^6 5s^2 4d^{10} 5p^5$ **b.** 7

1-5. a. 1 **b.** $4s$

1-6. a. Cl—CH$_3$ **b.** H—OH **c.** H—F **d.** Cl—CH$_3$

1-7. a. KCl **b.** Cl$_2$

1-10. a. $\overset{\delta-}{HO}$—$\overset{\delta+}{H}$ **c.** $\overset{\delta+}{H_3C}$—$\overset{\delta-}{NH_2}$ **e.** $\overset{\delta-}{HO}$—$\overset{\delta+}{Br}$ **g.** $\overset{\delta+}{I}$—$\overset{\delta-}{Cl}$

b. $\overset{\delta-}{F}$—$\overset{\delta+}{Br}$ **d.** $\overset{\delta+}{H_3C}$—$\overset{\delta-}{Cl}$ **f.** $\overset{\delta-}{H_3C}$—$\overset{\delta+}{MgBr}$ **h.** $\overset{\delta+}{H_2N}$—$\overset{\delta-}{OH}$

1-11. a. LiH and HF **b.** Its hydrogen has the greatest electron density. **c.** HF

1-12. a. oxygen **b.** oxygen **c.** oxygen **d.** hydrogen

1-15. a. CH$_3$CH$_2$OH CH$_3$OCH$_3$

b. CH$_3$CH$_2$CH$_2$OH CH$_3$CHCH$_3$ CH$_3$CH$_2$OCH$_3$
OH

1-16. a. CH$_3$CH$_2$N̈H$_2$ **c.** CH$_3$CH$_2$Ö̈H **e.** CH$_3$CH$_2$C̈l:

b. CH$_3$N̈HCH$_3$ **d.** CH$_3$Ö̈CH$_3$ **f.** HÖ̈NH$_2$

1-17. a. CH$_3$CH$_2$CH$_2$Cl **c.** CH$_3$CH$_2$C(=O)NCH$_2$CH$_3$
CH$_3$

b. CH$_3$C(=O)OCH$_2$CH$_3$ **d.** CH$_3$CH$_2$C≡N

1-18. a. Cl **b.** O **c.** N **d.** C and H **1-20.** yes **1-21. a.** π^* **b.** σ^* **c.** π **d.** σ

1-22. The C—C bonds are formed by sp^3–sp^3 overlap; the C—H bonds are formed by sp^3–s overlap. **1-24.** $> 104.5° < 109.5°$ **1-25.** $107.3°$

1-26. the nitrogen **1-27.** most = water; least = methane **1-28. a.** relative lengths: Br$_2$ > Cl$_2$; relative strengths: Cl$_2$ > Br$_2$ **b.** relative lengths: CH$_3$Br > CH$_3$Cl > CH$_3$F; relative strengths: CH$_3$F > CH$_3$Cl > CH$_3$Br

1-29. a. 1. C-I **2.** C-Cl **3.** H-Cl **b. 1.** C-Cl **2.** C-C **3.** H-H

1-30. σ **1-31.** sp^2–sp^2 is stronger because the more s character, the stronger the bond **1-33. a.** $109.5°$ **b.** $107.3°$ **c.** $109.5°$ **d.** $109.5°$ **1-35.** hydrogen

1-37. a, e, g, h **1-38. a. 1.** $^+$NH$_4$ **2.** HCl **3.** H$_3$O$^+$ **b. 1.** $^-$NH$_2$ **2.** Br$^-$ **3.** NO$_3^-$ **4.** HO$^-$ **1-39. a.** 5.2 **b.** 3.4×10^{-3} **1-40.** 8.16×10^{-8}

1-41. $K_a = 1.51 \times 10^{-5}$; weaker **1-43. a.** basic **b.** acidic **c.** basic

1-44. a. CH$_3$CH$_2$Ö̈H$_2$ **b.** CH$_3$CH$_2$OH

c. CH$_3$CH$_2$Ṅ̈H$_3$ **d.** CH$_3$CH$_2$C($^+$OH)OH

1-45. a. CH$_3$COO$^-$ **b.** $^-$NH$_2$ **c.** H$_2$O

1-46. CH$_3$NH$^-$ > CH$_3$O$^-$ > CH$_3$NH$_2$ > CH$_3$C(=O)O$^-$ > CH$_3$OH

1-50. a. 2.0×10^5 **b.** 3.2×10^{-7} **c.** 1.0×10^{-5} **d.** 4.0×10^{-13}

1-51. a. oxygen **b.** H$_2$S **c.** CH$_3$SH **1-52. a.** HBr **b.** CH$_3$CH$_2$CH$_2$Ö̈H$_2$

c. the one on the right **d.** H$_3$C—C(=O)—SH

1-53. a. F$^-$ **b.** I$^-$ **1-54. a.** HO$^-$ **b.** NH$_3$ **c.** CH$_3$O$^-$ **d.** CH$_3$O$^-$

1-55. a. CH$_3$OCH$_2$CH$_2$OH **b.** CH$_3$CH$_2$CH$_2$Ö̈H$_2$ **c.** CH$_3$CH$_2$OCH$_2$CH$_2$OH

d. CH$_3$CH$_2$C(=O)OH

1-56. CH$_3$CHCH$_2$OH > CH$_3$CHCH$_2$OH > CH$_2$CH$_2$CH$_2$OH > CH$_3$CH$_2$CH$_2$OH
F Cl Cl

1-57. a. CH$_3$CHC(=O)O$^-$ **b.** CH$_3$CHCH$_2$C(=O)O$^-$ **c.** CH$_3$CH$_2$C(=O)O$^-$ **d.** CH$_3$C(=O)CH$_2$CH$_2$O$^-$
Br Cl

1-59. CH$_3$S(=O)(=O)—OH **1-60. a.** resonance structures of carbonate

b. resonance structures of nitro group

1-61. a. CH$_3$C≡$^+$NH **b.** CH$_3$CH$_3$ **c.** F$_3$CC(=O)OH **d.** sp^2
e. HC≡CH > CH$_2$=CH$_2$ > CH$_3$CH$_3$ **f.** HNO$_3$

1-62. a. CH$_3$COO$^-$ **b.** CH$_3$CH$_2$Ṅ̈H$_3$ **c.** H$_2$O **d.** Br$^-$ **e.** $^+$NH$_4$ **f.** HC≡N
g. NO$_2^-$ **h.** NO$_3^-$ **1-63. b. 1.** charged **2.** charged **3.** charged
4. charged **5.** neutral **6.** neutral **c. 1.** neutral **2.** neutral **3.** neutral
4. neutral **5.** neutral **6.** neutral

1-64. a. CH$_3$CHC(=O)O$^-$
$^+$NH$_3$
b. no **c.** 6.02

1-65. a. 10.4 **b.** 2.7 **c.** 6.4 **d.** 7.3 **e.** 5.6

1-66. a. 1. 4.9 **2.** 10.7 **b. 1.** > 6.9 **2.** < 8.7 **1-67.** 10.4

1-68. a. CH$_3$COO$^-$ + H$^+$ ⇌ CH$_3$COOH

b. CH$_3$COOH + HO$^-$ ⇌ CH$_3$COO$^-$ + H$_2$O

Chapter 2

2-1. a. *n*-propyl alcohol or propyl alcohol **b.** dimethyl ether **c.** *n*-propylamine or propylamine

2-2. a. CH$_3$CHCH$_2$CH$_3$ **b.** CH$_3$CCH$_3$
CH$_3$ CH$_3$ / CH$_3$
2-methylbutane **2,2-dimethylpropane**

2-3.
1. CH$_3$CH$_2$CH$_2$CH$_2$Br CH$_3$CHCH$_2$Br CH$_3$CH$_2$CHCH$_3$ CH$_3$CBr
CH$_3$ Br CH$_3$ / CH$_3$
butyl bromide **isobutyl bromide** ***sec*-butyl bromide** ***tert*-butyl bromide**
or
***n*-butyl bromide**

2-4. c
2-5. a. CH$_3$CHOH **d.** CH$_3$CCH$_2$CH$_3$
CH$_3$ OH / CH$_3$

b. CH$_3$CHCH$_2$CH$_2$F **e.** CH$_3$CNH$_2$
CH$_3$ CH$_3$

c. CH$_3$CH$_2$CHI **f.** CH$_3$CH$_2$CH$_2$CH$_2$CH$_2$CH$_2$CH$_2$Br
CH$_3$

2-6. a. ethyl methyl ether **b.** methyl propyl ether **c.** *sec*-butylamine
d. *n*-butyl alcohol **e.** isobutyl bromide **f.** *sec*-butyl chloride

2-7. a. CH$_3$CHCHCH$_2$CH$_2$CH$_3$ **b.** CH$_3$CHCH$_2$C—CHCH$_2$CH$_3$
CH$_3$ CH$_3$ / CH$_3$ / CH(CH$_3$)$_2$

c. $CH_3CH_2CH_2\underset{\underset{CH_2CH_3}{|}}{\overset{\overset{CH_2CH_3}{|}}{C}}CH_2CH_2CH_2CH_2CH_3$ **d.** $CH_3\underset{\underset{CH_3}{|}}{\overset{\overset{CH_3}{|}}{C}}CH_2\underset{\underset{CH_2CH_2CH_3}{|}}{CH}CH_2CH_2CH_3$

e. $CH_3\overset{\overset{CH_3}{|}}{CH}CH_2\underset{\underset{CH_2CH(CH_3)_2}{|}}{\overset{\overset{CH_3}{|}}{CH}}CH_2CH_2CH_3$ **f.** $CH_3CH_2CH_2\underset{\underset{(CH_3)_2CCH_3}{|}}{CH}CH_2CH_2CH_3$

2-9. a. 2,2,4-trimethylhexane **b.** 2,2-dimethylbutane **c.** 3-methyl-4-propylheptane
d. 2,2,5-trimethylhexane **e.** 3,3-diethyl-4-methyl-5-propyloctane
f. 5-ethyl-4,4-dimethyloctane **g.** 3,3-diethylhexane **h.** 4-isopropyloctane
i. 2,5-dimethylheptane

2-10. a. $CH_3CH_2CH_2CH_2CH_3$ **c.** $CH_3\overset{\overset{CH_3}{|}}{CH}CH_2CH_3$
pentane 2-methylbutane

b. $CH_3\underset{\underset{CH_3}{|}}{\overset{\overset{CH_3}{|}}{C}}CH_3$ **d.** $CH_3\overset{\overset{CH_3}{|}}{CH}CH_2CH_3$
2,2-dimethylpropane 2-methylbutane

2-12. a. [structure] OH **d.** [structure] O
b. [structure] **e.** [structure] N H
c. [structure] **f.** [structure] Br

2-15. a. 1-ethyl-2-methylcyclopentane **b.** ethylcyclobutane
c. 4-ethyl-1,2-dimethylcyclohexane **d.** 3,6-dimethyldecane
e. 2-cyclopropylpentane **f.** 1-ethyl-3-isobutylcyclohexane **g.** 5-isopropylnonane
h. 1-sec-butyl-4-isopropylcyclohexane
2-16. a. 1. sec-butyl chloride, 2-chlorobutane, **secondary b.** cyclohexyl bromide,
bromocyclohexane, **secondary c.** isohexyl chloride, 1-chloro-4-methylpentane,
primary d. isopropyl fluoride, 2-fluoropropane, **secondary**
2-18. a. 1. methoxyethane **2.** ethoxyethane **3.** 4-methoxyoctane
4. 1-isopropoxy-3-methylbutane **5.** 1-propoxybutane **6.** 2-isopropoxypentane
b. no **c. 1.** ethyl methyl ether **2.** diethyl ether **4.** isopentyl isopropyl ether
5. butyl propyl ether
2-20. a. 1-pentanol, **primary b.** 5-chloro-2-methyl-2-pentanol, **tertiary**
c. 5-methyl-3-hexanol, **secondary d.** 2,6-dimethyl-4-octanol, **secondary**

2-21. $CH_3\underset{\underset{OH}{|}}{\overset{\overset{CH_3}{|}}{C}}CH_2CH_2CH_3$ $CH_3CH_2\underset{\underset{OH}{|}}{\overset{\overset{CH_3}{|}}{C}}CH_2CH_3$ $CH_3\underset{\underset{OH}{|}}{\overset{\overset{CH_3}{|}}{C}}-\underset{\underset{CH_3}{|}}{CH}CH_3$
2-methyl-2-pentanol 3-methyl-3-pentanol 2,3-dimethyl-2-butanol

2-22. a. 4-chloro-3-ethylcyclohexanol, **secondary b.** 7,8-dimethyl-3-nonanol,
secondary c. 1-bromo-5,5-diemthyl-3-heptanol, **secondary**
d. 4-methylcyclohexanol, **secondary 2-23. a.** tertiary **b.** tertiary **c.** primary
2-24. a. hexylamine, 1-hexanamine, **primary b.** sec-butylisobutylamine,
N-isobutyl-2-butanamine, **secondary c.** diethylmethylamine, N-ethyl-N-
methylethanamine, **tertiary d.** butylpropylamine, N-propyl-1-butanamine,
secondary e. diethylpropylamine, N,N-diethyl-1-propanamine, **tertiary**
f. no common name, N-ethyl-3-methylcyclopentanamine, **secondary**

2-25. a. $CH_3\overset{\overset{CH_3}{|}}{CH}CH_2NHCH_2CH_2CH_3$ **b.** $CH_3CH_2NHCH_2CH_3$
c. $CH_3\overset{\overset{CH_3}{|}}{CH}CH_2CH_2CH_2CH_2NH_2$ **d.** $CH_3CH_2CH_2\overset{\overset{CH_3}{|}}{N}CH_2CH_2CH_3$
e. $CH_3CH_2\underset{\underset{CH_3}{|}}{\overset{\overset{CH_2CH_3}{|}}{CH}}NCH_3$ **f.** [cyclohexyl]$-\overset{\overset{CH_3}{|}}{N}CH_2CH_3$

2-26. a. 6-methyl-1-heptanamine, isooctylamine, **primary**
b. cyclohexanamine, cyclohexylamine, **primary**
c. 3-methyl-N-propyl-1-butanamine, isopentylpropylamine, **secondary**
d. 2,5-dimethylcyclohexanamine, no common name, **primary**
2-27. a. 104.5° **b.** 107.3° **c.** 104.5° **d.** 109.5°
2-28. pentane
2-29. a. 1, 4, 5 **b.** 1, 2, 4, 5, 6

2-31.

HO[structure with two OH] > [structure with OH] > [structure with OH] > [structure with NH$_2$] >

[structure] > [structure]

2-33. a.

[structure OH/OH] > [structure OH O] > [structure OH] > [structure]

b. $HOCH_2CH_2CH_2OH > CH_3CH_2CH_2OH >$
$CH_3CH_2CH_2CH_2OH > CH_3CH_2CH_2CH_2Cl$
2-34. ethanol **2-36. a.** [Newman projection] **b.** [Newman projection] [Newman projection]

2-37. a. 135° **b.** 140° **2-38.** hexethal **2-40.** 6.2 kcal/mol **2-41.** 0.13 kcal/mol
2-42. 84% **2-43. a.** cis **b.** cis **c.** cis **d.** trans **e.** trans **f.** trans
2-44. cis-1-tert-butyl-3-methylcyclohexane **2-46. a.** one equatorial and one axial
b. both equatorial and both axial **c.** both equatorial and both axial
d. one equatorial and one axial **e.** one equatorial and one axial
f. both equatorial and both axial **2-47. a.** 3.6 kcal/mol **b.** 0

Chapter 3

3-1. a. C_5H_8 **b.** C_4H_6 **c.** $C_{10}H_{16}$ **d.** C_8H_{10} **3-2. a.** 3 **b.** 4 **c.** 1 **d.** 3 **e.** 13

3-4. a. [cyclopentene]$-CH_3$ **b.** $BrCH_2CH_2CH_2\underset{\underset{CH_3}{|}}{\overset{\overset{CH_3}{|}}{C}}=CCH_3$ **c.** $CH_3CH_2OCH\equiv CH_2$

d. $CH_2=CHCH_2OH$ **3-5. a.** 4-methyl-2-pentene **b.** 2-chloro-3,
4-dimethyl-3-hexene **c.** 1-bromocyclopentene **d.** 1-bromo-4-methyl-3-hexene
e. 1,5-dimethyl-cyclohexene **f.** 1-butoxy-1-propene **g.** 8,8-dimethyl-1-nonene
3-6. a. 5 **b.** 4 **c.** 4 **d.** 6 **3-7. a.** 1 and 3
3-9. $CH_3CH_2CH_2CH=CH_2$ $CH_3CH=\underset{\underset{CH_3}{|}}{C}CH_3$ $CH_3\underset{\underset{CH_3}{|}}{CH}CH=CH_2$

3-10. C **3-11. a.** $-I > -Br > -OH > -CH_3$
b. $-OH > -CH_2Cl > -CH\equiv CH_2 > -CH_2CH_2OH$ **3-14. a.** (E)-2-heptene
b. (Z)-3,4-dimethyl-2-pentene **c.** (Z)-1-chloro-3-ethyl-4-methyl-3-hexene
3-18. electrophiles: $CH_3\overset{+}{C}HCH_3$ nucleophiles: H^- CH_3O^- $CH_3C\equiv CH$ NH_3
3-22. a. all **b.** tert-butyl **c.** tert-butyl **d.** -1.7 kcal/mol or -7.1 kJ/mol
3-24. a. 1. $A + B \rightleftharpoons C$ **b.** none
 2. $A + B \rightleftharpoons C$
3-25. a. 1. $\Delta G° = -1.5$; $K_{eq} = 7.2 \times 10^{10}$ **2.** $\Delta G° = -16$; $K_{eq} = 1.8 \times 10^8$
b. the greater the temperature, the more negative is the $\Delta G°$
c. the greater the temperature, the smaller is the K_{eq}
3-26. a. -21 kcal/mol **b.** -36 kcal/mol **c.** exothermic **d.** exergonic
3-27. a. a and b **b.** b **c.** c
3-30. decreasing; increasing **3-31. a.** it will decrease it **b.** it will increase it
3-32. a. the first reaction **b.** the first reaction **3-34. a.** first step
b. revert to reactants **c.** second step **3-35. a.** 1 **b.** 2
c. see the Solutions Manual **d.** k_{-1} **e.** k_{-1} **f.** $B \longrightarrow C$ **g.** $C \longrightarrow B$

Chapter 4

4-1. a. 0 **b.** ethyl cation
4-2. a. 1. 3 **2.** 3 **3.** 6 **b.** sec-butyl cation
4-3. a. $CH_3CH_2\underset{\underset{CH_3}{|}}{\overset{+}{C}}CH_3 > CH_3CH_2\overset{+}{C}HCH_3 > CH_3CH_2CH_2\overset{+}{C}H_2$

b. $CH_3\overset{\overset{CH_3}{|}}{CH}CH_2\overset{+}{C}H_2 > CH_3\underset{\underset{Cl}{|}}{CH}CH_2\overset{+}{C}H_2 > CH_3\underset{\underset{F}{|}}{CH}CH_2\overset{+}{C}H_2$

4-4. a. products **b.** reactants **c.** reactants **d.** products

4-5. a. $CH_3CH_2\underset{\underset{Br}{|}}{CH}CH_3$ **c.** [cyclopentane with CH_3 and Br] **e.** [cyclohexane with CH_3 and Br]

b. $CH_3CH_2\underset{\underset{Br}{|}}{\overset{\overset{CH_3}{|}}{C}}CH_3$ **d.** $CH_3\underset{\underset{Br}{|}}{\overset{\overset{CH_3}{|}}{C}}CH_2CH_2CH_3$ **f.** $CH_3CH_2\underset{\underset{Br}{|}}{CH}CH_3$

4-6. a. $CH_2=CCH_3$ **c.** (structure: cyclohexyl with $C(CH_3)=CH_2$)

b. (cyclohexyl)$-CH_2CH=CH_2$ **d.** (cyclohexene)$=CHCH_3$ or (cyclohexenyl)$-CH_2CH_3$

4-7. a. $CH_3CH_2C(CH_3)=CH_2$ **b.** (methylenecyclohexane structure)

4-8. greater than -2.5 and less than 15   **4-9. a.** 3 **b.** 2 **c.** second step

4-10. a. $CH_3CH_2CH_2CHCH_3$ with OH **c.** $CH_3CH_2CH_2CHCH_2CH_3$ with OH and $CH_3CH_2CH_2CH_2CHCH_3$ with OH **d.** (1-methylcyclohexanol, CH_3, OH)

b. (cyclohexanol, OH)

4-16. a. $CH_3CCH_2CH_3$ with CH_3 and Br **b.** (methyl bromocyclohexane)

c. (bromo methyl cyclohexane)   **d.** $CH_3CHCH_2CHCH_3$ with CH_3 and Br

e. $CH_3CH-CCH_3$ with CH_3, CH_3, Br **f.** (methyl bromocyclohexane) and (methyl bromocyclohexane)

4-17. $CH_3CCH_2CH_3$ with CH_3 and Br **4-21.** $CH_3CH_2CHCH_2I$ with Cl

4-22. a. $CH_2CHCH_2CH_3$ with Br Br **c.** $CH_2CHCH_2CH_3$ with Br OCH_2CH_3

b. $CH_2CHCH_2CH_3$ with Br OH **d.** $CH_2CHCH_2CH_3$ with Br OCH_3

4-26. a. (epoxide)$-CH_2CH_2CH_3$ **c.** H_3C, O, CH_3 epoxide (H_3C, CH_3)

b. (epoxycyclohexane)   **d.** H_3C, O epoxide (H_3C, CH_2CH_3)

4-27. a. cyclohexene **b.** 1-butene   **4-28.** 2/3 mole

4-29. a. $CH_3CHCHCH_3$ with CH_3 and OH **b.** (methyl cyclohexanol, CH_3, OH)   **4-32.** A

4-33. a. (cyclohexene with CH_2CH_3, CH_2CH_3)   **b.** (cyclohexene with CH_2CH_3, CH_2CH_3)   **c.** (cyclohexene with CH_2CH_3, CH_2CH_3)

4-34. cis-3,4-dimethyl-3-hexene > $trans$-3-hexene > cis-3-hexene > cis-2,5-dimethyl-3-hexene

4-36. 3-Methylcyclohexanol would also be formed.

Chapter 5

5-1. a. $CH_3CH_2CH_2OH$ CH_3CHOH (with CH_3) $CH_3CH_2OCH_3$ **b.** 7

5-3. a., b., c., f., h.   **5-4. a.** P, F, J, L, G, R, Q, N, Z **b.** T, M, O, A, U, V, H, I, X, Y

5-5. a, c, and f   **5-7.** a, c, and f   **5-10.** A, B, and C

5-11. a. $-CH_2OH$ (1) $-CH_3$ (3) $-H$ (4) $-CH_2CH_2OH$ (2)

b. $-CH=O$ (2) $-OH$ (1) $-CH_3$ (4) $-CH_2OH$ (3)

c. $-CH(CH_3)_2$ (2) $-CH_2CH_2Br$ (3) $-Cl$ (1) $-CH_2CH_2CH_2Br$ (4)

d. $-CH=CH_2$ (2) $-CH_2CH_3$ (3)   (phenyl) (1) $-CH_3$ (4)

5-12. a. R **b.** R **c.** R **d.** R **5-13. a.** S **b.** R **c.** S **d.** S **5-14. a.** identical **b.** enantiomers **c.** enantiomers **d.** enantiomers   **5-16. a.** levorotatory **b.** dextrorotatory   **5-17.** $+168$ **5-18. a.** -24 **b.** 0   **5-19. a.** $+79$ **b.** 0 **c.** -79 **5-20. a.** do not know **b.** 98.5% dextrorotatory; 1.5% levorotatory   **5-23.** no   **5-24. a.** enantiomers **b.** identical **c.** diastereomers   **5-25. a.** 8 **b.** $2^8 = 256$ **5-29.** 1-chloro-1-methylcyclooctane, cis-1-chloro-5-methylcyclooctane, $trans$-1-chloro-5-methylcyclooctane   **5-31.** A = identical, B = enantiomer, C = diastereomer, D = identical   **5-32.** b, d, and f   **5-36.** asymmetric carbon on left = R; asymmetric carbon on right = R **5-38.** the second one   **5-39. a.** (2R,3R)-2,3-dichloropentane **b.** (2S,3S)-2-bromo-3-chloropentane **c.** (1R,3S)-1,3-cyclopentanediol **d.** (3R,4S)-3-chloro-4-methylhexane   **5-42.** S **5-43. a.** R **b.** R **c.** S **d.** S **5-44.** b   **5-45.** the one on the left   **5-47. a.** no **b.** no **c.** no **d.** yes **e.** no **f.** no   **5-50. a.** 1. $trans$-3-heptene 2. cis-3-heptene **b.** the enantiomer of each epoxide would also be formed

5-51. a. (cyclohexanol, OH)   **b.** (HO, CH_2CH_3) and (HO, CH_2CH_3)

c. (HO, CH_3, CH_3 cyclopentane) and (HO, CH_3, CH_3 cyclopentane)   **d.** (CH_3, C, H, CH_3CH_2, OH) and (CH_3, H, C, HO, CH_2CH_3)

5-58. a. 1-bromo-2-chloropropane **b.** equal amounts of R and S **5-60. a.** (R)-malate and (S)-malate **b.** (R)-malate and (S)-malate   **5-59.** $> 99\%$ **5-61.** hatched wedge

Chapter 6

6-1. $C_{14}H_{20}$

6-2. a. $ClCH_2CH_2C\equiv CCH_2CH_3$ **d.** $CH_3CH_2CHC\equiv CCH_2CHCH_3$ with CH_3 and CH_3

b. (cyclooctyne)   **e.** $HC\equiv CCH_2CCH_3$ with CH_3, CH_3

c. $CH_3CHC\equiv CH$ with CH_3 **f.** $CH_3C\equiv CCH_3$

6-4. a. 5-bromo-2-pentyne **b.** 6-bromo-2-chloro-4-octyne **c.** 1-methoxy-2-pentyne **d.** 3-ethyl-1-hexyne   **6-6. a.** 1-hepten-4-yne **b.** 4-methyl-1,4-hexadiene **c.** 5-vinyl-5-octen-1-yne **d.** 3-butyn-1-ol **e.** 1,3,5-heptatriene **f.** 2,4-dimethyl-4-hexen-1-ol

6-7. a. 1-bromo-1,3-pentadiene **b.** 1-hepten-5-yne **c.** 4-hepten-1-yne

6-8. pentane, 1-pentene, 1-pentyne   **6-9. a.** sp^2–sp^2 **b.** sp^2–sp^3 **c.** sp–sp^2 **d.** sp–sp^3 **e.** sp–sp **f.** sp^2–sp^2 **g.** sp^2–sp^3 **h.** sp–sp^3 **i.** sp^2–sp

6-10. If the less stable reactant has the more stable transition state or if the less stable reactant has the less stable transition state and the difference in stabilities of the reactants is greater than the difference in the stabilities of the transition states.

6-11. a. $CH_2=CCH_3$ with Br **b.** CH_3CCH_3 with Br **c.** $CH_3C=CCH_3$ with Br **d.** $HC-CCH_3$ with Br Br

e. $CH_3CH_2CCH_3$ with Br **f.** $CH_3CCH_2CH_3$ with Br + $CH_3CH_2CCH_2CH_3$ with Br

6-12. (H_3C, $C=C$, Br, Br, CH_3)

6-13. $CH_3CH_2CCH_2CH_2CH_2CH_3$ (with O) and $CH_3CH_2CH_2CCH_2CH_2CH_3$ (with O)

6-14. a. $CH_3C\equiv CH$ **b.** $CH_3CH_2C\equiv CCH_2CH_3$ **c.** $HC\equiv C-$(cyclohexyl with OH)

6-15. a. $CH_2=CCH_3$ with OH

b. $CH_3CH=CCH_2CH_2CH_3$ with OH and $CH_3CH_2C=CHCH_2CH_3$ with OH

c. $CH_2=C-$(cyclohexyl) with OH and CH_3C-(cyclohexyl) with OH

6-17. ethyne (acetylene)

6-18. **a.** $CH_3CH_2CH_2C\equiv CH$ or $CH_3CH_2C\equiv CCH_3$ $\xrightarrow{H_2}{Pd/C}$

b. $CH_3C\equiv CCH_3$ $\xrightarrow{H_2}{\text{Lindlar catalyst}}$ **c.** $CH_3CH_2C\equiv CCH_3$ $\xrightarrow{Na}{NH_{3(liq)}}$

d. $CH_3CH_2CH_2CH_2C\equiv CH$ $\xrightarrow{H_2}{\text{Lindlar catalyst}}$ or $\xrightarrow{Na}{NH_{3(liq)}}$

6-19. 25 **6-20.** The carbanion that would be formed is a stronger base than the amide ion. **6-21. a.** $CH_3CH_2CH_2\overset{-}{C}H_2 > CH_3CH_2CH=\overset{-}{C}H > CH_3CH_2C\equiv\overset{-}{C}$
b. $^-NH_2 > CH_3C\equiv\overset{-}{C} > CH_3CH_2O^- > F^-$

Chapter 7

7-1. a. 1. 4 2. 2 **b.** 1. 5 2. 5 **7-6. a.** all are the same length **b.** 2/3 of a negative charge

7-7. **a.** $CH_3CH_2CH=CH\overset{+}{C}H_2$ **c.** $CH_3\overset{O^-}{\overset{|}{C}}=CHCH_3$

b. $CH_3\overset{O}{\overset{||}{C}}CH=CHCH_3$ **d.** $CH_3-\overset{+NH_2}{\overset{||}{C}}-NH_2$

7-8. the dianion
7-9. conjugated > isolated > cumulated

7-10. $CH_3\overset{CH_3}{\overset{|}{C}}=CHCH=\overset{CH_3}{\overset{|}{C}}CH_3 > CH_3CH=CHCH=CHCH_3 >$
2,5-dimethyl-2,4-hexadiene   **2,4-hexadiene**

$CH_3CH=CHCH=CH_2 > CH_2=CHCH_2CH=CH_2$
1,3-pentadiene   **1,4-pentadiene**

7-11. a. [structure: cyclohexene with $\overset{+}{C}HCH_3$] **b.** $CH_3\overset{+}{N}HCH_2$ **c.** [phenyl isopropyl cation]

7-12. $\psi_3 = 3; \psi_4 = 4$
7-13. a. bonding $= \psi_1$ and ψ_2; antibonding $= \psi_3$ and ψ_4
b. symmetric $= \psi_1$ and ψ_3; antisymmetric ψ_2 and ψ_4 **c.** HOMO $= \psi_2$;
LUMO $= \psi_3$; **d.** HOMO $= \psi_3$; LUMO $= \psi_4$ **e.** If the HOMO is symmetric, the LUMO is antisymmetric and vice versa.
7-14. a. bonding $= \psi_1, \psi_2,$ and ψ_3; antibonding $= \psi_4, \psi_5,$ and ψ_6 **b.**
symmetric $= \psi_1, \psi_3,$ and ψ_5; antisymmetric $\psi_2, \psi_4,$ and ψ_6 **c.** HOMO $= \psi_3$;
LUMO $= \psi_4$ **d.** HOMO $= \psi_4$; LUMO $= \psi_5$
e. If the HOMO is symmetric, the LUMO is antisymmetric and vice versa.
7-15. a. $\psi_1 = 3; \psi_2 = 2$ **b.** $\psi_1 = 7; \psi_2 = 6$

7-16. a. $CH_3\overset{O}{\overset{||}{C}}OH$ **b.** $CH_3CH=CHOH$ **c.** $CH_3CH=CH\overset{+}{N}H$

7-17. a. ethylamine **b.** ethoxide ion **c.** ethoxide ion

7-18. [phenyl]—COOH > [phenyl]—OH > [phenyl]—CH$_2$OH

7-20. resonance electron donation
7-21. 1-bromo-1-phenylpropane

7-24. [structure]

7-25. a. $CH_3\overset{Cl}{\overset{|}{C}}HCHCH=CHCH_3$ + $CH_3\overset{Cl}{\overset{|}{C}}HCH=CH\overset{Cl}{\overset{|}{C}}HCH_3$

b. $CH_3CH_2\overset{Br}{\overset{|}{C}}-C=CHCH_3$ + $CH_3CH_2\overset{Br}{\overset{|}{C}}=C\overset{}{C}HCH_3$
      $\overset{|}{C}H_3\overset{}{C}H_3$ CH_3CH_3

c. [structures with Br]

7-29. a. Addition at C-1 forms the more stable carbocation. **b.** To cause the 1,2- and, 1,4-products to be different.
7-30. a. formation of the carbocation **b.** reaction of the carbocation with the nucleophile

7-33. a. [structure with two COCH$_3$ groups] **c.** [anhydride structure with CH$_3$ groups]

b. [structure with C≡N] **d.** [bicyclic structure with CH$_3$ groups]

7-34. [structure CH$_3$O— with CHO]

7-36. a. [structure CH$_3$, C≡N] + [structure with C≡N, CH$_3$]

b. [structure with C≡N, H$_3$C] + [structure H$_3$C, C≡N]

7-37. A and B **7-39. a.** The product is a meso compound. **b.** The product is a racemic mixture.

7-40. a. [diene] + [CHC≡N, CH$_2$] **c.** [cyclopentadiene] + $CH_3O\overset{O}{\overset{||}{C}}C\equiv C\overset{O}{\overset{||}{C}}OCH_3$

b. [furan structure O] + $HC\equiv CH$ **d.** [diene] + [cyclohexenone structure]

Chapter 8

8-1. It will be 0.50 of the original rate. **8-2.** decrease
8-3.

$CH_3CH_2CH_2CH_2CH_2Br > CH_3\overset{CH_3}{\overset{|}{C}}HCH_2CH_2Br > CH_3CH_2\overset{CH_3}{\overset{|}{C}}HCH_2Br > CH_3CH_2\overset{CH_3}{\overset{|}{C}}Br\overset{|}{}_{CH_3}$

8-4. a. (S)-2-butanol **b.** (R)-2-hexanol **c.** 3-pentanol **8-5. a.** aprotic **b.** aprotic **c.** protic **d.** aprotic **8-6. a.** RO^- **b.** RS^- **c.** RO^- **8-7. a.** Br^- **b.** Cl^- **c.** CH_3O^- **d.** CH_3O^- **e.** $^-NH_2$ **f.** $^-NH_2$ **g.** I^- **h.** Br^- **8-9. a.** $CH_3CH_2Br + HO^-$
b. $CH_3\overset{}{C}HCH_2Br + HO^-$ **c.** $CH_3CH_2Cl + CH_3S^-$ **d.** $CH_3CH_2Br + I^-$
  $\overset{|}{C}H_3$
8-11. a. $CH_3CH_2OCH_2CH_2CH_3$ **b.** $CH_3CH_2C\equiv CCH_3$ **c.** $CH_3CH_2\overset{+}{N}(CH_3)_3Br^-$
d. $CH_3CH_2SCH_2CH_3$

8-15. $CH_3\overset{CH_3}{\underset{CH_3}{\overset{|}{C}}}Br > CH_3\overset{CH_3}{\overset{|}{C}}HBr > CH_3CH_2CH_2Br > CH_3Br$

8-17.

$CH_3CH_2\overset{CH_3}{\underset{Br}{\overset{|}{C}}}CH_2CH_3 > CH_3\overset{CH_3}{\underset{Br}{\overset{|}{C}}}HCH_2CH_2CH_3 > CH_3\overset{}{\underset{Cl}{C}}HCH_2CH_2CH_3 >$

$ClCH_2CH_2CH_2CH_2CH_3$

8-18. A, B, C, E **8-19.** 3-aceto-3-methyl-1-butene and 1-aceto-3-methyl-2-butene

8-22. a. [structure Br] **b.** [structure Br] **c.** [phenyl Br] **d.** [phenyl]

e. [structure Br] **f.** [structure Br]

8-23.

a. [structure: Br on isopropyl] b. [structure: Br on pentyl] c. [structure: phenyl-CH2-CH(Br)-CH3] d. [structure: benzyl-CH2Br]

e. equally reactive f. [structure: CH=CH with Br and CH3]

8-26. a and b **8-28.** protic **8-29.** a. decrease b. decrease c. increase

8-30. a. $CH_3Br + HO^- \longrightarrow CH_3OH + Br^-$

b. $CH_3I + HO^- \longrightarrow CH_3OH + I^-$

c. $CH_3Br + NH_3 \longrightarrow CH_3\overset{+}{N}H_3 + Br^-$

d. $CH_3Br + HO^- \xrightarrow{DMSO} CH_3OH + Br^-$

e. $CH_3Br + NH_3 \xrightarrow{EtOH} CH_3\overset{+}{N}H_3 + Br^-$

8-32. dimethyl sulfoxide **8-33.** HO^- in 50% water/50% ethanol

8-34. a. HO⌒⌒⌒⌒Br

b. HO⌒⌒⌒⌒Br

c. HO⌒⌒⌒⌒⌒Br

Chapter 9

9-1. a. $CH_3\overset{\overset{CH_3}{|}}{C}=CHCH_3$ b. $CH_3\overset{\overset{CH_3}{|}}{C}=CHCH_3$ c. $CH_3CH_2\overset{\overset{CH_3}{|}}{\underset{\underset{CH_3}{|}}{C}}CH=CH_2$

9-2.

a. [structure with Br] b. [cyclohexyl-Br] c. [structure with Br] d. [structure with Cl]

9-4. a. $CH_3CH=CHCH_3$ d. $CH_2=CHCH_2CH_3$

b. $CH_3\overset{\overset{CH_3}{|}}{C}=CHCH_2CH_3$ e. [cyclohexene with CH3]

c. $CH_3CH=CHCH=CH_2$ f. $CH_3CHCH=CHCH_3$

9-5.

a. [structure with Br] b. [cyclohexene with Br] c. [structure with Br] d. [phenyl structure with Br]

9-6. $CH_3\overset{\overset{CH_3}{|}}{\underset{\underset{CH_3}{|}}{C}}=CHCH_2CH_3 >$ [structure] $>$ [structure] $> CH_3\overset{\overset{CH_2}{||}}{\underset{\underset{CH_3}{|}}{C}HCHCH_2CH_3}$

9-7. yes; elimination occurs through the carbocation **9-8.** a. B b. B c. B d. A

9-10. a. E2 $CH_3CH=CHCH_3$ d. E2 $CH_3\overset{\overset{CH_3}{|}}{C}=CH_2$

b. E1 $CH_3CH=CHCH_3$ e. E1 $CH_3\overset{\overset{CH_3}{|}}{C}=CCH_3$ with CH_3

c. E1 $CH_3\overset{\overset{CH_3}{|}}{C}=CH_2$ f. E2 $CH_3\overset{\overset{CH_3}{|}}{\underset{\underset{CH_3}{|}}{C}}CH=CH_2$

9-11. a. 96% b. 1.2%

9-12. a. 1. $CH_3CH_2CH=CCH_3$ with CH3 3. [structure] b. no 2. [structure]

9-13. b. 2-methyl-2-pentene c. (E)-4-methyl-3-heptene d. 1-methylcyclohexene
9-14. the eliminated atoms have to be in axial positions **9-15.** elimination only from the *cis* isomer occurs through the more stable conformer **9-17.** left to right 2, 5, 3, 1, 4 (1 is the most reactive, 5 the least reactive) **9-18.** ~1
9-19. it will increase **9-20.** When Br is in an axial position, both adjacent H's are in equatorial positions. **9-21.** a. 1-bromopropane b. iodocyclohexane
c. 2-bromo-2-methylbutane d. 3-bromocyclohexene **9-22.** a. 1. no reaction
2. no reaction 3. substitution and elimination 4. substitution and elimination
b. 1. primarily substitution 2. substitution and elimination 3. substitution and elimination 4. elimination **9-23.** a. S_N2 difficult because of steric hindrance; no S_N1 because cannot form a primary carbocation b. No E2 because there are no hydrogens on a β-carbon; no E1 because cannot form a primary carbocation.
9-24. a. $CH_3CH=CH_2$ b. $CH_3CH_2CH=CH_2$

9-26. $CH_3\overset{\overset{CH_3}{|}}{\underset{\underset{CH_3}{|}}{C}}OH + CH_3\overset{\overset{CH_3}{|}}{\underset{\underset{CH_3}{|}}{C}}OCH_2CH_3 + CH_3\overset{\overset{CH_3}{|}}{C}=CH_2$

Chapter 10

10-1. no lone pair **10-4.** $3° > 1° > 2°$

10-5. a. $CH_3CH_2\overset{}{\underset{\underset{Br}{|}}{C}}HCH_3$ c. $CH_3\overset{\overset{CH_3}{|}}{\underset{\underset{Br}{|}}{C}}\overset{}{C}HCH_3$ with CH_3

b. [cyclopentane with CH3 and Cl] d. [cyclohexane with CH3, CH2CH3, Cl]

10-8. D **10-9.** 1-bromo-1-methylcyclopentane

10-11. a. $CH_3CH_2\overset{\overset{CH_3}{|}}{C}HCH_2OH$ c. $CH_3CH_2\overset{}{\underset{\underset{OH}{|}}{C}}HCH_2CH_3$

b. [cyclohexane with CH3 and OH] d. [cyclohexane with CH2OH]

10-13.

a. $CH_3CH_2\overset{\overset{CH_3}{|}}{C}=\overset{}{\underset{\underset{CH_3}{|}}{C}}CH_3$ b. [cyclopentene with CH2CH3] c. [cyclohexene]

d. [cyclohexene with CH3] e. $CH_3CH_2\overset{\overset{CH_3}{|}}{C}=\overset{}{\underset{\underset{CH_3}{|}}{C}}CH_3$ f. [structure: CH_3CH_2 and H, C=C, H and CH3]

10-15. a. $CH_3CH_2\overset{\overset{O}{||}}{C}CH_2CH_3$ b. $CH_3CH_2CH_2CH_2\overset{\overset{O}{||}}{C}OH$ c. no reaction

d. $CH_3\overset{\overset{O}{||}}{C}CH_2\overset{\overset{O}{||}}{C}CH_2CH_3$ e. [cyclohexanone] f. $HO\overset{\overset{O}{||}}{C}CH_2CH_2\overset{\overset{O}{||}}{C}OH$

10-18. No, F^- is too poor a nucleophile.

10-20. a. $HOCH_2\overset{\overset{CH_3}{|}}{\underset{\underset{OCH_3}{|}}{C}}CH_3$ c. $HOCH\overset{\overset{OCH_3}{|}}{\underset{\underset{CH_3}{|}}{C}}CH_3$ with CH_3

b. $CH_3OCH_2\overset{\overset{OH}{|}}{\underset{\underset{CH_3}{|}}{C}}CH_3$ d. $CH_3OCH\overset{\overset{OH}{|}}{\underset{\underset{CH_3}{|}}{C}}CH_3$ with CH_3

10-21. noncyclic ether

10-23. $CH_3\overset{}{\underset{\underset{CH_3}{|}}{C}}=CH_2 + \overset{\overset{CH_3}{|}}{N}CH_2CH_2CH_3$ with CH_3

10-24. $CH_3\overset{}{\underset{\underset{CH_3}{|}}{C}}HCH_2\overset{}{\underset{\underset{CH_3}{|}}{N}}CH_3 + CH_2=CHCH_3$

10-25. The only difference is the leaving group.

10-26. a. $CH_2=CHCHCH_2CH_2NCH_3$ **c.** $CH_3NCH_2CHCH_2CH=CH_2$

(with CH$_3$, CH$_3$ substituents; CH$_2$ group; CH$_3$)

b. (methylenecyclohexane) $+$ $N(CH_3)_3$

10-28. a. 2-methyl-3-pentanamine **b.** 3-methylpyrrolidine   **10-30.** It has two sites that can be attacked by a nucleophile, and each site has an excellent leaving group.   **10-31.** The first one is too insoluble; the second is too reactive; the third is too unreactive.

Chapter 11

11-1. a. $CH_3CH_2CH_2CH_2CH_2OH$ **c.** (cyclohexyl)—CH_2CH_2OH

b. (phenyl)—$CH_2CH_2CH_2OH$

11-4. They all occur.   **11-5.** an organosodium compound   **11-6.** $(CH_3)_4Si$
11-8. The alkyl halide will undergo an elimination reaction instead of a substitution reaction
11-10. a. (para-substituted benzene with Br and propyl) **b.** (meta-substituted benzene with NO$_2$ and butyl)

11-11. a. (bromobenzene) **b.** (β-bromostyrene) **c.** (allylic bromide on benzene)

11-12. 1-pentyne

11-13. a. (conjugated diene nitrile, C≡N) **b.** (cinnamamide, with NH$_2$)

11-14. a. (methyl-substituted dienone) **b.** (longer chain dienone)

11-15. CH_3C(=O)—(phenyl)—Br   and $CH_2=CH$—(phenyl)—OCH_3

CH_3C(=O)—(phenyl)—$CH=CH_2$ and   Br—(phenyl)—OCH_3

11-19. a. 1,6-heptadiene **b.** *ortho*-allylstyrene **c.** 1-pentene

11-21. (phenyl)—C≡C—(phenyl)   and CH_3—(phenyl)—C≡C—(phenyl)—CH_3

Chapter 12

12-3. a. the one on the third carbon from the left (It is hidden behind the carbon.)
b. 6   **12-4. a.** 3 **b.** 3 **c.** 5 **d.** 1 **e.** 5 **f.** 4 **g.** 2 **h.** 1 **i.** 4   **12-7. a.** 2-bromo-2-methylbutane **b.** 82.6%   **12-8. a.** chlorination **b.** bromination **c.** no preference
12-10. a. D **b.** B **c.** no preference

12-12. a. $CH_3CCH_2CH_3$ (with CH$_3$, Br)   **c.** $CH_3CHCHCH_3$ (with CH$_3$, Br)

b. $CH_3CCH_2CH_3$ (with CH$_3$, Cl)   **d.** $CH_3CCH_2CH_3$ (with CH$_3$, Cl)

12-13. a. 2-methylpropane **b.** butane

Chapter 13

13-1. #2, #3, #5   **13-3.** $m/z = 57$ **13-6.** 8   **13-7.** 1 : 2 : 1   **13-8.** C_6H_{14}
13-10. a. 2-methoxy-2-methylpropane **b.** 2-methoxybutane **c.** 1-methoxybutane
13-12. $CH_2=\overset{+}{O}H$ **13-13. a.** 2-pentanone **b.** 3-pentanone   **13-16. a.** 3-pentanol
b. 2-pentanol   **13-17. a.** IR **b.** UV   **13-18. a.** $2000\,cm^{-1}$ **b.** $8\,\mu m$ **c.** $2\,\mu m$
12-18. a. $2500\,cm^{-1}$ **b.** $50\,\mu m$ **13-19.** C=O   **13-20. a.** 1. C≡C

2. C—H stretch **3.** C≡N **4.** C=O **b.** 1. C—O **2.** C—C
13-21. a. carbon–oxygen stretch of a phenol **b.** carbon–oxygen double-bond stretch of a ketone **c.** C—N stretch of aniline   **13-22.** sp^3 **13-23.** C—O bond of pentanoic acid has partial double bond character
13-24. a. (formaldehyde) > (acetaldehyde) > (acetone)

b. (δ-valerolactone) > (cyclohexanone) > (δ-valerolactam, NH)

13-25. ethanol dissolved in carbon disulfide   **13-26.** C—N stretch would be less intense   **13-27. a.** ketone **b.** tertiary amine   **13-30.** 2-butyne, H_2, Cl_2, ethene
13-31. *trans*-2-hexene   **13-32.** methyl vinyl ketone   **13-33.** does not have a π^* antibonding molecular orbital   **13-34.** $4.1 \times 10^{-5}\,M$ **13-35.** $10{,}000\,M^{-1}cm^{-1}$
13-36.
a. (phenyl)—CH=CH—(phenyl) > (biphenyl) > (phenyl)—CH=CH$_2$ > (phenyl) >
b. (phenyl)—$N(CH_3)_2$ > (phenyl)—$\overset{+}{N}(CH_3)_3$ > (cyclohexadienyl)—$N(CH_3)_2$ > (cyclohexenyl)—$N(CH_3)_2$

13-37. left = purple; right = blue   **13-38.** monitor increase in absorption at 340 nm   **13-39.** 5.0

Chapter 14

14-1. 43 MHz   **14-2. a.** 8.46 T **b.** 11.75 T   **14-3. a.** 2 **b.** 1 **c.** 3 **d.** 3 **e.** 1 **f.** 4
g. 3 **h.** 3 **i.** 5 **j.** 4 **k.** 2 **l.** 3 **m.** 3 **n.** 4 **o.** 3
14-5. (cyclopropane derivatives labeled 1, 2, 3 with Cl and H substituents)
1   **2**   **3**
14-6. a. 300 Hz **b.** 500 Hz   **14-7. a.** 2.0 ppm **b.** 2.0 ppm **c.** 200 Hz
14-8. a. 1.5 ppm **b.** 30 Hz   **14-9.** to the right of the TMS signal
14-10. a. in each structure it is the proton(s) on the carbon on the right-hand side of the structure **b.** in each structure it is the protons on the methyl group on the left-hand side of the structure
14-11. a. $CH_3CHCHBr$ (Br, Br underlined)   **c.** $CH_3CH_2CHCH_3$ (Cl underlined)   **e.** $CH_3CH_2CH=CH_2$ (underlined)

b. CH_3CHOCH_3 (CH$_3$ underlined)   **d.** $CH_3CHCCH_2CH_3$ (=O; CH$_3$ underlined)   **f.** $CH_3OCH_2CH_2CH_3$ (underlined)

14-12. a. $CH_3CH_2CH_2Cl$ (underlined)   **b.** $CH_3CH_2CHCH_3$ (Cl underlined)   **c.** CH_3CHCH (=O; underlined)

14-14. 9.25 ppm = hydrogens that protrude out;
−2.88 ppm = hydrogens that point in
14-15. The compounds have different integration ratios: 2 : 9, 1 : 3, and 2 : 1
14-17. B   **14-18.** first spectrum = 1-iodopropane
14-21. a. 2-chloropropanoic acid **b.** 3-chloropropanoic acid
14-26. a. propyl benzene **b.** 3-pentanone **c.** ethyl benzoate

14-31. CH_3O—(phenyl)—CH_3 **14-33. a.** A **b.** B and D   **14-36.** pure ethanol

14-38. CH_3CH_2—C(=O)—NH_2

14-42. a. $CH_3(CH_2)_4C(=O)(CH_2)_4CH_3$ **b.** Br—(phenyl)—CH_3CH_2 **c.** (cyclohexanone)=O

d. $CH_3CH_2CH=CHCH_2CH_3$

Chapter 15

15-1. a. 4 **b.** It will be aromatic if it is cyclic, if it is planar, and if every carbon in the ring has a p orbital.   **15-3. a.** cyclopropenyl cation **b.** cycloheptatrienyl cation   **15-4.** d and e   **15-5. b.** 5   **15-7. a.** sp^3 **b.** sp^2 **c.** sp
15-9. quinoline = sp^2; indole = p; imidazole = 1 is sp^2 and 1 is p;

purine = 3 are sp^2 and 1 is p; pyrimidine = both are sp^2 **15-10.** A and D
15-14. a. Cyclopentadiene has the lower pK_a. **b.** Cyclopropane has the lower
pK_a. **15-15.** 3-bromocyclopropene   **15-16.** c   **15-17.** one bonding, two
nonbonding, one antibonding; two π electrons in the bonding MO and one in
each of the nonbonding MOs   **15-18.** no

15-20. a. $CH_3CHCH_2CH_2CH_2CH_3$ **c.** $CH_3CH_2CHCH_2CH_3$

15-27. a. ethylbenzene **b.** isopropylbenzene **c.** *sec*-butylbenzene
d. *tert*-butylbenzene **e.** *tert*-butylbenzene **f.** 3-phenylpropene

Chapter 16

16-1. a.

16-3. a. *ortho*-ethylphenol **b.** *meta*-bromochlorobenzene
c. *meta*-bromobenzaldehyde **d.** *ortho*-ethyltoluene   **16-6. a.** 1,3,5-tribromobenzene
b. 3-nitrophenol **c.** *para*-bromotoluene **d.** 1,2-dichlorobenzene
16-7. a. donates electrons by resonance and withdraws electrons inductively
b. donates electrons by hyperconjugation **c.** withdraws electrons by resonance
and withdraws electrons inductively **d.** donates electrons by resonance and
withdraws electrons inductively **e.** donates electrons by resonance and
withdraws electrons inductively **f.** withdraws electrons inductively
16-8. a. phenol > toluene > benzene > bromobenzene > nitrobenzene
b. toluene > chloromethylbenzene > dichloromethylbenzene
> difluoromethylbenzene

16-11.

16-12. They are all meta directors.

16-14.

16-16. a. *o*-chlorobenzoic acid **b.** benzoic acid
16-18. a. no reaction   **c.** no reaction

16-19. a. yes **b.** yes

16-21. a.

16-22. a. 2 **b.** 1 **c.** 2   **16-26.** It would complex with the amino group,
converting it into a meta director.

16-32. CH_3CHCH_3 + CH_3CHCH_3 + $CH_3CH=CH_2$ + N_2

16-35.
a. 1-chloro-2, 4-dinitrobenzene > *p*-chloronitrobenzene > chlorobenzene
b. chlorobenzene > *p*-chloronitrobenzene > 1-chloro-2, 4-dinitrochlorobenzene

Chapter 17

17-2. a. butanenitrile, propyl cyanide **b.** ethanoic propanoic anhydride, acetic
propionic anhydride **c.** potassium butanoate; potassium butyrate **d.** pentanoyl
chloride, valeryl chloride **e.** isobutyl butanoate, isobutyl butyrate
f. *N,N*-dimethylhexanamide, *N,N*-dimethylcaproamide **g.** 2-azacyclopentanone,
γ-butyrolactam **h.** cyclopentanecarboxylic acid **i.** 5-methyl-2-oxacyclohexanone,
β-methyl-δ-valerolactone   **17-4.** B
17-6. The shortest bond has the highest frequency.

17-7. acyl chloride (1800 cm^{-1}); acid anhydride (1800 cm^{-1} and 1750 cm^{-1});
ester (1730 cm^{-1}); amide (1640 cm^{-1})   **17-8.** true   **17-9. a.** acetic acid
b. no reaction   **17-10. a.** acetyl chloride **b.** acetamide   **17-11. a.** no reaction
b. acetic acid **c.** acetic anhydride **d.** no reaction   **17-12. a.** new **b.** no reaction
c. mixture of two
17-13. a. $CH_3CH_2CH_2OH$ **b.** $CH_3CH_2NH_2$ **c.** $(CH_3)_2NH$ **d.** H_2O

17-20. a. carbonyl group of the ester is relatively unreactive, nucleophile is
relatively unreactive, leaving group is a strong base **b.** aminolysis
17-22. a. benzoic acid and ethanol **b.** butanoic acid and methanol
c. 5-hydroxypentanoic acid   **17-24. a.** protonated carboxylic acid, tetrahedral
intermediate I, tetrahedral intermediate III, H_3O^+, CH_3OH **b.** Cl^-, carboxylic
acid, tetrahedral intermediate II, H_2O, CH_3OH **c.** H_3O^+ **d.** H_3O^+ if excess
water were used; $CH_3OH_2^+$ if not.   **17-26. a.** isopropyl benzoate **b.** ethyl acetate
17-30. methyl butanoate and methanol   **17-31. a.** the alcohol **b.** the carboxylic
acid   **17-34. a.** butyrate ion and iodomethane **b.** acetate ion and 1-iodooctane
17-36. a. butanoyl chloride + ethylamine **b.** benzoyl chloride + dimethylamine
17-37. a. 2 and 5 **b.** 1: heat to 225 °C; 3: do not use CH_3O^-; 4: add HCl and heat
to 225 °C; 6: do not use HO^- **17-39.** C > B > D > A   **17-40. a.** pentyl
bromide **b.** isohexyl bromide **c.** benzyl bromide **d.** cyclohexyl bromide
17-42. a. 1-bromopropane **b.** 1-bromo-2-methylpropane **c.** bromocyclohexane
17-44. a. propanoic acid + thionyl chloride followed by phenol
b. benzoic acid + thionyl chloride followed by ethylamine
17-46. PDS

Chapter 18

18-1. if elsewhere would not be a ketone   **18-2. a.** 3-methylpentanal,
β-methylvaleraldehyde **b.** 4-heptanone, dipropyl ketone
c. 2-methyl-4-heptanone, isobutyl propyl ketone **d.** 4-phenylbutanal,
γ-phenylbutyraldehyde **e.** 4-ethylhexanal, γ-ethylcaproaldehyde

f. 1-hepten-3-one, butyl vinyl ketone   **18-3. a.** 6-hydroxy-3-heptanone
b. 2-oxocyclohexylmethanenitrile **c.** 3-formylpentanamide
18-4. a. 2-heptanone **b.** *para*-nitroacetophenone   **18-5. a.** 2-hexanol
b. 2-methyl-2-pentanol **c.** 1-methylcyclohexanol

18-6. CH₃CCH₂CH₃   +   CH₃CH₂CH₂MgBr

CH₃CH₂CCH₂CH₂CH₃   +   CH₃MgBr

18-7. a. two; (*R*)-3-methyl-3-hexanol and (*S*)-3-methyl-3-hexanol
b. one; 2-methyl-2-pentanol   **18-9.** B and D   **18-10.** A and C

18-12. RC≡C—C(OH)(R)—C≡CR

18-13. a. CH₃CHCH₂OH (CH₃) **c.** Ph—CH₂OH

b. cyclohexyl—OH **d.** Ph—CHCH₃(OH)

18-14. a. 1-butanol + ethanol **b.** benzyl alcohol **c.** benzyl alcohol + methanol
d. 1-pentanol

18-15. a. Ph—CNHCH₃   **c.** CH₃CNHCH₂CH₃

b. CH₃CNH₂ **d.** CH₃CN(CH₂CH₃)(CH₂CH₃)

18-17. no   **18-18.** The conjugate bases of the strong acids are weak and readily
eliminated.   **18-20.** the OH group withdraws electrons inductively
18-21. ~ 8.5   **18-22. a.** 1×10^{-12} **b.** 1×10^{-9} **c.** 3.1×10^{-3}
18-25. the lone pair of one nitrogen is delocalized, so it is not nucleophile
18-28. a secondary amine and a tertiary amine   **18-32.** the ketone with the nitro
substituents   **18-33. a.** 7 **b.** 2, 3 **c.** 1,8 **d.** 5 **e.** 4, 6

18-36. a. cyclohexane with OH and CH₂OH   **b.** NaBH₄   **18-39. a.** 26% **b.** 17%

18-43. a. Ph—C(OH)(CH₃)—CH₂CH₃   *S*   **c.** CH₃CC(OH)CH₂CH₂CH₃ (CH₃)
compound does not have an asymmetric center

b. CH₃—C(OH)(H)—Ph   *R* **d.** CH₃CH₂CH₂—C(CH₂CH₃)(CH₃)—CH₂CH₃   *S*

18-46. Nonsterically hindered

Chapter 19

19-1. The conjugate base of propene has delocalized electrons but they are
delocalized onto a carbon.

19-2. a. CH₃CCH₂C≡N **b.** CH₃OCCH₂COCH₃
a β-keto nitrile   a β-diester

19-3. The proton on the nitrogen is more acidic than the proton on the α-carbon.
19-4. Competing electron delocalization by the lone pair on N or O is more
important for the amide than for the ester.

19-5. a. CH₃CH > HC≡CH > CH₂=CH₂ > CH₃CH₃

b. CH₃CCH₂CCH₃ > CH₃CCH₂COCH₃ > CH₃OCCH₂COCH₃ > CH₃CCH₃

c. cyclohexanone > lactone > lactam(NCH₃)

19-7. a. enol/enolate = 1×10^{12} **b.** enol/enolate = 1×10^{8}
c. enol/enolate = 1×100

19-8. a. CH₃CH=CCH₂CH₃(OH) **c.** cyclohexenol

b. Ph—C(OH)=CH₂ **d.** cyclohexenone-OH (more stable) and cyclohexenone-OH

e. CH₃CH₂C=CHCCH₂CH₃(OH) (more stable) and CH₃CH=CCH₂CCH₂CH₃(OH)

f. Ph—CH=CCH₃(OH) (more stable) and Ph—CH₂C=CH₂(OH)

19-10. You need to replace three H's with halogens to get a leaving group that is
a weaker base than HO⁻.   **19-11.** hydroxide-ion promoted   **19-12.** The rate-
determining step must be removal of the proton from the α-carbon of the ketone.

19-16. cyclohexanone with D's (D, D, D, D)

19-21. a. cyclohexenone   +   CH₃CCH₂CCH₃ + HO⁻

b. CH₃CCH=CH₂   +   CH₃CH₂OCCH₂COCH₂CH₃   +   CH₃CH₂O⁻

19-23. a. CH₃CH₂CH₂CH **c.** cyclohexyl—CH₂CH   **19-25.** spiro-bicyclohexanone

b. CH₃CCH₃ **d.** CH₃CH₂CCH₂CH₃

19-32. a. CH₃CH₂CH₂CCHCOCH₃ (CH₂, CH₃) **b.** CH₃CHCH₂CCHCOCH₂CH₃ (CH₃, CHCH₃, CH₃)

19-33. A, B, and D

19-38. a. cyclobutane(OH, CH₃, CCH₃O) **b.** cyclooctanone(OH, CH₃)   **19-41. a.** decalone(OH)

b. HO-bicyclic ketone **c.** cyclohexane(OH, CH) **d.** bicyclic(OH, CCH₃O)

19-43. A and D
19-44. a. methyl bromide **b.** methyl bromide (twice) **c.** benzyl bromide
d. isobutyl bromide
19-47. a. ethyl bromide **b.** pentyl bromide **c.** benzyl bromide
19-50. 7
19-51. a. 3 **b.** 7

Chapter 20

20-1. a. reduction **b.** neither **c.** oxidation **d.** oxidation **e.** reduction **f.** neither
20-2. a. CH₃CH₂CH₂CH₂CH₂OH   **e.** no reaction
b. CH₃CH₂CH₂CH₂NH₂   **f.** CH₃CH₂OH

c. CH₃CH₂CH₂—C=C—CH₃/H (cis alkene)   **g.** CH₃CH

d. cyclohexyl—OH   **h.** cyclohexyl—NHCH₃

20-3. a. ethylmethylamine **b.** ethyldimethylamine

20-4. a.

d.

b.

e. $CH_3CH_2CH_2CH_2NHCH_2CH_3$

c. $CH_3CH_2CHCH_2CH_3$ (with OH)   **f.** $CH_3CH_2CH_2CH_2OH$

20-5. Yes, because the bonds are polar.   **20-7.** Na will cause a terminal alkyne to be converted to an acetylide ion.

20-14.

20-15. It is stereoselective and stereospecific, but not enantioselective.

20-16. a. CH_3C—$CHCH_2CH_3$ (with CH_3 and OH)   **b.**

20-18.

20-19. a.

b.

20-20. 2,3-diemthyl-2-butene   **20-22. a.** 2,3-dimethyl-2-butene **b.** cis-4-octene and trans-4-octene   **20-24.** whether the alkene has the cis or the trans configuration

Chapter 21

21-1. a. 2,2-dimethylaziridine **b.** 4-ethylpiperidine **c.** 3-methylazacyclobutane **d.** 2-methylthiacyclopropane **e.** 2,3-dimethyltetrahydrofuran **f.** 2-ethyloxacyclobutane   **21-2.** The electron-withdrawing oxygen stabilizes the-conjugate base.

21-3. a.

b. $pK_a \sim 8$ **c.** conjugate acid of 3-chloroquinuclidine

21-9. Both acidic and basic forms of pyrrole are aromatic; only the basic form of cyclopentadiene is aromatic.

21-11.

21-14.

21-16.

21-17.

21-18. Imidazole forms intramolecular hydrogen bonds that N-methylimidazole cannot form.   **21-19.** 24%   **21-21.** yes

Chapter 22

22-1. D-Ribose is an aldopentose. D-Sedoheptulose is a ketoheptose. D-Mannose is an aldohexose.   **22-3. a.** L-glyceraldehyde **b.** L-glyceraldehyde **c.** D-glyceraldehyde   **22-4. a.** enantiomers **b.** diastereomers   **22-5. a.** D-ribose **b.** L-talose **c.** L-allose   **22-6. a.** (2R,3S,4R,5R)-2,3,4,5,6-pentahydroxyhexanal **b.** (2S,3S,4R,5R)-2,3,4,5,6-pentahydroxyhexanal   **22-7.** D-psicose **22-8. a.** A ketoheptose has four asymmetric centers ($2^4 = 16$ stereoisomers). **b.** An aldoheptose has five asymmetric centers ($2^5 = 32$ stereoisomers). **c.** A ketotriose has no asymmetric centers; therefore, it has no stereoisomers. **22-11.** D-tagatose, D-galactose, and D-talose   **22-12. a.** D-iditol **b.** D-iditol and D-gulitol   **22-13. a.** 1. D-altrose 2. L-gulose 3. L-galactose **b.** 1. D-tagatose 2. D-psicose   **22-14. a.** L-gulose **b.** L-gularic acid **c.** D-allose and L-allose, D-altrose and D-talose, L-altrose and L-talose, D-galactose and L-galactose   **22-15. a.** D-arabinose and D-ribulose **b.** D-allose and D-psicose **c.** L-gulose and L-sorbose **d.** D-talose and D-tagatose   **22-16.** D-gulose and D-idose   **22-17. a.** D-gulose and D-idose **b.** L-xylose and L-lyxose

22-18. a. D-allose and D-altrose **b.** D-glucose and D-mannose **c.** L-allose and L-altrose

22-20. A = D-glucose **B** = D-mannose **C** = D-arabinose **D** = D-erythrose

22-24. a. the OH group at C-2 **b.** the OH group at C-2, C-3, and C-4 **c.** the OH group at C-3 and C-1

22-25. A protonated amine is not a nucleophile.

22-26. b. α-D-talose (reducing) **c.** methyl α-D-galactoside (nonreducing) **d.** ethyl β-D-psicoside (nonreducing)   **22-27.** −96.7

22-30. a. They cannot receive type A, B, or AB blood because these have sugar components that type O blood does not have. **b.** They cannot give blood to those with type A, B, or O blood because AB blood has sugar components that these other blood types do not have.

Chapter 23

23-2. a. (R)-alanine **b.** (R)-aspartate **c.** The α-carbon of all the D-amino acids except cysteine has the R-configuration.   **23-4.** Ile

23-5. because of the electron-withdrawing ammonium group

23-7. a.

b.

c.

d.

23-10. a. 5.43 **b.** 10.76 **c.** 5.68 **d.** 2.98   **22-11. a.** Asp **b.** Arg **c.** Asp **d.** Met **23-13.** 2-methylpropanal   **23-14.** Leucine and isoleucine have similar polarities and pI values, so they show up as one spot.   **23-17.** His > Val > Ser > Asp **23-18.** One equivalent of ammonia will be protonated by the carboxylic acid. **23-19. a.** L-Ala, L-Asp, L-Glu **b.** L-Ala and D-Ala, L-Asp and D-Asp, L-Glu and D-Glu   **23-20. a.** leucine **b.** methionine   **23-21. a.** 4-bromo-1-butanamine **b.** benzylbromide   **23-22. a.** alanine **b.** isoleucine **c.** leucine   **23-25.** A-G-M A-M-G M-G-A M-A-G G-A-M G-M-A   **23-27.** the bonds on either side of the α-carbon   **23-28.** both have the S configuration   **23-30.** Leu-Val and Val-Val **23-33. a.** 5.8% **b.** 4.4%   **23-37.** Gly-Arg-Trp-Ala-Glu-Leu-Met-Pro-Val-Asp **23-36.** Edman's reagent would release two amino acids in approximately equal amounts.   **23-39. a.** His-Lys Leu-Val-Glu-Pro-Arg Ala-Gly-Ala **b.** Leu-Gly-Ser-Met-Phe-Pro-Tyr Gly-Val   **23-41.** Leu-Tyr-Lys-Arg-Met-Phe-Arg-Ser   **23-43.** 110 Å in an α-helix and 260 Å in a straight chain **23-44.** nonpolar groups on the outside and polar groups on the inside **23-45. a.** cigar-shaped protein **b.** subunit of a hexamer

Chapter 24

24-1. $\Delta H^{\ddagger}, E_a, \Delta S^{\ddagger}, \Delta G^{\ddagger}, k_{rate}$ **24-3.** specific acid catalyzed   **24-7.** They do not have a negatively charged oxygen on one carbon and a carbonyl group on an adjacent carbon.   **24-9.** close to one

24-10.

24-11. Solvolysis of the unsubstituted compound and the thio-substituted compound are S_N1 reactions; the rate of the thio-substituted compound is slowed down by the inductively electron withdrawing thio substituent.

24-13. The nitro groups cause the phenolate ion to be a better leaving group than the carboxylate ion.   **24-16.** 2, 3, and 4   **24-17.** Ser-Ala-Phe **24-19.** Arginine forms a direct hydrogen bond; lysine forms an indirect hydrogen bond.   **24-21.** NAM   **24-22.** The acid denatures the enzyme.   **24-24.** lysine **24-25.** 2   **24-28.** Putting a substituent on cysteine with iodoacetic acid could interfere with binding or catalysis of the substrate.

Chapter 25

25-1. It increases the susceptibility of the carbonyl carbon to nucleophilic attack, increases the nucleophilicity of water, and stabilizes the negative charge on the transition state.

25-2.

+ NADH + H^+

25-3.

$$CH_3\text{–}CH(OH)\text{–}CO\text{–}O^- + NAD^+$$

25-4. pyrophosphate   **25-5. a.** 7 **b.** 3 isolated from 2 others
25-15. a. alanine **b.** aspartate   **25-18.** the one on the right
25-22.

$$CH_3CH_2\overset{O}{\underset{}{C}}SCoA \xrightarrow[\text{biotin}]{E} CH_3\underset{COO^-}{\underset{|}{CH}}\overset{O}{\underset{}{C}}SCoA \xrightarrow[\text{coenzyme } B_{12}]{E} \underset{COO^-}{\underset{|}{CH_2}}CH_2\overset{O}{\underset{}{C}}SCoA$$

25-23. the methylene group of N^5,N^{10}-methylene-THF

Chapter 26

26-5. The β-carbon has a partial positive charge.   **26-6.** eight   **26-7.** seven
26-9. a. conversion of glucose to glucose-6-phosphate; conversion of glucose-6-phosphate to glucose-1,6-diphosphate **b.** conversion of 1,3-diphosphoglycerate to 3-phosphoglycerate; conversion of 2-phosphoenolpyruvate to pyruvate
26-10. two   **26-11.** an aldehyde   **26-12.** thiamine pyrophosphate
26-13. a ketone   **26-14.** thiamine pyrophosphate   **26-16.** pyridoxal phosphate
26-17. pyruvate   **26-18.** a secondary alcohol   **26-19.** citrate and isocitrate
26-20. succinyl   **26-21.** succinyl-CoA synthetase

Chapter 27

27-2. hexanoic acid, 3 malonic acids, and glutaric acid   **27-3.** glyceryl tripalmitate   **27-8.** no   **27-9.** Integral proteins will have a higher percentage of nonpolar amino acids.   **27-10.** The bacteria could synthesize phosphoacylglycerols with more saturated fatty acids.   **27-15.** The two halves are synthesized in a head-to-tail fashion and then joined together in a tail-to-tail linkage.   **27-18.** one to reduce the ester to an aldehyde; the second to reduce the aldehyde to a primary alcohol   **27-22.** The reaction of dimethylallyl pyrophosphate and isopentenyl pyrophosphate is an S_N1 reaction.   **27-25.** biotin
27-26. cis fused; trans fused   **27-27.** a β-substituent   **27-30.** Two are axial substituents and one is an equatorial substituent.

Chapter 28

28-6. a. $3'$—C—C—T—G—T—T—A—G—A—C—G—$5'$ **b.** guanine
28-9. Thymine and uracil have the hydrogen bond donor and the hydrogen bond acceptor in the same place.   **28-10.** Met-Asp-Pro-Val-Ile-Lys-His
28-11. Met-Asp-Pro-Leu-Leu-Asn
28-13. $5'$—G-C-A-T-G-G-A-C-C-C-C-G-T-T-A-T-T-A-A-A-C-A-C—$3'$
28-15.

xanthine   hypoxanthine

28-17. a

Chapter 29

29-1. a. $CH_2\!=\!CHCl$ **b.** $CH_2\!=\!CCH_3$ (with $\overset{O}{\underset{}{COCH_3}}$ group)   **c.** $CF_2\!=\!CF$

29-2. poly(vinyl chloride)   **29-5.** beach balls

29-7. a. $CH_2\!=\!CH$–(C$_6$H$_4$–OCH$_3$) > $CH_2\!=\!CH$–(C$_6$H$_4$–CH$_3$) > $CH_2\!=\!CH$–(C$_6$H$_4$–NO$_2$)

b. $CH_2\!=\!CHO\overset{O}{\underset{}{C}}CH_3$ > $CH_2\!=\!CHCH_3$ > $CH_2\!=\!CH\overset{O}{\underset{}{C}}OCH_3$

c. $CH_2\!=\!CCH_3$(phenyl) > $CH_2\!=\!CH$(phenyl)

29-8. a. $CH_2\!=\!CH$–(C$_6$H$_4$–NO$_2$) > $CH_2\!=\!CH$–(C$_6$H$_4$–CH$_3$) > $CH_2\!=\!CH$–(C$_6$H$_4$–OCH$_3$)

b. $CH_2\!=\!CHC\!\equiv\!N$ < $CH_2\!=\!CHCl$ < $CH_2\!=\!CHCH_3$
29-9. The carbocation would be unstable because of the electron withdrawing ester group.

29-12. a. $CH_2\!=\!CCH_3$ (with CH_3) $+ BF_3 + H_2O$ **c.** (epoxide) $+ CH_3O^-$

b. $CH_2\!=\!CH$ (pyrrolidine) $+ BF_3 + H_2O$ **d.** $CH_2\!=\!CH$ (with $\overset{O}{\underset{}{COCH_3}}$) $+ BuLi$

29-13.

$$H_3C\text{–}(\text{oxetane})\overset{+}{O}\text{–}CH_2\underset{CH_3}{\overset{CH_3}{C}}CH_2OCH_2\underset{CH_3}{\overset{CH_3}{C}}CH_2OCH_2\underset{CH_3}{\overset{CH_3}{C}}CH_2OH$$

28-16. a. $-NHCH_2CH_2CH_2\overset{O}{\underset{}{C}}NHCH_2CH_2CH_2\overset{O}{\underset{}{C}}-$

b. $-NH(CH_2)_4NH\overset{O}{\underset{}{C}}CH_2CH_2\overset{O}{\underset{}{C}}NH(CH_2)_4NH\overset{O}{\underset{}{C}}CH_2CH_2\overset{O}{\underset{}{C}}-$

Chapter 30

30-1. a. electrocyclic reaction **b.** sigmatropic rearrangement
c. cycloaddition reaction **d.** cycloaddition reaction
30-2. a. bonding orbitals = ψ_1, ψ_2, ψ_3; antibonding orbitals = ψ_4, ψ_5, ψ_6;
b. ground-state HOMO = ψ_3; ground-state LUMO = ψ_4
c. excited-state HOMO = ψ_4; excited-state LUMO = ψ_5
d. symmetric orbitals = ψ_1, ψ_3, ψ_5; antisymmetric orbitals = ψ_2, ψ_4, ψ_6
e. The HOMO and LUMO have opposite symmetries.   **30-3. a.** 8 **b.** ψ_4 **c.** 7
30-6. a. conrotatory **b.** trans **c.** disrotatory **d.** cis   **30-7. a.** correct **b.** correct
c. correct   **30-8. 1. a.** conrotatory **b.** trans **2. a.** disrotatory **b.** cis   **30-11.** yes

30-13.

(reaction scheme with ^{14}C labels)

30-18. a. inversion **b.** retention   **30-19.** antarafacial

G L O S S A R Y

absolute configuration   the three-dimensional structure of a chiral compound. The configuration is designated by *R* or *S*.

absorption band   a peak in a spectrum that occurs as a result of the absorption of energy.

acetal

acetamidomalonic ester synthesis   a method used to synthesize an amino acid that is a variation of the *N*-phthalimidomalonic ester synthesis.

acetoacetic ester synthesis   synthesis of a methyl ketone, using ethyl acetoacetate as the starting material.

achiral (optically inactive)   an achiral molecule has a conformation identical to (superimposable upon) its mirror image.

acid (Brønsted)   a substance that donates a proton.

acid anhydride

acid–base reaction   a reaction in which an acid donates a proton to a base or accepts a share in a base's electrons.

acid catalyst   a catalyst that increases the rate of a reaction by donating a proton.

acid-catalyzed reaction   a reaction catalyzed by an acid.

acid dissociation constant   a measure of the degree to which an acid dissociates in solution.

activating substituent   a substituent that increases the reactivity of an aromatic ring. Electron-donating substituents activate aromatic rings toward electrophilic attack, and electron-withdrawing substituents activate aromatic rings toward nucleophilic attack.

active site   a pocket or cleft in an enzyme where the substrate is bound.

acyclic   noncyclic.

acyl adenylate   a carboxylic acid derivative with AMP as the leaving group.

acyl–enzyme intermediate   an intermediate formed when an amino acid residue of an enzyme is acetylated.

acyl group   a carbonyl group bonded to an alkyl group or to an aryl group.

acyl halide

acyl phosphate   a carboxylic acid derivative with a phosphate leaving group.

acyl pyrophosphate   a carboxylic acid derivative with a pyrophosphate leaving group.

1,2-addition (direct addition)   addition to the 1- and 2-positions of a conjugated system.

1,4-addition (conjugate addition)   addition to the 1- and 4-positions of a conjugated system.

addition polymer (chain-growth polymer)   a polymer made by adding monomers to the growing end of a chain.

addition reaction   a reaction in which atoms or groups are added to the reactant.

adrenal cortical steroids   glucocorticoids and mineralocorticoids.

alcohol   a compound with an OH group in place of one of the hydrogens of an alkane; (ROH).

alcoholysis   reaction with an alcohol.

aldaric acid   a dicarboxylic acid with an OH group bonded to each carbon. Obtained by oxidizing the aldehyde and primary alcohol groups of an aldose.

aldehyde

alditol   a compound with an OH group bonded to each carbon. Obtained by reducing an aldose or a ketose.

aldol addition   a reaction between two molecules of an aldehyde (or two molecules of a ketone) that connects the α-carbon of one with the carbonyl carbon of the other.

aldol condensation   an aldol addition followed by the elimination of water.

aldonic acid   a carboxylic acid with an OH group bonded to each carbon. Obtained by oxidizing the aldehyde group of an aldose.

aldose   a polyhydroxyaldehyde.

aliphatic   a nonaromatic organic compound.

alkaloid   a natural product, with one or more nitrogen heteroatoms, found in the leaves, bark, or seeds of plants.

alkane   a hydrocarbon that contains only single bonds.

alkene   a hydrocarbon that contains a double bond.

alkene metathesis   breaks the double bond of an alkene (or the triple bond of an alkyne) and then rejoins the fragments.

alkoxymercuration   addition of alcohol to an alkene, using a mercuric salt of a carboxylic acid as a catalyst.

alkylation reaction   a reaction that adds an alkyl group to a reactant.

alkyl halide   a compound with a halogen in place of one of the hydrogens of an alkane.

alkyl substituent (alkyl group)   formed by removing a hydrogen from an alkane.

alkyl tosylate   an ester of *para*-toluenesulfonic acid.

alkyne   a hydrocarbon that contains a triple bond.

allene   a compound with two adjacent double bonds.

allyl group $CH_2=CHCH_2-$

allylic carbon   an sp^3 carbon adjacent to a vinylic carbon.

allylic cation   a species with a positive charge on an allylic carbon.

alpha olefin   a monosubstituted olefin.

alternating copolymer   a copolymer in which two monomers alternate.

ambident nucleophile   a nucleophile with two nucleophilic sites.

amide

amine   a compound with a nitrogen in place of one of the hydrogens of an alkane; (RNH_2, R_2NH, R_3N)

amine inversion   the configuration of an sp^3 hybridized nitrogen with a nonbonding pair of electrons rapidly turns inside out.

amino acid   an α-aminocarboxylic acid. Naturally occurring amino acids have the *l* configuration.

amino acid analyzer   an instrument that automates the ion-exchange separation of amino acids.

amino acid residue   a monomeric unit of a peptide or protein.

aminolysis   reaction with an amine.

amino sugar   a sugar in which one of the OH groups is replaced by an NH_2 group.

amphoteric compound   a compound that can behave either as an acid or as a base.

anabolic steroids   steroids that aid in the development of muscle.

anabolism   reactions that living organisms carry out in order to synthesize complex molecules from simple precursor molecules.

anchimeric assistance (intramolecular catalysis)   catalysis in which the catalyst that facilitates the reaction is part of the molecule undergoing reaction.

androgens   male sex hormones.

angle strain   the strain introduced into a molecule as a result of its bond angles being distorted from their ideal values.

angstrom   unit of length; 100 picometers = 10^{-8} cm = 1 angstrom

angular methyl group   a methyl substituent at the 10- or 13-position of a steroid ring system.

anion-exchange resin   a positively charged resin used in ion-exchange chromatography.

anionic polymerization   chain-growth polymerization in which the initiator is a nucleophile; the propagation site therefore is an anion.

annulation reaction   a ring-forming reaction.

annulene   a monocyclic hydrocarbon with alternating double and single bonds.

anomeric carbon   the carbon in a cyclic sugar that is the carbonyl carbon in the open-chain form.

anomeric effect   the preference for the axial position shown by certain substituents bonded to the anomeric carbon of a six-membered-ring sugar.

anomers   two cyclic sugars that differ in configuration only at the carbon that is the carbonyl carbon in the open-chain form.

antarafacial bond formation   formation of two σ bonds on opposites sides of the π system.

antarafacial rearrangement   rearrangement in which the migrating group moves to the opposite face of the π system.

anti addition   an addition reaction in which two substituents are added at opposite sides of the molecule.

antiaromatic   a cyclic and planar compound with an uninterrupted ring of p orbital-bearing atoms containing an even number of pairs of π electrons.

antibiotic   a compound that interferes with the growth of a microorganism.

antibodies   compounds that recognize foreign particles in the body.

antibonding molecular orbital   a molecular orbital that results when two atomic orbitals with opposite signs interact. Electrons in an antibonding orbital decrease bond strength.

anticodon   the three bases at the bottom of the middle loop in tRNA.

anti conformer   the most stable of the staggered conformers.

anti elimination   an elimination reaction in which the two substituents that are eliminated are removed from opposite sides of the molecule.

antigene agent   a polymer designed to bind to DNA at a particular site.

antigens   compounds that can generate a response from the immune system.

anti-periplanar   parallel substituents on opposite sides of a molecule.

antisense agent   a polymer designed to bind to mRNA at a particular site.

antisense strand (template strand)   the strand in DNA that is read during transcription.

antisymmetric molecular orbital   a molecular orbital in which the left (or top) half is not a mirror of the right (or bottom) half.

antiviral drug   a drug that interferes with DNA or RNA synthesis in order to prevent a virus from replicating.

apoenzyme   an enzyme without its cofactor.

applied magnetic field   the externally applied magnetic field.

aprotic solvent   a solvent that does not have a hydrogen bonded to an oxygen or to a nitrogen.

aramide   an aromatic polyamide.

arene oxide   an aromatic compound that has had one of its double bonds converted to an epoxide.

aromatic   a cyclic and planar compound with an uninterrupted ring of p orbital-bearing atoms containing an odd number of pairs of π electrons.

Arrhenius equation   relates the rate constant of a reaction to the energy of activation and to the temperature at which the reaction is carried out ($k = Ae^{-E_a/RT}$).

aryl group   a benzene or a substituted-benzene group.

asymmetric center   an atom bonded to four different atoms or groups.

atactic polymer   a polymer in which the substituents are randomly oriented on the extended carbon chain.

atomic number   the number of protons (or electrons) that the neutral atom has.

atomic orbital   an orbital associated with an atom.

atomic weight   the average mass of the atoms in the naturally occurring element.

aufbau principle   states that an electron will always go into that orbital with the lowest available energy.

automated solid-phase peptide synthesis   an automated technique that synthesizes a peptide while its C-terminal amino acid is attached to a solid support.

autoradiograph   the exposed photographic plate obtained in autoradiography.

autoradiography   a technique used to determine the base sequence of DNA.

auxochrome   a substituent that when attached to a chromophore, alters the λ_{max} and intensity of absorption of UV/Vis radiation.

axial bond   a bond of the chair conformation of cyclohexane that is perpendicular to the plane in which the chair is drawn (an up–down bond).

aziridine   a three-membered-ring compound in which one of the ring atoms is a nitrogen.

azo linkage   an —N=N— bond.

back-side attack   nucleophilic attack on the side of the carbon opposite the side bonded to the leaving group.

bactericidal drug   a drug that kills bacteria.

bacteriostatic drug   a drug that inhibits the further growth of bacteria.

Baeyer–Villiger oxidation   oxidation of aldehydes or ketones with H_2O_2 to form carboxylic acids or esters, respectively.

banana bond   the σ bonds in small rings that are weaker as a result of overlapping at an angle rather than overlapping head-on.

base^1   a substance that accepts a proton.

base^2   a heterocyclic compound (a purine or a pyrimidine) in DNA and RNA.

base catalyst   a catalyst that increases the rate of a reaction by removing a proton.

base peak   the peak with the greatest abundance in a mass spectrum.

basicity   the tendency of a compound to share its electrons with a proton.

Beer–Lambert law   relationship among the absorbance of UV/Vis light, the concentration of the sample, the length of the light path, and the molar absorptivity ($A = cl\varepsilon$).

bending vibration   a vibration that does not occur along the line of the bond. It results in changing bond angles.

benzoyl group   ring bonded to a carbonyl group.

benzyl group

benzylic carbon   an sp^3 hybridized carbon bonded to a benzene ring.

benzylic cation   a compound with a positive charge on a benzylic carbon.

benzyne intermediate   a compound with a triple bond in place of one of the double bonds of benzene.

bicyclic compound   a compound containing two rings that share at least one carbon.

bifunctional molecule   a molecule with two functional groups.

bile acids   steroids that act as emulsifying agents so that water-insoluble compounds can be digested.

bimolecular reaction (second-order reaction)   a reaction whose rate depends on the concentration of two reactants.

biochemistry (biological chemistry)   the chemistry of biological systems.

biodegradable polymer   a polymer that can be broken into small segments by an enzyme-catalyzed reaction.

bioorganic compound   an organic compound found in biological systems.

biopolymer   a polymer that is synthesized in nature.

biosynthesis   synthesis in a biological system.

biotin   the coenzyme required by enzymes that catalyze carboxylation of a carbon adjacent to an ester or a keto group.

Birch reduction   the partial reduction of benzene to 1,4-cyclohexadiene.

blind screen (random screen)   the search for a pharmacologically active compound without any information about which chemical structures might show activity.

block copolymer   a copolymer in which there are regions (blocks) of each kind of monomer.

blue shift   a shift to a shorter wavelength.

boat conformation   the conformation of cyclohexane that roughly resembles a boat.

boiling point   the temperature at which the vapor pressure from a liquid equals the atmospheric pressure.

bonding molecular orbital   a molecular orbital that results when two in-phase atomic orbitals interact. Electrons in a bonding orbital increase bond strength.

bond length   the internuclear distance between two atoms at minimum energy (maximum stability).

bond strength   the energy required to break a bond homolytically.

brand name (proprietary name, trade name)   identifies a commercial product and distinguishes it from other products. It can be used only by the owner of the registered trademark.

bridged bicyclic compound   a bicyclic compound in which rings share two nonadjacent carbons.

Brønsted acid   a substance that donates a proton.

Brønsted base   a substance that accepts a proton.

buffer   a weak acid and its conjugate base.

carbanion   a compound containing a negatively charged carbon.

carbene   a species with a carbon that has a nonbonded pair of electrons and an empty orbital

carbocation   a species containing a positively charged carbon.

carbocation rearrangement   the rearrangement of a carbocation to a more stable carbocation.

carbohydrate   a sugar or a saccharide. Naturally occurring carbohydrates have the D configuration.

α-carbon   a carbon bonded to a leaving group or adjacent to a carbonyl carbon.

β-carbon   a carbon adjacent to an α-carbon.

carbon acid   a compound containing a carbon that is bonded to a relatively acidic hydrogen.

carbonyl addition (direct addition)   nucleophilic addition to the carbonyl carbon.

carbonyl carbon   the carbon of a carbonyl group.

carbonyl compound   a compound that contains a carbonyl group.

carbonyl group   a carbon doubly bonded to an oxygen.

carbonyl oxygen   the oxygen of a carbonyl group.

carboxyl group   COOH

carboxylic acid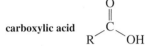

carboxylic acid derivative   a compound that is hydrolyzed to a carboxylic acid.

carboxyl oxygen   the single-bonded oxygen of a carboxlic acid or an ester.

carotenoid   a class of compounds (a tetraterpene) responsible for the red and orange colors of fruits, vegetables, and fall leaves.

catabolism   reactions that living organisms carry out in order to break down complex molecules into simple molecules and energy.

catalyst   a species that increases the rate at which a reaction occurs without being consumed in the reaction. Because it does not change the equilibrium constant of the reaction, it does not change the amount of product that is formed.

catalytic antibody   a compound that facilitates a reaction by forcing the conformation of the substrate in the direction of the transition state.

catalytic hydrogenation   the addition of hydrogen to a double or a triple bond with the aid of a metal catalyst.

cation-exchange resin   a negatively charged resin used in ion-exchange chromatography.

cationic polymerization   chain-growth polymerization in which the initiator is an electrophile; the propagation site therefore is a cation.

cephalin   a phosphoacylglycerol in which the second OH group of phosphate has formed an ester with ethanolamine.

cerebroside   a sphingolipid in which the terminal OH group of sphingosine is bonded to a sugar residue.

chain-growth polymer (addition polymer)   a polymer made by adding monomers to the growing end of a chain.

chain transfer   a growing polymer chain reacts with a molecule XY in a manner that allows X to terminate the chain, leaving behind Y to initiate a new chain.

chair conformation   the conformation of cyclohexane that roughly resembles a chair. It is the most stable conformation of cyclohexane.

chemical exchange   the transfer of a proton from one molecule to another.

chemically equivalent protons   protons with the same connectivity relationship to the rest of the molecule.

chemical shift   the location of a signal in an NMR spectrum. It is measured downfield from a reference compound (most often, TMS).

chiral (optically active)   a chiral molecule has a nonsuperimposable mirror image.

chiral auxiliary   an enantiomerically pure compound that, when attached to a reactant, causes a product with a particular configuration to be formed.

chirality center   a tetrahedral atom bonded to four different groups.

cholesterol   a steroid that is the precursor of all other animal steroids.

chromatography   a separation technique in which the mixture to be separated is dissolved in a solvent and the solvent is passed through a column packed with an absorbent stationary phase.

chromophore   the part of a molecule responsible for a UV or visible spectrum.

cine substitution   substitution at the carbon adjacent to the carbon that was bonded to the leaving group.

s-cis conformation   the conformation in which two double bonds are on the same side of a single bond.

cis fused   two cyclohexane rings fused together such that if the second ring were considered to be two substituents of the first ring, one substituent would be in an axial position and the other would be in an equatorial position.

cis isomer   the isomer with the hydrogens on the same side of the double bond or cyclic structure.

cis–trans isomers   geometric isomers.

citric acid cycle (Krebs cycle)   a series of reactions that converts the acetyl group of acetyl-CoA into two molecules of CO_2.

Claisen condensation   a reaction between two molecules of an ester that connects the α-carbon of one with the carbonyl carbon of the other and eliminates an alkoxide ion.

Claisen rearrangement   a [3,3] sigmatropic rearrangement of an allyl vinyl ether.

α-cleavage   homolytic cleavage of an alpha substituent.

Clemmensen reduction   a reaction that reduces the carbonyl group of a ketone to a methylene group using Zn(Hg)/ HCl.

codon   a sequence of three bases in mRNA that specifies the amino acid to be incorporated into a protein.

coenzyme   a cofactor that is an organic molecule.

coenzyme A   a thiol used by biological organisms to form thioesters.

coenzyme B_{12}   the coenzyme required by enzymes that catalyze certain rearrangement reactions.

cofactor   an organic molecule or a metal ion that certain enzymes need to catalyze a reaction.

coil conformation (loop conformation)   that part of a protein that is highly ordered, but not in an α-helix or a β-pleated sheet.

combination band   occurs at the sum of two fundamental absorption frequencies ($v_1 + v_2$).

combinatorial library   a group of structurally related compounds.

combinatorial organic synthesis   the synthesis of a library of compounds by covalently connecting sets of building blocks of varying structure.

common intermediate   an intermediate that two compounds have in common.

common name   nonsystematic nomenclature.

competitive inhibitor   a compound that inhibits an enzyme by competing with the substrate for binding at the active site.

complete racemization   the formation of a pair of enantiomers in equal amounts.

complex carbohydrate   a carbohydrate containing two or more sugar molecules linked together.

concerted reaction   a reaction in which all the bond-making and bond-breaking processes occur in one step.

condensation polymer (step-growth polymer)   a polymer made by combining two molecules while removing a small molecule (usually water or an alcohol).

condensation reaction   a reaction combining two molecules while removing a small molecule (usually water or an alcohol).

conducting polymer   a polymer that can conduct electricity.

configuration   the three-dimensional structure of a particular atom in a compound. The configuration is designated by R or S.

configurational isomers   stereoisomers that cannot interconvert unless a covalent bond is broken. Cis–trans isomers and optical isomers are configurational isomers.

conformation   the three-dimensional shape of a molecule at a given instant that can change as a result of rotations about σ bonds.

conformational analysis   the investigation of the various conformations of a compound and their relative stabilities.

conformers   different conformations of a molecule.

conjugate acid   a species accepts a proton to form its conjugate acid.

conjugate addition   1,4-addition to an α,β,-unsaturated carbonyl compound.

conjugate base   a species loses a proton to form its conjugate base.

conjugated double bonds   double bonds separated by one single bond.

conrotatory ring closure   achieves head-to-head overlap of p orbitals by rotating the orbitals in the same direction.

conservation of orbital symmetry theory   a theory that explains the relationship between the structure and configuration of the reactant, the conditions under which a pericyclic reaction takes place, and the configuration of the product.

constitutional isomers (structural isomers)   molecules that have the same molecular formula but differ in the way their atoms are connected.

contributing resonance structure (resonance contributor, resonance structure)   a structure with localized electrons that approximates the structure of a compound with delocalized electrons.

convergent synthesis   a synthesis in which pieces of the target compound are individually prepared and then assembled.

Cope elimination reaction   elimination of a proton and a hydroxyl amine from an amine oxide.

Cope rearrangement   a [3,3] sigmatropic rearrangement of a 1,5-diene.

copolymer   a polymer formed from two or more different monomers.

corrin ring system   a porphyrin ring system without one of the methine bridges.

COSY spectrum   a 2-D NMR spectrum that shows coupling between sets of protons.

coupled protons   protons that split each other. Coupled protons have the same coupling constant.

coupling constant   the distance (in hertz) between two adjacent peaks of a split NMR signal.

coupling reaction   a reaction that joins two alkyl groups.

covalent bond   a bond created as a result of sharing electrons.

covalent catalysis (nucleophilic catalysis)   catalysis that occurs as a result of a nucleophile forming a covalent bond with one of the reactants.

Cram's rule   the rule used to determine the major product of a carbonyl addition reaction in a compound with an asymmetric center adjacent to the carbonyl group.

cross-conjugation   nonlinear conjugation.

crossed (mixed) aldol addition   an aldol addition in which two different carbonyl compounds are used.

cross-linking   connecting polymer chains by intermolecular bond formation.

crown ether   a cyclic molecule that contains several ether linkages.

crown–guest complex   the complex formed when a crown ether binds a substrate.

cryptand   a three-dimensional polycyclic compound that binds a substrate by encompassing it.

cryptate   the complex formed when a cryptand binds a substrate.

crystallites   regions of a polymer in which the chains are highly ordered.

C-terminal amino acid   the terminal amino acid of a peptide (or protein) that has a free carboxyl group.

cumulated double bonds   double bonds that are adjacent to one other.

Curtius rearrangement   conversion of an acyl chloride into a primary amine with the use of azide ion ($^-N_3$).

cyanohydrin
$$\text{R}-\overset{\overset{\displaystyle \text{OH}}{|}}{\underset{\underset{\displaystyle \text{C}\equiv\text{N}}{|}}{\text{C}}}-\text{R(H)}$$

cycloaddition reaction   a reaction in which two π-bond-containing molecules react to form a cyclic compound.

[4 + 2] cycloaddition reaction   a cycloaddition reaction in which four π electrons come from one reactant and two π electrons come from the other reactant.

cycloalkane   an alkane with its carbon chain arranged in a closed ring.

deactivating substituent   a substituent that decreases the reactivity of an aromatic ring. Electron-withdrawing substituents deactivate aromatic rings toward electrophilic attack, and electron-donating substituents deactivate aromatic rings toward nucleophilic attack.

deamination   loss of ammonia.

decarboxylation   loss of carbon dioxide.

degenerate orbitals   orbitals that have the same energy.

dehydration   loss of water.

dehydrogenase   an enzyme that carries out an oxidation reaction by removing hydrogen from the substrate.

dehydrohalogenation   elimination of a proton and a halide ion.

delocalization energy (resonance energy)   the extra stability a compound achieves as a result of having delocalized electrons.

delocalized electrons   electrons that are shared by more than two atoms.

denaturation   destruction of the highly organized tertiary structure of a protein.

deoxygenation   removal of an oxygen from a reactant.

deoxyribonucleic acid (DNA)   a polymer of deoxyribonucleotides.

deoxyribonucleotide   a nucleotide in which the sugar component is D-2′ deoxyribose.

deoxy sugar   a sugar in which one of the OH groups has been replaced by an H.

DEPT ^{13}C NMR spectrum   a series of four spectra that distinguishes among $-CH_3$, $-CH_2$, and $-CH$ groups.

depurination   elimination of a purine ring.

detergent   a salt of a sulfonic acid.

deuterium kinetic isotope effect   ratio of the rate constant obtained for a compound containing hydrogen and the rate constant obtained for an identical compound in which one or more of the hydrogens have been replaced by deuterium.

dextrorotatory   the enantiomer that rotates polarized light in a clockwise direction.

diastereomer   a configurational stereoisomer that is not an enantiomer.

diastereotopic hydrogens   two hydrogens bonded to a carbon that when replaced with a deuterium, result in a pair of diastereomers.

1,3-diaxial interaction   the interaction between an axial substituent and the other two axial substituents on the same side of the cyclohexane ring.

diazonium ion $Ar\overset{+}{N}\equiv N$ or $R\overset{+}{N}\equiv N$.

diazonium salt   a diazonium ion and an anion ($Ar\overset{+}{N}\equiv NX^-$).

Dieckmann condensation   an intramolecular Claisen condensation.

dielectric constant   a measure of how well a solvent can insulate opposite charges from one another.

Diels–Alder reaction   a [4 + 2] cycloaddition reaction.

diene   a hydrocarbon with two double bonds.

dienophile   an alkene that reacts with a diene in a Diels–Alder reaction.

β-diketone   a ketone with a second carbonyl group at the β-position.

dimer   a molecule formed by the joining together of two identical molecules.

dinucleotide   two nucleotides linked by phosphodiester bonds.

dipeptide   two amino acids linked by an amide bond.

dipole–dipole interaction   an interaction between the dipole of one molecule and the dipole of another.

dipole moment (μ)   a measure of the separation of charge in a bond or in a molecule.

direct addition   1,2-addition.

direct displacement mechanism   a reaction in which the nucleophile displaces the leaving group in a single step.

direct substitution   substitution at the carbon that was bonded to the leaving group.

disaccharide   a compound containing two sugar molecules linked together.

disconnection   breaking a bond to carbon to give a simpler species.

disproportionation   transfer of a hydrogen atom by a radical to another radical, forming an alkane and an alkene.

disrotatory ring closure   achieves head-to-head overlap of p orbitals by rotating the orbitals in opposite directions.

dissociation energy   the amount of energy required to break a bond, or the amount of energy released when a bond is formed.

dissolving-metal reduction   a reduction brought about by the use of sodium or lithium metal dissolved in liquid ammonia.

distribution coefficient   the ratio of the amounts of a compound dissolving in each of two solvents in contact with each other.

disulfide bridge   a disulfide ($-S-S-$) bond in a peptide or protein.

DNA (deoxyribonucleic acid)   a polymer of deoxyribonucleotides.

double bond   a σ bond and a π bond between two atoms.

doublet   an NMR signal split into two peaks.

doublet of doublets   an NMR signal split into four peaks of approximately equal height. Caused by splitting a signal into a doublet by one hydrogen and into another doublet by another (nonequivalent) hydrogen.

drug   a compound that reacts with a biological molecule, triggering a physiological effect.

drug resistance   biological resistance to a particular drug.

drug synergism   when the effect of two drugs used in combination is greater than the sum of the effects obtained when the drugs are administered individually.

eclipsed conformation   a conformation in which the bonds on adjacent carbons are aligned as viewed looking down the carbon–carbon bond.

E conformation   the conformation of a carboxylic acid or carboxylic acid derivative in which the carbonyl oxygen and the substituent bonded to the carboxyl oxygen or nitrogen are on opposite sides of the single bond.

Edman's reagent   phenyl isothiocyanate. A reagent used to determine the N-terminal amino acid of a polypeptide.

effective magnetic field   the magnetic field that a proton "senses" through the surrounding cloud of electrons.

effective molarity   the concentration of the reagent that would be required in an intermolecular reaction for it to have the same rate as an intramolecular reaction.

E isomer   the isomer with the high-priority groups on opposite sides of the double bond.

elastomer   a polymer that can stretch and then revert to its original shape.

electrocyclic reaction   a reaction in which a π bond in the reactant is lost so that a cyclic compound with a new σ bond can be formed.

electromagnetic radiation   radiant energy that displays wave properties.

electron affinity   the energy given off when an atom acquires an electron.

electronegative element   an element that readily acquires an electron.

electronegativity   tendency of an atom to pull electrons toward itself.

electronic transition   promotion of an electron from its HOMO to its LUMO.

electron sink   site to which electrons can be delocalized.

electrophile   an electron-deficient atom or molecule.

electrophilic addition reaction   an addition reaction in which the first species that adds to the reactant is an electrophile.

electrophilic aromatic substitution   a reaction in which an electrophile substitutes for a hydrogen of an aromatic ring.

electrophilic catalysis   catalysis in which the species that facilitates the reaction is an electrophile.

electrophoresis   a technique that separates amino acids on the basis of their pI values.

electropositive element   an element that readily loses an electron.

electrostatic attraction   attractive force between opposite charges.

electrostatic catalysis   stabilization of a charge by an opposite charge.

elemental analysis   a determination of the relative proportions of the elements present in a compound.

α-elimination   removal of two atoms or groups from the same carbon.

β-elimination   removal of two atoms or groups from adjacent carbons.

elimination reaction   a reaction that involves the elimination of atoms (or molecules) from the reactant.

empirical formula   formula giving the relative numbers of the different kinds of atoms in a molecule.

enamine   an α,β-unsaturated tertiary amine.

enantiomerically pure   containing only one enantiomer.

enantiomeric excess (optical purity)   how much excess of one enantiomer is present in a mixture of a pair of enantiomers.

enantiomers   nonsuperimposable mirror-image molecules.

enantioselective reaction   a reaction that forms an excess of one enantiomer.

enantiotopic hydrogens   two hydrogens bonded to a carbon that is bonded to two other groups that are nonidentical.

endergonic reaction   a reaction with a positive $\Delta G°$.

endo   a substituent is endo if it is closer to the longer or more unsaturated bridge.

endopeptidase   an enzyme that hydrolyzes a peptide bond that is not at the end of a peptide chain.

endothermic reaction   a reaction with a positive $\Delta H°$.

enediol rearrangement   interconversion of an aldose and one or more ketoses.

enkephalins   pentapeptides synthesized by the body to control pain.

enolization   keto–enol interconversion.

enthalpy   the heat given off ($-\Delta H°$) or the heat absorbed ($+\Delta H°$) during the course of a reaction.

entropy   a measure of the freedom of motion in a system.

enzyme   a protein that is a catalyst.

epimerization   changing the configuration of an asymmetric center by removing a proton from it and then reprotonating the molecule at the same site.

epimers   monosaccharides that differ in configuration at only one carbon.

epoxidation   formation of an epoxide.

epoxide (oxirane)   an ether in which the oxygen is incorporated into a three-membered ring.

epoxy resin   substance formed by mixing a low-molecular-weight prepolymer with a compound that forms a cross-linked polymer.

equatorial bond   a bond of the chair conformer of cyclohexane that juts out from the ring in approximately the same plane that contains the chair.

equilibrium constant   the ratio of products to reactants at equilibrium or the ratio of the rate constants for the forward and reverse reactions.

equilibrium control   thermodynamic control.

E1 reaction   a first-order elimination reaction.

E2 reaction   a second-order elimination reaction.

erythro enantiomers   the pair of enantiomers with similar groups on the same side as drawn in a Fischer projection.

essential amino acid   an amino acid that humans must obtain from their diet because they cannot synthesize it at all or cannot synthesize it in adequate amounts.

essential oils   fragrances and flavorings isolated from plants that do not leave residues when they evaporate. Most are terpenes.

ester $\overset{\displaystyle O}{\underset{\displaystyle R}{\overset{\displaystyle \|}{C}}}\diagdown OR$

estrogens   female sex hormones.

ether   a compound containing an oxygen bonded to two carbons (ROR).

eukaryote   a unicellular or multicellular body whose cell or cells contain a nucleus.

excited-state electronic configuration   the electronic configuration that results when an electron in the ground-state electronic configuration has been moved to a higher energy orbital.

exergonic reaction   a reaction with a negative $\Delta G°$.

exhaustive methylation   reaction of an amine with excess methyl iodide to form a quaternary ammonium iodide.

exo   a substituent is exo if it is closer to the shorter or more saturated bridge.

exon   a stretch of bases in DNA that are a portion of a gene.

exopeptidase   an enzyme that hydrolyzes a peptide bond at the end of a peptide chain.

exothermic reaction   a reaction with a negative $\Delta H°$.

experimental energy of activation $(E_a = \Delta H^{\ddagger} - RT)$ a measure of the approximate energy barrier to a reaction. (It is approximate because it does not contain an entropy component.)

extrusion reaction   a reaction in which a neutral molecule (e.g., CO_2, CO, or N_2) is eliminated from a molecule.

fat   a triester of glycerol that exists as a solid at room temperature.

fatty acid   a long-chain carboxylic acid.

Favorskii reaction   reaction of an α-haloketone with hydroxide ion.

fibrous protein   a water-insoluble protein in which the polypeptide chains are arranged in bundles.

fingerprint region   the right-hand third of an IR spectrum where the absorption bands are characteristic of the compound as a whole.

first-order rate constant   the rate constant of a first-order reaction.

first-order reaction (unimolecular reaction)   a reaction whose rate depends on the concentration of one reactant.

Fischer esterification reaction   the reaction of a carboxylic acid with alcohol in the presence of an acid catalyst to form an ester.

Fischer projection   a method of representing the spatial arrangement of groups bonded to an asymmetric center. The asymmetric center is the point of intersection of two perpendicular lines; the horizontal lines represent bonds that project out of the plane of the paper toward the viewer, and the vertical lines represent bonds that point back from the plane of the paper away from the viewer.

flagpole hydrogens (transannular hydrogens)   the two hydrogens in the boat conformation of cyclohexane that are closest to each other.

flavin adenine dinucleotide (FAD)   a coenzyme required in certain oxidation reactions. It is reduced to $FADH_2$ which can act as a reducing agent in another reaction.

flavin mononucleotide (FMN)   a coenzyme required in certain oxidation reactions. It is reduced to $FMNH_2$, which can act as a reducing agent in another reaction.

formal charge   the number of valence electrons – (the number of nonbonding electrons + 1/2 the number of bonding electrons).

Fourier transform NMR   a technique in which all the nuclei are excited simultaneously by an rf pulse, their relaxation is monitored, and the data are mathematically converted to a spectrum.

free energy of activation $(\Delta G^{\ddagger})$ the true energy barrier to a reaction.

free-induction decay   relaxation of excited nuclei.

frequency   the velocity of a wave divided by its wavelength (in units of cycles/s).

Friedel–Crafts acylation   an electrophilic substitution reaction that puts an acyl group on a benzene ring.

Friedel–Crafts alkylation   an electrophilic substitution reaction that puts an alkyl group on a benzene ring.

frontier orbital analysis   determining the outcome of a pericyclic reaction with the use of frontier orbitals.

frontier orbitals   the HOMO and the LUMO.

frontier orbital theory   a theory that, like the conservation of orbital symmetry theory, explains the relationships among reactant, product, and reaction conditions in a pericyclic reaction.

functional group   the center of reactivity in a molecule.

functional group interconversion   the conversion of one functional group into another functional group.

functional group region   the left-hand two-thirds of an IR spectrum where most functional groups show absorption bands.

furanose   a five-membered-ring sugar.

furanoside   a five-membered-ring glycoside.

fused bicyclic compound   a bicyclic compound in which the rings share two adjacent carbons.

Gabriel synthesis   conversion of an alkyl halide into a primary amine, using phthalimide as a starting material.

gauche   X and Y are gauche to each other in this Newman projection:

gauche conformer   a staggered conformer in which the largest substituents are gauche to each other.

gauche interaction   the interaction between two atoms or groups that are gauche to each other.

gem-dialkyl effect   two alkyl groups on a carbon, the effect of which is to increase the probability that the molecule will be in the proper conformation for ring closure.

gem-diol (hydrate)   a compound with two OH groups on the same carbon.

geminal coupling   the mutual splitting of two nonidentical protons bonded to the same carbon.

geminal dihalide   a compound with two halogen atoms bonded to the same carbon.

gene   a segment of DNA.

general-acid catalysis   catalysis in which a proton is transferred to the reactant during the slow step of the reaction.

general-base catalysis   catalysis in which a proton is removed from the reactant during the slow step of the reaction.

generic name   a commercially nonrestricted name for a drug.

gene therapy   a technique that inserts a synthetic gene into the DNA of an organism that is defective in that gene.

genetic code   the amino acid specified by each three-base sequence of mRNA.

genetic engineering   recombinant DNA technology.

geometric isomers   cis–trans (or *E,Z*) isomers.

Gibbs standard free-energy change ($\Delta G°$)   the difference between the free- energy content of the products and the free-energy content of the reactants at equilibrium under standard conditions (1 M, 25 °C, 1 atm).

Gilman reagent   an organocuprate, prepared from the reaction of an organolithium reagent with cuprous iodide, used to replace a halogen with an alkyl group.

globular protein   a water-soluble protein that tends to have a roughly spherical shape.

gluconeogenesis   the synthesis of D-glucose from pyruvate.

glycol   a compound containing two or more OH groups.

glycolysis (glycolytic cycle)   the series of reactions that converts D-glucose into two molecules of pyruvate.

glycoprotein   a protein that is covalently bonded to a polysaccharide.

glycoside   the acetal of a sugar.

N-glycoside   a glycoside with a nitrogen instead of an oxygen at the glycosidic linkage.

glycosidic bond   the bond between the anomeric carbon and the alcohol in a glycoside.

α-1,4′-glycosidic linkage   a linkage between the C-1 oxygen of one sugar and the C-4 of a second sugar with the oxygen atom of the glycosidic linkage in the axial position.

β-1,4′-glycosidic linkage   a linkage between the C-1 oxygen of one sugar and the C-4 of a second sugar with the oxygen atom of the glycosidic linkage in the equatorial position.

graft copolymer   a copolymer that contains branches of a polymer of one monomer grafted onto the backbone of a polymer made from another monomer.

Grignard reagent   the compound that results when magnesium is inserted between the carbon and halogen of an alkyl halide (RMgBr, RMgCl).

ground-state electronic configuration   a description of which orbitals the electrons of an atom or molecule occupy when all of the electrons of atoms are in their lowest-energy orbitals.

Hagemann's-ester   a compound prepared by treating a mixture of formaldehyde and ethylacetoacetate with base and then with acid and heat.

half-chair conformation   the least stable conformation of cyclohexane.

haloform reaction   the reaction of a halogen and HO− with a methyl ketone.

halogenation   reaction with halogen (Br_2, Cl_2, I_2).

halohydrin   an organic molecule that contains a halogen and an OH group on adjacent carbons.

Hammond postulate   states that the transition state will be more similar in structure to the species (reactants or products) that it is closer to energetically.

Haworth projection   a way to show the structure of a sugar; the five- and six-membered rings are represented as being flat.

head-to-tail addition   the head of one molecule is added to the tail of another.

heat of combustion   the amount of heat given off when a carbon-containing compound reacts completely with O_2 to form CO_2 and H_2O.

heat of formation   the heat given off when a compound is formed from its elements under standard conditions.

heat of hydrogenation   the heat ($-\Delta H°$) released in a hydrogenation reaction.

Heck reaction   couples an aryl, benzyl, or vinyl halide or triflate with an alkene in a basic solution in the presence of $Pd(PPh_3)_4$.

Heisenberg uncertainty principle   states that both the precise location and the momentum of an atomic particle cannot be simultaneously determined.

α-helix   the backbone of a polypeptide coiled in a right-handed spiral with hydrogen bonding occurring within the helix.

Hell–Volhard–Zelinski (HVZ) reaction   heating a carboxylic acid with Br_2 + P in order to convert it into an α-bromocarboxylic acid.

Henderson–Hasselbalch equation $pK_a = pH + \log[HA]/[A^-]$

heptose   a monosaccharide with seven carbons.

HETCOR spectrum   a 2-D NMR spectrum that shows coupling between protons and the carbons to which they are attached.

heteroatom   an atom other than carbon or hydrogen.

heterocyclic compound (heterocycle)   a cyclic compound in which one or more of the atoms of the ring are heteroatoms.

heterogeneous catalyst   a catalyst that is insoluble in the reaction mixture.

heterolytic bond cleavage (heterolysis)   breaking a bond with the result that both bonding electrons stay with one of the atoms.

hexose   a monosaccharide with six carbons.

high-energy bond   a bond that releases a great deal of energy when it is broken.

highest occupied molecular orbital (HOMO)   the molecular orbital of highest energy that contains an electron.

high-resolution NMR spectroscopy   NMR spectroscopy that uses a spectrometer with a high operating frequency.

Hofmann degradation   exhaustive methylation of an amine, followed by reaction with Ag_2O, followed by heating to achieve a Hofmann elimination reaction.

Hofmann elimination (anti-Zaitsev elimination)   a hydrogen is removed from the β-carbon bonded to the most hydrogens.

Hofmann elimination reaction   elimination of a proton and a tertiary amine from a quaternary ammonium hydroxide.

Hofmann rearrangement   conversion of an amide into an amine by using Br_2/HO.

holoenzyme   an enzyme plus its cofactor.

homogeneous catalyst   a catalyst that is soluble in the reaction mixture.

homolog   a member of a homologous series.

homologous series   a family of compounds in which each member differs from the next by one methylene group.

homolytic bond cleavage (homolysis)   breaking a bond with the result that each of the atoms gets one of the bonding electrons.

homopolymer   a polymer that contains only one kind of monomer.

homotopic hydrogens   two hydrogens bonded to a carbon bonded to two other groups that are identical.

Hoogsteen base pairing   the pairing between a base in a synthetic strand of DNA and a base pair in double-stranded DNA.

Hooke's law   an equation that describes the motion of a vibrating spring.

hormone   an organic compound synthesized in a gland and delivered by the bloodstream to its target tissue.

Hückel's rule   states that, for a compound to be aromatic, its cloud of electrons must contain ($4n + 2)\pi$ electrons, where n is an integer. This is the same as saying that the electron cloud must contain an odd number of pairs of π electrons.

human genome the total DNA of a human cell.

Hund's rule states that when there are degenerate orbitals, an electron will occupy an empty orbital before it will pair up with another electron.

Hunsdiecker reaction conversion of a carboxylic acid into an alkyl halide by heating a heavy metal salt of the carboxylic acid with bromine or iodine.

hybrid orbital an orbital formed by mixing (hybridizing) orbitals.

hydrate (*gem*-diol)

$$R-\underset{\underset{\displaystyle OH}{|}}{\overset{\overset{\displaystyle OH}{|}}{C}}-R(H)$$

hydrated water has been added to a compound.

hydration addition of water to a compound.

hydrazone $R_2C=NNH_2$

hydride ion a negatively charged hydrogen.

1,2-hydride shift the movement of a hydride ion from one carbon to an adjacent carbon.

hydroboration–oxidation the addition of borane to an alkene or an alkyne, followed by reaction with hydrogen peroxide and hydroxide ion.

hydrocarbon a compound that contains only carbon and hydrogen.

α-hydrogen usually, a hydrogen bonded to the carbon adjacent to a carbonyl carbon.

hydrogenation addition of hydrogen.

hydrogen bond an unusually strong dipole–dipole attraction (5 kcal/mol) between a hydrogen bonded to O, N, or F and the nonbonding electrons of an O, N, or F of another molecule.

hydrogen ion (proton) a positively charged hydrogen.

hydrolysis reaction with water.

hydrophobic interactions interactions between nonpolar groups. These interactions increase stability by decreasing the amount of structured water (increasing entropy).

hyperconjugation delocalization of electrons by overlap of carbon–hydrogen or carbon–carbon σ bonds with an empty *p* orbital.

imine $R_2C=NR$

inclusion compound a compound that specifically binds a metal ion or an organic molecule.

induced-dipole–induced-dipole interaction an interaction between a temporary dipole in one molecule and the dipole the temporary dipole induces in another molecule.

induced-fit model a model that describes the specificity of an enzyme for its substrate: The shape of the active site does not become completely complementary to the shape of the substrate until after the enzyme binds the substrate.

inductive electron donation donation of electrons through σ bonds.

inductive electron withdrawal withdrawal of electrons through a σ bond.

inflection point the midpoint of the flattened-out region of a titration curve.

informational strand (sense strand) the strand in DNA that is not read during transcription; it has the same sequence of bases as the synthesized mRNA strand (with a U, T difference).

infrared radiation electromagnetic radiation familiar to us as heat.

infrared spectroscopy uses infrared energy to provide a knowledge of the functional groups in a compound.

infrared (IR) spectrum a plot of percent transmission versus wave number (or wavelength) of infrared radiation.

initiation step the step in which radicals are created, or the step in which the radical needed for the first propagation step is created.

in-line displacement mechanism nucleophilic attack on a phosphorus concerted with breaking a phosphoanhydride bond.

interchain disulfide bridge a disulfide bridge between two cysteine residues in different peptide chains.

intermediate a species formed during a reaction and that is not the final product of the reaction.

intermolecular reaction a reaction that takes place between two molecules.

internal alkyne an alkyne with the triple bond not at the end of the carbon chain.

intimate ion pair pair such that the covalent bond that joined the cation and the anion has broken, but the cation and anion are still next to each other.

intrachain disulfide bridge a disulfide bridge between two cysteine residues in the same peptide chain.

intramolecular catalysis (anchimeric assistance) catalysis in which the catalyst that facilitates the reaction is part of the molecule undergoing reaction.

intramolecular reaction a reaction that takes place within a molecule.

intron a stretch of bases in DNA that contain no genetic information.

inversion of configuration turning the configuration of a carbon inside out like an umbrella in a windstorm, so that the resulting product has a configuration opposite that of the reactant.

iodoform test addition of I_2/HO^- to a methyl ketone forms a yellow precipitate of triiodomethane.

ion–dipole interaction the interaction between an ion and the dipole of a molecule.

ion-exchange chromatography a technique that uses a column packed with an insoluble resin to separate compounds on the basis of their charges and polarities.

ionic bond a bond formed through the attraction of two ions of opposite charges.

ionization energy the energy required to remove an electron from an atom.

ionophore a compound that binds metal ions tightly.

iron protoporphyrin IX the porphyrin ring system of heme plus an iron atom.

isoelectric point (pI) the pH at which there is no net charge on an amino acid.

isolated double bonds double bonds separated by more than one single bond.

isomers nonidentical compounds with the same molecular formula.

isoprene rule rule expressing the head-to-tail linkage of isoprene units.

isopropyl split a split in the IR absorption band attributable to a methyl group. It is characteristic of an isopropyl group.

isotactic polymer a polymer in which all the substituents are on the same side of the fully extended carbon chain.

isotopes atoms with the same number of protons, but different numbers of neutrons.

iterative synthesis a synthesis in which a reaction sequence is carried out more than once.

IUPAC nomenclature systematic nomenclature of chemical compounds.

Kekulé structure a model that represents the bonds between atoms as lines.

ketal

$$R-\underset{\underset{\displaystyle OR}{|}}{\overset{\overset{\displaystyle OR}{|}}{C}}-R$$

keto–enol tautomerism (keto–enol interconversion) interconversion of keto and enol tautomers.

keto–enol tautomers a ketone and its isomeric α,β-unsaturated alcohol.

β-keto ester an ester with a second carbonyl group at the β-position.

ketone

$$\underset{R\qquad R}{\overset{\overset{\displaystyle O}{\|}}{C}}$$

ketose a polyhydroxyketone.

Kiliani–Fischer synthesis a method used to increase the number of carbons in an aldose by one, resulting in the formation of a pair of C-2 epimers.

kinetic control when a reaction is under kinetic control, the relative amounts of the products depend on the rates at which they are formed.

kinetic isotope effect a comparison of the rate of reaction of a compound with the rate of reaction of an identical compound in which one of the atoms has been replaced by an isotope.

kinetic product the product that is formed the fastest.

kinetic resolution separation of enantiomers on the basis of the difference in their rate of reaction with an enzyme.

kinetics the field of chemistry that deals with the rates of chemical reactions.

kinetic stability chemical reactivity, indicated by $\Delta G^{\ddagger}$. If $\Delta G^{\ddagger}$ is large, the compound is kinetically stable (not very reactive). If $\Delta G^{\ddagger}$ is small, the compound is kinetically unstable (highly reactive).

Knoevenagel condensation a condensation of an aldehyde or ketone with no α hydrogens and a compound with an α-carbon flanked by two electron-withdrawing groups.

Kolbe–Schmitt carboxylation reaction a reaction that uses CO_2 to carboxylate phenol.

Krebs cycle (citric acid cycle, tricarboxylic acid cycle, TCA cycle) a series of reactions that convert the acetyl group of acetyl-CoA into two molecules of CO_2

lactam a cyclic amide.

lactone a cyclic ester.

λ_{max} the wavelength at which there is maximum UV/Vis absorbance.

lead compound the prototype in a search for other biologically active compounds.

leaning   when a line drawn over the outside peaks of an NMR signal points in the direction of the signal given by the protons that cause the splitting.

leaving group   the group that is displaced in a nucleophilic substitution reaction.

Le Châtelier's principle   states that if an equilibrium is disturbed, the components of the equilibrium will adjust in a way that will offset the disturbance.

lecithin   a phosphoacylglycerol in which the second OH group of phosphate has formed an ester with choline.

levorotatory   the enantiomer that rotates polarized light in a counterclockwise direction.

Lewis acid   a substance that accepts an electron pair.

Lewis base   a substance that donates an electron pair.

Lewis structure   a model that represents the bonds between atoms as lines or dots and the valence electrons as dots.

ligation   sharing of nonbonding electrons with a metal ion.

linear combination of atomic orbitals (LCAO)   the combination of atomic orbitals to produce a molecular orbital.

linear conjugation   the atoms in the conjugated system are in a linear arrangement.

linear synthesis   a synthesis that builds a molecule step by step from starting materials.

lipid   a water-insoluble compound found in a living system.

lipid bilayer   two layers of phosphoacylglycerols arranged so that their polar heads are on the outside and their nonpolar fatty acid chains are on the inside.

lipoate   a coenzyme required in certain oxidation reactions.

living polymer   a nonterminated chain-growth polymer that remains active. This means that the polymerization reaction can continue upon the addition of more monomer.

localized electrons   electrons that are restricted to a particular locality.

lock-and-key model   a model that describes the specificity of an enzyme for its substrate: The substrate fits the enzyme as a key fits a lock.

London forces   Induced-dipole–induced-dipole interactions.

lone-pair electrons (nonbonding electrons)   valence electrons not used in bonding.

long-range coupling   splitting of a proton by a proton more than three σ bonds away.

loop conformation (coil conformation)   that part of a protein that is highly ordered, but not in an α-helix or β-pleated sheet.

lowest unoccupied molecular orbital (LUMO)   the molecular orbital of lowest energy that does not contain an electron.

Lucas test   a test that determines whether an alcohol is primary, secondary, or tertiary.

magnetic anisotropy   the term used to describe the greater freedom of a π electron cloud to move in response to a magnetic field as a consequence of the greater polarizability of π electrons compared with σ electrons.

magnetic resonance imaging (MRI)   NMR used in medicine. The difference in the way water is bound in different tissues produces a variation in signal between organs as well as between healthy and diseased tissue.

magnetogyric ratio   a property (measured in rad $T^{-1}s^{-1}$) that depends on the magnetic properties of a particular kind of nucleus.

major groove   the wider and deeper of the two alternating grooves in DNA.

malonic ester synthesis   the synthesis of a carboxylic acid, using diethyl malonate as the starting material.

Mannich reaction   condensation of a secondary amine and formaldehyde with a carbon acid.

Markovnikov's rule   the actual rule is "When a hydrogen halide adds to an asymmetrical alkene, the addition occurs such that the halogen attaches itself to the sp^2 carbon of the alkene bearing the lowest number of hydrogen atoms." A more universal rule is "The electrophile adds to the sp^2 carbon that is bonded to the greater number of hydrogens."

mass number   the number of protons plus the number of neutrons in an atom.

mass spectrometry   provides a knowledge of the molecular weight, molecular formula, and certain structural features of a compound.

mass spectrum   a plot of the relative abundance of the positively charged fragments produced in a mass spectrometer versus their m/z values.

materials science   the science of creating new materials to be used in place of known materials such as metal, glass, wood, cardboard, and paper.

Maxam–Gilbert sequencing   a technique used to sequence restriction fragments.

McLafferty rearrangement   rearrangement of the molecular ion of a ketone. The bond between the α- and β-carbons breaks, and a γ-hydrogen migrates to the oxygen.

mechanism-based inhibitor (suicide inhibitor)   a compound that inactivates an enzyme by undergoing part of its normal catalytic mechanism.

mechanism of a reaction   a description of the step-by-step process by which reactants are changed into products.

melting point   the temperature at which a solid becomes a liquid.

membrane   the material that surrounds a cell in order to isolate its contents.

mercaptan (thiol)   the sulfur analog of an alcohol (RSH).

meso compound   a compound that contains asymmetric centers and a plane of symmetry.

metabolism   reactions that living organisms carry out in order to obtain the energy and to synthesize the compounds they require.

meta-directing substituent   a substituent that directs an incoming substituent meta to an existing substituent.

metal-activated enzyme   an enzyme that has a loosely bound metal ion.

metal-ion catalysis   catalysis in which the species that facilitates the reaction is a metal ion.

metalloenzyme   an enzyme that has a tightly bound metal ion.

methine hydrogen   a tertiary hydrogen.

methylene group   a CH_2 group.

1,2-methyl shift   the movement of a methyl group with its bonding electrons from one carbon to an adjacent carbon.

micelle   a spherical aggregation of molecules, each with a long hydrophobic tail and a polar head, arranged so that the polar head points to the outside of the sphere.

Michael reaction   the addition of an α-carbanion to the β-carbon of an α,β-unsaturated carbonyl compound.

minor groove   the narrower and more shallow of the two alternating grooves in DNA.

mixed (crossed) aldol addition   an aldol addition in which two different carbonyl compounds are used.

mixed anhydride   an acid anhydride with two different R groups.

$$\underset{R}{\overset{\displaystyle O}{\|}}\underset{}{C}\underset{}{O}\underset{R'}{\overset{\displaystyle O}{\|}}C$$

mixed Claisen condensation   a Claisen condensation in which two different esters are used.

mixed triacylglycerol   a triacylglycerol in which the fatty-acid components are different.

molar absorptivity   the absorbance obtained from a 1.00 M solution in a cell with a 1.00-cm light path.

molecular ion (parent ion)   peak in the mass spectrum with the greatest m/z.

molecular modeling   computer-assisted design of a compound with particular structural characteristics.

molecular modification   changing the structure of a lead compound.

molecular orbital   an orbital associated with a molecule.

molecular orbital theory   describes a model in which the electrons occupy orbitals as they do in atoms, but with the orbitals extending over the entire molecule.

molecular recognition   the recognition of one molecule by another as a result of specific interactions; for example, the specificity of an enzyme for its substrate.

molozonide   an unstable intermediate containing a five-membered ring with three oxygens in a row that is formed from the reaction of an alkene with ozone.

monomer   a repeating unit in a polymer.

monosaccharide (simple carbohydrate)   a single sugar molecule.

monoterpene   a terpene that contains 10 carbons.

MRI scanner   an NMR spectrometer used in medicine for whole-body NMR.

multiplet   an NMR signal split into more than seven peaks.

multiplicity   the number of peaks in an NMR signal.

multistep synthesis   preparation of a compound by a route that requires several steps.

mutarotation   a slow change in optical rotation to an equilibrium value.

$N + 1$ rule   an ^1H NMR signal for a hydrogen with N equivalent hydrogens bonded to an adjacent carbon is split into $N + 1$ peaks. A ^{13}C NMR signal for a carbon bonded to N hydrogens is split into $N + 1$ peaks.

natural-abundance atomic weight   the average mass of the atoms in the naturally occurring element.

natural product   a product synthesized in nature.

neurotransmitter   a compound that transmits nerve impulses.

nicotinamide adenine dinucleotide (NAD⁺)   a coenzyme required in certain oxidation reactions. It is reduced to NADH, which can act as a reducing agent in another reaction.

nicotinamide adenine dinucleotide phosphate (NADP⁺)   a coenzyme required in certain oxidation reactions. It is reduced to NADPH, which can act as a reducing agent in another reaction.

NIH shift   the 1,2-hydride shift of a carbocation (obtained from an arene oxide) that leads to an enone.

nitration   substitution of a nitro group (NO_2) for a hydrogen of a benzene ring.

nitrile   a compound that contains a carbon–nitrogen triple bond ($RC \equiv N$).

nitrosamine (N-nitroso compound) $R_2NN \!=\! O$

NMR spectroscopy   the absorption of electromagnetic radiation to determine the structural features of an organic compound. In the case of NMR spectroscopy, it determines the carbon–hydrogen framework.

node   that part of an orbital in which there is zero probability of finding an electron.

nominal mass   mass rounded to the nearest whole number.

nonbonding electrons (lone-pair electrons)   valence electrons not used in bonding.

nonbonding molecular orbital   the p orbitals are too far apart to overlap significantly, so the molecular orbital that results neither favors nor disfavors bonding.

nonpolar covalent bond   a bond formed between two atoms that share the bonding electrons equally.

nonreducing sugar   a sugar that cannot be oxidized by reagents such as Ag^+ and Cu^+. Nonreducing sugars are not in equilibrium with the open-chain aldose or ketose.

normal alkane (straight-chain alkane)   an alkane in which the carbons form a contiguous chain with no branches.

N-phthalimidomalonic ester synthesis   a method used to synthesize an amino acid that combines the malonic ester synthesis and the Gabriel synthesis.

N-terminal amino acid   the terminal amino acid of a peptide (or protein) that has a free amino group.

nucleic acid   the two kinds of nucleic acid are DNA and RNA.

nucleophile   an electron-rich atom or molecule.

nucleophilic acyl substitution reaction   a reaction in which a group bonded to an acyl or aryl group is substituted by another group.

nucleophilic addition–elimination–nucleophilic addition reaction   a nucleophilic addition reaction that is followed by an elimination reaction that is followed by a nucleophilic addition reaction. Acetal formation is an example: An alcohol adds to the carbonyl carbon, water is eliminated, and a second molecule of alcohol adds to the dehydrated product.

nucleophilic addition–elimination reaction   a nucleophilic addition reaction that is followed by an elimination reaction. Imine formation is an example: An amine adds to the carbonyl carbon, and water is eliminated.

nucleophilic addition reaction   a reaction that involves the addition of a nucleophile to a reagent.

nucleophilic aromatic substitution   a reaction in which a nucleophile substitutes for a substituent of an aromatic ring.

nucleophilic catalysis (covalent catalysis)   catalysis that occurs as a result of a nucleophile forming a covalent bond with one of the reactants.

nucleophilic catalyst   a catalyst that increases the rate of a reaction by acting as a nucleophile.

nucleophilicity   a measure of how readily an atom or a molecule with a pair of nonbonding electrons attacks an atom.

nucleophilic substitution reaction   a reaction in which a nucleophile substitutes for an atom or a group.

nucleoside   a heterocyclic base (a purine or a pyrimidine) bonded to the anomeric carbon of a sugar (D-ribose or D-2′-deoxyribose).

nucleotide   a heterocycle attached in the β-position to a phosphorylated ribose or deoxyribose.

observed rotation   the amount of rotation observed in a polarimeter.

octet rule   states that an atom will give up, accept, or share electrons in order to achieve a filled shell. Because a filled second shell contains eight electrons, this is known as the octet rule.

off-resonance decoupling   the mode in ^{13}C NMR spectroscopy in which spin–spin splitting occurs between carbons and the hydrogens attached to them.

oil   a triester of glycerol that exists as a liquid at room temperature.

olefin   an alkene.

olefin metathesis   breaks the double bond of an alkene (or the triple bond of an alkyne) and then rejoins the fragments.

oligomer   a protein with more than one peptide chain.

oligonucleotide   3 to 10 nucleotides linked by phosphodiester bonds.

oligopeptide   3 to 10 amino acids linked by amide bonds.

oligosaccharide   3 to 10 sugar molecules linked by glycosidic bonds.

open-chain compound   an acyclic compound.

operating frequency   the frequency at which an NMR spectrometer operates.

optical isomers   stereoisomers that contain chirality centers.

optically active   rotates the plane of polarized light.

optically inactive   does not rotate the plane of polarized light.

optical purity (enantiomeric excess)   how much excess of one enantiomer is present in a mixture of a pair of enantiomers.

orbital   the volume of space around the nucleus in which an electron is most likely to be found.

orbital hybridization   mixing of orbitals.

organic compound   a compound that contains carbon.

organic synthesis   preparation of organic compounds from other organic compounds.

organometallic compound   a compound containing a carbon–metal bond.

oriented polymer   a polymer obtained by stretching out polymer chains and putting them back together in a parallel fashion.

orphan drugs   drugs for diseases or conditions that affect fewer than 200,000 people.

ortho-para-directing substituent   a substituent that directs an incoming substituent ortho and para to an existing substituent.

osazone   the product obtained by treating an aldose or a ketose with excess phenylhydrazine. An osazone contains two imine bonds.

overtone band   an absorption that occurs at a multiple of the fundamental absorption frequency ($2v$, $3v$).

oxidation   loss of electrons by an atom or a molecule.

β-oxidation   a series of four reactions that removes two carbons from a fatty acyl-CoA.

oxidation reaction   a reaction in which the number of C—H bonds decreases or the number of C—O, C—N, or C—X (X = a halogen) increases.

oxidative cleavage   an oxidation reaction that cuts the reactant into two or more pieces.

oxidative phosphorylation   a series of reactions that converts a molecule of NADH and a molecule of $FADH_2$ into 3 and 2 molecules of ATP, respectively.

oxime $R_2C \!=\! NOH$

oxirane (epoxide)   an ether in which the oxygen is incorporated into a three-membered ring.

oxonium ion   a compound with a positively charged oxygen.

oxyanion   a compound with a negatively charged oxygen.

oxymercuration   addition of water using a mercuric salt of a carboxylic acid as a catalyst.

ozonide   the five-membered-ring compound formed as a result of the rearrangement of a molozonide.

ozonolysis   reaction of a carbon–carbon double or triple bond with ozone.

packing   the fitting of individual molecules into a frozen crystal lattice.

paraffin   an alkane.

parent hydrocarbon   the longest continuous carbon chain in a molecule.

parent ion (molecular ion)   peak in the mass spectrum with the greatest m/z.

partial hydrolysis   a technique that hydrolyzes only some of the peptide bonds in a polypeptide.

partial racemization   formation of a pair of enantiomers in unequal amounts.

Pauli exclusion principle   states that no more than two electrons can occupy an orbital and that the two electrons must have opposite spin.

pentose   a monosaccharide with five carbons.

peptide   polymer of amino acids linked together by amide bonds. A peptide contains fewer amino acid residues than a protein does.

peptide bond   the amide bond that links the amino acids in a peptide or protein.

peptide nucleic acid (PNA)   a polymer containing both an amino acid and a base designed to bind to specific residues on DNA or mRNA.

Perkin condensation   a condensation of an aromatic aldehyde and acetic acid.

pericyclic reaction   a concerted reaction that takes place as the result of a cyclic rearrangement of electrons.

peroxyacid   a carboxylic acid with an OOH group instead of an OH group.

perspective formula   a method of representing the spatial arrangement of groups bonded to an asymmetric center. Two bonds are drawn in the plane of the paper; a solid wedge is used to depict a bond that projects out of the plane of the paper toward the viewer, and a hatched wedge is used to represent a bond that projects back from the plane of the paper away from the viewer.

pH the pH scale is used to describe the acidity of a solution (pH = −log[H$^+$]).

pH-activity profile a plot of the activity of an enzyme as a function of the pH of the reaction mixture.

phase-transfer catalysis catalysis of a reaction by providing a way to bring a polar reagent into a nonpolar phase so that the reaction between a polar and a nonpolar compound can occur.

phase-transfer catalyst a compound that carries a polar reagent into a nonpolar phase.

phenone

$$C_6H_5 \overset{\overset{\displaystyle O}{\|}}{\underset{\displaystyle}{C}} R$$

phenyl group $\langle \rangle$— C_6H_5—

phenylhydrazone $R_2C=NNHC_6H_5$

pheromone a compound secreted by an animal that stimulates a physiological or behavioral response from a member of the same species.

phosphatidic acid a phosphoacylglycerol in which only one of the OH groups of phosphate is in an ester linkage.

phosphoacylglycerol (phosphoglyceride) a compound formed when two OH groups of glycerol form esters with fatty acids and the terminal OH group forms a phosphate ester.

phosphoanhydride bond the bond holding two phosphoric acid molecules together.

phospholipid a lipid that contains a phosphate group.

phosphoryl transfer reaction the transfer of a phosphate group from one compound to another.

photochemical reaction a reaction that takes place when a reactant absorbs light.

photosynthesis the synthesis of glucose and O_2 from CO_2 and H_2O.

pH-rate profile a plot of the observed rate of a reaction as a function of the pH of the reaction mixture.

pi (π) bond a bond formed as a result of side-to-side overlap of p orbitals.

pi-complex a complex formed between an electrophile and a triple bond.

pinacol rearrangement rearrangement of a vicinal diol.

pK_a describes the tendency of a compound to lose a proton (pK_a = −log K_a, where K_a is the acid dissociation constant).

plane of symmetry an imaginary plane that bisects a molecule into mirror images.

plasticizer an organic molecule that dissolves in a polymer and allows the polymer chains to slide by each other.

β-pleated sheet the backbone of a polypeptide that is extended in a zigzag structure with hydrogen bonding between neighboring chains.

point of symmetry any line through a point of symmetry encounters identical environments at the same distance.

polar covalent bond a covalent bond between atoms of different electronegativites.

polarimeter an instrument that measures the rotation of polarized light.

polarizability an indication of the ease with which the electron cloud of an atom can be distorted.

polarized light light that oscillates only in one plane.

polar reaction the reaction between a nucleophile and an electrophile.

polyamide a polymer in which the monomers are amides.

polycarbonate a step-growth polymer in which the dicarboxylic acid is carbonic acid.

polyene a compound that has several double bonds.

polyester a polymer in which the monomers are esters.

polymer a large molecule made by linking monomers together.

polymerase chain reaction (PCR) a method that amplifies segments of DNA.

polymer chemistry the field of chemistry that deals with synthetic polymers; part of the larger discipline known as materials science.

polymerization the process of linking up monomers to form a polymer.

polynucleotide many nucleotides linked by phosphodiester bonds.

polypeptide many amino acids linked by amide bonds.

polysaccharide a compound containing more than 10 sugar molecules linked together.

polyunsaturated fatty acid a fatty acid with more than one double bond.

polyurethane a polymer in which the monomers are urethanes.

porphyrin ring system consists of four pyrrole rings joined by one-carbon bridges.

primary alcohol an alcohol in which the OH group is bonded to a primary carbon.

primary alkyl halide an alkyl halide in which the halogen is bonded to a primary carbon.

primary alkyl radical a radical with the unpaired electron on a primary carbon.

primary amine an amine with one alkyl group bonded to the nitrogen.

primary carbocation a carbocation with the positive charge on a primary carbon.

primary carbon a carbon bonded to only one other carbon.

primary hydrogen a hydrogen bonded to a primary carbon.

primary structure (of a nucleic acid) the sequence of bases in a nucleic acid.

primary structure (of a protein) the sequence of amino acids in a protein.

principle of microscopic reversibility states that the mechanism for a reaction in the forward direction has the same intermediates and the same rate-determining step as the mechanism for the reaction in the reverse direction.

prochiral carbonyl carbon a carbonyl carbon that will become an asymmetric center if it is attacked by a group unlike any of the groups already bonded to it.

prochirality center a carbon bonded to two hydrogens that will become an asymmetric center if one of the hydrogens is replaced by deuterium.

prodrug a compound that does not become an effective drug until it undergoes a reaction in the body

promoter site a short sequence of bases at the beginning of a gene.

propagating site the reactive end of a chain-growth polymer.

propagation step in the first of a pair of propagation steps, a radical (or an electrophile or a nucleophile) reacts to produce another radical (or an electrophile or a nucleophile) that reacts in the second to produce the radical (or the electrophile or the nucleophile) that was the reactant in the first propagation step.

proprietary name (trade name, brand name) identifies a commercial product and distinguishes it from other products.

pro-R hydrogen replacing this hydrogen with deuterium creates an asymmetric center with the R configuration.

pro-S hydrogen replacing this hydrogen with deuterium creates an asymmetric center with the S configuration.

prostacyclin a lipid, derived from arachidonic acid, that dilates blood vessels and inhibits platelet aggregation.

prosthetic group a tightly bound coenzyme.

protecting group a reagent that protects a functional group from a synthetic operation that it would otherwise not survive.

protein a polymer containing 40 to 4000 amino acids linked by amide bonds.

protein prenylation attaching isopentenyl units to proteins.

protic solvent a solvent that has a hydrogen bonded to an oxygen or a nitrogen.

proton a positively charged hydrogen (H$^+$); a positively charged particle in an atomic nucleus.

proton-decoupled ^{13}C NMR spectrum a ^{13}C NMR spectrum in which all the signals appear as singlets because there is no coupling between the nucleus and its bonded hydrogens.

proton transfer reaction a reaction in which a proton is transferred from an acid to a base.

protoporphyrin IX the porphyrin ring system of heme.

proximity effect an effect caused by one species being close to another.

pseudo-first-order reaction a second-order reaction in which the concentration of one of the reactants is much greater than the other, allowing the reaction to be treated as a first-order reaction.

pyranose a six-membered-ring sugar.

pyranoside a six-membered-ring glycoside.

pyridoxal phosphate the coenzyme required by enzymes that catalyze certain transformations of amino acids.

pyrosequencing a technique used to determine the sequence of bases in a polynucleotide by detecting the identity of each base that adds to a primer.

quantitative structure–activity relationship (QSAR) the relation between a particular property of a series of compounds and their biological activity.

quantum numbers numbers arising from the quantum mechanical treatment of an atom that describe the properties of the electrons in the atom.

quartet an NMR signal split into four peaks.

quaternary ammonium ion an ion containing a nitrogen bonded to four alkyl groups (R_4N^+).

quaternary ammonium salt   a quaternary ammonium ion and an anion ($R_4N^+X^-$).

quaternary structure   a description of the way the individual polypeptide chains of a protein are arranged with respect to each other.

racemic mixture (racemate, racemic modification)   a mixture of equal amounts of a pair of enantiomers.

radical   an atom or a molecule with an unpaired electron.

radical addition reaction   an addition reaction in which the first species that adds is a radical.

radical anion   a species with a negative charge and an unpaired electron.

radical cation   a species with a positive charge and an unpaired electron.

radical chain reaction   a reaction in which radicals are formed and react in repeating propagating steps.

radical inhibitor   a compound that traps radicals.

radical initiator   a compound that creates radicals.

radical polymerization   chain-growth polymerization in which the initiator is a radical; the propagation site is therefore a radical.

radical reaction   a reaction in which a new bond is formed by using one electron from one reagent and one electron from another reagent.

radical substitution reaction   a substitution reaction that has a radical intermediate.

random coil   the conformation of a totally denatured protein.

random copolymer   a copolymer with a random distribution of monomers.

random screen (blind screen)   the search for a pharmacologically active compound without any information about what chemical structures might show activity.

rate constant   a measure of how easy or difficult it is to reach the transition state of a reaction (to get over the energy barrier to the reaction).

rate-determining step (rate-limiting step)   the step in a reaction that has the transition state with the highest energy.

rational drug design   designing drugs with a particular structure to achieve a specific purpose.

R configuration   after assigning relative priorities to the four groups bonded to an asymmetric center, if the lowest priority group is on a vertical axis in a Fischer projection (or pointing away from the viewer in a perspective formula), an arrow drawn from the highest priority group to the next-highest-priority group goes in a clockwise direction.

reaction coordinate diagram   describes the energy changes that take place during the course of a reaction.

reactivity–selectivity principle   states that the greater the reactivity of a species, the less selective it will be.

receptor site   the site at which a drug binds in order to exert its physiological effect.

recombinant DNA   DNA that has been incorporated into a host cell.

reduction reaction   a reaction in which the number of C—H bonds increases or the number of C—O, C—N, or C—X (X = a halogen) decreases.

red shift   a shift to a longer wavelength.

reducing sugar   a sugar that can be oxidized by reagents such as Ag^+ or Br_2. Reducing sugars are in equilibrium with the open-chain aldose or ketose.

reduction   gain of electrons by an atom or a molecule.

reductive amination   the reaction of an aldehyde or a ketone with ammonia or with a primary amine in the presence of a reducing agent (H_2/Raney Ni).

reference compound   a compound added to a sample whose NMR spectrum is to be taken. The positions of the signals in the NMR spectrum are measured from the position of the signal given by the reference compound.

Reformatsky reaction   reaction of an organozinc reagent with an aldehyde or a ketone.

regioselective reaction   a reaction that leads to the preferential formation of one constitutional isomer over another.

relative configuration   the configuration of a compound relative to the configuration of another compound.

relative rate   obtained by dividing the actual rate constant by the rate constant of the slowest reaction in the group being compared.

replication   the synthesis of identical copies of DNA.

replication fork   the position on DNA at which replication begins.

resolution of a racemic mixture   separation of a racemic mixture into the individual enantiomers.

resonance   a compound with delocalized electrons is said to have resonance.

resonance contributor (resonance structure, contributing resonance structure)   a structure with localized electrons that approximates the true structure of a compound with delocalized electrons.

resonance electron donation   donation of electrons through p orbital overlap with neighboring π bonds.

resonance electron withdrawal   withdrawal of electrons through p orbital overlap with neighboring π bonds.

resonance energy (delocalization energy)   the extra stability associated with a compound as a result of its having delocalized electrons.

resonance hybrid   the actual structure of a compound with delocalized electrons; it is represented by two or more structures with localized electrons.

resonances   NMR absorption signals.

restriction endonuclease   an enzyme that cleaves DNA at a specific base sequence.

restriction fragment   a fragment that is formed when DNA is cleaved by a restriction endonuclease.

retro Diels–Alder reaction   a reverse Diels–Alder reaction.

retrosynthesis (retrosynthetic analysis)   working backwards (on paper) from the target molecule to available starting materials.

retrovirus   a virus whose genetic information is stored in its RNA.

rf radiation   radiation in the radiofrequency region of the electromagnetic spectrum.

ribonucleic acid (RNA)   a polymer of ribonucleotides.

ribonucleotide   a nucleotide in which the sugar component is D-ribose.

ribosome   a particle composed of about 40% protein and 60% RNA on which protein biosynthesis takes place.

ribozyme   an RNA molecule that acts as a catalyst.

ring current   the movement of π electrons around an aromatic benzene ring.

ring-expansion rearrangement   rearrangement of a carbocation in which the positively charged carbon is bonded to a cyclic compound and, as a result of rearrangement, the size of the ring increases by one carbon.

ring-flip (chair–chair interconversion)   the conversion of the chair conformer of cyclohexane into the other chair conformer. Bonds that are axial in one chair conformer are equatorial in the other.

ring opening polymerization   a chain-growth polymerization that involves opening the ring of the monomer.

Ritter reaction   reaction of a nitrile with a secondary or tertiary alcohol to form a secondary amide.

RNA (ribonucleic acid)   a polymer of ribonucleotides.

RNA splicing   the step in RNA processing that cuts out nonsense bases and splices informational pieces together.

Robinson annulation   a Michael reaction followed by an intramolecular aldol condensation.

Rosenmund reduction   reduction of an acyl chloride to an aldehyde by using a deactivated palladium catalyst.

Ruff degradation   a method used to shorten an aldose by one carbon.

Sandmeyer reaction   the reaction of an aryl diazonium salt with a cuprous salt.

saponification   hydrolysis of an ester (such as a fat) under basic conditions.

saturated hydrocarbon   a hydrocarbon that is completely saturated (i.e., contains no double or triple bonds) with hydrogen.

Schiemann reaction   the reaction of an arenediazonium salt with HBF_4.

Schiff base $R_2C{=}NR$

S configuration   after assigning relative priorities to the four groups bonded to an asymmetric center, if the lowest priority group is on a vertical axis in a Fischer projection (or pointing away from the viewer in a perspective formula), an arrow drawn from the highest priority group to the next-highest priority group goes in a counterclockwise direction.

secondary alcohol   an alcohol in which the OH group is bonded to a secondary carbon.

secondary alkyl halide   an alkyl halide in which the halogen is bonded to a secondary carbon.

secondary alkyl radical   a radical with the unpaired electron on a secondary carbon.

secondary amine   an amine with two alkyl groups bonded to the nitrogen.

secondary carbocation   a carbocation with the positive charge on a secondary carbon.

secondary carbon   a carbon bonded to two other carbons.

secondary hydrogen   a hydrogen bonded to a secondary carbon.

secondary structure   a description of the conformation of the backbone of a protein.

second-order rate constant   the rate constant of a second-order reaction.

second-order reaction (bimolecular reaction)   a reaction whose rate depends on the concentration of two reactants.

sedimentation constant   designates where a species sediments in an ultracentrifuge.

selection rules   the rules that determine the outcome of a pericyclic reaction.

selenenylation reaction conversion of an α-bromoketone into an α,β-unsaturated ketone via the formation of a selenoxide.

semicarbazone $R_2C{=}NNHCNH_2$ (with O double-bonded to C)

semiconservative replication the mode of replication that results in a daughter molecule of DNA having one of the original DNA strands plus a newly synthesized strand.

sense strand (informational strand) the strand in DNA that is not read during transcription; it has the same sequence of bases as the synthesized mRNA strand (with a U, T difference).

separated charges a positive and a negative charge that can be neutralized by the movement of electrons.

sesquiterpene a terpene that contains 15 carbons.

shielding phenomenon caused by electron donation to the environment of a proton. The electrons shield the proton from the full effect of the applied magnetic field. The more a proton is shielded, the farther to the right its signal appears in an NMR spectrum.

sigma (σ) bond a bond with a cylindrically symmetrical distribution of electrons.

sigmatropic rearrangement a reaction in which a σ bond is broken in the reactant, a new σ bond is formed in the product, and the π bonds rearrange.

Simmons–Smith reaction formation of a cyclopropane using $CH_2I_2 + Zn(Cu)$.

simple carbohydrate (monosaccharide) a single sugar molecule.

simple triacylglycerol a triacylglycerol in which the fatty acid components are the same.

single bond a σ bond.

singlet an unsplit NMR signal.

site-specific mutagenesis a technique that substitutes one amino acid of a protein for another.

site-specific recognition recognition of a particular site on DNA.

skeletal structure shows the carbon–carbon bonds as lines and does not show the carbon–hydrogen bonds.

S_NAr reaction a nucleophilic aromatic substitution reaction.

S_N1 reaction a unimolecular nucleophilic substitution reaction.

S_N2 reaction a bimolecular nucleophilic substitution reaction.

soap a sodium or potassium salt of a fatty acid.

solid-phase synthesis a technique in which one end of the compound being synthesized is covalently attached to a solid support.

solvation the interaction between a solvent and another molecule (or ion).

solvent-separated ion pair the cation and anion are separated by a solvent molecule.

solvolysis reaction with the solvent.

specific-acid catalysis catalysis in which the proton is fully transferred to the reactant before the slow step of the reaction takes place.

specific-base catalysis catalysis in which the proton is completely removed from the reactant before the slow step of the reaction takes place.

specific rotation the amount of rotation that will be caused by a compound with a concentration of 1.0 g/mL in a sample tube 1.0 dm long.

spectroscopy study of the interaction of matter and electromagnetic radiation.

sphingolipid a lipid that contains sphingosine.

sphingomyelin a sphingolipid in which the terminal OH group of sphingosine is bonded to phosphocholine or phosphoethanolamine.

spin-coupled ^{13}C NMR spectrum a ^{13}C NMR spectrum in which each signal of a carbon is split by the hydrogens bonded to that carbon.

spin coupling the atom that gives rise to an NMR signal is coupled to the rest of the molecule.

spin decoupling the atom that gives rise to an NMR signal is decoupled from the rest of the molecule.

spin–spin coupling the splitting of a signal in an NMR spectrum described by the $N + 1$ rule.

α-spin state nuclei in this spin state have their magnetic moments oriented in the same direction as the applied magnetic field.

β-spin state nuclei in this spin state have their magnetic moments oriented opposite the direction of the applied magnetic field.

spirocyclic compound a bicyclic compound in which the rings share one carbon.

splitting diagram a diagram that describes the splitting of a set of protons.

squalene a triterpene that is a precursor of steroid molecules.

stacking interactions van der Waals interactions between the mutually induced dipoles of adjacent pairs of bases in DNA.

staggered conformation a conformation in which the bonds on one carbon bisect the bond angle on the adjacent carbon when viewed looking down the carbon–carbon bond.

step-growth polymer (condensation polymer) a polymer made by combining two molecules while removing a small molecule (usually of water or an alcohol).

stereochemistry the field of chemistry that deals with the structures of molecules in three dimensions.

stereoelectronic effects the combination of steric effects and electronic effects.

stereogenic center (stereocenter) an atom at which the interchange of two substituents produces a stereoisomer.

stereoisomers isomers that differ in the way their atoms are arranged in space.

stereoselective reaction a reaction that leads to the preferential formation of one stereoisomer over another.

stereospecific reaction a reaction in which the reactant can exist as stereoisomers and each stereoisomeric reactant leads to a different stereoisomeric product or set of products.

steric effects effects due to the fact that groups occupy a certain volume of space.

steric hindrance refers to bulky groups at the site of a reaction that make it difficult for the reactants to approach each other.

steric strain (van der Waals strain, van der Waals repulsion) the repulsion between the electron cloud of an atom or a group of atoms and the electron cloud of another atom or group of atoms.

steroid a class of compounds that contains a steroid ring system.

Stille reaction couples an aryl, a benzyl, or a vinyl halide or triflate with a stannane in the presence of $Pd(PPh_3)_4$.

stop codon a codon at which protein synthesis is stopped.

Stork enamine reaction uses an enamine as a nucleophile in a Michael reaction.

straight-chain alkane (normal alkane) an alkane in which the carbons form a continuous chain with no branches.

Strecker synthesis a method used to synthesize an amino acid: An aldehyde reacts with NH_3, forming an imine that is attacked by cyanide ion. Hydrolysis of the product gives an amino acid.

stretching frequency the frequency at which a stretching vibration occurs.

stretching vibration a vibration occurring along the line of a bond.

structural isomers (constitutional isomers) molecules that have the same molecular formula but differ in the way their atoms are connected.

structural protein a protein that gives strength to a biological structure.

α-substituent a substituent on the side of a steroid ring system opposite that of the angular methyl groups.

β-substituent a substituent on the same side of a steroid ring system as that of the angular methyl groups.

α-substitution reaction a reaction that puts a substituent on an α-carbon in place of an α-hydrogen.

substrate the reactant of an enzyme-catalyzed reaction.

subunit an individual chain of an oligomer.

suicide inhibitor (mechanism-based inhibitor) a compound that inactivates an enzyme by undergoing part of its normal catalytic mechanism.

sulfide (thioether) the sulfur analog of an ether (RSR).

sulfonate ester the ester of a sulfonic acid (RSO_2OR).

sulfonation substitution of a hydrogen of a benzene ring by a sulfonic acid group (SO_3H)

suprafacial bond formation the formation of two σ bonds on the same side of the π system.

suprafacial rearrangement rearrangement in which the migrating group remains on the same face of the π system.

Suzuki reaction couples an aryl, a benzyl, or a vinyl halide with an organoborane in the presence of $Pd(PPh_3)_4$.

symmetrical anhydride an acid anhydride with identical R groups:

$$R{-}\overset{\overset{O}{\|}}{C}{-}O{-}\overset{\overset{O}{\|}}{C}{-}R$$

symmetrical ether an ether with two identical substituents bonded to the oxygen.

symmetric molecular orbital a molecular orbital in which the left half is a mirror image of the right half.

symmetry-allowed pathway a pathway that leads to overlap of in-phase orbitals.

symmetry-forbidden pathway   a pathway that leads to overlap of out-of-phase orbitals.

syn addition   an addition reaction in which two substituents are added to the same side of the molecule.

syndiotactic polymer   a polymer in which the substituents regularly alternate on both sides of the fully extended carbon chain.

syn elimination   an elimination reaction in which the two substituents that are eliminated are removed from the same side of the molecule.

syn-periplanar   parallel substituents on the same side of a molecule.

synthetic equivalent   the reagent actually used as the source of a synthon.

synthetic polymer   a polymer that is not synthesized in nature.

synthetic tree   an outline of the available routes to get to a desired product from available starting materials.

synthon   a fragment of a disconnection.

systematic nomenclature   nomenclature based on structure.

target molecule   desired end product of a synthesis.

tautomerism   interconversion of tautomers.

tautomers   rapidly equilibrating isomers that differ in the location of their bonding electrons.

template strand (antisense strand)   the strand in DNA that is read during transcription.

terminal alkyne   an alkyne with the triple bond at the end of the carbon chain.

termination step   when two radicals combine to produce a molecule in which all the electrons are paired.

terpene   a lipid, isolated from a plant, that contains carbon atoms in multiples of five.

terpenoid   a terpene that contains oxygen.

tertiary alcohol   an alcohol in which the OH group is bonded to a tertiary carbon.

tertiary alkyl halide   an alkyl halide in which the halogen is bonded to a tertiary carbon.

tertiary alkyl radical   a radical with the unpaired electron on a tertiary carbon.

tertiary amine   an amine with three alkyl groups bonded to the nitrogen.

tertiary carbocation   a carbocation with the positive charge on a tertiary carbon.

tertiary carbon   a carbon bonded to three other carbons.

tertiary hydrogen   a hydrogen bonded to a tertiary carbon.

tertiary structure   a description of the three-dimensional arrangement of all the atoms in a protein.

tetraene   a hydrocarbon with four double bonds.

tetrahedral bond angle   the bond angle (109.5°) formed by adjacent bonds of an sp^3 hybridized carbon.

tetrahedral carbon   an sp^3 hybridized carbon; a carbon that forms covalent bonds by using four sp^3 hybridized orbitals.

tetrahedral intermediate   the intermediate formed in a nucleophilic acyl substitution reaction.

tetrahydrofolate (THF)   the coenzyme required by enzymes that catalyze reactions that donate a group containing a single carbon to their substrates.

tetraterpene   a terpene that contains 40 carbons.

tetrose   a monosaccharide with four carbons.

therapeutic index   the ratio of the lethal dose of a drug to the therapeutic dose.

thermal cracking   using heat to break a molecule apart.

thermal reaction   a reaction that takes place without the reactant having to absorb light.

thermodynamic control   when a reaction is under thermodynamic control, the relative amounts of the products depend on their stabilities.

thermodynamic product   the most stable product.

thermodynamics   the field of chemistry that describes the properties of a system at equilibrium.

thermodynamic stability   is indicated by $\Delta G°$. If $\Delta G°$ is negative, the products are more stable than the reactants. If $\Delta G°$ is positive, the reactants are more stable than the products.

thermoplastic polymer   a polymer that has both ordered crystalline regions and amorphous noncrystalline regions; it can be molded when heated.

thermosetting polymers   cross-linked polymers that, after they are hardened, cannot be remelted by heating.

thiamine pyrophosphate (TPP)   the coenzyme required by enzymes, which catalyze a reaction that transfers a two-carbon fragment to a substrate.

thiirane   a three-membered-ring compound in which one of the ring atoms is a sulfur.

thin-layer chromatography   a technique that separates compounds on the basis of their polarity.

thioester   the sulfur analog of an ester:

thioether (sulfide)   the sulfur analog of an ether (RSR).

thiol (mercaptan)   the sulfur analog of an alcohol (RSH).

threo enantiomers   the pair of enantiomers with similar groups on opposite sides when drawn in a Fischer projection.

titration curve   a plot of pH versus added equivalents of hydroxide ion.

Tollens test   an aldehyde can be identified by observing the formation of a silver mirror in the presence of Tollens' reagent (Ag_2O/NH_3).

trademark   a registered name, symbol, or picture.

trade name (proprietary name, brand name)   identifies a commercial product and distinguishes it from other products.

transamination   a reaction in which an amino group is transferred from one compound to another.

transannular hydrogens (flagpole hydrogens)   the two hydrogens in the boat conformation of cyclohexane that are closest to each other.

s-trans conformation   a conformation in which two double bonds are on opposite sides of a single bond.

transcription   the synthesis of mRNA from a DNA blueprint.

transesterification reaction   the reaction of an ester with an alcohol to form a different ester.

trans fused   two cyclohexane rings fused together such that if the second ring were considered to be two substituents of the first ring, both substituents would be in equatorial positions.

transimination   the reaction of a primary amine with an imine to form a new imine and a primary amine derived from the original imine.

transition metal catalyst   a catalyst containing a transition metal, such as $Pd(PPh_3)_4$, that is used in coupling reactions.

trans isomer   the isomer with the hydrogens on opposite sides of the double bond or cyclic structure. the isomer with identical substituents on opposite sides of the double bond.

transition state   the highest point on a hill in a reaction coordinate diagram. In the transition state, bonds in the reactant that will break are partially broken and bonds in the product that will form are partially formed.

transition state analog   a compound that is structurally similar to the transition state of an enzyme-catalyzed reaction.

translation   the synthesis of a protein from an mRNA blueprint.

transmetallation   metal exchange.

triacylglycerol   the compound formed when the three OH groups of glycerol are esterified with fatty acids.

triene   a hydrocarbon with three double bonds.

trigonal planar carbon   an sp^2 hybridized carbon.

triose   a monosaccharide with three carbons.

tripeptide   three amino acids linked by amide bonds.

triple bond   a σ bond plus two π bonds.

triplet   an NMR signal split into three peaks.

triterpene   a terpene that contains 30 carbons.

twist-boat conformation (skew-boat conformation)   a conformation of cyclohexane.

ultraviolet light   electromagnetic radiation with wavelengths ranging from 180 to 400 nm.

umpolung   reversing the normal polarity of a functional group.

unimolecular reaction (first-order reaction)   a reaction whose rate depends on the concentration of one reactant.

unsaturated hydrocarbon   a hydrocarbon that contains one or more double or triple bonds.

unsymmetrical ether   an ether with two different substituents bonded to the oxygen.

urethane   a compound with a carbonyl group that is both an amide and an ester.

UV/Vis spectroscopy   the absorption of electromagnetic radiation in the ultraviolet and visible regions of the spectrum; used to determine information about conjugated systems.

valence electron   an electron in an unfilled shell.

valence shell electron-pair repulsion (VSEPR) model   combines the concept of atomic orbitals with the concept of shared electron pairs and the minimization of electron pair repulsion.

van der Waals forces (London forces)   induced-dipole–induced-dipole interactions.

van der Waals radius   a measure of the effective size of an atom or a group. A repulsive force occurs (van der Waals repulsion) if two atoms approach each other at a distance less than the sum of their van der Waals radii.

vector sum   takes into account both the magnitudes and the directions of the bond dipoles.

vicinal dihalide   a compound with halogens bonded to adjacent carbons.

vicinal diol (vicinal glycol)   a compound with OH groups bonded to adjacent carbons.

vinyl group $CH_2=CH-$

vinylic carbon   a carbon in a carbon–carbon double bond.

vinylic cation   a compound with a positive charge on a vinylic carbon.

vinylic radical   a compound with an unpaired electron on a vinylic carbon.

vinylogy   transmission of reactivity through double bonds.

vinyl polymer   a polymer in which the monomers are ethylene or a substituted ethylene.

visible light   electromagnetic radiation with wavelengths ranging from 400 to 780 nm.

vitamin   a substance needed in small amounts for normal body function that the body cannot synthesize at all or cannot synthesize in adequate amounts.

vitamin KH_2   the coenzyme required by the enzyme that catalyzes the carboxylation of glutamate side chains.

vulcanization   increasing the flexibility of rubber by heating it with sulfur.

wave equation   an equation that describes the behavior of each electron in an atom or a molecule.

wave functions   a series of solutions of a wave equation.

wavelength   distance from any point on one wave to the corresponding point on the next wave (usually in units of μm or nm).

wavenumber   the number of waves in 1 cm.

wax   an ester formed from a long-chain carboxylic acid and a long-chain alcohol.

wedge-and-dash structure   a method of representing the spatial arrangement of groups. Wedges are used to represent bonds that point out of the plane of the paper toward the viewer, and dashed lines are used to represent bonds that point back from the plane of the paper away from the viewer.

Williamson ether synthesis   formation of an ether from the reaction of an alkoxide ion with an alkyl halide.

Wittig reaction   the reaction of an aldehyde or a ketone with a phosphonium ylide, resulting in the formation of an alkene.

Wohl degradation   a method used to shorten an aldose by one carbon.

Wolff–Kishner reduction   a reaction that reduces the carbonyl group of a ketone to a methylene group with the use of NH_2NH_2/HO^-.

Woodward–Fieser rules   allow the calculation of the λ_{max} of the $\pi \longrightarrow \pi^*$ transition for compounds with four or fewer conjugated double bonds.

Woodward–Hoffmann rules   a series of selection rules for pericyclic reactions.

ylide   a compound with opposite charges on adjacent covalently bonded atoms with complete octets.

Zaitsev's rule   the more substituted alkene product is obtained by removing a proton from the β-carbon that is bonded to the fewest hydrogens.

Z conformation   the conformation of a carboxylic acid or a carboxylic acid derivative in which the carbonyl oxygen and the substituent bonded to the carboxyl oxygen or nitrogen are on the same side of the single bond.

Ziegler–Natta catalyst   an aluminum–titanium initiator that controls the stereochemistry of a polymer.

Z isomer   the isomer with the high-priority groups on the same side of the double bond.

zwitterion   a compound with a negative charge and a positive charge on non-adjacent atoms.

I N D E X

Note: Page numbers in **boldface** indicate definitions; page numbers followed by f indicate illustrations; page numbers followed by t indicate tables.

Periodic Table of the Elements

Main groups

Main groups

Transition metals

	1A 1	2A 2		3B 3	4B 4	5B 5	6B 6	7B 7	8B 8	8B 9	8B 10	1B 11	2B 12	3A 13	4A 14	5A 15	6A 16	7A 17	8A 18
1	1 H 1.00794																		2 He 4.002602
2	3 Li 6.941	4 Be 9.012182												5 B 10.811	6 C 12.0107	7 N 14.0067	8 O 15.9994	9 F 18.998403	10 Ne 20.1797
3	11 Na 22.989770	12 Mg 24.3050												13 Al 26.981538	14 Si 28.0855	15 P 30.973761	16 S 32.065	17 Cl 35.453	18 Ar 39.948
4	19 K 39.0983	20 Ca 40.078		21 Sc 44.955910	22 Ti 47.867	23 V 50.9415	24 Cr 51.9961	25 Mn 54.938049	26 Fe 55.845	27 Co 58.933200	28 Ni 58.6934	29 Cu 63.546	30 Zn 65.39	31 Ga 69.723	32 Ge 72.64	33 As 74.92160	34 Se 78.96	35 Br 79.904	36 Kr 83.80
5	37 Rb 85.4678	38 Sr 87.62		39 Y 88.90585	40 Zr 91.224	41 Nb 92.90638	42 Mo 95.94	43 Tc [98]	44 Ru 101.07	45 Rh 102.90550	46 Pd 106.42	47 Ag 107.8682	48 Cd 112.411	49 In 114.818	50 Sn 118.710	51 Sb 121.760	52 Te 127.60	53 I 126.90447	54 Xe 131.293
6	55 Cs 132.90545	56 Ba 137.327		71 Lu 174.967	72 Hf 178.49	73 Ta 180.9479	74 W 183.84	75 Re 186.207	76 Os 190.23	77 Ir 192.217	78 Pt 195.078	79 Au 196.96655	80 Hg 200.59	81 Tl 204.3833	82 Pb 207.2	83 Bi 208.98038	84 Po [208.98]	85 At [209.99]	86 Rn [222.02]
7	87 Fr [223.02]	88 Ra [226.03]		103 Lr [262.11]	104 Rf [261.11]	105 Db [262.11]	106 Sg [266.12]	107 Bh [264.12]	108 Hs [269.13]	109 Mt [268.14]	110 Ds [271.15]	111 Rg [272.15]	112 [277]		114 [285]		116 [289]		

*Lanthanide series	57 *La 138.9055	58 Ce 140.116	59 Pr 140.90765	60 Nd 144.24	61 Pm [145]	62 Sm 150.36	63 Eu 151.964	64 Gd 157.25	65 Tb 158.92534	66 Dy 162.50	67 Ho 164.93032	68 Er 167.259	69 Tm 168.93421	70 Yb 173.04
†Actinide series	89 †Ac [227.03]	90 Th 232.0381	91 Pa 231.03588	92 U 238.02891	93 Np [237.05]	94 Pu [244.06]	95 Am [243.06]	96 Cm [247.07]	97 Bk [247.07]	98 Cf [251.08]	99 Es [252.08]	100 Fm [257.10]	101 Md [258.10]	102 No [259.10]

[a] The labels on top (1A, 2A, etc.) are common American usage. The labels below these (1, 2, etc.) are those recommended by the International Union of Pure and Applied Chemistry.

The names and symbols for elements 112 and above have not yet been decided.

Atomic weights in brackets are the masses of the longest-lived or most important isotope of radioactive elements.

Further information is available at *http://www.shef.ac.uk/chemistry/web-elements/* .

The production of element 116 was reported in May 1999 by scientists at Lawrence Berkeley National Laboratory.

Common Functional Groups

Alkane RCH_3

Alkene

internal   terminal

Alkyne $RC{\equiv}CR$ $RC{\equiv}CH$

internal   terminal

Nitrile $RC{\equiv}N$

Nitroalkane RNO_2

Ether $R-O-R$

Epoxide

Thiol $R-SH$

Sulfide $R-S-R$

Disulfide $R-S-S-R$

Sulfonium salt $R-\overset{R}{\underset{}{S^{\pm}}}-R\ X^-$

Quaternary ammonium salt $R-\overset{R}{\underset{R}{N^{\pm}}}-R\ X^-$

Aniline

Phenol

Carboxylic acid

Acyl halide

acyl chloride   acyl bromide

Acid anhydride

Ester

Amide

Aldehyde

Ketone

	primary	secondary	tertiary
Alkyl halide	$R{-}CH_2{-}X$	$R-\overset{R}{\underset{}{C}}H-X$	$R-\overset{R}{\underset{R}{C}}-X$
	X = F, Cl, Br, or I		
Alcohol	$R-CH_2-OH$	$R-\overset{R}{\underset{}{C}}H-OH$	$R-\overset{R}{\underset{R}{C}}-OH$
Amine	$R-NH_2$	$R-\overset{R}{\underset{}{N}}H$	$R-\overset{R}{\underset{R}{N}}$